". . . and lo, there was a great earthquake . . . and every mountain and island were moved out of their places."   REVELATION 6:12, 14

The Great Alaska Earthquake of 1964

GEOLOGY

National Research Council

∧ COMMITTEE ON THE ALASKA EARTHQUAKE ,
OF THE
DIVISION OF EARTH SCIENCES
NATIONAL RESEARCH COUNCIL

NATIONAL ACADEMY OF SCIENCES
WASHINGTON, D.C.
1971

Geology

Seismology and Geodesy

Hydrology

Biology

Oceanography and Coastal Engineering

Engineering

Human Ecology

Summary and Recommendations

Available from
Printing and Publishing Office
National Academy of Sciences
2101 Constitution Avenue
Washington, D.C. 20418

ISBN 0-309-01601-0

Library of Congress Catalog Card Number 68-60037

Printed in the United States of America

FRONTISPIECE   The rails in this approach to a bridge near the head of Turnagain Arm were torn from their ties and buckled laterally by streamward movement of the riverbanks. Photograph by M. G. Bonilla.

COMMITTEE ON THE ALASKA EARTHQUAKE

Foreword

Soon after the Alaska earthquake of March 27, 1964, President Lyndon B. Johnson wrote to Donald F. Hornig, his Special Assistant for Science and Technology:

It is important we learn as many lessons as possible from the disastrous Alaskan earthquake. A scientific understanding of the events that occurred may make it possible to anticipate future earthquakes, there and elsewhere, so as to cope with them more adequately.

I, therefore, request that your office undertake to assemble a comprehensive scientific and technical account of the Alaskan earthquake and its effects. . . .

In defining the scientific and technical questions involved and the related informational requirements for collection and assessment, I hope that you will be able to enlist the aid of the National Academy of Sciences. . . .

In discussions that followed, the Academy was requested by Dr. Hornig to establish the Committee on the Alaska Earthquake, to be charged with three principal tasks—to evaluate efforts being made to gather scientific and engineering information about the earthquake and its effects, to encourage the filling of gaps in the record, and to compile and publish a comprehensive report on the earthquake.

Under the chairmanship of Konrad B. Krauskopf of Stanford University, a twelve-man committee was formed of specialists from related scientific and technical disciplines. Their first meeting was held on June 15, 1964.

The resulting documents, prepared by the Committee and its seven specialized panels, constitute perhaps the most comprehensive and detailed account of an earthquake yet compiled. The Committee has attempted to compile from the available information and analysis a useful resource for present and future scholars in this field. As a result of the present study, much that is new and useful has been learned about earthquakes as well as about natural disasters in general.

Although considerable literature on the geological aspects of the earthquake is already in print, the Committee concluded that the Academy series on this earthquake would be incomplete without an appropriate representative section on geology. Thus, the Committee compiled a balanced selection of the best available material, drawing heavily on previously published papers. This compilation, which constitutes the content of this volume, will have the effect of preserving essential geological findings on the Alaska earthquake as a part of this comprehensive permanent record.

In addition to the membership of the central committee, the work of several hundred scientists and engineers is represented in the Committee's report. Many of these are staff members of government agencies that have gathered facts and data about the earthquake and its effects; others are from universities and nongovernmental scientific organizations with an interest in earthquake-related research. Their help and cooperation in making this report possible is deeply appreciated.

PHILIP HANDLER
President
National Academy of Sciences

Preface

South central Alaska (Figure 1), including Prince William Sound and the Aleutian area, is one of the world's most active seismic regions. On March 27, 1964, at about 5:36 p.m. local time (0336, or 3:36 a.m. GMT, March 28), an earthquake of unusual severity struck the Prince William Sound area. Seismologists record earthquake occurrences in Greenwich mean time (GMT). The U.S. Coast and Geodetic Survey, therefore, uses 03h 36m 14.0 ± 0.2s GMT, March 28, 1964, as the time of the earthquake. The coordinates of the epicenter of the main shock have been calculated as lat. $61.04° ± 0.05°$ N and long. $147.73° ± 0.07°$ W, and the focus was within a few tens of kilometers of the surface. Not only was this earthquake of large magnitude (between 8.3 and 8.6 on the Richter scale, on which the greatest known earthquake is 8.9), but its duration (3 to 4 minutes) and the area of its damage zone (50,000 mi^2) were extraordinary. Probably twice as much energy was released by the Alaska earthquake as by the one that rocked San Francisco in 1906.

The shock was felt over 500,000 mi^2. A tsunami (a train of long waves impulsively generated, in this case by movement of the sea floor) or "tidal wave" swept from the Gulf of Alaska across the length of the Pacific and lapped against Antarctica. Water levels in wells as far away as South Africa jumped abruptly, and shock-induced waves were generated in the Gulf of Mexico. An atmospheric pressure wave caused by the earthquake was recorded at La Jolla, California, more than 2,000 mi away. Seismic surface waves, with periods of many seconds, moved the ground surface of most of the North American continent by as much as 2 in.

The magnitude of the earthquake can be calculated only from teleseismic records, and its duration can be estimated only from eyewitness accounts, because no seismic instruments capable of recording strong ground motion were in Alaska at the time. The range of uncertainty in the magnitude calculations (8.3–8.6) is far greater in terms of energy release than the figures suggest; from the most generally accepted relation of magnitude to energy release, it can be

calculated that magnitude 8.6 represents approximately twice the energy release of magnitude 8.3.

Measured crustal deformation was more extensive than the deformation related to any known previous earthquake. Areas of uplift and subsidence were separated by a line of zero land-level change trending both southwestward and eastward from the vicinity of the epicenter, about 80 mi east-southeast of Anchorage; this line parallels the major tectonic features of the region. Areas north and northwest of the zero line subsided as much as 7.5 ft; areas south and southeast rose, over wide areas, as much as 6 ft. Locally the uplift was much greater: 38 ft on Montague Island and more than 50 ft on the sea floor southwest of the island. The zone of uplift was along the continental margin of the Aleutian Trench. Not only was the earth's crust displaced vertically, but horizontal movements of tens of feet took place, in which the landmass moved southeastward relative to the ocean floor. The area of crustal deformation was more than 100,000 mi^2.

The mechanism of the earthquake remains to some extent uncertain. Fault-plane solutions for the main shock and the principal aftershocks, of which there were 10 of magnitudes greater than 6.0 within 24 hours after the initial shock, are consistent either with thrusting of the continent over the ocean floor along a plane dipping $5°$–$15°$ north or northwest, or with downward slip of the continent along a near-vertical plane; in either case the strike of the fault is northeast in the vicinity of Kodiak Island to east in Prince William Sound, parallel to the dominant tectonic trend. Although the fault-plane solutions do not permit an unambiguous decision between the two possible planes, several other lines of evidence strongly favor the low-angle thrust alternative.

The strong ground motion induced many snowslides, rockfalls, and landslides, both subaerial and submarine. The submarine landslides created local sea waves or tsunamis, which, together with the major tsunami generated by the crustal deformation, smashed port and harbor facilities,

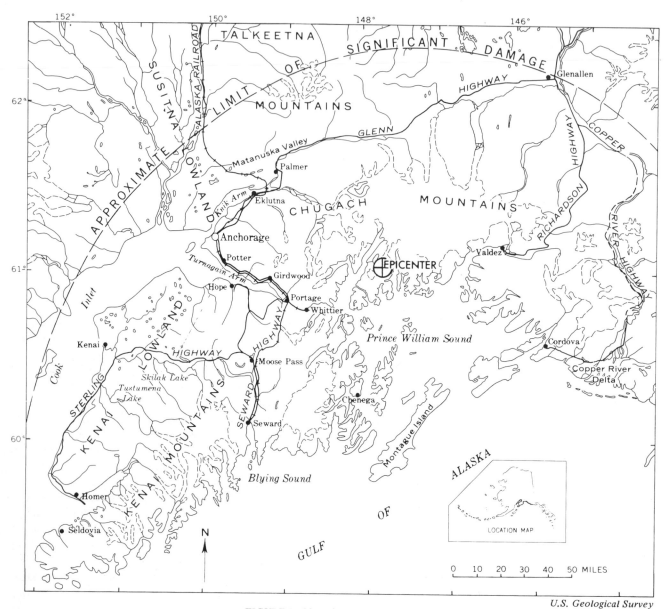

FIGURE 1   Map of south central Alaska.

U.S. Geological Survey

covered sessile organisms and salmon-spawning beds with silt, disturbed and killed salmon fry, leveled forests, and caused saltwater invasion of many coastal freshwater lakes.

The tectonic elevation and depression caused extensive damage to the biota of coastal forests, migratory-bird nesting grounds, salmon-spawning waters and gravels, as well as shellfish habitats, and initiated long-term changes in littoral and stream morphology. Clams, barnacles, algae, and many other marine and littoral organisms perished in areas of uplift. Spawning beds, trees, and other vegetation were destroyed in areas of depression.

Except for the major tsunami, which caused extensive damage in British Columbia and took 16 lives in Oregon

and California, violence to man and his structures was restricted to the area of tectonic land-level change. Tsunamis, major and local, took the most lives. Landslides caused the most damage.

The number of lives lost in Alaska, 115, was very small for an earthquake of this magnitude. Factors that contributed to the light loss of life were the sparse population, the fortuitous timing of the earthquake, a low tide, the absence of fire in residential and business areas, the generally clement weather, and the fact that the earthquake occurred during the off-season for fishing. The earthquake came on the evening of a holiday, when the schools were empty and most offices deserted, but when most people were still wearing their warm clothing. The low tide and the absence of fishermen and cannery workers mitigated the destruction and loss of life from tsunamis.

Public and private property loss was over $300 million. Hundreds of homes were destroyed. A multistory apartment building (fortunately not occupied), a department store, and other buildings in Anchorage collapsed. Oil storage tanks at Valdez, Seward, and Whittier ruptured and burned. Many other structures were destroyed or damaged. Most of downtown Kodiak was inundated by the major tsunami.

Damage to surface transportation facilities was extensive. The Alaska Railroad lost its port facility at Whittier, its docks at Seward, and numerous bridges on the Kenai Peninsula. Many highway bridges, especially on the Seward and Copper River highways, were damaged. Many port and harbor facilities, especially at Seward, Valdez, Kodiak, Whittier, Cordova, and Homer, were destroyed.

The earthquake crippled Alaska's economy because nearly half the people of the state live within the damage area and because the land- and sea-transport facilities on which the economy depends were knocked out.

Relief came quickly. The extensive military establishment proved a great source of strength in implementing emergency measures designed to reduce the loss of life, to ease immediate suffering, and to restore needed services promptly. Financial assistance for relief purposes was provided immediately by the Office of Emergency Planning under provisions of the Federal Disaster Act.

Recovery was rapid. Of major importance in the reconstruction effort was a congressional program to provide additional federal aid not possible under existing authority. This program was recommended by the Federal Reconstruction and Development Planning Commission for Alaska, a unique body appointed by President Lyndon B. Johnson on April 2, 1964. The additional aid included transitional grants to maintain essential public services; an increase in the federal share of highway reconstruction costs; a decrease in the local share of urban renewal projects; debt adjustments on existing federal loans; federal purchase of state bonds; and grants for a state mortgage-forgiveness program. An estimated $330 million of government and private funds financed Alaska's recovery from the earthquake.

The Alaska earthquake is the best documented and most thoroughly studied earthquake in history. Attempts have been made to draw lessons from both the physical event and the human experience. Strong-motion seismographs and accelerographs were installed in Alaska shortly after the earthquake, providing a basis for study of the stronger aftershocks. The tsunami warning system for the North Pacific was greatly improved within a few months, mainly by establishment of three new seismograph stations in south central Alaska as the basic elements in the system. Risk maps for Anchorage, Homer, Seward, and Valdez, based upon exten-

sive geological studies, were prepared by the Scientific and Engineering Task Force of the Reconstruction Commission and were used discriminatingly as a basis for federal aid to reconstruction and as guides to future builders. The entire town of Valdez was relocated. Communities and state and professional organizations in seismic areas outside Alaska reexamined codes and programs related to earthquake hazard in light of the Alaska experience. Finally, the Alaska earthquake turned the nation's attention again, and sharply, to the problems of improving the elements of a national natural-disaster policy: zoning and construction codes; prediction and warning systems; rescue and relief organizations; disaster-data collection and analysis; and disaster insurance and reconstruction aids.

Thus the earthquake had many facets. It was a natural scientific experiment on a grand scale, providing data on a variety of long-standing problems regarding the mechanism and effects of earthquakes. It served as a test of man-made structures under extreme conditions, and as a guide to improvements in the location and design of such structures to make them better able to withstand seismic shocks. It was an object lesson in human response to disaster, pointing the way to increased effectiveness of warning systems, of emergency measures during disasters, and of relief and recovery operations.

The charge to the Committee on the Alaska Earthquake was made to ensure that as much technical and scientific information as possible would be wrung from the earthquake experience and that the results would be assembled into a comprehensive report. At its first meeting the Committee decided that its initial task of evaluating and encouraging efforts to gather scientific and technical information could best be carried out by panels representing the major disciplines involved in the data-gathering: engineering, geography (human ecology), geology, hydrology, oceanography, and seismology. Biology, at first included within oceanography, was later made the basis of a separate panel.

As information for a comprehensive report accumulated, it became clear that the report itself could most appropriately follow the panel structure. Accordingly, this report appears in eight volumes, seven put together by the separate panels and a summary volume prepared by the full Committee.

In the early meetings of the Committee, and especially as it became apparent that many of the physical-science and some of the engineering aspects of the earthquake would be treated comprehensively in government publications and individual studies, there was considerable discussion of the appropriate content of the Committee's final report.

The Committee finally decided that the advantages of having available, under one cover and in one place in a library, a truly comprehensive report on the earthquake would justify the expense of duplicating some material already published. In addition, the Committee agreed, a complete report would provide a better basis for the inclusion of cross-disciplinary papers, for pointing out lessons learned from the Alaska experience, and for making recommendations designed to reduce the loss of life and property in subsequent major earthquakes.

As a model for its work, the Committee could look back to the classic report on the 1906 San Francisco earthquake, published by the Carnegie Institution in 1908. To emulate the comprehensiveness of this magnificent report seemed possible, but not the unity and coherence that it gained from the encyclopedic knowledge of its editor and principal author, A. C. Lawson. The breadth and depth of scientific interest in earthquakes have increased so greatly since 1906 that no one man can hope to master, as Lawson did, a great part of existing technical knowledge on all aspects of earthquakes. A report today must necessarily have many authors and must reflect in its length and diversity the extraordinary development of disciplines and instruments over the past half century.

Despite the Committee's attempt to make the report broadly comprehensive, there are unfortunate and obvious gaps in the record, mainly in those subject-matter fields not included in the work of government agencies. Such gaps are identified in the appropriate volumes of the report.

Apart from these gaps, the report covers a wide variety of subjects in engineering, natural science, and social science. Ranging from seismology to human ecology, it sets forth what is known about the structure of the earth's crust in south central Alaska, especially in relation to possible earthquake mechanisms and to tsunami generation; describes the effects of the earthquake on geologic processes, rocks, and soils; outlines the seismic history of Alaska and gives the seismic parameters of the earthquake; presents the results of energy-release, strain-release, and focal-mechanism studies of the main shock and aftershocks; describes the effects of the earthquake on groundwater and surface-water bodies and on glaciers and snowfields; discusses the generation, propagation, and effects of earthquake-induced tsunamis; describes immediate as well as long-term effects on plants and animals of abrupt land elevation and depression and of slides and tsunamis; sets forth in detail, with analyses, the response of man-made structures to the earthquake; chronicles in narrative form both the physical and human events of the earthquake; describes the impact of the earthquake on individuals, communities, and organizations; and puts forward recommendations that range from geologic mapping for hazard zoning, through methods of assuring site-suited earthquake-resistant construction, to means of improving the human response to disaster.

This volume on geology is one of the eight that make up the report. It brings together theoretical papers on the mechanism of the earthquake, descriptive accounts of geo-logic effects on surface features, papers describing effects on communities, and analyses of geologic effects on utilities, roads, and railroads. In large part it is a compilation of papers published separately over a period of several years by the U.S. Geological Survey with a few from other sources. Although most of the papers were already in print, it seemed worthwhile to collect between the covers of a single volume the most important papers dealing primarily with geologic aspects of the earthquake.

Geology plays a prominent role in several other volumes of this series. The relationship to Seismology and Geodesy is particularly close, for much of the evidence bearing on the controversy between the vertical-fault and thrust-fault hypotheses comes from geophysical theory and geodetic measurement. Geologic changes produced by the earthquake in streams, lakes, and glaciers, as well as the characteristics of earthquake-generated avalanches, are described in the volume on Hydrology. The Oceanography and Coastal Engineering volume includes such geologic subjects as changes in beaches and stream mouths resulting from large-scale uplift and subsidence, erosional effects of the major tsunami and local tsunamis, and differential vertical movements of the sea bottom. In the Engineering volume the detailed treatment of soil movement as related to response of man-made structures supplements the discussion of soil and bedrock behavior here.

Scientists, who flocked to Alaska immediately after the earthquake, found many geologic effects that were spectacular and perhaps unprecedented, particularly the uplift and subsidence of huge areas. Landslides in cities, landslides on glaciers, and submarine landslides in fiords provided favorite subjects for study and speculation. One effect that was confidently expected but not found was a major break of the earth's surface along a fault. There were small scarps, both on land and on the sea bottom, but no long line of fracture to which the major movement could be ascribed. The extensive vertical movement and near-absence of surface breaks provided a major puzzle about the earthquake mechanism, a puzzle about which geologists and seismologists still argue: vertical movement along a steeply inclined fault at depth, or thrust movement along a gently inclined surface dipping under the land. Either hypothesis can account for most of the data, and neither can be established definitively as correct. The weight of geologic evidence, as built up over the years since the earthquake and described in detail in this volume, is heavily on the side of the thrust-fault hypothesis. It seems probable that one of the major scientific results to emerge from study of the Alaska earthquake will be the careful documentation for the first time of the effects of sudden movement along a major zone of thrusting.

Not only theoretical geology but the practical application of geology to land-use planning has benefited from detailed work on effects of the earthquake. The papers in this volume relating the behavior of buildings, bridges, and other man-made structures to the kinds of soil and bedrock beneath them will provide both stimulus and background for geologic studies in other earthquake-prone areas. On these studies, maps of earthquake risk that will serve as guides to engineers and city planners can be based.

The Alaska earthquake provided a rare chance for geologists to expand their knowledge of the earth's crust by observing the immediate effects of a major tectonic event. How well they used the opportunity and how important are the scientific and practical results obtained may be judged from the papers in this volume.

KONRAD B. KRAUSKOPF
Stanford University

EDITORIAL NOTE

Although the Committee has used Donald J. Orth's 1967 *Dictionary of Alaska Place Names*, Geological Survey Professional Paper 567, to standardize the spelling of place names in its report, the reader may still detect alternate spellings, such as Ouzinkie in one place and Uzinki in another. Such differences result largely from our decision to reproduce a sizable portion of this volume directly from the page negatives of the original publications by the Geological Survey. Where no ambiguity exists, we have ignored style and format differences; page numbers in italics at the *bottom* of the page will alert the reader to changes we have listed under the heading of Clarifications at the end of each paper.

The large folded plates and a plate index may be found in Part B, the accompanying map portfolio; each plate has been lettered alphabetically according to the order in which it has first been referred to in the text.

Acknowledgments

The Committee on the Alaska Earthquake and the Panel on Geology are particularly indebted to the National Science Foundation, the U.S. Coast and Geodetic Survey, the U.S. Geological Survey, the Office of Emergency Preparedness, the Army Research Office, the Atomic Energy Commission, the Advanced Research Projects Agency, the Office of Naval Research, the Office of Civil Defense, and the Department of Transportation for support of the Committee under Contract NSF C-310, Task Order 89; to the Department of Housing and Urban Development for similar support under Contract H-1229; to the Department of the Interior for special support; to the National Science Foundation for publication support under Contract NSF C-310, Task Order 208; and also to those agencies with projects that culminated in papers appearing in this volume.

The Committee and Panel greatly appreciate the time and effort provided by Creighton A. Burk, John C. Maxwell, John T. Rouse, and Carl S. Benson and his colleagues for their comments and suggestions as reviewers for the Division of Earth Sciences.

They are also grateful to the U.S. Geological Survey, The Geological Society of America, the Society of Economic Paleontologists and Mineralogists, and the American Geophysical Union for the use of their previously published professional papers, journal articles, and previously unpublished materials.

The Panel thanks the various government and private organizations that made available the time of the authors whose works appear in this volume. Special recognition is due The Geological Society of America, the U.S. Geological Survey, the California Institute of Technology, the University of California at Berkeley, the U.S. Coast and Geodetic Survey, the Environmental Science Services Administration, and the National Oceanic and Atmospheric Administration for making it possible for some of their personnel to serve as Panel members, authors, and reviewers. Similarly, the Panel expresses its appreciation to Stanford University, the California Institute of Technology, Texas A&M University, the University of Hawaii, the U.S. Geological Survey, The Geological Society of America, The Ohio State University, the University of Colorado, the U.S. Bureau of Commercial Fisheries, the University of Southern California, Clark University, the University of California at Berkeley, the U.S. Coast and Geodetic Survey, the Environmental Science Services Administration, and the National Oceanic and Atmospheric Administration for making available their personnel for service on the parent Committee; and also to the Office of Science and Technology, the National Science Foundation, the Department of Defense, the Army Research Office, the Advanced Research Projects Agency, the U.S. Coast and Geodetic Survey, the Environmental Science Services Administration, the National Oceanic and Atmospheric Administration, the U.S. Geological Survey, the Office of Emergency Preparedness, the Atomic Energy Commission, the Office of Naval Research, the Department of the Interior, and the Department of Housing and Urban Development for the time and assistance provided by their liaison representatives to the Committee.

The Panel is grateful to the University of Idaho, the U.S. Geological Survey, and Emory University for making the services of editors and indexers available; to the U.S. Geological Survey for assistance with reports, maps, and illustrations; to the U.S. Army and the U.S. Air Force for transportation to the affected areas; and to the U.S. Geological Survey for furnishing meeting places for the Panel on Geology.

Since 1964, reorganizations within federal agencies and departments have involved several of the Committee's supporting agencies. On July 13, 1965, the U.S. Coast and Geodetic Survey (USC&GS) and other component agencies were combined to form the Environmental Science Services Administration (ESSA), under the Department of Commerce. On October 3, 1970, ESSA together with several other organizations became the National Oceanic and Atmospheric Administration (NOAA), also under the Department of Commerce. Although the USC&GS and ESSA no longer exist as organizations, their names are used for historical accuracy, as is that of the Office of Emergency Planning, which was renamed the Office of Emergency Preparedness on October 21, 1968.

Contents

General Introduction: Relations between Geology and Effects of the Earthquake—*Edwin B. Eckel* ... 1

Setting and Effects of the Earthquake—*Wallace R. Hansen* and *Edwin B. Eckel* ... 5

I. REGIONAL AND AREAL EFFECTS

Tectonics—*George Plafker* ... 47
Gravity Survey and Regional Geology of the Prince William Sound Epicentral Region—*J. E. Case,*
    D. F. Barnes, George Plafker, and *S. L. Robbins* ... 123
Surface Faults on Montague Island—*George Plafker* ... 135
Geologic Effects on the Kodiak Island Area—*George Plafker* and *Reuben Kachadoorian* ... 177
Effects on Shore Processes and Beach Morphology—*Kirk W. Stanley* ... 229
Effects on Some Shallow-Water Sediments in Prince William Sound—*Peter J. Barrett* ... 250
Effects of the Earthquake and Tsunami on Recent Deltaic Sediments—*Erk Reimnitz* and *Neil F. Marshall* ... 265
Slide-Induced Waves, Seiching, and Ground Fracturing at Kenai Lake (Abstract)—*David S. McCulloch* ... 279
Ground Breakage and Associated Effects in the Cook Inlet Area (Abstract)—*Helen L. Foster* and
    Thor N. V. Karlstrom ... 280
Erosion and Deposition on a Raised Montague Island Beach (Abstract)—*M. J. Kirkby* and *Anne V. Kirkby* ... 281
Effects in the Copper River Basin Area (Abstract)—*Oscar J. Ferrians, Jr.* ... 282
Geomorphic Effects in the Martin-Bering Rivers Area (Abstract)—*Samuel J. Tuthill* and *Wilson M. Laird* ... 284
The Puget Peak Avalanche (Abstract)—*Marcus C. Hoyer* ... 285

II. EFFECTS ON COMMUNITIES

Effects at Anchorage—*Wallace R. Hansen* ... 289
Effects at Valdez—*Henry W. Coulter* and *Ralph R. Migliaccio* ... 359
Effects at Seward—*Richard W. Lemke* ... 395
Effects at Whittier—*Reuben Kachadoorian* ... 439
Effects in the Homer Area—*Roger M. Waller* ... 461
    Beach Changes on Homer Spit—*Kirk W. Stanley* ... 480
Effects on Various Communities—*George Plafker, Reuben Kachadoorian, Edwin B. Eckel,* and
    Lawrence R. Mayo ... 489
Effects on the Communities of Kodiak and Nearby Islands (Abstract)—*Reuben Kachadoorian* and
    George Plafker ... 539

III. EFFECTS ON TRANSPORTATION AND UTILITIES

Effects on the Alaska Railroad—*David S. McCulloch* and *Manuel G. Bonilla*   543
Effects on the Alaska Highway System—*Reuben Kachadoorian*   641
Effects on Air and Water Transport, Communications, and Utilities Systems—*Edwin B. Eckel*   705
Effect on the Eklutna Hydroelectric Project, Anchorage (Abstract)—*Malcolm H. Logan*   732

IV. SUMMARY

Landslide Susceptibility in and near Anchorage as Interpreted from Topographic and Geologic Maps—
  Ernest Dobrovolny   735
Lessons and Conclusions—*Edwin B. Eckel*   747

APPENDIXES

English–Metric and Metric–English Conversion Tables   794
Annotated Bibliography   796
Contributors to This Volume   815

INDEX   817

General Introduction: Relations between Geology and Effects of the Earthquake

In geologic terms, the Alaska earthquake of 1964 was but a tiny, momentary episode in the history of the earth. Huge parts of the earth's crust—entire continents, in fact—have in the past been displaced laterally or horizontally over great distances by a long succession of earth movements. The sea has many times encroached on dry land or withdrawn to expose new land, and each time it has destroyed living things or forced them to adapt to new environments. But all such large-scale changes in the earth's surface required untold millenia of time or took place long ago. Thus it is difficult for man to understand what has happened to the earth, either in general or in detail. Usually, all he can do is to draw inferences from bits and pieces of evidence still left in the geologic record. Only seldom can he witness large-scale changes in the earth actually occurring before his eyes.

Insignificant as it was in the entire history of the earth, nevertheless, the Alaska earthquake had enormous importance for geologists and seismologists throughout the world. It was one of the greatest earthquakes of all recorded history: Because it shook the earth longer than most, natural and man-made structures were subjected to prolonged stresses; and it took place in an area that was accessible for study. More important than these circumstances, however, is the fact that in

3 to 4 minutes the Alaska earthquake provided easily visible or measurable examples of a great variety of geologic features or processes in a variety of geologic settings. A portion of the earth's surface tilted, and a huge segment moved horizontally several tens of feet. Faults broke the surface locally. Far greater breaks deep within the crust betrayed themselves, indicating a kind of fault movement that had never before been well documented. The sea adjusted to changes in its bottom, and in so doing produced destructive local waves and a tsunami that traversed the entire Pacific Ocean. The earthquake's vibrations, both in the rocks and in the atmosphere, left records on sensitive instruments the world over. Water levels in wells and lakes were changed on several continents. Besides these major geologic events, the secondary effects of a great earthquake—landslides of many kinds, avalanches, ground fractures, compaction of unconsolidated sediments, and many others—left an abundance of evidence of their origin and meaning for all to see and study.

In short, the Alaska earthquake created an unprecedented opportunity for study by scientists, whether they sought to test older theories or to find new facts on which to build new theories. Geologists therefore hastened to Alaska, or to observation posts else-

where, immediately after the earthquake struck. The result of this scientific invasion was perhaps the most thorough and far-reaching study of a great geologic phenomenon that has ever been accomplished. The geologic studies that have been completed are so voluminous that they could not possibly be presented here in full, and some direct studies are still in progress. This volume can only attempt to give the highlights of the information learned by 1971 from the massive attack on the geology of the earthquake and to guide the serious reader to sources of more detailed information.

The first Chairman of the Panel on Geology of the Committee on the Alaska Earthquake was James Gilluly of the U.S. Geological Survey, who served briefly during 1964 and 1965. In April 1965, Edwin B. Eckel, an engineering geologist with the U.S. Geological Survey, who had been Chairman of the Scientific and Engineering Task Force (Task Force 9) Field Team, became Chairman of the Panel. Other members of the Panel include Clarence Allen, Professor of Geology and Geophysics at the California Institute of Technology, a specialist on the San Andreas and other faults in California and the director of the Institute's Seismological Laboratory; Ernest Dobrovolny, Research Geologist with the Engineering Geology Division of the U.S. Geological Survey, with many years of experience in the Anchorage area; George Gates, Assistant Chief Geologist, U.S. Geological Survey, Menlo Park, California, formerly chief of the Survey's Alaska Geology Branch; H. B. Seed, Professor of Civil Engineering at the University of California at Berkeley, who has specialized in seismically triggered soil failures; and Charles Whitten, Chief Geodesist, Office of National Geodetic Survey, National Ocean Survey, National Oceanic and Atmospheric Administration, who is widely known for his work in gravimetry and geodesy. Mr. Whitten is also a member of the Panel on Seismology, which is producing the Seismology and Geodesy volume.

The Panel's primary duties, as defined by its members and by the parent Committee, were to maintain surveillance of all the geologic investigations that were active or proposed, to identify gaps in coverage and to take steps to fill them where possible, and to coordinate the geologic effort with the investigations of other scientific and engineering disciplines.

An equally important duty of the Panel was to encourage publication in the formal literature of all significant results of the field and laboratory investigations that were being made, to the end that the lessons and procedures learned would not be lost but would be available to students of future earthquakes.

The Panel's final duty was to decide on how best to present the geologic story in the Committee's series of reports on all facets of the Alaska earthquake, and to winnow from a vast quantity of data those reports that might together tell the story completely but succinctly.

The work of the Panel was accomplished by a series of meetings, by its representation in the deliberations of the parent Committee, and by voluminous correspondence. Because all Panel members were deeply involved in investigations of the earthquake for other purposes than those of the Panel,

each member had special knowledge and dedicated interest in the problems involved.

The bulk of geologic studies of the earthquake was performed by the U.S. Geological Survey, making the work of the Committee's Panel on Geology generally simpler than that of other Panels, but in some respects more difficult. The Survey possessed a large corps of geologists who were intimately familiar with the geology of Alaska or with the application of geologic knowledge to man and his structures. More important, a farsighted management immediately recognized that the earthquake had provided one of the grandest opportunities of all time for geologic research. To seize the opportunity, people and funds were quickly allocated to make and publish the studies that were necessary to piece together a complete story of the geology of the great earthquake.

The impression of a dominant role by the Survey was emphasized when, where necessary, it reached outside its own resources to fill gaps in the record. It persuaded geologists, engineers, hydrologists, and even news-media representatives, all of whom had done their basic research under other auspices, to publish their observations in its series of Professional Papers on the earthquake. Moreover, the Survey's work could not possibly have been as complete or fruitful had it not been closely coordinated with, and drawn heavily on, the published and unpublished findings of innumerable other workers in seismology, geodesy, and other related fields.

The work of the Panel on Geology was thus comparatively easy, for a single institution already had a well-coordinated and well-financed program to provide the needed research and to publish the results. The Panel, and indeed the entire Committee on the Alaska Earthquake, followed closely the U.S. Geological Survey's investigations and acted in many ways as an independent advisor to the Sur-

vey, watching to make sure that all facets of the geology were being adequately covered. A few gaps in the Survey's program were identified and brought to its attention. Most of these were filled by the Survey, but in one case the Panel arranged for use of some of the Committee's funds to support a needed study that could not be included directly in the Survey program.

The Panel's final duty—that of deciding on the contents of this volume—was greatly facilitated by the Survey's effective program of publishing geologic, hydrologic, and engineering papers in its Professional Paper series from both Survey and non-Survey authors. At the same time, the task was made somewhat more difficult and even a trifle embarrassing by the broad scope and significance of the Survey reports, which obviously dominate the geologic literature on this earthquake. The Panel was thus faced with the prospect that its Geology volume—a basic and essential part of the Committee's series of reports—would perforce be composed almost entirely of reprints of already-published government reports. This situation led to the difficult task of selecting those papers that were to be published in full or in condensed form, while keeping within the limits of expenditures and size of volume that could be handled by the Committee on the Alaska Earthquake.

The choice of which of the many reports on the geology of the earthquake should be included in full or in abstract form was made by the Panel members. In general, the aim has been to give as complete a presentation of the geologic aspects as is possible within the space limitations available. Survey papers excluded, or given in abstract form, duplicate to some extent the material in other papers, or describe comparatively insignificant or ephemeral effects or events. Such papers are at least cited, if not summarized or abstracted. Future serious students of the geology of the Alaska earthquake, therefore, will find the salient facts in these pages and will be referred directly to the primary literature for the rest.

The volume begins with a semitechnical sketch of the geology of the earthquake-affected part of Alaska and its place in the continental framework. The effects of the earthquake are summarized also with stress on the geologic effects and the relationships between geology and earthquake damage to the works of man. The preliminary description is designed to provide perspective for the four major parts, including a summary, that follow.

Part I contains 13 papers, in full or in abstract, that describe the regional and areal effects of the earthquake. The first paper, on the tectonics of the earthquake, details the deep-seated movements in the earth's crust that constitute the real story of the earthquake as a geologic phenomenon; the tectonics caused both lateral and horizontal shifts of land and sea at the surface, which in turn, caused all the earthquake-related damages. The other papers in Part I describe the effects of uplift, subsidence, and shaking on all the various kinds of geologic materials, including water, that underlie the areas that were most strongly affected by the earthquake.

Part II describes in seven chapters the earthquake's effects on most of the cities and smaller communities in south central Alaska that bore the brunt of the damage. The effects differed greatly from town to town, depending largely on their physiographic and geologic settings. Anchorage, Alaska's largest city, was damaged most by seismic vibrations and by huge translatory landslides caused by the shaking. Other towns, particularly Valdez and Seward, sustained their greatest losses when huge slices of steep-fronted deltas slid off into deep water. Still other communities, such as Kodiak and many of the small villages, were flooded or even wiped out by giant tsunamis or by other water waves. Postearthquake studies in all these places not only provided clear understanding of the causes of earthquake damage but also led to well-substantiated warnings as to where it is safe or unsafe to site future communities.

Part III, comprising most of four Survey chapters, describes the earthquake's effects on the region's transportation and utility systems. Of these, the highway network and The Alaska Railroad were hardest hit. Terminals and dockside facilities, such as those at Seward, Anchorage, and Whittier, were ruined by vibrations or by offshore slides. Scores of bridges were smashed and many miles of highway and rail alignments twisted askew by myriad ground fractures and by horizontal slippages of soil (called landspreading) toward free faces such as stream- and riverbanks. As was true of the urban studies reported in Part II, investigations of the transportation and utility systems not only yielded information on the earthquake's effects on structures, but also presented opportunities for much new geologic mapping that adds to our understanding of south central Alaska.

The volume closes with the summary, Part IV, in which one of the two chapters describes the application of new knowledge yielded by the earthquake to forecasts of slope stability in various parts of Anchorage, should another great earthquake strike. The final chapter summarizes the lessons to be learned and the conclusions to be drawn from studies of the Alaska earthquake of 1964 that might help in preparing for future earthquakes here or elsewhere.

EDWIN B. ECKEL
The Geological Society of America

WALLACE R. HANSEN
U.S. GEOLOGICAL SURVEY

EDWIN B. ECKEL*
U.S. GEOLOGICAL SURVEY

Reprinted with minor changes from
U.S. Geological Survey Professional Paper 541,
"A Summary Description of the Alaska Earthquake–Its Setting and Effects"

Setting and Effects of the Earthquake

INTRODUCTION

One of the greatest geotectonic events of our time occurred in southern Alaska late in the afternoon of March 27, 1964. Beneath a leaden sky, the chill of evening was just settling over the Alaskan countryside. Light snow was falling on some communities. It was Good Friday, schools were closed, and the business day was ending. Suddenly without warning half of Alaska was rocked and jarred by the most violent earthquake to occur in North America this century.

The descriptive summary that follows is based on the work of many investigators. A large and still-growing scientific literature has accumulated since the earthquake, and this literature has been freely drawn upon here. In particular, the writers have relied upon the findings of their colleagues in the Geological Survey. Some of these findings have been published, but some are still being prepared for publication. Moreover, some field investigations are still in progress.

TIME AND MAGNITUDE

Seismologic events such as earthquakes are normally recorded in the scientific literature in Greenwich mean time. Greenwich time provides a worldwide standard of reference that obviates the difficulties of converting one local time to another. The Alaskan earthquake of 1964 thus began at about 5:36 p.m., Friday, March 27, 1964, Alaska standard time, but its onset is officially recorded in the seismological literature as 03:36:11.9 to 12.4, Saturday, March 28, 1964, Greenwich mean time (U.S. Coast and Geodetic Survey, 1964, p. 30).

This earthquake has become renowned for its savage destructiveness, for its long duration, and for the great breadth of its damage zone. Its magnitude has been computed by the U.S. Coast and Geodetic Survey as 8.3–8.4 on the Richter scale. Other observatories have calculated its magnitude as 8.4 (Pasadena) and 8.5–8.75 (Berkeley). These computations indicate something of the great size of the earthquake. Few earthquakes in history have been as large. In minutes, thousands of people were made homeless, 114 lives were lost, and the economy of an entire State was disrupted. Seismic sea waves swept the Pacific Ocean from the Gulf of Alaska to Antarctica; they caused extensive damage in British Columbia and California and took 12 lives in Crescent City, Calif., and 4 in Oregon. Unusually large waves, probably seiches, were recorded in the Gulf of Mexico. The entire earth vibrated like a tuning fork.

EPICENTER

The epicenter of this great earthquake has been located in a forlorn wilderness of craggy peaks, glaciers, and fjords at the head of Prince William Sound, on the south flank of the rugged Chugach Mountains, about 80 miles east-southeast of Anchorage (fig. 1, next page). Computations by the Coast and Geodetic Survey fix the epicenter at lat 61.1° N., long 147.7° W.±15 km. The hypocenter, or point of origin, was at a depth of 20–50 km. However, it is not meant to imply that the earthquake had a point source: During the quake, energy was released from a broad area south and southwest of the epicenter underlying and adjacent to Prince William Sound and the Gulf of Alaska (U.S. Coast and Geodetic Survey, 1964, p. 31; Grantz and others, 1964, p. 3). Epicenters of most aftershocks were dispersed throughout an area of about 100,000 square miles, mainly along the continental margin of the Aleutian Trench between Prince

---

*Now with The Geological Society of America.

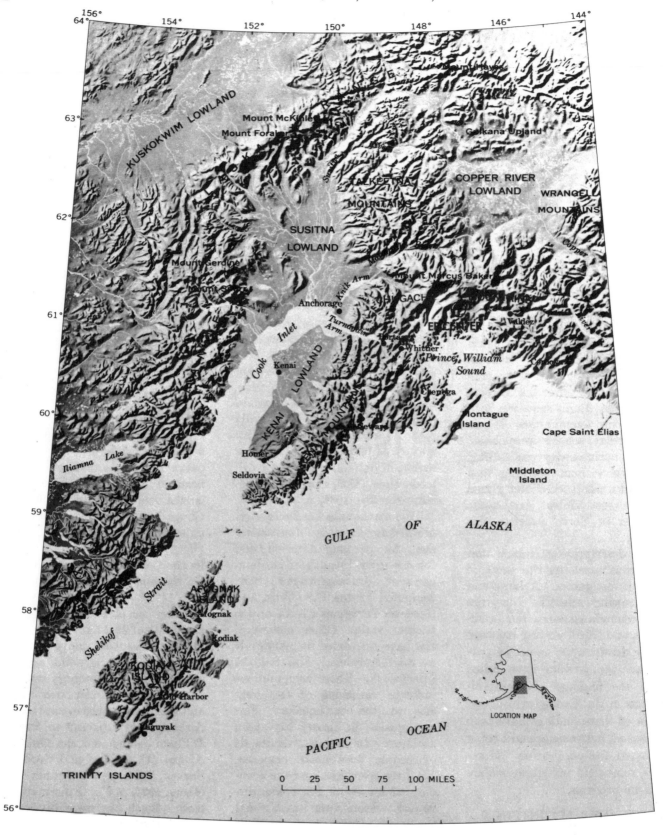

1.—Physiographic setting of south-central Alaska, including the area principally involved in the Alaska earthquake of 1964. The epicenter of the main shock is near the north end of Prince William Sound.

William Sound and the seaward side of Kodiak Island (fig. 9). This area coincides with a zone of tectonic uplift (Plafker, 1965).

DURATION AND EXTENT

The total effect of the earthquake was intensified by the long duration of strong ground motion. The elapsed time can only be surmised from the estimates of eyewitnesses, inasmuch as no recording instruments capable of measuring the duration of the shock were in the affected area at the time. Several such instruments have since been installed. Some witnesses timed the quake by wrist or pocket watch, and their timings ranged from 1½ to 7 minutes or more. Most such timings ranged from 3 to 4 minutes, whether measured at Anchorage, Seward, Valdez, or elsewhere. By comparison, the great San Francisco earthquake of 1906 is said to have lasted about 1 minute.

Several factors besides the human element may influence the variation from place to place of the estimated duration of the shock. Shocks are more intense in some geologic settings than in others; the character and amplitude of seismic waves passing through one medium are unlike those passing through another of different elastic properties. Ground motion is more intense and sometimes more prolonged over thick unconsolidated fills as at Anchorage or Valdez than over firm bedrock, as in the Chugach Mountains. Under certain ground conditions the intensity of ground motion may be amplified by resonance. Motions are stronger in high buildings than in low ones, so an observer in a tall building is likely to record a longer duration than an observer in a low building. And under certain conditions, shaking may be prolonged locally after direct seismic motion has stopped: for example, if landslides or avalanches, triggered by the earthquake, are in progress in the vicinity. At any rate, even the shortest estimates indicated an earthquake of unusual duration, a duration that had marked effects on the behavior of earth materials and manmade structures and on their susceptibility to damage.

The main shock was reportedly felt throughout most of Alaska, including such remote points as Cape Lisburne, Point Hope, Barrow, and Umiat on the Arctic slope of Alaska and at Unimak Island beyond the tip of the Alaska Peninsula—points 600–800 miles distant from the epicenter. The earthquake was recorded by seismographs throughout the world. It caused significant damage to ground and structures throughout a land area of about 50,000 square miles and it cracked ice on rivers and lakes throughout an area of about 100,000 square miles (Grantz and others, 1964, p. 2). Marked fluctuations of water levels in recording wells were noted at places as far distant as Georgia, Florida, and Puerto Rico (Waller and others, 1965, p. 131).

Effects of so great an earthquake hold the utmost interest of scientists and engineers. Few earthquakes have had such marked effects on the crust of the earth and its mantle of soil. Perhaps the effects of no earthquake have been better documented. Early investigation has provided a clear picture of much that happened, but years will pass before all the effects are understood. In fact, secondary effects are still in progress. In the fjords and along the shores at tectonically disturbed tidal zones, wholesale extermination of sessile organisms has been followed by a slow restoration of the biotic balance. Marine shellfish are now seen attaching themselves to the branches of drowned spruce trees (Hanna, 1964, p. 26). Rivers are regrading their channels to new base levels. Long-term effects on glaciers, shorelines, and the ground-water regimen will bear further watching.

But despite its magnitude and its impressive related tectonic effects, the earthquake ranks far below many other great natural disasters in terms of property damaged and lives lost. Less violent earthquakes have killed many more people. The reasons are many: The damage zone of the Alaskan quake has a very low population density; much of it is uninhabited. In Anchorage, the one really populous area in the damage zone, many modern buildings had been designed and constructed with the danger of earthquakes in mind.

The generative area of the earthquake was also sparsely inhabited, and the long-period seismic vibrations that reached the relatively distant inhabited areas wreaked heavy damage on tall and wide-area buildings but caused mostly light damage to small one-family dwellings of the type prevalent in Alaska (Steinbrugge, 1964, p. 71). According to White (1965, p. 91), attenuation of sinusoidal seismic waves at low frequencies should vary as the square of the frequency. Thus, destructive short-period vibrations presumably were attenuated to feeble amplitudes not far from their points of origin. Most residential buildings, moreover, were cross-braced wood-frame construction, and such buildings usually fare well in earthquakes.

Severe earthquakes during last 1,100 years, and resulting casualties

[After Hill, 1965, p. 50]

Year	Place	Deaths
856	Corinth, Greece	45,000
1038	Shansi, China	23,000
1057	Chihli, China	25,000
1170	Sicily	15,000
1268	Silicia, Asia Minor	60,000
1290	Chihli, China	100,000
1293	Kamakura, Japan	30,000
1456	Naples, Italy	60,000
1531	Lisbon, Portugal	30,000
1556	Shenshi, China	830,000
1667	Shemaka, Caucasia	80,000
1693	Catania, Italy	60,000
1693	Naples, Italy	93,000
1731	Peking, China	100,000
1737	Calcutta, India	300,000
1755	Northern Persia	40,000
1755	Lisbon, Portugal	30,000–60,000
1783	Calabria, Italy	50,000
1797	Quito, Ecuador	41,000
1811–12	New Madrid, Missouri, U.S.A.	------------
1819	Cutch, India	1,500
1822	Aleppo, Asia Minor	22,000
1828	Echigo (Honshu) Japan	30,000
1847	Zenkoji, Japan	34,000
1868	Peru and Ecuador	25,000
1875	Venezuela and Columbia	16,000
1896	Sanriku, Japan	27,000
1897	Assam, India	1,500
1898	Japan	[1] 22,000
1906	Valparaiso, Chile	1,500
1906	San Francisco, U.S.A	500
1907	Kingston, Jamaica	1,400
1908	Messina, Italy	160,000
1915	Avezzano, Italy	30,000
1920	Kansu, China	180,000
1923	Tokyo, Japan	143,000
1930	Apennine Mountains, Italy.	1,500
1932	Kansu, China	70,000
1935	Quetta, Baluchistan	60,000
1939	Chile	30,000
1939	Erzincan, Turkey	40,000
1946	Alaska-Hawaii, U.S.A	[1] 150
1948	Fukui, Japan	5,000
1949	Ecuador	6,000
1950	Assam, India	1,500
1953	Northwestern Turkey	1,200
1954	Northern Algeria	1,600
1956	Kabul, Afghanistan	2,000
1957	Northern Iran	2,500
1957	Western Iran	1,400
1957	Outer Mongolia	1,200
1960	Southern Chile	5,700
1960	Agadir, Morocco	12,000
1962	Northwestern Iran	12,000
1963	Taiwan, Formosa	100
1963	Skopje, Yugoslavia	1,000
1964	Southern Alaska, U.S.A	[2] 114

[1] Principally from seismic sea wave.
[2] Does not include 12 deaths in California and 4 deaths in Oregon, by drowning.

The timing of the earthquake undoubtedly contributed to the low casualty rate. It was a holiday; many people who would otherwise have been at work or returning from work were at home. Schools were closed for the holiday. In coastal areas the tide was low; had tides been high, inundation and destruction by sea waves would have been much more severe. Nevertheless, sea waves caused more deaths than all other factors combined.

Hill (1965, p. 58) has compiled a chronological list of severe earthquakes dating back more than 1,100 years. Her list, reproduced at left, places the Alaskan earthquake of 1964 in a proper perspective so far as deaths are concerned.

Throughout history, earthquakes have ranked high among the causes of sudden disaster and death, but many other causes have added as much or more to the misfortunes of mankind. Some of these, such as dam failures, for example, man has brought on himself. Others he has not. The great epidemics of the past are not likely to recur, but disease, famine, floods, and landslides all still take huge tolls. Single tornadoes in the American midcontinent have taken more lives than the Alaska earthquake of 1964; so have mine explosions. In East Pakistan, thousands of lives were lost in 1965 to floods and hurricanes ("cyclones"). It would be irrelevant to enlarge here on natural and manmade disasters. Hill, however, has compiled another table that sheds pertinent further light on some of the causes of human misery in the past 600 years, other than earthquakes. Wars have been omitted.

Deaths (rounded) from some of the world's worst man-made accidents and natural disasters

[After Hill, 1965, p. 57]

Date	What and where	Deaths
1347–51___	Bubonic plague in Europe and Asia.	75,000,000
1918_____	Influenza throughout the world.	22,000,000
1878_____	Famine in China_____	9,500,000
1887_____	Flood in China_____	900,000
1556_____	Earthquake in China_____	830,000
1881_____	Typhoon in Indochina_____	300,000
1902_____	Eruption of Mount Pelee, West Indies.	40,000
1883_____	Eruption of Krakatoa, near Sumatra.	36,000
1941_____	Snow avalanche in Peru_____	5,000
1963_____	Overflow of Vaiont Dam in Italy.	2,000
1942_____	Mine explosion Manchuria_____	[1] 1,500
1912_____	Sinking of the *Titanic*_____	[2] 1,500
1871_____	Forest fire, Wisconsin_____	1,000
1925_____	Tornado in south-central United States.	700
1944_____	Train stalled in Italy_____	[3] 500
1928_____	Collapse of St. Francis Dam, California.	500
1960_____	Airliners collided over New York City.	[4] 134

[1] Actual count 1,549.
[2] Known dead 1,513.
[3] Passengers suffocated when the train was caught in a tunnel; actual count 521.
[4] Including casualties on the ground.

Some of the tolls listed in Hill's tables differ substantially from those reported by other authorities for the same disasters. Perhaps this difference is not surprising in view of the chaos and lack of communication that generally accompany great natural disasters and the varying casualty estimates, therefore, that appear in the subsequent literature. Hill did not cite the sources of her data, and the some of her figures are questionable; she lists 143,000 deaths in the Tokyo earthquake of 1923, for example, whereas Richter (1958, p. 561, citing Imamura) lists 99,331. For the Messina earthquake of 1908 Hill lists 160,000 deaths, whereas other authors list from 82,000 to 100,000. Nevertheless, used with caution, Hill's tables help to equate the magnitudes of past tragedies, and they provide some basis for comparing one disaster with another. Compared with the eruption of Mount Pelee in 1902, for exam-ple, or the sinking of the Titanic in 1912, the Alaska earthquake of 1964 took a small toll of lives. In view of the magnitude of the event, the relatively small size of the toll is in some ways remarkable.

AFTERSHOCKS

The long series of aftershocks that followed the main Alaska earthquake gradually diminished in frequency and intensity over a period of several months. Within 24 hours the initial shock was followed by 28 aftershocks, 10 of which exceeded Richter magnitude 6. The epicenters of these shocks were disposed in a zone 50–60 miles wide reaching from Prince William Sound southwest to the Trinity Islands area south of Kodiak (fig. 9). Fifty-five aftershocks with magnitudes greater than 4 were recorded within 48 hours after the main earthquake, including a shock of magnitude 6.7 on March 29 at 4:18 p.m. (March 30, 02:18:05.6 Gmt). Within a week 75 shocks with magnitudes greater than 4 had been recorded by the U.S. Coast and Geodetic Survey (1964, table 2). In the 45 days following the earthquake, 728 aftershocks were recorded (Jordan and others, 1965, p. 1323). According to Press and Jackson (1965) about 12,000 aftershocks with magnitudes equal to or greater than 3.5 probably occurred in the 69-day period after the main shock, and several thousand more were recorded in the next year and a half (U.S. Coast and Geodetic Survey, 1965a, p. 44).

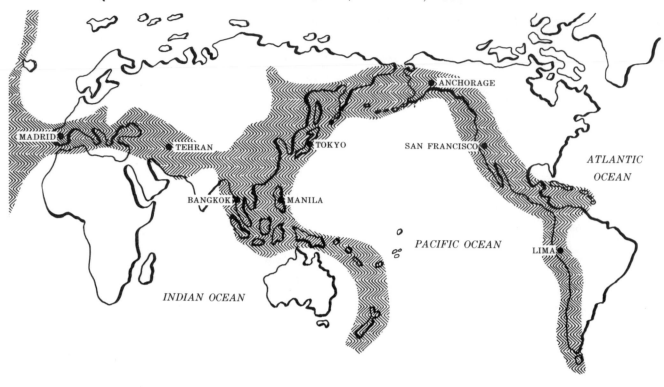

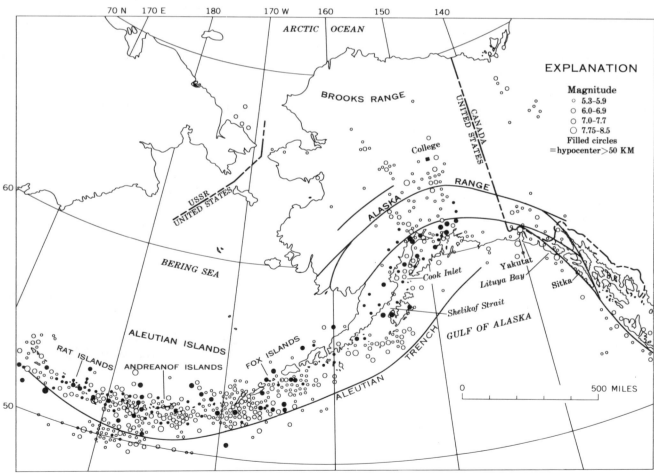

PREVIOUS ALASKAN EARTHQUAKES

Southern Alaska and the adjoining Aleutian Island chain together constitute one of the world's most active seismic zones. Extending from Fairbanks on the north to the Gulf of Alaska on the south, the Alaskan seismic zone is but a part of the vast, near-continuous seismically active belt that circumscribes the entire Pacific Ocean basin (fig. 2). Figure 3 shows the distribution of earthquake epicenters of magnitude 5.3 and greater recorded in Alaska since instrumental measurements began, through 1961. Between 1899 and May 1965, seven

2 (left).—Earthquake belts of the world. These belts coincide with the earth's orogenic zones and contain most of the earth's active volcanoes.

Alaska earthquakes have equaled or exceeded Richter magnitude 8, and more than 60 have equaled or exceeded magnitude 7 (Davis and Echols, 1962). According to Gutenberg and Richter (1949, table 7) about 7 percent of the seismic energy released annually on the globe originates in the Alaskan seismic zone.

This highly active zone is circumferential to the Gulf of Alaska and parallel to the Aleutian Trench. It embraces the rugged mountainous region of southern Alaska, Kodiak and the Aleutian Islands, the continental shelf, and the continental slope of the Aleutian Trench. Most of the earthquakes originate at shallow to intermediate depths—mostly less

3 (left).—Epicenters of major Alaskan earthquakes, 1898–1961. Reproduced from Davis and Echols (1962). More recent earthquakes include the Alaska earthquake of 1964 (magnitude 8.3–8.4) and the Rat Islands earthquake of 1965 (magnitude 7.75).

than 50 km—between the Aleutian Trench and the Aleutian Volcanic Arc. Foci are generally deeper away from the trench toward the arc (Gutenberg and Richter, 1949, fig. 7).

PHYSIOGRAPHIC AND GEOLOGIC SETTING OF THE EARTHQUAKE

It was noted above that the earthquake was felt throughout nearly all of Alaska, although for various reasons it was not felt in certain local areas distant from the epicenter. The level of intensity diminished appreciably northward from mountainous southern Alaska to the intermontane plateaus of the interior. Damage, moreover, was restricted generally to an arcuate area within about 150 miles of Prince William Sound (Grantz and others, 1964, fig. 1). This area coincided approximately with the area of tectonic land-level change. The

cardinal geographic setting of the earthquake, therefore, was southern Alaska south of the Alaska Range, west of the "Panhandle," and east of the Alaska Peninsula.

The four major physiographic divisions of Alaska are shown in figure 4. Each division is a northwesterly extension of a major physiographic division of Canada and conterminous United States. Tectonic effects of the earthquake and significant damage were confined largely to the southernmost division of Alaska, the Pacific Mountain System.

Physiographic divisions of Alaska are definitively described and summarized by Wahrhaftig (1966). They are outlined concisely by Wahrhaftig and Gates (1964, p. 27). Those parts of Alaska principally involved in the earthquake have been described by Miller, Black, Barnes, and Wahrhaftig in a summary volume

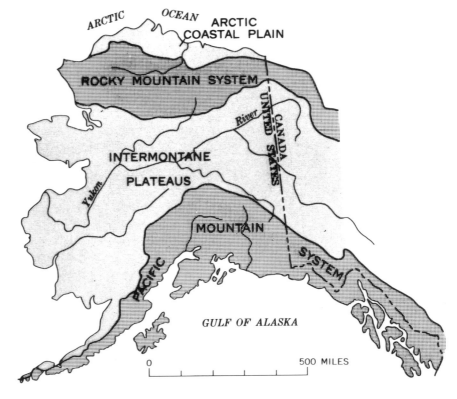

4.—Major physiographic divisions of Alaska.

"Landscapes of Alaska," edited by Howell Williams (1958). The geotectonic setting and structural history of Alaska have been outlined by Gates and Gryc (1963) and by Gates (1964). Most of the information that follows is abstracted from the several reports noted above. The physiographic nomenclature is that of Wahrhaftig, who followed and elaborated the early nomenclature of Brooks (1906, 1911).

The Pacific Mountain System extends from the southern part of the conterminous United States north through British Columbia and Yukon into Alaska. Not surprisingly, therefore, subdivisions of the system in Alaska have geologic and physiographic counterparts in the conterminous States. In mainland Alaska the Pacific Mountain System forms a broad arc, concave toward the south. Two mountainous belts are separated by a discontinuous belt of lowlands—the Alaska-Aleutian Ranges on the north, the Coastal Trough province in the center, and the Pacific Border Ranges on the south. The Alaska-Aleutian Ranges are analogous to the Cascade-Sierra Nevada Ranges of Washington, Oregon, and California—these provinces contain eugeosynclinal suites of graywacke, argillite, and volcanic rocks that are variably metamorphosed, are intruded by batholithic plutons, and are surmounted in places by Pleistocene and Recent volcanoes. The Coastal Trough province of Alaska is analogous to the Puget Sound-Willamette Valley-Great Valley of California lowland—these provinces contain thick fills of Cretaceous and Tertiary sedimentary rocks. The Pacific Border Ranges of Alaska are analogous to the Olympic Mountains and Coast Ranges.

They contain suites of graywacke, slate, and phyllite tightly folded and intruded by silicic to ultramafic plutons.

The Pacific Mountain System in Alaska is a region of dramatic physiographic contrasts—glacier-clad mountains, active volcanoes, lake-dotted lowlands, great rivers, fjords, and waterfalls framed in a setting of primeval forest on the one hand and trackless tundra on the other. Local relief in some places is astonishing: Mount McKinley at 20,269 feet, the highest summit in North America, looms above lowlands only a few hundred to 3,000 feet above sea level. In the nearby Wrangell Mountains, 12,000- to 16,000-foot peaks rise above the floor of the Copper River valley at an altitude of less than 1,000 feet. The abrupt relief of the St. Elias Range to the southeast is legendary—Mount St. Elias, visible from tidewater, is 18,008 feet high; Mount Fairweather, only 15 miles from the Gulf of Alaska, is 15,300 feet high.

ALASKA-ALEUTIAN PROVINCE

The Alaska-Aleutian province, a region of extreme seismic-tectonic activity, includes the Aleutian Island chain, the contiguous Aleutian Range on the Alaska Peninsula, and the Alaska Range (figs. 1 and 4). Together they form a great sigmoid wall concave northward on the west (the Aleutian Arc) and concave southward on the east, altogether totaling about 3,200 miles in length and averaging, on land, about 60 miles across.

ALEUTIAN RANGE

The Aleutian Range and its seaward extension, the Aleutian Islands, surmount a partly submerged ridge 20–60 miles wide extending 1,600 miles from Mount

Gerdine west of Anchorage to Attu Island at the west end of the chain. About 80 Quaternary volcanoes, some deeply dissected but many of them historically active (Coats, 1950), stand 2,000 to more than 12,000 feet above sea level. Mount Gerdine, the highest peak (but not a volcano), stands 12,600 feet above sea level at the north end of the arc. The volcanoes themselves rest on a platform made up largely of deeply eroded volcanic rocks of Tertiary age, interbedded with sedimentary rocks of volcanic provenance, all cut by dikes and irregular bodies of gabbro, diorite, and granite (Powers, in Williams, 1958, p. 61). Although the Alaska earthquake of 1964 was felt throughout much of the Aleutian Range, tectonic and geomorphic effects apparently were negligible. Reportedly, there was ground breakage on the flanks of Augustine Island volcano (R. M. Waller, oral commun., 1964). Landslides were triggered along steeper slopes as far south as Mount Iliamna. There was extensive ground cracking in the alluvial flats of most rivers and some lake deltas, and ice cracked in all the larger lakes.

ALASKA RANGE

The Alaska Range forms a great semicircular barrier about 600 miles long that merges imperceptibly with the Aleutian Range on the southwest and with the Wrangell and St. Elias Ranges on the southeast. Its faulted northern slope is one of the most abrupt mountain fronts in the world (Reed, 1961, p. A3). Despite its height and formidable aspect, however, the Alaska Range is breached by several low passes and river valleys utilized for transportation routes. The crestline of the range is mostly 7,000–9,000 feet high. Isolated massifs of great jagged peaks rise much higher, each the center of extensive systems of icecaps and valley glaciers. The two icy summits of Mount McKinley (19,370 and 20,269 ft) and their sister peak, Mount Foraker (17,280 ft), dominate the range. McKinley and Foraker both are visible on clear days from Anchorage, 130 miles to the south. About 140 miles east of Mount McKinley a second group of high peaks culminates in Mount Hayes (13,700 ft).

Internally the Alaska Range consists of a great synclinorium flanked by large longitudinal faults (Brooks, 1911, p. 111). In general, Cretaceous rocks along the center of the fold are bounded by Paleozoic and Precambrian rocks in the limbs. All are intruded by bodies of granitic rock, some batholithic in size. Most of the higher peaks, including the Mount McKinley group, consist of granitic rock. The north peak of Mount McKinley is slate and graywacke (Reed, 1961, fig. 2).

The Alaska Range was mostly outside the area markedly affected by the earthquake. Strong ground motion was felt well north of the range, however, and releveling suggests possible uplift of nearly a foot (U.S. Coast and Geodetic Survey, 1965a, p. 16).

COASTAL TROUGH PROVINCE

The Coastal Trough province sustained severe damage in the March 27 earthquake. Damage to properties and manmade structures was related especially to the relatively high local population density and to the behavior of c e r t a i n Pleistocene formations that underlay parts of the area. Landslides, ground cracks, subsidence, and vibration were the chief causes of damage. The province consists of two main lowland belts, the Cook Inlet-Susitna Lowland and the Copper River Lowland, separated by the Talkeetna Mountains. On the east, the Wrangell Mountains project deep into the Copper River Lowland. Wahrhaftig has divided the Coastal Trough province into several sections on the basis of geologic and physiographic distinctions.

COOK INLET-SUSITNA LOWLAND

The Cook Inlet-Susitna Lowland is a deep structural basin more than 200 miles long and about 60–70 miles across. It is bounded by the Alaska and Aleutian Ranges on the west and north and by the Kenai, Chugach, and Talkeetna Mountains on the east. Its surface is mostly less than 500 feet above sea level, and much of it is submerged beneath the Cook Inlet. It contains such well-known subdivisions as the populous Anchorage Lowland, the agricultural Matanuska Valley, and the petroleum-rich Kenai Lowland. It is underlain by thick sequences of poorly consolidated coal-bearing rocks of Tertiary age mantled with glacial, glaciofluvial, and glaciomarine deposits, and flanked by hard-rock mountains on the east and west. Parts of the area

5.—A rock avalanche on the Surprise Glacier near Harriman Fjord, about 50 miles east of Anchorage. Photograph taken May 29, 1964.

6.—Debris flow (avalanche) and Upper Miles Glacier, in the Chugach Mountains near mouth of the Copper River. View east from 6,300 feet, April 19, 1964. The flow is approximately 2 kilometers long.

have been described by Capps (1916) and by Martin, Johnson, and Grant (1915). The Quaternary geology has been described in detail by Karlstrom (1964).

TALKEETNA MOUNTAINS

The little known Talkeetna Mountains are a dissected highland of diverse topography and geology, about 100 miles long north to south and 60–70 miles across west to east. Extremely rugged glacier-covered peaks and ridges in the central part, standing 6,000–8,000 feet above sea level, are carved from a large Jurassic batholith that has intruded older Jurassic volcanics and pre-Jurassic rocks. On the south a large fault (Lake Clark-Castle Mountain fault) separates the hard rocks of the mountains from the softer Cretaceous and Tertiary rocks of the Matanuska Valley. The southeast part of the

Talkeetna Mountains consists of soft Jurassic and Cretaceous sandstones and shales overlain by thick Tertiary basalt flows (Brooks, 1911, pl. 9; Capps, 1940, pl. 2; Grantz, 1961). During the earthquake the southern part of the range subsided as much as 2 feet (U.S. Coast and Geodetic Survey, 1965a, p. 16). Avalanches and landslides were triggered in the upper Matanuska Valley and doubtless occurred in the mountains also.

COPPER RIVER LOWLAND

The Copper River Lowland as here described includes all the area between the Alaska Range on the north, the Wrangell Mountains on the east, the Chugach Mountains on the south, and the Talkeetna Mountains on the west. As thus limited, it includes marginal areas called the Gulkana Upland in the northwest part of the area and

the Lake Louise Plateau in the west (Wahrhaftig, 1966). Thus delineated, it is drained not only by the Copper River itself, but also by the Susitna, which arises in the Alaska Range, flows south into the lowland, then west across the Talkeetna Mountains, and by the Delta River, which heads in the Gulkana upland and flows north across the Alaska Range to the Tanana River. A low pass at the south end of the Talkeetna Mountains connects the Copper River Lowland with the Cook Inlet area by way of the Matanuska Valley. The surface of the lowland ranges in altitude from less than 1,000 feet above sea level where the Copper River enters the Chugach Mountains at Wood Canyon (alt 581 ft at Chitina) to more than 3,500 feet in the Gulkana Upland. Most of the area is underlain by perennially frozen ground, and the surface consequently is dotted with shallow lakes. Several large lakes are of glacial origin. Bedrock in the northern and western parts of the lowland consists chiefly of greenstone and other metavolcanic rocks of late Paleozoic and Triassic age. In the southern part of the lowland, bedrock consists chiefly of sedimentary rock of Mesozoic age. Most of the lowland, however, is mantled with unconsolidated deposits of Pleistocene age. On the east is the volcanic pile of the Wrangell Mountains.

The earthquake caused avalanches, landslides, and ground breakage in the Copper River Lowland. Several buildings were s h i f t e d on their foundations. Throughout the lowland, ice was cracked on lakes and rivers.

WRANGELL MOUNTAINS

The Wrangell Mountains, austere and beautiful, dominate the landscape of the Copper River region. They are a cluster of great ice-capped volcanoes crowded into an area about 100 miles long, northwest to southeast, and 60

miles across, northeast to southwest. To the southeast they merge with the St. Elias Range. Several volcanoes exceed 14,000 feet in altitude, including Mount Blackburn (16,523 ft) the highest in the range, and Mount Sanford (16,208 ft). Historically active Mount Wrangell (14,163 ft) still emits steam and vapors. At least a dozen summits exceed 12,000 feet. The volcanoes rest on a base of deformed Paleozoic and Mesozoic sedimentary and volcanic rocks. During the earthquake the apparent subsidence was less than a

7.—Clastic dikes composed of sand and silt were intruded along fissures into near-surface sediments and overlying snow and ice in the delta of Snow River, Kenai Peninsula. The dikes were left in relief when the snow and ice melted.

foot at the southwest front of the range. Extensive ground cracks formed in the alluvial flats of the larger rivers in the McCarthy area.

PACIFIC BORDER RANGES PROVINCE

The Pacific Border Ranges province contains the epicenter of the March 27 earthquake and most of the land areas of major tectonic deformation. It consists of several mountain ranges, most of which merge laterally with one another. Including some of the world's most rugged mountains, the province forms the mountainous and adjacent coastal lowland border of the Gulf of Alaska, an arcuate belt about 1,000 miles long and 20–110 miles across stretching from Kodiak Island on the southwest to Sitka Island on the southeast. Included as subdivisions are the Kodiak Mountains, Kenai-Chugach Mountains, Gulf of Alaska coastal section, St. Elias Mountains, Fairweather Range, and the mountains of the western part of the Alexander Archipelago (Wahrhaftig and Gates, 1964, p. 27). Only the Kodiak Mountains, Kenai-Chugach Mountains, and the Gulf of Alaska coastal section, described below, were significantly involved in the earthquake, although a large clay-silt mudflow was triggered on Admiralty Island in the Alexander Archipelago near Juneau, 480 miles from the epicenter (oral commun., Keith Hart, Alaska Department of Highways, to Robert D. Miller, U.S. Geological Survey, 1965).

KODIAK MOUNTAINS

The Kodiak Mountains (Wahrhaftig, 1966) are a structural-topographic continuation of the Kenai-Chugach Mountains. They form a rugged northeast-trending divide 2,000–4,000 feet high along

the crestline of Kodiak Island and slope abruptly to the southeast and more gradually to the northwest to an irregular coastline modified by many fjords and islands. The mountains consists mostly of argillite and graywacke of Mesozoic age intruded along the main divide by an elongate granitic batholith of Tertiary age (Dutro and Payne, 1957). Eocene sedimentary rocks along the southeast border of Kodiak Island and in the Trinity Islands to the south are downfaulted against the older rocks. Most of Kodiak Island subsided during the earthquake, but a narrow zone along the southeast coast had no displacement, and the outermost headlands on the southeast coast were elevated. Other effects of the earthquake included landslides and avalanches on the steeper slopes, local subsidence and cracking of many unconsolidated deposits, and the cracking of lake ice (Reuben Kachadoorian and George Plafker, written commun., 1966).

KENAI-CHUGACH MOUNTAINS

The Kenai-Chugach Mountains form the landward closure of Prince William Sound. The greater part of this region subsided during the earthquake, although part of it was elevated. Landslides, avalanches, and ground cracks were abundant (Hackman, 1965, p. 608; Ragle and others, 1965; Post, 1965; Tuthill and Laird, 1966). Wahrhaftig's description (1966, p. 40) of the general topography and geology is quoted as follows:

The Kenai-Chugach Mountains form a rugged barrier along the north coast of the Gulf of Alaska. High segments of the mountains are dominated by extremely rugged east-trending ridges 7,000 to 13,000 feet high. Low segments consist of discrete massive moun-

tains 5 to 10 miles on a side and 3,000 to 6,000 feet high, separated by a reticulate system of through valleys and passes ½ to 1 mile wide that are eroded along joints and cleavage. The entire range has been heavily glaciated and the topography is characterized by horns, aretes, cirques, U-shaped valleys and passes, rock-basin lakes, and grooved and mammilated topography. The south coast is deeply indented by fiords and sounds, and ridges extend southward as chains of islands. The north front is an abrupt mountain wall.

The Kenai-Chugach Mountains are composed chiefly of dark-gray argillite and graywacke of Mesozoic age [some of these rocks are now known to be of Tertiary age (George Plafker, written commun., 1965)], mildly metamorphosed and with a pronounced vertical cleavage that strikes parallel to the trend of the range. In the Prince William Sound area large bodies of greenstone are associated with the argillite and graywacke. A belt of Mesozoic and Paleozoic schist, greenstone, chert, and limestone lies along the north edge of the Kenai and Chugach Mountains. All these rocks are cut by granitoid masses.

All the higher parts of the range are buried in great icefields, from which valley and piedmont glaciers radiate. Many glaciers on the south side of the mountains are tidal.

Although the earthquake caused many snow and rock-slides that avalanched onto glaciers in the Kenai-Chugach Mountains, there were relatively few slides that seemed to be large enough to materially alter the regimens of the glaciers in the manner proposed by Tarr and Martin (1912; Ragle and others, 1965, p. 31, 42). Tarr and Martin attributed rapid advances of glaciers in southeastern Alaska in the first decade of the 20th century to avalanching caused by the great Yakutat earthquakes of 1899, a view disputed recently by Post (1965). The long-term effect of the snow added to the surfaces of the glaciers in the Chugach Mountains, however, will require years to evaluate.

8.—The Hanning Bay fault scarp, Montague Island, looking northeast. Vertical displacement in the foreground, in rock, is about 12 feet; the maximum measured displacement of 15 feet is at the beach ridge near trees in background.

Rock avalanches were more numerous in the Chugach Mountains than in the Kenai Mountains (Ragle and others, 1965, p. 31). A notably large one fell onto the Sherman glacier near Cordova (Post, 1965; George Plafker, oral commun., 1965).

From a study of aerial photographs, Hackman (1965, p. 609) identified 1,958 avalanches and snow slides, 58 combined snow and rock slides, and 20 rock slides in the mountainous areas adjoining Prince William Sound after the March 27 earthquake. It is not known what the normal incidence of spring avalanching is in the Chugach Mountains adjacent to Prince William Sound, or how many of the avalanches were caused by the earthquake, but Hackman suspected that most of them were caused by the earthquake.

GULF OF ALASKA COASTAL SECTION

Wahrhaftig (1966) describes the Gulf of Alaska coastal section as an area of diverse topography carved in Tertiary rocks. It extends about 340 miles along the coast in a strip 2–40 miles wide from the vicinity of Cordova on the west to Icy Point on the east, between the Gulf of Alaska to the south and the high Chugach and St. Elias Mountains to the north. It is basically a coastal plain marked by beach and dune ridges, belts of morainal topography, outwash plains, marine terraces, and enormous piedmont glaciers. It is deeply indented locally by large fjords and by the valley of the Copper River but, for the most part, its coastline is less irregular than that of the rest of southern Alaska. The largest of the piedmont glaciers, the Malaspina, covers an area the size of Rhode Island. The Bering Glacier is almost as large.

Large thrust faults separate the Tertiary rocks of the coast from the older rocks in the mountains. During the earthquake the western part of the section was tectonically elevated; the eastern part was little affected. Uplift died out between the Bering Glacier and Yakataga (Plafker, 1965, p. 1679). Other great earthquakes have centered in this area in the past, including the great Yakutat earthquake of 1899 (Richter magnitude 8.6) and the Lituya Bay earthquake of 1958 (magnitude 8), the latter remembered for the giant waves generated by avalanching of rock into Lituya Bay (Miller, 1960). As a result of the March 27, 1964, earthquake, slides and slumps occurred as far east as Yakataga; unconsolidated deposits cracked and slumped eastward to Yakutat Bay and lake ice cracked as far east as Lituya Bay.

ST. ELIAS MOUNTAINS AND FAIRWEATHER RANGE

The colossal St. Elias Mountains and Fairweather Range are largely peripheral to the region affected markedly by the earthquake but they have had a long history of seismic activity. Iceclad and drained by glaciers, they are the highest coastal mountains in the world. Among them also are some of the highest and most impressive peaks in North America, including Mount Logan (19,850 ft) entirely in Canada, Mount St. Elias (18,008 ft), Mount Vancouver (15,700 ft), Mount Hubbard (14,950 ft), and Mount Fairweather (15,300 ft), all along the international boundary and all visible from tidewater (Bostock, 1948, p. 92). Many other peaks range in height from 12,000 to 17,000 feet. Little is known of the geology. The Alaska part of the mountains is topographically continuous with the Chugach Moun-

tains and is geologically similar. The St. Elias Mountains also merge with the Wrangell Mountains and also contain volcanic rocks. Reconnaissance in the Fairweather-Yakutat Bay area indicates bedded sedimentary and volcanic rocks of Paleozoic and Mesozoic age intensely folded and faulted. Many of the higher peaks are carved from granitic intrusive rocks (Miller, in Williams, 1958, p. 21).

TECTONIC EFFECTS

Tectonic effects of the Alaska earthquake of 1964 have been studied and described in detail by Plafker (1965). Crustal deformation associated with the earthquake was more extensive than any known deformation related to any known previous earthquake. From the Wrangell Mountains at the northeast to the Trinity Islands south of Kodiak, the zone of land-level changes extended southwest through the epicenter a distance of more than 500 miles (Plafker, 1965, fig. 5). From northwest to southeast it extended at least from the west shore of Cook Inlet to Middleton Island in the Gulf of Alaska, a distance of about 200 miles. Crustal warping may have extended inland as far as the Alaska Range and seaward out onto the continental slope of the Aleutian Trench (U.S. Coast and Geodetic Survey, 1965a, p. 15–16). East along the Alaska coast, deformation died out somewhere between the Bering Glacier and Yakataga (Grantz and others, 1964, p. 5). An area of at least 70,000 square miles and possibly 110,000 square miles or more was tectonically elevated or depressed during the earthquake (fig. 9).

Areas of uplift and subsidence are separated by a zero line or axis of tectonic tilting that trends southwestward from the vicinity

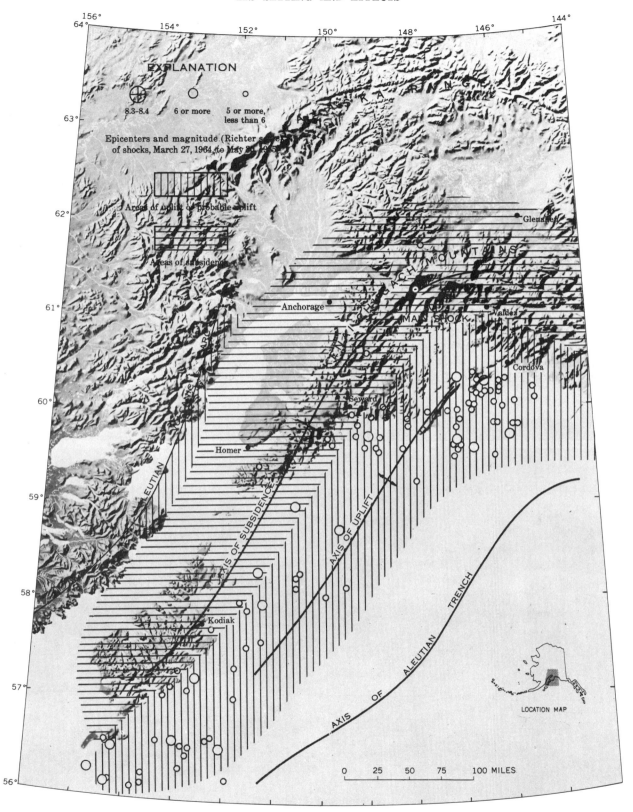

9.—Map of south-central Alaska, showing epicenter of March 27, 1964, earthquake, major aftershocks, and areas of tectonic land-level changes. Most aftershocks centered in the area of uplift along the continental margin of the Aleutian Trench between the Trinity Islands and the epicenter of the main shock. Data chiefly from reports by the U.S. Coast and Geodetic Survey (1964, 1965a), Grantz, Plafker, and Kachadoorian (1964), and Plafker (1965).

[19]

of the epicenter to the seaward side of Kodiak and the Trinity Islands (fig. 9). East from the epicenter the zero line passes approximately through Port Valdez fjord, trends along Heiden Canyon east of Valdez (H. W. Coulter, written commun., 1965), and crosses the Copper River Valley about 50 miles above the mouth (Plafker, 1965, fig. 5; Coulter and Migliaccio, 1966). Areas north and northwest of the hingeline subsided; areas south and southeast arose. A line of maximum subsidence about coincided with the mountain axes of the Kenai Peninsula and Kodiak Island, where downwarping exceeded 6 feet; uplift over wide areas of Prince Wil-

10 (left).—Reddish-brown spruce trees in foreground were drowned when gravel spit in Resurrection Bay area subsided about 3 feet.

liam Sound exceeded 6 feet and, in an area of surface rupture on Montague Island, locally exceeded 30 feet (Plafker, 1965). This uplift deleteriously affected shipping lanes and harbor facilities in parts of Prince William Sound; docks at Cordova and elsewhere were left high and dry during times of low tide.

Southwest from Montague Island, where bottom soundings show seaward continuations of new fault scraps along old fault lines on the island, the sea bottom was uplifted locally more than 50 feet (Malloy, 1964, p.

11 (left).—Uplifted sea floor at Cape Clear, Montague Island, in the area of greatest recorded uplift on land (33 feet). The white coating, about a quarter of a mile wide, consists of the remains of calcareous marine organisms that were killed by dessication when their sea-floor home was lifted above high tide.

1048). Inferred large-scale uplift of the continental shelf and slope southeast of Montague Island probably generated the seismic sea waves that spread across the Pacific Ocean (Van Dorn, 1964, p. 186; Plafker, 1965, p. 1680). Much, if not all, of the uplift probably accompanied the few minutes of most violent ground shaking during the earthquake (Plafker, 1965, p. 1680).

Tectonic changes, both up and down, caused extensive damage to the biota in such areas as coastal forests, migratory-bird nesting grounds, salmon spawning waters, and shellfish habitats. These effects are described further in subsequent paragraphs. Land-level changes at Alaskan coastal communities are shown in table 1 (p. 19).

EFFECTS ON COMMUNITIES

Earthquake damage to the cities, towns, and villages of southern Alaska was caused by direct seismic vibration, ground breakage, mud or sand emission from cracks, ground lurching, subaerial and submarine landslides, fires, sea waves, and land-level changes (Grantz and others, 1964). Not all these factors caused damage in every community. Some communities were devastated by only one; the village of Chenega, for example, was destroyed by a sea wave. Overall, landslides probably caused the most damage to manmade structures and property, but sea waves took the most lives.

Effects of one factor cannot always be separated from effects of another. Thus, at Seward (Grantz and others, 1964, p. 15; Lemke, 1966) the waterfront was racked by vibration, slides, sea waves, fires, subsidence, and ground cracks. All these factors

contributed significantly to the havoc, and all in combination wiped out the economic base of the town. Comparable damage at Valdez, plus the threat of recurrent damage in the future, forced relocation of the village and abandonment of the present townsite (Coulter and Migliaccio, 1966).

Most of the small coastal villages in the earthquake zone were damaged chiefly by sea waves, subsidence, or both (Kachadoorian, 1965). Among the larger towns, only Cordova was significantly damaged by uplift, but the native village of Tatitlek and several canneries and residences at Sawmill Bay on Evans Island were also adversely affected by uplift.

Direct vibratory damage was significant chiefly in Anchorage and Whittier, although minor vibratory damage was widespread through the area of intense shaking. At Anchorage several buildings were destroyed by vibration, and nearly all multistory buildings were damaged (Berg and Stratta, 1964; McMinn, 1964; National Board of Fire Underwriters and Pacific Fire Rating Bureau, 1964; Hansen, 1965). At Seward, Valdez, and Whittier, ground vibrations ruptured oil storage tanks, and the spilled petroleum quickly caught fire.

Ground breakage caused extensive damage in Anchorage, Seward, Whittier, and Valdez, not only to buildings but also to buried utilities such as water, sewer, gas, electric, and telephone lines. Cracked ground resulted from the passage of sinusoidal seismic waves through the soil, from lurching, from lateral spreading of soils under gravity, especially near the heads of landslides, and from differential settlement of alluvial and artificial fills.

Mud and sand were pumped from ground cracks throughout the damage zone where water tables were shallow in saturated granular soil. At Valdez, and to a lesser extent at Seward (Forest Acres), large volumes of sediment were ejected from cracks into cellars and crawl spaces (Coulter and Migliaccio, 1966; R. W. Lemke, oral commun., 1965).

Submarine and subaerial landslides triggered by the earthquake caused spectacular damage in Anchorage, Seward, Valdez, Whittier, and Homer (Engineering Geology Evaluation Group, 1964; Grantz and others, 1964; Shannon and Wilson, Inc., 1964; Hansen, 1965; Lemke, 1966; Coulter and Migliaccio, 1966; Kachadoorian, 1965; Waller, 1966). Four large slides in built-up parts of Anchorage were caused by failures along bluff lines in soft, sensitive silty clay whose water content at critical depths exceeded its liquid limit. Failure at Anchorage was mostly subaerial, although the large Turnagain Heights slide failed partly below sea level and slipped part way down the mudflat into Knik Arm of Cook Inlet. At Valdez and Seward, violent shaking spontaneously liquified granular deltaic materials; slumping which initiated well below sea level carried away the waterfronts of both towns. The seaward slopes of the deltas, moreover, were left less stable after the earthquake than they were before.

Estimates by the Federal Reconstruction a n d Development Planning Commission for Alaska, as of August 12, 1964, indicated that total property damage to Alaska by the earthquake exceeded $311 million (fig. 13). This figure does not include loss of personal property or in-

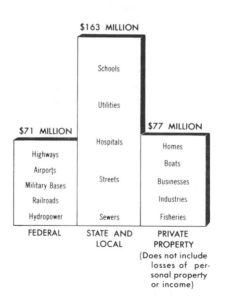

12 (above).—Transverse fissure in Valdez at corner of McKinley St. and Keystone Ave. Note damage to cinderblock building where the main fissure, foreground, intersects it. Similar ground fractures, with or without sand and mud spouts caused much damage to streets, utilities, and buildings in many parts of the earthquake-affected area.

13 (left).—Earthquake damages in Alaska. From estimates by the Office of Emergency Planning (1964a).

come. Not only was the economic base of entire communities destroyed, but the resultant loss of income severely crippled the economy of the whole State and deprived Alaska of a major share of its tax base at the time when funds were most needed to aid in restoration.

As also pointed out by the Federal Reconstruction and Development Planning Commission, the disaster struck at the heart of the State's economy, inasmuch as nearly half the people of the State reside in the stricken area. About 100,000 of the State's estimated 265,000 people live in the greater Anchorage area alone. Anchorage, because of its size, bore the brunt of property damage, but the per capita damage and the actual death toll were much greater in many smaller towns. Although

the combined population of Chenega, Kodiak, Seward, Valdez, and Whittier is less than 9,000 people, each of these communities lost more lives than Anchorage.

Despite the extensive damage at Anchorage to residence and business properties, utilities, and transportation, a large segment of the economy was intact, and recovery was relatively rapid. But at many small towns and villages, where virtually entire populations were dependent on one or two industrial enterprises—fisheries, for example—the effects of the earthquake were staggering. Whole fishing fleets, harbor facilities, and canneries were destroyed.

The native villages of Chenega, Kaguyak, Old Harbor, and Afognak, all remote waterfront fishing villages, were nearly or completely destroyed by waves, especially

Chenega, population 80 before the earthquake. There, 23 lives were lost, and only the schoolhouse remained of the village's buildings. Six homes were left standing at Old Harbor, where there had been about 35. There were nine homes in Kaguyak and a Russian Orthodox Church; all were carried away or destroyed. At Afognak, four homes, the community hall, and the grocery store were carried away by waves; several other homes were moved partly off their foundations (Alaska Depart. Health and Welfare, 1964b); and subsidence made the townsite uninhabitable. The sites of Chenega, Kaguyak, and Afognak have been abandoned in favor of new townsites.

Earthquake damages to communities of Alaska are summarized in table 1.

TABLE 1.—*Summary of earthquake damages to Alaskan communities*

Place	Population [1] 1960	Deaths (total, 114)	Subsidence	Uplift	Landslides — Land	Landslides — Submarine	Ground cracks	Vibration	Waves	Fire	Townsite acreage (est.) Total	Damaged	Percent	Premises (est.) Total	Damaged	Homes	Business and public	Military	Harbor	Water supply	Other utilities	Highways	Airports
Afognak	190	0	×						×		20	2	10	38	23	×	×		×	×	0	×	
Anchorage	[2] 44,237	9			×		×	×			4,500	700	14	15,000	750	×	×	×	×	×	0	×	×
Cape St. Elias	4	1			×				×														
Chenega	80	23		×					×		20	20	100	20	20	×							
Chugiak	51	0												0	0					×			
Cordova	1,128	0		×			×		×		200	20	10	400	40	×	×		×	×	×		
Cordova FAA airport	40	0					×	×			20	1	5	0	0	×	×			×		×	×
Eagle River	130	0		×													×			×			
Ellemar	1	0														×	×						
Girdwood	63	0	×				×									×	×						
Homer	1,247	0	×			×			×							×	×			×			
Hope	44	0	×								10	3	30		10	×							
Kadiak Fisheries Cannery	2		×				×		×					15	15	×	×		×	×			
Kaguyak	36	3							×		15			15	15	×	×						
Kodiak	[3] 2,628	15	×						×		285	31	11	1,100	130	×	×	×	×	×	×	×	×
McCord	8						×		×							×	×						
Old Harbor	193	0							×		30			38	35	×	×		×	×	0		
Ouzinkie	214	0	×						×		50		10	38	6	×	×						
Point Nowell	1	1							×					1	1	×							
Point Whitshed		1			×				×						10	×							
Portage	71	0	×				×						20			×	×			0		×	
Port Ashton		1							×					0		×							
Port Nellie Juan	3	3	×						×					0		×	×		×	×			
Seldovia	460	0	×													×	×		×				
Seward	1,891	13	×			×	×		×	×	400	400	100	700	200	×	×	×	×	×	×	×	×
Tatitlek		0			×											×	×						
Valdez	1,000	31	×			×	×		×	×	300	300	100	200	40	×	×		×	×	×	×	×
Whittier	70	13	×				×	×	×	×	30	10	35	30	10	×	×	×	×	×	×	×	×

[1] Alaska Depart. Health and Welfare (1964).
[2] 82,833 including military personnel.
[3] 4,788 including personnel at Kodiak Naval Station.

[23]

14 (left).—Remains of the Native village of Chenega, Prince William Sound, after devastation by waves.

15 (below).—Damage to railroad yard and petroleum tank farm at Seward, looking northwest. The extensive damage at Seward, as at Whittier and some other towns, was caused by a combination of submarine slides, waves and fire.

16 —Hinchinbrook Coast Guard dock, raised above all but the highest tides by regional uplift in Prince William Sound. Docks at Cordova and elsewhere were also made useless by the same uplift.

17 (below).—Scarp at the subsidence trough or graben of the Fourth Avenue slide, Anchorage. The graben dropped 11 feet in response to 14 feet of horizontal movement of the slide block.

18.—The 1200 L Street apartment building in Anchorage that was severely damaged by shaking during the earthquake. Note X-shaped fractures caused by vertical shear.

19.—The Alaska Sales and Service building in Anchorage, which was under construction, partially collapsed during the earthquake. The building was constructed of prestressed concrete roof T's which rested on precast reinforced concrete T-columns; it had precast reinforced concrete walls.

20.—Store building in Anchorage wrecked by seismic shaking.

21.—Toe of Turnagain Heights landslide exposed at low tide as viewed from new bluff line, looking northeast toward Anchorage waterfront. Trees that formerly stood 70 feet above sea level were swept downward and outward into Knik Arm by mass movement of landslide.

22.—A wooden fence which lay athwart the toe of the L Street landslide, Anchorage, was buckled and shortened by compression.

DAMAGE TO TRANSPORTATION FACILITIES

THE ALASKA RAILROAD

Damage to The Alaska Railroad, totaling about $27 million (Office of Emergency Planning, 1964a), has been described briefly by Grantz, Plafker, and Kachadoorian (1964, p. 24). It has been investigated more fully by McCulloch and Bonilla. Most of the damage was along the 150 miles of trackage between the terminal at Seward and Anchorage (fig. 24). Damage to the terminal and marshaling yards at Seward (described by Lemke, 1966), was caused by submarine slumping and waves. Two railroad docks valued at $4 million were completely destroyed, together with $2 million of freight and 50 freight cars. Between Seward and Anchorage, damage was caused by direct seismic shaking, landslides, subsidence, ground cracks and lurching, and inundation by high tides. Seventeen bridges were damaged or destroyed. Ground slumping along the right-of-way was severe at Kenai Lake and at Potter. Inundation and current scour were severe near Portage. Snow avalanches covered trackage along Turnagain Arm. At Anchorage,

23.—Rail and highway net of south-central Alaska. Damage to these routes was heaviest between Anchorage and Seward. Heavy damage was sustained also along the Copper River Highway east of Cordova.

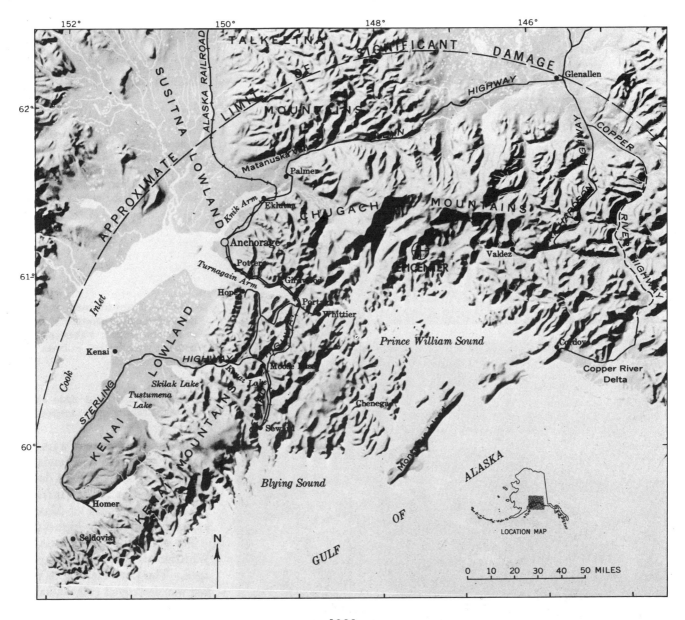

24 (above).—The rails in this approach to a bridge near the head of Turnagain Arm were torn from their ties and buckled laterally by streamward movement of the riverbanks.

25 (left).—Railroad yard and warehouse damage at Seward caused by submarine slides, waves and fire. Looking west toward railroad warehouses and docks.

26 (left).—Potter Hill slide on The Alaska Railway near Anchorage.

shops and rolling stock were damaged by vibration and landslides. North of Anchorage light damage was reported as far as Hurricane. Trackage just south of Matanuska was inundated by high tides.

The spur line from Portage to Whittier was also severely damaged. The port facility at Whittier was destroyed (Kachadoorian, 1965).

HIGHWAYS

Most of the following information is abstracted from Grantz, Plafker, and Kachadoorian (1964). Subsequent, more detailed studies have been made by Kachadoorian. Highway damage resulted chiefly from destruction of bridges and cracking, collapse, or differential compaction of fills that rested on unconsolidated deposits. Estimates for repairs alone came to about $21 million (Alaska Construction Consultants Committee, 1964). Repairs plus upgrading to higher standards may come to $55–$65 million. The Seward Highway was severely damaged between Ingram Creek and Potter, where 22 bridges were

27 (right).—Fissures in Seward Highway near The Alaska Railroad station at Portage, at head of Turnagain Arm. Many bridges were also damaged and at some places tectonic subsidence and consolidation of alluvial materials dropped both highway and railroad below high-tide levels.

destroyed. Between Potter and Anchorage there were many pavement breaks caused by differential subsidence of fills. Damage was light on the Richardson Highway between Glennallen and Valdez. Lurching displaced the alinement laterally at mile 69, and just outside Valdez there were many pavement breaks where large ground cracks crossed the highway (Coulter and Migliaccio, 1966).

28 (right).—Richardson Highway near mile 69, showing offsets of center line stripe caused by lurching. Road embankment shifted to right without appreciable vertical offset. Chugach Mountains in background.

[31]

29.—One span of the Million Dollar truss bridge of the former Copper River and Northwestern Railroad was dropped into the Copper River by the earthquake, and the other truss spans were shifted on their piers.

30.—Twentymile River Bridge near Turnagain Arm of Cook Inlet. The bridge fell into the river and some of the wood piles were driven through the reinforced concrete deck. The adjacent steel railroad bridge (upper right) survived with only minor damage. Both bridges were founded on thick deposits of soft alluvium and tidal flat mud and were subjected to severe seismic vibration.

The partly completed Copper River Highway was severely damaged from Allen glacier to Cordova. Nearly every bridge along the route was seriously damaged or destroyed, including the famous Million Dollar Bridge.

North from Anchorage the Glenn Highway received mostly minor damage. Part of the highway, however, was inundated by high tides near Eklutna, and the piers of the Knik River Bridge were damaged. Damage was light on the Sterling Highway between Moose Pass and Homer, except that a bridge was destroyed across the outlet of Kenai Lake (McCulloch, 1966). At Homer, about 4½ miles of road along Homer Spit was inundated by high tides and damaged by waves and currents. Homer Spit subsided 4–6 feet during the earthquake (Waller, 1966; Stanley in Waller, 1966).

Near Kodiak, highways were severely damaged by sea waves and by tectonic subsidence.

AIRPORTS

Damage to airports was relatively minor, although loss estimates totaled about $3.3 million (Alaska Construction Consultants Committee, 1964). Greatest damage was at Anchorage International Airport, where a life was lost when the control tower collapsed under sustained seismic vibration and where minor damage was sustained by other buildings. Also, 20,000 barrels of aviation fuel was lost from a ruptured storage tank. Runways and taxi strips were only slightly damaged.

At Elmendorf Air Force Base just north of Anchorage, the control tower was damaged by cracks from its base to a height of about 15 feet. In Cordova, Homer, Kodiak Naval Station, Seldovia, Seward, and Valdez, damage to runways and taxi strips was mostly light.

31 (right).—An indication of the violence of the surge-waves that struck Whittier.

32 (below).—Ground cracks damaged runway at Cordova Airport. Similar cracks formed on the taxiways.

33.—Fire, wave, and submarine slide damage to railroad and port facilities at Whittier.

PORTS AND HARBORS

Water transportation is one of Alaska's vital links with the outside world and is the base for one of her major industries, commercial fishing. Many Alaska communities can be reached only by water or air. The severe damage to port and harbor facilities, therefore, was a staggering blow to the State's economy and health. Moreover, destruction of The Alaska Railroad terminal and port facilities at Seward and Whittier, coupled with the destruction of the highway port at Valdez, deprived Alaska of any ice-free, all-weather ship terminals.

Ports and harbors sustained heavy damage from several different causes. Damage by direct seismic vibration generally was subordinate to other secondary causes. Submarine slides, sea waves, ground cracks, fires, subsidence, and uplift all took large tolls. Hardest hit in terms of port and harbor facilities damaged or destroyed were Seward, Valdez, Kodiak, Whittier, Cordova, and Homer. Listed below are estimated major damage losses to ports and harbors; these figures have been gathered from several sources, but mainly from estimates by the

Alaska Construction Consultant Committee (1964).

Community	Damage
Seward	$15, 375, 000
Valdez	3, 585, 000
Kodiak (excluding Naval facilities)	2, 165, 000
Whittier	[1] 5, 000, 000
Cordova	1, 645, 000
Homer	[2] 460, 000
Woody Island FAA Station	158, 000
Seldovia	[3] 25, 000
Kodiak Naval Station	11, 000, 000

[1] Total damage—port facilities not itemized separately.
[2] Excludes $1,250,000 estimate for new small-boat harbor.
[3] Estimated cost of raising canneries, commercial buildings, and boardwalk is additional $1,750,000.

Submarine sliding at Seward, Valdez, and Whittier generated large local waves that added to the destruction already caused by the slides and shaking (Kachadoorian, 1965; Coulter and Migliaccio, 1966; Lemke, 1966). Except at Whittier, subsequent damage was then caused by seismic sea waves generated in the Gulf of Alaska or possibly by seiches (standing waves: Van Dorn, 1964, p. 166; Plafker, 1965; Plafker and Mayo, 1965). When seismic vibration sundered petroleum storage tanks in Seward, Valdez, and Whittier, the contents quickly caught fire and added to the devastation. At Seward and Valdez, burning oil that was swept into the bay by submarine sliding was carried back across the waterfront by the returning surge of water; docks, piers, and small-boat harbors were thus destroyed by water and fire. At Seward, tugs, fishing boats, and a tanker were washed ashore. At Valdez, more than 40 boats were smashed. At Whittier, the railroad port facilities were swept away.

At Kodiak, damage was caused mostly by a succession of huge seismic sea waves, intensified by tectonic subsidence of 5–6 feet. Forty percent of the business district and many homes were destroyed, as well as 30 percent of the fishing industry facilities and most of the fishing fleet (Tudor, 1964, table 1 and p. 41). Some vessels were washed several city blocks inland where they collided with buildings and houses like great battering rams. At Kodiak Naval Station more than $11 million damage was inflicted on buildings, materials, and equipment by 30-foot sea waves and by subsidence (Tudor, 1964, fig. 3). Piers were covered by 10 feet of water, and the buoyed-up superstructure of the cargo pier shifted off its pilings. Boat-repair shops, gear-storage buildings, and warehouses were damaged or swept out to sea (Stroh, 1964, p. 254).

Port and harbor facilities at Cordova were damaged chiefly by tectonic uplift of about 6 feet and subordinately by sea waves. Although the immediate effect of uplift was to minimize wave

34.—Fire and wave damage to Seward port facilities.

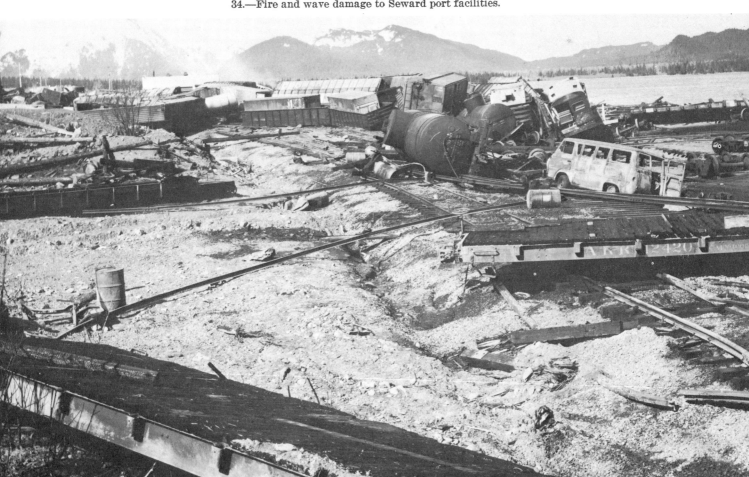

damage, it placed docks and piers beyond reach of shipping during low tides. Boats were grounded in the small boat harbor, Orca Inlet shoaled, and passages through the adjacent islands became unnavigable.

Facilities at Homer were damaged by subsidence and submarine landsliding. Wave damage was minimal (Waller, 1966). The small-boat harbor disappeared into a "funnel-shaped" pool, and a lighthouse that had been on the harbor breakwater subsided into 40–50 feet of water (Grantz and others, 1964, p. 24). Homer Spit,

a gravel bar that extends 5 miles into Kachemak Bay and on which various commercial buildings and storage tanks were placed, subsided 4–6 feet, partly by local compaction and lateral spreading and partly by regional tectonic lowering (Grantz and others, 1964). During subsequent high tides, facilities on the bar were inundated.

Facilities at Seldovia sustained damage chiefly from subsidence. At Woody Island FAA facility outside Kodiak, docks and storage tanks were damaged by seismic sea waves and subsidence. A cannery at Shearwater Bay was

thrown off its foundations by the earthquake and later destroyed by waves. At Cape St. Elias lighthouse, about 135 miles southeast of the epicenter, a coastguardsman was injured by a rockslide and later drowned by seismic waves (Grantz and others, 1964, p. 6).

The Port of Anchorage was damaged by ground displacements along fractures and by direct seismic shaking. The main pier lurched laterally 5–19 inches. It sustained large longitudinal and transverse cracks, and several buildings were cracked. Gantry

35.—Tsunamis washed many vessels into the heart of Kodiak. A section of the harbor and partly submerged breakwater can be seen in upper left.

cranes on the pier were damaged when they jumped their tracks. Approach roads settled as much as 18 inches. Cement-storage tanks were toppled. Bulk petroleum tanks were ruptured, and large quantities of fuel were lost (Berg and Stratta, 1964, p. 44).

Throughout coastal areas of the damage zone many fishing vessels and other small craft were destroyed by direct wave action or by being battered against docks or the shore. Boats in harbors or tied to docks were hit hardest; vessels underway in deep water were generally undamaged; one fishing boat was sunk with all hands while underway in shallow waters near Kodiak.

ATMOSPHERIC EFFECTS

Widespread atmospheric effects are sometimes associated with large earthquakes; some have been documented (Richter, 1958, p. 128; Benioff and Gutenberg, 1939, p. 421; Van Dorn, 1964, p. 174). An atmospheric pressure wave attributed to the Alaskan earthquake was recorded by microbarographs at Scripps Institute of Oceanography at La Jolla, Calif., more than 2,000 miles from the epicenter, and at the University of California at Berkeley (Van Dorn, 1964, p. 174; Christensen and Bolt, 1964, p. 1208). This wave must have passed unnoticed at many other stations. It resembled air waves previously recorded from the detonation of large nuclear explosions. The wave traveled at acoustical velocity, reaching La Jolla 3 hours and 19 minutes after the onset of the earthquake (at 06:55 Gmt, March 28, 1965); it was, therefore, the atmospheric counterpart of the seismic sea waves generated in the Gulf of Alaska. Like the seismic sea waves, the air wave must have been caused by the tectonic uplift of the sea floor and the overlying water column. To displace the atmosphere in the form of a pressure wave, uplift must have been very rapid over a very large area, and must have coincided with the time of the most violent earth tremors (Van Dorn, 1964, p. 173–174; Plafker, 1965, p. 1680).

The earthquake also generated ordinary sound waves of very low subaudible frequencies in the atmosphere.[1] These sound waves were recorded by the National Bureau of Standards at microphone stations in Washington, D.C., Boulder, Colo., and Boston, Mass. Sound waves were radiated by the earthquake at the epicenter and by seismic waves passing through the earth remote from the epicenter, exciting the atmosphere with their passage. Thus, the Rocky Mountains and the Mississippi delta were local sources of sound as they vibrated with the passage of the shock. In addition, Rayleigh waves (surface seismic waves) crossing the continent displaced the ground surface about 2 inches in the conterminous United States and produced strong subaudible sound waves that traveled vertically upward to the ionosphere, amplifying greatly as they ascended. The ionosphere, in turn, oscillated up and down at a rate of several hundred yards per second in motions that were detected by means of reflected radio waves broadcast from one ground station to another.

Atmospheric waves coupled to surface seismic waves were also recorded by a barograph at Berkeley. These waves started at Berkeley about 14 minutes after the onset of the quake and lasted about 4 hours (Christensen and Bolt, 1964, p. 1208).

Localized atmospheric effects in Alaska were related to avalanches triggered by the earthquake in the Chugach Mountains (Tuthill and Laird, 1966). Around the peripheries of large snow avalanches, trees were toppled by pressure blasts as the snow plummeted downward. Air blasts commonly accompany large fast-moving avalanches, whether such avalanches are triggered by earthquakes or not. The chief prerequisite is a large cross section of dense swiftly traveling snow (or rock), and the accompanying blast may be caused both by the frontal thrust of the snow and the vacuum created by its passage (Church, 1942, p. 135). Another local effect was a distribution of dust as thin coatings on glaciers adjacent to rock avalanches throughout the Prince William Sound region.

POSSIBLE MAGNETIC EFFECTS

Magnetic disturbances that began 1 hour 4 minutes before the earthquake momentarily increased the magnetic field at Kodiak by as much as 100 gammas (Moore, 1964, p. 508). Moore has inferred a possible causal relationship between the magnetic disturbances and the earthquake, and a possible means, therefore, of predicting major earthquakes by magnetic monitoring. Why abrupt magnetic disturbances should precede an earthquake is unknown, but "one possibility is that the magnetic events which preceded the Alaska earthquake resulted from piezomagnetic effects of rocks undergoing a change in stress" (Moore, 1964, p. 509).

---

[1] Reported by J. M. Young and R. K. Cook in papers presented at the meeting of the Acoustical Society of America in Washington, D.C., June 2–5, 1965.

36.—Uplifted wave-cut sea floor at Cape Clear, Montague Island. Shows white coating of desiccated calcareous marine organisms and brown stipes or "stalks" of kelp. The stalks are about 2 feet long.

BIOLOGIC EFFECTS

Probably few earthquakes have so strongly affected the fauna and flora of a region as did the Alaska earthquake of 1964. Moreover, because of the complex interrelations of one organism to another, the total biologic effects will not be known for a long time. In the littoral zones of the Prince William Sound region, of the Kenai Peninsula, Kodiak and elsewhere, large communities of organisms were adversely affected when pronounced crustal changes completely altered the ecologic setting of the shore. Broad expanses of shore and sea bottom were elevated above tide water in Prince William Sound, and innumerable marine organisms were exterminated. Effects were equally marked in the subsided upper end of Turnagain Arm near Girdwood and Portage, where coastal marshlands and forest were inundated by salt water—areas that formerly had provided winter forage for moose and nesting grounds for migratory birds. Extensive forested and grassland areas on Kodiak and Afognak Islands were drowned, also.

Hanna (1964, p. 24) has summarized the biologic effects of the earthquake in the littoral zone of Prince William Sound, and he portrays the extent of the depopulation in the following passage:

The exposed areas spread out before the observer are many hundreds of square miles, once densely populated by a varied fauna and flora, now completely desolated. Many of the great array of marine animals that you read about when you study zoology are dead. There is now no littoral zone anywhere that the land went up 10 feet or more. Most of the soft-bodied creatures had decomposed or had become food for birds by the time of our visit, 2 months after the earthquake, so the odor was not overpowering. The great array of living marine plants, so conspicuous along most coastlines, was gone. The *Fucus* had turned black from thirst; the calcareous algae were bleached white and so were the many species of green algae. The great fields of big brown kelp were gone, but the individual stalks left their stems and holdfasts, black and bent over, a menace to the unwary footman.

In many places there were great accumulations of dried starfish; and in one, the dried necks of clams formed a solid mass covering about a square yard. We left to speculation the manner in which these objects came to congregate. In some places a shovel could have been used to collect almost pure concentrations of small shells. Bleached remains of Bryozoa and calcareous algae were so white that the rocky beaches rivalled the snow covered adjacent mountains in brightness.

During studies that are still in progress, G D. Hanna and George Plafker jointly examined the distribution of tectonically disturbed zones of sessile organisms. Some of these organisms, such as barnacles and various algae, grow in response to rigorous water-depth controls, and their postearthquake vertical distribution above or below mean high-tide level provides a reliable measure of land displacement where geodetic control is unavailable (Tarr and Martin, 1912, p. 29; Plafker, 1965).

Other deleterious effects on organisms were caused by sea waves.

In addition to the enormous direct destruction caused by the waves themselves, salt water invaded many coastal lakes and destroyed, at least temporarily, the fresh-water habitat. Spawning beds for salmon in some instances were destroyed by siltation in river deltas. Direct kills of eggs and fry were caused by disturbance of the gravel beds of streams (Alaska Dept. Fish and Game, 1965).

Fish populations were also destroyed when streams and lakes temporarily lost water into ground cracks, or when streams were dammed by landslides (Alaska Dept. Fish and Game, 1965). On the other hand, subsidence in some areas opened miles of new spawning habitat by

inundating previously impassable falls and velocity barriers in coastal streams.

The salmon fishery is one of Alaska's foremost resources, and the full impact of the quake on this fishery will not be realized until the matured 1964 hatch returns from the sea to spawn. Spawning areas for pink and chum salmon, which are intertidal spawners, received major damage in nearly all coastal sections affected by sea waves, uplift, or subsidence (Thorsteinson, 1964). On Kodiak and Afognak Islands, moreover, the waves struck at a critical time when pink salmon fry were just moving from the spawning beds into the stream estuaries. Spawning areas for red

37.—Tectonically elevated shoreline, Latouche Island, Prince William Sound. Heavy white encrustation of barnacles, topped by reddish-brown fucus, marks former mean high-water line. Uplift was about 10 feet.

and silver salmon were little affected by the earthquake (Alaska Dept. Fish and Game, 1965).

Sport fisheries, including salmon, trout, char, and smelt, all were damaged by environmental disturbances, chiefly by subsidence, emergence, and salt-water pollution, especially in spawning areas.

Vast numbers of red snapper (red rock cod) were exterminated in Port Valdez, Port Wells, and in the area between Knight Island, Chenega Island, and Evans Island, possibly by turbulence or sudden upwelling associated with submarine slumping, or perhaps by sudden pressure changes caused by the passage of high-amplitude surface waves (H. W. Coulter, written commun., 1965). Countless thousands of these fish, which normally are bottom dwellers in deep water, were left floating dead at the surface (Grantz and others, 1964, p. 13; Hanna, 1964, p. 25; Coulter and Migliaccio, 1966).

Mortalities of dungeness crab were noted in the Copper River delta area after the earthquake, but the commercial catch appears to have been unaffected. King Crab, a deeper water species, apparently was not significantly affected by the earthquake.

Although the total crab population itself was not markedly affected by the earthquake, the crab industry was severely damaged by the loss of boats, gear, harbor facilities, and canneries. The loss of fishing vessels amounted to about $7 million and of related facilities to about $13 million. To some extent the loss was offset on the market by unusually heavy catches of crab during the 1964 season, so that the crab harvest was actually larger than usual (Office of Emergency Planning, 1964a, p. 23).

Much of the commercial clam habitat in Prince William Sound and in the Copper River delta was damaged or destroyed (Alaska Dept. Fish and Game, 1965, p. 52). The estimated total loss of clam habitat in the sound was 43 percent, and the reduction in the amount of commercially accessible clam habitat was 31 percent. (More recent observations by G D. Hanna, oral commun., 1965, led him to believe that the clam mortality was closer to 90 percent.) In the Copper River delta and vicinity there was a high mortality of razor clams, duck clams, and cockles. At the Cordova small-boat harbor, for example, the loss of commercial size cockles was about 3.6 per square foot. Razor clams were exterminated on the higher bars of the Copper River delta. The mortality of duck clams was as high as 324 per square foot in the Martin River Slough on the east side of the Copper River delta. Duck clams are an important food for sea ducks, divers, and other birds, as well as for the starry flounder. Recovery of clams as a commercial resource is expected to be slow. Many of the new beach areas are now unsuited for clam habitat. In suitable areas, moreover, reseeded clams will require 8 to 12 years of growth before reaching commercial size (Alaska Dept. Fish and Game, 1965, p. 52).

The effects of the earthquake on terrestrial wildlife are mixed, and some short-term effects have even been beneficial. Again, only time will disclose the long-term effects. In the mountains, some mountain goats are reported to have been killed by avalanches, and there probably was some mortality among mountain sheep, deer, and moose. Although uplift adversely affected shellfish habi-

tats, it favorably altered nesting habitats of ducks, geese, and trumpeter swans by eliminating flood dangers. The long-term ecology may be less favorable—a new balance will be established as brush gradually invades upland areas and emergent vegetation spreads over former mudflats; nesting places will shift accordingly (Olson, 1964; J. W. Brooks, Director, Div. Game, Alaska Dept. Fish and Game, written commun. to U.S. Bureau Commercial Fisheries, Jan. 12, 1965). In tectonically subsided areas where extensive fresh-water marshlands and meadows have been invaded by salt water, populations of moose and other grazing animals will have to readjust downward to the new restricted food supply.

DAMAGE OUTSIDE ALASKA

Secondary damage effects of the earthquake reached far beyond Alaska as seismic sea waves generated on the continental shelf in the Gulf of Alaska spread rapidly across the Pacific Ocean to Hawaii, Japan, and Antarctica. The source mechanism of the waves has been investigated by Van Dorn (1964), who concluded that the waves were caused by the sudden displacement of water in the Gulf of Alaska, accompanying the uplift of thousands of square miles of sea floor. A maximum wave height of 4 feet was reported in the Antarctic Peninsula (Palmer Peninsula), but heights in Japan were only a foot or so (Van Dorn, 1964, p. 187). Hilo, Hawaii, had a 7-foot wave, but received only minor damage. Apparently the source was directional, the waves radiating preferentially southeastward. Wave heights thus were greater along the North American coast than they were in the Aleutian Islands at comparable distances from the source.

As the train of sea waves advanced southward it spread damage in British Columbia, Washington, Oregon, and California. Heavy damage was localized in Alberni and Port Alberni, B.C., in Hot Springs Cove, B.C., and in Crescent City, Calif. (U.S. Coast and Geodetic Survey, 1964, p. 40). At Alberni and Port Alberni, damage to houses and a forest-industries complex totaled several million dollars; 260 houses were damaged, 60 heavily. Of the 17 homes at Hot Springs Cove, 5 were washed away and 10 were heavily damaged.

The coast of Washington was damaged lightly. In Grays Harbor County, the waves destroyed a bridge across the Copalis River and overturned several trailer houses (Tudor, 1964, p. 4).

The Oregon coast was struck by 10- to 14-foot waves. Damage was concentrated in estuaries; a family of four was drowned at De Poe Bay. At Seaside, where a trailer park was flooded as water backed up the Necanicum River, damaged totalled about $250,000. At Cannon Beach, damages totalled $250,000; power and telephone services were cut off and several houses were toppled off their foundations. At Gold Coast, docks and small boats were smashed in the Rogue River (Tudor, 1964, p. 4). At Coos Bay, an initial wave 10 feet above mean high water was attenuated by crossing wide tidal flats before it reached Pony Point 7 miles up the channel, but at Florence an 8-foot wave travel-ing up a narrow channel was negligibly dissipated (Schatz and others, 1964, p. 231).

In California, minor harbor damage was sustained as far south as San Diego where small craft were destroyed and dock installations were damaged. In San Francisco Bay, water surging through the Golden Gate set adrift a ferry boat and a house boat, and caused about $1 million damage to small boats and berthing facilities at San Rafael. At Santa Cruz, a 35-foot floating dredge was set adrift and a 38-foot power cruiser was crushed (Tudor, 1964, p. 4).

At Crescent City, which bore the brunt of wave damage in California, 12 lives were lost despite a 1-hour tsunami warning. Eight boats were sunk, 3 are unaccounted for, and 15 capsized. Docks, harbor facilities, and the seawall were heavily damaged. Fifty-four homes were destroyed, 13 were heavily damaged, and 24 were slightly damaged. Forty-two small business buildings were destroyed, 118 were heavily damaged, and 29 were slightly damaged. Fires were started by the rupture and explosion of 5 bulk-storage oil tanks (Tudor, 1964, p. 61–64).

The fifth seismic sea wave to arrive at Crescent City caused most of the damage and took all 12 lives. After the first wave crested at 14.5 feet above mean low low water (MLLW), a second wave slacked off to 12 feet, followed by two much smaller waves. The townspeople, thinking that the tsunami was over, had begun to return to the flood-ed area when the fifth wave—coming in on a high tide—crested at 20.5 feet above MLLW.

Seiches were generated in various places remote from Alaska by amplification of direct seismic vibrations (Donn, 1964, p. 261). In the Gulf of Mexico off Texas—completely separated physically from any possible effects of tsunamis—waves as much as 6 feet high damaged small craft. In addition, water was agitated in many swimming pools in Texas and Louisiana (U.S. Coast and Geodetic Survey, 1964, p. 41). Surface-water gages recorded fluctuations in Texas, Louisiana, Arkansas, Missouri, Kentucky, Tennessee, Alabama, Georgia, and Pennsylvania (Waller and others, 1965, p. 130).

The ground-water regimen was affected throughout much of North America. Water-level fluctuations were noted in wells throughout the conterminous United States and at points as distant as Puerto Rico, the Virgin Islands, and Denmark. Fluctuations of as much as 6 cm were recorded in wells in Denmark (R. C. Vorhis, written commun., 1965). The maximum reported fluctuation was 23 feet in a well at Belle Fourche, S. D. Fluctuations apparently were greatest in a broad belt extending southeast from South Dakota and Wisconsin, through Missouri and Illinois, and on through Georgia and Florida to Puerto Rico (Waller and others, 1965, p. 131). Most level changes in wells were temporary, but some were permanent. The water in some wells was temporarily muddied.

ILLUSTRATION CREDITS

U.S. Geological Survey: Figures 1, 2, 3, 4, 9, 13, 18, 23
George Plafker: Figures 5, 8, 10, 11, 14, 15, 17, 31, 32, 36, 37
John E. Sater: Figure 6
Manuel G. Bonilla: Figures 7, 22, 24, 30

Troy L. Péwé: Figure 12
U.S. Army: Figures 16, 25, 27, 33, 34
Arthur Grantz: Figures 19, 20

Wallace R. Hansen: Figures 21, 28
Reuben Kachadoorian: Figures 26, 29
U.S. Navy: Figure 35

REFERENCES

Alaska Department of Fish and Game, 1965, Post - earthquake fisheries evaluation; an interim report on the March, 1964 earthquake effects on Alaska's fishery resources: Juneau, Alaska, 72 p.

Alaska Department of Health and Welfare, 1964a, Good Friday earthquake called on resources of all in State: Alaska's Health and Welfare, v. 21, June 1964, p. 5–7.

——— 1964b, Preliminary report of earthquake damage to environmental health facilities and services in Alaska: Juneau, Alaska Dept. Health and Welfare, Environmental Health Br., 46 p.

Alaskan Construction Consultants Committee [1964], Reconstruction and development survey of earthquake damages in Alaska: Prepared for Federal Reconstruction and Development Planning Commission for Alaska, 98 p.

Benioff, Hugo, and Gutenberg, Beno, 1939, Waves and currents recorded by electromagnetic barographs: Bull. Am. Meteorol. Soc., v. 20, p. 421–426.

Berg, G. V., and Stratta, J. L., 1964, Anchorage and the Alaska earthquake of March 27, 1964: New York, Am. Iron and Steel Inst., 63 p.

Bostock, H. S., 1948, Physiography of the Canadian Cordillera, with special reference to the area north of the 55th parallel: Canada Geol. Survey Mem. 247, pub. 2483, 106 p.

Brooks, A. H., 1906, The geography and geology of Alaska, a summary of existing knowledge: U.S. Geol. Survey Prof. Paper 45, 327 p.

——— 1911, The Mount McKinley region, Alaska: U.S. Geol. Survey Prof. Paper 70, 234 p.

Capps, S. R., 1916, The Turnagain-Knik region: U.S. Geol. Survey Bull. 642–E, p. 147–194.

——— 1940, Geology of The Alaska Railroad region: U.S. Geol. Survey Bull. 907, 201 p.

Christensen, M. N., and Bolt, B. A., 1964, Earth movements—Alaskan earthquake, 1964: Science, v. 145, no. 3637, p. 1207–1216.

Church, J. E., 1942, Snow and snow surveying; ice, in Meinzer, O. E.,

Hydrology: New York, Dover Pub., Inc. p. 83–148.

Coats, R. R., 1950, Volcanic activity in the Aleutian arc: U.S. Geol. Survey Bull. 974–B, p. 35–49.

Coulter, H. W., and Migliaccio, R. R., 1966 Effects of the March 27, 1964, earthquake at Valdez, Alaska: U.S. Geol. Survey Prof. Paper 542–C, 36 p.

Davis, T. N., and Echols, Carol, 1962, A table of Alaska earthquakes 1788–1961: Alaska Univ. Geophys. Inst., Geophys. Research Rept. 8 [UAG–R131], 43 p.

Donn, W. L., 1964, Alaskan earthquake of 27 March 1964: remote seiche stimulation: Science, v. 145, no. 3629, p. 261–262.

Dutro, J. T., Jr., and Payne, T. G., 1957, Geologic map of Alaska: U.S. Geol. Survey map, scale 1 :2,500,000.

Engineering Geology Evaluation Group, 1964, Geologic report—27 March 1964 earthquake in Greater Anchorage area: Prepared for Alaska Housing Authority and the City of Anchorage, Anchorage, Alaska, 34 p., 12 figs., pls. 1–17.

Gates, G. O., 1964, Geologic and tectonic setting in Mineral and water resources of Alaska: U.S. 88th Cong., 2d sess., Senate Comm. Interior and Insular Affairs, Comm. Print 31–068, p. 32–39.

Gates, G. O., and Gryc, George, 1963, Structure and tectonic history of Alaska, in Childs, O. E., and Beebe, B. W., Backbone of the Americas: Am. Assoc. Petroleum Geologists Mem. 2, p. 264–277.

Grantz, Arthur, 1961, Geologic map and cross sections of the Anchorage (D–2) quadrangle and northeasternmost part of the Anchorage (D–3) quadrangle, Alaska: U.S. Geol. Survey Misc. Geol. Inv. Map I–342, scale 1 :48,000.

Grantz, Arthur, Plafker, George, and Kachadoorian, Reuben, 1964, Alaska's Good Friday earthquake, March 27, 1964—a preliminary geologic evaluation: U.S. Geol. Survey Circ. 491, 35 p.

Gutenberg, Beno, and Richter, C. F., 1949, Seismicity of the earth and associated phenomena: Princeton, N. J., Princeton Univ. Press, 273 p.

Hackman, R. J., 1965, Photointerpretation of post-earthquake photographs, Alaska: Photogrammetric Eng., v. 31, no. 4, p. 604–610.

Hanna, G. D., 1964, Biological effects of an earthquake: Pacific Discovery, v. 17, no. 6, p. 24–26.

Hansen, W. R., 1965, Effects of the earthquake of March 27, 1964, at Anchorage, Alaska: U.S. Geol. Survey Prof. Paper 542–A, 68 p.

Hill, M. R., 1965, Earth hazards—an editorial: California Div. Mines and Geology Mineral Inf. Service, v. 18, no. 4, p. 57–59.

Jordan, J. N., Lander, J. F., and Black, R. A., 1965, Aftershocks of the 4 February 1965 Rat Island earthquake: Science, v. 148, no. 3675, p. 1323–1325.

Kachadoorian, Reuben, 1965, Effects of the earthquake of March 27, 1964, at Whittier, Alaska: U.S. Geol. Survey Prof. Paper 542–B, 21 p.

Karlstrom, T. N. V., 1964, Quaternary geology of the Kenai Lowland and glacial history of the Cook Inlet region, Alaska: U.S. Geol. Survey Prof. Paper 443, 69 p.

Lemke, R. W., 1966, Effects of the earthquake of March 27, 1964, at Seward, Alaska: U.S. Geol. Survey Prof. Paper 542–E. (In press.)

McCulloch, D. S., 1966, Slide-induced waves, seiching, and ground fracturing caused by the earthquake of March 27, 1964, at Kenai Lake, Alaska: U.S. Geol. Survey Prof. Paper 543–A, 41 p.

McMinn, J. H., 1964, The verdict of Anchorage—good structural design survived: Eng. News-Record, v. 172, no. 15, p. 22–25.

Malloy, R. J., 1964, Crustal uplift southwest of Montague Island, Alaska: Science, v. 146, no. 3647, p. 1048–1049.

Martin, G. C., Johnson, B. L., and Grant, U.S., 1915, Geology and mineral resources of Kenai Peninsula, Alaska: U.S. Geol. Survey Bull. 587, 243 p.

Moore, G. W., 1964, Magnetic disturbances preceding the Alaska earthquake: Nature, v. 203, no. 4944, p. 508–509.

National Board of Fire Underwriters and Pacific Fire Rating Bureau,

1964, The Alaska earthquake, March 27, 1964: Distributed by American Insurance Assoc., 465 California St., San Francisco, Calif., 35 p.

Office of Emergency Planning, 1964a, Impact of earthquake of March 27, 1964, upon the economy of Alaska: Prepared for Federal Reconstruction and Development Planning Commission for Alaska, 27 p.

Olson, S. T., chief [1964], Reconnaissance of Copper River Delta following the March 27, 1964, earthquake: U.S. Forest Service Br. Wildlife Management, Region 10, 6 p.

Plafker, George, 1965, Tectonic deformation associated with the 1964 Alaska earthquake: Science, v. 148, no. 3678, p. 1675–1687.

Plafker, George, and Mayo, L. R., 1965, Tectonic deformation, subaqueous slides and destructive waves associated with the Alaskan March 27, 1964, earthquake—an interim geologic evaluation: U.S. Geol. Survey open-file report, 21 p.

Post, A. S., 1965, Alaskan glaciers—recent observations in respect to the earthquake-advance theory: Science, v. 148, no. 3668, p. 366–368.

Press, Frank, and Jackson, David, 1965, Alaskan earthquake, 27 March 1964—Vertical extent of faulting and elastic strain energy release: Science, v. 147, no. 3660, p. 867–868.

Ragle, R. H., Sater, J. E., and Field, W. O., 1965, Effects of the 1964 Alaskan earthquake on glaciers and related features: Arctic, v. 18, no. 2, p. 135–137; also *in* Arctic Inst. North America Research Paper 32.

Reed, J. C., Jr., 1961, Geology of the Mount McKinley quadrangle, Alaska: U.S. Geol. Survey Bull. 1108–A, p. A1–A36.

Richter, C. F., 1958, Elementary seismology: San Francisco, W. H. Freeman and Co., 768 p.

Schatz, C. E., Curl, Herbert, Jr., and Burt, W. V., 1964, Tsunamis on the Oregon coast; The Ore Bin, v. 26, no. 12, p. 231–232, Portland, Oregon Dept. Geol. and Mineral Industries.

Shannon and Wilson, Inc., 1964, Preliminary report to U.S. Army Corps of Engineers on 4th Avenue Slide, Anchorage, Alaska: Seattle, Wash., 9 p.

Steinbrugge, K. V., 1964, Engineering seismology aspects, *in* Prince William Sound, Alaskan earthquakes, March–April 1964: U.S. Coast and Geod. Survey, Seismology Div. prelim. rept., p. 58–72.

Stroh, Alfred, Jr., 1964, Navy operations at Kodiak: The Military Engineer, v. 56, no. 372, p. 254–255.

Thorsteinson, F. V., 1964, Effects of the Alaska earthquake on pink and chum salmon runs in Prince William Sound: U.S. Bur. Commercial Fisheries Biol. Lab., Auke Bay, Alaska, 16 p.; 1965, *in* Science in Alaska, 1964: Alaskan Sci. Conf., 15th, College, Alaska, 1964, Proc., p. 267–280.

Tudor, W. J., 1964, Tsunami damage at Kodiak, Alaska, and Crescent City, California, from Alaskan earthquake of 27 March 1964: Port Hueneme, Calif., U.S. Naval Civil Eng. Lab. Tech. Note N–622, 124 p.

Tuthill, S. J., and Laird, W. M., 1966, Geomorphic effects of the earthquake of March 27, 1964, in the Martin-Bering Rivers area, Alaska: U.S. Geol. Survey Prof. Paper 543–B, 29 p.

U.S. Coast and Geodetic Survey, 1964, Prince William Sound, Alaskan earthquakes, March–April 1964: U.S. Coast and Geod. Survey, Seismology Div., prelim. rept., 83 p.

———1965a, Assistance and recovery, Alaska, 1964: A report covering the activities of the U.S. Coast and Geodetic Survey in conjunction with the Prince William Sound, Alaska, earthquake of 1964 for the period March 27–December 31, 1964: 45 p.

Van Dorn, W. G., 1964, Source mechanism of the tsunami of March 28, 1964, in Alaska: Coastal Eng. Conf., 9th, Lisbon, 1964, Proc., p. 166–190.

Wahrhaftig, Clyde, 1966, Physiographic divisions of Alaska: U.S. Geol. Survey Prof. Paper 482, 52 p.

Wahrhaftig, Clyde, and Gates, G. O., 1964, Physiographic setting, *in* Mineral and water resources of Alaska: U.S. 88th Cong., 2d sess., Senate Comm. Interior and Insular Affairs, Comm. Print 31–068, p. 27–32.

Waller, R. M., 1966a, Effects of the earthquake of March 27, 1964, in the Homer area, Alaska: U.S. Geol. Survey Prof. Paper 542–D, 28 p.

Waller, R. W., Thomas, H. E., and Vorhis, R. C., 1965, Effects of the Good Friday earthquake on water supplies: Am. Water Works Assoc., Jour., v. 57, no. 2, p. 123–131.

White, J. E., 1965, Seismic waves—radiation, transmission, and attenuation: New York, McGraw Hill Co., 302 p.

Williams, Howel, ed., 1958, Landscapes of Alaska—their geologic evolution: Berkeley, California Univ. Press, 148 p.

CLARIFICATIONS

Geology Vol. Page	USGS Page	Column	Line	Remarks
5	1	2	31	Also reported as 115 lives lost in Alaska
5	1	3	1	Also reported as 11 lives lost in Crescent City
5	1	3	18, 19	Later computed at 61.04°N; 147.73°W
41	37	2	21, 40	Otherwise reported as 11 deaths in Crescent City, California

I
REGIONAL
AND
AREAL
EFFECTS

GEORGE PLAFKER
U.S. GEOLOGICAL SURVEY

Reprinted with minor changes from
U.S. Geological Survey Professional Paper 543-I,
"Tectonics of the March 27, 1964, Alaska Earthquake"

Tectonics

ABSTRACT

The March 27, 1964, earthquake was accompanied by crustal deformation—including warping, horizontal distortion, and faulting—over probably more than 110,000 square miles of land and sea bottom in south-central Alaska. Regional uplift and subsidence occurred mainly in two nearly parallel elongate zones, together about 600 miles long and as much as 250 miles wide, that lie along the continental margin. From the earthquake epicenter in northern Prince William Sound, the deformation extends eastward 190 miles almost to long 142° and southwestward slightly more than 400 miles to about long 155°. It extends across the two zones from the chain of active volcanoes in the Aleutian Range and Wrangell Mountains probably to the Aleutian Trench axis.

Uplift that averages 6 feet over broad areas occurred mainly along the coast of the Gulf of Alaska, on the adjacent Continental Shelf, and probably on the continental slope. This uplift attained a measured maximum on land of 38 feet in a northwest-trending narrow belt less than 10 miles wide that is exposed on Montague Island in southwestern Prince William Sound. Two earthquake faults exposed on Montague Island are subsidiary northwest-dipping reverse faults along which the northwest blocks were relatively displaced a maximum of 26 feet, and both blocks were upthrown relative to sea level. From Montague Island, the faults and related belt of maximum uplift may extend southwestward on the Continental Shelf to the vicinity of the Kodiak group of islands. To the north and northwest of the zone of uplift, subsidence forms a broad asymmetrical downwarp centered over the Kodiak-Kenai-Chugach Mountains that averages 2½ feet and attains a measured maximum of 7½ feet along the southwest coast of the Kenai Peninsula. Maximum indicated uplift in the Alaska and Aleutian Ranges to the north of the zone of subsidence was 1½ feet. Re-triangulation over roughly 25,000 square miles of the deformed region in and around Prince William Sound shows that vertical movements there were accompanied by horizontal distortion, involving systematic shifts of about 64 feet in a relative seaward direction. Comparable horizontal movements are presumed to have affected those parts of the major zones of uplift and subsidence for which retriangulation data are unavailable.

Regional vertical deformation generated a train of destructive long-period seismic sea waves in the Gulf of Alaska as well as unique atmospheric and ionospheric disturbances that were recorded at points far distant from Alaska. Warping resulted in permanent tilt of larger lake basins and temporary reductions in discharge of some major rivers. Uplift and subsidence relative to sea level caused profound modifications in shoreline morphology with attendant catastrophic effects on the nearshore biota and costly damage to coastal installations. Systematic horizontal movements of the land relative to bodies of confined or semiconfined water may have caused unexplained short-period waves—some of which were highly destructive—observed during or immediately after the earthquake at certain coastal localities and in Kenai Lake. Porosity increases, probably related to horizontal displacements in the zone of subsidence, were reflected in lowered well-water levels and in losses of surface water.

The primary fault, or zone of faults, along which the earthquake occurred is not exposed at the surface on land. Focal-mechanism studies, when considered in conjunction with the pattern of deformation and seismicity, suggest that it was a complex thrust fault (megathrust) dipping at a gentle angle beneath the continental margin from the vicinity of the Aleutian Trench. Movement on the megathrust was accompanied by subsidiary reverse faulting, and perhaps wrench faulting, with-in the upper plate. Aftershock distribution suggests movement on a segment of the megathrust, some 550–600 miles long and 110–180 miles wide, that underlies most of the major zone of uplift and the seaward part of the major zone of subsidence.

According to the postulated model, the observed and inferred tectonic displacements that accompanied the earthquake resulted primarily from (1) relative seaward displacement and uplift of the seaward part of the block by movement along the dipping megathrust and subsidiary faults that break through the upper plate to the surface, and (2) simultaneous elastic horizontal extension and vertical attenuation (subsidence) of the crustal slab behind the upper plate. Slight uplift inland from the major zones of deformation presumably was related to elastic strain changes resulting from the overthrusting; however, the data are insufficient to permit conclusions regarding its cause.

The belt of seismic activity and major zones of tectonic deformation associated with the 1964 earthquake, to a large extent, lie between and parallel to the Aleutian Volcanic Arc and the Aleutian Trench, and are probably genetically related to the arc. Geologic data indicate that the earthquake-related tectonic movements were but the most recent pulse in an episode of deformation that probably began in late Pliocene time and has continued intermittently to the present. Evidence for progressive coastal submergence in the deformed region for several centuries preceding the earthquake, in combination with transverse horizontal shortening indicated by the retriangulation data, suggests pre-earthquake strain directed at a gentle angle downward beneath the arc. The duration of strain accumulation in the epicentral region, as interpreted from the time interval during which the coastal submergence occurred, probably is 930–1,360 years.

INTRODUCTION

Among the most notable aspects of the 1964 Alaska earthquake was the great areal extent and amount of the tectonic movements that accompanied it. From the epicenter in northern Prince William Sound, the region affected by tectonic deformation parallels the trends of the Aleutian Volcanic Arc, the Aleutian Trench, and the Gulf of Alaska coast for about 600 miles (fig. 1). In south-central Alaska, where the northeastern end of the arc intersects the continent at an oblique angle, the pattern of deformation can be observed in an exceptionally complete profile extending more than 200 miles northward from the seaward edge of the Continental Shelf across the northeastern end of the volcanic arc. Within this region, tectonic displacements on land include absolute vertical movements ranging from as much as 38 feet of uplift to 7½ feet of subsidence, relative horizontal movements of about 64 feet, and dip-slip offset on reverse faults of as much as 26 feet. Furthermore, the available data indicate that these movements extended over a large segment of the adjacent offshore area where they may have been as large, or larger, than those measured on land.

This report substantially enlarges upon a preliminary summary and interpretation of the tectonic movements that accompanied the 1964 earthquake (Plafker, 1965). It presents the available data on the distribution and nature of the earthquake-related displacements and of the manifold, often disastrous, effects of these movements. Geologic, geodetic, and seismologic data pertinent to the tectonics that were available to the writer prior to

completion of this report in July 1967 are summarized. Implications of the data for the earthquake mechanism are reviewed, and a tentative qualitative model is outlined, which attempts to explain most of the observations.

ACKNOWLEDGMENTS

Field mapping of the vertical shoreline displacements and surface faults was accomplished by a party headed by the writer from mid-May through August 1964 and during 1 month in 1965. Geological Survey personnel included L. R. Mayo, J. E. Case, S. L. Robbins, and William Bastian during 1964, and Mayo and M. G. Bonilla during 1965. An especially large part of the fieldwork and data compilation were carried out by L. R. Mayo during both field seasons. G Dallas Hanna, marine biologist of the California Academy of Sciences, spent 3 weeks with the party in Prince William Sound in 1964, during which time he studied effects of the earthquake on the ecology of the intertidal fauna and flora and provided invaluable advice on the use of sessile marine organisms for determining changes in land level.

The U.S. Geological Survey research vessel, *Don J. Miller*, was used as a base of operations for work in Prince William Sound and Resurrection Bay during the 1964 season. Helicopters and fixed-wing aircraft were used during both field seasons for work along shorelines elsewhere. Outstanding logistical support of the field investigations was provided—often under difficult circumstances—by the crew of the *Don J. Miller*, which consisted of Capt. John Stacey and cook-seaman John

Muttart of the U.S. Geological Survey, and by bush pilots Jim Osborne, Glenn Wheeler, "Stinky" Myers, Al Cratty, Bob Leonard, Oren Hudson, and Bob Barnett.

R. L. Detterman, Reuben Kachadoorian, T. N. V. Karlstrom, G. W. Moore, and B. L. Reed, all of the Geological Survey, contributed data on changes in land level as determined by coastal residents of Cook Inlet and the Kodiak group of islands. Many residents of Alaska gave helpful information on earthquake effects, including tectonic changes, in about 150 interviews with the writer and on numerous form questionnaires.

Virtually all the seismologic, geodetic, and marine data incorporated in this report were obtained by the U.S. Coast and Geodetic Survey as part of their massive investigations of this major seismic event. I am especially indebted to the numerous individuals in the U.S. Coast and Geodetic Survey who freely made available unpublished data and have discussed their interpretations of these data with the writer on many occasions. Among these, special thanks for assistance are due S. T. Algermissen of the Seismology Division, W. D. Barbee, R. J. Malloy, and E. W. Richards of the Office of Oceanography, and C. A. Whitten, E. J. Parkin and J. B. Small of the Geodesy Division.

Postearthquake vertical aerial photographs were provided through the courtesy of Col. M. L. Fallwell, U.S. Army, Fort Richardson, and H. R. Cravat of the Photogrammetry Division, U.S. Coast and Geodetic Survey. R. A. Page, Jr., of the Lamont Geological Observatory furnished a computer plot of the larger magnitude

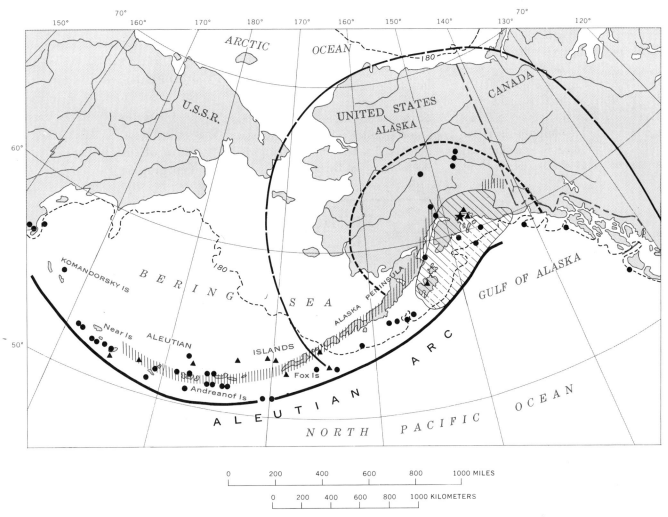

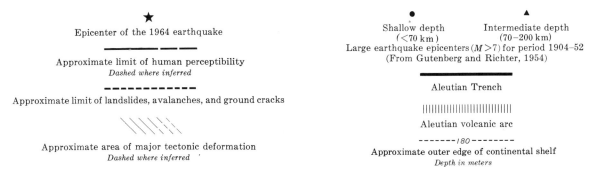

EXPLANATION

★

Epicenter of the 1964 earthquake

———————

Approximate limit of human perceptibility
Dashed where inferred

— — — — — — —

Approximate limit of landslides, avalanches, and ground cracks

⦀⦀⦀⦀⦀

Approximate area of major tectonic deformation
Dashed where inferred

●   ▲
Shallow depth   Intermediate depth
(<70 km)   (70–200 km)
Large earthquake epicenters ($M > 7$) for period 1904–52
(From Gutenberg and Richter, 1954)

————————

Aleutian Trench

|||||||||||||||||||||||||||||

Aleutian volcanic arc

- - - - - - - 180 - - - - - - - -

Approximate outer edge of continental shelf
Depth in meters

1.—Map of Alaska and adjacent areas showing the location of the 1964 earthquake, the area affected by the earthquake, epicenters of previous major earthquakes, belts of active volcanism, and the Aleutian Trench.

aftershock epicenters. William Stauder, S. J., provided data on focal mechanisms of the earthquake and its aftershock sequence in advance of his own publication. D. F. Barnes and Roland von Huene of the Geological Survey made available unpublished results of submarine geophysical and geological studies carried out in south-central Alaska after the earthquake.

I am grateful to colleagues in the Geological Survey for very helpful discussions of the various tectonic aspects of the earthquake during which many of the ideas incorporated in this report were generated. The manuscript has been improved through critical reviews by E. B. Eckel and G. D. Eberlein and reviews of portions by D. F. Barnes, R. R. Coats, R. O. Burford, and C. B. Raleigh. Vector shifts for the readjustment of triangulation data were calculated by J. T. Minta and C. R. Lloyd of the Geological Survey's Topographic Division.

SEISMICITY

THE MAIN SHOCK

The 1964 earthquake was centered in a sparsely inhabited, mountainous area of northern Prince William Sound in south-central Alaska near the eastern end of the Aleutian Arc (fig. 1). Its epicenter was located by the U.S. Coast and Geodetic Survey (Wood, 1966, p. 62) at lat 61.06° N., long 147.44° W. and its origin time was at about 5:36 p.m., Friday, March 27, 1964, A.s.t. (03:36:13.5, Saturday, March 28, 1964, G.m.t.). The hypocenter, or focus, could not be determined more closely than between 12 and 31 miles (20–50 km) in depth.

Magnitude of the earthquake, based upon surface-wave amplitudes (M_s) is estimated to have been about 8.4 (Pasadena seismograph station). Earthquake vibrations were felt over an area in excess of a million square miles in Alaska and adjacent parts of Canada (fig. 1), and they caused widespread damage throughout an area of about 50,000 square miles in south-central Alaska. The manifold effects of the shaking, which have been described in numerous reports are concisely summarized by Hansen and Eckel (1966) in the previous paper of this series of reports.

Rupture along a fault of considerable length is suggested from (1) the exceptionally long duration of strong ground motion, (2) the character of the radiated seismic surface and body waves, and (3) the extensive belt over which aftershocks were distributed.

Eyewitness accounts indicate that both the amplitude and duration of ground motion definitely tended to be largest in areas of relatively unconsolidated saturated deposits and least in areas of crystalline or metamorphic rocks. Within the immediate area affected by the earthquake, the only known instrumental records of the duration of shaking were made on several automatic recording charts in a steam powerplant built on bedrock at Whittier. On the clearest of these records, trace vibrations lasted for nearly 4 minutes. At other bedrock sites on Kodiak Island and on the Kenai Peninsula, where the motion was timed by observers with pocket watches or clocks, it was 2½–5 minutes. Anomalously short durations, ranging from only 15 seconds to 1½ minutes, were reported by residents at Seldovia and in two nearby localities in areas underlain by metamorphic rock at the southwestern tip of the Kenai Mountains (Plafker, Kachadoorian, Eckel, and Mayo, 1969).

According to most eyewitness accounts, the earthquake started without prior warning as a gentle rolling motion that lasted for a period of 20 seconds to 1 minute, shook hard for as much as 4 minutes, and then gradually subsided. There were no foreshocks perceptible to observers such as are known to immediately precede many great earthquakes. A few observers heard premonitory low rumbling sounds several seconds before the earthquake was felt. The ground motion was variously described as a rolling wavelike motion, a strong horizontal acceleration, or a hard jarring motion. A few individuals noted that the ground motion during the earthquake periodically eased up for a short period and then resumed with increased violence.

Reports of the directions of vibrations vary widely, and at some places, prevailing vibration directions reportedly changed during the earthquake. The majority of the reports indicate a tendency for ground oscillation to be grouped in the quadrants between northwest-southeast and northeast-southwest although it also was reported from all other quadrants. A westward propagation of vibrations between Anchorage and Kenai is indicated by the fact that power failure due to shaking in the Anchorage area caused an overload of the circuits at the interconnected Bernice Lake power-plant near Kenai, 53 miles farther from the epicenter, some 15–20 seconds before the plant superintendent felt the tremors.

On the basis of a study of seismic surface waves, Toksöz, Ben-Menahem, and Harkrider (1965, p. 154) determined that the rupture propagated S. 50° W. from the epicenter of the main shock for a distance of about 370 miles (600 km) at an average velocity of 3 km per sec. Furumoto (1967) found from analysis of Rayleigh waves recorded by the Kipapa, Hawaii, strain seismometer that the rupture more probably propagated S. 30 ± 5° W. for 500 miles (800 km) at this same velocity. A detailed study of P-phases by Wyss and Brune (1967) suggests that the rupture actually broke in a complex series of events at an average propagation velocity of 3.5 km per sec and that each event was characterized by more or less distinct high-amplitude bursts or events. Their data further indicate that, although the rupture propagated initially in various azimuthal directions, after an elapsed time of 44 seconds it continued only in a southwesterward direction.

THE AFTERSHOCKS

The epicenters and depth distributions of 598 aftershocks with Richter magnitudes equal to or greater than 4.4 recorded through December 31, 1964, are shown on figure 2. Of these, the largest shock had a magnitude of 6.7, six were larger than 6.0, 127 were between 5.0 and 6.0, and the remainder were less than 5.0 (U.S. Coast and Geodetic Survey, Preliminary Determination of Epicenter cards). During this same period of time, thousands of smaller aftershocks were also recorded.

The aftershock sequence diminished rapidly in frequency and intensity. All aftershocks with magnitudes larger than 6.0 recorded teleseismically by the U.S. Coast and Geodetic Survey, occurred within the first several hours and most of those that were strongly felt occurred within 3 weeks of the main event. Daily frequency of all shocks dropped rapidly from a high of about 120 the first day after the earthquake to 30 in 5 days, 15 in 10 days, and a steadily decreasing number thereafter (Jordan, Lander, and Black, 1965, p. 1324). As noted by Jordan and associates, the number of aftershocks at the beginning of the series may be much larger than indicated, because the first aftershocks are commonly masked by the train of large amplitude waves generated by the main shock and these waves may have a duration of several hours at distant stations.

The larger aftershocks ($M \geqq 4.4$) were concentrated mainly in an arcuate belt 600 miles long by as much as 200 miles wide that roughly parallels the continental margin. From the epicenter of the main shock it extends 425 miles southwestward to the vicinity of the Trinity Islands and about 175 miles eastward nearly to long 142° W. (fig. 2). Most of the largest aftershocks in this belt ($M \geqq 5.0$) were situated over that part of the belt lying seaward from the zero isobase between the major zones of uplift and subsidence. Smaller aftershocks ($M \geqq 4.4$) were spread over a larger area that extends inland from the zero isobase beneath the coastal mountains that border the Gulf of Alaska, and the smallest aftershocks ($M < 4.4$) were scattered over an even larger area. There was a distinct concentration of activity within the aftershock belt on the Continental Shelf at the southwestern end and in the area southeast of Prince William Sound

near the northeastern end. Burk (1965, p. 150) noted that the fairly sharp southwestern limit of the aftershock belt approximately coincides with a transverse structural boundary on the Alaska Peninsula, and he suggested the possibility that a transverse fault marks the southwestern margin of the crustal block involved in the 1964 earthquake. Only about 3 percent of the aftershocks with magnitudes of 4.4 or more were outside the main belt of activity along the continental margin. Their epicenters were widely scattered, mainly in the Shelikof Strait-Cook Inlet areas and on the ocean floor seaward from the Aleutian Trench axis. Significantly, none of the aftershocks were centered as far inland as the chain of active volcanoes in the Aleutian Range, southern Alaska Range, and the Wrangell Mountains. The possibility that they were directly related to vulcanism is thus ruled out.

Depth distribution of the aftershocks is less perfectly defined than their epicentral positions because of (1) inherent errors in the determination of hypocenters in areas of uncertain crustal structure and seismic velocity, and (2) the wide spacing of the seismographs on which the shocks were recorded. Algermissen (1965) found that hypocenters of aftershocks with magnitudes greater than 5.0 were at depths between 3 and 25 miles (5–40 km) and they average about 12 miles (20 km). Only 25 of the earthquakes with magnitudes of 4.4 or more were deeper than 22 miles (35 km), the deepest ones being less than 56 miles (90 km). According to Page (1967; also unpub. data), the microaftershocks—which had a spatial distribution similar to that of the aftershocks—were at depths of 22 miles (35 km) or less. He

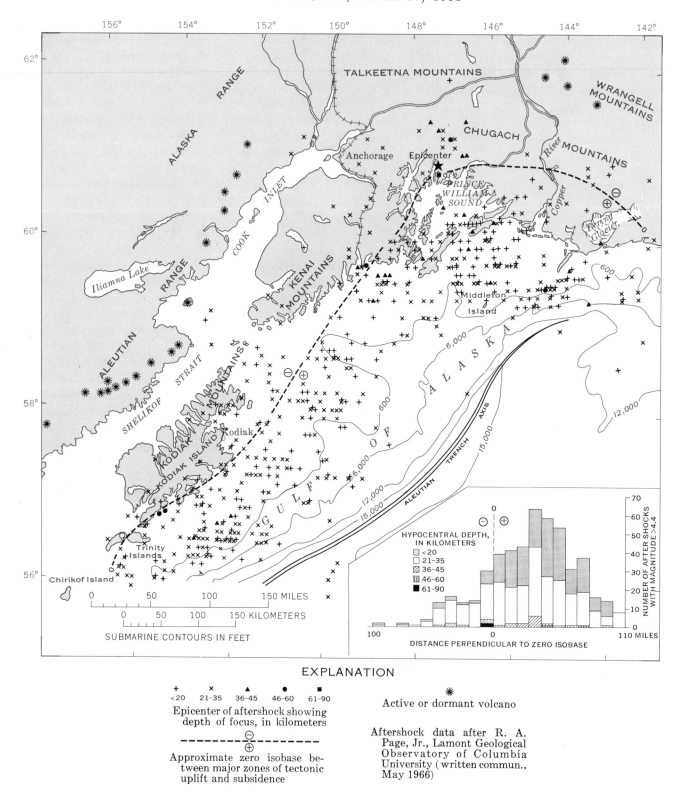

EXPLANATION

+   ×   ▲   ●   ■
<20   21–35   36–45   46–60   61–90

Epicenter of aftershock showing
depth of focus, in kilometers

⊖
– – – – – – – – – – – – – – – –
⊕

Approximate zero isobase between major zones of tectonic
uplift and subsidence

✳   Active or dormant volcano

Aftershock data after R. A.
Page, Jr., Lamont Geological
Observatory of Columbia
University (written commun.,
May 1966)

2.—Distribution and depth of aftershocks (4.4≦M≧6.7) from March 27, to December 31, 1964.

suggests that subcrustal earthquakes in and near the aftershock region may have represented the normal seismicity of the region. Aftershock hypocenters do not fall into any well-defined planar zone although there is a vague tendency towards a slight deepening of their lower limit beneath the continent. The proportion of hypocenters deeper than 12 miles relative to those shallower than 12 miles also shows an increase in the same direction (fig. 2).

Large earthquakes at shallow and intermediate depths are thought by most geologists and geophysicists to result from sudden rupture, or faulting, in strained rocks. Aftershocks which follow large earthquakes presumably represent continuous adjustments of the strained volume of rock, or focal region, within which faulting occurred (Benioff, 1951). According to this model, therefore, faulting associated with the 1964 earthquake was largely confined to the part of the continental margin extending roughly 150–200 miles northward from the axis of the Aleutian Trench, it was limited in depth to the crust, or perhaps the uppermost part of the mantle, and its lower limit may deepen slightly beneath the arc.

FOCAL MECHANISM STUDIES

Mechanism studies of the main shock, of a number of larger aftershocks, and of one preshock that occurred about 7 weeks prior to the earthquake provide data relevant to the fault orientation and sense of displacement at the earthquake foci. Body-wave solutions define a pair of orthogonal planes at the focus, one of which presumably contains the active fault surface. Inherent in the focal mechanism studies are the basic assumptions of an elastic-rebound source and initial displacements at the earthquake foci that approximately reflect the regional stress field.

Focal mechanism studies of P-waves for the main shock yield one well-defined nodal plane that strikes between N. 61° and 66° E. and dips 82°–85° SE. (Stauder and Bollinger, 1966. Algermissen, 1965; written commun., March 19, 1965). The alternative low-angle plane is restricted by the data to a plane that dips towards the northwest; Algermissen's solution suggests an inclination of about 8°. If the well-defined nodal plane is regarded as the fault plane, its strike was N. 61°–66° E. and the motion was predominantly dip-slip on a steep reverse fault with the southeast side relatively upthrown. Alternatively, if the steep nodal plane is considered to be normal to the motion, the fault would be a northwest-dipping thrust. Focal mechanism studies of the main shock alone cannot distinguish which of these two planes is the fault plane. Surface-wave studies that define the direction of rupture may permit distinction between the fault and auxiliary planes in cases where the strikes of the two planes differ significantly. However, as noted by Savage and Hastie (1966, p. 4900), surface waves do not permit a unique solution for the 1964 earthquake because the direction of rupture propagation is essentially the same for either plane.

Stauder and Bollinger (1966) determined focal mechanisms, based on combined P-wave first-motion and S-wave polarization data, for a preshock and 25 aftershocks in the Kodiak Island and Prince William Sound areas. Most of these solutions have one near-vertical nodal plane that resembles the well-defined nodal plane for the main shock; the other dips 5°–15° to the northwest or north. Strike of the steep plane is between N. 50° and 72° E. to the southwest of Prince William Sound; it is variable in the Prince William Sound area and nearly east-west to the east of the sound. This systematic variation in orientation of the steep nodal plane tends to follow a change in trend of tectonic features along the coastal belt. Four aftershock solutions in the Prince William Sound area and one located seaward from the Aleutian Trench off Kodiak Island, however, are anomalous in that they do not correspond to this general pattern.

The preshock and all the aftershock fault-plane solutions are subject to the same ambiguity of interpretation as the main shock. Thus, on the basis of all the individual solutions (except for the five apparently anomalous ones) the motion at the source of the earthquake and the related pre- and aftershocks may be (1) almost entirely dip-slip on a steeply dipping reverse fault along which the seaward side is relatively upthrown or (2) dip-slip on a northward-dipping thrust fault along which the landward block overrides the seaward block in an average S. 25° E. direction to the southwest of Prince William Sound and in a S. 10°–15° W. direction to the east of Prince William Sound (Stauder and Bollinger, 1966, p. 5295). In considering the solutions in relation to one another, Stauder and Bollinger observe that in the first alternative the faulting may consist of en echelon segments that follow a sinuous path roughly paralleling the curving trend of both the aftershock belt and the zero isobase between the major zones of earthquake-related vertical tectonic deformation (fig. 2). In the second alternative the thrust plane has a dip of less than 14° beneath the continent, displacement of the upper plate is relatively seaward, and the direction of motion is roughly normal to the trend of the aftershock belt and the zones of tectonic deformation.

The steep plane in solutions of the main shock, the preshock, and most aftershocks differs in strike from the tectonic trends of the region, the orientation of the earthquake focal region, and the pattern of vertical displacements associated with the earthquake.

These differences suggest to Stauder and Bollinger (1966, p. 5293–5294) that the steep plane corresponds to the auxiliary plane rather than the fault plane. They also interpret the spatial distribution of foci for which mechanism studies were made and the nature of the inferred motions as being more compatible with thrusting on the shallowly dipping plane than to movement on the steep plane.

Solutions for the main shock and most of the other shocks suggest a maximum-stress axis at the foci of these earthquakes oriented approximately normal, or at a small oblique angle, to major structural elements within the focal region. Within the limitations of the data, this orientation is in reasonably good agreement with geodetic and geologic data cited in subsequent sections (p. I 49) that suggest dominantly tangential compressive stress on land within the region affected by tectonic movements during the earthquake.

DEFORMATION

Crustal deformation, including both vertical and horizontal movements, associated with the 1964 Alaska earthquake was more extensive than any known to have been related to a single tectonic event. Vertical movements occurred over an arcuate region that roughly parallels the continental margin for almost 600 miles from the southwestern tip of the Kodiak group of islands northeastward through Prince William Sound and thence eastward to about long 142° W. (fig. 3). In a northwest to southeast direction, the deformation extends at least 200 miles from the west shore of Cook Inlet to Middleton Island at the seaward edge of the Continental Shelf. In addition, crustal warping appears to extend inland as far as the Alaska Range and it may extend seaward to the axis of the Aleutian Trench.

Observable tectonic deformation involved (1) regional crustal warping, including both uplift and subsidence relative to sea level, in broad zones that roughly parallel the trend of the continental margin, (2) systematic regional horizontal extension and shortening in a direction approximately transverse to that of the zones of warping, (3) displacement across longitudinal reverse faults exposed on land and on the sea floor, and (4) possible displacement on at least one wrench fault. Evidence for these various movements, their manifold effects, and their tectonic significance are discussed below.

REGIONAL VERTICAL DISPLACEMENTS

Notable tectonic changes in land level during the 1964 earthquake occurred over an area of at least 70,000 square miles, and probably more than 110,000 square miles, of south-central Alaska. The areal distribution and approximate amount of the vertical displacements are summarized on figure 3. Plates 1 and 2 show data points where quantitative measurements of vertical displacement were made, as well as the method used and year of measurement. Also shown on the figure and plates are isobase contours, or lines of equal vertical displacement based on these data, and the approximate axes of the major upwarped and downwarped zones. The deformation includes two broad major zones of warping, each about 600 miles long and as much as 130 miles wide. The seaward zone is one of uplift that includes a fringe of coast along the Gulf of Alaska, the adjacent Continental Shelf, and perhaps the continental slope; it is bordered to the northwest and west by a zone of subsidence. Slight uplift also occurred in at least three areas extending inland from the major zone of subsidence as far northward as the Alaska Range.

METHODS OF MEASUREMENT

Quantitative information on vertical displacements along the coast (pls. 1, 2) comes mainly from (1) comparison of pre- and post-earthquake tide gage readings, (2) the position of the upper growth limit of certain sessile intertidal organisms relative to sea level, (3) differences in the pre- and post-earthquake positions of the upper growth limits of sessile intertidal organisms or the lower growth limit of terrestrial vegetation, (4) differences in the heights of pre- and postearthquake storm beaches, (5) estimates or measurements of changes in the position of shoreline

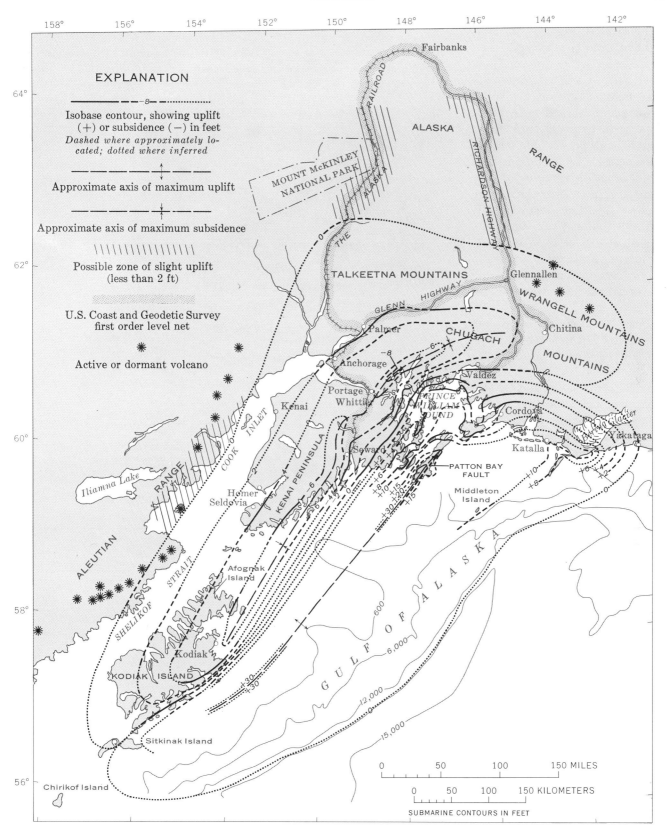

3.—Map showing the distribution of tectonic uplift and subsidence in south-central Alaska.

markers by local residents, and (6) measured changes in the height of tidal bench marks relative to sea level. For those offshore areas where detailed preearthquake bathymetry was available, approximate vertical displacements were also obtained from comparison of pre- and postearthquake depth s o u n d i n g s. The amount and distribution of the vertical displacements inland from the coast (pls. 1, 2) was precisely determined along the highway-railroad routes between Seward, Anchorage, Fairbanks, and Valdez by comparison of pre- and postearthquake level lines tied to tidal bench marks.

Isobase contours plotted on plates 1 and 2, which were derived from all the sources listed above, represent absolute changes in altitude related to the earthquake. The accuracy of the contouring varies greatly from place to place depending upon the type and amount of data, but, because it is essentially an averaging process, the contouring tends to be most accurate in areas where many data points are available, and least accurate in areas where data are sparse. In general, contours shown as solid or dashed lines are estimated to be accurate at least to within ±1 contour interval; at most places they are probably accurate to within half an interval.

The various techniques used for determining vertical displacement, estimates of their relative precision, and sources of data are outlined below.

COMPARISON OF PRE- AND POSTEARTHQUAKE TIDE-GAGE READINGS

The directions and relative amounts of vertical displacement were determined from coupled pre- and postearthquake tide-gage readings made by the U.S. Coast and Geodetic Survey at two

TABLE 1.—*Land-level changes based on comparison of pre- and postearthquake tide series at tide stations in south-central Alaska*

[After Small (1966, p. 19–22) and U.S. Coast and Geodetic Survey (unpub. data, April 22, 1966). Asterisk indicates station is plotted in fig. 10; double asterisk indicates standard tide-gage station operational before and after the earthquake]

Location	Length of tide series		Land movement (feet)
	Preearthquake	Postearthquake	
Prince William Sound			
*Cordova_____	1950–1951 (2 years)	May–Nov. 1964	+6. 2
		May–Nov. 1965	+6. 2
*Port Gravina_____	July 17–Sept. 26, 1913	July 3–31, 1964	+4. 5
	June 15–Aug. 19, 1915	May 16–June 16, 1965	+4. 2
Port Fidalgo_____	Aug. 24–26, 1915	June 18–July 17, 1965	+2. 4
Valdez_____	1924–26 (3 years)	May–July 1964	−. 9
		July–Nov. 1965	[1] −3. 5
*Whittier_____	June 12–29, 1956	May–June 1964; Oct.–Dec. 1964	−5. 4
		July–Nov. 1965	[1] −5. 7
*Chenega Island___	July–Aug. 1957	July 7–Aug. 4, 1964	+4. 8
Green Island_____	Aug. 23–Sept. 20, 1911	August, 1965	+6. 6
*Port Chalmers____	July–Sept. 1933 (3 months)	May 19–30; July 7–Aug. 6, 1964	+10. 5
		July 19–Aug. 23, 1965	+10. 5
*Sawmill Bay, Evans Island___	May, 1927 (1 month)	May 20–June 1; June 14–July 7, 1964	+7. 2
		July 29–Aug. 31, 1965	+7. 2
Hogg Bay_____	June 15–July 21, 1927	July 20–Aug. 16, 1965	+5. 8
Kenai Peninsula and Cook Inlet			
Day Harbor_____	May 20–July 13, 1928	May 7–June 30, 1965	−. 5
**Seward_____	1926–38 (13 years)	June 1964–Jan. 1965	−3. 6
		Jan.–Sept. 1965	−3. 6
Aialik Bay_____	July 6–Sept. 21, 1912	May–June 1965	−4. 5
*Two Arm Bay_____	July 20–Sept. 18, 1928	May 14–June 30, 1965	−5. 4
Chance Cove_____	May 14–July 25, 1930	May 15–June 30, 1965	−6. 6
Shelter Cove_____	June–Aug. 1927 (3 months)	July 1965	−5. 4
*Port Dick_____	Aug. 1–Sept. 26, 1930	May 21–June 30, 1965	−6. 2
**Homer_____	Oct. 3–Nov. 17, 1962	June–Dec. 1964; Sept.–Nov. 1965	−5. 4 [1] −5. 8
*Port Chatham_____		May 22–June 4, 1965	−4. 6
*Seldovia_____	April 30–Oct. 8, 1908	June–Oct. 1964	−3. 9
	May 8–Sept. 29, 1910	April–July 1965	−3. 8
Nikiski_____		June 18–July 31, 1964	−. 9

See footnote at end of table.

TABLE 1.—*Land-level changes based on comparsion of pre- and postearthquake tide series at tide stations in south-central Alaska*—Continued

| Location | Length of tide series | | Land movement (feet) |
	Preearthquake	Postearthquake	
Kenai Peninsula and Cook Inlet—Continued			
Anchorage_____	June–Sept. 1910; June–Oct., Dec. 1922; May–Nov. 1923; May–Sept. 1924; May–Oct. 1925	May–Oct. 1964	− 2. 6
		April–Oct. 1965	− 2. 3
Kodiak group of islands			
Carry Inlet_____	July 1931	July 8–Aug. 7, 1965	− 3. 2
Redfox Bay_____	July–Aug. 1926	July 1–Aug. 8, 1965	− 3. 4
*Tonki Bay_____	Aug. 23–31, 1932	July 10–Aug. 7, 1965	− 5. 2
Nachalni Island___	July 30–Sept. 8, 1941	June 14–July 10, 1965	− 3. 9
Dolphin Point____	Sept. 10–Oct. 1, 1941	June 7–July 8, 1965	− 2. 9
St. Paul Harbor___		June–Oct. 1964 May–Nov. 1965	− 5. 5 − 5. 0
*Ugak Bay_____	August 1932	June 12–July 10, 1965	− 4. 2
Port Hobron_____	June 1–Sept. 19, 1928	July 26–Aug. 27, 1965	− . 7
Jap Bay_____	July 1931	July 28–Aug. 24, 1965	. 0
*Lazy Bay_____	May 16–Sept. 29, 1929	June 11–30, July 1–Aug. 14, 1964	− . 4
	June 1–Sept. 30, 1930	July 28–Aug. 15, Aug. 20–24, 1965	− . 2
*Larsen Bay_____	Aug. 19–22, 1929	June 13–Aug. 31, 1964	− 2. 5
		July 18–Aug. 17, 1965	− 2. 4
Uyak Bay_____	July 14–30, 1908	July 22–Aug. 17, 1965	− 1. 9
*Port O'Brien_____	June 22–July 30, 1929	July Aug. 1964	− 3. 6
		June 8–July 19, 1965	− 3. 6
**Women's Bay_____	1950–59 (10 years)	April–July 1964	− 5. 6
Alaska Peninsula			
**Kukak Bay_____	July–Aug. 1949 (2 months)	July 17–Aug. 16, 1965	− . 5

[1] Change between 1964 and 1965 possibly due to surficial compaction.

operative standard stations, and 34 temporary stations within the region affected by tectonic movements during the earthquake (table 1). Such measurements were made at localities where a series of pre-earthquake tidal observations had been made and where tidal bench marks had been established that were not destroyed during or before the earthquake.

The Seward and Womens Bay (Kodiak) stations were equipped with standard automatic tide gages; readings could therefore be compared for series taken immediately before and after the earthquake. These determinations of vertical displacement are probably accurate to within a few tenths of a foot. The only other standard station in the region, at Homer Spit in Kachemak Bay, could not be used directly to measure vertical tectonic displacement because it was inoperative at the time of the earthquake, and the tectonic subsidence was augmented by pronounced surficial settlement of the unconsolidated deposits that made up the spit. Because the amount of surficial settling was known from level lines to areas of relatively firm ground (Waller, 1966a, p. D13), net tectonic subsidence could be obtained by subtracting the surficial effect from total subsidence relative to sea level at the gage. This difference amounted to about 2.9 feet.

Accuracy of the changes determined at the temporary stations depends largely on the length of the preearthquake series of observations, some of which were as short as 4 days, and also on the time interval between the pre- and postearthquake series, which at one station is 54 years and at many is more than 30 years (table 1). Positions of the preearthquake tidal datum planes at these stations may not have been precisely determined originally, and (or) they may have changed from their original values because of relative land-level changes in the time interval between tide observations. At most of the temporary stations such errors are believed to be small because, where other sources of data such as estimates by local residents or measured differences between pre- and postearthquake shoreline features are available in the immediate vicinity, they tend to agree with the tide data within 0.5 foot or less. An exception is the 7.0-foot uplift of the Sawmill Bay station on Evans Island, Prince William Sound, derived from the tidal observations(table 1). It is about 2 feet too low when compared with (1) the 9.0-foot estimated uplift of shoreline features whose preearthquake heights were precisely known to residents of the area and (2) the 8.9 feet of uplift indicated by differences in the pre- and postearthquake upper growth limit of barnacles (pl. 2). The preearthquake tidal observations at this particular station consist of a 1-month series taken in 1927, 37 years before the postearthquake series with which it was compared. Therefore, either about 2 feet of uplift occurred in the area during the 37 years prior to the earthquake or the tidal measurements are in error. Because Sawmill Bay had been continuously inhabited during this time interval and because there was no indication of preearthquake changes in land level, it appears probable that the latter alternative is the correct one.

THE UPPER GROWTH LIMIT OF SESSILE INTERTIDAL ORGANISMS RELATIVE TO SEA LEVEL

Vertical displacements in coastal areas were determined mainly from more than 800 measurements of the upper growth limits of intertidal sessile marine organisms relative to sea level along the long, intricately embayed rocky coast. In Prince William Sound and Resurrection Bay, where we used outboard-motor-powered skiffs for studying these changes during 1964, measurements were made continuously along the shore at spacings of about 1–5 miles except in those places where cliffs, heavy surf, or floe ice in fiords prevented boat landings or where the upper growth limits were not well-defined. During both the 1964 and 1965 seasons, measurements of vertical displacement were also made at localities shown on plates 1 and 2 that were accessible by light plane or helicopter along the ocean coast, on the offshore islands, and around the shores of the Kodiak group of islands.

In measuring land-level change from the displacement of sessile marine organisms relative to sea level, the zonation of plants and animals between tide marks was used—a zonation that has long been recognized by marine ecologists. The intertidal zone along the predominantly steep and rocky coastline of south-central Alaska is inhabited by certain species of organisms—notably barnacles, mussels, and algae—whose vertical growth limits are usually well defined (pl. 3A, facing p. I 16; fig. 4). The zonation of intertidal organisms in the Prince William Sound region was studied in detail by a party headed by G Dallas Hanna of the California Academy of Sciences in 1965. To the writer's knowledge, there were no published preearthquake data on the intertidal ecology for any part of the Gulf of Alaska coast.

In particular, the common acorn barnacle, *Balanus balanoides* (Linnaeus), and closely similar forms such as *B. glandula* are widely distributed on rocky shores and form a conspicuous band with a sharply defined, readily recognizable upper limit (figs. 5–7) The common olive-green rockweed (*Fucus distichus*), which has an upper growth limit near that of the barnacles, served as a useful datum for measuring land-level changes along shores where barnacles were absent or poorly developed (pl. 3B, facing p. I14). The upper limit of this zone, referred to as the "barnacle line," corresponds roughly to the top of the Balanoid or Midlittoral Zone of Stephenson and Stephenson (1949); to Zone 2, the High Tide Region, or the Upper Horizon of Ricketts and Calvin (1962); and the Upper Intertidal Zone of Rigg and Miller (1949). The barnacle line usually, but not always, approximates the lower growth limit of the dark-gray-to-black encrusting lichen (*Verrucaria*) which commonly forms a black band in the splash zone immediately above the barnacles and *Fucus* (pl. 3A, facing p. I16; fig. 4).

The upper limit of all intertidal organisms depends mainly on the ability of immature individuals to survive prolonged exposure to air and on the tidal characteristics at any given locality (Kaye, 1964, p. 591–592). In referring to the survival ability of barnacles, Kaye has termed this maximum exposure interval the "lethal limit." He found experimentally that it was close to 150 hours for yearling barnacles and ranged to an absolute maximum of 192 hours for mature barnacles. *Fucus*, which has a nearly identical upper growth range, must have approximately the same "lethal limit." To a lesser extent the upper growth limit of barnacles and *Fucus* depends upon a number of other factors which, in parts of Prince William Sound, locally cause the barnacle line to deviate as much as 0.6 foot from its average height at any given locality. Wave action during the lowest annual neap tides and protection from desiccation by shady locations tend to elevate the upper growth limit; exposure to fresh water near large streams or tidewater glaciers tends to depress it. Annual variations in sea level may cause further slight upward or downward shifts of the organisms' upper growth limits.

4.—Characteristic parallel bands formed by zoned intertidal marine organisms along unlifted west shore of Knight Island, Prince William Sound. Encrusting lichens form the upper dark band and brown laminarians form the lower one; light-colored barnacle zone is between the two. Photograph taken at about 2-foot tide stage, May 20, 1964.

5.—Measuring height of the barnacle line at Port Bainbridge in an area of the Kenai Peninsula uplifted 5.7 feet. Photograph taken at 4.4-foot tide stage, June 21, 1964.

6.—Barnacle line clearly marked by upper limit of light-gray barnacles and desiccated rockweed in dark patches and by the lower growth limit of dark-gray encrusting lichens of the splash zone. Uplift of 3.2 feet in Whale Bay, western Prince William Sound. Photograph taken at 3.0-foot tide stage, June 22, 1964.

7.—Barnacle line on hull of S.S. *Coldbrook*, Middleton Island. The upper growth limit of the dark band of barnacles on this vertical surface is clearly defined and at a uniform level, even though it is in a locality that was exposed to open-coast surf conditions prior to the earthquake. Indicated uplift is 11.7 feet. Photograph taken at 6.5-foot tide stage, July 26, 1965.

8.—Variations of mean tide range in areas of south-central Alaska where tide levels were used as a datum in measuring vertical displacement of the coast. Triangles show locations of permanent tide gages prior to the earthquake. Data from U.S. Coast and Geodetic Survey (1964).

planes corresponding to mean tide ranges of 6.4 feet to 15.9 feet in south-central Alaska.[1] Kaye (1964) has reviewed the definition of these tidal planes, the way in which they are derived from tide-gage records, and the control they exert on the zonation of intertidal organisms.

Field procedure for determining land-level changes by the barnacle-line method was to measure the height of the upper limit of barnacle or *Fucus* growth above or below water level at any stage of tide. On smooth steep rocky slopes sheltered from heavy surf, this line is sharply defined and can be readily determined to within 0.2 foot or less. On sloping shores or shores exposed to heavy surf it tends to be less regular, although even under such conditions it generally can be determined with confidence to within 0.5 foot. At most places where the barnacle line was above water, its height was measured with a hand level or surveyor's level and stadia rod. Where the barnacle line was visible under water, its depth below the surface was measured directly with the stadia rod.

Stage of tide at the time of measurement was then determined from the U.S. Coast and Geodetic Survey table of predicted tides for

Specific data on the normal upper growth limit of barnacles and *Fucus* relative to tide levels were unavailable for the part of coastal south-central Alaska that was affected by vertical tectonic displacements associated with the earthquake at the time this study was made. However, elsewhere on the Pacific Coast of North America and in other areas of the world the height of the barnacle line roughly approximates annual mean high water along shores with a small or moderate tidal range. In the region where measurements of vertical displacements were made during this study, tidal range, and hence the height of the barnacle line, differs from place to place along the coast. For example, the mean tide range (that is the difference in height between mean high and mean low water) varies from a minimum of 6.4 feet along the ocean coast of the Kodiak group of islands to a maximum of 15.9 feet at Homer near the entrance to Cook Inlet (fig. 8). Even higher tides—as high as 30.3 feet—prevail within Cook Inlet. However, the exceptionally large tidal range, in combination with a general lack of stable rocky shores and an increasingly impoverished marine fauna toward the head of the inlet precluded use of marine organisms for measuring vertical displacement.

On figure 9 are shown the variations in the 1964 positions of six of the important sea-level datum

[1] Extreme high and low water are the highest and lowest predicted annual tides; the extreme high-water line is also the approximate lower limit for growth of terrestrial vegetation along shores sheltered from wave splash. Because tides in south-central Alaska are of the semidiurnal type. the levels of the two daily high and low tides differ, varying between a maximum (spring tides) and a minimum (neap tides), depending on the interactions of the tide-producing forces. Thus, mean high water (MHW) and mean low water (MLW) are the average heights of all high and low tides during the period of measurement. Mean lower low water (MLLW), the mean of the spring tides, is the tidal datum plane commonly used as the zero datum by the U.S. Coast and Geodetic Survey. Mean tide level (MTL) is the exact midpoint of the range MHW–MLW. It differs by a few tenths of a foot from mean sea level, the average of all hourly tide readings over a given period, because the tidal curve is not a simple sine curve, but rather is compounded of a number of simple sine curves, some of which have fixed phase relationships with respect to each other (Marmer, 1951, p. 70).

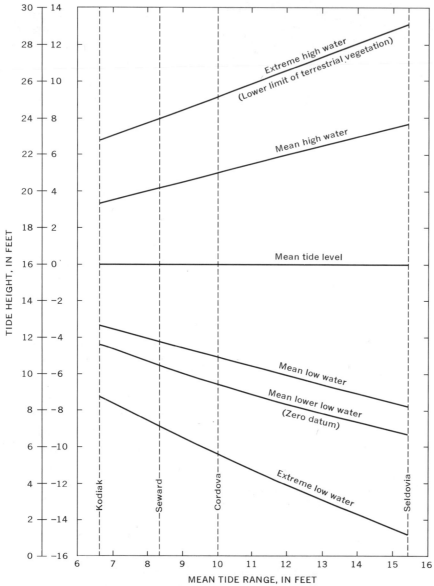

9.—Tidal parameters in areas of south-central Alaska where tide levels were used as a datum in measuring vertical displacement of the coast. Data from U.S. Coast and Geodetic Survey (1964).

the closest reference station, and, finally, the position of the barnacle line relative to the mean lower low water (MLLW) datum was calculated. For measurements made close to the 16 U.S. Coast and Geodetic Survey tide gages that were installed in the area immediately following the earthquake, we later made corrections to the actual, rather than the predicted, tides. During the period of fieldwork, it was found that few tides deviated by as much as 1.5 feet from predictions; most were within a few tenths of a foot of predicted values.

Differences in the height of the barnacle line in local areas of similar tide range provided a powerful tool for determining relative changes in land level along the coast even where the absolute change was not known. Absolute uplift or subsidence relative to sea level at any given locality was taken as the difference in height between the measured elevation of the barnacle line and the "normal" preearthquake upper growth limit for the barnacles and Fucus as indicated in figure 10.

The "normal" preearthquake upper growth limit of barnacles and Fucus relative to MLLW was determined empirically at the 17 localities listed on figure 10 where the amount of vertical displacement was known from Coast and Geodetic Survey tide gage readings. Its position at these localities was taken as the measured height relative to MLLW corrected for the amount of tectonic uplift or subsidence indicated by the tide-gage readings. On figure 10 these heights are plotted against the mean tide range at the station. The least-square curve through these points represents the average pre-earthquake height of the barnacle line for mean tides ranging from 6.4 to 15.9 feet in the study area. The curve suggests that the pre-earthquake barnacle line was close to mean high water for the lowest mean tides and that it lowered progressively relative to MHW with an increase in mean tide range. For the lower tides of 6.4–10.0 feet which prevail along most of the Gulf of Alaska and in Prince William Sound, it ranged from MHW to 0.6 foot below MHW level; for the higher mean tides of as much as 15.4 feet at Seldovia in lower Cook Inlet and Shelikof Strait, the barnacle line dropped to 1.7 feet below MHW.

The derived curve for the approximate height of the barnacle line is only a crude approximation to the actual position of the barnacle line. In addition to uncertainties in measurement of the position of the postearthquake barnacle line relative to sea level, it incorporates inherent errors in the determination of land-level change at the temporary tide-gage stations as discussed previously (p. I 11).

EFFECTS OF THE EARTHQUAKE ON INTERTIDAL ORGANISMS

A (right).—Sharply zoned intertidal marine organisms along west shore of Port Bainbridge. The barnacle line, uplifted 6.1 feet, is at the contact between the upper black band of encrusting lichens and the light-gray band of barnacles. Greenish material in the lower part of the rock face is marine algae; its upper limit marks the approximate position of the postearthquake barnacle line. Photograph taken at 3.1-foot tide stage, June 18, 1964.

This photograph is printed in color in the USGS original.

B (left).—Barnacle line defined by upper growth limit of olive-brown rockweed and lower limit of dark-gray encrusting lichens. Shoreline shown (Malina Bay, Afognak Island) subsided about 3 feet during the earthquake. Photograph taken at 6.5-foot tide stage, July 20, 1964.

This photograph is printed in color in the USGS original.

C (right).—Postearthquake yearling barnacles (light gray) among preearthquake barnacles (yellow). Within 4 months after the earthquake the new crop of barnacles had base diameters of as much as 0.3 inch. Large divisions in upper scale are inches. Photograph taken August 2, 1964.

This photograph is printed in color in the USGS original.

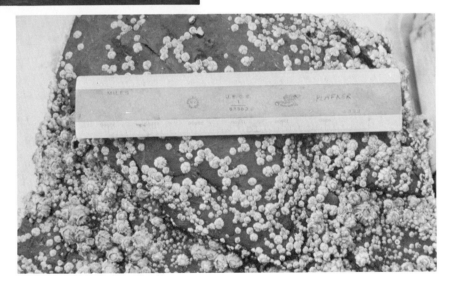

EFFECTS OF THE EARTHQUAKE ON SHORELINE FEATURES

A.—Living (olive-green) and desiccated (dark-brown) *Fucus* along the shore of Glacier Island, Prince William Sound. The top of the band of desiccated algae was near the preearthquake barnacle line and the top of the band of living algae was near the postearthquake barnacle line. The 3.0-foot difference between their elevations was a measure of the tectonic uplift in this area. Photograph taken at 8.8-foot tide stage, June 13, 1964.

This photograph is printed in color in the USGS original.

B.—Extensive area of brown terrestrial vegetation at Kiliuda Bay, Kodiak Island, killed by salt-water immersion after about 4 feet of tectonic subsidence and an unknown amount of surficial subsidence. Dikelike gray ridge of beach gravel was built up in adjustment to the new higher base level. The area behind this beach ridge may eventually become a shallow lagoon. Photograph taken July 17, 1964.

This photograph is printed in color in the USGS original.

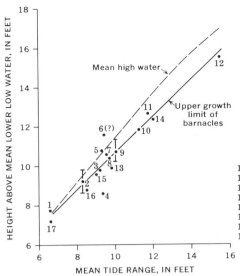

Data Points

1. Womens Bay, Kodiak Island
2. Seward, Kenai Peninsula (average of 2 measurements, range indicated by vertical bar)
3. Chenega Island, Prince William Sound
4. Lazy Bay, Kodiak Island
5. Port Chalmers, Montague Island, Prince William Sound
6. Sawmill Bay, Evans Island, Prince William Sound
7. Port Gravina, Prince William Sound
8. Whittier, Prince William Sound
9. Cordova, Prince William Sound (average of 28 measurements; range indicated by vertical bar)
10. Larsen Bay, Kodiak Island
11. Port O'Brien, Kodiak Island
12. Seldovia, Kenai Peninsula
13. Port Dick, Kenai Peninsula
14. Port Chatham, Kenai Peninsula
15. Two Arm Bay, Kenai Peninsula
16. Tonki Bay, Afognak Island
17. Ugak Bay, Kodiak Island

10.—Height of upper growth limit of barnacles above mean lower low water for mean tide ranges of 6.4–15.9 feet in south-central Alaska. The least-square curve for the upper growth limit of barnacles is based on measurements made at 17 stations (dots) where the vertical displacement was determined independently by the U.S. Coast and Geodetic Survey (Small, 1966) from tide-gage observations. Standard deviation is 0.627 foot.

However, the validity of using the empirically determined barnacle line was generally confirmed by our observations in late 1964 and in 1965 that the upper growth limits of new postearthquake barnacles and *Fucus* were generally within about ±1 foot of this line.

The precision of the land-level changes determined by the barnacle-line method varies within wide limits because of the numerous variables involved in making the measurements and the assumptions inherent in the presumed preearthquake position of the barnacle line. The measurements are generally within 1 foot of changes estimated by local residents or found by means of other techniques. Under the least favorable combination of circumstances, such as along segments of the coast exposed to heavy surf or swells or in areas of high and erratic tides in Cook Inlet and Shelikof Strait, measurements may locally be in error by as much as 2½ feet. In such areas, however, more reliance was placed on changes indicated by those techniques that do not require use of tide level as a datum.

DIFFERENCES IN THE EXTREME PRE- AND POSTEARTHQUAKE GROWTH LIMITS OF SESSILE INTERTIDAL ORGANISMS AND TERRESTRIAL VEGETATION

Throughout the region affected by tectonic land-level movements, postearthquake changes in the upper growth limit of barnacles and *Fucus* or in the lower growth limit of terrestrial vegetation provided direct indications of the direction and approximate amount of movement. Thus, along uplifted shores a band of dead barnacles, *Fucus*, and other sessile organisms developed within 2 months after the earthquake. The height of this band reflected the amount of uplift (pl. 4*A*). By July of 1964 a new postearthquake line of young barnacles, and in some places *Fucus*, was well established on most shores. The height of this line above or below the preearthquake line furnished a direct measure of the amount of uplift or subsidence (pl. 3*C*; fig. 11). Similarly, at many places, the amount of subsidence could be clearly determined within 2 months after the earthquake from certain ephemeral features such as the elevation to which the highest spring tides inundated terrestrial vegetation (fig. 12). By the 1965 field season, land plants had become sufficiently well established over much of the uplifted shore that the approximate amount of uplift could be determined from differences in the pre- and postearthquake lower growth limits (fig. 13). This method was particularly useful in areas of uplift such as Middleton Island where, for some unknown reason, barnacles and *Fucus* had not become established in the intertidal zone even a year after the earthquake.

Land-level changes determined from differences in pre- and postearthquake positions of the barnacle line or of the lower limits of terrestrial vegetation provide reasonably precise values for the tectonic movements where the postearthquake growth limits have had time to reach a position in equilibrium with the local tides and where the earthquake-related displacements have not caused significant changes in the tidal characteristics. Such measurements are thought to represent the actual vertical change at least to within 1.0 foot, and probably to within 0.5 foot in most places.

DIFFERENCES IN THE HEIGHTS OF PRE- AND POSTEARTHQUAKE STORM BEACHES

Along uplifted sandy shores on Montague Island in Prince William Sound and along the linear stretch of coast east of Kayak Island, the amount of uplift could be approximated in 1965 from the relative positions of pre- and postearthquake storm beaches (fig. 14). The accuracy of such measurements is difficult to evaluate, although where they could be

11.—Conspicuous white band of postearthquake barnacles along the shore of Kizhuyak Bay, Kodiak Island. The difference in elevation between the upper growth limit of the yearling barnacles in the photograph and the preearthquake barnacles, which were at water level, indicates at least 3 feet of tectonic subsidence. Photograph taken July 20, 1964.

12.—Drowned brush and trees along shore of Harriman Fiord, Prince William Sound. The color change (arrow) between the dead brown foliage (light gray) below and the green foliage (darker gray) reflects the position of the postearthquake extreme high-tide line. The difference in elevation between the lower growth limit of terrestrial vegetation and the new extreme high-tide line provided a measure of tectonic subsidence, which was 7.2 feet at this locality. Photograph taken at 0.9-foot tide stage, June 10, 1964.

13.—Wild flowers and grass growing among dead barnacles (white) on shore of Middleton Island uplifted about 11 feet. The differences in the lower growth limits of pre- and postearthquake terrestrial vegetation provided a direct indication of the approximate amount of uplift. Photograph taken July 26, 1965.

14.—Coast at Cape Suckling uplifted about 13 feet during the earthquake. The difference in elevation between the postearthquake storm beach (marked by band of light-colored driftwood) and the preearthquake storm beach, which was above the base of the sea cliff, provided a crude measure of the uplift. The smooth area between the upper limits of driftwood and the sea cliff is now a marine terrace, and the former island in the foreground is a stack on its surface. The flat surface on the stack is probably an older marine terrace. Photograph taken at about zero tide stage, July 24, 1965.

compared with changes at nearby rocky shores, they appear to give results consistent, within about 3 feet, with those obtained from barnacle lines. The measurements between Kayak Island and Yakataga (pl. 1) are particularly uncertain because the shore there consists of active sand dunes that had partially concealed the old storm-beach line by the time measurements were made in 1965. This method was used only where no other means was available for measuring vertical displacement.

ESTIMATES OR MEASUREMENTS BY LOCAL RESIDENTS

Where possible, data on local land-level changes were obtained from local residents in interviews and on form questionnaires. The amount of these changes and the confidence limits expressed by observers are shown on plates 1 and 2. Most of the estimates were made by fishermen, mariners, loggers, and other coastal residents who had long experience in observing the levels of local tides relative to familiar shoreline features. Consequently, most of their estimates or measurements of the vertical displacements are probably correct to within a foot or less.

HEIGHT OF TIDAL BENCH MARKS RELATIVE TO SEA LEVEL

At a few localities in Prince William Sound, changes in land level were determined by leveling from the water surface to U.S. Coast and Geodetic Survey tidal bench marks of known preearthquake elevation. The accuracy of these determinations, which depends mainly upon the precision of leveling and the degree to which the actual tides at the time of measurement correspond with predicted tides, is believed to be within 0.5 foot.

Submarine control for the off-shore uplift indicated southwest of Montague Island is provided by comparisons of detailed bottom soundings taken by the U.S. Coast and Geodetic Survey in 1927 and after the earthquake in 1964 (Malloy, 1964, p. 1048–1049; 1965, p. 22–26). Because of the technical problems involved in carrying out such surveys, however, the inferred submarine displacements could locally be in error by 10 feet or more.

COMPARISON OF PRE- AND POSTEARTHQUAKE LEVELINGS

The amount and distribution of the vertical tectonic movements inland from the coast were defined by the U.S. Coast and Geodetic Survey's prompt releveling of 722 miles of previously surveyed first-order level lines connecting the cities of Seward, Anchorage, Valdez and Fairbanks (pl. 1; fig. 3). Details of the methods used in these surveys were presented by Small (1966); changes in elevation between successive levelings at bench marks along these routes have been tabulated by Wood (1966, p. 124–130). The changes indicated by this method are probably accurate to within a few tenths of a foot.

Small (1966, p. 2) has cautioned that observed divergences in the results of the original leveling dating from 1923 and the postearthquake leveling in 1964 and 1965 may not be due entirely to movement associated with the earthquake because there is evidence for minor gradual regional movement along some lines where repeated levelings were made prior to 1964. At a few bench marks along these routes, which were located on unconsolidated deposits, the indicated subsidence was anomalously large. Such anomalous measurements obviously represented changes caused by accidental displacement of the bench marks or by local phenomena such as frost heaving, surficial settling, or thawing of permafrost rather than to tectonic movements; they are not shown on plate 1.

DISTRIBUTION OF LAND-LEVEL CHANGES

Figure 3 summarizes the known and inferred areal distribution of land-level changes. The deformation extends for almost 600 miles along the Gulf of Alaska coast from the southwest tip of the Kodiak group of islands through the Prince William Sound region and eastward to the vicinity of Yakataka where it seems to die out. The deformed region consists essentially of (1) a broad zone of subsidence centered along the axis of the Kodiak-Kenai-Chugach Mountains, (2) a major zone of uplift that borders it on the seaward side and extends from the coast onto the sea floor, and (3) a zone of slight uplift that borders it on the landward side and extends northward into the Alaska and Aleutian Ranges. The distribution of subsidence and uplift in these three zones is described below.

THE ZONE OF SUBSIDENCE

The zone of tectonic subsidence includes almost all of the Kodiak group of islands, most of the Kenai Peninsula, the northern and western parts of Prince William Sound, and probably the western segment of the Chugach Mountains (pls. 1, 2; fig. 3). Areas of subsidence in most rocky embayed coastal areas are clearly defined by the various criteria outlined in the preceding section or by qualitative indicators of shoreline submergence. In sheltered embayments the changes may be noticeable where the subsidence is as little as 1 foot. Such effects were most pronounced in areas of lowest mean annual tide range (fig. 8), inasmuch as both the frequency and duration of shoreline immersion for a given amount of subsidence vary inversely with the tidal range.

Along coasts with large tidal ranges and nonrocky shores, such as the part of Cook Inlet north of Homer, the subsidence is known only from tide gage readings near Kenai and at Anchorage, from a few observations by local residents, and from leveling along the coast near the head of the inlet. In this area, and along Shelikof Strait, the northwestern limit of the zone of subsidence is poorly defined. It seems to be close to the west side of the inlet from Redoubt Bay southwestward to Kamishak Bay and probably extends inland between the south side of that bay and the general area of Katmai Bay.

Control on the distribution and absolute amount of subsidence inland from the coast is provided by the Coast and Geodetic Survey's releveling of the first-order net shown on figure 3. Subsidence was indicated on all these lines south of the approximate southern margin of the Alaska Range except in the immediate vicinity of Valdez where a few bench marks were uplifted less than 0.2 foot (pl. 2). The leveling clearly demonstrates that the subsidence extends as a broad warp without abrupt changes of level across the Kenai Mountains northward from Seward and across the Chugach Mountains north of Valdez (pl. 1). Within the Chugach Mountains, subsidence of about half a foot extends eastward at least to Chitina. The northern limits of the zone are approximately defined by the leveling along The Alaska Railroad and Richardson Highway. Because of the small measured land-level changes on those lines, errors of as little as 0.5 foot could cause shifts of as much as 30 miles in the position of the northern boundary of the zone.

MAJOR ZONE OF UPLIFT

The main zone of uplift on land, as determined from shoreline changes, includes (1) a narrow fringe of points, capes, and small islands along the seaward side of the Kodiak group of islands, (2) all but the extreme northwestern and northern parts of the Prince William Sound region, and (3) the coastal belt extending about 120 miles east of the sound. Direct indications of uplift of parts of the contiguous Continental Shelf are afforded by emergence of all the offshore islands and reefs, including Middleton Island near the edge of the Continental Shelf (pl. 1, 2; fig. 1).

The extreme southwestern limit of the zone is believed to lie between Sitkinak Island, which was uplifted about 1½ feet according to a local resident (Mr. Hall Nelson), and Chirikof Island, where there apparently was no change in level (Neal Hoisington, written commun., 1965). Its eastern limit is probably at, or just west of, Yakataga.

The trend of the isobase contours in the northeastern part of the zone of uplift (fig. 3) and the distribution of aftershocks (fig. 2) seem to justify the inference that uplift also occurred over much of the submarine part of the continental margin in a broad zone extending southwestward at least to the latitude of southern Kodiak Island. Seaward projection of the trend of the isobase contours from the area between Yakataga and Middleton Island also suggests that uplift occurred over much of the continental slope and could have extended to the toe of the

continental slope, as is shown in figure 3 and on plate 1.

Independent evidence for uplift over a large segment of the Continental Shelf and slope comes from the seismic sea waves (tsunami) generated by the submarine movements. Because seismic sea waves are gravity waves set up in the ocean mainly by vertical disturbances of the sea bottom, the sense of displacement in the generative area can be determined under favorable conditions from the initial water motion at suitably situated tide stations. Tide-gage records outside the immediate area affected by the earthquake show an initial rise that indicates a positive wave resulting from upward motion of the sea bottom (Van Dorn, 1964, p. 166). The initial direction of water movement along the coast of the Gulf of Alaska within the area affected by the earthquake is less clear, however, because there were no operative tide gages, and in many localities the water movements reported by eyewitnesses were complicated by (1) changes of land level along the coast, (2) local waves generated mainly by submarine landslides, and (3) seiches, or other water disturbances related to horizontal tectonic displacement.

The shape of the source area within which the train of seismic sea waves was generated can be approximated from an envelope of imaginary wave fronts projected back toward the wave source from observation stations along the shore at which arrival times are known. Distances traveled by the waves can be determined if both the wave velocity along the propagation path and the travel time are known. Because of their long wavelengths, seismic sea waves move as shallow water waves even in the deepest ocean,

and their approximate velocity is given by La Grange's equation (in Lamb, 1932, p. 257):

$$V = \sqrt{gh}$$

were g is the gravitational constant, and h is the water depth along the travel path (as determined from nautical charts). Travel time is taken as the elapsed time between the main shock and the arrival of the first wave crest at shore stations. The distribution of tide gage stations outside the seismic sea-wave generative area precludes precise delineation of the source by this method. However, its general position as derived by Van Dorn (1964, fig. 8), Pararas-Carayannis (1967), and M.G. Spaeth (oral commun., Sept. 1964) is consistent with uplift in the broad zone that lies roughly between the Aleutian Trench axis and the coast and extends from the general area offshore from Yakataga southwestward to about the latitude of Kodiak.

The position of the axis of the wave source shown on figure 15 was inferred from the arrival times of the initial wave crest along the adjacent coast, the general distribution of wave damage, and the reported movement directions of the initial wave. Approximate travel times to shore stations, sense of initial water motion, and the data sources are given in table 2. These data suggest that the wave crest was generated along one or more line sources within an elongate belt that extends about 350 miles from the vicinity of Montague Island in Prince William Sound to the area offshore from Sitkalidak Island in the Kodiak group. This inference is supported by the fact that at the northeast end of this axis on Montague Island warping and faulting have resulted in uplift of 38 feet in a

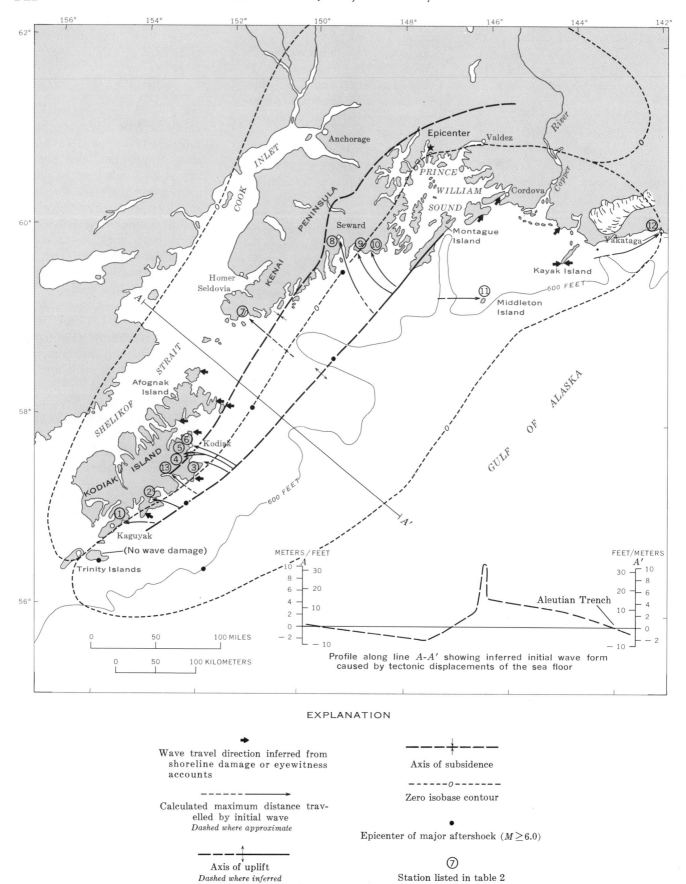

EXPLANATION

Wave travel direction inferred from shoreline damage or eyewitness accounts

Calculated maximum distance travelled by initial wave
Dashed where approximate

Axis of uplift
Dashed where inferred

Axis of subsidence

Zero isobase contour

Epicenter of major aftershock ($M \geq 6.0$)

Station listed in table 2

15.—Submarine extension of the zone of maximum uplift and faulting on Montague Island as inferred from movement directions and calculated travel distances of seismic sea waves generated by the tectonic displacements.

TABLE 2.—*Travel times of seismic sea-wave crest to near-source observation stations*

[Locations shown on figure 15. Travel time from start of the earthquake (5:36 p.m., A.s.t.)]

Station		Travel time (minutes)	Reported sense of first motion	Data source
No. (fig. 15)	Name			
1	Kaguyak____	38±5	?	Larry Matfay (radioed message received at Old Harbor).
2	Old Harbor___	48	Up_____	Larry Matfay.
3	Cape Chiniak_	38	Up_____	Fleet Weather Central, Kodiak Naval Station.
4	Kalsin Bay___	70	?	U.S. Geological Survey stream gage.
5	Kodiak Naval Station.	63	Up_____	Fleet Weather Central, Kodiak Naval Station.
6	Kodiak_____	45±3	Down____	Jerry Tilley.
7	Rocky Bay___	[1] 30	Down____	Guy Branson.
8	Seward_____	30±5	Up_____	Scottie McRae.
9	Whidbey Bay_	19½±½	Up_____	Bill Sweeney.
10	Puget Bay____	20±2	Up_____	Sam Hatfield.
11	Middleton Island	[1] 20	Down____	Dwight Meeks
12	Cape Yakataga.	60±1	Down____	Charlie Bilderback.
13	Saltery Cove__	[1] 30	?	Ron Hurst.

[1] Approximate.

belt about 6 miles wide (Plafker, 1968), and comparable displacements are known to have occurred on the adjacent sea floor (Malloy, 1964). Similarities in maximum wave-runup heights along physiographically comparable segments of coast, both on the Kenai Peninsula opposite Montague Island and on the ocean coast of Kodiak Island, suggest that the vertical sea-floor displacements that generated the waves in these two areas could be of the same order of magnitude. If so, the initial wave form resulting from sea-floor displacement had the approximate shape shown by profile A–A′, figure 15. Other factors, however, such as rate of uplift, initial slope at the wave source, and energy loss along the propagation path preclude direct correlation of runup heights with displacement at the source.

PROBABLE ZONE OF SLIGHT UPLIFT

Minor uplift, probably associated with the earthquake, has been detected in three areas adjacent to, and inland from, the zone of subsidence (fig. 3). The distribution of uplift in these three areas strongly suggests the possibility that they may be part of a continuous zone, roughly 100 miles wide, that parallels the major zones of subsidence and uplift.

Slight uplift in the Alaska Range is indicated by U.S. Coast and Geodetic Survey releveling along both the Richardson Highway and The Alaska Railroad (Small, 1966, fig. 9). Comparison of the 1964 leveling with a line run in 1952 shows general uplift along the Richardson Highway in a zone from about 25 miles north of Glennallen to within 50 miles of Fairbanks (fig. 3). Maximum uplift recorded on this line was 0.89 foot near the center of the zone, with irregular but generally progressive decreases toward the north and south. Land-level changes indicated by comparison of 1922 and 1964 levelings along The Alaska Railroad are less con-

sistent but they are predominantly positive and are as much as 0.36 foot in a zone where the line crosses the Alaska Range. The relatively large amount of change (0.89 ft) in only 12 years between the successive surveys on the Richardson Highway strongly suggests that at least the major part of the measured changes were probably associated with the earthquake. Furthermore, the fairly systematic rise and fall in the amounts of uplift across the Alaska Range suggest that uplift is not due to surveying errors or errors inherent in tying the level lines to tidal datum planes. Thus, it is tentatively concluded that the uplift along these two lines represents earthquake-related uplift over a broad zone centered in the general area of the Alaska Range.

Residents along the Iliamna, Chinitna, and Tuxedni Bays on the northwest shore of Cook Inlet (pl. 1; fig. 3) report a decrease in the height of tides after the earthquake that suggests shoreline uplift of 1–2 feet. There is little doubt about the validity of these estimates, particularly in Iliamna and Tuxedni Bays, where reference marks existed whose pre-earthquake relationship to tide levels were precisely known. Between 1963 and 1965 a slight uplift, presumably related to the earthquake, occurred also on the west side of Augustine Island (R. L. Detterman, oral commun., 1965) where beach berms have been lowered ½–1½ feet. The observed changes along the northwest side of Cook Inlet strongly suggest slight tectonic uplift of the shoreline during the earthquake. They cannot be explained by changes in the tidal characteristics due to regional subsidence of the entrance to Cook Inlet, inasmuch as deepening of the entrance would be expected to increase, rather than decrease, the height of the tides by facilitating diurnal movement of the tidal prism.

GEOMETRY OF THE DEFORMATION

The pattern of absolute vertical deformation associated with the earthquake is indicated by the isobase contours and profiles of plates 1 and 2 and is shown at a smaller scale in figure 3. The isobase contours may be pictured as the amounts of vertical displacement of an imaginary surface that was horizontal before the earthquake. The resulting map, therefore, is a special form of structure-contour map showing the configuration of the deformed surface. The maps and profiles indicate that the deformation occurred in three broad elongate warps, each of which is from 100 to 130 miles wide and has axes that roughly parallel the trend of the continental margin. Subsidence occurred in the middle warp and uplift in the adjacent warps on the seaward and landward sides. The zero isobases between the zone of subsidence and the adjacent zones of uplift are axes of tilt across which the sense of vertical displacement relative to the preearthquake position changes gradually. No abrupt changes of level have been found between the adjacent zones that would indicate vertical fault displacement between them.

ZONE OF SUBSIDENCE

The zone of subsidence is a synclinal downwarp whose axis is situated roughly along the crest of the coastal mountain ranges. The axis of subsidence plunges gently northeastward from the Kodiak Mountains and southwestward from the Chugach Mountains to a low of 7½ feet on the south coast of the Kenai Peninsula. In cross section the down-

warp is strongly asymmetrical with an average tilt in the middle part of the deformed region of about 1 foot per 14 miles from the landward side towards the axis and a much steeper average tilt of 1 foot per 2–3½ miles on the seaward side. The prevailing simple synclinal form of the downwarp is broken only by the slight warping of the tilted surface near the axis of subsidence immediately north of Seward in an area where both triangulation and geologic data suggest the possibility of minor earthquake-related movement on a conspicuous north-south-trending lineament.

Apparent reduction in crustal volume within the zone of subsidence, as calculated by summing the average volumes included between successive isobase contours on plate 1, is about 29 cubic miles. Total area of the zone affected by subsidence is about 48,000 square miles, and the average amount of subsidence within it is roughly 2½ feet.

MAJOR ZONE OF UPLIFT

The major zone of uplift along the continental margin is a broad upwarp with a maximum amplitude of 15 feet, upon which is superimposed a narrow belt, less than 10 miles wide, in which there has been strong uplift associated with displacement on reverse faults. The axis of the uplifted zone trends southwestward from Montague Island, presumably to the area offshore from Sitkalidak Island in the Kodiak group. Maximum uplift along this axis on Montague Island is 38 feet and it may be as much as 50 feet on the sea floor.

The position of the axis of uplift to the northeast of Montague Island is uncertain; it may continue offshore from Hinchinbrook Island and the Copper River Delta to intersect the coast at Cape Suck-

ling where 13 feet of uplift was measured. Because of the scarcity of data points in the Cape Suckling area, the shape of the deformed surface there cannot be closely defined and the possibility cannot be ruled out that the large amount of uplift there may reflect local warping or faulting.

The part of the upwarp available for observation in Prince William Sound has an irregular shape that suggests combined tilting and warping. As indicated by profiles A–A' and B–B' on plate 1, the landward slope outside the narrow belt of extreme uplift averages 1 foot per 2.1 miles northwest of Montague Island and only 1 foot per 7.4 miles north of Hinchinbrook Island. Local tilts as high as 1 foot in 185 feet occur within the belt of extreme uplift and surface faulting in southern Montague Island. The isobases in the central and southeastern part of Prince William Sound reflect a broad undulating platform 4–8 feet above its preearthquake position. In at least two areas of western Prince William Sound, local flattening or even reversals of slope are indicated.

Data on the configuration of the upwarped surface in the Kodiak Island area, although less conclusive, suggest northwestward tilting that is as steep as 1 foot per mile at Narrow Cape.

Little is known about the shape of that part of the upwarped zone that is seaward from the axis of uplift because only a few points are available for observation. The slope between the most southeasterly capes of Montague Island and Middleton Island 50 miles to the southeast averages 1 foot per 11 miles, but the shape of the surface in the water-covered area between these points is conjectural. Nor is it known whether the uplift seaward from Middleton Island dies out gradually toward the toe of the continental slope, as inferred on the profiles on plate 1, or whether it terminates abruptly in one or more faults or flexures on the slope.

The apparent increase in crustal volume within the major zone of uplift is much less certain than that involved in subsidence, because the distribution of uplift in extensive submarine areas must be inferred from the trend of isobase contours in the northeastern part of the zone and a few offshore control points. If the deformation has the general form shown by the profiles on plate 1, the volume increase would be approximately 89 cubic miles, or roughly three times the decrease in the zone of subsidence. Total area of the uplifted zone is inferred to be roughly 60,000 square miles. Average amount of uplift is about 6 feet, except in the narrow axial belt of uplift and faulting extending southwestward from Montague Island, where it is probably 30 feet or more.

PROBABLE ZONE OF SLIGHT UPLIFT

Where the broad slight upwarp landward from the zone of subsidence is crossed by level lines, its axis seems to be centered along the crest of the Alaska Range and its maximum indicated uplift is 0.89 foot on the Richardson Highway line and 0.35 foot on The Alaska Railroad line. The upwarp crossed by these two lines of leveling may be part of a continuous zone that extends into the Aleutian Range of the Alaska Peninsula where uplift of as much as 1.5 feet has been reported at several places in the Kamishak Bay-Tuxedni Bay area. A rough estimate of the apparent increase in crustal volume in the zone of slight uplift, based on an average uplift of 0.3 foot and an area of 24,000 square miles is about 1.0 cubic miles.

EARTHQUAKE FAULTS

Faults on land associated with the 1964 earthquake were found only at two localities on southwestern Montague Island in Prince William Sound and on the subsea continuation of one of these faults southwest of the island. Comparable faults entirely on the sea floor may have gone undetected. As far as could be determined no definite movement occurred along any other faults on land, although faulting at depth is suspected in some areas of unconsolidated surficial deposits characterized by linear zones of landslides or surficial cracks.

MONTAGUE ISLAND FAULTS

The location of, and displacement across, the earthquake faults on and near Montague Island are shown on plate 1. Their surface characteristics and tectonic significance are briefly summarized in the following paragraphs. In a separate volume of the Geological Survey's series of papers on the Alaska earthquake, they are described in more detail (Plafker, 1967b).

The longer of the two faults, the Patton Bay fault, is represented by a complex system, 22 miles long, of en echelon reverse faults and associated flexures with an average N. 37° E. strike. Surface dip of the fault is northwest at about 85° near its southern end and 50°–75° elsewhere along the scarp. Displacement on the fault is almost entirely dip slip—the northwest side upthrown relative to the southeast side. The maximum measured vertical component of slip is 20–23 feet, and maximum indicated dip slip is about 26 feet. A left-lateral displacement component of less than 2 feet near the southern end of the fault is probably a local phenomenon related to

a change in strike of the fault that causes it to trend at an oblique angle to the N. 53° W. principal horizontal stress direction.

The Patton Bay fault system was traced by the U.S. Coast and Geodetic Survey (Malloy, 1964) for at least 17 miles on the sea floor southwest of Montague Island. Indirect evidence, from the distribution of large aftershocks associated with the earthquake and from the distribution of submarine scarps, suggests that the faulting on and near Montague Island occurred at the northeastern end of a reactivated submarine fault system. This system approximately coincides with the axis of uplift inferred from seismic sea waves between the southeast coast of Kodiak Island and Montague Island (fig. 15). The fault apparently dies out on its northwestern end, although the possibility cannot be ruled out that it is offset en echelon towards the southeast (in a righthanded sense) and continues northeastward offshore from Montague Island at least as far as Hinchinbrook Island.

The shorter of the two faults, the Hanning Bay fault, is a virtually continuous reverse fault with an average strike of N. 47° E. and a total length of about 4 miles. Dip of the fault is 52°–75° NW. at the surface. Displacement is dip slip except for a left-lateral strike-component of about a third of a foot near the southern limit of the exposure. The maximum measured vertical component of slip is $16\frac{1}{3}$ feet near the middle of the fault, the indicated dip slip at that locality being about 20 feet.

The two reverse faults on Montague Island and the postulated submarine extension of the Patton Bay fault constitute a zone within which crustal attenuation and maximum known uplift occurred during the earthquake. Nevertheless, there are no significant lithologic differences in the rock sequences across them to suggest that these faults form major tectonic boundaries. Furthermore, their spatial distribution relative to the regional zone of tectonic uplift associated with the earthquake, to the earthquake focal region, and to the epicenter of the main shock suggests that they are probably subsidiary features, rather than the primary faults along which the earthquake originated.

OTHER POSSIBLE EARTHQUAKE FAULTS ON LAND

As far as could be determined, there are no other surface faults on land along which movement occurred during the earthquake. A careful search for renewed movement on known preexisting faults did not reveal any detectable surface displacements. Nor were any anomalous abrupt changes found in amounts of vertical movement along the coast or along level lines inland from the coast that would suggest significant displacement on concealed faults. All reports of suspected faulting that were checked in the field proved to be landslides or surficial cracks in unconsolidated deposits. It is reasonably certain that if additional faulting did indeed occur, its surface expression is far more subtle than that on Montague Island.

Some of the linear belts of concentrated surficial cracking and landsliding may reflect displacements on concealed faults. Foster and Karlstrom (1967, p. F24) suggested that movement on a concealed fault may have produced a northeast-trending linear belt of conspicuous surface fissures on the Kenai Lowland in the western part of the Kenai Peninsula. However, no evidence has been found for ver-

tical displacements where the belt crosses the U.S. Coast and Geodetic Survey level line south of Anchorage, and there is a notable absence of aftershock activity along the postulated fault.

A second possible line of fault movement lies along the broad north-south-trending topographic depression, referred to here as the "Kenai lineament," that extends northward from Resurrection Bay through the valley containing the eastern arm of Kenai Lake (pl. 1). Faulting is suggested (1) by local concentrations of fissures seemingly unrelated to seismic shaking along The Alaska Railroad (D. S. McCulloch, oral commun., October 1967), (2) by reported angular changes between points on either side of the lineament as indicated by comparison of pre- and postearthquake triangulation surveys, and (3) by a distinct change in trend of isobase contours across the lineament (pl. 1). The geodetic data have been interpreted as suggesting left-lateral displacement of as much as 5 feet between stations about 4 miles apart on either side of the lineament (Wood, 1966, p. 122). These data, if correct, could indicate either slight movement on a north-south-trending concealed fault or crustal warping localized along the lineament.

HORIZONTAL DISPLACEMENTS

Although the vertical displacements that occurred during the earthquake are unusually large, they appear to be secondary to the horizontal displacements indicated by retriangulation over much of the deformed region. During 1964–65, the U.S. Coast and Geodetic Survey carried out revisional triangulations in the area shown in figure 16. The resurvey includes an area of about 25,000 square miles

bounded on the west by the Seward-Anchorage highway, on the north by the Glenn Highway, and on the east by the Richardson Highway and the east coast of Prince William Sound. To the south, the resurvey extends to stations on the Gulf of Alaska coast and on Middleton Island 50 miles offshore from the coast. A tellurometer traverse was also run around the south coast of the Kenai Peninsula from Seward to Homer and from Homer to Moose Pass (at Kenai Lake) via Kenai. Because the precision of station locations obtained by the tellurometer traverse is probably too low to yield meaningful data on earthquake-related horizontal displacements, the stations are not shown in figure 16 and the indicated shifts of these stations are not considered here.

METHODS OF MEASUREMENT

Parkin (1966, p. 2–5) has described the procedures used in adjusting the pre- and postearthquake surveys. The preearthquake net consisted of: (1) a primary arc extending along the highway route from Anchorage northeastward to Valdez via Glennallen, surveyed in 1941 and 1944, (2) a second-order arc across the north shore of Prince William Sound from Valdez to Perry Island, surveyed in 1947–48, (3) a third-order arc surveyed from Perry Island to Anchorage between 1910 and 1914, (4) third-order triangulation between 1900 and 1961 for chart control across Prince William Sound and extending south to Middleton Island and westward along the southern Kenai Peninsula to Seward, and (5) a double arc from Seward north to connections at Turnagain Arm, surveyed by the U.S. Army Corps of Engineers in 1941–42. All these observations were combined into a single composite network and a

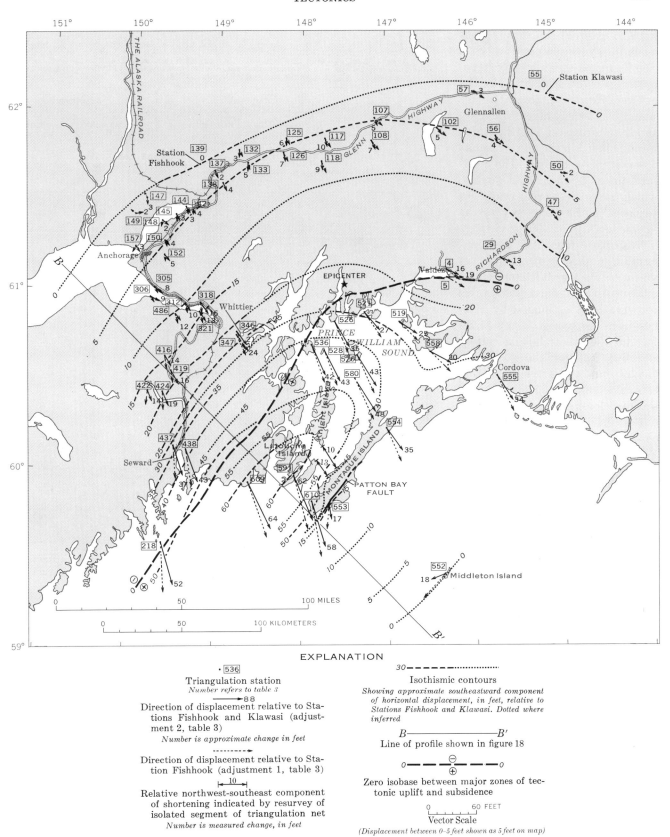

EXPLANATION

• 536
Triangulation station
Number refers to table 3

→ 88
Direction of displacement relative to Stations Fishhook and Klawasi (adjustment 2, table 3)
Number is approximate change in feet

- - - - →
Direction of displacement relative to Station Fishhook (adjustment 1, table 3)

├─ 10 ─┤
Relative northwest-southeast component of shortening indicated by resurvey of isolated segment of triangulation net
Number is measured change, in feet

30 — — — · · · · · ·
Isothismic contours
Showing approximate southeastward component of horizontal displacement, in feet, relative to Stations Fishhook and Klawasi. Dotted where inferred

B——————B'
Line of profile shown in figure 18

0 — ⊖ — — — 0
  ⊕
Zero isobase between major zones of tectonic uplift and subsidence

0 ▬▬ 60 FEET
Vector Scale
(Displacement between 0-5 feet shown as 5 feet on map)

16.—Map showing horizontal tectonic displacements in the Prince William Sound region and nearby areas. Horizontal displacements based on triangulation surveys by U.S. Coast and Geodetic Survey (Parkin, 1966, table 1).

free adjustment (an adjustment with no external constraints) was made in which one position—Station Fishhook—was held fixed. Internal scale and orientation for the net were furnished from 5 Laplace azimuths, 15 short taped base lines, and 1 tellurometer length, which were included in the adjustment as observation equations. The postearthquake triangulation survey, which was all first-order work, was adjusted in the same way as the earlier work.

Probable errors in the geographic positions of stations in southern Prince William Sound relative to the fixed station, as conservatively estimated by Parkin from the residuals, are 15–20 feet for the preearthquake survey and 6–8 feet for the postearthquake survey. These probable errors decrease progressively for stations closer to the fixed station.

The horizontal shift of recovered stations relative to Station Fishhook between the pre- and postearthquake surveys, as computed by Parkin, are listed in table 3 as adjustment 1 and are shown graphically as displacement vectors (dashed) in figure 16. Because the postearthquake net was not carried northward to an area of stability, changes shown are relative rather than absolute. However, small angular shifts in the northern part of the net, as compared with those farther south, suggest that the northern part of the resurveyed net probably approaches an area that was not strongly affected by horizontal distortion during the earthquake. Anomalous aspects of the adjustment are (1) a gradual increase in displacement along the Glenn Highway arc east of Station Fishhook to almost 13 feet at Station Klawasi, and (2) an apparent 32-foot shift of Middleton Island southwestward in a direction al-

TABLE 3.—*Pre- and postearthquake differences in triangulation station plane coordinates*

[Data after U.S. Coast and Geodetic Survey (Parkin, 1966, and B. K. Meade, written commun., June 24, 1966). Adjustment 1: station 139 (Fishhook) held fixed; orientation and scale from azimuths and baselines of preearthquake net (Parkin, 1966, table 1). Adjustment 2: stations 139 (Fishhook) and 55 (Klawasi) held fixed for additional orientation and scale of preearthquake net. Station locations are shown in figure 16 except for stations 180, 184, 186, 188, and 218. Azimuth: north=0°.]

| Station | Adjustment 1 | | | | Adjustment 2 | | | |
| | Position shifts (feet) | | Resultant vector | | Position shifts (feet) | | Resultant vector | |
	ΔX (east (+)-west (−))	ΔY (north (−)-south (+))	Length (feet)	Azimuth	ΔX (east (+)-west (−))	ΔY (north (−)-south (+))	Length (feet)	Azimuth
4	+18.74	−13.73	23.23	125°	+15.51	−4.65	16.18	117°
5	+21.66	−11.50	24.52	120°	+18.60	−2.32	18.72	97°
29	+17.32	−15.39	23.17	130°	+12.37	−5.23	13.43	113°
47	+11.17	−14.32	18.16	140°	+4.17	−4.73	6.30	139°
50	+8.45	−11.84	14.55	145°	+1.96	−0.54	2.03	105°
55 (Klawasi)	+10.06	−7.82	12.74	130°	0	0	0	------
56	+10.08	−10.47	14.53	135°	+2.23	−3.29	3.97	146°
57	+10.74	−6.82	12.72	120°	+2.25	−1.23	2.56	119°
102	−10.05	−9.03	13.51	130°	+3.34	−3.60	4.91	137°
107	+8.47	−7.73	11.47	130°	+2.99	−4.16	5.12	144°
108	+8.01	−10.23	12.99	140°	+3.14	−6.13	7.05	154°
117	+5.26	−8.88	10.32	150°	+1.57	−6.20	6.40	166°
118	+4.64	−12.48	13.31	160°	+1.62	−9.30	9.44	170°
125	+3.83	−7.09	8.06	150°	+1.10	−5.41	5.52	169°
126	+3.88	−9.23	10.01	155°	+1.54	−7.29	7.45	168°
132	+1.46	−3.91	4.17	160°	+0.17	−3.12	3.12	177°
133	+1.45	−6.61	6.77	170°	+0.23	−5.40	5.40	178°
137	+0.83	−2.37	2.51	160°	+0.81	−1.81	1.97	157°
138	+1.55	−4.74	4.99	160°	+1.42	−3.75	4.01	159°
139 (Fishhook)	0	0	0	------	0	0	0	------
142	+0.58	−4.71	4.75	175°	+1.93	−3.76	4.22	153°
144	+0.40	−3.68	3.70	175°	+1.82	−2.90	3.42	148°
145	−0.49	−3.41	3.45	190°	+1.35	−2.70	3.02	153°
147	−1.84	+3.15	3.65	330°	+0.37	−2.61	2.64	172°
148	−0.51	−2.04	2.10	195°	+1.88	−1.53	2.42	129°
149	−2.46	+2.06	3.21	310°	+0.42	+1.68	1.73	76°
150	−0.07	−4.38	4.38	180°	+2.70	−3.27	4.24	140°
152	+0.58	−5.56	5.59	175°	+3.70	−4.18	5.25	143°
157	−1.54	−2.43	2.88	210°	+2.19	−1.95	2.93	132°
218	+5.08	−58.20	58.42	175°	+15.34	−49.67	51.98	163°
305	+2.77	−4.83	5.57	150°	+6.99	−2.80	7.55	112°
306	+3.29	−5.50	6.41	150°	+7.79	−3.40	8.50	114°
312	+2.96	−10.69	11.09	165°	+6.80	−7.51	10.11	138°
318	+3.26	−15.58	15.92	170°	+6.66	−12.07	15.81	140°
321	+3.94	−14.22	14.76	165°	+7.58	−10.51	12.96	144°
346	+9.68	−21.89	23.93	155°	+12.96	−16.78	21.20	142°
347	+10.72	−24.23	26.50	155°	+14.12	−19.00	23.67	143°
416	+2.63	−14.85	15.08	170°	+8.26	−10.89	13.67	143°
419	+2.64	−18.23	18.42	170°	+8.46	−13.89	16.26	149°
422	−1.08	−17.25	17.28	185°	+5.88	−12.91	14.19	156°
424	+1.85	−21.59	21.67	175°	+8.35	−16.88	18.83	154°
437	+5.34	−41.20	41.54	175°	+12.88	−34.86	37.16	160°
438	+8.84	−46.34	47.18	170°	+16.26	−39.65	42.85	158°
486	+4.09	−11.98	12.66	160°	+8.41	−8.89	12.24	137°
519	+22.13	−22.78	31.76	135°	+21.22	−13.76	25.29	123°
521	+19.46	−28.40	34.43	145°	+18.18	−20.46	27.37	138°
526	+18.01	−37.17	41.30	155°	+18.70	−29.84	35.22	148°
528	+18.19	−45.85	49.33	160°	+19.76	−38.18	42.99	153°
536	+16.68	−44.77	47.78	160°	+18.67	−37.72	42.09	154°
552	−21.56	−22.61	31.24	225°	−17.02	−6.32	18.16	250°
553	−3.14	−28.77	28.94	185°	+2.34	−17.05	17.31	172°
554	+18.63	−39.50	43.67	155°	+20.81	−28.26	35.09	144°
555	+20.85	−41.30	46.26	155°	+19.35	−28.32	34.29	146°
558	+25.94	−23.87	35.25	135°	+25.18	−13.30	29.45	118°
576	+22.24	−45.30	50.46	155°	+23.51	−36.48	43.40	147°
580	+23.59	−48.63	54.05	155°	+25.25	−39.43	47.82	147°
591	+18.60	−67.40	69.92	165°	+23.88	−57.59	62.34	157°
609	+22.06	−66.56	70.19	160°	+28.91	−57.49	64.34	153°
610	+11.30	−66.35	67.30	170°	+17.12	−55.23	57.82	163°

most normal to that of stations along the coast.

The first of these anomalies is eliminated, and the second considerably reduced, by an alternative preferred adjustment of the data in which two stations, Fishhook and Klawasi spaced 140 miles apart, are held fixed to provide additional orientation and scale of the postearthquake net (fig. 17).

The assumption that the base line remained relatively stable in length and azimuth is justified on the basis of its position in the seismically inactive part of the net where there was only slight vertical displacement and by its orientation roughly parallel to the trend of isobase contours and normal to the trend of the horizontal shifts. The revised adjustment involves a

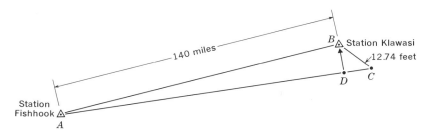

17.—Schematic diagram illustrating the method of deriving triangulation adjustment 2 from adjustment 1. According to adjustment 1, the postearthquake position of line *AB* is given by *AC*; point *B* shifted 12.74 feet S. 50° E. to point *C*. For adjustment 2, which assumes no change in distance or azimuth between *A* and *B*, the postearthquake net was rotated counterclockwise 0.0000124277 radians (angle *BAC*) and reduced in scale by the amount *DC*, or a factor of 0.9999881256 (the ratio of *AB/AC*).

counterclockwise rotation of the earthquake net of 0.0000124277 radians and a decrease in scale by a factor of 0.9999881256—changes probably well within the limits of error of these surveys. The resulting horizontal shifts, which appear to be more consistent with the vertical displacements, are given in table 3 as adjustment 2 and are plotted vectorially in figure 16 as solid lines. Unless otherwise specified, horizontal displacements referred to in the following sections are those of adjustment 2.

AMOUNT AND DISTRIBUTION OF THE DISPLACEMENTS

Absolute magnitudes and precise directions of the horizontal changes cannot be determined because the preearthquake triangulation net consisted mainly of third-order surveys and because the postquake survey, all of which was precise first-order work, was not carried northward to an area unaffected by the earthquake. Nevertheless, most of the changes are so large and systematic that there can be little doubt that they are in the general direction and are of the order of magnitude indicated by comparison of the two surveys. The true orientation and amount of displacement of the stations on the southeast shore of Montague Island (553) and on Middleton Island (552) are especially un-

certain. This uncertainty exists because (1) both stations are in a part of the net where large differential earthquake-related vertical movements may have caused significant horizontal shifts in their positions, (2) the preearthquake triangulation involving these stations was only third order and the stations were tied to the net in Prince William Sound through several figures that are geometrically weak, and (3) the stations are situated near the extremity of the net where errors in displacement relative to the fixed stations are likely to be at a maximum. As a consequence, errors inherent in the adjustments could equal or exceed the observed displacements of these two stations in either of the two alternative adjustments.

The pattern of horizontal displacements relative to stations Fishhook and Klawasi during the time between the surveys is brought out by the displacement vectors (solid) in figure 16. Except for Middleton Island (552), they show relative seaward movements that are predominantly toward the south-southeast in the western part of the area, almost due southeast in the central part, and east-southeast in the eastern part. Over the central part of the net, the magnitude of the displacements relative to the base

line increases progressively from the base line to a maximum of 64 feet at station 609 on the mainland immediately west of Prince William Sound, after which it decreases towards the southeast. In the western and eastern parts of the net, displacements show a progressive increase in magnitude to the most seaward stations amounting to as much as 52 feet south-southwest from Seward (218) and 34 feet near Cordova (555). In addition, resurveys of small isolated triangulation nets spanning the straits from Latouche and Knight Islands to Montague Island indicate relative shortening of 10–13 feet in a northwest-southeast direction (fig. 16).

The overall pattern of movement relative to the fixed stations is emphasized by the isothismic contours (lines of equal horizontal movement) in figure 16 which show the approximate component of horizontal displacement in a S. 45° E. direction, or nearly parallel to the average trend of the vectors in the same area. Contours are based on the displacement vectors (adjustment 2, table 3) and on relative horizontal movements within an isolated segment of the triangulation net between Montague, Latouche, and Knight Islands (Parkin, 1966, p. 9; C. A. Whitten, written commun., 1965).

Isothismic contours in figure 16 indicate that the entire area from the northern arc of the net to southwestern Prince William Sound showed a relative extension in a seaward direction, whereas the part of the net southeast of the Knight Island-Latouche Island area showed a relative shortening in a northwest-southeast direction. In other words, the position of Middleton Island, and perhaps the area southeast of the

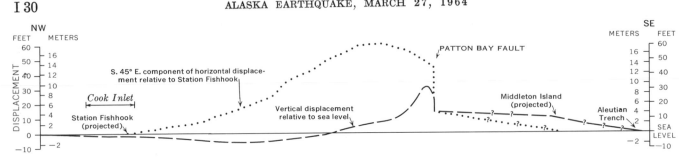

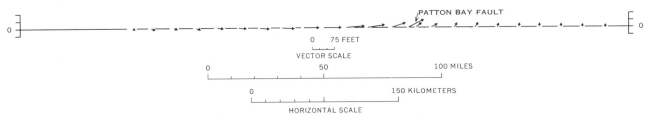

18.—Profile showing measured and inferred tectonic displacements (above) and vectorial sum of the horizontal and vertical movements (below) along section B–B' of plate 1 and figure 16.

island, remained essentially fixed relative to the base line, whereas the intervening area was displaced in a relative seaward direction, the amount of displacement attaining a maximum in the Latouche-Knight Island area.

Triangulation data indicating shortening across Montague Island agree well with the observed imbrication on reverse faults in this area (Plafker, 1967b, p. G40–G41). However, the exact amount of shortening is uncertain because the geographic positions of the stations on the seaward side of Montague Island (553) and on Middleton Island (552) are subject to large errors that may equal or exceed the indicated amounts of displacement at these stations. If the S. 45° W. component of displacement dies out at Middleton Island, as inferred in figure 16, the average contraction between that point and the 60-foot isothismic contour is 60 feet. That this amount of contraction may not be unreasonable is indicated by (1) the 10- to 13-foot shortening in a northwest-southeast direction indicated by reobservation of the

small isolated triangulation net spanning Montague Strait between Montague Island and Latouche and Knight Islands, (2) the horizontal shortening of at least 9.3 feet, and possibly as much as 19 feet, across the Patton Bay fault that is indicated by surface mapping, and (3) the pronounced crustal warping that occurred on and near Montague Island.

RELATIONSHIP TO REGIONAL VERTICAL DISPLACEMENTS AND SURFACE FAULTS

A genetic relationship between the horizontal and vertical regional displacements is strongly suggested by the orientation of the horizontal displacement vectors in a direction roughly normal to the trend of the isobases and by approximate coincidence of the maximum vertical displacements with areas of maximum transverse extension or contraction. This relationship is brought out by the profiles in figure 18 which show magnitudes of the horizontal displace-

ments in a relative S. 45° E. direction and the vertical displacements relative to sea level along line B–B' of figure 16. Also shown in figure 18 are the vectorial sums of the horizontal and vertical displacements along the line of profile, that is, the direction and relative amount of movement of points on the ground surface along this line.

The horizontal displacement data indicate that the zone of subsidence extended tranversely by an average of 1.1×10^{-4}, or 1.1 parts in 10,000, and reached a maximum of about 3×10^{-4} slightly seaward from the axis of the subsided zone. By contrast, at least part of the zone of uplift seems to be one of net transverse shortening resulting from crustal warping and reverse faulting. Average contraction across the uplifted zone as far seaward as Middleton Island is about 10^{-4} and it averages as much as 8×10^{-4} across the narrow belt of maximum uplift on Montague Island. Presumably, a comparable relationship exists between horizontal displacements and the earthquake-related vertical movements that ocurred outside the retriangulated area. Extension of the retriangulation net over this area could provide a definitive test of this assumption.

In a general way, the displacement vectors on either side of the Patton Bay fault (stations 610 and 553) are consistent with the field observations that the fault has undergone reverse movement with resultant crustal shortening by imbrication in the dip direction. In detail, however, there is an unresolved discrepancy between the observed dip-slip movement on the Patton Bay fault and the apparent left-lateral strike-slip shift of triangulation stations on either side of it (Plafker, 1967b, fig. 35). The discrepancy was reduced by the readjustment (adjustment 2, table 3) used here, but not altogether eliminated. Absence of an observable component of lateral slip on the fault suggests either that the displacement was taken up largely by horizontal distortion between the fault and the two triangulation stations or, more probably, that an error has been introduced into this part of the triangulation adjustment through a slight clockwise rotation of displacement vectors.

It is significant that, regardless of the details of the horizontal displacements, the triangulation data suggest rebound of a broad segment of the continental margin that had been elastically compressed and shortened by at least 64 feet prior to the earthquake. The vectors in figure 16 show the general sense and amount of the rebound within the retriangulated area. This indicated rebound implies preearthquake regional compression oriented parallel to the trend of the vectors, or roughly normal to the continental margin and trend of the eastern end of the Aleutian Arc.

TIME AND RATE OF THE DEFORMATION

Instrumental records of the time and rate of tectonic movements in the deformed area are nonexistent. Three standard tide gages at Seward, Kodiak, and Homer were located where they might have been able to record the vertical land movements relative to sea level had they been operative during the earthquake. However, the Seward gage was destroyed in a submarine landslide at the time of the earthquake, the Kodiak gage with the marigram for the month of March was lost when it was washed away by seismic sea waves half an hour after the earthquake, and the Homer gage was made inoperative by the shaking. There were no accelerographs in the affected region to record the horizontal movements. As a consequence, the time and rate of the movements can only be inferred from the reports of eyewitnesses, from photographs taken after the earthquake, and from the water and atmospheric disturbances generated by the movements.

EARTHQUAKE-RELATED MOVEMENTS

Numerous eyewitness reports of immediate withdrawals of water from uplifted coastal areas indicate that much, if not all, of the deformation occurred during the 1½–5 minutes of violent tremors. In most places, however, immediate water disturbances resulting from submarine slides or other causes precluded estimates of relative changes in level for several hours or days after the earthquake. In an area uplifted 6.3 feet, one eyewitness (Gordon McMahon, oral commun., 1964), thought that the displacements were perceptible as a series of distinct upward accelerations during the earthquake. Another eyewit-

ness (Guy Branson, oral commun., 1964), from an area that subsided 5 feet, described a definite dropping or sinking sensation toward the end of the strong ground motion "as when a plane hits an air pocket." No other observers reported perceptible accelerations in the direction of the tectonic displacements.

All of the uplift and surface faulting at the southwest tip of Montague Island occurred prior to March 30th. On this date the uplifted platform at Cape Cleare and a part of the Patton Bay fault were photographed during a reconnaissance flight (fig. 20). Jim Osborne, a bush pilot who knows the Prince William Sound area intimately and is an exceptionally perceptive observer, informed me that all of the shoreline displacements took place prior to the morning of March 28—the day he first flew over the area after the earthquake. According to Osborne, there were no noticeable shoreline changes after the 28th. His evaluation is corroborated by residents along the coast in all areas affected by the tectonic displacements. Movement along strongly uplifted shores occurred at least fast enough to trap many mobile marine animals such as small fish, starfish, and snails above the tide level (fig. 24; p. I 36).

That a substantial fraction of the net vertical displacement occurred very rapidly is also suggested by the pattern of seismic air and sea waves. The peaks between compression and rarefaction on the La Jolla microbarograph record (Van Dorn, 1964, fig. 5) were 7 minutes apart, a difference which suggests a peak-to-peak separation at the origin of about 83 miles; this figure is in close agreement with the observed spacing between the axes of uplift and subsidence. As noted by Van Dorn, the recorded disturbance could only have been produced by vertical motions over a very large area, and in a time interval of the order of that required for an acoustic wave to propagate across the dimensions of the generator. The elapsed time between the earthquake and the arrival of the initial wave crest along the ocean coast of the Kenai Peninsula further suggests that the initiating disturbance along the submarine extension of the axis of maximum uplift southwest of Montague Island (fig. 15) occurred during, or within a few minutes after, the earthquake.

There is no direct evidence as to when the horizontal displacements, which in some inhabited localities were as much as 60 feet, occurred. No observers reported strong systematic horizontal movements at any time during the main shock, nor could such movements be inferred with confidence from the incomplete data on the directions in which objects or structures fell. Nevertheless, as suggested on page I39, horizontal displacements probably occurred during the earthquake, and at a rate fast enough to cause waves in some bodies of surface water. Accelerations due to the permanent displacements probably were undetected by observers because they were masked by the strong ground motions resulting from the transient elastic seismic waves.

PREEARTHQUAKE MOVEMENTS

Vertical changes in the position of the shore relative to sea level have been noted within a period of hours prior to some major earthquakes in Japan (Imamura, 1930, p. 141). These changes, which have been termed "acute" tiltings or deformations by Japanese scientists, have been a subject of special interest because of their obvious potential importance in earthquake prediction.

During the field investigation of the 1964 Alaska earthquake, an effort was made to ascertain whether any premonitory changes of level were noted by residents in coastal areas or were recorded on operative tide gages. The only suggestion of preseismic changes was an observation made by an officer of Fleet Weather Central at the Kodiak Naval Station to the effect that tides in the area were at least 1½, and possibly 2½, feet lower than normal a few days before the earthquake and that the low tides were apparently unrelated to atmospheric conditions (Lt. C. R. Barney, oral commun., 1964). However, the loss of the March marigram prevented documentation of the reported low tides. The Seward and Homer marigrams for the time preceding the earthquake do not show evidence of preseismic changes, nor have such changes been reported elsewhere by coastal residents.

POSTEARTHQUAKE MOVEMENTS

Relevelings, tidal observations, and gravity readings suggest either no postearthquake vertical changes or, perhaps, slight changes in the earthquake-affected region.

The most convincing indication of continued postearthquake movement comes from releveling in May–June and in October 1964 of a line 22 miles long extending northwestward from Portage on Turnagain Arm and a third releveling from Portage to Anchorage in the summer of 1965. Between the preearthquake leveling and the initial postearthquake leveling, Portage subsided 5.6 feet, the area 22 miles to the northwest subsided about 4.9 feet, and Anchorage subsided about 2.3 feet (pl. 1). Comparison of the two

1964 relevelings shows a progressive increase in divergence from northwest to southeast, which suggests additional relative subsidence of about 0.16 foot at Portage in the period between surveys (Small, 1966, p. 13). Comparison of the May–June 1964 and the 1965 leveling suggests relative postearthquake subsidence of 0.36 foot at Anchorage and 0.52 foot at Portage during this interval (Small, 1966, p. 17). Unfortunately, neither the October 1964 line nor the 1965 line was tied to tidal bench marks, so the absolute postearthquake displacements are uncertain. Furthermore, because both Anchorage and Portage are situated in areas of extensive thick unconsolidated deposits, the possibility cannot be ruled out with the data available that some or all of the indicated subsidence may be due to continued consolidation of soft sediments.

Small (1966, p. 18) also reports a gravity increase of about 0.18 mgal on Middleton Island relative to an Anchorage base station. This increase occurred between the time of a postearthquake 1964 measurement and one made in 1965 which would indicate about 2 feet of additional uplift between surveys. However, the possibility that this large difference in the successive gravity readings may be due to meter drift in one or both surveys is suggested by the fact that residents of the island did not notice changes in relative tide levels during this same interval. Two feet of uplift at Middleton Island should have been readily detectable along the shore.

A comparison of tidal observations made in 1964 and 1965 provides data on the postearthquake land-level changes at 14 of the stations listed in table 1. However, it is difficult to separate purely tectonic movements from meteorological effects and the effects of surficial compaction at gages situated on soft sediments. Tidal observations in the zone of uplift at Cordova, Port Chalmers, and Sawmill Bay showed no detectable change suggestive of continued tectonic movements, but one station, Port Gravina, apparently subsided 0.3 foot between 1964 and 1965. In the zone of subsidence, gages at Seward and Port O'Brien had no detectable change in mean sea level; five gages at bedrock sites showed slight rises ranging from 0.1 to 0.5 foot, possibly suggestive of postearthquake tectonic uplift. Comparisons of 1964 and 1965 tidal observations at Valdez, Whittier, and Homer, in the zone of subsidence, indicated apparent continued subsidence ranging from 2.6 feet at Valdez to 0.3 foot at Whittier. The postearthquake subsidence at Valdez is definitely related to seaward extension and subsidence of the thick prism of deltaic deposits on which the tide gage is situated; much or all of the subsidence at the other two sites, both of which are on thick deposits of unconsolidated sediment, could also have resulted from surficial effects.

The available data on postearthquake changes outlined above are internally inconsistent and inconclusive with reference to postearthquake vertical movements. Disregarding the Valdez, Whittier, and Homer stations, where superficial subsidence of unconsolidated deposits is known or suspected to be large, the repeated postearthquake tidal observations indicate either recovery (by uplift) of as much as 0.5 foot or no change in the subsided zone. However, the repeated levelings on the Portage-Anchorage line and repeated gravity readings at Anchorage have been interpreted as indicating either continued subsidence or sta-

bility in that part of the zone of subsidence. On the other hand, tidal observations in the zone that was uplifted during the earthquake suggests either postearthquake subsidence of as much as 0.3 foot or stability, whereas the pair of gravity measurements at Middleton Island in this zone suggest additional uplift of about 2 feet. Repeated tidal observations, levelings, and gravity readings over a longer time period will be required before definite conclusions may be drawn concerning the postearthquake pattern of adjustments in the deformed region. It is abundantly clear, from available data, however, that there was no large rapid postearthquake recovery of vertical displacement comparable to the recoveries reported after some major earthquakes along the coasts of Japan and South America.

EFFECTS OF THE TECTONIC DISPLACEMENTS

Regional vertical tectonic displacements, both upward and downward, have caused profound modifications in shoreline morphology and attendant widespread effects on the biota. Changes in the position of the shorelines relative to sea level directly affected numerous coastal installations, shipping, and the fishing and shellfish industries. A major indirect effect of the vertical movements was the generation of a train of destructive seismic sea waves that were responsible for 35 of the 115 fatalities and for much of the property damage attributable to the earthquake. The movements also appear to have generated atmospheric and ionospheric disturbances that were detectable at several places in the conterminous United States.

The systematic regional horizontal displacements may have caused waves in certain confined and semiconfined bodies of surface water, and related porosity changes may have caused temporary water losses from surface streams and lakes as well as drops in water levels of some wells that tap confined aquifers.

Because the displacements were along faults that are under water and in uninhabited places on land they did not damage any works of man. Had they occurred in inhabited areas, however, these displacements surely would have caused extensive damage to structures built across them. It is also reasonably certain that phenomena related to the reverse faulting, such as the landsliding, extension cracking, and severe warping that occurred in a belt as much as 3,000 feet wide adjacent to the fault traces (Plafker, 1967b), would have been a definite hazard for engineering works.

Most of the effects resulting from vertical movement of the shoreline have been known from other earthquakes in coastal areas throughout the world. Especially detailed descriptions have been given by Tarr and Martin (1912) of the various physiographic and biologic effects of uplift and subsidence associated with the great earthquakes of 1899, centered near Yakutat Bay along the Gulf of Alaska coast. Effects of such movements on the works of man have also been amply documented for numerous major earthquakes along the coasts of South America, New Zealand, India, Japan, and elsewhere, most of which have been summarized by Richter (1958). Although submarine tectonic movements have long been suspected as the most probable generative mechanism for seismic sea waves, the 1964 Alaska earthquake provides what is probably the clearest evidence for a cause-and-effect relationship between these two phenomena. Atmospheric disturbances of the type associated with the 1964 earthquake have been recorded previously after large volcanic explosions and nuclear detonations, but they have never before been observed in association with tectonic earthquakes. To the writer's knowledge, there are no published reports relating surface-water disturbances or ground-water changes to horizontal tectonic displacements during previous earthquakes.

PHYSIOGRAPHIC CHANGES

Tectonic subsidence, augmented locally by surficial subsidence of unconsolidated deposits, resulted in narrowing or, in extreme cases, complete submergence of beaches. Sea water inundated the lower reaches of some streams in subsided areas as much as 4,500 feet inland from the former mouths, and salt water encroached upon former beach-barred lakes at stream mouths or bay heads (Plafker and Kachadoorian, 1966, p. D27). Beach berms and deltas in subsided areas rapidly shifted landward and built up into equilibrium with the new, relatively higher sea levels (pl. 4B). Former reefs and low-lying islands along the coast were submerged, and some tombolo-tied points or capes became islands. Wave action at the higher sea levels caused rapid erosion of shorelines—especially those composed of poorly consolidated deposits that were brought within reach of the tides (fig. 19). An irreplaceable loss resulting from such accelerated erosion of these deposits was destruction of coastal archaeological sites at several places in the Kodiak Island group and on the southern Kenai Peninsula.

The major effect of tectonic uplift was to shift the extreme high-

19.—Spruce trees on a spit near the mouth of Resurrection Bay killed by salt-water immersion and undermined by erosion after the land subsided about 3 feet. Photograph taken at a 9-foot tide stage, July 10, 1964.

tide line seaward and thereby expose parts of the littoral and, at some places, the sublittoral zones (frontispiece; figs. 14, 20). In the areas of maximum uplift on southwestern Montague Island, the emergent sea floor is as much as 1,800 feet wide (Plafker, 1967b, pl. 1, 2). As a consequence, former beaches and sublittoral marine deposits were rapidly incised by streams that cut down through them to new, relatively lower base levels (fig. 21). In many places, beach-barred lakes were drained in varying degrees by incision of their outlet streams. About 8 or 9 feet of uplift at the outlet of shallow Bering Lake, which formerly was reached by high tides, caused the lake to be suddenly reduced in area by about 4 square miles to a third its preearthquake size. Beaches and deltas developed below, and seaward from, their previous positions (fig. 14). Along the uplifted shores, preearthquake beaches, sea cliffs, driftwood lines, sea caves, notches, stacks, and benches were elevated above their normal position relative to sea level. Similarly, in offshore areas,

uplift created new islands and exposed reefs at stages of tide when they formerly were under water.

TILTING OF LAKE BASINS

Regional tilting or warping of the land surface seems to have caused permanent shoreline changes at Kenai and Tustumena lakes on the Kenai Peninsula. It may have had comparable effects on other lakes for which observational data are unavailable.

Tilting of Kenai Lake, which is about 25 miles long, is indicated by changes in the relative position of the bench marks that had been established near its ends prior to the earthquake. Although the accuracy of some of the recovered bench mark positions is open to question, the postearthquake survey suggests that the western end of the lake sank 3.0 feet with respect to the east end, and that the dip of the tilted surface is N. 72° W. at 1 foot per 5.4 miles (McCulloch, 1966, p. A29). These data are corroborated by the fact that the west end of the lake is close to the axis of subsidence (pl. 1) and that residents report a relative lower-

20.—Rocky surf-cut platform a quarter of a mile wide at Cape Cleare, Montague Island, exposed by 26 feet of tectonic uplift. The white band on the upper part of the platform consists mainly of barnacles and calcareous worm tubes; brown algae, or "kelp," cover much of the surface below the barnacle zone. Photograph taken at about zero tide stage, March 31, 1964. Compare with frontispiece, taken 2 months later in same general area.

21.—Bay-head deposits in MacLeod Harbor, Montague Island, deeply incised by stream erosion following about 33 feet of uplift. Arrows indicate the positions of pre- and postearthquake high-tide shorelines. Photograph taken August 6, 1965.

ing of the lake level at the eastern end after the earthquake (McCulloch, 1966).

The long axis of the 20-mile-long Tustumena Lake and its outlet stream, the Kasilof River, are oriented northwest-southeast, or almost normal to the projected trend of isobase contours in the area (pl. 1). After the earthquake, water levels at the inlet end of the lake reportedly rose above the banks; about 2 feet of southeastward tilt of the lake basin is thus suggested (J. D. Reardon, oral commun., 1965). The amount of tilt across the basin, as indicated by reported relative changes in lake levels, is in good agreement with that suggested by the spacing of isobase contours projected from the coast into the Kenai Lowland area (pl. 1).

TILTING OF RIVER DRAINAGES

Regional tilting may also have temporarily reduced the flow of certain rivers, such as the Copper, Kenai, and Kasilof Rivers, whose flow directions were opposite to the regional tilt (pl. 1). The Kasilof River was reduced to a trickle the day after the earthquake (Alaska Dept. Fish and Game, 1965, p. 23) and the Copper River reportedly ceased flowing at its mouth for several days. Immediately after the earthquake the Kenai River for almost a mile below the Kenai Lake outlet temporarily reversed its direction and flowed back towards Kenai Lake (McCulloch, 1966, p. A28), but it is not clear to what extent this reversal was due to tilting and to what extent it was related to the seiching of the lake.

Because rivers and lakes were approximately at their lowest annual levels when the tilting occurred, slight changes in gradient caused disproportionately large changes in discharge. The changes probably were largely related to upstream tilting of the larger lake basins in the drainage systems with consequent reductions or reversals of discharge until the basins once again filled to the spillover point. To some extent, however, the reduced flow in the river channels may have resulted from the lowered gradient of the beds. The regional tilting averaged 1 foot per 4.8 miles in the lower Copper River drainage and 1 foot per 10 miles or less in the Kenai Lowland. Other causes, such as channel blockage by river ice or landslides, may also have contributed to the reported temporary declines in discharge.

BIOLOGIC CHANGES

Vertical displacements of the shoreline strongly affected both the fauna and the flora over a vast segment of coastal south-central Alaska. Some of these effects were apparent within days after the earthquake; others, which depend upon the complex interrelations of one organism to another and to their habitat, will not be known for a long time. G Dallas Hanna, who studied the biologic effects of the earthquake in the littoral zone, has given a graphic summary of these earthquake-related changes (Hanna, 1964). The results of detailed governmental and private studies of the effects of the earthquake on intertidal organisms, land plants, and fish are to be reported in the Biology Volume of the planned series of publications of the Committee on the Alaska Earthquake of the National Academy of Sciences (W. L. Petrie, oral commun., 1968).

The most conspicuous effect of subsidence was the fringe of terrestrial vegetation killed by saltwater inundation at periods of high tides (pl. 4*B*; figs. 12, 19).

22.—Spruce trees in Nuka Passage on the southern Kenai Peninsula killed by repeated inundation with salt water in an area of 6.3 feet of tectonic subsidence. Algae and animals of the upper littoral have encroached upward into the former terrestrial environment. Inset shows a barnacle (white) and numerous *Littorina* or "periwinkles" (gray) on the roots of a tree. Photograph taken July 22, 1965.

Virtually all noncliffed shorelines that subsided more than 3 feet clearly showed fringes of dead vegetation within 2 months after the earthquake. In some sheltered localities at which vegetation extended down to the extreme high-tide line, dead vegetation was noticeable even where subsidence was as little as 1 foot.

Trees, bushes, beach grass, and muskeg along many former beaches were killed and partially buried in gravel or sand. Extensive areas of coastal marshland and forest that formerly had provided winter forage for grazing animals or nesting grounds for migratory birds were inundated. In such places, marine organisms encroached upward into the new littoral zone and it was not uncommon to find barnacles, limpets, and algae living on or among the remains of land plants (fig. 22).

The effects of subsidence on sessile intertidal marine organisms submerged below their normal growth positions were not readily apparent. Undoubtedly, individuals near the lower depth range of the species were adversely affected by the changed conditions and were gradually replaced by other organisms better adjusted to the deeper water environment.

Effects of uplift on the biota of the littoral zone were more striking than those resulting from subsidence, because the uplift caused complete extermination of organisms that were permanently elevated above their normal ranges. The width of the resultant band of dead organisms depended, of course, on both the amount of uplift and the slope of the uplifted shore. In areas where uplift exceeded the local tide range, as on islands in southern Prince William Sound, on parts of the mainland coast to the east of the Sound, and on several offshore islands on the Continental Shelf, destruction of the sessile organisms was almost absolute. Even many of the mobile forms—including starfish, gastropods, and small fish—did not survive. Some of the effects of uplift

23.—Closeup view of surf-cut surface at Cape Cleare, Montague Island, shown in frontispiece. The white coating on the rocks consists primarily of desiccated calcareous algae and bryozoans; the dark ropelike objects are stipes of laminarians ("kelp"). Photograph taken June 1, 1964.

of shellfish—including commercially important razor clams—has been estimated to be as high as 90 percent by G Dallas Hanna (oral commun., 1965). At many places where uplift exceeds the normal tide range, the clam population was literally wiped out. In such areas, the populations of birds, fish, and other animals that normally feed on shellfish must eventually readjust downward to the reduced food supply.

The potential effect of the land-level changes on the important salmon runs in the affected areas cannot be fully evaluated until the matured 1964 hatch returns from the sea to spawn. Spawning areas for pink and chum salmon, which are intertidal spawners, received major damage due to changes in land level and seismic sea waves (Alaska Dept. Fish and Game, 1965, p. 3; Thorsteinson, 1965). Spawning areas of upstream migrants, including the red and silver salmon, where relatively unaffected by the earthquake.

on organisms of the littoral zone are illustrated by plates 3A, 4A; figures 5, 23, and 24. The dramatic change with time in the appearance of the shore and sea floor after about 26 feet of uplift at the southwest end of Montague Island may best be appreciated by comparing the aerial photograph taken on March 30th, 3 days after the earthquake (fig. 20), with one taken 2 months later on May 30th (frontispiece).

By August 1964 a few land plants had encroached onto the fringe of shore reclaimed from the sea, and in the summer of 1965 scattered clumps of grasses and wildflowers grew everywhere, on raised beaches and deltas and in favorable localities on rock benches amid the dead and dried remains of marine organisms (fig. 13). In a few years the bleak aspect of these fringes of uplifted shore should become subdued by a luxuriant cover of brush and timber comparable to that growing on older uplifted marine terraces in the area. By July 1965,

land plants had covered much of the raised platform on Middleton Island and sea birds had already begun nesting in the former intertidal zone.

Throughout the uplifted areas in and near Prince William Sound, the mortality of all types

Many low-lying coastal lakes that were important habitats for

24.—Mass of dead starfish in a depression on the uplifted platform shown on figure 23. Photograph taken May 31, 1964.

waterfowl and for fresh-water fish were damaged mainly by salt-water pollution related to subsidence or to draining in varying degrees resulting from uplift and incision of their outlet streams. A few of the uplifted lakes that formerly received salt water through their outlets during high tides become entirely fresh with consequent changes in the number and species of fish they can support.

GENERATION OF SEISMIC SEA WAVES

Most major earthquakes in coastal areas that involve vertical tectonic displacements beneath the sea are accompanied by seismic sea waves, and the 1964 earthquake generated one of the larger seismic sea waves of recent times (Grantz and others, 1964, p. 11–12; Van Dorn, 1964; Plafker and Mayo, 1965; Plafker and Kachadoorian, 1966; Pararas-Carayannis, 1967). Between the southern tip of Kodiak Island and Kayak Island, these waves took 20 lives and caused destruction all along the ocean coast. The waves were especially destructive along the ocean coast of the Kodiak group of islands and the Kenai Peninsula areas that had been lowered relative to sea level by tectonic subsidence or by the combination of tectonic subsidence and compaction of unconsolidated deposits during the earthquake. In addition, the waves, which were recorded on tide gages throughout the Pacific Ocean, caused 15 deaths and major damage in British Columbia, Oregon, and California.

The wave-source mechanism was initially investigated by Van Dorn (1964), who concluded that the waves were generated by a dipolar displacement of water resulting from regional tectonic warping. He inferred that the positive pole of this disturbance included much of the shallow Continental Shelf bordering the Gulf of Alaska within the major zone of uplift, and that the negative pole lay largely under land or beneath Cook Inlet and Shelikof Strait in the major zone of subsidence. From preliminary data on the amount and distribution of vertical displacements along the shore, Van Dorn (1964, p. 17) calculated that the total potential energy imparted to the positive part of the seismic sea wave by submarine uplift (assuming (1) vertical displacement of 6 feet that increases progressively from zero at the southwest end to 6 feet at the northwest end and (2) source dimensions of 240 miles by 100 miles), was 1.7×10^{14} ft-lbs (2.3×10^{21} ergs), or only about 0.1–0.05 percent of the approximately 10^{24} to 2×10^{24} ergs of seismic-wave energy released by the main shock. Pararas-Carayannis (1967), using source dimensions of 93 miles (150 km) by 435 miles (700 km) and the same average uplift as inferred by Van Dorn, arrived at a total water-wave energy of 5.88×10^{21} ergs.

The Geological Survey's subsequent studies of the vertical displacements on land and their probable extension beneath the sea provide additional data relevant to the probable configuration of the initial positive wave and its energy content. These data suggest that the initial wave form, due to vertical displacement of the sea floor on the Continental Shelf, probably had the general cross-sectional shape indicated by the profile in figure 15 and that the offshore areas involved in the uplift and the amounts of sea-floor displacement are considerably greater than was indicated by preliminary reconnaissance surveys. Thus, the general shape of the deformed surface on the Continental Shelf may be roughly approximated by a broad low-amplitude upwarp with minimum dimensions of 400 by about 75 miles, superimposed upon which is a narrow belt of maximum uplift about 6 miles wide that is inferred to extend some 350 miles southwestward from Montague Island. As indicated on profiles A–A', B–B' C–C' plate 1, average uplift across the broad upwarp is roughly about 12 feet and that across the narrow zone is probably at least 30 feet. Because this highly simplified model does not consider the additional wave energy at the ends of the deformed region, where uplift gradually falls off to zero, or in that part lying seaward from the edge of the Continental Shelf where the deformation field is unknown, the calculated energy should be considered as a minimum.

If the initial wave form approximates that of the uplift, total potential energy transferred to the water, E_t was the sum of the energy in both the broad low-amplitude part of the wave (E_1) and in the narrow superimposed high-amplitude part (E_2). Total potential energy transferred to the water, E_t, derived by using Iida's equation (1963, p. 65), was

$$E_t = E_1 + E_2 = \frac{\rho g (h_1)^2 A_1}{2} + \frac{\rho g (h_2)^2 A_2}{2}$$

where ρ is the density of sea water, g is the gravitational acceleration, h is the average vertical displacement, and A is the area over which the deformation occurred. Therefore, by substitution,

$E_1 = (1.1)(32)(15)^2(6)(350)(5,280)^2$
$= 4.6 \times 10^{14}$ ft-lbs (6.2×10^{21} ergs);
$E_2 = (1.1)(32)(6)^2(75)(400)(5,280)^2$
$= 1.06 \times 10^{15}$ ft-lbs (1.4×10^{22} ergs);

and their sum,

$E_t = 1.5 \times 10^{15}$ ft-lbs (2×10^{22} ergs).

These figures suggest that the total potential energy in the positive part of the wave may be about an order of magnitude larger than that derived by Van Dorn, or 1.0–0.5 percent of the seismic wave energy release. According to the model used, roughly one-third of the energy was concentrated in the narrow high-amplitude part of the wave along the axis of maximum uplift and two-thirds was distributed over the low-amplitude part of the wave which has an area roughly 15 times larger. Thus, the relatively greater damage and higher wave runups along the outer coast of the Kodiak group of islands and the Kenai Peninsula, as compared to the ocean coast of Prince William Sound and the mainland east of the sound, appears to be a function of proximity to the narrow zone of high wave-energy concentration along the axis of maximum uplift.

ATMOSPHERIC EFFECTS

An atmospheric pressure wave that was the atmospheric counterpart of the seismic sea waves was recorded on microbarographs at the University of California at Berkeley and at the Scripps Institute of Oceanography at La Jolla, Calif. The wave traveled at the speed of sound in air (roughly 1,050 ft per sec in the lower atmosphere), reaching Berkeley, 1,950 miles from the epicenter, 2 hours and 40 minutes after start of the earthquake (Bolt, 1964, p. 1095) and La Jolla 39 minutes later (Van Dorn, 1964, fig. 5). Travel times to these stations correspond to an initiating disturbance in the epicentral region during the earthquake. The pressure wave's signature further suggests that it was caused by the vertical tectonic displacements of the land and sea surfaces that accompanied the earthquake.

The atmospheric pressure wave also seems to have caused a traveling ionospheric disturbance that was observed in Hawaii, Alaska, and the conterminous United States on high-frequency radio sounders (Row, 1966). The disturbance at Boulder, Colo., was characterized by an abrupt onset, speeds appropriate to sound waves above 100 km in altitude, an oscillatory long-period tail, and an initial negative doppler. Computations by Row indicate that the essential features of the observations may be reproduced by sudden vertical ground displacement of the type observed in the epicentral region below a plane isothermal gravitating atmosphere.

WATER DISTURBANCES POSSIBLY RELATED TO HORIZONTAL DISPLACEMENTS

Water disturbances that accompanied the earthquake in some lakes, fiords, and rivers may have been generated by inertial effects of the water bodies as the land mass was displaced horizontally beneath them. Horizontal movement of a deep steep-sided basin or fiord, if it occurred fast enough, would be expected to impart potential energy to a contained water mass by changing its surface configuration as illustrated diagrammatically by figure 25. Thus, because of its inertia, water would tend to pile up above its original level along shores on the side of the basin opposite to the direction of displacement, and it would simultaneously be lowered along shores in the direction of displacement. For a given amount and rate of displacement, the effect of horizontal movement on the water mass would be proportionally greatest where orientation of shores is normal to the direction of horizontal movement and relatively steep basin sides permitted the maximum energy to be

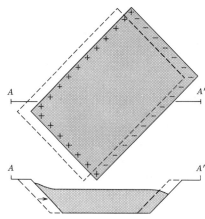

25.—Schematic diagram illustrating the postulated effect of a sudden horizontal displacement on water in an enclosed basin, the amount of displacement assumed to be small relative to the dimensions of the basin. Dashed lines indicate the original position of the basin, solid lines the position after displacement. Symbols along the basin margin in the plan view (above) indicate shores along which an initial rise (+) or drop (−) in water level would occur; profile A–A' shows a possible configuration of the water surface immediately after the displacement.

transferred from the basin to the contained water mass.

McCulloch (1966, p. A39) has reported uninodal and multinodal seiche waves in Kenai Lake with half-wave amplitudes of 5–6 feet and initial runup heights that were locally as much as 30 feet. He inferred that they were generated by a tectonic tilting of the lake basin that amounted to no more than 3 feet. A possible alternative explanation, however, is that the waves and seiche in Kenai Lake—a lake which lies in a long narrow steep-sided glacial valley—resulted mainly from the 15–25 feet of south-southeast horizontal translation of the lake basin that accompanied the earthquake in that area (fig. 16). Because of the irregular shape of the basin and uncertainties regarding the rate at which the horizontal displacements occurred, it is not possible to determine quantitatively whether the horizontal displacements alone or in combination with tectonic tilting could generate the waves recorded at Kenai Lake.

Sudden rises of water level during or immediately after the earthquake, observed at numerous coastal localities where there was no evidence for submarine sliding, strong tilting, or faulting could also have been caused by the horizontal displacements. Within Prince William Sound, where horizontal displacements in a south-to-southeast direction ranged from about 20 to 62 feet (fig. 16), local waves of unknown origin were responsible for the loss of at least 28 lives and caused extensive property damage at Chenega, Port Ashton, Port San Juan, Port Oceanic, Perry Island, and probably at Port Nellie Juan and Point Nowell (Plafker and others, 1969). Similar waves that did not cause damage also were reported at Port Wells, Unakwik Inlet, Tatitlek, Naked Island, and several other localities in Prince William Sound. Much of the damage from local waves was concentrated along east-west- to northeast-southwest-trending shores in semiconfined bays or along deep steep-sided fiords and straits. These waves, which appeared at widely separated localities in the sound within minutes after the earthquake was first felt, must have been generated locally and almost simultaneously. Most eyewitnesses observed a single large wave with runup as high as 70 feet (as at Chenega), preceded or followed by much smaller waves at intervals of a few minutes. The sudden onset, short period, and local distribution of the waves distinguish them from the train of long-period seismic sea waves generated in the Gulf of Alaska that did not reach the outer coast

of the Kenai Peninsula until about 20 minutes after the start of the earthquake. That the waves may have been generated by relative seaward movement of the land mass in Prince William Sound is suggested by (1) their appearance during the earthquake, (2) their occurrence in an area where there were large horizontal displacements, and by (3) the orientation and configuration of the affected shorelines.

Unexplained waves were also observed in widely scattered coastal areas of the Kenai Peninsula and Kodiak Islands, where retriangulation data are unavailable but where significant horizontal displacements probably occurred. For example, waves as high as 9 feet were reported by eyewitnesses in the Homer area during and immediately after the earthquake. Such waves could not be attributed to sliding, slumping, or other causes (Waller, 1966a, p. D3–D4). The curious breaking and surging of the waves on the tidal flats suggested to one observer that "the land was being shoved under the bay" (Waller, 1966a, p. D4). Rapid, calm rises in water level of 9 feet at Kodiak (Plafker and Kachadoorian, 1966, p. D30) and of about 26 feet at Whittier (Plafker and Mayo, 1965, p. 15) that cannot be readily ascribed to any other cause may also have been related to horizontal displacement of the land.

In summary, horizontal displacements of the magnitude indicated by retriangulation data, if they occurred fast enough, should theoretically generate waves in water bodies of suitable size and configuration. This movement may have been the cause, or a contributing cause, of some waves observed in certain localities during or immediately after the earthquake that cannot be directly re-

lated to vertical tectonic displacements, regional tilting, seismic shaking, or submarine landslides.

CHANGES IN ARTESIAN-WELL LEVELS

Systematic long-term drops in water levels of wells tapping confined aquifers in Pleistocene and late Tertiary strata were recorded at various widely spaced localities within the zone of tectonic subsidence (Waller, 1966a, p. D16–D18; 1966b, p. A18–A26). Records of seven representative artesian wells from Anchorage, Chugiak, and four communities on the Kenai Peninsula are shown in figure 26. The residual drops in well levels at the time of the earthquake range from about 7 to 25 feet, and none of the wells showed full recovery within a year after the earthquake.

Observed long-term changes in well levels suggest changes in the physical structure of the aquifers and a net increase in aquifer-pore space. Such changes could be caused by rearrangement of grains or fractures as a result of the horizontal extension (on the order of 2×10^{-4}) and (or) the elastic dilatation that is known or inferred to have affected the areas in which these wells are located.

A similar effect was looked for, but not found, in the oil wells of the Swanson River oil field located in the zone of tectonic subsidence near Kenai (R. I. Levorsen, written commun., 1966). Any small strain change that may have occurred probably was masked by changes in volume of the relatively compressible oil-water-gas mixture filling the pore space of the field reservoir.

The only artesian water wells in the zone of tectonic uplift are in a thick deposit of glacial drift at Cordova (Waller, 1966b, p. A20–A21). Because these wells did not have recorders installed in them, their response to the earth-

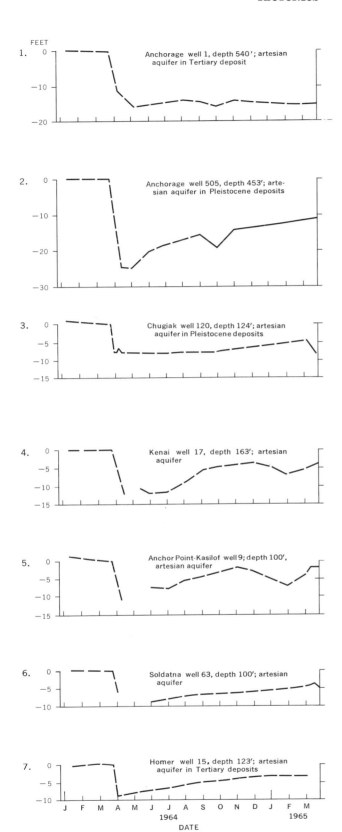

26.—Artesian well records from the zone of tectonic subsidence showing systematic drop in water levels at the time of the earthquake. After Waller (1966a, fig. 13 ; 1966b, figs. 14, 20, 22).

quake cannot be correlated with that of the wells in the zone that subsided. However, comparison of measurements in three wells made in July 1962 with measurements made 4 months after the earthquake showed about a 1-foot rise in water level, rather than the residual drop that characterized wells in the subsided zone.

STREAMFLOW, LAKE LEVELS, AND SHALLOW WELLS

Changes in the levels of many lakes, streams, and shallow wells in unconfined aquifers were observed at numerous localities within the zone of tectonic subsidence. In general, the reported changes involved temporary water losses (Waller, 1966b, p. A8–A11; Plafker and Kachadoorian, 1966, p. D23–D24). One of the more probable causes for such changes is an increase of intergranular or fracture porosity in the surrounding materials consequent upon horizontal extension and elastic dilatation across the subsided zone during the earthquake.

COASTAL FACILITIES AND SHIPPING

Regional land-level changes— including both subsidence and uplift—caused direct and costly damage to homes, canneries, transportation routes, airfields, docks, harbors, and other facilities throughout the affected areas (figs. 27, 28). Many facilities that had otherwise been unaffected either by the earthquake or the destructive water waves associated with it were damaged by land-level changes. Such changes had relatively few short-term beneficial effects on the works of man. Because the various forms of damage resulting from vertical tectonic movements have already been described in detail in the various reports of this series on effects to communities (U.S. Geol. Survey Professional Paper 542) and were

27.—Road along Womens Bay, Kodiak Island, in an area of about 5.5 feet of tectonic subsidence and an unknown, but probably substantial, amount of local settling of unconsolidated deposits. Since subsidence, the road has been flooded at high tide and subject to erosion by waves. Photograph taken at 4.0-foot tide stage, July 20, 1964.

28.—Canneries and fishermen's homes along Orca Inlet in Prince William Sound placed above the reach of most tides due to about 6 feet of uplift. Photograph was taken on July 27, 1964, at a 9-foot tide stage, which would have reached beneath the docks prior to the earthquake.

summarized by Hansen and Eckel (1966) and Eckel (1967), they need not be described here.

GRAVITY CHANGES

Vertical displacements were accompanied by measurable changes in gravity at several stations where comparative pre- and postearthquake gravity readings were made (D. F. Barnes, 1966; oral commun. 1966). The stations were distributed in both the zones of subsidence and the zones of uplift where changes in elevation ranged from −5.8 feet at Portage to about +11 feet at Middleton Island. Corresponding gravity changes were between +0.5 milligals to −0.67 milligals. Barnes (1966, p. 455) noted that the gravity changes, at least in the uplifted area, tend to approximate the Bouguer, rather than the free-air, gradients. Although uncertainties in relocating some of the station positions preclude firm conclusions, the data suggest that there has been a redistribution of mass in at least those parts of the deformed region where the changes correspond to Bouguer gradients.

COMPARISON WITH OTHER EARTHQUAKES

In terms of areal extent of deformation and amount of residual horizontal and vertical displacement, the 1964 Alaska earthquake is one of the most impressive tectonic events ever recorded. This fact is brought out by table 4, which compares the deformation associated with the 1964 event with that of selected great earthquakes for which quantitative data are available.

The area of observable crustal deformation, or probable deformation, that accompanied the 1964 earthquake is larger than any such area known to have been associated with a single earthquake in historic times. Comparable tectonic deformations have probably occurred during other great historic earthquakes, but if so they were beneath the sea, along linear coast lines, or inland, where it generally is not possible to determine the areal extent of such features with any degree of confidence. For example, the area affected by vertical displacements during the great series of Chilean earthquakes in May and June of 1960 extended

TABLE 4.—*Comparative deformations of the 1964 Alaska earthquake and some other great earthquakes*

Earthquake	Date	Approximate Magnitude (Richter scale)	Probable area of surface warping (square miles)	Maximum vertical warping relative to sea level (feet)	Maximum relative horizontal distortion (feet)	Maximum relative fault displacement (feet) (H, horizontal; V, vertical)	Data source
1964 Alaska	March 27, 1964	8.4+	108,000 (major zones only).	+38, −7½	64	2H?; 20–23V	This paper.
Niigata, Japan	June 16, 1964	7.7	≈20,000	+4.9, −1.5	No data	Submarine only, displacement unknown.	Earthquake Research Institute (1964).
1960 Chile	May 22, 1960	8.3	17,000+	+10–13, −7.2	...do	No known surface faults.	Saint-Amand (1961).
Lituya Bay, Alaska	July 10, 1958	8.0	No data; fault rupture 115+ miles long.	None reported	...do	21.5H; 6V	Tocher (1960).
Gobi-Altai, Mongolia	December 4, 1957. (G.)	8.6	≈32,000 (area of faulting).	No data	...do	29H; 30V	Florensov and Solonenko (1963).
Nankaido, Japan	December 20, 1946.	8.5	20,000+	+2.9, −2.0	6.2	No known surface faults.	Inoue (1960, p. 84–85).
Hawkes Bay, New Zealand	February 3, 1931	7.9	2,000 (minimum)	+9, −2 to 3	No data	6–7H; 6–8V?	Henderson (1933).
Kwanto, Japan	September 1, 1923.	8.3	10.+	+6.6, −5.3	15	6.6V	Muto (1932); Inamura (1930).
San Francisco, Calif	April 18, 1906	8.3	No data; fault rupture 270 miles long.	Minor	≈20	21H; 3V	Richter (1958, p. 476–486).
Yakutat Bay, Alaska	September 1899	8.5–8.6	1,300 (minimum)	+47, −7(?)	No data	8+H?; 8V (on subsidiary faults).	Tarr and Martin (1912).
Assam, India	June 12, 1897	8.7	2,000 (minimum)	No data	...do	0H?; 35V	Richter (1958, p. 49–50).

north-south some 420 miles along the Pacific Ocean coast, and at least 40 miles in an east-west direction at the Gulf of Ancud near the southern end of the affected area (Saint-Amand, 1961). If the inland extent of deformation to the north is comparable to that in the Gulf of Ancud, the minimum area of surface warping on land would be 17,000 square miles. The distribution of aftershocks and the source area of the destructive train of seismic sea waves associated with the earthquake suggest further that significant movements occurred over an extensive area of the sea floor adjacent to the deformed Pacific coast of Chile.

Other major earthquakes in which long sections of the west coast of South America reportedly changed elevation occurred in 1751, 1822, 1835, 1837, and 1906 (Richter, 1958); data on the areal distribution of the changes, however, are scarce. Warping associated with one of these, the violent Chilean earthquake of 1822, gave rise to speculation that an area of some 100,000 square miles of coastal Chile had been uplifted (Lyell, 1874, p. 94), but there are few data to support this asser-

tion. Imamura (1930) lists 26 Japanese earthquakes that resulted in vertical displacements. Regional warping has accompanied some of the more recent Japanese earthquakes, notably the 1946 Nankaido earthquake (Inoue, 1960, p. 85) and the 1964 Niigata earthquake (Hatori, 1965, p. 133–136). Elsewhere in the circum-Pacific region, additional large-scale vertical tectonic deformation was reported following the major earthquakes of 1848, 1855, and 1931 in New Zealand, and 1762 in India and Burma. Known areas of deformation associated with all of these earthquakes, however, are but small fractions of that involved in the 1964 Alaska event.

The 38 feet of uplift on Montague Island during the 1964 earthquake is known to have been exceeded only by the 47.3 feet of uplift that occurred during the earthquakes of 1899 that were centered at Yakutat Bay, 185 miles to the east (Tarr and Martin, 1912, pl. 14). Reported submarine vertical displacement offshore from Montague Island, however, may equal or perhaps exceed the 1899 movements (Malloy, 1964, p. 1048).

Subsidences roughly equal to,

or slightly larger than, the 7½ feet that accompanied the 1964 earthquake have been recorded during previous seismic events, although at many places determination of the absolute amount has been complicated by surficial slumping or compaction effects in unconsolidated deposits. For example, the largest reported coastal subsidence, 17 feet, which accompanied the Great Cutch earthquake (Lyell, 1874, p. 98) was at the mouth of the Indus River in an area where significant surficial compaction of deltaic deposits was to be expected.

Following the 1923 Kwanto, Japan, earthquake, unusually large submarine displacements, involving as much as 825 feet of uplift and 1,320 feet of subsidence on the sea floor in Sagami Bay, were inferred from a comparison of pre- and postearthquake soundings (Richter, 1958, p. 570–571). However, because of (1) possible errors in the positioning of the preearthquake survey and (2) the effects of submarine sliding, these data are of doubtful value for inferring tectonic movement; consequently they are not included in table 4.

The regional horizontal displacements associated with the 1964 earthquake, which were about 64 feet, are significantly larger than any previously recorded. By contrast, regional displacements associated with the great 1923 Kwanto earthquake, as indicated by retriangulation, were less than 15 feet (Muto, 1932, fig. 6), and the maximum relative displacement resulting from combined distortion and fault offsets associated with the 1906 California earthquake was roughly 21 feet (Reid, 1911).

Measured vertical displacements across the two subsidiary earthquake faults on Montague Island—the Patton Bay fault (20–23 ft) and Hanning Bay fault (16⅓ ft)—are considerably larger than any others of definite reverse type previously described (Plafker, 1967b). A few normal or oblique-slip faults, however, have undergone larger vertical displacements. The largest of these was associated with the 1897 Indian earthquake and reportedly was as much as 35 feet (Richter, 1958, p. 51).

TECTONIC SETTING

In the following sections the 1964 earthquake is viewed from the perspective of its broad relationship to the Aleutian Arc and to other major structural elements of south-central Alaska. Emphasis is placed on the geological and geophysical evidence for late Cenozoic tectonic movements in the immediate region affected by the earthquake. Earlier tectonic features and events, and contemporaneous features and events outside the region affected by the earthquake, are not of primary interest here, although they are mentioned where necessary to provide the setting of the principal features and events that are treated.

Most of Alaska has been studied geologically in a reconnaissance manner, but detailed mapping is still relatively uncommon and is largely confined to a few mining districts and to outcrops of potentially petroliferous or coal-bearing rocks around the margins of sedimentary basins. Gross aspects of the lithology and structure in outcrop areas are reasonably well known, but present knowledge of the geologic record in most places is inadequate for a detailed interpretation of the tectonic history. Subsurface investigations in the vast terrestrial areas of sparse outcrops and in the submarine parts of the Continental Shelf and Aleutian Arc are in a state so rudimentary that geological interpretations based upon them must be considered as very tentative. The spatial distribution of earthquakes and the rapidly increasing number of available fault-plane solutions provide valuable indirect evidence for the orientation and nature of displacements that have given rise to the earthquakes. Recent improvements in locating hypocenters of Alaskan earthquakes should contribute substantially to resolving the precise relationship of the earthquakes to known structural features.

THE ALEUTIAN ARC

The 1964 earthquake occurred in the tectonically complex region where northeast-trending structural elements associated with the Aleutian Arc overlap and merge with arcuate structures of south-central Alaska. The belt of seismic activity and the major zones of tectonic deformation associated with the 1964 earthquake lie largely between and parallel to the chain of active volcanoes and the oceanic trench that constitute the arc and are presumably related genetically to it (fig. 1). Consequently, it is pertinent to review briefly the data and current hypotheses relevant to tectonic processes within the arc.

MAJOR FEATURES

The Aleutian Arc, which sweeps 1,800 miles (2,800 km) across the North Pacific Ocean from Kamchatka to southern Alaska, exhibits all of the striking features characteristic of the festoons of arcs that ring the Pacific basin. These are (1) an arcuate deep oceanic trench — the Aleutian Trench—which is convex toward the ocean basin except near its eastern end, (2) a subparallel volcanic chain on the concave, or inner, side, away from the ocean basin—the Aleutian volcanic arc, (3) an associated belt of active seismicity between the trench and volcanic chain in which the lower limit of hypocenters tends to deepen from the vicinity of the trench toward the arc, and (4) parallel zones of isostatic gravity lows over the trench bottom and gravity highs between the trench bottom and volcanic arc.

The Aleutian Arc differs from most other arcs in that it partly traverses and partly follows along the margin of the oceanic basin (fig. 1). In its western part the arc consists of the Aleutian Ridge, which is surmounted by a chain of volcanoes that comprise the Aleutian Islands, and the Aleutian Trench, which lies at a distance of less than 155 miles (250 km) on the convex (south) side of the ridge. As it approaches south-central Alaska, the distance between the volcanic arc and the trench gradually increases to more than 250 miles (400 km), the belt of seismic activity becomes broader and less well defined, and the trench gradually shallows to become indistinguishable from the floor of the North Pacific Ocean. It is in this eastern portion of the arc that the line of volcanoes and the belt of seismicity overlap and in part merge with preexisting structural elements that roughly parallel the margin of the Gulf of Alaska (fig. 29). The group of volcanoes in the Wrangell Mountains, which are separated from Mount Spurr, the most northerly volcano of the Aleutian Range, by a gap of 420 miles, are similar in age and composition to the Aleutian Arc volcanoes. These similarities, and their position near the eastern end of the Aleutian Trench and its associated belt of intermediate-depth earthquakes, suggest that the Wrangell Mountains volcanoes may also be genetically related to the arc.

The geology of the Aleutian Islands segment of the arc was summarized by Coats (1962), that of the Aleutian Range and nearby areas by Burk (1965). Both of these writers presented thorough reviews of available bathymetric, seismologic, and marine geophysical data as well as hypotheses concerning origin of the arc. Results of detailed marine geophysical surveys along the eastern end of the Aleutian Arc, carried out during 1964 and 1965 by the Scripps Institution of Oceanography and the U.S. Coast and Geodetic Survey,

had not been published at the time this report was completed.

SEISMICITY

Figures 1 and 30 indicate that, in plan, most of the belt of concentrated seismic activity is between the trench and the volcanic chain along the length of the arc; a small number of earthquakes occurred on the south wall of the Aleutian Trench and north of the volcanic chain. Shallow-depth (<70 km) earthquakes have occurred throughout the area included between the Aleutian Trench and the Aleutian volcanic arc, but most of the intermediate-depth earthquakes (70–170 km) were located in the northern part of this area or north of the volcanic chain. The most easterly intermediate-depth earthquakes have been along the coast of the North Pacific Ocean at long 145° W. in the vicinity of the Wrangell Mountains. In south-central Alaska the belt of seismicity associated with the Aleutian Arc bifurcates into a broad zone of shallow and intermediate depth shocks that sweeps northward into central Alaska and a belt of shallow-focus earthquakes that extends eastward along the continental margin. Comparison of figures 2 and 31 shows that the spatial distribution of the seismicity associated with the 1964 Alaska earthquake closely follows the pattern of previously recorded earthquakes along the arc and thereby implies a genetic relationship between them, as suggested by Arthur Grantz, shortly after the event (Grantz and others, 1964, p. 2).

From studies of earthquake distribution along the Aleutian Arc, Benioff (1954, p. 391) concluded that the hypocenters lie in a broad zone that dips northward from the vicinity of the Aleutian Trench at an average angle of 28°. Saint-

Amand (1957, p. 1348) interprets the same data as indicative of a zone dipping at an angle of about 45° between long 172° and 179° W. and at a "somewhat lower angle" in the eastern part of the arc. Detailed studies of seismicity associated with the 1964 earthquake suggest that some planes within the earthquake focal region dip beneath the arc at angles of less than 15°.

Benioff postulated that the dipping seismic zone marked the location of a complex "reverse" fault (termed a "megathrust" by Coats, 1962, p. 103) along which the arc relatively overrides the ocean basin. According to the sea floor spreading hypothesis advanced by Hess (1962, p. 617) and Dietz (1961), arc structures are sites of down-welling mantle-convection currents, and the planar seismic zones dipping beneath them mark the zone of shearing produced by downward-moving material thrust against a less mobile block of the crust and upper mantle. This hypothesis is in general consistent with other data suggestive of active spreading of the sea floor in a northwest-southeast direction away from the East Pacific Rise (Vine, 1966, p. 1412), and with active regional shoreline submergence suggestive of a downward-directed component of deformation near the eastern end of the arc (p. I 60).

Because of the scarcity of standard seismograph stations in Alaska as well as incomplete travel-time data for Alaska earthquakes prior to 1964, the horizontal and vertical distribution of earthquakes could not be defined precisely enough to resolve details of structure within the broad seismic zone either at depth or laterally along it. As a result, large uncertainties exist regarding the

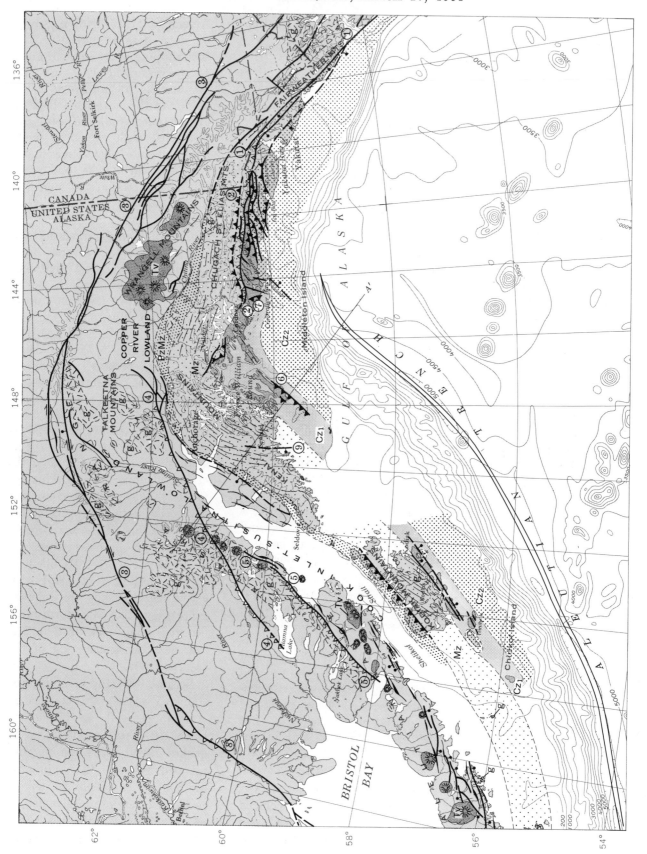

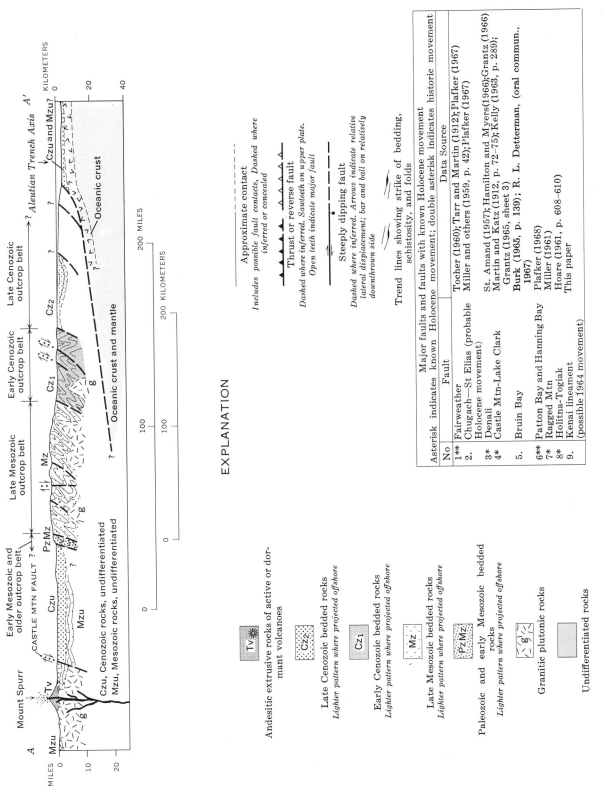

EXPLANATION

Tv — Andesitic extrusive rocks of active or dormant volcanoes

Czu₂ — Late Cenozoic bedded rocks
Lighter pattern where projected offshore

Cz₁ — Early Cenozoic bedded rocks
Lighter pattern where projected offshore

Mz — Late Mesozoic bedded rocks
Lighter pattern where projected offshore

PzMz — Paleozoic and early Mesozoic bedded rocks

g — Granitic plutonic rocks

— Undifferentiated rocks

——— Approximate contact
Includes possible fault contacts. Dashed where inferred or concealed

▲▲▲▲ Thrust or reverse fault
Dashed where inferred. Sawteeth on upper plate. Open teeth indicate major fault.

— — • Steeply dipping fault
Dashed where inferred. Arrows indicate relative lateral displacement; bar and ball on relatively downthrown side

—— Trend lines showing strike of bedding, schistosity, and folds

Major faults and faults with known Holocene movement
Asterisk indicates known Holocene movement; double asterisk indicates historic movement

No	Fault	Data Source
1**	Fairweather	Tocher (1960); Tarr and Martin (1912); Plafker (1967)
2.	Chugach—St Elias (probable Holocene movement)	Miller and others (1959, p. 42); Plafker (1967)
3*	Denali	St. Amand (1957); Hamilton and Myers(1966);Grantz (1966)
4*	Castle Mtn–Lake Clark	Martin and Katz (1912, p. 72–75);Kelly (1963, p. 289); Grantz (1965, sheet 3)
5.	Bruin Bay	Burk (1965, p. 139); R. L. Detterman, (oral commun., 1967)
6**	Patton Bay and Hanning Bay	Plafker (1968)
7*	Ragged Mtn	Miller (1961)
8*	Holitna-Togiak	Hoare (1961, p. 608–610)
9.	Kenai lineament (possible 1964 movement)	This paper

29.—Generalized tectonic map and idealized vertical section showing selected rock units and structural features of south-central Alaska. Indicated displacement direction on faults is the net late Cenozoic movement only. Geology modified from a manuscript tectonic map of Alaska by P. B. King and from unpublished U.S. Geological Survey data; the thickness of crustal layers and the structure shown in the section are largely hypothetical.

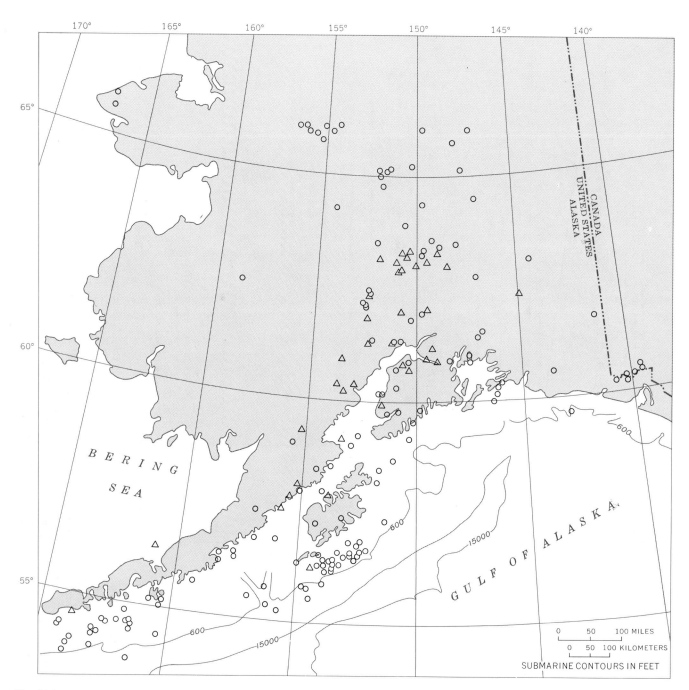

30.—Epicenters of earthquakes ($M \geq 4$) in central Alaska during the period January 1954 to March 1963. Shallow depth (≤ 70 km) earthquakes indicated by circles; intermediate depth (≥ 70 km) indicated by triangles. Data after Tobin and Sykes (1966).

precise orientation and lower depth limits of planes within the zone along which earthquakes originate. Nor is it known to what extent movement on subordinate faults within the upper plate contributes to the recorded seismicity.

Focal mechanism studies of arc earthquakes suggest that the pattern of faulting is extremely complex and that it changes significantly laterally along the arc. The small number of fault-plane solutions of arc earthquake sequences that are based on both P and S waves tend to group in pairs of dip-slip and strike-slip (Bollinger and Stauder, 1965; Stauder, 1967. p. 218–219); those based solely on P waves are almost entirely strike-slip (Hodgson, 1957, p. 641). The dip-slip solutions may be interpreted as representing northwestward-dipping planes that parallel the trend of the eastern part of the arc and are oblique to it in the central part. Coats (1962, p. 95) observed that solutions yielding predominantly strike-slip movement on steeply dipping planes may originate on transverse tear or wrench faults oriented at a large oblique angle to the arc trend. Coats further suggested that the positions of individual volcanoes may be localized by transverse fractures and that their regular position relative to the trench is determined by the distance at which tensional fractures can penetrate through the upper plate to tap eruptible material.

The predominance of transverse faults and other linear elements on land and offshore from the Aleutian Islands (Coats, 1962, fig. 2; Gates and Gibson, 1956, fig. 12) and relatively abrupt transverse boundaries for aftershock sequences of the February 1964 Rat Island earthquake (Jordan and others, 1965), the 1957 earthquake sequence in the Andreanof-Fox

Island region (Brazee, 1965), and the 1964 earthquake (p. I 15), all lend support to the inference that transverse faults segment the plate above the megathrust into large tectonic blocks. Conversely, there is no seismological or geological evidence of systematic dextral strike-slip displacement parallel to the arc in support of the speculation that it marks the trace of a major fault along which the North Pacific Ocean basin is rotating counterclockwise relative to North America, as was suggested by Saint-Amand (1957, p. 1367).

INFERRED REGIONAL STRESS PATTERN

According to the sea-floor spreading hypothesis, compressive forces should be directed roughly normal to the arcs and the deep-sea trenches would be interpreted as due to dragging down of the oceanic crust above a descending mantle convection current (Hess, 1955, 1957, 1962). In the Aleutian Arc, transverse compression landward from the trench axis is suggested by (1) the orientation of major stress axes derived from mechanism studies of most, but not all, previous arc earthquakes (Balakina and others, 1961; Lensen, 1961, fig. 4); (2) the orientation of the axes of folded late Cenozoic rocks in the Aleutians, on the Alaska Peninsula and around the Gulf of Alaska roughly parallel to the arc trend (Coats, 1962, p. 93; Burk, 1965, p. 3; fig. 29); and (3) the distribution and nature of the seismicity, surface faulting, and warping associated with the 1964 earthquake. Both the pattern of residual displacements in 1964 (fig. 3), and the late Cenozoic fold-fault pattern (fig. 29) near the eastern end of the arc suggest that regional compressional deformation extends across it, from at least the outer edge of

the Continental Shelf to the vicinity of the volcanic arc.

On the other hand, reconnaissance marine-geophysical studies across the Aleutian Trench and along the north wall of the trench have revealed an apparent lack of features indicating transverse compression or the existence of a megathrust intersecting the sea floor. From interpretations of gravity and magnetic data over the Aleutian Trench and outer margin of the arc southwest of Kodiak Island, Peter, Elvers, and Yellin (1965, p. 366) concluded that there probably exists "crustal tension, rather than compression, underthrust, or downbuckle." Marine reflection-refraction data suggest that the trench, with its relatively undeformed veneer of acoustically transparent sediments, reflects an origin by tension or vertical movements of the crust (Shor, 1966, p. 221; Ewing and others, 1965, p. 4599; Von Huene and others, 1966, p. 176).

It should be emphasized, however, that the geophysical investigations, particularly along the north wall of the trench, have provided direct information only on the approximate geometry and properties of the crust; they do not permit unambiguous conclusions regarding the deformations or the nature of the causative forces. More data, including a knowledge of the lithology and internal structure of the crustal rock in these areas, are required to determine whether features that seem to indicate absence of compression actually reflect the regional stress pattern. The seismic and geologic evidence in the eastern part of the Aleutian Arc suggests to me that any regional stress, other than transverse compression, must be largely limited to the part of the arc that lies seaward from the edge of the Continental Shelf.

SUMMARY OF THE PRE-HOLOCENE (RECENT) TECTONIC HISTORY OF SOUTH-CENTRAL ALASKA

The tectonic history along the eastern end of the Aleutian Arc and adjacent parts of south-central Alaska may be interpreted from the geologic record of folding and faulting. This record suggests that the present orogenic cycle, which probably began in Pliocene time, has resulted in regional compressive deformation in a general northwest-southeast to north-south direction around the margin of the Gulf of Alaska. It further indicates that at least three previous major orogenies c u l m i n a t e d in south-central Alaska during (1) late Eocene to early Oligocene time, (2) Late Cretaceous to earliest Tertiary time, and (3) Middle(?) Jurassic to Late Jurassic or Early Cretaceous time. These earlier orogenies are indicated by major unconformities that divide the exposed section into four laterally continuous time-stratigraphic units that constitute gross subdivisions of the stratigraphic record. For brevity they are referred to in the following discussion as the late Cenozoic, early Cenozoic, late Mesozoic, and early Mesozoic and older sequences. They are described in the order named because it is the youngest deformation that is of primary concern here and because each successive orogeny tends to mask earlier events and thereby obscure to a large extent the earlier tectonic history.

Each of the four orogenies involved significant structural shortening of thick eugeosynclinal or geosynclinal sequences along the continental margin through folding and imbricate faulting. Deformation of coeval rocks inland from the continental margin was

significantly less severe. This relationship may reflect a progressive reduction in horizontal compressive stress away from the continental margin, an increase in crustal competence, or a combination of both factors. In the mountains bordering the Gulf of Alaska and on the continental margin, the four major sequences form laterally continuous outcrop bands, commonly bounded by faults, which progressively increase in age from south to north (fig. 29). The d i s t r i b u t i o n of coeval sequences to the north of the coastal mountains is not shown in figure 29 because the sequences exhibit complex overlapping relationships and are obscured to a large extent by plutonic intrusions, young volcanic rocks, water, or a veneer of unconsolidated deposits. The larger plutons and active or dormant volcanoes in south-central Alaska are delineated on figure 29.

A concise summary of the physiography and general geology of the area affected by tectonic movements during the earthquake, based on the compilation by Wahrhaftig (1966), has been given by Hansen and Eckel (1967) in the previous paper of this volume. It is not necessary to repeat it here. The broad tectonic setting and structural history of Alaska has been presented by Payne (1955) and by Gates and Gryc (1963). The stratigraphy and general geology of sedimentary basins in south-central Alaska were discussed by Miller, Payne, and Gryc (1959). Burk (1965) synthesized the geology of the western Alaska Peninsula and analyzed the relationship of the peninsula to the Aleutian Arc and continental margin. Grantz (1966) summarized data on strike-slip faults in Alaska and evaluated their role in the tectonic evolution

of Alaska. All these writers included exhaustive bibliographies in their publications. Recent geologic maps along the Gulf of Alaska margin include a 1:500,000-scale compilation of the area between Prince William Sound and southeastern Alaska (Plafker, 1967a) and a 1:250,000-scale compilation of most of the Kodiak group of islands (Moore, 1967). The following section is based largely on the publications cited above, but includes some modifications of the Cenozoic history based on previously unpublished U.S. Geological Survey data.

POST-MIOCENE DEFORMATION

The orogeny, which began in Pliocene time and continued to the present, resulted in differential uplift and faulting throughout southern Alaska (Miller and others, 1959, p. 17). Folding was severe along the margin of the Gulf of Alaska, but gentle elsewhere except in the immediate vicinity of major faults. During this orogeny, the coastal mountains were uplifted and in places, especially to the west of Yakutat Bay, were thrust relatively southward against the Pacific basin along a system of high-angle faults (fig. 29). Major faults and folds in the late Cenozoic sequence tend to parallel the trends of the older structures in the Pacific Border Ranges; there is a general increase in the intensity of folding and magnitude of fault displacements from south to north across the deformed belt.

Transverse trends occur in the structurally complex Controller Bay area east of Prince William Sound where folds involving Oligocene and Miocene strata are typically of small amplitude, tightly compressed, and asymmetric or overturned; axial planes are inclined to the west or north.

Horizontal shortening of upper Oligocene and lower Miocene strata along one 5-mile north-south structure section in the Controller Bay area averages close to 25 percent (Don J. Miller, unpub. data).

To the east of the Controller Bay area the upper Cenozoic rocks form broad synclines and tightly appressed asymmetrical anticlines cut by north-dipping overthrust faults that strike roughly parallel to the coast. At least some of these faults probably represent the leading edges of thrust sheets developed by gravitational gliding off the uplifted Chugach-Saint Elias Mountains. On the south limbs of many of these anticlines, strata as young as late Pliocene are steeply dipping or overturned towards the north. At least two major intraformational unconformities in the upper part of the sequence record pronounced folding and uplift during late Pliocene time. Minor unconformities and thick beds of coarse conglomeratic sediments in the sequence reflect intervals of local uplift and erosion beginning in early Miocene time.

Marine sedimentary rocks of early Pleistocene or younger age on Middleton Island near the edge of the Continental Shelf have been titled northwestward at an average angle of 28°, truncated, raised above sea level, and displaced by active minor faults. A pervasive conjugate system of shear joints cutting the sequence reflects compressive stress directed northwest-southeast, normal to the strike of the beds.

Bedded rocks of Oligocene through middle Miocene age exposed in narrow belts along the southeast coast of the Kodiak Islands, and Oligocene rocks on Chirikof Island, are tightly folded about northeast-trending axes and are locally overturned (Moore,

1967). Relatively undeformed Tertiary rocks are exposed along the margin of the Gulf of Alaska only in the Trinity Islands and on Chirikof Island. On Chirikof, late Pliocene strata are exposed in homoclines with dips of less than 10°.

Late Cenozoic deposits along the Aleutian Volcanic Arc, in the Cook Inlet-Susitna lowland and around the Copper River lowland, were uplifted and slightly deformed during Pliocene and Quaternary time into generally open folds, most of which trend nearly parallel with the main arc or at a slightly oblique angle (Payne, 1955; Coats, 1962, p. 93; Burk, 1965, p. 121; Wolfe and others, 1966, p. A13). Most of the Eocene or younger Tertiary sedimentary rocks around the margin of the Cook Inlet lowland are nearly flat lying, gently tilted, or folded into broad, open structures with flank dips generally less than 10°. Thinning of individual stratigraphic units over anticlinal crests in the subsurface and the occurrence of topographic anomalies in areas mantled with Quaternary deposits suggest continuous active growth of some of these structures during late Cenozoic time (Kelly, 1963, p. 289, 296).

LATE EOCENE TO EARLY OLIGOCENE DEFORMATION

A major episode of deformation and plutonic activity began in late Eocene time and probably culminated in early Oligocene time. This episode resulted in complex folding, faulting, and mild metamorphism of early Tertiary rocks in the coastal belt (Plafker and MacNeil, 1966, p. 68) and probable minor warping and faulting of the age-equivalent strata exposed in the northern part of the Cook Inlet-Susitna lowland (Miller and others, 1959, p. 18). Folds

in the southern belt commonly are of short wavelength, tightly appressed with flank dips in excess of 50° and locally overturned both toward the north and south. Individual folds are of small amplitude and lateral extent and are complicated by intricate drag folding and minor overthrust faults. Horizontal shortening across a typical folded section, such as that shown in figure 31, commonly exceeds 45 percent, exclusive of imbrication on faults. Net shortening across the outcrop belt of lower Tertiary rocks is indeterminate because the structure has not been mapped in detail and traceable key horizons are generally absent. Conceivably, it could average as much as 45 percent or more across the entire outcrop belt; a net surface shortening of at least 30 miles in the Prince William Sound area. In a gross sense the strikes of bedding planes and fold axes tend to parallel the structural trends of the older rocks. They are notably divergent and complex in northeastern Prince William Sound and in the area immediately east of the sound (fig. 29), possibly because these areas are situated close to the axis of Carey's postulated Alaska orocline (1958, p. 209–212). Postorogenic potash-rich granite plutons of probable early Oligocene age (Lanphere, 1966, p. D197) with pronounced thermal aureoles are intrusive into the early Tertiary and older rocks in and near the Prince William Sound region.

Deformation of the early Tertiary rocks in the Cook Inlet-Susitna lowland during the early Cenozoic and later orogenies is characterized by broad open folding, flank dips commonly being less than 50° except in the immediate vicinity of faults. The strike of fold axes and of the steeply dipping faults of moderate dis-

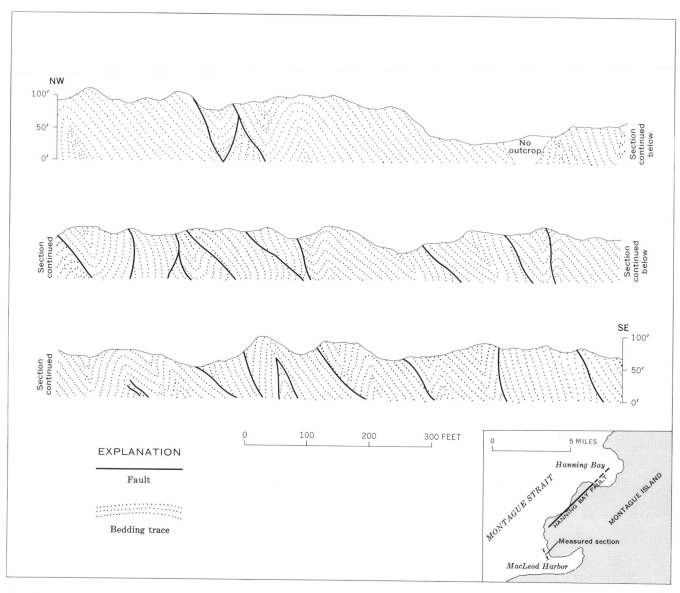

31.—Structure of the early Tertiary Orca Group exposed in a sea cliff along the north shore of MacLeod Harbor, Montague Island, Prince William Sound.

placement that offset the sequence is roughly parallel or at a slightly oblique angle to the trend of the adjacent mountain ranges. Horizontal shortening of Paleocene or Eocene strata through folding and faulting along a 5-mile-long northwest-southeast section across the Matanuska Valley (Barnes, 1962, section A–A') is about 25 percent. This figure undoubtedly approaches the approximate maximum amount of shortening in the sequence, because the section is located in a narrow structurally complex trough bounded on its north side by the active Castle Mountain fault.

LATE CRETACEOUS TO EARLY TERTIARY DEFORMATION

A major episode of diastrophism, corresponding to an early phase of the Laramide orogeny in the time interval from Late Cretaceous to early Tertiary, resulted in regional deformation and widespread intrusive activity in the Kodiak-Kenai-Chugach Mountains (Chugach Mountains geosyncline of Payne, 1955) and in the Alaska Range (Alaska Range geosyncline of Payne, 1955), with relatively slight deformation of rocks in the intervening area (Matanuska geosyncline of Payne, 1955). Figure 32 shows the style of deformation in one particularly well exposed outcrop area of probable late Mesozoic rocks along the south coast of the Kenai Peninsula immediately west of Prince William Sound. Structural shortening by folding across the section is about 55 percent, and there is an unknown amount of additional

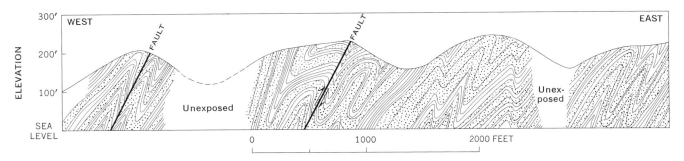

32.—Structure of probable late Mesozoic rocks along the southeast coast of the Kenai Peninsula immediately west of Prince William Sound (Martin and others, 1915, p. 216).

shortening by imbrication on overthrust faults. A comparable amount of deformation across the entire late Mesozoic outcrop belt would have resulted in a net shortening of the original sequence by 40–60 miles. Deformation of the sequence was accompanied by emplacement of stocks and small batholiths, predominantly of quartz diorite and related plutonic rocks, and by metamorphism and penetrative deformation of rocks in the cores of the eastern Chugach Mountains, the Saint Elias Mountains, and the Fairweather Range.

During the Late Cretaceous to early Tertiary orogeny, deformation inland from the coastal mountains was mainly by uplift, broad open folding, and displacement on steeply dipping faults as indicated diagrammatically on section A–A', figure 29. Published structure sections across the sequence around the margins of the Copper River lowland (Grantz, 1965, sheet 3; Miller and MacColl, 1964) and on the Alaska Peninsula (Burk, 1965, figs. 21, 22) indicate structural shortening of Late Cretaceous strata that ranges from 5 to 20 percent and probably averages no more than 10 percent.

MIDDLE (?) JURASSIC TO EARLY CRETACEOUS DEFORMATION

All the older rocks in south-central Alaska were strongly affected by the major orogenic episode, roughly corresponding to the Nevadan orogeny, that began between latest Early Jurassic and earliest Middle Jurassic time and may have continued intermittently into earliest Cretaceous time. Rocks in the Seldovia geanticline were folded, complexly faulted, and regionally metamorphosed; deformation in the Talkeetna geanticline was considerably more variable and depended largely upon proximity to major batholiths. The orogeny was accompanied or immediately followed by emplacement of (1) numerous plutonic masses that range in composition from peridotite to granodiorite in the coastal mountains belt and (2) plutons of felsic composition and of batholithic size on the Alaska Peninsula and in the Talkeetna Mountains, with resultant contact metamorphism of the enclosing bedded rocks. The prevailing schistosity and slaty cleavage in the rocks of the coastal mountains are nearly vertical and have a variable strike that generally parallel roughly, or is at a small oblique angle to, the trend of the mountains.

A slight unconformity between rocks of Permian and Middle Triassic age in the Talkeetna Mountains (MacKevett and others, 1964) and the apparent absence of bedded rocks of Pennsylvanian, part of Permian, and Early Triassic age throughout the region suggest that these times were intervals of uplift and erosion.

MAJOR SURFACE FAULTS IN SOUTH-CENTRAL ALASKA

The longer coastal faults, or systems of faults, in south-central Alaska tend to follow the arcuate grain of the mountain ranges and the margin of the Gulf of Alaska; larger faults inland from the coast trend obliquely across some of the mountain ranges (fig. 29). In detail the faults do not form simple arcs but instead consist of linear segments of variable length, the included angles between adjacent segments being as little as 150°. Two minor north-south trending faults with Holocene movement intersect the regional grain at large oblique angles in the Controller Bay area (Ragged Mountain fault) and in the central Kenai Mountains (Kenai lineament).

Of the major faults delineated on figure 29, all but the Bruin Bay fault and the reverse fault along the northwest side of the Kodiak Island group exhibit evidence of post-Miocene movement; several have been active during post-Pleistocene (Holocene) time. Surface deformation was recorded in Alaska in conjunction with only three previous historic earthquakes along the Gulf of Alaska, at Chirikof Island in 1880 (George W. Moore, 1962, unpubl. data), at Yakutat Bay in 1899 (Tarr and Martin, 1912), and along the Fairweather fault in 1958 (Tocher,

TABLE 5.—*Radiocarbon-dated samples used in determining the relative ages of shoreline features*

[Locations of sample sites shown on fig. 33]

Locality No.	Lab. No.	Location	Age (B.P.)	Submergence (−) or emergence (+) relative to preearthquake datum (feet)	Data source	Comments
1	P-1039	Kodiak Island	3,279	[1]−3.3	Clark (1966, p. 370)	Archaeologic site in submerged beach deposits.
2	P-1034	Sitkalidak Island	5,519±78	Slight emergence	do	Archaeologic site in elevated beach ridge.
3	P-1036	do	3,945±65	do	do	Do.
4		Kukak Bay, Shelikof Strait	1,460±95	No apparent change	D. E. Dumond (written commun., March 28, 1966).	Archaeologic site in present beach ridge.
5		do	1,450±130	do	do	Do.
6		do	1,075±100	do	do	Do.
7		do	775±110	do	do	Do.
8	P-138	Yukon Island, Kachemak Bay	1,369±102	−4 to −10	Rainey and Ralph (1959)	Antler bone from archaeological site in submerged beach deposits.
9	P-139	do	2,706±118	[1]−16	do	Do.
10	W-299	Girdwood, Turnagain Arm	2,800±180	[1]−15	Karlstrom (1964, p. 48)	Peat in tidal silts and bog deposits. Possible significant surficial subsidence.
11	W-175	do	700±250	−2½	do	Do.
12	W-1720	Seward	≈200	[1]−7	Plafker and Rubin (1967)	Rooted stump on delta. Indicated submergence may be due to significant surficial slumping of unconsolidated deltaic deposits.
13	W-1589	Perry Island, Prince William Sound	3,680±300	−11.2	do	Rooted stump on submerged beach.
14	W-1588	Point Nowell, Prince William Sound	930±200	−17	do	Wood fragment from interbedded peat and gravel on submerged beach.
15	W-1592	Columbia Bay, Prince William Sound	1,140±250	−6	do	Rooted stump on submerged beach.
16	W-1591	Latouche Island, Prince William Sound	230±200	−8.5	do	Do.
17	W-1590	MacLeod Harbor, Prince William Sound	560±200	−9.7	do	Do.
18	W-1764	do	380±200	[1]−8	M. J. Kirkby (written commun., 1967).	Rooted stump in submerged river delta.
19	W-1766	Patton Bay, Montague Island	600±200	[1]−12	do	Wood fragment from submerged peat and gravel deposits.
20	W-1770	do	2,070±200	[1]+20	do	Peat on elevated beach deposits.
21	LJ-943	Copper River Delta area	1,360±50	−16.8	Reimnitz (1966, p. 85)	
22	LJ-945	do	380±20	−13.9	do	Rooted stumps on deltaic and marsh deposits. Submergence may be exaggerated owing to surficial subsidenc.
23	LJ-0032	do	700±50	−16.8	do	
24	LJ-939	do	725±35	−15.8	do	
25	LJ-938	do	700±30	−16.8	do	
26	I-6	Katalla area	7,650±330	[1]+180	Heusser (1960, p. 94)	Peat from elevated terrace.
27	I-7	do	3,770±200	[1]+40	do	Do.
28	W-376	Cape Suckling	390±160	[1]−14	Rubin and Alexander (1958).	Rooted stump on submerged rock platform.
29	W-1729	do	710±200	−14	Plafker and Rubin (1967)	Do.
30	W-462	do	5,120±220	[1]+20	Rubin and Alexander (1958).	Shells on elevated terrace.
31	W-1724	Middleton Island	1,350±200	+22	do	Driftwood on elevated terrace.
32	W-1404	do	2,390±200	+58	Levin and others (1965, p. 392).	Do.
33	W-1405	do	4,470±250	+137	Levin and others (1965, p. 392-393).	Do.
34	W-1722	Stockdale Harbor, Prince William Sound	>200	−8	Plafker and Rubin (1967)	Rooted stump on submerged beach.
35	LJ-0033	Copper River Delta area	860±50	−15.9	Reimnitz (1966, p. 85)	Rooted stump on deltaic and marsh deposits.
36	LJ-0034	do	1,700±100	−22.0	do	Do.

[1] Approximate.

1960). Although surface breakage may have occurred along faults during other earthquakes in Alaska, such features could easily have gone undetected had they occurred in the vast uninhabited parts of the State.

The sense of late Cenozoic displacement on the faults shown in figure 29 is given where known. In general, faults in south-central Alaska that trend northeast or east are predominantly overthrusts or oblique overthrusts that dip northward at moderate to steep angles, with north sides relatively upthrown. Horizontal movements on major longitudinal faults are largely restricted to the northwest-trending Fairweather fault and to the northwest and east-west trending parts of the Denali fault system, both of which are predominantly right-lateral. Geologic relationships across many of the faults suggest that they have undergone recurrent movement during Cenozoic and much of Mesozoic time and that the sense of displacement along some of them has changed with time. The orientation and the Quaternary displacement on these faults reflects tangential compression oriented north-south to northwest-southeast along the margin of the Gulf of Alaska, perhaps rotating to a more nearly east-west direction in central Alaska. The broad fault pattern implies that the Pacific Ocean basin is moving north to northwest relative to the mainland. Thus, the ocean basin appears to be shearing relatively past the mainland of British Columbia and southeastern Alaska along the system of northwest-trending right-lateral strike-slip faults, whereas it shears relatively beneath the continental margin and Aleutian Arc in central and western Alaska along a system of imbricate thrust (underthrust?) faults.

THE PREEARTHQUAKE HOLOCENE (RECENT) RECORD OF VERTICAL SHORELINE MOVEMENTS

Numerous records of preearthquake differential shoreline movements relative to sea level provide data on the history of vertical tectonic movements during Holocene time. Reconnaissance studies of the displaced shorelines have brought out (1) a general similarity between the pattern of earthquake displacements and the long-term trend of Holocene coastal emergence or submergence, and (2) a remarkable recent widespread submergence over much of the zone that was uplifted during the 1964 earthquake and over at least part of the zone that subsided. In addition, radiocarbon dating of material from coastal sites has provided quantitative data on the duration and rates of these Holocene movements.

Data and interpretations presented in this section are largely taken from a preliminary paper by Plafker and Rubin (1967). All radiocarbon-dated samples referred to, sources, and other pertinent data are listed in table 5; sample locations are shown on figure 33.

As used herein, the terms "uplift" and "subsidence" describe a tectonic rise or fall of the land; "emergence" and "submergence" indicate relative movements that may be the sum of both tectonic movements and eustatic sea-level changes. Tectonic movements include those that result from both diastrophic and isostatic processes. "Long-term" refers to shoreline changes relative to sea level having durations measured in thousands of years; "short-term" refers to the general submergence that occurred during the 1,350 years or less prior to the earthquake.

Some of the observed recent submergence in areas shown on figure 33 is undoubtedly exaggerated by the local vibration-induced compaction or slumping of unconsolidated deposits during the earthquakes that frequently rock this seismically active region. As was demonstrated during the 1964 earthquake, surficial submergence may be substantial in areas of thick unconsolidated saturated deposits—especially in those deposits that are not constrained on one or more sides, such as deltas, spits, and barrier beaches. Consequently, rooted tree stumps, on bedrock or on thin beach deposits overlying bedrock, were used to determine amounts and rates of pre-1964 vertical displacement wherever possible.

In the absence of a reliable local eustatic sea-level record for southern Alaska, it is assumed that Holocene sea levels were probably comparable to those in more tectonically stable parts of the world where the sea-level record has been worked out in some detail. Three recent interpretations of eustatic sea levels are shown on figure 34. Most of these studies suggest either (1) a rather rapid rise in sea level at an average rate of about 0.08 inch per year until it reached approximately its present level between 2,000 and 6,000 years ago (Coleman and Smith, 1964), or (2) that sea level has been rising slowly and continuously from about −33 feet to its present level during the past 7,000 years with a generally rising, but fluctuating, sea level between about 15,000 and 7,000 years B.P. (Curray, 1961). Some authorities believe that sea level reached its present position from 3,000 to 5,000 years ago and has been fluctuating above and below its present position by about 3–6 feet ever since (Fairbridge, 1961). For present purposes, it is significant to note that none of these studies suggest that eustatic sea-level fluctuations during the last 10,000 years were large enough alone to explain the relative shoreline displacements found along the coast of south-central Alaska.

LONG-TERM HOLOCENE EMERGENCE AND SUBMERGENCE

The record of Holocene displacements in the area affected by the earthquake, as deduced from shoreline morphology and from radiocarbon dates, is outlined in the following section. Places referred to and the spatial distribution of radiocarbon-dated shoreline samples in relation to the 1964 deformation are shown in figure 33. The age and pre-1964 position of these samples relative to sea level is shown in figure 34.

Much of the shore in the mountainous southern part of the area that subsided during the earthquake exhibits the characteristic features of a deeply drowned coast. Submerged shorelines occur along most of Kodiak and the adjacent islands, the southern Kenai Peninsula, the south shore of Kachemak Bay, and part of Turnagain Arm. The northern and eastern parts of the Prince William Sound region also appear to be submergent, although the evidence for relative shoreline movements is somewhat obscured by recent glaciation in most of the fiords. In these submerged mountainous areas, former rocky ridges are now peninsulas or islands, and

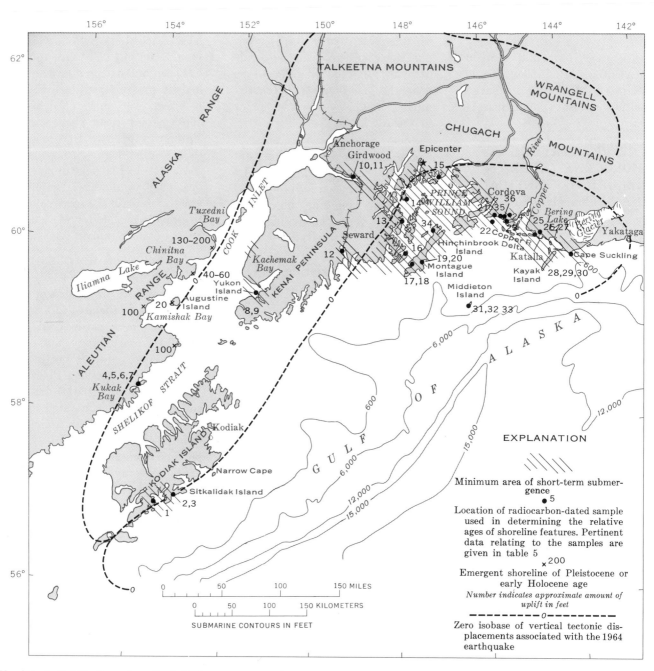

33.—Areal distribution of vertical displacements associated with the 1964 earthquake, areas of preearthquake submergence, and locations of radiocarbon-dated samples used to determine relative ages of shoreline features.

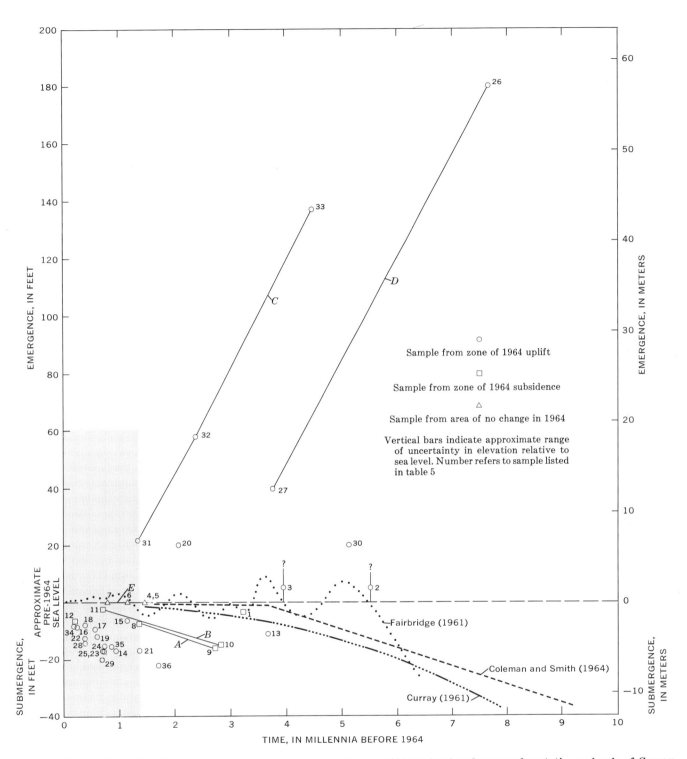

34.—Pre-1964 positions of radiocarbon-dated samples relative to the pre-1964 sea level and proposed eustatic sea levels of Curray (1961), Fairbridge (1961), and Coleman and Smith (1964). The duration of the inferred period of short-term subsidence is indicated by the stippled area. Sample locations at Yukon Island (A), Girdwood (B), Middleton Island (C), Katalla (D), and Kukak Bay (E) are connected by solid lines.

35.—Deeply submerged coast along the southern Kenai Peninsula. Embayments, which give the shore a distinctive scalloped appearance, are cirques whose floors are drowned to depths of as much as 300 feet below sea level. Shoreline shown was submerged an additional 2–5 feet in 1964. Photograph by T. L. Péwé.

drowned river valleys or glacial cirques have become embayments (fig. 35). The general scarcity of well-developed sea cliffs, beaches, and similar shore features attests to the recency of the submergence. Elsewhere in the subsided zone, coastal bogs of terrestrial peat and some aboriginal dwelling sites that are now inundated by high tides also indicate long-continued submergence relative to sea level.

The most pronounced submergence appears to be in the vicinity of the axis of maximum subsidence during the 1964 earthquake—a region which roughly coincides with the crest of the Kenai and Kodiak Mountains (pl. 1). Although the absolute maximum amount of postglacial submergence cannot be determined, an indication of it is provided by differences in the altitudes of cirque floors of probable Wisconsin age along this part of the coast which presumably were formed at a fairly uniform level. The lowest cirque floors along the outer coast of Prince William Sound and in

most of the Kodiak Island group— areas away from the region of maximum submergence—lie at altitudes ranging from 800 to 1,000 feet above sea level, but cirque floors along the south coast of the Kenai Peninsula range in altitude from 300 feet below sea level to 800 feet above sea level. This difference in cirque levels suggests at least 300, and perhaps as much as several hundred feet, of submergence in the Kenai Peninsula area.

In contrast to the zone of subsidence, the coast in those areas where the land has risen relative to the sea is generally smoother in outline and commonly exhibits, among other features, one or more wave-cut terraces or uplifted beaches rising to elevations of at least 200 feet (figs. 36, 37). In the major zone of uplift such features are characteristic of the points and capes on the seaward side of Kodiak Island, the islands of the southern and eastern Prince William Sound region, much of the mainland coast east of Cape Suckling, and Middleton Island on the

Continental Shelf. Comparable emergent shores with postglacial terraces as much as 1,700 feet high occur all along the mainland coast to the east of the area that was affected by the 1964 earthquake.

Relatively stable or emergent shores occur along parts of the Cook Inlet and Shelikof Strait coasts in areas that either subsided slightly, remained unchanged, or were slightly uplifted during the 1964 earthquake (fig. 33). Many of these emergent shorelines are probably pre-Holocene features related to high eustatic sea levels rather than to tectonic movements (Hopkins and others, 1965, p. 1113; Karlstrom, 1964, p. 34–37).

The record of long-term Holocene deformation within the major zone of uplift in the area between the Copper River Delta and Cape Suckling is seemingly anomalous in that uplifted surfaces described as marine terraces, and drowned forests or sphagnum-peat horizons, occur in close association with one another. Dated marine terraces at Katalla (nos. 26, 27, fig. 34) and Cape Suckling (no. 30, fig. 34) record net Holocene emergence; recent net submergence is indicated by (1) a dated wood sample from the Copper River Delta (no. 36, fig. 34) that was submerged 22 feet in the 1,700 years prior to the earthquake but was uplifted only about 6 feet at the time of the earthquake, (2) a widespread horizon of terrestrial peat of unknown age that was penetrated in borings at depths as much as 40 feet below sea level in the lower Copper River Delta and to a depth of 30 feet at Bering Lake (Tarr and Martin, 1914, p. 462–463), and (3) forest horizons in the Katalla and Cape Suckling areas submerged prior to the earthquake by amounts that were considerably larger than the earthquake-related uplift at these same

36.—Muskeg-covered preearthquake marine terrace on Middleton Island at an altitude of 110–125 feet. It is one of five uplifted terraces on the island, and surf-cut rock platform exposed between the base of the sea cliff and the new high-tide level is a sixth terrace formed by uplift of about 11 feet in 1964. White specks are seagulls. Photograph taken near 7-foot tide stage, April 4, 1964.

37.—The linear tree-covered beach ridge in this view is one of nine elevated beach ridges near Katalla, east of the Copper River Delta. Uplift of about 9 feet in 1964 shifted the shoreline several hundred feet seaward where another beach ridge is in process of formation. Photograph taken near zero tide stage, July 28, 1964.

localities. The relative ages of dated samples in these areas suggest that the long-term displacement may have reversed direction from uplift to submergence during the time interval between about 3,770 and 1,700 years B.P.

Radiocarbon dating of organic material from terraces, peat bogs, and archaeological sites in coastal areas affected by the earthquake has provided some preliminary data on average long-term displacement trends relative to sea level at a number of localities. Displacement-time curves at the five localities (A–E) in the area for which multiple samples are available are shown in figure 34. Points on the graph are the preearthquake position relative to mean lower low water plotted against age in millenia of radiocarbon-dated material from these five sites. The available dated samples were collected by several different workers over a period of 30 years and were analyzed in three different laboratories. In spite of the small number of samples at each site, uncertainties in their exact positions relative to sea level, and the ever-present problem of analytical or sampling errors, it is noteworthy that the results appear to be remarkably consistent with one another and with the displacements that occurred in 1964.

These data indicate that the two localities at Yukon Island (A) and Girdwood (B) have subsided relative to present sea level at an average rate of about 0.7–1.0 foot per century during the time interval from 2,800 to 700 years B.P., whereas those at Middleton Island (C) and Katalla (D) in the uplifted area have risen at the much greater average rate of at least 3.3 feet per century between 7,650 and 1,350 years B.P. The rate of uplift would be increased somewhat if any of the deduced eustatic sea levels are used in place of the 1964 sea level. The shore at Kukak Bay (E), which was not affected by the earthquake, has apparently undergone no detectable net change in its present position relative to sea level since at least 1,450 B.P.

Detailed study of the emergent shorelines shows that the long-term vertical movements occurred, at least in part, as a series of upward pulses separated by intervals of stability or even gradual submergence. Evidence for periodic uplift is exceptionally well displayed on Middleton Island where the surface consists of a flight of five gently sloping and well-developed marine terraces separated by wave-cut cliffs or rises ranging from 20 to 30 feet each (Miller, 1953; Plafker, unpub. data, 1963, 1964, 1965). The highest terrace, forming the flat central part of the island, has a general altitude of 130–165 feet. Sudden uplift of 10–13 feet during the 1964 earthquake, which exposed a sixth surf-cut terrace (shown on fig. 36), suggests that perhaps the earlier terraces may also have been exposed by a series of upward pulses during previous earthquakes. Radiocarbon-dated driftwood from the highest and lowest of these preearthquake platforms on Middleton Island dates initial uplift of the island at 4,470±250 years ago and uplift of the lowest preearthquake terrace at approximately 1,350±200 years B.P. (nos. 33, 31, table 5). Thus, the extrapolated average time interval between successive uplifts of the three intervening terraces would be close to 800 years.

Because most of the dated samples were taken from deposits laid down when the postglacial eustatic sea level was rising gradually or was at about its present stand, the emergent shorelines probably result almost entirely from tectonic movements. Although some slightly submerged shorelines may be attributed to the effects of a late Holocene rise of sea level and to local surficial subsidence of unconsolidated deposits, in most instances the submergence is so large when compared to deduced eustatic curves that it must also be at least partly due to tectonic subsidence.

Regional submergence of the Kenai and Kodiak Mountains is clearly anomalous in that the movements are in a direction that tends to reduce the elevation of these youthful mountain ranges. Furthermore, because the net load of glacial ice on the mountains has been steadily diminished since the Pleistocene, isostatic adjustments, if any, should be upward. Thus, the submergence is a counter-isostatic process that can only be attributed to regional diastrophic movements.

Less certain is the extent to which the regional postglacial uplift reflects isostatic compensation resulting from unloading of ice and the extent to which it is caused by diastrophic movements. Both processes are undoubtedly involved. However, the known seismic activity of the region, the evidence for pulsating rather than continuous emergence, and the apparent late Holocene reversals in the sense of the net displacements over part of the region suggest that the movements were also, to a large extent, diastrophic in nature.

SHORT-TERM TECTONIC SUBMERGENCE

Much of the coast in the region affected by tectonic movements during the 1964 earthquake had experienced a pronounced submergence for several centuries prior to that event. This phenomenon was probably first recorded by the great English navigator, George Vancouver, who explored Prince William Sound between May 25 and June 17, 1794 (Vancouver, 1801, v. 5, p. 335–336). He noted that on northern Montague Island "The shores are in general low, and as had been already observed, very swampy in many places, on which the sea appears to be making more rapid encroachments than I ever before saw or heard of * * * [trees along the shore] were reduced to naked, dead white stumps, by the encroachment of the sea water to their roots; and some stumps of trees, with their roots still fast in the ground, were also found in no very advanced state of decay nearly as low down as the low water of spring tides." The fact that low water of spring tides is about 13 feet below the normal lower growth limit of trees in this area indicates almost that amount of submergence prior to 1794. The characteristic appearance of these drowned forests in Prince William Sound and along the coast at Cape Suckling east of the Sound is illustrated by figures 38 and 39.

Evidence for active submergence along the coast of the type first described by Vancouver was subsequently noted by geologists, archaeologists, and botanists in the following places: (1) the Controller Bay area east of Prince William Sound (Tarr and Martin, 1914), (2) the Copper River region (Schrader, 1900, p. 404; Reimnitz, 1966, p. 112–125), (3) around Prince William Sound (Grant and Higgins, 1910; Moffitt, 1954; Dachnowski-Stokes, 1941; De Laguna, 1956, (4) around Kachemak Bay on the southern Kenai Peninsula (De Laguna, 1934), (5) in the upper Cook Inlet region (Karlstrom, 1964, p. 48), and (6) in at least two localities on Kodiak Island (Clark, 1966).

Reconnaissance studies by the Geological Survey of all these shorelines after the 1964 earthquake suggest that the submergence observed is a regional phenomenon that has affected much, if not all, of the Prince William Sound region, the mainland coast and islands east of Prince William Sound, the south coast of the Kenai Peninsula at least as far as Kachemak Bay, parts of Turnagain Arm, and segments of the southeastern coast of the Kodiak group of islands. Undoubtedly, many more such localities could be found by detailed examination of the shorelines. Areas within

38.—Bleached trunks of spruce trees on Latouche Island, Prince William Sound, killed by salt-water immersion and partially buried in beach gravel as a result of about 8 feet of submergence below preearthquake extreme high-tide level. The locality was exposed by 8 feet of uplift in 1964. Photograph taken May 28, 1964.

39.—Spruce tree stumps (foreground) rooted in a thin layer of peat on a surf-cut bedrock surface about 14 feet below preearthquake extreme high water (indicated by the top of the line of driftwood below the present forest edge in the background). Radiocarbon age of a stump near the base of the stadia rod was 710±200 years (no. 29, fig. 34). These stumps were exposed by about 16 feet of uplift in 1964. Photograph taken July 24, 1964.

which there is evidence of pre-earthquake submergence are indicated on figure 33 and the ages and positions relative to sea level of the dated samples are shown on figure 34. In a few scattered localities within Prince William Sound, evidence of stable shorelines or of possible recent slight uplift (no more than 4 ft) was found. This evidence suggests that small areas may have acted as independent tectonic units that did not take part in the general submergence.

The available data is insufficient for determining whether the submergence, which affected the offshore islands from Kayak Island to the Copper River Delta, extended as far out on the Continental Shelf as Middleton Island. Preearthquake sea levels that reached to the base of the prominent sea cliff encircling much of the island indicate either a long period of relative stability and erosion or some submergence since the last uplift of the island roughly 1,350 years ago.

The record of preearthquake submergence in the zone that was lowered in relation to sea level is much less complete than that for the zone that was raised, mainly because much of the evidence is now below lowest low tide. Available data suggest that submergence occurred along parts of the coast of the Kenai Peninsula and the Kodiak group of islands but that submergence probably was much less than in the area from Prince William Sound to Cape Suckling. No change in mean sea level attributable to tectonic movements was detected in a 21-year tidal record at Seward and a 15-year record at Kodiak. An apparently large preearthquake submergence on the delta of Spruce Creek near Seward of about 6.9 feet in less than 200 years, as indicated by drowned rooted tree stumps (no. 12, fig. 34), may be partly due to slumping and (or) compaction of deltaic deposits.

Radiocarbon dates from drowned terrestrial plants that were probably killed by sea-water encroachment provide data that permit a crude estimate of the duration and average rate of the short-term preearthquake submergence. Ages in radiocarbon years versus amount of submergence of samples taken from the most deeply submerged terrestrial vegetation at each site are plotted in the stippled area on figure 34. The fairly regular linear distribution of 14 out of 16 samples, all from the area between Seward and Cape Suckling, suggests a general submergence at a rate that averaged roughly 1.7 feet per century for about 930 years. On the other hand, positions of two samples (nos. 15, 21, fig. 34) from this same general area, both of which are older than 930 years, reflect lower rates of submergence, as do three samples from the Cook Inlet region (nos. 8, 11, 15, fig. 34). The maximum indicated average rate of submergence is 8.6 feet in 230 years or about 3.7 feet per century on Latouche Island in Prince William Sound.

Absence of historic records of sudden earthquake-related relative sea-level changes and of geomorphic evidence for such movements suggest that the submergence was probably gradual or that it occurred in numerous small increments over a long period of time. This time interval, as inferred from dated submerged shorelines, was at least 930 years in the Prince William Sound region. The upper limit for the duration of the submergence is far less certain; if it corresponds to the oldest dated submerged-forest sample along the coast (no. 21, fig. 34) and the time of uplift of the

lowest preearthquake marine terrace on Middleton Island (no. 31, fig. 34), it could be as much as 1,350 years.

Short-term submergence occurred at a time when sea level was at or near its present stand and in a region where overall isostatic displacements in response to glacial unloading should have been upward. Isostatic adjustments between major earthquakes such as the 1964 event could conceivably be responsible for some of the submergence in areas of tectonic uplift. However, such adjustments are inadequate to explain either short-term submergence in the Copper River Delta-Cape Suckling area that exceeds earthquake-related uplift or submergence in areas of the Kenai Peninsula and Kodiak Island that subsided both before and during the earthquake. By implication, this fact suggests that the submergence was caused at least partly by diastrophism that involved a significant downward-directed component of regional strain of variable amount and rate over much of the coastal belt affected by vertical displacements during the 1964 earthquake.

TECTONIC IMPLICATIONS OF THE RECORD OF HOLOCENE VERTICAL MOVEMENTS

The history of Holocene vertical movements in the region affected by the 1964 earthquake, and in nearby areas, is a fragmentary one based largely on a rapid reconnaissance after the earthquake and on incidental investigations by others. Additional work—involving far more radiocarbon dating—is required to obtain detailed data on vertical movements at selected localities in areas of net Holocene emergence and submergence. However, the following four tentative conclusions regarding the prehistoric tectonic move-

ments seem to be indicated by the available data:

1. Areas of net Holocene emergence or submergence broadly correspond with those areas in which significant amounts of uplift and subsidence occurred during the 1964 earthquake. Thus, the tectonic movements that accompanied the earthquake were apparently but one pulse in a long-continuing trend of deformation. This trend has resulted in regional emergence of parts of the continental margin, simultaneous submergence of the Kenai-Kodiak Mountains belt, and either relative stability or emergence along the shores of Cook Inlet and parts of Shelikof Strait.

2. The amounts of net long-term Holocene emergence and submergence of the coast, which are locally considerably larger than the postulated eustatic sea-level changes for the same time interval, indicate that differential displacement of the shoreline results largely from tectonic movements. Progressive submergence of youthful mountains recently unloaded of ice and pulsating emergence of the Continental Shelf and Gulf of Alaska coast are suggestive of a dominant regional diastrophic deformation.

3. Steplike flights of Holocene marine surf-cut terraces at a number of localities along the coast suggest that the long-term vertical movements occurred as a series of upward pulses that were separated by intervals of stability or even gradual subsidence that locally average 800 years or more in duration. These upward pulses probably represent earthquake-related movements comparable in origin to those which affected parts of the same coast in 1964.

4. Gradual tectonic submergence prevailed during at least the past 900 years, and perhaps as long as 1,360 years, over much of the zone that was uplifted and over at least part of the zone that subsided during the 1964 earthquake. This widespread submergence is tentatively interpreted as direct evidence for a significant downward-directed component of regional strain preceding the earthquake and its duration as the approximate time interval since the last major tectonic earthquake in this same region.

MECHANISM OF THE EARTHQUAKE

GENERAL CONSIDERATIONS

According to the classic elastic rebound theory of earthquake generation (Reid, 1911), which is generally accepted by western geologists and geophysicists, shallow earthquakes are generated by sudden fracture or faulting following a period of slow deformation during which energy is stored in the form of elastic strain within rock adjacent to the fault. When the strength of the rock is exceeded, failure in the form of faulting occurs, the material on opposite sides of the fault tends to rebound into a configuration of elastic equilibrium, and elastic strain potential is released in the form of heat, crushing of rock, and seismic-wave radiation. The drop in elastic strain potential is possibly augmented or partially absorbed by net changes in gravitational potential associated with vertical tectonic displacements.

Field investigations demonstrate that there is little likelihood that the primary fault along which the 1964 earthquake occurred is exposed at the surface on land, nor is there evidence for movement on any of the known major continental faults. If the earthquake originated by rupture along one or more faults, the two most plausible models for the orientation and sense of movement on the primary fault consistent with the available fault-plane solutions and dislocation-theory analyses of the re-

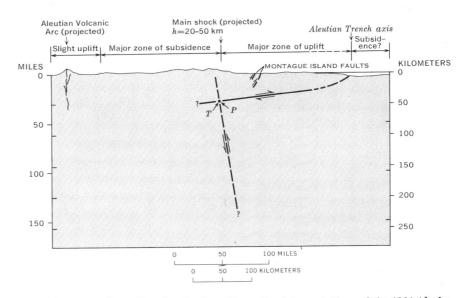

40.—Diagrammatic section showing two alternative interpretations of the 1964 Alaska earthquake based on focal mechanism studies (S. T. Algermissen, written commun., March 1965) and analyses of residual vertical displacements by dislocation theory (Savage and Hastie, 1966). Section is oriented through the focus of the main shock and roughly normal to the regional structural trend. P and T axes are the approximate orientations of the principal pressure and tension axes, respectively, at the hypocenter of the main shock indicated by the focal mechanism studies.

sidual vertical displacements are (1) relative seaward thrusting along a fault that dips northwestward beneath the continental margin at a low angle, and (2) dipslip movement on a near-vertical fault, the ocean side being relatively upthrown, that strikes approximately along the zero isobase between the major zones of uplift and subsidence (fig. 40). These two models, which are discussed in the following sections, are referred to as the "thrust-fault model" and the "steep-fault model."

Whether the postulated shearing resulted from the overcoming of frictional resistance to sliding, as set forth in the elastic rebound theory of Reid (1911), or from some other process such as brittle fracture, creep instability, or propagation of flaws cannot be ascertained from available data. Several writers (O r o w a n, 1960; Griggs and Handin, 1960; Evison, 1963, p. 863–884) have pointed out deficiencies in the elastic rebound mechanism for earthquakes at depths of more than a few miles, where frictional stress on dry fault planes must vastly exceed the rock strength. However, such considerations generally do not take into account the effect of pore fluids which must exist in the real earth down to the depths of the deepest hydrated mineral phases. Recent laboratory studies (Raleigh and Patterson, 1965, p. 3977–3978; Griggs and Blacic, 1965; Raleigh, 1967) suggest the possibility that the Reid mechanism may extend to depths at least as great as the lower crust and upper mantle in regions where frictional resistance to sliding on faults may be reduced by local anomalously high pore pressures or where the strength of the rock is lowered sufficiently in the presence of pore fluids to permit brittle fracture.

An alternative mechanism to be considered is one that explains tectonic earthquakes as originating from sudden expansion and (or) contraction of large volumes of rock due to rapid phase changes (Evison, 1963). According to this concept, faulting is the result rather than the cause of earthquakes. No evidence has yet been found from either natural or experimental petrologic systems to support the idea that reconstructive solid-solid or solid-liquid reactions can occur fast enough throughout sufficiently large volumes of rock to generate major earthquakes or to produce regional vertical displacements (Ghent, 1965). Aside from the theoretical objections, it is difficult to conceive of a reasonable combination of equidimensional volume changes that could cause the observed pattern of vertical and horizontal displacements that accompanied this earthquake. For these reasons, there is little likelihood that phase

changes were a primary mechanism for the 1964 earthquake, and this possibility will not be pursued further.

THRUST-FAULT MODEL

Most of the preliminary data available by the end of the 1964 field season suggested that the earthquake and the associated tectonic deformation resulted from a relative seaward thrusting along the continental margin that was accompanied by elastic horizontal extension behind the thrust block (Plafker, 1965, p. 1686). The t h r u s t - f a u l t model has been strongly reinforced by data subsequently obtained from (1) more detailed fieldwork on the surface displacements and preearthquake movements by the Geological Survey during 1965, (2) comparison of pre- and post-earthquake triangulation surveys for a large segment of the deformed region (Parkin, 1966, fig. 4), and (3) detailed focal-mechanism studies of the main shock and larger aftershocks (Stauder and Bollinger, 1966). The essential features of the suggested model, which are illustrated diagrammatically by figure 41, are presented below.

OUTLINE OF THE MODEL

According to the thrust-fault model, the earthquake resulted from shear failure along an inferred major zone of movement, or megathrust, which dips northwestward beneath the continental margin from the vicinity of the Aleutian Trench, and on subsidiary faults within the overthrust plate. The zone within which movement occurred, as delineated by the belt of major aftershocks, parallels the Aleutian Trench on the northwest for a distance of some 600 miles and is from 110 to 180 miles wide (fig. 2). It lies almost entirely within the major zone of uplift and the portion of the adjacent zone of

subsidence that is on the seaward side of the axis of subsidence.

The pattern of earthquake-related horizontal displacements (fig. 16) and the evidence for regional preearthquake shoreline submergence along the continental margin (fig. 33) suggest that shear failure followed a long period of elastic strain accumulation (930–1,360 years) during which the upper plate was horizontally compressed roughly normal to the trend of the Aleutian Arc and probably simultaneously depressed relative to sea level. A hypothetical deformation cycle is illustrated diagrammatically in figure 42. The data suggest that the dynamic drive was probably provided by underthrust of the lower plate, with a downward-directed component of movement. R. K. Hose has pointed out that distortional drag due to an underthrust would have generated a shear couple in which the relative strains and orientation of potential shear planes coincide reasonably well with those deduced from fault-plane solutions for the main shock and many or the larger aftershocks (oral commun., Nov. 1965). Alternative mechanisms such as movement of the continental margin over the oceanic basin, or almost horizontal movements, could not be responsible for the combination of both horizontal shortening and regional submergence indicated by the available data.

Previous seismicity in the region during the strain-accumulation phase of the 1964 earthquake may have resulted from adjustments within the strained volume of rock involving predominantly lateral offsets or relatively local dip-slip displacement. This possibility is suggested by the fact that, although prior historic earthquakes with magnitudes of 7 or more have been recorded

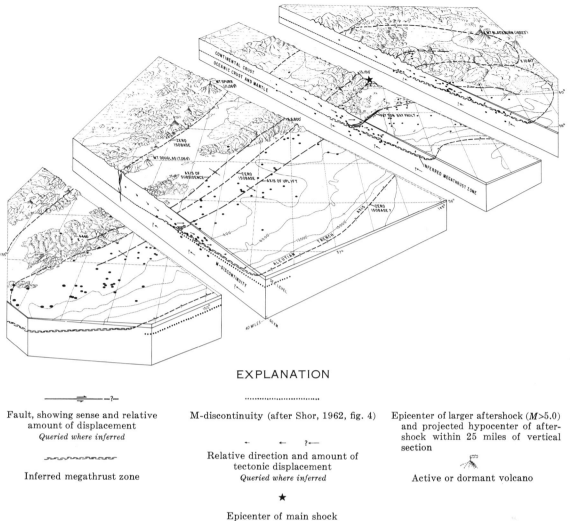

EXPLANATION

⇒ ──?─
Fault, showing sense and relative
amount of displacement
Queried where inferred

∙∙∙∙∙∙∙∙∙∙∙∙∙∙∙∙∙∙∙∙∙∙∙
M-discontinuity (after Shor, 1962, fig. 4)

←   ←   ?←
Relative direction and amount of
tectonic displacement
Queried where inferred

Epicenter of larger aftershock (*M*>5.0)
and projected hypocenter of aftershock within 25 miles of vertical
section

Active or dormant volcano

∼∼∼∼∼∼∼∼∼∼∼∼∼
Inferred megathrust zone

★
Epicenter of main shock

41.—Schematic block diagram showing the postulated relationship of the seismic activity and tectonic displacement associated with the 1964 Alaska earthquake to major structural elements of south-central Alaska. Horizontal and vertical scales equal below sea level; vertical scale above sea level exaggerated × 4. Drawn by H. T. Koelbl.

(Wood, 1966, p. 24), none of these were accompanied by known regional tectonic deformation—and certainly none with deformation on the scale of the 1964 earthquake.

Faulting at the time of the earthquake presumably was initiated at the hypocenter of the main shock in northern Prince William Sound, from which point it propagated simultaneously updip towards the Aleutian Trench and along strike both towards the southwest and east within the area encompassed by the aftershocks. Shear failure was accompanied by elastic rebound in the upper plate

above the thrust, which resulted in (1) relative seaward displacement and uplift of a part of the continental margin by movement along the inferred megathrust and the subsidiary reverse faults that break through the upper plate to the surface, and (2) simultaneous elastic horizontal extension and vertical attenuation (subsidence) of the crustal slab behind the upper plate. These movements, possibly in combination with unidentified submarine faulting and (or) underthrusting of the lower plate in the opposite direction, resulted in the observed and inferred

tectonic displacements at the surface.

Indicated stress drops at the surface across the zone of subsidence (on the order of a few hundred bars) are comparable in magnitude to those reported for other tectonic earthquakes. For the idealized case of homogeneous strain and purely elastic distortion of the crust, the stress drop (*P*) is a function of Young's modulus (*E*) of the slab and the reduction of horizontal strain (ϵ) across it:

$$\triangle P = E\epsilon$$

For an average *E* of 3×10^5 bars

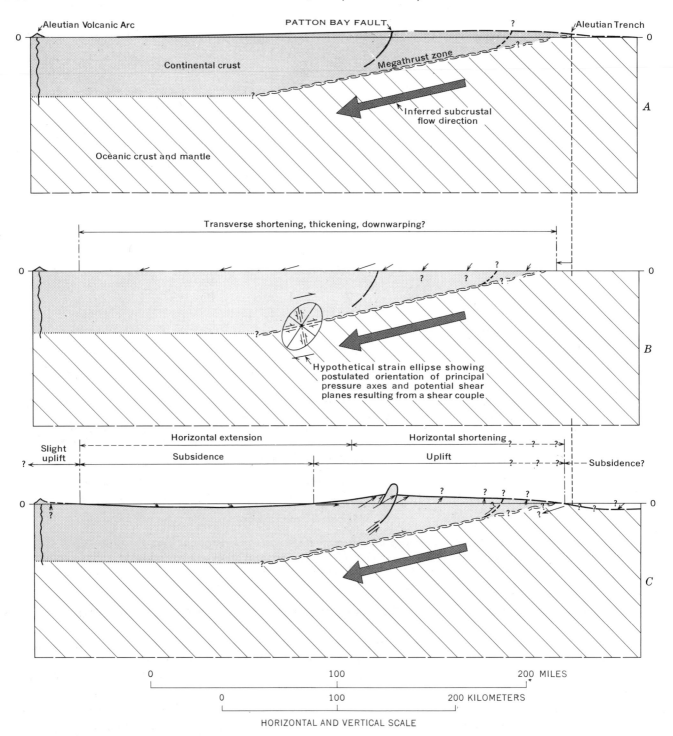

42.—Diagrammatic time-sequential cross sections through the crust and upper mantle in the northern part of the region affected by the 1964 earthquake. A, Relatively unstrained condition after the last major earthquake. B, Strain buildup stage during which the continental margin is shortened and downwarped. C, Observed and inferred displacements at time of the earthquake during which a segment of the continental margin is thrust seaward relative to the continent. Datum is the upper surface of the crust beneath the cover of water and low-velocity sediments. Vertical displacements at the surface, which are indicated by the profiles and by arrows showing sense and relative amount of movement, are about × 1,000 scale of the figure.

$(7 \times 10^{11}$ dynes cm^{-2}), and average and maximum strain across the subsided zone of 1.1×10^{-4} and 3×10^{-4}, respectively, the average stress drop was only about 77 bars $(77 \times 10^6$ dynes cm^{-2}). The maximum drop, which occurs near the axis of subsidence, was about 210 bars $(210 \times 10^6$ dynes cm^{-2}).

The megathrust in the earthquake focal region dips north to northwest at an angle of 9°–15°, according to fault-plane solutions of the main shock and several aftershocks, but its precise depth and configuration are uncertain. The limited available data on focal depths of the earthquake (p. I 4) and on deep crustal structure (Shor, 1962, fig. 4; Hales and Asada, 1966, p. 420) suggest that the megathrust may coincide with the unstable interface at the base of the continental crust beneath the continental slope and shelf. It probably extends into the upper mantle toward the north to some unknown depth (no deeper than the deepest hypocenters in the region) where stress relaxation is sufficiently rapid to absorb the applied force by plastic, rather than elastic, deformation.

MAJOR UNRESOLVED PROBLEMS

The cause of the slight uplift that occurred to the north of the major zone of subsidence is uncertain. Presumably, this uplift involves an elastic distortion related to strain changes resulting from seaward thrusting along the continental margin at the time of the earthquake. It could represent an increase in vertical strain (Poisson bulge) resulting from a sudden increment in the regional horizontal compressive strain oriented roughly normal to the zone (R. O. Burford, written commun., 1966). If this explanation for the uplift is correct, retriangulation within

the areas of slight uplift should show transverse horizontal shortening. A test of the suggestion could be made if the postearthquake triangulation net were extended northward into this zone.

A second major problem is that there exists an apparent asymmetry in the volumes of uplift (89 cu mi, 372 cu km) and subsidence (29 cu mi, 122 cu km) in the two major zones that implies a substantial increase in net gravitational potential. By making the assumptions that the displacements decrease linearly from a maximum at the surface to zero at the base of the continental crust, that there were no density changes within the affected volume of crust, and that the crust has an average density of 2.7, the approximate upper limit for this change may be calculated. An average lowering of 2½ feet (75 cm) in a crustal block having the dimensions of the zone of subsidence would result in a potential energy loss of 2.7×10^{19} ft-lbs $(3.6 \times 10^{26}$ ergs). The increase in gravitational potential in the uplifted area would be about 4.1×10^{19} ft-lbs $(5.6 \times 10^{26}$ ergs), assuming an average uplift against gravity of roughly 6 feet (1.8 m) for a wedge-shaped block with a length of 475 miles (760 km), a width of 115 miles (185 km), and an average thickness of about 11 miles (18 km).

These data suggest an apparent net increase in gravitational potential of about 1.5×10^{19} ft-lbs $(2 \times 10^{26}$ ergs). Even with the assumption that vertical displacements extend only halfway through the slab, the indicated gravitational potential increase is still roughly two orders of magnitude larger than the total released seismic-wave energy of about $1-2 \times 10^{24}$ ergs (calculated from the empirically derived Gutenberg-Richter relationship between

energy and earthquake magnitude $\log E = 11.4 + 1.5\,M$; Richter, 1958, p. 366).

In fact, however, the net change in gravitational potential due to elastic-rebound mass redistribution in the crust must be considered as indeterminate because data are unavailable on (1) the seaward and continentward limits of the displacement field, (2) possible elastic density changes attendant upon stress drops within and behind the upper plate, and (3) the extent to which the movements may have been compensated by elastic depression of the denser mantle beneath zones of uplift and a corresponding rise beneath the zone of subsidence.

REPRESENTATION BY DISLOCATION THEORY

Savage and Hastie (1966) and Stauder and Bollinger (1966) have used dislocation theory to compare theoretical profiles of vertical surface displacement for various gently dipping and horizontal overthrust models to the observed and inferred profile. Their assumed models, with the corresponding profiles along a vertical plane oriented normal to the fault strike, are plotted to a common scale on figure 43. These models have, of necessity, been highly generalized to permit a mathematical analysis by dislocation theory, and, in part, the studies are based upon preliminary and incomplete observational data.

The basic assumption in this procedure is that the observed displacements can be modeled by the corresponding fields of a planar dislocation sheet in a homogeneous, isotropic, elastic half-space with displacement discontinuity matching the observed or inferred fault slip. Inasmuch as the depth, configuration, and net slip on the postulated faults are to a large degree speculative, considerable latitude exists in the parameters used for those calculations. Furthermore, because faults that break to the surface are not dislocations in a semi-infinite medium, their contribution to the deformation can only be examined qualitatively.

Figure 43 shows that, although each of the assumed models can approximately account for the observed subsidence, none of them gives a close fit between the theoretical and actual profiles in the uplifted zone. Stauder and Bollinger (1966, p. 5293) suggest that the observed tectonic surface displacements can be approximated to any desired degree by assuming combined differential-slip motion and a shallowly dipping thrust plane. Such a model would be more nearly in accord with the data which suggest a dipping master fault having the approximate configuration shown in figure 43A with differential slip as indicated in figure 43B. To be realistic, however, it would also have to include the effects of (1) imbrication along known and suspected thrust or reverse faults that break to the surface, (2) possible breaking to the surface along the shallowing leading edge of the megathrust, and, perhaps (3) possible simultaneous underthrusting of the lower plate along an inclined fault plane.

STEEP-FAULT MODEL

OUTLINE OF THE MODEL

According to the steep-fault model, the earthquake resulted from elastic rebound on a near-vertical fault that strikes approximately along the line of zero change in land level, with the southeast block up and the northwest block down relative to sea level. A steeply dipping fault was suggested by a preliminary fault-plane solution based on surface waves (Press and Jackson, 1965,

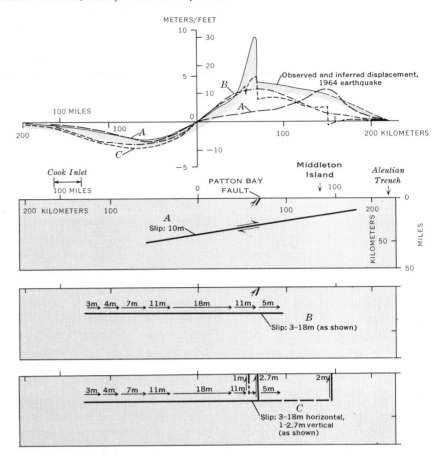

43.—Comparison of observed and inferred profile of surface displacement along line B–B′ of plate 1 (shaded line) with computed profiles for movement on faults of slip and cross-sectional configuration shown in diagrams below the profiles. Model A from Savage and Hastie (1966, fig. 3); models B and C from Stauder and Bollinger (1966, fig. 7).

p. 867; Press, 1965, p. 2404). However, Savage and Hastie (1966, p. 4899–4900) have pointed out that a unique surface-wave solution for the fault orientation cannot be inferred from the surface waves, inasmuch as the direction of rupture propagation is along the null axis and therefore the radiation of seismic waves will be essentially the same for either of the two possible fault planes.

The main appeal of the steep-fault model is that it can readily account for the gross distribution of uplift and subsidence in two major zones, as well as the occurrence of the earthquake epicenter close to the zero isobase between these zones.

However, as noted elsewhere (Plafker, 1965, p. 1686), there are no compelling geologic, seismologic, or geodetic data in support of the steep-fault model. Aftershocks are not grouped along its postulated trace, but instead lie mainly in a broad belt along the continental margin mainly to the south of the zero isobase (fig. 2). Furthermore no field evidence exists for new surface breakage in the vicinity of the zero isobase—despite the fact that it intersects the coast in more than 15 localities (fig. 3). And finally there is no evidence that the line corresponds to a major geologic boundary with the seaward side relatively upthrown, as might be expected if it marked the trace of a major fault

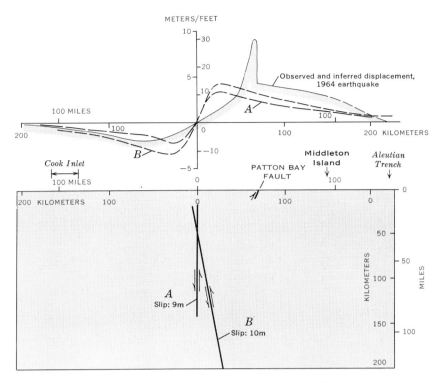

44.—Comparison of observed and inferred profile of surface displacement along line B–B' of plate 1 (shaded line) with computed profiles for movement on steeply dipping faults of slip and cross-sectional configuration shown in the diagram below the profiles. Model A from Press and Jackson (1965, fig. 1); model B from Savage and Hastie (1966, fig. 3).

along which vertical movement has occurred in the past. On the contrary the overwhelming majority of surface faults that parallel the coast in this part of Alaska have exactly the opposite sense of displacement (fig. 29).

The apparent absence of a surface dislocation along the zero isobase between the major zones prompted the suggestion that the displacement represents flexure above a near-vertical fault at depth (Press and Jackson, 1965, p. 868; Press, 1965, p. 2405). Such a fault would have to extend to the considerable depth of 62–124 miles (100–200 km) below the free surface to account for the areal distribution of residual vertical displacements normal to its inferred strike.

REPRESENTATION BY DISLOCATION THEORY

Observed residual tectonic displacements have been compared to the theoretical surface displacements that would occur on faults of varying inclination, slip, and dimension by application of dislocation theory (Press and Jackson, 1965; Press, 1965; Savage and Hastie, 1966). These analyses are subject to the same basic assumptions as were previously outlined. Assumed models, with corresponding profiles along a vertical plane oriented normal to the fault strike, are plotted to a common scale on figure 44. The resultant profiles show the same general spatial distribution of uplift and subsidence as the profile of observed and inferred vertical

displacements along a northwest-southeast line through the southwest tip of Montague Island. They differ fundamentally, however, in that the axes of uplift and subsidence are too close together by at least 50 miles (80 km), or a factor of one-half, and the indicated changes within the two major zones are notably more equal in amplitude than in the observed profile. The distance between the two axes would tend to decrease even further if the faulting is shallow—as is suggested by the spatial distribution of the aftershocks. Even if the vertical displacements could be explained by these models, no reasonable combination of fault dimensions, slip, and dip could also duplicate the systematic horizontal displacements observed in the field (fig. 18).

SUMMARY AND CONCLUSIONS

The earthquake of March 27, 1964, was accompanied by regional vertical and horizontal displacements over an area probably in excess of 110,000 square miles in south-central Alaska. Major deformation and related seismic activity were largely limited to an elongate segment of the continental margin lying between the Aleutian Trench and the chain of late Cenozoic volcanoes that comprise the Aleutian Volcanic Arc.

Geologic evidence in the earthquake-affected region suggests that the earthquake was but the most recent pulse in an episode of deformation that probably began in late Pliocene time and has continued intermittently to the present. The net effect of these movements has been uplift along the Gulf of Alaska coast and continental margin by warping and imbricate faulting; subsidence or relative stability characterized most of the adjacent landward zone extending inland approximately to the Aleutian Volcanic Arc. The length of time since the last major tectonic earthquake that involved regional warping, as inferred from radiocarbon-dated displaced shorelines in the epicentral region, appears to have been about 930–1,360 years.

Because the primary fault or zone of faulting along which the earthquake is presumed to have occurred is not exposed at the surface on land, a unique solution for its orientation and sense of slip cannot be made. Nevertheless, the vertical displacements, when considered in relationship to the focal-mechanism studies and spatial distribution of seismicity, strongly favor the hypothesis that the primary fault was a major thrust fault, or megathrust. The data suggest that the segment of the megathrust along which slippage occurred was 550–600 miles long and 110–180 miles wide and that it dips from the vicinity of the Aleutian Trench at a gentle angle beneath the continental margin.

According to the thrust-fault hypothesis, the observed regional uplift and transverse shortening along the continental margin during the earthquake resulted from (1) relative seaward displacement of the upper plate along the dipping primary thrust, (2) imbrication on the known subsidiary reverse faults that break through the upper plate to the surface, and (3) crustal warping. Movement on other subsidiary submarine reverse faults, as well as rebound of the lower plate toward the continent, may have contributed to the uplift. Simultaneous subsidence in the zone behind the fault block presumably reflects an elastic horizontal extension and vertical attenuation of previously compressed crustal material. Stored elastic-strain energy within the thrust block and the segment of crust behind the block that was affected by subsidence was the primary source of energy dissipated during the earthquake in the form of seismic waves, heat, crushing of rock, and, perhaps, net changes in gravitational potential. Major unresolved problems are the cause of the slight uplift in the area north of the two major zones of deformation and the apparent large increase in potential energy over the displacement field.

The implication of a genetic relationship between the 1964 Alaska earthquake and the Aleutian Arc appears inescapable in view of the nature of the surface deformation and seismic activity associated with the earthquake. Available geologic, geodetic, and geophysical data from the region affected by tectonic deformation during the earthquake are compatible with the concept that arc structures are sites of down-welling mantle convection currents and that planar seismic zones dipping beneath them mark the zone of shearing produced by downward-moving material thrust against a less mobile block of the crust and upper mantle. Conversely, the data provide severe constraints for alternative hypotheses that relate deformation in the eastern Aleutian Arc, at least, primarily to transverse regional extension or to movement on major longitudinal strike-slip faults or shallow steep dip-slip faults.

Preearthquake strain directed at a gentle angle downward beneath the arc in the epicentral region is suggested by geodetic evidence for horizontal shortening of as much as 64 feet roughly normal to the Gulf of Alaska coast and by geologic evidence for progressive coastal submergence in the same region in excess of 16 feet. If the duration of preearthquake strain accumulation, as inferred from radiocarbon-dated drowned shorelines, was about 930–1,360 years, average annual horizontal displacement was about 0.59–0.83 inch per year (1.5 to 2.1 cm per year). The indicated shortening, which is probably a minimum value inasmuch as there probably also was some permanent shortening, is reasonably compatible with seafloor spreading rates of about 2.9 cm per year in a northwesterly direction from the Juan de Fuca ridge. Such rates and spreading directions have been deduced from paleomagnetic studies of the northeastern Pacific ocean floor (Vine, 1966, p. 1407). Alternative driving mechanisms, in which the upper

plate overrides the ocean basin or in which the regional strain is directed horizontally, do not readily account either for the widespread preearthquake subsidence relative to sea level that accompanied hori-

zontal shortening in coastal areas affected by earthquake-related tectonic deformation or for the orientation of principal stress axes at the hypocenter of the main shock and many of its aftershocks.

REFERENCES CITED

Alaska Department of Fish and Game, 1965, Post-earthquake fisheries evaluation; an interim report on the March 1964 earthquake effects on Alaska's fishery resources: Juneau, Alaska, 72 p.

Algermissen, S. T., 1965, Prince William Sound, Alaska earthquake of March 28, 1964, and aftershock sequence [abs.]: Geol. Soc. America Spec. Paper 82, p. 2.

Balakina, L. M., Shirokova, H. I., and Vvedenskaya, A. V., 1961, Study of stresses and ruptures in earthquake foci with the help of dislocation theory: Ottawa Dominion Observatory Pub., v. 24, no. 10, p. 321–327.

Barnes, D. F., 1966, Gravity changes during the Alaska earthquake: Jour. Geophys. Research, v. 71, no. 2, p. 451–456.

Barnes, F. F., 1962, Geologic map of the lower Matanuska Valley, Alaska: U.S. Geol. Survey Misc. Geol. Inv. Map I–359, scale 1 : 63,360.

Benioff, Hugo, 1951, Earthquakes and rock creep; pt. 1, Creep characteristics of rocks and the origin of aftershocks: Seismol. Soc. America Bull., v. 41, no. 1, p. 31–62.

——— 1954, Orogenesis and deep crustal structure—additional evidence from seismology: Geol. Soc. America Bull., v. 65, no. 5, p. 385–400.

Bollinger, G. A., and Stauder, William, 1965, Geometry of earthquake foci stresses [abs.]: Seismol. Soc. America, Eastern Sec., Earthquake Notes, v. 36, nos. 3–4, p. 22.

Bolt, B. A., 1964, Seismic air waves from the great 1964 Alaska earthquake: Nature, v. 202, no. 4937, p. 1095–1096.

Brazee, R. J., 1965, A study of T phases in the Aleutian earthquake series of March and April 1957: Seismol. Soc. America, Eastern Sec. Earthquake Notes, v. 36, nos. 1–2, p. 9–14.

Burk, C. A., 1965, Geology of the Alaska Peninsula—island arc and continental margin: Geol. Soc. America Mem. 99, pt. 1, 250 p.

Carey, S. W., 1958, The tectonic approach to continental drift, in Continental drift—a symposium: Hobart, Australia, Tasmania Univ. Geol. Dept. [1956], p. 177–355.

Clark, D. W., 1966, Perspectives in the prehistory of Kodiak Island, Alaska: Am. Antiquity, v. 31, no. 3, p. 358–371.

Coats, R. R., 1962, Magma type and crustal structure in the Aleutian Arc, in The crust of the Pacific Basin: Am. Geophys. Union. Geophys. Mon. 6, p. 92–109.

Coleman, J. M., and Smith, W. G., 1964, Late Recent rise of sea level: Geol. Soc. Am. Bull., v. 75, no. 9, p. 833–840.

Curray, J. R., 1961, Late Quaternary sea level—a discussion: Geol. Soc. Am. Bull., v. 72, no. 11, p. 1707–1712.

Dachnowski-Stokes, A. P., 1941, Peat resources in Alaska: U.S. Dept. Agriculture Tech. Bull. 769, 84 p.

De Laguna, Frederica, 1934, The archaeology of Cook Inlet, Alaska, with a chapter on Skeletal material, by Bruno Oetteking: Philadelphia Univ., Pa., Pennsylvania Press, 263 p.

——— 1956, Chugach prehistory; the archaeology of Prince William Sound, Alaska: Seattle, Washington Univ. Press, 289 p.

Detterman, R. L., and Reed, B. L., 1964, Preliminary map of the geology of the Iliamna quadrangle, Alaska: U.S. Geol. Survey Misc. Geol. Inv. Map I–407, scale 1 : 250,000.

Dietz, R. S., 1961, Continent and ocean basin evolution by spreading of the sea floor: Nature, v. 190, no. 4779, p. 854–857.

Earthquake Research Institute, 1964, Report of the Niigata earthquake of June 16, 1964: Spec. Bull. Tokyo Univ., Earthquake Research Inst., v. 8, 133 p. [In Japanese].

Eckel, E. B., 1967, Effects of the earthquake of March 27, 1964, on air and water transport, communications, and utilities systems in south-central Alaska: U.S. Geol. Survey Prof. Paper 545–B, p. B1–B27.

Evison, F. F., 1963, Earthquakes and faults: Seismol. Soc. America Bull., v. 53, no. 5, p. 873–891.

Ewing, Maurice, Ludwig, W. J., and Ewing, John, 1965, Oceanic structural history of the Bering Sea: Jour. Geophys. Research, v. 70, no. 18, p. 4593–4600.

Fairbridge, R. W., 1961, Eustatic changes in sea level, in Physics and chemistry of the earth: New York, Pergamon Press, v. 4, p. 99–185.

Florensov, N. A., and Solonenko, V. P., eds., 1963, The Gobi-Altai earthquake: Izdatelo Akad. Nauk SSSR, 391 p. [in Russian; English translation, U.S. Dept. of Commerce, 1965.]

Foster, H. L., and Karlstrom, T. N. V., 1967, Ground breakage and associated effects in the Cook Inlet area, Alaska, resulting from the March 27, 1964, earthquake: U.S. Geol. Survey Prof. Paper 543–F, p. F1–F28.

Furumoto, A. S., 1967, Analysis of Rayleigh waves, pt. 2 of Source mechanism of the Alaska earthquake and tsunami of 27 March 1964: Pacific Sci., v. 21, no. 3, p. 311–316.

Gates, G. O., and Gryc, George, 1963, Structure and tectonic history of Alaska: Am. Assoc. Petroleum Geologists Mem. 2, p. 264–277.

Gates, Olcott, and Gibson, W. M., 1956, Interpretation of the configuration of the Aleutian Ridge [Alaska]: Geol. Soc. America Bull., v. 67, no. 2, p. 127–146.

Ghent, E. D., 1965, Comments on phase changes and shallow focus earthquakes: New Zealand Jour. Geology and Geophysics, v. 8, no. 5, p. 820–832.

Grant, U. S., and Higgins, D. F., 1910, Reconnaissance of the geology and mineral resources of Prince William Sound, Alaska: U.S. Geol. Survey Bull. 443, 89 p.

Grantz, Arthur, 1965, Geologic map and cross sections of the Nelchina area, south-central Alaska: U.S. Geol. Survey open-file map, 4 sheets, scale 1:63,360.

———— 1966, Strike-slip faults in Alaska: U.S. Geol. Survey open-file report, 82 p.

Grantz, Arthur, Plafker, George, and Kachadoorian, Reuben, 1964, Alaska's Good Friday earthquake, March 27, 1964, a preliminary geologic evaluation: U.S. Geol. Survey Circ. 491, 35 p.

Griggs, D. T., and Blacic, J. D., 1965, Quartz—anomalous weakness of synthetic crystals: Science, v. 147, no. 3655, p. 292–295.

Griggs, D. T., and Handin, J. W., 1960, Observations on fracture and a hypothesis of earthquakes: Geol. Soc. America Mem. 79, p. 347–363.

Gutenberg, Beno, and Richter, C. F., 1954, Seismicity of the earth and associated phenomena, 2d ed.: Princeton, N.J., Princeton Univ. Press, 310 p.

Hales, A. L., and Asada, T., 1966, Crustal structure in coastal Alaska, in The earth beneath the continents: Am. Geophys. Union Geophys. Mon. 10, p. 420–432.

Hamilton, Warren, and Myers, W. B., 1966, Cenozoic tectonics of the western United States: Reviews of Geophysics, v. 4, no. 4, p. 509–549.

Hanna, G D., 1964, Biological effects of an earthquake: Pacific Discovery, v. 17, no. 6, p. 24–26.

Hansen, W. R., and Eckel, E. B., 1966, A summary description of the Alaska earthquake—its setting and effects, in Hansen, Eckel, and others, The Alaska earthquake, March 27, 1964: Field investigations and reconstruction effort: U.S. Geol. Survey Prof. Paper 541, p. 1–37.

Hatori, Tokutaro, 1965, on the tsunami which accompanied the Niigata earthquake of June 16, 1964—source deformation, propagation, and tsunami run-up: Tokyo Univ., Earthquake Research Inst. Bull., v. 43, no. 1, p. 129–148.

Henderson, J., 1933, The geological aspects of the Hawke's Bay earthquakes [New Zealand]: New Zealand Jour, Sci. Technology, v. 15, no. 1, p. 38–75.

Hess, H. H., 1955, The oceanic crust: Jour. Marine Research, v. 14, no. 4, p. 423–439.

———— 1957, The Vening Meinesz negative gravity anomaly belt of island arcs 1926–56: Koninkl. Nederl. Geol.-Mijnbouwk. Genoot., Verh., Geol. Ser., v. 18, 183–188.

———— 1962, History of ocean basins, in Petrologic studies (Buddington volume): Geol. Soc. America, p. 599–620.

Heusser, C. J., 1960, Late-Pleistocene environments of North Pacific North America—an elaboration of late-glacial and postglacial climatic, physiographic, and biotic changes: Am. Geog. Soc. Spec. Pub. 35, 308 p.

Hoare, J. M., 1961, Geology and tectonic setting of lower Kuskokwim-Bristol Bay region, Alaska: Am. Assoc. Petroleum Geologists Bull., v. 45, no. 5, p. 594–611.

Hodgson, J. H., 1957, Nature of faulting in large earthquakes: Geol. Soc. America Bull., v. 68, no. 5, p. 611–643.

Hopkins, D. M., MacNeil, F. S., Merklin, R. L., and Petrov, O. M., 1965, Quaternary correlations across Bering Strait: Science, v. 147, no. 3662, p. 1107–1114.

Iida, K., 1963, A relation of earthquake energy to tsunami energy and the estimation of the vertical displacement in a tsumami source: Nagoya [Japan] Univ. Inst. Earth Sci., Earth Sci. Jour., v. 11, no. 1, p. 49–67.

Imamura, Akitsune, 1930, Topographical changes accompanying earthquakes or volcanic eruptions: Japan Imperial Earthquake Inv. Comm., Foreign Languages Pubs., no. 25, 143 p.

Inoue, E., 1960, Land deformation in Japan: Japan Geog. Survey Inst. Bull., v. 6, pt. 2–3, p. 73–134.

Jordan, J. N., Lander, J. F. and Black, R. A., 1965, Aftershocks of the 4 February 1965 Rat Island Earthquake: Science, v. 148, no. 3675, p. 1323–1325.

Karlstrom, T. N. V., 1964, Quaternary geology of the Kenai Lowland and glacial history of the Cook Inlet region, Alaska: U.S. Geol. Survey Prof. Paper 443, 69 p.

Kaye, C. A., 1964, The upper limit of barnacles as an index of sea level change on the New England Coast during the past 100 years: Jour. Geology, v. 72, no. 5, p. 580–600.

Kelly, T. E., 1963, Geology and hydrocarbons in Cook Inlet basin, Alaska: Am. Assoc. Petroleum Geologists Mem. 2, p. 278–296.

Lamb, Horace, 1932, Hydrodynamics, 6th ed.: England, Cambridge Univ. Press, 738 p.

Lanphere, M. A., 1966, Potassium-argon ages of Tertiary plutons in the Prince William Sound region, Alaska, in Geological Survey research 1966: U.S. Geol. Survey Prof. Paper 550–D, p. D195–D198.

Lensen, G. J., 1961, Principal horizontal stress directions as an aid to the study of crustal deformation, in A symposium on earthquake mechanism: Ottawa Dominion Observatory Pub., v. 24, no. 10, p. 389–397.

Levin, Betsy, Ives, P. C., Oman, C. L., and Rubin, Meyer, 1965, U.S. Geological Survey radiocarbon dates VIII: Radiocarbon, v. 7, p. 372–398.

Lyell, Sir Charles, 1874, Principles of geology: New York, D. Appleton and Co., v. 2, 652 p.

McCulloch D. S., 1966, Slide-induced waves, seiching, and ground fracturing caused by the earthquake of March 27, 1964, at Kenai Lake, Alaska: U.S. Geol. Survey Prof. Paper 543–A, p. A1–A41.

MacKevett, E. M., Jr., Berg, H. C., Plafker, George, and Jones, D. L., 1964, Preliminary geologic map of the McCarthy C–4 quadrangle, Alaska: U.S. Geol. Survey Misc. Geol. Inv. Map I–423, scale 1:63,360.

Malloy R. J., 1964, Crustal uplift southwest of Montague Island, Alaska: Science, v. 146, no. 3647, p. 1048–1049.

———— 1965, Gulf of Alaska—Seafloor upheaval: Geo-Marine Technology, v. 1, no. 5, p. 22–26.

Marmer, H. A., 1951, Tidal datum planes, revised ed.: U.S. Coast and Geodetic Survey Spec. Pub. 135, 142 p.

Martin, G. C., Johnson, B. L., and Grant, U.S., 1915, Geology and mineral resources of the Kenai Peninsula, Alaska: U.S. Geol. Survey Bull. 587, 243 p.

Martin, G. C., and Katz, F. J., 1912, Geology and coal fields of the lower Matanuska Valley, Alaska: U.S. Geol. Survey Bull. 500, 98 p.

Miller, D. J., 1953, Late Cenozoic marine glacial sediments and marine terraces of Middleton Island, Alaska: Jour. Geology, v. 61, no. 1, p. 17–40.

———1961, Geology of the Katalla district, Gulf of Alaska Tertiary province, Alaska: U.S. Geol. Survey open-file map, scale 1:96,000, 2 sheets.

Miller, D. J., and MacColl, R. S., 1964, Geologic map and sections of the northern part of the McCarthy A–4 quadrangle, Alaska: U.S. Geol. Survey Misc. Geol. Inv. Map I–410, scale 1:63,360.

Miller, D. J., Payne, T. G., and Gryc, George, 1959, Geology of possible petroleum provinces in Alaska, with an annotated bibliography by E. H. Cobb: U.S. Geol. Survey Bull. 1094, 131 p.

Moffit, F. H., 1954, Geology of the Prince William Sound region, Alaska: U.S. Geol. Survey Bull. 989–E, p. 225–310.

Moore, G. W., 1967, Preliminary geologic map of Kodiak Island and vicinity, Alaska: U.S. Geol. Survey open-file map, scale 1:250,000.

Muto, K., 1932, A study of displacements of triangulation points: Tokyo Univ., Earthquake Research Inst. Bull., v. 10, p. 384–392.

Orowan, E., 1960, Mechanism of seismic faulting: Geol. Soc. America Mem. 79, p. 323–345.

Page, R. A., Jr., 1967, Aftershocks as a near-surface phenomenon [abs.]: Am. Geophys. Union Trans., v. 48, no. 1, p. 205.

Pararas-Carayannis, George, 1967, Water waves, pt. 1 of Source mechanism study of the Alaska earthquake and tsunami of 27 March 1964: Pacific Science, v. 21, no. 3, p. 301–310.

Parkin, E. J., 1966, Horizontal displacements, pt. 2 of Alaskan surveys to determine crustal movement: U.S. Coast and Geodetic Survey, 11 p.

Payne, T. G., 1955, Mesozoic and Cenozoic tectonic elements of Alaska: U.S. Geol. Survey Misc. Geol. Inv. Map I–84, scale 1:5,000,000.

Peter, G., Elvers, D., Yellin, M., 1965, Geological structure of Aleutian Trench southwest of Kodiak Island: Jour. Geophys. Research, v. 70, no. 2, p. 353–66.

Plafker, George, 1965, Tectonic deformation associated with the 1964 Alaskan earthquake: Science, v. 148, no. 3678, p. 1675–1687.

———1967a, Geologic map of the Gulf of Alaska Tertiary Province, Alaska: U.S. Geol. Survey Misc. Geol. Inv. Map I–484, scale 1:500,000.

———1967b, Surface faults on Montague Island associated with the 1964 Alaska earthquake: U.S. Geol. Survey Prof. Paper 543–G, p. G1–G42.

Plafker, George, and Kachadoorian, Reuben, 1966, Geologic effects of the March 1964 earthquake and associated seismic sea waves on Kodiak and nearby islands, Alaska: U.S. Geol. Survey Prof. Paper 543–D, p. D1–D46.

Plafker, George, Kachadoorian, Reuben, Eckel, Edwin B., and Mayo, L. R., 1969, Effects of the earthquake of March 27, 1964, on various communities: U.S. Geol. Survey Prof. Paper 542–G, G1–G50.

Plafker, George, and MacNeil, F. S., 1966, Stratigraphic significance of Tertiary fossils from the Orca Group in the Prince William Sound region, Alaska, in Geological Survey research 1966: U.S. Geol. Survey Prof. Paper 550–B, p. B62–B68.

Plafker, George, and Mayo, L. R., 1965, Tectonic deformation, subaqueous slides, and destructive waves associated with the Alaskan March 27, 1964, earthquake—an interim geologic evaluation: U.S. Geol. Survey open-file report, 21 p.

Plafker, George, and Rubin, Meyer, 1967, Vertical tectonic displacements in south-central Alaska during and prior to the great 1964 earthquake: Jour. Geosciences (Osaka City Univ.), v. 10, art. 1–7, p. 1–14.

Press, Frank, 1965, Displacements, strains, and tilts at teleseismic distances: Jour. Geophys. Research, v. 70, no. 10, p. 2395–2412.

Press, Frank, and Jackson, David, 1965, Alaskan earthquake, 27 March 1964—vertical extent of faulting and elastic strain energy release: Science, v. 147, no. 3660, p. 867–868.

Rainey, F. G., and Ralph, Elizabeth, 1959, Radiocarbon dating in the Arctic: Am. Antiquity, v. 24, no. 4, p. 365–374.

Raleigh, C. B., 1967, Tectonic implications of serpentinite weakening: Royal Astron. Soc. Geophys. Jour., v. 14, p. 113–118.

Raleigh, C. B., and Patterson, M. S., 1965, Experimental deformation of serpentinite and its tectonic implications: Jour. Geophys. Research, v. 70, no. 16, p. 3965–3985.

Reid, H. F., 1911, The California earthquake of April 18, 1906. The mechanics of the earthquake: Carnegie Inst. Washington Pub. 87, v. 2, 192 p.

Reimnitz, Erk, 1966, Late Quaternary history and sedimentation of the Copper River Delta and vicinity: California Univ., San Diego, unpublished Ph. D. thesis, 160 p.

Richter, C. F., 1958, Elementary seismology: San Francisco, Calif., W. H. Freeman and Co., 768 p.

Ricketts, E. F., and Calvin, Jack, 1962, Between Pacific tides; an account of the habit and habitats of some 500 of the common, conspicuous seashore invertebrates of the Pacific Coast between Sitka, Alaska, and northern Mexico, 3d ed.: Stanford, Calif., Stanford Univ. Press, 516 p.

Rigg, G. B., and Miller, R. C., 1949, Intertidal plant and animal zonation in the vicinity of Neah Bay, Washington: California Acad. Sci. Proc., 4th ser., v. 26, no. 10, p. 323–351.

Row, R. V., 1966, On the ionospheric long-period acoustic-gravity wave pulse launched by the great Alaskan earthquake of March 1964 [abs.]: Am. Geophys. Union Trans., v. 47, no. 1, p. 51.

Rubin, Meyer, and Alexander, Corrinne, 1958, U.S. Geological Survey radiocarbon dates IV: Science, v. 127, no. 3313, p. 1476–1487.

Saint-Amand, Pierre, 1957, Geological and geophysical synthesis of the tectonics of portions of British Columbia, the Yukon Territory, and Alaska: Geol Soc. America Bull., v. 68, no. 10, p. 1343–1370.

———1961, Los terremotos de mayo – Chile 1960 * * * an eyewitness account of the greatest catastrophe in recent history: China Lake, Calif., Michelson Lab., U.S. Naval Ordnance Test Sta. Tech. Art. 14, 39 p.

Savage, J. C., and Hastie, L. M., 1966, Surface deformation associated with dip-slip faulting: Jour. Geophys. Research, v. 71, no. 20, p. 4897–4904.

Schrader, F. C., 1900, A reconnaissance of a part of Prince William Sound and the Copper River district, Alaska, in 1898: U.S. Geol. Survey 20th Ann. Rept., pt. 7, p. 341–423.

Shor, G. G., Jr., 1962, Seismic refraction studies off the coast of Alaska 1956–1957: Seismol. Soc. America Bull., v. 52, no. 1, p. 37–57.

———1966, Continental margins and island arcs of western North America, in Continental margins and island arcs: Canada Geol. Survey Paper 66–15, p. 126–222.

Small, J. B., 1966, Vertical bench mark displacement, pt. 1 of Alaskan surveys to determine crustal movement: U.S. Coast and Geod. Survey, 24 p.

Stauder, William, 1967, Seismic evidence of present deformation in island arc structures [abs.]: Am. Geophys. Union Trans., v. 48, no. 1, p. 218–219.

Stauder, William, and Bollinger, G. A., 1964, the S wave project for focal mechanism studies—Earthquakes of 1962: Seismol. Soc. America Bull., v. 54, no. 6, pt. B, p. 2199–2208.

———1966, The focal mechanism of the Alaska earthquake of March 28, 1964, and of its aftershock sequence: Jour. Geophys. Research, v. 71, no. 22, p. 5283–5296.

Stephenson, T. A., and Stephenson, Anne, 1949, The universal features of zonation between tide-marks on rocky coasts: Jour. Ecology, v. 37, p. 289–305.

Tarr, R. S., and Martin, Lawrence, 1912, The earthquake at Yakutat Bay, Alaska, in September, 1899, with a preface by G. K. Gilbert: U.S. Geol. Survey Prof. Paper 69, 135 p.

———1914, Alaskan glacier studies of the National Geographic Society in the Yakutat Bay, Prince William Sound and lower Copper River Regions: Washington, D.C., Natl. Geog. Soc., 498 p.

Thorsteinson, F. V., 1965, Effects of the Alaska earthquake on pink and chum salmon runs in Prince William Sound: Auke Bay, Alaska, U.S. Bur. Commercial Fisheries Biol. Lab., 16 p.

Tobin, D. G., and Sykes, L. R., 1966, Relationship of hypocenters of earthquakes to the geology of Alaska: Jour. Geophys. Research, v. 71, no. 6, p. 1659–1667.

Tocher, Don, 1960, The Alaska earthquake of July 10, 1958—Movement on the Fairweather fault and field investigation of southern epicentral region: Seismol. Soc. America Bull., v. 50, no. 2, p. 267–292.

Toksoz, M. N., Ben-Menahem, Ari, and Harkrider, D. G., 1965, Source mechanism of Alaska earthquake from long-period seismic surface waves [abs.]: Am. Geophys. Union Trans., v. 46, no. 1, p. 154.

U.S. Coast and Geodetic Survey, 1964, Tide tables, high and low water predictions, 1964, West Coast North and South America including the Hawaiian Islands: U.S. Coast and Geod. Survey, 224 p.

Vancouver, John, ed., 1801, A voyage of discovery to the North Pacific Ocean and around the world * * * in the years 1790–1795 * * * under the command of Captain George Vancouver * * *, new ed.: London, printed for J. Stockdale, 6 v.

Van Dorn, W. G., 1965, Source mechanism of the tsunami of March 28, 1964, in Alaska: Coastal Eng. Conf., 9th, Lisbon 1964, Proc., p. 166–190.

Vine, F. J., 1966, Spreading of the ocean floor—new evidence: Science, v. 154, no. 3755, p. 1405–1415.

Von Huene, Roland, Shor, G. R., Jr., and Saint-Amand, Pierre, 1966, Active faults and structure of the continental margin in the 1964 Alaskan aftershock sequence area [abs.]: Am. Geophys. Union Trans., v. 47, no. 1, p. 176.

Wahrhaftig, Clyde, 1965, The physiographic provinces of Alaska: U.S. Geol. Survey Prof. Paper 482, 52 p.

Waller, R. M., 1966a, Effects of the earthquake of March 27, 1964 in the Homer area, Alaska with a section on Beach changes on Homer Spit, by K. W. Stanley: U.S. Geol. Survey Prof. Paper 542–D, p. D1–D28.

Waller, R. M., 1966b, Effects of the March 1964 Alaska earthquake on the hydrology of south-central Alaska: U.S. Geol. Survey Prof. Paper 544–A, p. A1–A28.

Wolfe, J. A., Hopkins, D. M., and Leopold, E. B., 1966, Tertiary stratigraphy and paleobotany of the Cook Inlet region, Alaska: U.S. Geol. Survey Prof. Paper 398–A, p. A1–A29.

Wood, F. J., ed., 1966, Operational phases of the Coast and Geodetic Survey program in Alaska for the period March 27 to December 31, 1964, v. 1 of The Prince William Sound, Alaska, earthquake of 1964 and aftershocks: U.S. Coast and Geodetic Survey, 263 p.

Wyss, Max, and Brune, J. N., 1967, The Alaska earthquake of 28 March 1964—A complex multiple rupture: Bull. Seis. Soc. America, v. 57, no. 5, p. 1017–1023.

CLARIFICATIONS

Geology Vol. Page	USGS Page	Column	Line	Remarks
50	I 4	1	21, 22	Later computed as 61.04°N; 147.73°W
54	I 8	2	13	Plates 1 and 2 are Plates A and B, respectively, in Part B, the accompanying map case
82	I 34	2	4	For "frontispiece," read "Figure 11 of previous paper"
83	I 35	Fig. 20	5	For "frontispiece," read "Figure 11 of previous paper"
85	I 37	1	12, 13	For "frontispiece," read "Figure 11 of previous paper"
85	I 37	Fig. 23	2	For "frontispiece," read "Figure 11 of previous paper"
103	I 55	3	4	B.P. (before present)

J. E. CASE*
U.S. GEOLOGICAL SURVEY
D. F. BARNES
U.S. GEOLOGICAL SURVEY

GEORGE PLAFKER
U.S. GEOLOGICAL SURVEY
S. L. ROBBINS
U.S. GEOLOGICAL SURVEY

Reprinted with minor changes from
U.S. Geological Survey Professional Paper 543-C,
"Gravity Survey and Regional Geology of the
Prince William Sound Epicentral Region, Alaska"

Gravity Survey and Regional Geology of the Prince William Sound Epicentral Region

ABSTRACT

Sedimentary and volcanic rocks of Mesozoic and early Tertiary age form a roughly arcuate pattern in and around Prince William Sound, the epicentral region of the Alaska earthquake of 1964. These rocks include the Valdez Group, a predominantly slate and graywacke sequence of Jurassic and Cretaceous age, and the Orca Group, a younger sequence of early Tertiary age. The Orca consists of a lower unit of dense—average 2.87 g per cm³ (grams per cubic centimeter)—pillow basalt and greenstone intercalated with sedimentary rocks and an upper unit of lithologically variable sandstone interbedded with siltstone or argillite. Densities of the clastic rocks in both the Valdez and Orca Groups average about 2.69 g per cm³. Granitic rocks of relatively low density (2.62 g per cm³) cut the Valdez and Orca Groups at several localities.

Both the Valdez and the Orca Groups were complexly folded and extensively faulted during at least three major episodes of deformation: an early period of Cretaceous or early Tertiary orogeny, a second orogeny that probably culminated in late Eocene or early Oligocene time and was accompanied or closely followed by emplacement of granitic batholiths, and a third episode of deformation that began in late Cenozoic time and continued intermittently to the present.

About 500 gravity stations were established in the Prince William Sound region in conjunction with postearthquake geologic investigations. Simple Bouguer anomaly contours trend approximately parallel to the arcuate geologic structure around the sound. Bouguer anomalies decrease northward from +40 mgal (milligals) at the southwestern end of Montague Island to −70 mgal at College and Harriman Fiords. Most of this change may be interpreted as a regional gradient caused by thickening of the continental crust. Superimposed on the gradient is a prominent gravity high of as much as 65 mgal that extends from Elrington Island on the southwest, across Knight and Glacier Islands to the Ellamar Peninsula and Valdez on the northeast. This high coincides with the wide belt of greenstone and pillow basalt of the Orca Group and largely reflects the high density of these volcanic rocks. A large low in the east-central part of the sound is inferred to have a composite origin, and results from the combined effects of low-density sedimentary and granitic rocks.

The Prince William Sound gravity high extends southwest-northeast without major horizontal offset for more than 100 miles. Thus the belt of volcanic rocks causing the high constitutes a major virtually continuous geologic element of south-central Alaska.

INTRODUCTION

Following the Alaska earthquake of March 27, 1964, the U.S. Geological Survey made an intensive investigation of the effects of the earthquake in the Prince William Sound region where the epicenter was located. Concurrent investigations included studies of the regional geology, changes of land level, faulting, and effects of waves on shorelines which were summarized by Plafker and Mayo (1965). At the same time, this gravity survey, mentioned briefly by Barnes and Allen (1965), was conducted in order to establish the regional geologic and tectonic setting of the earthquake. Geologic sections of this report were prepared by Plafker and Case, the gravity sections by Case, Barnes, and Robbins.

STRATIGRAPHY

The geologic map of Prince William Sound (fig. 1) has been generalized and modified from published small-scale geologic maps compiled by Grant and Higgins (1910) and Moffit (1954). Structural data were gained from reconnaissance studies by George Plafker, L. R. Mayo, and J. E. Case in 1964. Some geologic details on Knight Island are based on recent mapping by Richter (1965). The ages of the

*Now with the University of Missouri.

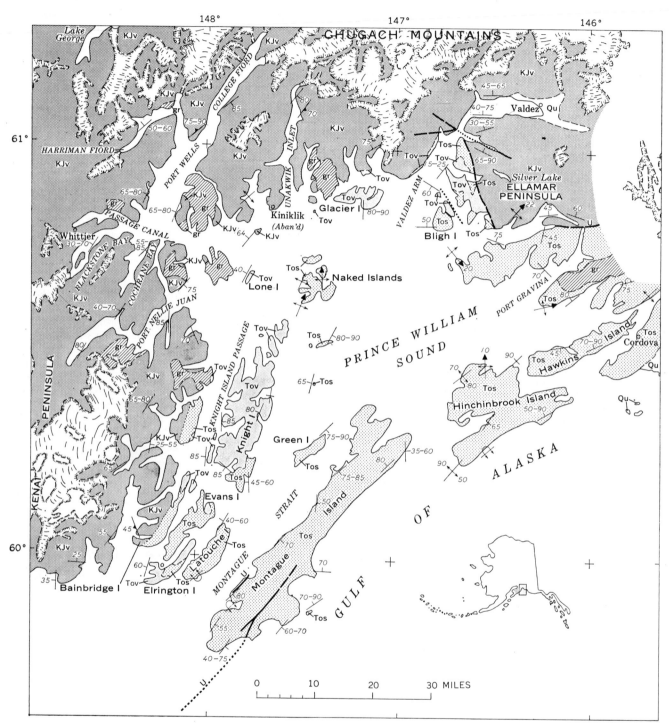

Geology compiled from Moffit (1954) and Grant and
Higgins (1910) supplemented with reconnaissance
mapping by George Plafker, L. R. Mayo, and
J. E. Case during 1964

1.—Generalized geologic map of the

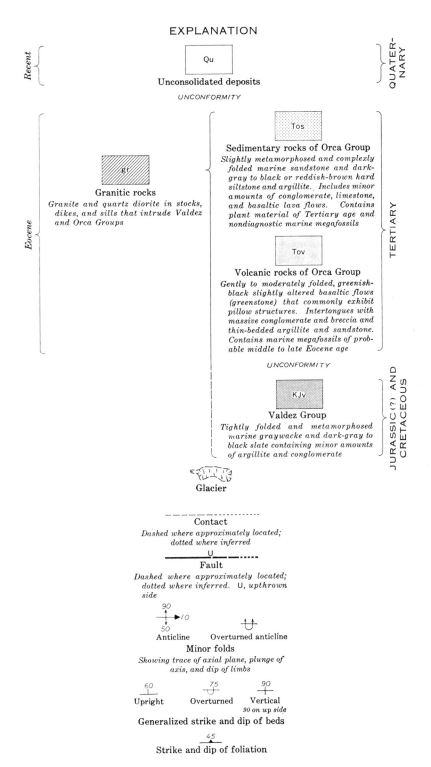

EXPLANATION

Recent

Qu

Unconsolidated deposits

UNCONFORMITY

Eocene

gr

Granitic rocks

Granite and quartz diorite in stocks, dikes, and sills that intrude Valdez and Orca Groups

Tos

Sedimentary rocks of Orca Group

Slightly metamorphosed and complexly folded marine sandstone and dark-gray to black or reddish-brown hard siltstone and argillite. Includes minor amounts of conglomerate, limestone, and basaltic lava flows. Contains plant material of Tertiary age and nondiagnostic marine megafossils

Tov

Volcanic rocks of Orca Group

Gently to moderately folded, greenish-black slightly altered basaltic flows (greenstone) that commonly exhibit pillow structures. Intertongues with massive conglomerate and breccia and thin-bedded argillite and sandstone. Contains marine megafossils of probable middle to late Eocene age

UNCONFORMITY

KJv

Valdez Group

Tightly folded and metamorphosed marine graywacke and dark-gray to black slate containing minor amounts of argillite and conglomerate

QUATER-NARY

TERTIARY

JURASSIC (?) AND CRETACEOUS

Glacier

- - - - - - - - - - - - - - - - -
Contact
Dashed where approximately located; dotted where inferred

⎯⎯⎯ U ⎯ ⎯ · · · · ·
Fault
Dashed where approximately located; dotted where inferred. U, upthrown side

90
→ 10
50
Anticline   Overturned anticline
Minor folds
Showing trace of axial plane, plunge of axis, and dip of limbs

60   75   90
Upright   Overturned   Vertical
90 on up side
Generalized strike and dip of beds

45
Strike and dip of foliation

Prince William Sound region, Alaska.

Valdez and Orca Groups have been revised by reinterpretation of the collections from the Valdez Group and by studies of a new fossil collection from the Orca Group (Plafker and MacNeil, 1966).

The geologic units in Prince William Sound shown on figure 1 include: (1) the Valdez Group, a sequence of eugeosynclinal clastic rocks of Jurassic(?) and Cretaceous age; (2) the Orca Group, a sequence of early Tertiary age which can be subdivided, in a general way, into a lower predominantly volcanic unit and an upper predominantly sedimentary unit; (3) bodies of granitic rocks which intrude both the Valdez and Orca Groups; and (4) unconsolidated continental and marine deposits of Quaternary age.

VALDEZ GROUP

The Valdez Group includes the oldest bedded rocks exposed in the Prince William Sound region. As defined by Schrader (1900, p. 408), the Valdez is a lithologically monotonous sequence of slate, argillite, and metamorphosed graywacke that is exposed along the northern and western shores of the sound and also underlies much of the adjacent Chugach and Kenai Mountains. The sequence is characterized by thin to thick beds of light-gray or tan-weathering poorly sorted sandstone of graywacke type which is rhythmically interbedded with thin-bedded, finely laminated dark-gray to black argillite and slate. In the vicinity of granitic intrusive rocks, the slate and argillite are locally altered to phyllite and the graywacke to semischist. Thin units of stretched pebble or cobble conglomerate and lenses of altered basaltic flows or intrusives occur locally within the sequence.

The sedimentary sequence assigned to the Valdez Group is probably tens of thousands of feet thick. The thickness cannot be accurately measured because the sequence lacks key beds and the units are duplicated and interrupted by complex folding and faulting.

Determinative fossils from the Valdez Group, and probably equivalent sequences elsewhere along the margin of the Gulf of Alaska, include *Inoceramus* and *Aucella* that indicate a Jurassic(?) and Cretaceous age for the Valdez (D. L. Jones, oral commun., Nov. 24, 1965).

ORCA GROUP

The predominantly volcanic unit that forms the lower part of the Orca Group crops out in a discontinuous belt 52 miles long and up to 12 miles wide that trends from the mainland east of Valdez Arm southwestward through Glacier, Lone, Knight, Bainbridge, Evans, and Elrington Islands (fig. 1). The unit consists principally of slightly altered greenish-black dense basaltic lava flows, pillow lavas, flow breccias, and coarser textured diabase intrusives which have collectively been termed "greenstone." Most of the flows are characterized by strikingly well formed pillow structures. The volcanic rocks intertongue with thick beds of conglomeratic argillite, conglomerate, dark-gray siltstone or argillite, and graywacke sandstone. The thickness of the unit differs markedly along the length of the outcrop belt. Along the southeast shore of Valdez Arm it is several thousand feet thick (Capps and Johnson, 1915, p. 45). The greatest thickness of the unit probably occurs on and near Knight Island. The volcanic rocks dip 40°–80° W. across most of an outcrop belt as much as 11 miles wide. The breadth and dips indicate an apparent thickness of about 40,000 feet, but it is entirely possible that there has been significant repetition by folding and faulting. Marine megafossils collected during the 1964 reconnaissance survey indicate that the volcanic unit is of early Tertiary (probably middle to late Eocene) age (Plafker and MacNeil, 1966).

The predominantly sedimentary unit that comprises the upper part of the Orca Group includes the bedded rocks that occur especially on the eastern and southern shores of the sound and on the islands of the central part of the sound (fig. 1). In its gross aspects the unit is distinguished from the Valdez Group by a somewhat more variable lithology and a generally lower degree of metamorphism. The sequence consists mainly of thin to thick beds of graywacke sandstone, but also includes light-colored arkosic, carbonaceous, tuffaceous, calcareous and conglomeratic sandstones. The sandstone commonly is interbedded with dark-gray to black or reddish-brown dense hard siltstone or argillite which locally contains abundant carbonized plant remains. Minor amounts of light-gray-weathering limestone occur as thin beds and concretions within the siltstone or argillite. Tabular and lenticular masses of basaltic lavas are locally interbedded with the clastic rocks, most notably on Hinchinbrook Island and the adjacent mainland to the east. The unit is at least several thousand feet thick, but complex folding and faulting preclude a reliable measurement.

The only fossils diagnostic of age that have been obtained from the sedimentary unit are *Alnus* pollen that indicates a post-Mesozoic age (W. R. Evitt, written commun., Nov. 10, 1964). The unit overlies, and probably is in part interbedded with, the volcanic sequence of the Orca Group from which lower Tertiary fossils have been collected.

GRANITIC ROCKS

Granitic rocks intrude the Valdez Group at numerous localities in the northwestern part of Prince William Sound, and a single large intrusive mass cuts the Orca Group on the mainland in the eastern part of the sound. The intrusive rocks consist mainly of pale-pink to pinkish-gray porphyritic biotite granite and light-gray hornblende-biotite quartz diorite. The granite body that cuts the Orca Group on the mainland in the eastern part of the sound can be no older than the rocks it intrudes (early Tertiary) and may be slightly younger. The remaining granitic bodies that intrude the Valdez Group are lithologically similar and probably belong to the same epoch of intrusion, although the available data do not preclude a pre-Orca age.

UNCONSOLIDATED DEPOSITS

The Mesozoic and Tertiary rocks of the Prince William Sound region are overlain with marked angular unconformity by nearly flat-lying fluvial, glacial, and marine deposits of gravel, sand, mud, and till. The various types of these unconsolidated deposits are not differentiated on figure 1.

ROCK DENSITIES

The densities of approximately 50 hand specimens representing the major lithologic units (except the unconsolidated sediments) were measured by comparing their weight in air and water (table 1). No effort was made to determine the effect of porosity on the measured densities, but tests of the influence of porosity on densities of similar rocks from other parts of Alaska have shown that the effect is negligible.

The heaviest rocks in the assemblage are volcanic rocks of the Orca Group and the lightest are the granitic intrusive rocks. The sampling is not sufficiently representative to establish definitely the lack of density contrast between the Orca sedimentary rocks and the older, more metamorphosed Valdez sedimentary rocks. However, seven slate samples from the combined groups had an average density of 2.74 g per cm^3 (grams per cubic centimeter), whereas 17 argillite and graywacke samples averaged 2.67 g per cm^3. Furthermore, four metagraywacke samples from the Valdez Group averaged 2.69 against 2.66 for the four less-metamorphosed graywacke samples from the Orca Group. Thus, overall densities of the two formations would depend on the relative abundance of these rock types. No samples were obtained from the Quaternary deposits which probably have an average density of about 2 g per cm^3.

TABLE 1.—*Densities of Prince William Sound rock units*

Rock unit	Specimens	Densities (g per cm³)		
		Minimum	Maximum	Average
Granite	8	2.58	2.69	2.62
Sedimentary rocks of Orca Group	16	2.63	2.75	2.69
Volcanic rocks of Orca Group	8	2.78	2.96	2.87
Sedimentary rocks of Valdez Group	10	2.64	2.74	2.69

STRUCTURE

The Valdez Group was intensely folded and faulted during a major period of orogeny which is tentatively placed in the time interval from Early Cretaceous to early Tertiary. The strike of bedding planes and the trend of fold axes are almost east-west in the region east of Valdez Arm, and the trend swings abruptly southwestward in the region west of the arm. Folds are characteristically tightly appressed and overturned toward the south; drag folds and minor thrust faults are common.

A second major period of orogeny that probably culminated in late Eocene or early Oligocene time (Plafker and MacNeil, 1966) complexly folded and faulted the Orca Group and intensified the deformation of older rocks. It was accompanied by, or closely followed by, emplacement of granitic batholiths. The strike of bedding planes and fold axes approximately parallels the structural trends of the older rocks, but they are notably divergent at many localities. The folds range from open to tightly appressed and locally are overturned both towards the north and south. They are of small amplitude and lateral extent and are complicated by intricate drag folding and minor thrust faults.

The most recent period of deformation, which has continued intermittently since late Cenozoic time, is attested by the uplift of the adjacent Chugach and Kenai Mountains, by the frequent earthquakes in the region, and by recent surface faulting.

All the rocks of the Prince William Sound region are intensely fractured and complexly faulted. The major lineaments show up on aerial photographs as conspicuous linear depressions and have been delineated in photogeological studies by Condon and Cass (1958) and Condon (1965). Two preexisting faults that displace sedimentary rocks of the Orca Group on Montague Island (fig. 1) were reactivated during the March 27 earthquake (Plafker, 1965). The only faults thus far recognized in the region that juxtapose lithologically distinctive sequences are in the Valdez Arm area (fig. 1) where rocks of the Valdez Group have been thrust from the northeast over the younger rocks of the Orca Group (Capps and Johnson, 1915, p. 62–63). Topographic and geologic evidence suggests the presence of major faults at other places where

contact relationships are obscured by the lack of key beds, the presence of brecciation and shearing associated with minor folding and faulting, and the extensive areas covered by water, unconsolidated deposits, or vegetation. According to Moffit (1954, p. 275), there are no known depositional contacts between the Valdez and Orca Groups anywhere in Prince William Sound.

At least seven major shear zones as much as 1,000 feet wide transect the area mapped by Richter (1965, p. 14) on Knight Island. Richter reports that there is no good evidence to indicate the sense or motion

along the shear zones, but left-lateral strike-slip movement of as much as half a mile is weakly suggested by the supposed dislocation of a coarse-grained gabbro body along one of the zones.

On Knight Island the thick sequence of volcanic rocks dips westward beneath probably older rocks of the Valdez Group which crop out west of Knight Island Passage. Here, the structural relationships suggest the possibility that the two units may be separated by a westward-dipping overthrust concealed beneath Knight Island Passage.

GRAVITY

Gravity was measured at approximately 500 stations within the sound (fig. 2). Most of the measurements were made with LaCoste and Romberg portable geodetic meter G–17, but approximately 75 measurements were made with a World-Wide meter. The measurements are based on absolute gravity values of 981,954.90 mgal beneath bench mark "A71" at Cordova Post Office, 982,008.00 mgal at bench mark "H11" in Valdez, and 981,921.30 mgal at bench mark "L31" in Anchorage that were established by at least three postquake ties to the North American Standardization Pendulum station (Woollard and Rose, 1963) at Fairbanks. These values differ by as much as 0.5 mgal from previous values measured near the stations established by Thiel and others (1958) prior to the earthquake. These deviations reflect small differences in location, adjustments in the North American gravity network, and changes caused by the Alaska earthquake (Barnes, 1966). During the survey,

float-plane flights were used to establish 10 subsidiary base stations within the sound. Most of the remaining measurements were made at shoreline points reached by small-boat traverses. Base stations were occupied at intervals of 1–4 days. A few inland stations were reached by automobile or aircraft trips. The drift and calibration characteristics of meter G–17 are such that the accuracy of 95 percent of observed gravity values should be better than 0.2 mgal. Contouring in the water-covered parts of Prince William Sound was helped by surface-ship gravity measurements made by the U.S. Coast and Geodetic Survey ship *Surveyor*. W. H. Bastian and L. R. Mayo assisted in the collection of the gravity data, and L. J. LaPointe made some of the computations.

Most of the gravity stations were located on beaches or rocks along the shoreline. Elevation control was obtained by measuring the height of the station above water level and making a tide correction to obtain an elevation relative to

mean sea level. A few stations were occupied at tidal bench marks and a few at geodetic bench marks established prior to the earthquake. Elevations at bench marks with respect to mean sea level had changed, owing to the tectonic deformation that accompanied the earthquake, so corrections to postearthquake mean sea level were required for these stations. Elevations of all shoreline stations are probably correct to within 3 feet, and the elevations of the few stations not on the seacoast should be correct to within 20 feet. Location control was provided by topographic maps of the Geological Survey, scale 1:63,360. Simple Bouguer anomalies were computed with a reduction factor corresponding to a density of 2.67 g per cm³. Simple Bouguer anomaly values are probably accurate to within about 1 mgal. Terrain corrections were made for a few stations close to the line $A-A'$ (fig. 3) and ranged from 0.2 to 13.5 mgal for terrain through zone O of Hayford-Bowie (Swick, 1942).

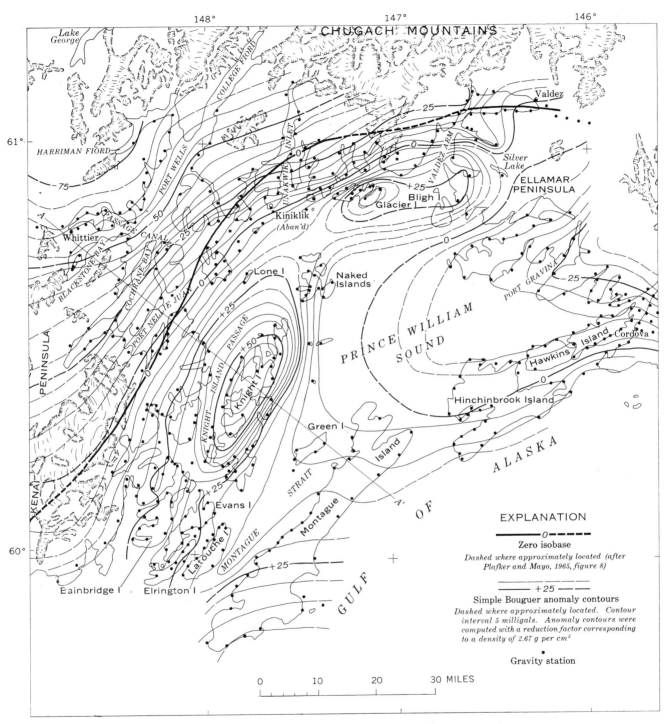

2.—Simple Bouguer anomaly map, Prince William Sound region, Alaska.

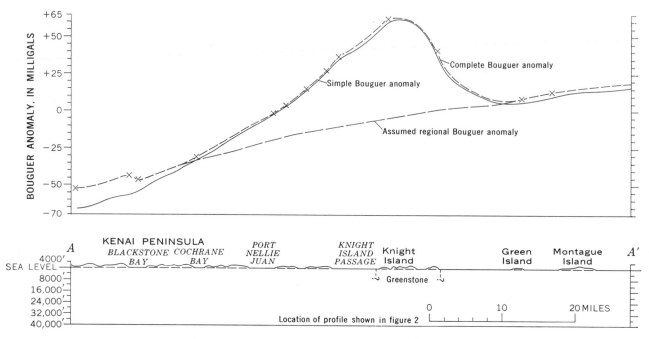

3.—Gravity anomalies and profile across Prince William Sound.

GENERAL FEATURES OF THE GRAVITY MAP

The simple Bouguer anomaly contours indicate a general trend from positive values over the Alaskan Continental Shelf to negative values on the mainland. Values are as high as +40 mgal at the southwestern part of Montague Island and decrease to −70 mgal at College and Harriman Fiords (fig. 2). Contours are crudely arcuate around Prince Willian Sound, roughly paralleling the dominant trend of the geologic structure. Superimposed on this regional pattern are the arcuate Prince William Sound gravity high, which is largest over Knight Island, and the broad gravity low covering Port Gravina and the southeastern part of the sound. The high coincides with a belt of greenstone and pillow basalt and is inferred to be caused by these rocks. The low is probably caused by a thick accumulation of recent sedimentary deposits, a granitic intrusive rock, and, in some areas, terrain effects. In part the low is an "apparent" low due to the combined effect of the high to the

northwest and the regional gradient. No other major correlations between the pattern of gravity anomalies and the mapped geologic features are apparent at this stage of interpretation.

The new data provide a more complete gravity map of the Prince William Sound area than was available from the limited number of measurements made by Thiel and others (1959) which served as the basis for earlier Alaskan gravity maps (Woollard and others, 1960, fig. 2; Ivanhoe, 1961). These maps showed the high gravity values in the southern part of the sound and the low values in the Chugach Mountains. However, neither the magnitude nor the estent of the Prince William Sound high to the north and northeast was recognized, although Woollard and others correctly interpreted the anomaly as being caused by mafic rock (1960, p. 1029). Furthermore, we have measured lower gravity values in the Chugach Mountains than did Thiel's group, so the gradient on the northwest side of Prince William Sound high is steeper, and causes a

much larger gravity difference than had been previously indicated by Woollard and others (1960). Between Knight Island and Harriman Fiord there is a total change of 135 mgal in 40 miles, in contrast to the change of about 60 mgal shown by Woollard and others. Between College Fiord and Kiniklik (near a low part of the Prince William Sound positive anomaly) there is a change of 70 mgal in 20 miles, in contrast to the change of about 50 mgal shown by Woollard and others.

The zero isobase separating the areas of subsidence and uplift during the Alaska earthquake of March 27, 1964 (Plafker, 1965, fig. 2; Plafker and Mayo, 1965, fig. 8) approximately coincides with the steepest part of the gradient along the northwest side of the sound and locally parallels the gravity contours. This relationship could be purely coincidental, or it could be that the gradient represents, at least in part, a fault or hinge line at depth along which movement occurred during the earthquake. Press and Jackson (1965, p. 867) have postulated a near-vertical fault which lies within 15 kilometers of the surface beneath the zero isobase and extends to a depth of 100–200 km. However, such a fault could explain only a part of the gradient on the north side of Knight Island, and its postulated configuration appears to be contrary to most of the available geologic and seismologic data (Plafker, 1965, p. 1686).

The large steep gradient on the south side of the island suggests that the relatively dense greenstones are the real cause of the Knight Island anomaly. Such interpretation, based on observed geology and measured density variations, seems preferable in view of the data presently available, and it forms the basis of the remaining discussion. However, future data may show that some of the Prince William Sound anomalies are caused by tectonic features that have not yet been recognized.

REGIONAL GRAVITY GRADIENT

In order to delineate the regional gravity field, which is presumed to reflect variations in crustal thickness and density, the local anomalies due to the greenstone belt must be removed by analytical or graphical methods. Conversely, in order to isolate the anomaly caused by the greenstone belt, a regional gravity gradient must be removed. Obviously, a unique solution in removal of either the local anomaly or the regional is impossible, but reasonable approximations can be made for both the regional and local anomalies.

Relationships between local geology, simple Bouguer anomaly, and complete Bouguer anomaly along a profile extending from southeast of Montague Island to the head of Passage Canal are shown in figure 3. The complete Bouguer anomaly profile is approximate: values at stations near the line of

profile for which terrain corrections were made were projected to the line of profile. The complete Bouguer anomaly profile shows a regional gravity gradient that is nearly linear or slightly convex upward. For the following analysis, it is assumed that the regional gravity gradient is determined by the complete Bouguer gravity values at Montague Island and at the Kenai Peninsula. The assumed regional gradient between these points is shown by the long-dashed line (fig. 3). Data obtained from the U.S. Coast and Geodetic Survey ship *Surveyor* on the Continental Shelf and by Thiel and others (1959) at Middleton Island, about 50 miles southeast of Montague Island, suggest that approximately the same regional gradient extends to the continental slope. The gradient may be assumed to represent a gradual increase in crustal thickness from the continental margin to the northeast side of the sound.

Woollard and others (1960) showed a similar gravity gradient and inferred increase in crustal thickness from about 24 km at Middleton Island to 33 km at Cordova and 37 km under the Chugach Mountains on their north-south profile through Middleton Island, Cordova, and Valdez. However, from reinterpretation of seismic data obtained by Tatel and Tuve (1956) from shots fired in College Fiord, Woollard and others believe that the crust is thicker beneath Prince William Sound than the gravity data suggested. They derived a crustal thickness in Prince William Sound of about 50 km. The traveltime curves show high velocities east of Valdez, suggestive of mafic rocks where our new data show a possible extension of the Prince William Sound gravity high.

Analysis of the new gravity data indicates that the regional gravity gradient is reasonably consistent with a change in crustal thickness

from about 50 km near College Fiord (Woollard and others, 1960) to about 20 km near the continental margin, as measured by Shor (1962) southeast of Kodiak.

PORT GRAVINA GRAVITY LOW

The broad gravity low in the southeastern part of the Prince William Sound is best developed at the eastern end of Port Gravina. There it is in part related to the granitic pluton that extends from Port Gravina eastward into the Chugach Mountains (fig. 1), although the outcrop area is small in comparison to the area of the gravity anomaly. However, the anomaly probably also reflects a thick accumulation of poorly consolidated sediments in the central and eastern parts of the sound. Its apparent extension into Montague Strait is influenced by terrain effects. Sample terrain corrections for two stations along the steep shoreline of the strait showed that the complete Bouguer anomalies at these stations are as much as 10 mgal higher than the simple Bouguer values contoured on the map. Corrections of this magnitude would tend to straighten the +15 and +20-mgal contours in Montague Strait and to eliminate much but not all of the tonguelike low shown by the contours on figure 2. The gravity low is also an apparent low imposed by the Prince William Sound high on the regional gravity gradient.

The low which would remain in Montague Strait after terrain corrections and much of the low which occupies the central and southeastern part of the sound in part represent thick, poorly consolidated glacial and marine sedimentary deposits. The average water depths in the central and eastern parts of the sound are shallow, about 300–800 feet, whereas water depths of 1,000–2,000 feet are common in the northwestern part of the sound and in some of the narrower passages and fiords. If the sound were once glaciated to a depth equivalent to the present water depths in the fiords, poorly consolidated material as much as 1,000–1,500 feet thick may be present at the site of the gravity low. However, sparker data obtained from the U.S. Coast and Geodetic Survey ship *Surveyor* (R. C. Malloy, oral commun., 1964, 1965) suggest that 500 feet of sediment may be the maximum accumulation in most of the southeastern part of the sound. This thickness would account for not more than 10 mgal of the gravity low.

The main cause of the gravity low in the southeastern part of the sound is thus presumed to be the granitic rocks which crop out near Port Gravina and which probably extend westward beneath the cover of sedimentary rocks. Although the one sample obtained from the Port Gravina pluton had a density as high as the average of the Valdez and Orca sedimentary rocks, samples from plutons on the opposite side of the sound indicate that the average density of the Prince William Sound granite is about

0.07 g per cm³ less than the densities of the Valdez and Orca sedimentary rocks. The absence of gravity lows over the intrusive bodies on the northwestern side of the sound suggests that they are smaller and that the Port Gravina intrusive is larger and possibly less dense. However, terrain corrections and precise contouring might also show small negative anomalies associated with the intrusive rocks on the northwest.

PRINCE WILLIAM SOUND GRAVITY HIGH

When the assumed regional Bouguer anomaly values are subtracted from the observed Bouguer anomaly profile, a residual positive anomaly of as much as 67 mgal can be isolated over the Knight Island greenstone (fig. 4). The residual anomaly is asymmetrical: the gradient on the southeast flank is much steeper than on the northwest flank of the anomaly. The steepness of the gradient on the southeast flank indicates that most of the relatively dense rock mass causing the anomaly probably lies at shallow depth— within the upper 10 km of the crust.

The greenstones and pillow basalts in general dip steeply. Richter (1965) has postulated that the belt of greenstone cut by shear zones may represent a complex anticlinal structure whose axis follows the approximate centerline of Knight Island. The breadth of exposures on Knight Island is about 8 miles, or 42,000 feet, and the sequence probably extends downward at least an equivalent amount if the steep dips are maintained at depth.

Available density measurements for rocks in Prince William Sound indicate that the average density of the greenstones is greater than that of the graywacke, slate, and granite with which the greenstones are in contact (table 1). The average density of the greenstone is 2.87 g per cm³, the slate and graywacke is 2.69 g per cm³, and the granitic rock is 2.60 g per cm³. Thus the density contrast between greenstone and the adjacent rocks is about 0.1–0.2 g per cm³.

A simplified model of the greenstone mass on Knight Island has a computed gravitational effect which approximates the residual anomaly (fig. 4). In construction of the model and computation of its gravitational effects, the following

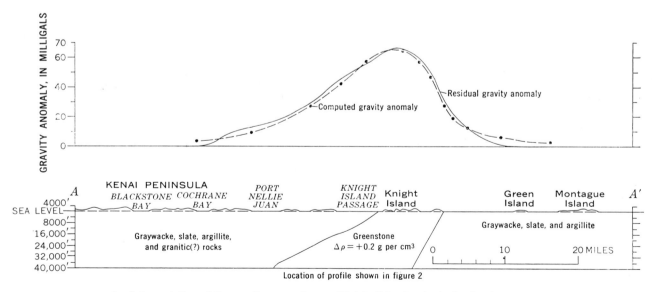

4.—Interpretation of the gravity anomaly over Knight Island. Δρ is the density contrast.

assumptions were made: (1) the source of the anomaly is two-dimensional, that is, its length is great with respect to its breadth; (2) the average density contrast of the greenstone mass is about +0.2 g per cm³; (3) the width of the anomalous mass at the surface is about 40,000 feet; (4) it extends downward to a depth of about 40,000 feet below sea level, and (5) the contacts of the anomalous mass dip northwest, and the northwestern contact dips more gently than the southeastern. Thus the model represents a mass whose breadth increases with depth. This configuration is consistent with Richter's hypothesis that the volcanic rocks form a major anticline.

Gravitational effects of the simplified model were computed by the method described by Hubbert (1948). The computed effects approximately coincide with the residual anomaly, both in total amplitude and in gradient. Slight changes in density contrast or in dimensions of the mass would produce an exact match, but these changes are not warranted because the dimensional assumptions and the regional gradient are more uncertain. The significant facts are: (1) a large greenstone mass is the most probable cause of the Knight Island anomaly; (2) its density is slightly greater than that of the adjacent rocks; (3) the mass probably extends to great depth, 40,000 feet or more below sea level; and (4) the gravity data indicate that faults may border both flanks of the Knight Island greenstone.

The gravity highs form a continuous belt from the greenstone outcrops on Elrington and Latouche Islands, through the area of maximum width of outcrop on Knight Island, to another high over the greenstone outcrops on Glacier Island, and then across Valdez Arm to the outcrops on Ellamar Peninsula. No large greenstone outcrops have been mapped northeast of the Ellamar outcrops, and a Bouguer gravity measurement of −1.3 mgal at the southeast end of Silver Lake suggests that the greenstones there are deeper and smaller. However, uncompleted surveys show positive gravity values 10 miles east of Valdez on the Richardson Highway, and 40–50 miles east of Valdez along the Tasnuna River up to its junction with the Copper River which could be continuous with the Prince William Sound high. If so, the incomplete data thus suggest that the belt of gravity highs may extend for 150 miles from Elrington Island at the coast to a point on the Copper River, where it is more than halfway across the Chugach Mountains. The computed profile (fig. 4) crosses the greenstone belt where the gravity anomaly associated with it is largest. Although the magnitude of the high varies along the belt, the fact that there are no major horizontal offsets of the anomaly northeast of Elrington Island suggests that no major post-Eocene faults having strike-slip displacement measureable in tens of miles obliquely cut the belt of gravity highs. The gravity survey has thus shown that the greenstone belt, which may be part of an ancient volcanic arc, constitutes one of the more continuous and significant geologic units along the Gulf of Alaska coastline.

REFERENCES CITED

Barnes, D. F., 1966, Gravity changes during the Alaskan earthquake: Jour. Geophys. Research, v. 71, no. 2, p. 451–456.

Barnes, D. F., and Allen, R. V., 1965, Progress report on Alaskan gravity surveys [abs.]: Alaskan Sci. Conf., 15th, College, Alaska, 1964, Proc., p. 165–166.

Capps, S. R., and Johnson, B. L., 1915, The Ellamar district, Alaska: U.S. Geol. Survey Bull. 605, 125 p.

Condon, W. H., 1965, Map of eastern Prince William Sound area, Alaska, showing fracture traces inferred from aerial photographs: U.S. Geol. Survey Misc. Geol. Inv. Map I–453, scale 1:125,000.

Condon, W. H., and Cass, J. T., 1958, Map of a part of the Prince William Sound area, Alaska, showing linear geologic features as shown on aerial photographs: U.S. Geol. Survey Misc. Geol. Inv. Map I–273, scale 1:125,000.

Grant, U. S., and Higgins, D. F., 1910, Reconnaissance of the geology and mineral resources of Prince William Sound, Alaska: U.S. Geol. Survey Bull. 443, 89 p.

Hubbert, M. K., 1948, A line-integral method of computing the gravimetric effect of two-dimensional masses: Geophysics, v. 13, no. 2, p. 215–225.

Ivanhoe, L. F., 1961, Bouguer gravity map of Alaska [abs.]: Am. Assoc. Petroleum Geologists Bull., v. 45, no. 1, p. 128–129.

Moffit, F. H., 1954, Geology of the Prince William Sound region, Alaska: U.S. Geol. Survey Bull. 989–E, p. 225–310.

Plafker, George, 1965, Tectonic deformation associated with the 1964 Alaska earthquake: Science, v. 148, no. 3678, p. 1675–1687.

Plafker, George, and MacNeil, F. S., 1966, Stratigraphic significance of Tertiary fossils from the Orca Group (Mesozoic), Prince William Sound, Alaska: U.S. Geol. Survey Prof. Paper 550–B, p. B62–B68.

Plafker, George, and Mayo, L. R., 1965, Tectonic deformation, subaqueous slides, and destructive waves associated with the Alaskan March 27, 1964, earthquake—an interim geologic evaluation: U.S. Geol. Survey open-file report, 21 p.

Press, Frank, and Jackson, David, 1965, Alaskan earthquake, 27 March 1964 —Vertical extent of faulting and elastic strain energy release: Science, v. 147, no. 3660, p. 867–868.

Richter, D. H., 1965, Geology and mineral deposits of central Knight Island, Prince William Sound, Alaska: Alaska Div. Mines and Minerals Geol. Rept. 16, 37 p.

Schrader, F. C., 1900, A reconnaissance of a part of Prince William Sound and the Copper River district, Alaska, in 1898: U.S. Geol. Survey Ann. Rept. 20, pt. 7, p. 341–423.

Schrader, F. C., and Spencer, A. C., 1901, The geology and mineral resources of a portion of the Copper River dis-

trict, Alaska: U.S. Geol. Survey Spec. Pub., 94 p.

Shor, G. G., Jr., 1962, Seismic refraction studies off the coast of Alaska 1956–1957: Seismol. Soc. America Bull., v. 52, no. 1, p. 37–57.

Swick, C. H., 1942, Pendulum gravity measurements and isostatic reductions: U.S. Coast and Geod. Survey Spec. Pub. 232, 82 p.

Tatel, H. E., and Tuve, M. A., 1956, The earth's crust, seismic studies: Carnegie Inst., Washington, Year Book 1955–1956, p. 81–85.

Thiel, Edward, Ostenso, N. A., Bonini,

W. E., and Woollard, G. P., 1958, Gravity measurements in Alaska: Woods Hole Oceanogr. Inst. Tech. Rept. Ref. 58–54, 104 p.

——1959, Gravity measurements in Alaska: Arctic, v. 12, no. 2, p. 67–76.

Woollard, G. P., Ostenso, N. A., and Thiel, Edward, 1960, Gravity anomalies, crustal structure, and geology in Alaska: Jour. Geophys. Research, v. 65, no. 3, p. 1021–1037.

Woollard, G. P., and Rose, J. C., 1963, International gravity measurements: Wisconsin Univ. Geophys. and Polar Research Center, 518 p.

GEORGE PLAFKER
U.S. GEOLOGICAL SURVEY

Reprinted with minor changes from
U.S. Geological Survey Professional Paper 543-G,
"Surface Faults on Montague Island Associated with the 1964 Alaska Earthquake"

Surface Faults on Montague Island

ABSTRACT

Two reverse faults on southwestern Montague Island in Prince William Sound were reactivated during the earthquake of March 27, 1964. New fault scarps, fissures, cracks, and flexures appeared in bedrock and unconsolidated surficial deposits along or near the fault traces. Average strike of the faults is between N. 37° E. and N. 47° E.; they dip northwest at angles ranging from 50° to 85°. The dominant motion was dip slip; the blocks northwest of the reactivated faults were relatively upthrown, and both blocks were upthrown relative to sea level. No other earthquake faults have been found on land.

The Patton Bay fault on land is a complex system of en echelon strands marked by a series of spectacular landslides along the scarp and (or) by a zone of fissures and flexures on the upthrown block that locally is as much as 3,000 feet wide. The fault can be traced on land for 22 miles, and it has been mapped on the sea floor to the southwest of Montague Island an additional 17 miles. The maximum measured vertical component of slip is 20 to 23 feet and the maximum indicated dip slip is about 26 feet. A left-lateral strike-slip component of less than 2 feet occurs near the southern end of the fault on land where its strike changes from northeast to north. Indirect evidence from the seismic sea waves and aftershocks associated with the earthquake, and from the distribution of submarine scarps, suggests that the faulting on and near Montague Island occurred at the northeastern end of a reactivated submarine fault system that may extend discontinuously for more than 300 miles from Montague Island to the area offshore of the southeast coast of Kodiak Island.

The Hanning Bay fault is a minor rupture only 4 miles long that is marked by an exceptionally well defined almost continuous scarp. The maximum measured vertical component of slip is 16⅓ feet near the midpoint, and the indicated dip slip is about 20 feet. There is a maximum left-lateral strike-slip component of one-half foot near the southern end of the scarp. Warping and extension cracking occurred in bedrock near the midpoint on the upthrown block within about 1,000 feet of the fault scarp.

The reverse faults on Montague Island and their postulated submarine extensions lie within a tectonically important narrow zone of crustal attenuation and maximum uplift associated with the earthquake. However, there are no significant lithologic differences in the rock sequences across these faults to suggest that they form major tectonic boundaries. Their spatial distribution relative to the regional uplift associated with the earthquake, the earthquake focal region, and the epicenter of the main shock suggest that they are probably subsidiary features rather than the causative faults along which the earthquake originated.

Approximately 70 percent of the new breakage along the Patton Bay and the Hanning Bay faults on Montague Island was along obvious preexisting active fault traces. The estimated ages of undisturbed trees on and near the fault trace indicate that no major displacement had occurred on these faults for at least 150 to 300 years before the 1964 earthquake.

INTRODUCTION

The great earthquake of March 27, 1964, in south-central Alaska was accompanied by regional tectonic warping that caused both extensive subsidence and uplift relative to sea level. During the months after the earthquake geologists made a concerted search for evidence of surface faulting. A U.S. Geological Survey field party headed by the writer found two reverse faults on southwestern Montague Island in Prince William Sound through combined air reconnaissance and studies of shoreline displacements. Although it is assumed that the fault displacements occurred during the main shock, or possibly during some of the subsequent large aftershocks, there were no eyewitnesses to fix the precise time of rupture.

The faulting definitely occurred prior to March 31 (4 days after the earthquake), when a part of one scarp was photographed during a reconnaissance flight over the island. The faults could not be examined on the ground until 2 months later, at the end of May.

As far as could be determined, no movement occurred along any other surface faults on land during the earthquake. A diligent search was made for indications of renewed movement on known pre-existing faults, particularly in the vicinity of the zero isobase between the major zones of regional tectonic uplift and subsidence, but no measurable surface faulting was found. There were no anomalous abrupt changes in amounts of uplift or subsidence along the coast or along level lines inland from the coast suggestive of displacement along concealed faults. All reported suspected surface faulting that was checked in the field turned out to be linear zones of landslides or surficial cracks in unconsolidated deposits. Although some of these lines of landsliding or cracking could possibly reflect fault movements at depth, no direct evidence for such movements is available.

This report substantially enlarges upon preliminary summaries of the nature and tectonic significance of the surface faulting that were based on data acquired during the 1964 field season (Plafker, 1965; Plafker and Mayo, 1965). It presents details of the varied and unusually well exposed surface manifestations of the faults on Montague Island which have an important bearing on tectonic analyses of the earthquake. The methods used in de-

termining the location, displacement, and surface dip of the faults are fully described because detailed descriptions of overthrusts involving predominantly reverse or thrust movements are scarce compared to the literature on strike-slip or normal faulting. Such data are of increasing practical importance to geologists and others who are concerned with identifying potentially a c t i v e faults and evaluating the possible effects of renewed activity on engineering works.

Previous descriptions of the surface manifestations of overthrust faults are limited to studies of the great earthquake of 1931 centered on Hawke Bay, New Zealand (Henderson, 1933), the 1945 Mikawa earthquake in southeastern Honshu, Japan (Tsuya, 1950), the 1952 Kern County, Calif., earthquakes (Buwalda and St. Amand, 1955), and the great 1957 Gobi-Altai earthquake in Mongolia (Florensov and Solonenko, 1963). With the possible exception of some Gobi-Altai faults, the relative displacements on the faults on Montague Island are considerably larger than any overthrusts previously described. They are also unique in that absolute, as well as relative, displacements could be determined across these faults at four points where they intersect the shoreline.

I am grateful to colleagues in the U.S. Geological Survey for assistance in the field and for much stimulating and helpful discussion. Field mapping of the faults was carried out by a boat-based and helicopter-supported U.S. Geological Survey party from May 30 to June 3, 1964, and by a helicopter-supported party from July 31 to August 7, 1965. L. R. Mayo and J. E. Case assisted in the 1964 fieldwork, and L. R. Mayo and M. G. Bonilla collected much of the data during the 1965 season. Additional critical observations on the northeastern segment of the Patton Bay fault were made by L. C. Cluff, of the firm Woodward-Clyde-Sherard and Associates, who visited the area briefly during the summer of 1966. The faults and related features were mapped on postearthquake vertical and oblique aerial photographs taken by the U.S. Army at scales of 1:15,000 and 1:20,000 and on vertical photographs taken by the U.S. Coast and Geodetic Survey at scales ranging from 1:4,000 to 1:20,000. Preearthquake vertical photographic coverage available for the entire island at a scale of 1:20,000 proved to be invaluable for determining the relationship of the fault movements to older geologic structures.

REGIONAL TECTONIC SETTING

The surface breaks on Montague Island lie within the focal region of the earthquake, as defined by aftershock distribution, and within a region of tectonic deformation associated with the earthquake (fig. 1). The regional deformation has been described briefly in preliminary reports (Grantz and others, 1964; Plafker and

Mayo, 1965; Plafker, 1965). Only the broad aspects of the regional tectonic movements will be outlined here to provide a proper perspective for the tectonic significance of these surface faults. A detailed description and analysis of the overall tectonic displacements will be given in a separate chapter on regional earthquake effects in

this series.

Tectonic movements, both vertical and horizontal, occurred over an area of at least 70,000 square miles, and possibly more than 110,000 square miles, of south-central Alaska. The deformed region, which is more than 500 miles long and as much as 200 miles wide, is roughly parallel to the Gulf of

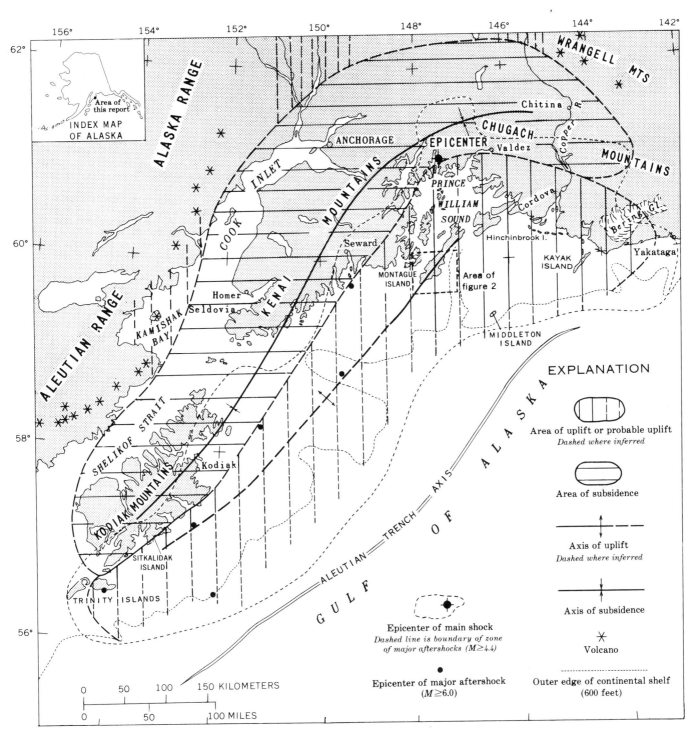

1.—Setting of Montague Island with respect to regional tectonic deformation and seismicity that accompanied the **March 27,** 1964, earthquake.

Alaska coast from the Kodiak group of islands northeastward to Prince William Sound and thence eastward to about long 143° W. It consists of a major seaward zone of uplift bordered on the northwest and north by a major zone of subsidence. These two zones are separated by a line of zero land-level change that trends northeastward to intersect the mainland between Seward and Prince William Sound. It then curves eastward through the western part of Prince William Sound to the vicinity of Valdez and crosses the Copper River valley about 50 miles above the mouth of the river.

The zone of subsidence includes most of the Kodiak group of islands, Cook Inlet, the Kenai Mountains, and the Chugach Mountains. The axis of maximum subsidence within this zone trends roughly northeastward along the crest of the Kodiak and Kenai Mountains and then bends eastward in the Chugach Mountains. Maximum recorded downwarping is about 7½ feet on the south coast of the Kenai Peninsula.

In the northern part of the deformed area, uplift that averages about 6 feet occurred over a wide zone including most of the Prince William Sound region, the mainland east of the sound, and offshore islands as far southwest as Middleton Island at the edge of the Continental Shelf. Large-scale uplift of the Continental Shelf and slope southwest of Montague Island is inferred from the trend of isobase contours in the northeastern part of the deformed zone and from the presence of a fringe of uplifted capes and points along the outer coast of the Kodiak Island area. The minimum extent of this inferred offshore zone of uplift is thought to be roughly outlined by the earthquake focal region, or belt of major aftershocks, shown in figure 1.

Montague Island lies within the earthquake focal region along the axis of maximum tectonic uplift. Combined surface faulting and regional warping have elevated the southwestern end of the island relative to sea level by as much as 38 feet (fig. 2). Southwest of Montague Island the sea bottom may have been uplifted more than 50 feet where pre- and postearthquake bottom soundings show residual vertical displacements at least as large as those on the adjacent land. As discussed later (p. G26), there is indirect evidence which suggests that the axis of maximum uplift and faulting may extend southwestward more than 300 miles to the area off the southeast coast of Kodiak Island.

GEOGRAPHIC AND GEOLOGIC SETTING

Montague Island is the most southerly of three long narrow islands that trend northeast across the south side of Prince William Sound (fig. 2). The island, which is 51 miles long by 4 to 12 miles wide, consists of a topographically rugged mountainous backbone ridge with average summit altitudes of 2,400 feet and a maximum altitude of 2,841 feet. A dense growth of timber and brush mantles much of the valley floors, raised beaches, and lower mountain slopes below an altitude of 1,000 feet. Access through the vegetated areas is difficult, and is mainly along streams, beaches, and bear trails. Open areas of muskeg—a mat of sphagnum moss several feet thick—sedge, and open-growth scrub occur wherever drainage is impeded by low and gently sloping topography or by impermeable soils. There are no permanent roads or inhabitants on the island although a few loggers and hunters usually live there intermittently during the summer months. No one was on Montague Island during the earthquake.

The geology of Montague Island is known only in a general way from regional reconnaissance studies (Grant and Higgins, 1910; Moffitt, 1954; Case and others, 1966; Plafker and MacNeil, 1966). The bedrock is part of the Orca Group, which consists of a thick sequence of well-indurated interbedded sandstone and siltstone, minor amounts of limestone as thin beds or lenses, and tabular to lenticular masses of basaltic lava. The Orca is at least in part of early Tertiary (probably middle to late Eocene) age.

The rocks were complexly folded and faulted in early Tertiary time. They generally strike northeast parallel to the trend of the island, but there are numerous local deviations from this trend. Folds on the island are characteristically overturned towards the northwest with near-horizontal axes; folds in most of the remainder of Prince William Sound are overturned mainly toward the southeast. Faults associated with the folding are mainly southeast-dipping overthrusts. Well-developed sets of steeply dipping conjugate shear joints trend at high angles to the strike of fold axes and faults in

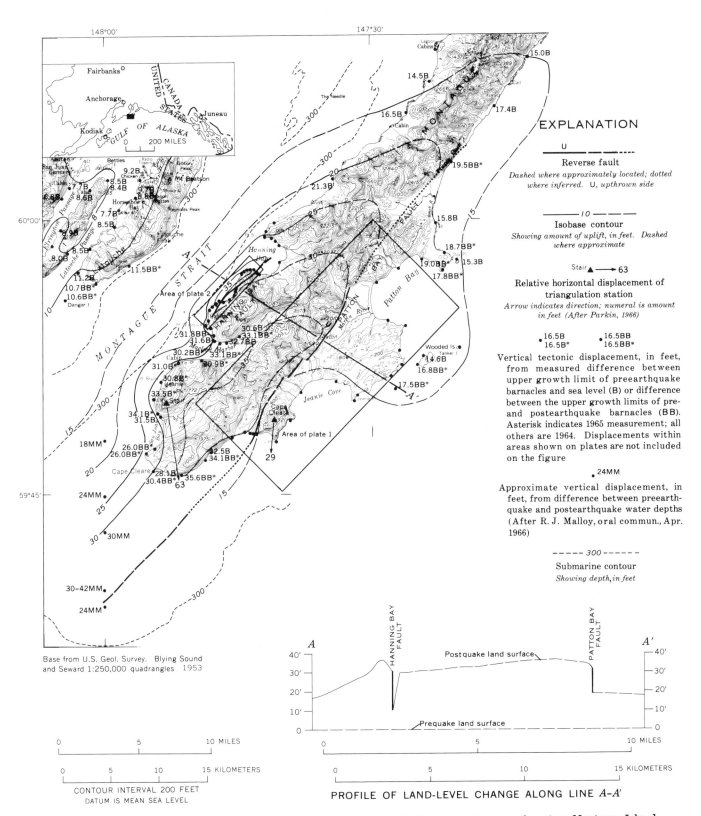

EXPLANATION

U
————— · · · · · · ·
Reverse fault
Dashed where approximately located; dotted where inferred. U, upthrown side

————— 10 —————
Isobase contour
Showing amount of uplift, in feet. Dashed where approximate

Stair ▲ ——► 63
Relative horizontal displacement of triangulation station
Arrow indicates direction; numeral is amount in feet (After Parkin, 1966)

· 16.5B   · 16.5BB
16.5B*   16.5B*
Vertical tectonic displacement, in feet, from measured difference between upper growth limit of preearthquake barnacles and sea level (B) or difference between the upper growth limits of pre- and postearthquake barnacles (BB). Asterisk indicates 1965 measurement; all others are 1964. Displacements within areas shown on plates are not included on the figure

· 24MM
Approximate vertical displacement, in feet, from difference between preearthquake and postearthquake water depths (After R. J. Malloy, oral commun., Apr. 1966)

————— 300 —————
Submarine contour
Showing depth, in feet

Base from U.S. Geol. Survey. Blying Sound and Seward 1:250,000 quadrangles 1953

0   5   10 MILES

0   5   10   15 KILOMETERS

CONTOUR INTERVAL 200 FEET
DATUM IS MEAN SEA LEVEL

PROFILE OF LAND-LEVEL CHANGE ALONG LINE *A–A'*

2.—Map and profile showing faults and horizontal and vertical tectonic displacements on southwestern Montague Island.

the southwestern part of the island. Surface faults associated with the 1964 earthquake parallel or cut obliquely across the strike of the older bedrock folds and faults at a small angle and are clearly discordant with the dip of these structures.

Unconsolidated Quaternary glacial till of variable thickness veneers bedrock on low-lying parts of the island, and thick deposits of coarse alluvium occur along the lower reaches of the larger streams. Talus, landslide deposits, and frost rubble commonly conceal bedrock on and at the base of the steeper slopes.

DESCRIPTION OF THE FAULTS

The locations of mapped fault traces on Montague Island and the distribution of vertical uplift relative to sea level are summarized in figure 2, and details of the features associated with the Patton Bay and Hanning Bay faults are shown on plates 1 and 2, respectively. The following general features are common to both the Patton Bay and Hanning Bay faults: (1) Both strike northeast almost parallel to the long axis of Montague Island; (2) both blocks are uplifted relative to sea level, with the northwest blocks upthrown relative to the southeast blocks; (3) the faults are northwest-dipping r e v e r s e faults; (4) both faults may have small components of left-lateral strike-slip displacement near their southern limits of exposure amounting to less than one tenth the dip-slip component; and (5) the new breakage occurred along or near the traces of preexisting faults which appear to have undergone earlier Holocene displacements.

Measurement of the inclination of the fault plane and the dip-slip component of displacement is hampered by the general tendency (1) for the slip plane to be concealed by slumping or landsliding across the steep to overhanging fault scarps or (2) for bedrock displacements to be reflected at the surface by flexing and fissuring of overlying unconsolidated deposits and surface vegetation. Approxi-

mate surface dips could be determined from the inclination of sheared rock at several places along the fault scarps (pls. 1, 2); the dip of the Patton Bay fault is also visible in the sea cliff where the fault intersects the coast.

Absolute, as well as relative, vertical displacements could be determined at shoreline intersections of the faults by measurement of shoreline changes relative to sea level. The isobase contours of figure 2 show the amount and direction of vertical displacement that accompanied the earthquake. Directions and relative amounts of change were determined at about 75 localities on southwestern Montague Island from measurements of the displacement of the upper growth limit of sessile intertidal organisms along the seashore and from changes in the altitudes of storm beach berms. Measurements were made at 14 of these localities both in 1964 and 1965. Data-point locations and measured vertical displacements are shown in figure 2 and on plates 1 and 2.

The technique used for measuring vertical displacements from the height of the upper growth limit of barnacles above tidal planes has been outlined elsewhere (Plafker, 1965, p. 1675–1679) and, consequently, will not be elaborated upon here. Those measurements based on differences in pre- and postearthquake altitudes of the upper growth limits of bar-

nacles are thought to be generally accurate to about 1 foot. Many of the 1964 measurements, however, are based only on the postearthquake altitude of these organisms above sea level; they contain inherent errors due to deviation of sea level from predicted heights and to variations in the growth limits of these organisms resulting from local factors of exposure, rock type, and water characteristics. The measurements made on the eastern side of the islands are estimated to be accurate to within $1\frac{1}{2}$ feet in sheltered bays and to within $2\frac{1}{2}$ feet on segments of the coast exposed to heavy surf and swells along the ocean side. At two localities on sandy stretches of beach where barnacles were not present, the vertical movements were determined from differences in altitude of the pre- and postearthquake storm beach berms. The accuracy of these measurements is unknown, although they give results consistent with those obtained from barnacle-line measurements at nearby rocky shores.

Submarine control for the isobase contours southwest of Montague Island is provided by comparisons of pre- and postearthquake bathymetric charts. Because of navigational and other technical problems in carrying out such surveys, the inferred submarine displacements could locally be in error by 10 feet or more.

Measurements of vertical displacement away from the shore are based mainly on the heights of slope breaks in surficial deposits which may or may not accurately reflect the vertical displacement within the underlying bedrock. In those rare instances where the displacement is apparently localized along a scarp in bedrock, the scarp height is taken as the net vertical displacement. Only the vertical component of surface displacement is shown on plates 1 and 2; dip-slip displacements may be as much as 25 percent greater, depending on the indicated dip of the fault at any given locality.

PATTON BAY FAULT

After the earthquake, the Patton Bay fault was traceable by a succession of exceptionally interesting and complex features, such as fresh fault scarps, surface flexures, and gigantic landslides. From the place where the fault strikes out to sea 1½ miles west of Neck Point, the rupture extends 11 miles northeastward to the valley of the Patton River (pl. 1). Northeast of Patton River, displacement is distributed across a broad zone of subparallel fissures as much as half a mile wide that can be traced an additional 11 miles as far as Purple Bluff on the southeast coast of the island.

In the following account, the fault on land is described from southwest to northeast. Places referred to, including the locations photographed and diagramed, are shown on the map of the surface ruptures (pl. 1). The northeastern segment of the fault is not shown on the detailed map, but is shown at a smaller scale in figure 2. Figure 2 also shows the measured and inferred vertical displacements relative to sea level at and near the two faults and along a section across them.

BEACH AND SEA CLIFF NEAR NECK POINT

The Patton Bay fault is best exposed at its southwestern end at the beach and sea cliff 1½ miles west of Neck Point. It is marked by a pronounced scarp 6 to 8½ feet high which trends north-south across the beach and the newly uplifted surf-cut platform seaward from the beach (figs. 3, 4, following pages). Beach gravel draped across the scarp conceals the actual fault plane everywhere except at the one small outcrop at the toe of the beach prism where a 4-foot-wide zone of sheared siltstone dips westward at an angle that averages about 85° (fig. 5).

The near-vertical fissure exposed in the sea cliff is along the most probable continuation of the fault. Its steep dip, which is consistent with the fault attitude indicated by the sheared siltstone along the scarp, may represent only a near-surface steepening of the fault plane where it breaks to the surface along the most direct path. Previous movement could have occurred along the dipping faults exposed in the sea cliff (fig. 3), which are undoubtedly associated with this same line of faulting but which apparently were not reactivated during the earthquake.

The position of the barnacle line along the shore in the vicinity of the fault provides an excellent means of determining the absolute vertical displacement of the blocks at and near the fault as well as the relative vertical displacement. The measurements indicate that both blocks are uplifted relative to sea level and that the western block is upthrown 20 to 23 feet in relation to the eastern (pl. 1, section A–A'). Uplift of the western block decreases progressively from 35 to 38 feet at a distance of 800 feet from the fault scarp to 21 to 23½ feet at the scarp; uplift of the eastern block is about 15 feet at the scarp. Only 6 to 8½ feet of the displacement occurred along the fault scarp that cuts the beach gravel and the reef at the shore (fig. 3); the remainder of the offset takes the form of a pronounced downwarping of the upthrown block within 800 feet of the fault.

Numerous surface cracks as much as 170 feet long formed in bedrock on the reef part of the upthrown block within 400 feet of the scarp. These newly opened cracks can be readily differentiated from preearthquake cracks because they expose fresh surfaces that do not have a white coating of calcareous algae. Locations, orientations, and displacements of the largest and most conspicuous of these cracks, which were mapped by a pace-and-compass survey, are shown in figure 6. Three typical cracks are illustrated in figures 7–9; the photographs were taken at the locations indicated in figure 6. No newly opened cracks were found near the fault in the downthrown block; close to the fault, however, this block is largely covered by beach deposits.

The cracks all dip steeply or are vertical, and they appear to occur exclusively along bedding planes and preexisting joints. Displacement in the overwhelming majority of cracks is an extension perpendicular to the crack face ranging from less than 0.01 to 0.4 foot. Locally, the cracks are substantially widened where loose narrow wedge-shaped rock slivers as much as 1.4 feet wide have dropped down along them. Left-lateral displacements occurred along two of the cracks. One of the two trends northeast at an oblique angle to the fault scarp and was displaced 1.0 foot (fig. 9). The other crack, which is almost parallel to the scarp, had 0.4 foot of lateral offset.

3.—Patton Bay fault (heavy solid and dotted line) at the beach and sea cliff near Jeanie Point. Note the vertical offset of contact between beach deposits (Qb) and talus (Qt). The man (circled) is standing at the base of a scarp 8½ feet high. Light dotted lines are bedding traces in the Orca Group (To); heavy dashed lines are probable fault traces on which there apparently was no movement during the earthquake. Location shown in figure 6.

4.—View south from top of the sea cliff in figure 3. Arrows indicate fault trace which displaces the elevated beach prism and cuts obliquely across bedrock structures in the surf-cut platform on the upthrown block. The lower part of the scarp was partially obliterated with newly deposited marine sand and gravel by the time this photograph was taken in August 1965.

5.—Near-vertical zone of sheared quartz-veined argillite and graywacke along the Patton Bay fault trace at the shore. Location shown in figure 6.

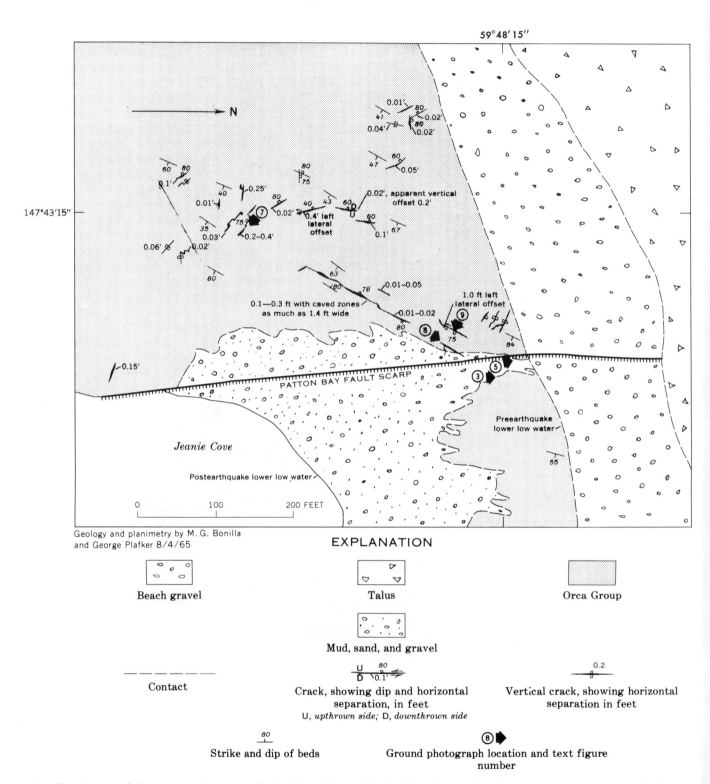

59°48'15"

147°43'15"

N

7

6

0.1'
0.25'
0.01'
0.02'
0.06'
0.02'
0.03'
0.2-0.4'
0.4' left
lateral
offset
80
80
40
43
60
D
75
80
35

0.01'
0.04'
0.02'
0.02'
47
80
80

0.05'
60
47

0.02', apparent vertical
offset 0.2'
60
0.1'
67

63
78
0.01-0.05
0.1-0.3 ft with caved zones
as much as 1.4 ft wide
80
0.01-0.02

1.0 ft left
lateral offset
9
8
75
84

0.15'
PATTON BAY FAULT SCARP
5
3

Preearthquake
lower low water

55

Jeanie Cove

Postearthquake lower low water

0   100   200 FEET

Geology and planimetry by M. G. Bonilla
and George Plafker 8/4/65

EXPLANATION

Beach gravel   Talus   Orca Group

Mud, sand, and gravel

Contact

U 80
D 0.1'
Crack, showing dip and horizontal
separation, in feet
U, *upthrown side;* D, *downthrown side*

0.2
Vertical crack, showing horizontal
separation in feet

80
Strike and dip of beds

8
Ground photograph location and text figure
number

6.—Sketch map of the scarp and open cracks in the upthrown block of the Patton Bay fault at the shore near Jeanie Point.

7.—Crack 0.2 to 0.4 foot wide and at least 2 feet deep in the warped relatively up-thrown block of the Patton Bay fault. Crack follows preexisting bedding and joint planes. Location shown in figure 6.

8.—Looking down on vertical crack 0.01 to 0.015 foot wide along preexisting joints in a hard graywacke bed. Location shown in figure 6.

9.—Crack along bedding plane in massive indurated sandstone; 1 foot of left-lateral separation. Location shown in figure 6.

One crack was found on the uplifted wave-cut bedrock surface of the relatively upthrown block approximately 1,000 feet southwest of the fault. It is as much as 0.2 foot wide and had possible right-lateral movement of less than 0.1 foot and dip-slip displacement of less than 0.2 foot.

The open cracks that occur in the reef on the upthrown block are probably tension cracks associated with the downwarping near the fault. Left-lateral displacements observed on two of these cracks suggest a possible small strike-slip component of movement of less than 1½ feet on the Patton Bay fault at this locality. No conclusive evidence for horizontal offset of the preearthquake beach strand lines that cross the fault scarp was found on the ground, although an apparent slight tendency for left-lateral bending of these lines was noted on the large-scale vertical aerial photographs.

FROM THE SEA CLIFF TO TORTUOUS CREEK

From the sea cliff to Tortuous Creek the Patton Bay fault trace is poorly defined by a discontinuous zone of fissures, warped surfaces, small landslides, and poorly exposed shear zones in rock (figs. 10–13). The fault in this segment angles obliquely across the structural and topographical grain of heavily timbered low rolling terrain with less than 700 feet of relief. It gradually changes strike from due north at the shore to N. 37° E. at its northern end. In this segment the fault trace is anomalous in that it does not coincide with a major topographic or structural lineament. Features such as alined swampy muskegs subtly suggest that some prior small vertical displacement occurred in Holocene time. The prominent northwest-trending lin-

10.—One of the larger fissures along the trace of the Patton Bay fault. The fissure, which is 3 feet wide and 7 feet deep, is in unconsolidated glacial till.

eaments and imposing scarps along Deception Creek and upper Slide Creek immediately to the west of the 1964 rupture apparently define a major fault trace along which large vertical up-to-the-northwest movements occurred previously but which shows no evidence of reactivation during this earthquake (pl. 1).

The fault trace cannot be located precisely within a few hundred feet inland from the top of the sea cliff, because it is obscured by the headwall scarps of enormous incipient landslide blocks that occur all along the upper part of the cliff. It reappears some 500 feet inland from the cliff where it coincides with the linear edge of a muskeg swamp. The fault trace here consists of a north-south trending zone of parallel surface fissures and flexures in glacial till and sphagnum peat. Individual fissures that parallel the trace are open as much as 3 feet (fig. 10) and have vertical offsets of as

much as 5 feet with the west (downhill) sides upthrown relative to the east sides. Net vertical displacement across the fissures is about 7 feet; the amount of vertical movement resulting from warping is not known. A possible left-lateral component of horizontal displacement is indicated by a 17-inch offset of segments of a log that had been frozen into the ground in a position almost normal to the trend of one of the larger surface breaks. A few gaping cracks that trend N. 15° W. at an oblique angle to the fault trace are also suggestive of some left-lateral strike-slip movement. No evidence for lateral offsets was found anywhere else along the fault trace.

The fault continues for a mile as a line of poorly defined fissures and flexures through densely timbered terrain to the point where it intersects a muskeg bog about 500 feet long by 100 feet wide that was

formerly flat and was crossed by a small meandering stream. Faulting has resulted in a pronounced eastward tilt of the eastern half of the muskeg and a slight anticlinal flexing of the central part. The tilted segment is now partly inundated by a lake that is more than 8 feet deep where it is dammed against an erosional scarp that borders the meadow on the east; the lake shallows toward the center of the muskeg (fig. 11). The anticlinal flexure forms a low north-south trending ridge immediately west of the lake.

On the flood plain of Strike Creek, the fault trace is vaguely defined by partially diverted drainage and tilted trees. Immediately to the west of Strike Creek, where it cuts through a muskeg bog in a N. 35° E. direction, the fault trace is clearly visible as a broad flexure through the formerly horizontal bog surface and

11 (above).—Formerly flat muskeg that was warped and tilted eastward along the Patton Bay fault trace. The newly formed lake is more than 8 feet deep at the eastern (left) margin of the muskeg. Photograph by L. R. Mayo.

12 (above right).—Warped and fissured muskeg surface along the Patton Bay fault trace. West (left) side of this formerly flat meadow is uplifted 16½ feet relative to the east side. Tilted trees in the background are along the flexure zone that marks the fault trace. Note the characteristic tilt of tree crowns toward the downthrown block. Arrows indicate fissures.

13 (bottom right).—Part of the zone of tectonic fissures north of Tortuous Creek. Two of the larger laterally persistent fissures (arrows) that trend obliquely across the slopes are visible above the brush line. The cracks and scars below the brush line result from earthquake-induced landslides and soil flows. Photograph by M. G. Bonilla.

the adjacent wooded area. A continuous sharp flexure about 60 feet wide in the muskeg is broken by a series of open fissures parallel to the trend of the fault that displace the muskeg-covered surface and underlying stream gravel (fig. 12). Relative vertical displacement across the part of the flexure in the bog is roughly 16½ feet. This estimate of the vertical movement is minimal, because it includes only part of the zone of surface warping associated with the fault. The total width of the zone, as indicated by the distribution of spruce trees which are tilted towards the downthrown block owing to warping of the surface, is roughly 125 feet at this locality.

From Strike Creek to Tortuous Creek the fault trends across heavily timbered terrain in which the trace is indicated by a vaguely defined discontinuous broad zone of tilted trees, ground fissures, and small landslides. These features were mapped from vertical and oblique photographs and from aerial observation. An outcrop consisting of highly sheared siltstone was observed in the bank of Slide Creek at about the point where the fault trace would cross the creek, but no indications of new surface displacement were found in the densely vegetated valley bottom.

Immediately to the north of Tortuous Creek, displacement is indicated by a zone of fissuring about half a mile wide that lies between the southern and central segments of the fault (pl. 1; fig. 13). The fissures range from a few hundred to more than 1,000 feet in length, and most have east-facing scarps. The more continuous of these fissures are clearly tectonic features inasmuch as they ignore topography and trend obliquely across mountain slopes and even over ridges as high as

1,800 feet. However, apparent tectonic fissures that nearly parallel the contours of steep slopes are difficult to distinguish from scarps at the heads of incipient landslides. Scarps parallel to the slopes that show evidence of downhill movement of the downhill side are arbitrarily mapped as landslide scarps; undoubtedly some represent fissures along which sliding has subsequently developed.

TORTUOUS CREEK TO THE VALLEY OF PATTON RIVER

The 5¾-mile-long segment of the Patton Bay fault between Tortuous Creek and the valley of Patton River trends N. 35° E. and is the most continuous and impressive of all the segments. It lies at the base of a line of imposing ridge spurs which are part of the modified scarp formed on the upthrown block of the Patton Bay fault. Along the ridge spurs the fault is marked by a spectacular series of gigantic landslides with headwall scarps as high as 300 feet, soil flows, and surface cracks associated with incipient slides on the slopes (figs. 14–16). The line of landslides along these spurs is broken only at the valleys of deeply incised streams that dissect the upthrown block intersecting the fault approximately at right angles. In some of these incised-stream valleys the actual fault trace could be seen, but in the interfluves the trace was concealed by the chaotic mass of crushed and pulverized landslide debris and a virtually impenetrable tangle of fallen brush and timber. The process by which landslide debris tends to bury the fault trace where it follows along the base of a prominent scarp is illustrated diagrammatically in figure 17. This process of automatic self-concealment undoubtedly occurs on most active overthrust faults and is

probably one of the major reasons why faults of this type are commonly difficult to recognize and map by surface geologic methods.

These ridge spurs were especially susceptible to mass gravitational movements through a combination of (1) steep slopes composed in part of unstable debris resulting from prior faulting; (2) bedding dips that tend to parallel the slopes; and (3) local zones of sheared and shattered bedrock along the fault plane and near it within the upthrown block. In view of this inherent instability, it is not surprising that oversteepening resulting from renewed

---

14.—Looking southwest along the Patton Bay fault in the vicinity of Jeanie Creek. Fault trace (dashed) is marked by the line of landslides at the base of the prominent scarp that is formed on the relatively upthrown block. →

---

uplift along a steep or overhanging fault scarp at the base of the slopes, coupled with transient accelerations due to the elastic ground vibrations and tectonic displacements during the earthquake, should have caused the massive slope failures. The transient movements alone seem to have been sufficient to trigger landslides under comparable circumstances elsewhere in the area, such as along upper Slide Creek, even where renewed faulting did not occur.

From Tortuous Creek to Jeanie Creek the fault trace is marked by a line of landslides at the base of an imposing eastward-facing slope that rises 1,500 feet at an average

---

15.—Patton Bay fault (dashed) looking northeast toward Jeanie Creek. The segment of the fault north of Jeanie Creek is offset about 0.4 mile to the east relative to the segment south of the creek. →

A

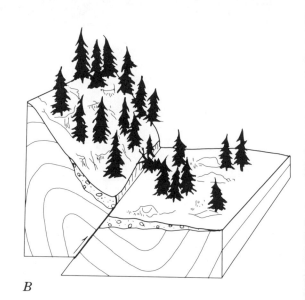

B

C

EXPLANATION

Bedrock

Colluvium, alluvium, and glacial till

[152]

18.—Shattered lenticular boudins of light-gray indurated sandstone in a matrix of sheared black argillite dipping 75° to 85° northwest along the Patton Bay fault at Jeanie Creek.

16 (above left).—Landslide scars as high as 200 feet (arrows) on the relatively upthrown block of the Patton Bay fault (dashed) near Nellie Martin River. The fault is exposed in the river channel where it dips about 50° northwest (right) and has at least 16 feet of vertical displacement.

angle in excess of 30°. Sheared rock is exposed along the fault trace in an isolated bedrock outcrop 2 feet wide along the south bank of a small stream 0.8 mile north of Tortuous Creek. The outcrop consists of intensely frac-

17 (below left).—Sequential diagram illustrating stages in growth of landslides along the base of a fault scarp of the reverse type upon renewed dip-slip displacement. A, preearthquake condition; B, overhanging scarp formed near base of slope by renewed fault movement; C, collapse of unstable slope above the fault scarp.

tured argillite and graywacke that contain lenticular veinlets of quartz and thin seams of dark-gray clay gouge less than 1 inch wide dipping 65° to 75° NW. Except for this one outcrop, the stream valley was so choked with slide debris that no information could be obtained on the displacement.

Between the south and north forks of Jeanie Creek the fault is offset about 0.4 mile to the east (fig. 15). The base of the slope in this area is entirely concealed by landslide debris, so whether the two segments of the fault here are connected by an abrupt bend or whether they are offset en echelon in a right-handed sense is not known.

Part of the fault zone is exposed in a 3-foot-wide outcrop in the bank of Jeanie Creek. The outcrop consists of shattered lenticular boudins of light-gray fine- to medium-grained arkosic sandstone in a matrix of sheared black argillite (fig. 18) that strikes N. 65° E. and dips 75° to 85° northwest. On the north side of the creek the fault passes through a terrace deposit of stream gravel which has been displaced into four gently sloping steps 10 to 20 feet wide separated by three fissured rises of comparable width that are strongly tilted toward the downthrown (east) block. Minimum cumulative vertical displacement of 10 to 12 feet is represented by the rises that displace the terrace.

[153]

One mile farther north the fault plane is again exposed in the banks of Nellie Martin River; its trace is clearly defined where it crosses the broad alluvial flood plain of the river. The fault zone in the upthrown block along the river consists of 75 feet of intensely sheared siltstone containing veins and lenticular masses of quartz less than half an inch wide; bedrock is concealed by stream deposits in the downthrown block. The siltstone in this zone is so fractured throughout that it can be readily broken into chips by hand. The sheared rock trends N. 35° E. and dips northwest at angles ranging from 50° to near vertical. By August of 1965 the Nellie Martin River, which flows directly across the strike of the bedding and the fault, had incised its channel below the preearthquake level, through 4 feet of stream gravel and 12 feet of bedrock immediately upstream from the fault trace. The amount of incision suggests a minimum of 16 feet of relative vertical displacement across the fault at this locality (fig. 19).

Both north and south of the river channel, the fault trace is marked by a well-defined flexure of the alluvial deposits and the usual associated ground fissures and tilted trees. A profile perpendicular to the strike of the flexure zone about 300 feet north of Nellie Martin River is shown as B–B' on plate 1. Open extension cracks as much as 1 foot wide parallel the upper part of the flexure; steeply tilted and downed trees, with crowns pointing downslope, were found along its base. It may be assumed that, if there was no previous break in slope along the new flexure, the vertical displacement is the offset of the sloping alluvial fan surface across the flexure zone.

19.—Incised channel of the Nellie Martin River immediately upstream from t[...] gravel and 12 feet of bedrock at this locality between March 27, 1964, and Aug[...]

Labels in figure:
Preearthquake river bed
4 ft.
Bedrock-gravel contact
Bedding trace
12 ft
Postearthquake bed of Nellie Martin River

...tton Bay fault scarp. The rejuvenated river has eroded about 4 feet of boulder 1965. Photograph by L. R. Mayo.

As shown in the profile, the indicated maximum vertical displacement at this locality is about 20 feet.

To the north, the fault trace is again concealed by landslides for a distance of almost 1½ miles until it reappears as a zone of fissures and tilted trees in the alluvial fan deposits of Braided Creek and the nearby streams. Individual fissures have as much as 4 feet of vertical displacement, the northwest sides invariably upthrown. At one point along this trace, the fault zone is defined by a 40- to 60-foot-wide swath of trees tilted at a uniform angle of about 70°, resulting from a southeastward surface tilt of 20°. Approximate vertical displacement across the zone, as calculated from its width and surface slope is 14½ to 22 feet.

North of Braided Creek the fault follows the contact between predominantly massive greenstone tuff along the base of the mountain front on the upthrown block and the alluvial flats on the downthrown side. At the most northerly point on this segment, where it strikes into the alluvial valley of Patton River, the fault is exposed in a dry creekbed as a 3-foot-wide zone of sheared, crumpled, and sericitized siltstone that strikes N. 10°E. and dips 67° northwest. On the flood plain immediately north of this outcrop, a vertical displacement of roughly 21 feet is indicated by an average 12° downslope tilt of the surface over a zone about 100 feet wide (determined from the tilting of trees).

PATTON RIVER VALLEY SEGMENT

The Patton River Valley segment of the Patton Bay fault is unique in that it is entirely in an area of low relief underlain by thick deposits of unconsolidated alluvium. A climax forest of Sitka spruce composed of imposing trees as much as 4 feet in base diameter and 140 feet in height occupies the entire valley floor except for the poorly drained swampy areas or active stream channels. Within this forest, the fault trace is defined by a remarkably persistent line of discontinuous surface cracks and associated tilted trees that can be traced to the northern margin of the valley, a distance of nearly a mile.

The cracks, which occur in peat moss and soil, are subparallel and trend N. 10° to 30° E. They are open 1 to 4 inches at the surface and show a few down-to-the southeast dip-slip displacements of 2 to 3 inches and no measurable strike-slip components. A minor set of cracks with a general N. 55° E. orientation was observed near the north end of the segment. All the cracks occurred in a well-defined zone a few hundred feet wide; no other newly opened cracks were found outside this zone in the same general area of the valley floor.

Tilted trees are associated with the line of cracks, particularly south of Patton River (fig. 20), where average tree heights of more than 125 feet make tilts of as little as 5° from the vertical readily apparent.

PATTON RIVER VALLEY TO PURPLE BLUFF

The character of the surface displacements along the Patton Bay fault zone changes markedly to the north of Patton River valley. In this 11-mile-long segment (pl. 1; figs. 21, 22), tectonic movements are strongly suggested by numerous peculiar subparallel northeast-trending fissures consisting of open cracks or normal faults with small vertical displacements that, for the most part, are unin-

20.—Looking southwest along the Patton Bay fault in the alluviated valley of Patton River. The fault trace is indicated by the tilted giant Sitka spruce trees and by ground fissures that roughly parallel the zone of tilted trees.

fluenced by the topography. The southeastern margin of this zone of fissures is a conspicuous lineament, trending N. 30° E., similar to much of the Patton Bay fault to the south in that it forms a boundary between an imposing rugged ridge on the northwest and terrain of lower relief on the southeast, but different in not having a single continuous scarp or well-

defined narrow zone of displacement. The character of the fissures in this segment suggests the possibility that the displacement here is taken up mainly by a broad anticlinal flexure of the upthrown block and that the longitudinal zone of extension cracks and minor normal faults results from local tensile stress along the crest of the flexure.

21.—Part of the zone of tectonic fissures at 3,000 feet altitude on the ridge summit north of Patton River. The fissures, some of which are indicated by arrows, could be traced almost continuously to the northeast through the peak (center of photograph) and the notch on the skyline to the left of the peak.

22.—Subparallel minor normal faults within the area shown in figure 21. Note that some of these fissures coincide with pre-existing linear scarps.

The fissures were studied in detail only at one locality on the ridge immediately north of the Patton River valley (pl. 1, profile *C–C′*). Here the fissures occur over a zone about 1,500 feet wide and are generally subparallel. Their average strike is N. 20° E. parallel to the ridge crest, although some individual fissures and segments of nonlinear fissures trend at an oblique angle to the zone—between N. 80° W. and N. 70° E. Some of the fissures are several hundred feet long and as much as 17 inches wide. Most are nearly vertical with dip-slip displacement of as much as 21 inches (figs. 21, 22; pl. 1, profile *C–C′*). The overall width of this zone of fissures is difficult to determine because cracks on the steep southeast-facing ridge slope cannot be readily differentiated from incipient landslides. The zone shown on plate 1, which is 3,000 feet wide, includes the entire area in which surface cracks of possible tectonic origin have been observed.

That the fissures on the ridge are tectonic features is indicated by (1) the linearity and lateral continuity of the zone; (2) the fact that most of the fissures displace bedrock; (3) the occurrence of some fissures in which uplift on the downhill side, in relation to the uphill, precludes the possibility of landslide origin (fig. 23); and (4) coincidence of many of the fissures with preexisting linear scarps in rock along which previous movements may have occurred.

The fissure zone could be readily followed northward from the area shown on profile *C–C′* of plate 1 across the highest peak on the ridge at an altitude of 2,200 feet. Beyond this point it is discontinuously evident from subparallel cracks and landslide scarps on the steep mountain slopes that were

23.—Minor normal faults along a preexisting linear groove on a steep ridge slope. The downhill side is uplifted 16 inches. Patton River valley visible in the background.

traced to Purple Bluff by aerial reconnaissance.

Two localities in this zone of fissures that were examined on the ground by L. C. Cluff of Woodward-Clyde-Sherard and Associates in July 1966 are worthy of special mention. One is at the slope break near the base of the ridge 2 miles north of the Patton River valley, where a southeast-facing scarp about half a mile long and 4 feet high displaces vegetation and soil. The length of this scarp and evidence of surface displace-

ment suggest that it may be a fault. The second locality is at the northern end of the zone, where renewed vertical surface displacement of no more than a few inches occurred along several preexisting lineaments that extend inland from Purple Bluff for a distance of about 1,600 feet (figs. 2, 24). Some of these fissures near the upper edge of the bluff may be along the heads of gigantic landslide blocks, but most of them, including many with relatively uplifted downhill sides, seem to be

24.—Vertical aerial photograph in the vicinity of Purple Bluff showing conspicuous lineaments (arrows) along the inferred northeastward extension of the Patton Bay fault. Renewed displacement occurred on some of these lineaments after the 1964 earthquake. A large earthquake-induced landslide may be seen at the base of the high bluff at bottom center. Photograph by U.S. Coast and Geodetic Survey, August 25, 1964.

of tectonic origin. The fissures strike about N. 30° E. and intersect the coast at an acute angle immediately north of Purple Bluff. No detailed studies of shoreline displacement were made across the zone of fissures at the coast; the available measurements of shoreline changes (fig. 2) suggest that the displacement here is no more than a few feet or that there may be no displacement at all.

An alternative possibility is that the fault may once again be offset en echelon to the southeast and that it continues northeastward as a submarine feature. Although there is no direct evidence for such an offset, the precipitous linear coast of Montague Island northeast of Purple Bluff, a concentration there of aftershock activity, and the occurrence of abrupt submarine scarps in the vicinity of Hinchinbrook Island (von Huene and others, 1966) are suggestive of possible active faulting in this area.

SUBMARINE EXTENSION OF PATTON BAY FAULT

Subsequent to the discovery of the faults on Montague Island, the U.S. Coast and Geodetic Survey made hydrographic and seismic surveys of the ocean floor southwest of the island. These surveys have revealed a prominent southeast-facing bedrock scarp 40 to 90 feet high that is in line with, and inferred to be a continuation of, the Patton Bay fault (fig. 2). Comparison of detailed bottom soundings taken in 1927 with others taken after the earthquake in 1964 indicates that the vertical uplift of the bottom on either side of this scarp is in the same sense as, and is comparable in amount to, that recorded on land for a distance of at least 17 miles southwest of the point where the fault strikes out to sea near Neck Point (Mal-

loy, 1965a, p. 1048–1049; 1965b, p. 22–26). The hydrographic surveys do not come closer than 6½ nautical miles to the fault trace on land, so it is not known whether the onshore and offshore segments of the fault scarp are a continuous strand or perhaps are offset en echelon.

Malloy (1965b, figs. 6, 7) believes that a sharp 18-foot-high break in slope on the continuous sounding and seismic profiles closest to shore may represent the 1964 movement; an underwater photograph of what appears to be fresh breakage of the sea floor at this locality tends to support this interpretation. It is also significant that the vertical displacement across the submarine scarp indicated by the bathymetric surveys is compatible with the displacement of 20 to 23 feet measured across the scarp and warped upper plate along the nearby shore at the southern end of the fault.

The fault probably continues farther southwestward, although the 1964 reconnaissance surveys did not track it as a continuous scarp beyond the limits of the pre-1964 hydrographic survey, which was confined mainly to shoal waters. The lines of evidence discussed below suggest that the Patton Bay fault may be but the northern end of a fault, or of a system of discontinuous faults, that extends southwestward an additional 300 miles to the area offshore from Sitkalidak Island in the Kodiak Island group.

1. That this postulated line of faulting is along a narrow zone of probable maximum submarine uplift is inferred from the spatial distribution and runup heights of the seismic sea waves associated with the earthquake (Van Dorn, 1964, fig. 6; Plafker and Mayo, 1965, p. 11; Plafker

and Kachadoorian, 1966, p. 38–39). The waves clearly were generated on the Continental Shelf within the zone of regional uplift by vertical displacements of the sea floor. The direction of travel and reported arrival times of the initial wave crest—the crest that struck the shores of the Kenai Peninsula nearest to Montague Island within 19 minutes and the southeast coast of Kodiak Island within 38 minutes after start of the earthquake—indicate that the wave crest was generated within the regional zone of uplift along one or more line sources in a narrow elongate belt that extends southwestward from Montague Island approximately along the axis of maximum uplift shown in figure 1. Furthermore, the similarities in maximum wave runup heights along physiographically comparable segments of coast, both on the Kenai Peninsula opposite Montague Island and on Kodiak Island, suggest that the vertical sea-floor displacements which generated the waves in these two areas may be of the same order of magnitude.

2. The inferred zone of fault displacement also has an especially large concentration of features that seem to be a result of recent subbottom tectonic movements (D. F. Barnes, unpub. data, 1966; von Huene and others, 1966). These features include sharply defined submarine fault scarps similar to those near Montague Island, subbottom discontinuities that displace possible Holocene deposits, and small folds in the Holocene deposits.

25.—View southwest along Hanning Bay fault. Northwest block (right) has overthrust the southeast block. Note warped surface and overhanging muskeg mat on the scarp in the foreground. Tree in the background has been tilted by the overthrusting. Location shown in figure 27.

3. The concentration of aftershock activity and release of seismic-wave energy which apparently occurred in this area could indicate postearthquake fault adjustments (S. T. Algermissen, written commun., March 1965). Much of the seismic-wave energy released during the aftershock sequence was contained in the six recorded aftershocks shown in figure 1 with Richter magnitudes equal to or larger than 6.0 (as determined by the U.S. Coast and Geodetic Survey). Of these, two were almost directly in the postulated fault zone, one was on its southwestward projection in the Trinity Islands,

two were northwest of the belt in positions where they could conceivably lie on the down-dip extension of northwest-dipping reverse faults, and only one was clearly unrelated to this postulated belt of extreme uplift and faulting.

HANNING BAY FAULT

The Hanning Bay fault extends about 4 miles from the south shore of Hanning Bay almost to MacLeod Harbor (pl. 2; figs. 25–39). After the earthquake, the fault trace was exceptionally well exposed along nearly its entire length, either as a single steep scarp or as a narrow zone of surface warping. Descriptions of

surface features along the fault are divided geographically into three segments as follows: (1) south of Fault Cove, (2) Fault Cove, and (3) Fault Cove to Hanning Bay. Places referred to, including the locations of illustrative photographs and diagrams, are shown by the map and photomosaic on plate 2. Vertical displacements relative to sea level at and near the fault are shown on plate 2 and are contoured at a smaller scale in figure 2.

SOUTH OF FAULT COVE

The mile-long segment of the Hanning Bay fault south of Fault Cove trends N. 35° E. and is marked by a southeast-facing

26.—Overhanging scarp of Hanning Bay fault in glacial till dipping 80° northwest. About 4 inches of left-lateral displacement is indicated by the rake of roots extending across the scarp. Scale is 6½ inches long. Location shown in figure 27.

scarp in surficial deposits, tilted or toppled trees, and gaping extension cracks. The scarp is clearly visible along the extreme southern part of the fault where it crosses open ground along a slight preexisting break in slope. The fault trace is marked by a scarp as much as 5½ feet high; the surficial muskeg layer and underlying glacial till on the northwest block has ridden up and over the southeastern block to form a prominent pressure ridge (fig. 25). Where visible beneath the surface vegetation, the overhanging scarp in till dips about 80° NW. At its southern end the scarp becomes progressively lower and finally disappears. No indication of fault displacement was found anywhere along the north shore of MacLeod Harbor—an area which was examined in some detail.

The displacement is entirely dip-slip except for about 4 inches of left-lateral strike-slip displacement near the south end of the fault. The lateral component of movement is indicated by rootlets that trend obliquely across the scarp (fig. 26), by the rake of striations in the fault plane, and by the regular right-handed en echelon arrangement of gaping fissures that follow the general course of the flexure but intersect it at an angle of about 15° (fig. 27). The absence of lateral displacements elsewhere along the fault, or of systematically offset drainage across the fault trace, demonstrates that the strike-slip component of displacement during this earthquake and during earlier movements was relatively minor.

27 (left).—Segment of Hanning Bay fault trace looking northeast showing surface flexure 3 to 5 feet high broken by gaping sub-parallel right-handed en echelon cracks, 3 to 6 feet apart. Gullies that intersect the scarp at right angles show no evidence of lateral offset that would suggest strike-slip displacement. Arrow indicates location of figure 25.

North of the locality shown in figure 27, the fault trace trends in a N. 35° E. direction along the heavily timbered channel of a small stream, which drains into the beach-barred lake at the shore. For most of this distance the fault parallels the northwest edge of the stream channel except at one point where it cuts across a meander and through a small bedrock hill on the opposite side of the creek. The trace is clearly marked by a break in slope with associated ground cracks and a swath of tilted and downed trees whose crowns all point toward the relatively downthrown block. In one locality the slope break is 8½ feet high and 24 feet wide; right-handed en echelon tension cracks trending N. 15° E. at the top of the slope are as much as 1 foot wide and 6½ feet deep.

At the north end of this segment, the fault scarp forms the linear southwest shore of the beach-barred lake. An overhanging scarp that dips 80° northwest displaces glacially derived pebble-cobble gravel in a blue-gray silty-clay matrix. Striations in the soft clay are in the direction of dip.

AT FAULT COVE

By far the most spectacular segment of the Hanning Bay fault is the part shown in figure 28 (next page). It crosses a former inconspicuous embayment in the coastline, which has been transformed by vertical displacement during the earthquake into a shallow cove (christened Fault Cove). The movement produced a single continuous scarp 1.4 miles long that displaces bedrock and sediments of the former sea floor and beach deposits along the shore. The fault trace curves gradually from N. 35° E. to N. 45° E. as it crosses the cove. At extreme low tide it is exposed at the surface almost continuously except for the per-

manently submerged part at the cove entrance which, however, is readily visible from the air (fig. 29).

The existence of a preearthquake submarine scarp in bedrock at this locality is clearly indicated by the fact that unconsolidated deposits were ponded on the shoreward side of the scarp, whereas bare rock is exposed almost everywhere else on the upthrown block.

Along the south shore of Fault Cove, the scarp is a prominent southeast-facing break in slope about 8½ feet high; marine sand and pebble-cobble-boulder gravel that constitute the beach prism have slumped across the scarp and thereby concealed the actual fault surface (fig. 30). Linear strand lines on the uplifted beach, and bands of marine sand and gravel on the former submarine part of the beach that cross the fault at an oblique angle, show no evidence of lateral offset.

The part of the fault trace along the north shore of Fault Cove in the area seaward from the former beach prism is marked by an abrupt scarp in bedrock or in bedrock mantled with a thin veneer of unconsolidated marine deposits. The scarp trends either parallel to the strike of bedding planes in the bedrock or intersects them at an acute angle of less than 10°. It varies in height from 12½ to 13½ feet, and along most of its length it consists of slumped bedrock and the overlying unconsolidated deposits (fig. 31). Segments of the scarp that originally were vertical or overhanging have subsequently slumped back to the steep angle of repose shown in figure 31. In part, the slumping was accelerated by undercutting of the scarp toe and by removal of slump debris both by stream runoff diverted along the uphill-facing scarp and by current scouring. A shallow pond oc-

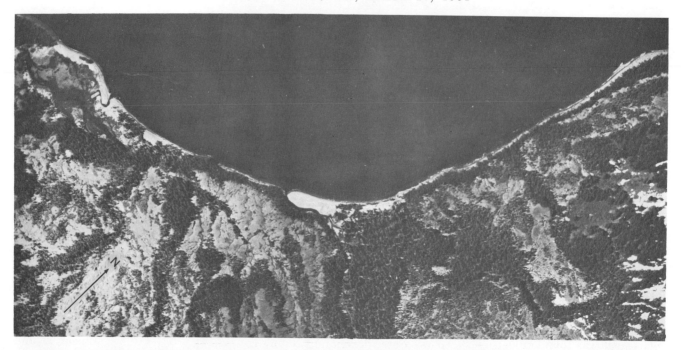

28.—Pre- and postearthquake high-tide shorelines at Fault Cove. The cove was formed by relative uplift of the former sea floor northwest of the fault scarp. The white color on the elevated bedrock surface northwest of the fault results from dessication of calcareous algae and other calcareous marine organisms. Upper photograph by U.S. Forest Service, June 8, 1959; lower photograph by U.S. Coast and Geodetic Survey, April 17, 1964.

29.—Hanning Bay fault at Fault Cove approximately at low tide. The northwest (right) block is uplifted as much as 16⅓ feet relative to the southeast block. Both blocks are uplifted relative to sea level. As a consequence, the cove is virtually dry at low tide, and the elevated beach and former offshore deposits are deeply dissected by streams. Veneer of unconsolidated deposits on the former submarine part of the downthrown block accumulated behind a preexisting fault scarp.

30.—View southwest along Hanning Bay fault. Scarp 8½ feet high has displaced the elevated beach at south side of Fault Cove, and beach deposits draped across the scarp conceal the fault plane. Comparative photographs show that modification of the scarp was negligible between May 30, 1964 (above), and August 4, 1965 (below). Bottom photograph by M. G. Bonilla.

31.—Hanning Bay fault scarp 13½ feet high in bedrock at north side of Fault Cove. The fault dips at about 55° NW. (left), but slumping along the trace has formed a scarp that is nearly vertical or dips steeply southeast. The slumping process is accelerated by erosion along the base of the uphill-facing scarp. Location shown in figure 34.

32.—View northwest toward cobble-gravel storm beach at north side of Fault Cove which was displaced 16⅓ feet vertically across the Hanning Bay fault scarp. Pond at right occupies a shallow tectonic depression. Photograph by M. G. Bonilla.

cupies a tectonic depression along the scarp base immediately below the elevated beach berm.

At the one locality where the fault plane is exposed, it consists of a 1½-foot-wide zone of sheared siltstone and intensely shattered graywacke containing thin seams of interstitial clay gouge and quartz veinlets. Planar elements within the shear zone dip 50°–60° northwest and cut obliquely across the prevailing southeast dips of the bedding.

The maximum amount of measured vertical displacement along the Hanning Bay fault is at the uplifted beach ridge shown in figure 32; here the surface of the former beach berm was displaced 16⅓ feet. Maximum dip-slip displacement at this locality is almost 20 feet.

Bedrock in the upthrown block of the Hanning Bay fault in the area of maximum uplift was broken by numerous cracks that commonly trend at high angles to the fault trace. Individual cracks are as much as 200 feet long and 0.4 foot wide, and are open to depths of more than 7 feet (fig. 33). They are extension features without vertical or lateral displacement except for short sections where local caving has occurred. All but one of the cracks are in the upthrown block in a zone that extends 650 feet northwest from the fault scarp and 1,000 feet laterally along the scarp on the northeast side of Fault Cove. The largest and most continuous cracks are shown in figure 34. A careful search found no other newly opened cracks elsewhere in the exposed bedrock platform along the shore in either block except for one crack as much as 0.3 foot wide that opened along a preexisting fault in the uplifted surf-cut platform immediately south of Fault Cove.

The relationship of these exten-

33.—Near-vertical extension crack on uplifted block of Hanning Bay fault at Fault Cove. Crack is 0.2 foot wide and at least 7 feet deep. Hole in foreground is caused by local caving at the intersection of two cracks. Location shown in figure 34.

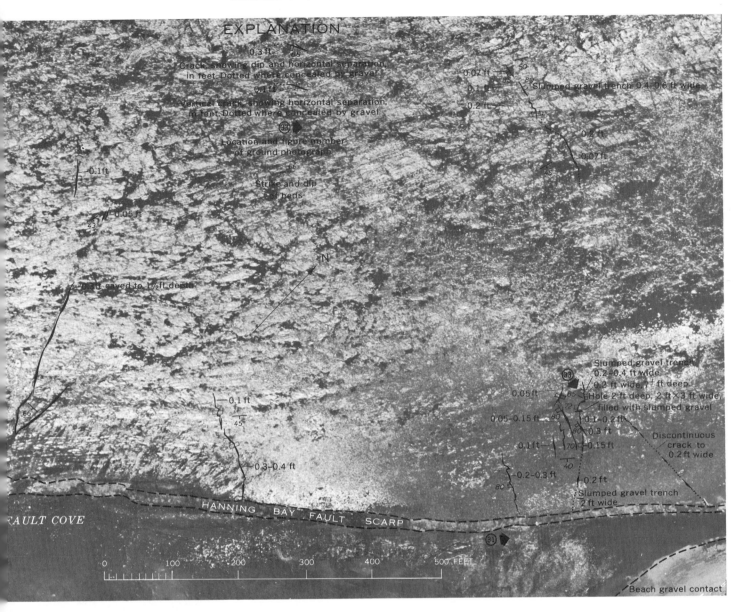

34.—Sketch map of the larger tectonic cracks in the upthrown block of the Hanning Bay fault at Fault Cove. Numerous smaller cracks in the same general area are not plotted. Location of photograph is shown on plate 2. Geology by M. G. Bonilla and George Plafker August 1, 1965. Base photograph by U.S. Coast and Geodetic Survey, July 28, 1964.

sion cracks to the Hanning Bay fault is uncertain. One possibility is that the cracks result from local tensional stresses due to surface flexing at the culmination of a distinct anticlinal warp that parallels the fault trace within the upthrown block in this area (fig. 2, profile A–A').

FAULT COVE TO HANNING BAY

North of Fault Cove the apparent strike of the Hanning Bay

fault swings to N. 50° E. as it crosses the 850-foot-high drainage divide between Fault Cove and Hanning Bay (fig. 35, next page). South of the divide, the fault trace follows along the northwest side of alined incised linear stream valleys that undoubtedly are controlled by a preexisting fault. The fault trace in this heavily timbered and topographically rugged segment is marked by a swath of fallen trees and brush, intermin-

gled with debris from soil slips and small landslides (fig. 36). Ponds have formed where two small streams flow across the uphill-facing scarp (fig. 37). Soundings made near the scarp at the downstream end of these ponds, indicate a minimum vertical fault displacement of 10 feet.

North of the ponds, the fault scarp follows a peculiar course that is northwest of, and parallel to, the incised linear stream valley

35.—Hanning Bay fault north of Fault Cove. The average 65°-NW. (left) dip of this segment of the fault causes the trace (dashed) to be deflected uphill (right) as it crosses the 850-foot-high ridge between Fault Cove and Hanning Bay. The pond, at the intersection of the fault scarp and the former beach ridge, occupies a closed tectonic depression in the downthrown block.

36.—A typical swath of tilted and fallen trees in timbered areas along the Hanning Bay fault. The upthrown block was overthrust from right to left.

37.—Pond more than 10 feet deep formed where a stream flows across the uphill-facing fault scarp (arrows). Streamflow is toward the observer. Rubble and tangle of fallen trees slid from the steep valley walls.

38.—Hanning Bay fault looking southwest from the bay. The fault trace on the ridge is marked by active landslides.

39.—Flexure and scarp with net vertical displacement of 7 feet in boulder-gravel beach along the Hanning Bay fault at south shore of Hanning Bay. Scarp 4 feet high in foreground is at the upper margin, and pond at right side of view is dammed against the base. The fault does not reappear on the north shore of Hanning Bay, which is visible in the background.

that heads at the divide on the ridge (pl. 2). The actual rupture is well uphill from the valley bottom, and, at one locality, a zone of discontinuous scarps crosses a meadow on the ridge about 200 feet above the valley bottom. The main scarp is about 6 feet high in bedrock and trends N. 35° to 40° E. along the edge of the meadow at the break in slope on the ridge. Discontinuous subparallel scarps or flexures with two sets of associated extension cracks trending N. 25° E. and N. 75° E. are exposed in an area about 150 feet wide on the ridge summit within the upthrown block.

From the meadow the fault can be traced northward to the drainage divide as a line of scarps with associated landslides and tilted or fallen trees. The fault plane is exposed in a scarp 6 feet high on the northwest side of the prominent notch at the drainage divide (pl. 2; fig. 38). Its dip, as indicated by sheared argillite and brecciated soft sandstone, is 52° NW. This estimate is reasonably compatible with a dip of 65° for the fault plane at this locality, as calculated from the altitudes and relative positions on published topographic maps of the fault trace at the divide and at the shorelines of Fault Cove and Hanning Bay. (This calculation was not made on plate 2 because distortion of photographs used in making the planimetric map does not show these three points in their correct relative horizontal positions.)

From the drainage divide to the shore of Hanning Bay the fault trace is concealed beneath blocky talus derived from a large landslide on the uphill side of the fault (pl. 2, fig. 38). The landslide predates the earthquake, but a substantial amount of debris with freshly exposed surfaces was apparently shaken down during the earthquake.

Where the fault crosses the uplifted boulder beach and former submarine platform along the shore of Hanning Bay, there is a pronounced flexure zone about 30 feet wide with a nearly vertical scarp as much as 5 feet high in boulder gravel at the head of the flexure (fig. 39). A small pond fills a depression in the downthrown block along the northeastern margin of this flexure, and the drainage is diverted along the base of the scarp, which faces upslope. Net vertical displacement across the fault zone is uncertain because many boulders have slumped along the scarp and the top and bottom

of the flexure are not clearly defined. Measurements of the height of the barnacle line on either side of the zone indicate that the northwest block is upthrown about 7 feet in relation to the southeast block (pl. 2).

The fault apparently dies out

somewhere beneath Hanning Bay. A detailed examination of the northeast shore along its projected strike did not reveal any of the features characteristics of the fault trace on land or any anomalous vertical displacements of the shoreline.

HORIZONTAL DISPLACEMENTS INDICATED BY GEODETIC MEASUREMENTS

A re-triangulation, by the U.S. Coast and Geodetic Survey, of part of the network of primary horizontal control stations in the vicinity of Montague Island suggests that both the horizontal shortening and left-lateral component of displacement in this area may be substantially greater than is indicated by the surface ruptures (Parkin, 1966, fig. 4).

Differences in displacement of two stations in the triangulation net—Stair (610) and Cape Cleare (553)—which straddle the Patton Bay fault as shown in figure 2, provide a geodetic check on the indicated fault movement obtained from field geologic studies. Station Cape Cleare is on the downthrown block 1 mile east of the fault trace; Station Stair is on the upthrown block 7 miles west of Station Cape Cleare and about 6 miles from the fault. Consequently, the indicated relative displacement between the two stations results from both movement on the fault and deformation of the crust between each of the stations and the fault.

Unfortunately, the stations are not tied together directly across Montague Island, but rather are connected through a third-order triangulation net (containing a number of geometrically weak figures), which extends around the

40.—Orientation of horizontal displacement vectors (solid arrows) at triangulation stations Stair and Cape Cleare relative to the average strike of the Patton Bay fault. Dashed arrows are the indicated components of horizontal displacement perpendicular to, and parallel to, the fault. Numerals are horizontal displacement in feet relative to station Fishhook (40 miles northeast of Anchorage), which was held fixed in the adjustment. Triangulation data from Parkin (1966, table 1).

northeast end of the island. As a consequence, the original position of Station Cape Cleare relative to the remainder of the net is especially uncertain. Added to this uncertainty is the fact that during the earthquake all stations in this area experienced large differential vertical movements with resultant

shifts in horizontal positions of the stations at high altitudes. Nevertheless, the general similarity in orientation of the two vectors and their striking difference in magnitude are suggestive of substantial relative movements between them.

As shown in figure 40, the principal vector of horizontal movement derived from the geodetic data is between N. 10° W. and N. 5° E. at an oblique angle to the fault system, whereas the direction indicated by the predominantly dip-slip displacements across the scarps is actually about N. 53° W., or approximately normal to the average strike of the faults. The re-triangulation data further indicate that the two stations moved 34 feet relatively toward one another in the direction of fault dip and that they were relatively displaced 21 feet in a left-lateral sense (fig. 40). The dip-slip shortening could have been taken up by bending of the upthrown block in addition to the fault displacement. The strike-slip displacement, on the other hand, should have been readily observable had it occurred along the fault. Absence of a large lateral-slip component on the fault suggests that either the displacement was taken up mostly by warping between the fault and the stations or, more probably, that an error has been introduced into this part of the triangulation adjustment through a slight clockwise rotation of displacement vectors.

SUMMARY AND CONCLUSIONS

The Patton Bay fault on land is represented by a complex system of right-handed en echelon reverse faults and associated flexures that has an average N. 37° E. strike. The fault at the surface dips about 85° NW. near its southern end and 50° to 75° elsewhere along the scarp. Displacement on the fault is almost entirely dip slip, the northwest side upthrown relative to the southeast side. The maximum measured vertical component of slip is 20 to 23 feet and maximum indicated dip slip is about 26 feet. A left-lateral displacement component of less than 2 feet near the southern end of the fault is probably a local phenomenon related to a change in strike of the fault that causes it to trend at a small oblique angle to the principal horizontal stress direction.

The fault system can be traced on land for 22 miles from shore to shore and is known to continue seaward to the southwest for at least 17 miles. Indirect evidence suggests that the fault system may extend southwestward on the sea floor more than 300 miles. The fault apparently dies out on its northwestern end but it could be offset en echelon in a right-handed sense and continue northeastward offshore from Montague Island at least as far as Hinchinbrook Island.

The Hanning Bay fault is a virtually continuous reverse fault with an average strike of N. 47° E., a total length of about 4 miles, and surface dips of 52° to 75° NW. Displacement is almost entirely dip slip except for a left-lateral strike-slip component of about a third of a foot near the southern limit of exposure. The maximum measured vertical component of slip is 16⅓ feet, and the maximum indicated dip slip is about 20 feet.

The reverse faults on Montague Island and the postulated submarine extension of the Patton Bay Fault lie within a tectonically important zone of crustal shortening and maximum known uplift associated with the earthquake. The principal horizontal stress direction is oriented roughly normal to the average strike of the faults in a general N. 53° W. to S. 53° E. direction.

The displacements that occurred along these two faults during the earthquake are large, but there are four convincing indications that the faults are not the primary features along which the earthquake occurred: (1) The lithology of the rock sequences is not significantly different on the two sides of the faults, as it commonly is along faults that form major tectonic boundaries. (2) Displacement along these known and postulated faults is insufficient to explain the areal extent of regional uplift—particularly the uplift seaward from the known and inferred trace. (3) Not enough movement occurred on these faults to account for the size and spatial distribution of the earthquake focal region, as defined by the aftershocks; this region extends in all directions far beyond the maximum conceivable limits of the known and postulated surface faults. (4) The epicenter of the main shock is roughly 90 miles away from the fault traces and in a position where it is not likely to lie on the down-dip projection of the fault planes.

Both the Patton Bay and the Hanning Bay faults on Montague Island are along prominent linear breaks in slope or linear stream valleys that, for the most part, were clearly visible on aerial photographs taken before the earthquake (Condon and Cass, 1958). Only the southern segment of the Patton Bay fault, for a distance of 3.3 miles, does not follow a well-established prior fault trace but instead breaks away from a pronounced scarp along which much of the previous movements undoubtedly occurred. Net Quaternary vertical displacement on and near the Patton Bay fault, as indi-cated by maximum topographic relief across it, could be 1,500 feet; it is probably no more than 100 feet on the Hanning Bay fault.

Many of the preearthquake scarps along these faults are sharp postglacial topographic features. The straight spruce trees along the faults, including many giants as much as 4 feet in base diameter that are probably 150 to 300 years old (J. Standerwick, U.S. Forest Service, oral commun., Oct. 4, 1966), indicate that no major displacement has occurred for at least that length of time.

REFERENCES

Buwalda, J. P., and St. Amand, Pierre, 1955, Geological effects of the Arvin-Tehachapi earthquake: California Div. Mines Bull. 171, pt. 1, Geology, p. 41–56.

Case, J. E., Barnes, D. F., Plafker, George, and Robbins, S. L., 1966, Gravity survey and regional geology of the Prince William Sound epicentral region, Alaska: U.S. Geol. Survey Prof. Paper 543–C, p. C1–C12.

Condon, W. H., and Cass, J. T., 1958, Map of a part of the Prince William Sound area, Alaska, showing linear geologic features as shown on aerial photographs: U.S. Geol. Survey Misc. Geol. Inv. Map I–273, scale 1:125,000.

Florensov, N. A., and Solonenko, V. P., eds., 1963, Gobi-Altayskoye zemletryasyeniye: Akad. Nauk SSSR, 391 p. *Also*, 1965, The Gobi-Altai earthquake: U.S. Dept. Commerce, 424 p. [English translation.]

Grant, U. S., and Higgins, D. F., 1910, Reconnaissance of the geology and mineral resources of Prince William Sound, Alaska: U.S. Geol. Survey Bull. 443, 89 p.

Grantz, Arthur, Plafker, George, and

Kachadoorian, Reuben, 1964, Alaska's Good Friday earthquake, March 27, 1964: U.S. Geol. Survey Circ. 491, 35 p.

Henderson, J., 1933, The geological aspects of the Hawke's Bay earthquakes: New Zealand Jour. Sci., v. 15, no. 1, p. 38–75.

Malloy, R. J., 1965a, Crustal uplift southwest of Montague Island, Alaska: Science, v. 146, no. 3647, p. 1048–1049.

——— 1965b, Seafloor upheaval: Geo-Marine Technology, v. 1, p. 22–26.

Moffitt, F. H., 1954, Geology of the Prince William Sound region, Alaska: U.S. Geol. Survey Bull. 989–E, p. 225–310.

Parkin, E. J., 1966, Horizontal displacements, pt. 2 *of* Alaskan surveys to determine crustal movement: U.S. Coast and Geodetic Survey, 11 p.

Plafker, George, 1965, Tectonic deformation associated with the 1964 Alaska earthquake: Science, v. 148, no. 3678, p. 1675–1687.

Plafker, George, and Kachadoorian, Reuben, 1966, Geologic effects of the March 27, 1964, earthquake and associated seismic sea waves on Kodiak and nearby islands, Alaska:

U.S. Geol. Survey Prof. Paper 543–D, p. D1–D46.

Plafker, George, and MacNeil, F. S., 1966, Stratigraphic significance of Tertiary fossils from the Orca Group in the Prince William Sound region, Alaska: U.S. Geol. Survey Prof. Paper 550–B, p. B62–B68.

Plafker, George, and Mayo, L. R., 1965, Tectonic deformation, subaqueous slides, and destructive waves associated with the Alaskan March 27, 1964, earthquake—an interim geologic evaluation: U.S. Geol. Survey open-file report, 21 p.

Tsuya, Hiromichi, ed., 1950, The Fukui earthquake of June 28, 1948: Tokyo, Report of the special committee for the study of the Fukui earthquake, 197 p.

Van Dorn, W. G., 1964, Source mechanism of the tsunami of March 28, 1964, in Alaska: Coastal Eng. Conf., 9th, Lisbon 1964, Proc., p. 166–190.

von Huene, Roland, Shor, G. R., Jr., and St. Amand, Pierre, 1966, Active faults and structure of the continental margin in the 1964 Alaskan aftershock area [abs.]: Am. Geophys. Union, 47th Ann. Mtg., April 19–22, 1966, p. 176.

CLARIFICATIONS

Geology Vol. Page	USGS Page	Column	Line	Remarks
140	G 6	1	15	Plates 1 and 2 are Plates C and D, respectively, in Part B, the accompanying map case
140	G 6	2	43	See also Plafker, USGS PP 543-I, p. 58, this volume

GEORGE PLAFKER
U.S. GEOLOGICAL SURVEY

REUBEN KACHADOORIAN
U.S. GEOLOGICAL SURVEY

Reprinted with minor changes from
U.S. Geological Survey Professional Paper 543-D,
"Geologic Effects of the March 1964 Earthquake and Associated Seismic Sea Waves
on Kodiak and Nearby Islands, Alaska"

Geologic Effects on the Kodiak Island Area

ABSTRACT

Kodiak Island and the nearby islands constitute a mountainous landmass with an aggregate area of 4,900 square miles that lies at the western border of the Gulf of Alaska and from 20 to 40 miles off the Alaskan mainland. Igneous and metamorphic rocks underlie most of the area except for a narrow belt of moderately to poorly indurated rocks bordering the Gulf of Alaska coast and local accumulations of unconsolidated alluvial and marine deposits along the streams and coast. The area is relatively undeveloped and is sparsely inhabited. About 4,800 of the 5,700 permanent residents in the area live in the city of Kodiak or at the Kodiak Naval Station.

The great earthquake, which occurred on March 27, 1964, at 5:36 p.m. Alaska standard time (March 28, 1964, 0336 Greenwich mean time), and had a Richter magnitude of 8.4–8.5, was the most severe earthquake felt on Kodiak Island and its nearby islands in modern times. Although the epicenter lies in Prince William Sound 250 miles northeast of Kodiak—the principal city of the area, the areal distribution of the thousands of aftershocks that followed it, the local tectonic deformation, and the estimated source area of the subsequent seismic sea wave, all suggest that the Kodiak group of islands lay immediately adjacent to, and northwest of, the focal region from which the elastic seismic energy was radiated. The duration of strong ground motion in the area was estimated at 2½–7 minutes. Locally, the tremors were preceded by sounds audible to the human ear and were reportedly accompanied in several places by visible ground waves.

Intensity and felt duration of the shocks during the main earthquake and aftershock sequence varied markedly within the area and were strongly influenced by the local geologic environment. Estimated Mercalli intensities in most areas underlain by unconsolidated Quaternary deposits ranged from VIII to as high as IX. In contrast, intensities in areas of upper Tertiary rock ranged from VII to VIII, and in areas of relatively well indurated lower Tertiary and Mesozoic rocks, from VI to VII.

Local subsidence of as much as 10 feet was widespread in noncohesive granular deposits through compaction, flow, and sliding that resulted from vibratory loading during the earthquake. This phenomenon, which was largely restricted to saturated beach and alluvial deposits or artificial fill, was locally accompanied by extensive cracking of the ground and attendant ejection of water and water-sediment mixtures.

Numerous landslides, including a wide variety of rockfalls, rockslides, and flows along steep slopes, were triggered by the long-duration horizontal and vertical accelerations during the earthquake. The landslides are most numerous in a narrow belt along the southeast coast of Kodiak Island and the nearby offshore islands. Their abundance appears to be related to an area underlain predominantly by Tertiary rocks.

Temporary and permanent changes of level occurred after the earthquake in some wells, lakes, and streams throughout the area; ice was cracked, and the salinity of a few wells increased. Permanent change of water level at some localities appears to be related to readjustments of fracture porosity by earthquake-induced movements of bedrock blocks. Increased salinity of wells in coastal areas resulted from encroachment of sea water into aquifers after subsidence during the earthquake, and to flooding of watersheds by seismic sea waves.

Vertical displacements, both downward and upward, occurred throughout the area as a result of crustal warping along a northeast-trending axis. Most of Kodiak and all of Afognak, Shuyak, and adjacent islands are within a regional zone of subsidence whose trough plunges gently northeastward and approximately coincides with the mountainous backbone of Kodiak Island. Subsidence in excess of 6 feet occurred throughout the northern part of the zone—a maximum subsidence of 6½–7 feet having occurred on Marmot and eastern Afognak Islands. Southeast of the axis of tectonic tilting, uplift of at least 2½ feet occurred in a narrow zone that includes most of the southeasterly capes of Kodiak Island, the southeastern half of Sitkalidak Island, and Sitkinak Island. The uplift is inferred to extend offshore over much or all of the continental shelf adjacent to the Kodiak group of islands. Within the affected area, tectonic subsidence, which was locally augmented by surficial subsidence of unconsolidated deposits, caused widespread inundation of shorelines and attendant damage to intertidal organisms, nearshore terrestrial vegetation, and salmon-spawning areas.

The most devastating effect of the earthquake on Kodiak Island and nearby islands resulted from seismic sea waves that probably originated along a linear zone of differential uplift in the Gulf of Alaska. A train of at least seven seismic sea waves, having initial periods of 50–55 minutes, struck along all the southeast coast of the island group from 38 to 63 minutes after the earthquake. The southeast shores were repeatedly washed by destructive waves having runup heights along exposed coasts of perhaps as much as 40 feet above existing tide level, and of 8–20 feet along protected shores. Runup heights of the waves were much less on the northwest and southwest sides of the islands, and no wave damage was incurred there. Locally, high-velocity currents that accompanied the waves caused intense erosion and redistribution of unconsolidated natural and artificial shore deposits and of shallow sea-floor deposits.

The Alaska earthquake was the greatest natural catastrophe to befall the Kodiak Island area in historic time. The combination of seismic shock and the earthquake-related tectonic deformation and seismic sea waves took 18 lives, destroyed property worth about $45 million, and resulted in estimated losses of income to the fishing industry of an additional $5 million.

Most of the damage and all of the loss of life were directly attributable to the seismic sea waves that crippled the city of Kodiak, wiped out the village of Kaguyak, and destroyed most of the village of Old Harbor and parts of the villages of Afognak and Uzinki. Bridges and segments of the highways in the vicinity of the city of Kodiak were washed out, and parts of the Kodiak Naval Station were inundated and damaged. Especially serious to all the damaged communities was the loss of fishing boats, seafood processing plants, and other waterfront installations, which had been the mainstay of the economy.

Additional heavy losses resulted from the combined regional tectonic and local surficial subsidence that occurred during the earthquake. Widespread shoreline flooding by high tides necessitated raising, protecting, or removing many installations otherwise undamaged by the earthquake or waves.

Structural damage attributable to seismic shock during the earthquake was relatively light and was restricted to areas underlain by saturated unconsolidated deposits. The chief structural failure in the area as a result of shaking was the collapse of part of a cannery built on saturated beach deposits that were partially liquefied during the earthquake. Minor structural damage resulted from differential settlement and cracking of the ground on natural granular deposits and artificial fills. The overwhelming majority of structures are constructed on indurated bedrock; none of these sustained damage other than small losses resulting from shifting about and breakage of their contents.

INTRODUCTION

The great earthquake of March 27, 1964 was strongly felt throughout Kodiak Island and the nearby islands. Earth tremors triggered numerous landslides and avalanches, caused the ground to crack and subside in some areas of unconsolidated deposits, and affected water levels of streams, lakes, and wells. The earthquake was accompanied by regional tectonic warping that resulted in both extensive subsidence and local uplift of the land relative to sea level. It was followed after about half an hour by a train of at least seven destructive large-amplitude seismic sea waves that repeatedly inundated low-lying segments of the shore.

The loss of 18 lives and most of the property damage were due to seismic sea waves that battered the southeastern coast of the islands. Additional heavy losses resulted from inundation of coastal lowlands and waterfront installations as a result of the combined tectonic and local subsidence. Structural damage directly attributable to seismic shock during the earthquake was light and was largely due to foundation failure of varying degrees. Total earthquake-related property damage in the area is estimated at about $45 million (table 1), and income losses to the fishing industry amount to an additional $5 million.

PURPOSE AND SCOPE OF INVESTIGATION

This report presents the results of a reconnaissance study of the earthquake effects over the vast uninhabited parts of the islands. The regional setting of the islands, and the effects of the earthquake at localities other than the urban areas are described. Detailed accounts of specific damage at the communities will be given in a separate volume of this series on earthquake effects on Kodiak and other communities on the Kodiak Islands.

An effort was made to evaluate the local geologic factors that control the distribution and character of the shock-induced effects because these factors have potential significance in the design and construction of engineering works in seismically active areas. A reconnaissance of the tectonic changes in land level was made to delineate the areal extent and nature of these movements on the islands, and their relationship to the deformation that occurred elsewhere in south-central Alaska. These data are pertinent to any critical interpretation of the mechanics of the earthquake and

TABLE 1.—*Estimated property losses on Kodiak and nearby islands*

Location	Nature of damage	Estimated replacement cost	Source of data
Kodiak City.............	Losses of private, commercial, and public property.	$24,746,000	Tudor (1964).
Afognak; village site abandoned.	Losses of private and public property.	816,000	Bur. Indian Affairs (written commun., Sept. 25, 1964).
Old Harbor	.... do	707,000	Do.
Kaguyak; village site abandoned.	.... do	321,000	Do.
Uzinki	.... do	49,800	Do.
Entire area except city of Kodiak.	Commercial	2,140,000	Alaska Dept. Fish and Game (1965).
Entire area	Vessels damaged and lost.	2,466,500	Do.
Kodiak Island exclusive of Kodiak Naval Station.	Bridge and highway damage.	3,359,000	Alaska Dept. Highways (written commun., April 1, 1964).
Kodiak Naval Station.	Structures and equipment including bridges and highway.	10,936,800	Tudor (1964).

to the origin of the seismic sea waves that followed. Incidental to the geologic studies enumerated above, information was also obtained on the arrival times, runup heights, and characteristics of the seismic sea waves and the damage caused by them.

The present report is based largely on studies made by Plafker from float-equipped fixed-wing aircraft and helicopter during the periods July 14–20, 1964, and July 15–21, 1965; on studies made by Kachadoorian at Kodiak and vicinity July 14–18, 1964; and on observations on earthquake effects made by G. W. Moore May 13–21, 1964. Moore also provided unpublished data on the geology of the islands. These observations were supplemented with studies of U.S. Coast and Geodetic Survey vertical aerial photography by the writers and W. H. Condon. Additional data

was obtained from the numerous individuals and organizations listed in the acknowledgments. Kachadoorian wrote the section on damage to the highways; the remainder of the report was written by Plafker.

ACKNOWLEDGEMENTS

We are greatly indebted to numerous individuals who provided us, in interviews and on form questionnaires, with eyewitness accounts of their experiences during and immediately after the earthquake.

Personnel of the Fleet Weather Central, Kodiak Naval Station (Comdr. A. L. Dodson, Commanding Officer), obtained critical data on the seismic sea-wave sequence and the change in tide levels at the Naval base in Womens Bay and furnished helicopter transportation to an otherwise inaccessible area of Narrow Cape. Dexter Lall

and other biologists of the Alaska Department of Fish and Game provided unpublished data and numerous photographs of the earthquake effects on coastal lakes and streams. June Brevdy of the U.S. Navy Radiological Laboratory furnished photographs, newspaper clippings, and published data on structural damage from seismic sea waves in the Kodiak area. Lt. Comdr. W. D. Barbee, of the U.S. Coast and Geodetic Survey, provided tide records and data on changes in land level at tide-gage stations on Kodiak Island. The U.S. Coast and Geodetic Survey and the U.S. Army furnished postearthquake aerial photographs. Pierre St. Amand, of the U.S. Naval Ordnance Test Station, made available data obtained during an aerial reconnaissance of the area immediately after the earthquake. Fred O. Jones, consulting geologist, provided photographs and data on earthquake effects in the Terror River drainage basin.

Pilots Bob Leonard and Al Cratty flew Plafker around the islands and freely shared with him their intimate knowledge of the Kodiak Islands area and of earthquake-induced changes that had occurred there.

GEOGRAPHIC SETTING

The group of islands described in this report, of which Kodiak Island is the largest, lies at the western border of the Gulf of Alaska in the north Pacific Ocean between lat 56°30′ and 58°40′ N. and long 150°40′ and 154°50′W. (fig. 1). The group has an aggregate land area of 4,900 square miles, extends for a distance of 177 miles in a northeast direction, and is 67 miles wide at its greatest width. The largest islands of the group are shown on figure 2.

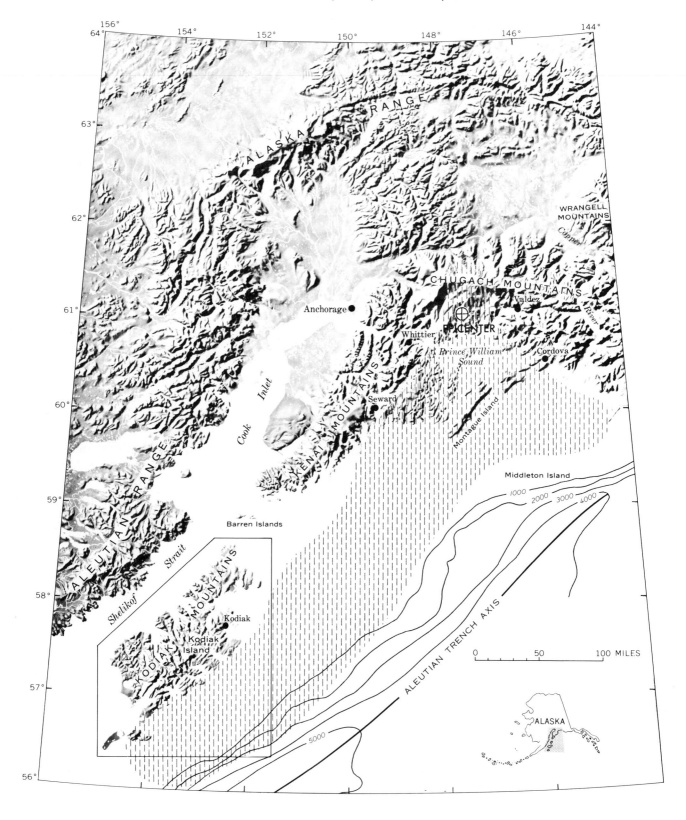

1. — Physiographic map of south-central Alaska showing location of the Kodiak group of islands with respect to the epicenter of the March 27 earthquake and its zone of major aftershocks (lined pattern). Submarine contours in meters.

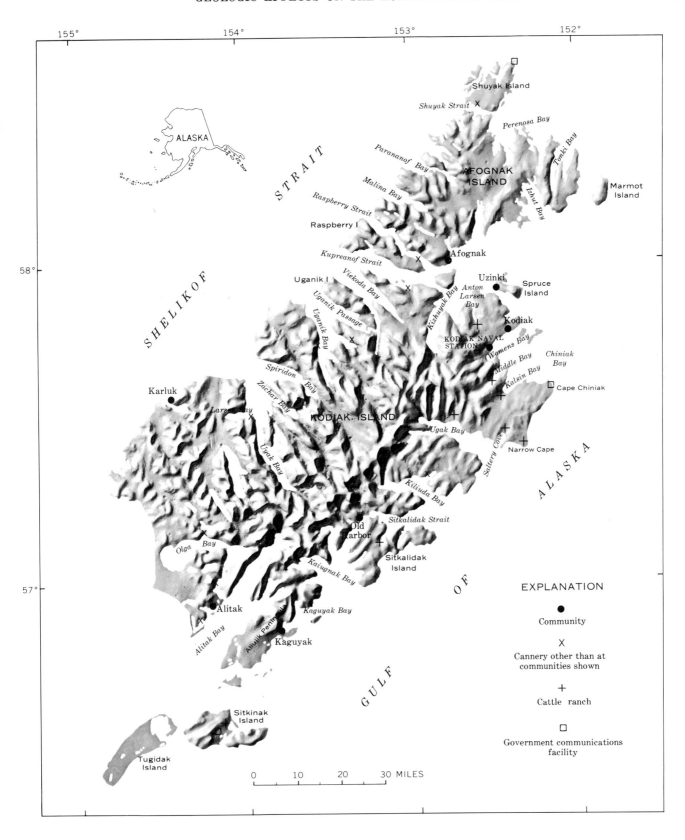

2. — Physiographic map of Kodiak and nearby islands.

The population of the Kodiak group of islands is sparse, only about 3,600 permanent residents being reported in the 1960 census, in addition to 2,160 personnel at the Kodiak Naval Station.

The city of Kodiak and nearby Kodiak Naval Station have the only large concentrations of population on the islands. The remaining settlements are small fishing villages. Permanent population of these settlements in 1960 was as follows:

Community	Population
Afognak	190
Akhiok	72–75
Kaguyak	36
Karluk	129
Kodiak	2,628
Larsen Bay	72
Old Harbor	193
Uzinki	214

Of the total of some 5,700 persons living on these islands, more than 5,300 live within 20 miles of the city of Kodiak. Throughout the rest of the area the population is concentrated in the villages with the exception of a few remote cattle ranches and Government communications facilities. Several large canneries on the island employ numerous workers during the summer; at the time of the earthquake none of the canneries were in operation and their only occupants were the winter watchmen.

Kodiak and the nearby islands are the structural extension of the Kenai-Chugach Mountains (fig. 1). This group of islands, and the Barren Islands that lie between the group and the Kenai Mountains, have been named the Kodiak Mountains section of the Pacific Border Ranges province (Wahrhaftig, 1965, p. 39). As a whole, the islands are mountainous, being lowest on the islands at the extreme north and south and highest in the middle (fig. 2).

TABLE 2. — *Tidal constants at selected stations along the coasts of Kodiak and nearby islands*

[Station: A, on the Gulf of Alaska; B, on Shelikof Strait. Predicted time and height of tides from U.S. Coast and Geodetic Survey (1964a). Local (Alaska standard) time; tide measurements in feet above lower low water]

Station (fig. 2)	Annual tide			Predicted tide, March 27–28, 1964			
	Diurnal range	Mean	Highest	Low, evening, March 27		High, morning, March 28	
				Time	Height	Time	Height
Perenosa Bay (A)	11.3	5.9	13.4	7:34 p.m.	0.1	1:29 a.m.	11.4
Izhut Bay (A)	8.9	4.5	11.0	7:16 p.m.	— .2	1:13 a.m.	10.0
Kizhuyak Bay (A)	9.6	4.9	11.7	7:06 p.m.	— .2	1:07 a.m.	9.7
Kodiak Harbor (A)	8.5	4.3	10.6	6:52 p.m.	— .3	0:57 a.m.	8.6
Ugak Bay (A)	8.4	4.3	10.6	6:35 p.m.	— .1	0:32 a.m.	8.6
Sitkalidak Island (A)	8.3	4.4	10.6	6:49 p.m.	— .1	0:43 a.m.	8.6
Alitak Bay (AB)	11.7	6.2	14.9	7:10 p.m.	.1	0:59 a.m.	10.1
Uyak Bay (B)	13.8	7.3	13.8	7:23 p.m.	— .4	1:24 a.m.	15.2
Uganik Bay (B)	14.6	7.6	17.7	7:22 p.m.	— .3	1:25 a.m.	15.8
Malina Bay (B)	14.5	7.7	17.7	7:24 p.m.	— .3	1:26 a.m.	16.0

The western part of Kodiak Island has many broad alluviated valleys and coastal lowlands that are underlain by thick glacial deposits. Sitkinak Island, at the south end of the group, has a maximum altitude of 1,470 feet. The surface of nearby Tugidak Island is a marine terrace that rises only about 100 feet above sea level. Shuyak Island and the northern part of Afognak Island are hilly lowlands.

The coastline is extremely steep and irregular and is characterized by many deep narrow fiords and rocky islets. Narrow marine terraces occur at intervals on the outer capes along the southeast coast of Kodiak and Sitkalidak Islands. Bars and spits have formed across the mouth of many of the bays and inlets. Numerous shallow lagoons and lakes occur behind low barrier beaches along the shore.

There is a marked difference in the range of tides on the ocean side and on the Shelikof Straits side of the islands. Mean annual tide range is 13 to 14½ feet along Shelikof Strait in contrast to 8.2 to 11.3 feet at most places on the ocean coast. Furthermore, the difference in maximum annual tide height on the two sides of

the island may be as much as 7 feet. These differences are significant to this study because they strongly influenced the amount and distribution of the damage caused by seismic sea waves and by tectonic subsidence along the coast. Table 2 shows the tidal constants at selected localities, and the time and height of high and low tide during the period when seismic sea waves struck the coast on the night of March 27.

On March 27, 1964, the weather was mild; highest and lowest reported temperatures were 37° F. and 20° F.; there was little or no snow on the ground at sea level, but traces of snow fell during the day at Kodiak Naval Station and Larsen Bay (U.S. Weather Bureau, 1964). Winds were light with scattered high overcast. All the lakes were frozen over.

GEOLOGIC SETTING

The oldest rocks in the area lie along the northwest coast of Kodiak Island and consist chiefly of metavolcanic and marine sedimentary rocks of Triassic and Jurassic age that are cut by mafic intrusives. Younger Mesozoic marine sedimentary rocks of probable Cretaceous age, complexly deformed and extensively intruded by granitic rocks, underlie the axial part of the Kodiak Mountains. Northeast-trending belts of downfaulted lower Tertiary rocks make up the southeast side of Kodiak Island, Sitkalidak, Tugidak, and Sitkinak Islands. These belts are composed of a sequence of highly inclined and intensely folded sandstone, shale, conglomerate, and altered volcanic rocks that are locally cut by felsic intrusives. Overlying the older rocks are poorly consolidated upper Tertiary marine sedimentary rocks that have been gently to moderately folded. Fold axes and major faults strike northeast, the northwest blocks of the faults generally being upthrown. Distribution of the major lithologic units is shown in figure 3 (next page).

On Kodiak and the nearby islands, unconsolidated deposits as a rule are thin and discontinuous. They consist mainly of glacial debris, alluvial and delta deposits, and beach deposits. Local thick accumulations of colluvium occur along the bases of the steeper slopes, particularly in areas underlain by Tertiary rocks. Most of the coast consists of rugged rocky bluffs; extensive and well-developed beaches are uncommon.

A significant proportion of the alluvial deposits in an east-west belt across the central part of the islands consists of virtually uncompacted volcanic ash and pumice deposited in the spring of 1912 during the eruption of Katmai Volcano, on the Alaska Peninsula to the west (Capps, 1937, p. 170–171).

The thickest and most extensive alluvial and glacial deposits are delineated on figure 3. Areas where bedrock is covered by thin deposits of soil, colluvium, glacial debris, stream gravel, marine beach deposits, or artificial fill are not shown.

THE EARTHQUAKE AND ITS AFTERSHOCKS

LOCATION AND MAGNITUDE

The earthquake began at 5:35:12.15±0.25 p.m. Alaska standard time (S. T. Algermissen, U.S. Coast and Geodetic Survey, oral commun., April 22, 1965); its hypocenter is 12–31 miles deep (20–50 km); and the epicenter is located at lat 61.1° N., long 147.7° W. in northern Prince William Sound, 250 miles northeast of the Kodiak group of islands (fig. 1). Estimates of Richter magnitude, based upon surface wave amplitudes (M_s) are in the range of 8.4 to 8.5 according to the U.S. Coast and Geodetic Survey. The focal region, or zone of probable fault breakage during the earthquake, is approximately outlined by the spatial distribution of aftershocks. As shown by figure 1, this zone extends 400 miles southwestward from the epicenter in a broad belt that includes much of the continental shelf and southeastern margin of the Kodiak group of islands.

Perhaps related to the earthquake was an apparent instantaneous increase in the magnetic field by about 100 gamma on a continuously recording magnetometer in the city of Kodiak (Moore, 1964, p. 508). It is possible, however, that the anomaly, which occurred 1 hour and 4 minutes before the tremors were first felt, was caused by a local surface disturbance unrelated to the earthquake.

During the first month after the earthquake, more than 7,500 aftershocks were recorded at seismograph stations in the focal region (S. T. Algermissen, oral commun., April 22, 1965). Locations of the larger aftershocks (magnitudes of 5.0 or greater) with epicenters in the vicinity of the Kodiak group of islands are indicated on figure 4. Except for two aftershocks centered in the western part of the islands (p. D9) they all lie along the southeast coast of Kodiak, Sitkalidak, and Sitinak Islands and on the adjacent continental shelf. The largest aftershock recorded in the mapped area had a magnitude of 6.1. Focal depths range from about 9 to 19 miles (15–30 km).

GROUND MOTION IN THE INITIAL SHOCK

Strong ground motion that lasted from 2½ to 7 minutes was experienced throughout the study area. However, marked variations in the duration, intensity, and nature of the shaking were reported in different parts of the islands. According to most observers, the earthquake started with a gentle rolling motion for a period of 20 seconds to 1 minute, shook hard for about 2½ minutes, and then gradually subsided. The ground motion was generally described as rolling like sea waves, or as a strong horizontal oscillation. The jarring motion that was felt in

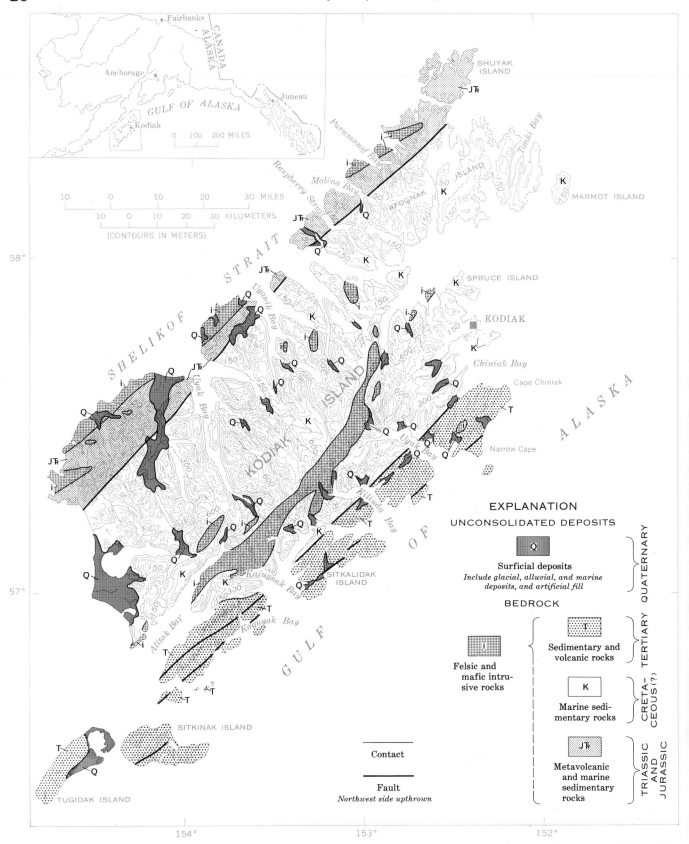

3. — Geologic sketch map of Kodiak and nearby islands. Geology generalized after Capps (1937) and from unpublished data by G. W. Moore.

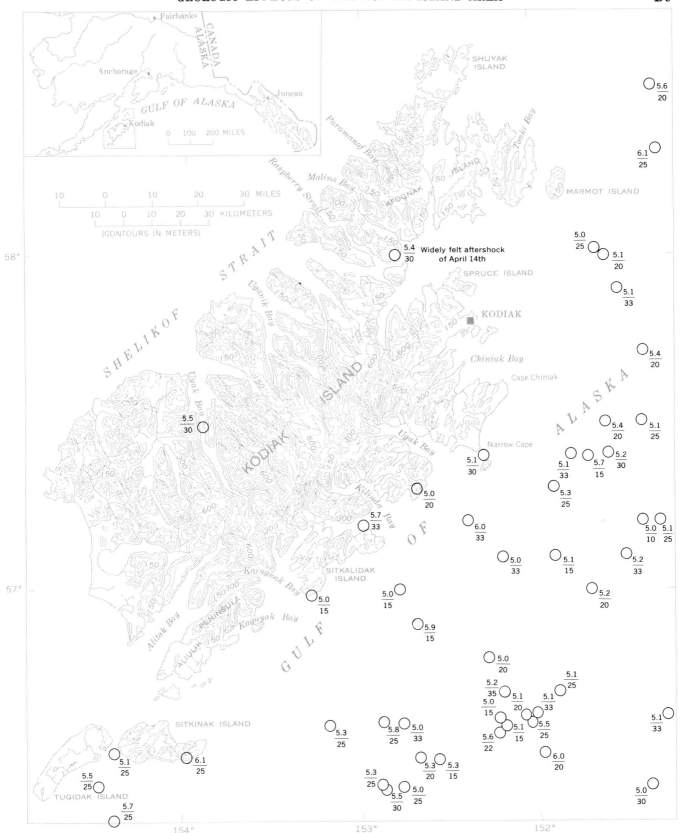

4. — Aftershock distribution (magnitude greater than 5.0) in the Kodiak Island area. Numbers indicate Richter magnitude (above) and focal depth in kilometers (below). Data after U.S. Coast and Geodetic Survey, Preliminary determination of epicenter cards, 1964.

5. — Reported ground motion, sounds, ground waves, and assigned Mercalli intensities on Kodiak and nearby islands. The directions of reported ground motion are shown by arrows; localities at which sound was reported are shown by solid circles, localities at which ground waves were reported by open circles, and assigned Mercalli intensities by Roman numerals.

DROWNED STREAM ESTUARY AT EAGLE HARBOR ALONG SOUTH SHORE OF UGAK BAY

Extensive brown area of terrestrial vegetation has been killed by salt-water immersion after 4 feet of tectonic subsidence and an unknown amount of surficial subsidence. The gray ridge of beach gravel in the left part of view (arrows) has been eroded back and built up in adjustment to the new higher base level of deposition. The fact that the effects of inundation are scarcely visible along the steep bedrock shore in the background suggests that much of the subsidence at the estuary deposits was surficial rather than tectonic.

This photograph is printed in color in the USGS original.

DEBRIS AVALANCHE ON THE PENINSULA BETWEEN UGAK AND KILIUDA BAYS

A slide of Tertiary rocks from the 1,500-foot-high peak at upper right flowed into the uninhabited valley below at about 300-foot altitude where it spread out as a debris lobe roughly 1,500 feet across.   The narrow streak of light-colored debris in the lower right corner is part of the slide mass that overflowed the near flank of the landslide scar.

This photograph is printed in color in the USGS original.

6. — The Kadiak Fisheries cannery site in Shearwater Bay along the north shore of Kiliuda Bay. Cannery buildings in the foreground were split during the earthquake and the seaward parts of the structures were later washed away by seismic sea waves. The former locations of the buildings and dock are outlined by timber pile foundations in the beach and water. The entire beach is now inundated at high tide as a result of about 4 feet of tectonic subsidence and 2-10 feet of surficial subsidence of the beach deposits. The barge behind the cusp is a floating cannery that replaces the destroyed facility on land. Location of cannery shown on figure 5.

some areas closer to the epicenter was not experienced on Kodiak or the nearby islands during the initial shock, although it was reported in some of the larger aftershocks. A local resident, Mr. Rudy Lorensen, timed the duration of the strongest ground motion as 2½ minutes on a bedrock site near the city of Kodiak.

Reports of the directions of vibrations show a wide variation. The apparent variations may be in part due to the difficulty in determining the direction from which a shock comes during such a distressing experience. In part they may result from a change in the source of the vibrations as the rupture propagated southwestward from its epicenter in Prince William Sound or to local variations in ground conditions.

Figure 5 shows that the reported vibration directions were mostly northeast-southwest to north-south, although in a few instances they were northwest-southeast.

The intensity, or the destructive potential, of the vibrations in the area varied markedly from place to place and appeared to be closely controlled by the local geologic environment. The generalization that both the intensity and duration of earthquake vibrations are enhanced in unconsolidated ground, particularly on water-soaked unconsolidated deposits (Gutenberg, 1957), is strikingly borne out by the distribution of vibration-induced damage in the area.

The most severe shaking occurred in areas of thick saturated unconsolidated Quaternary de-

posits throughout the islands. In these areas, structural damage resulted mainly from foundation failure attributable to partial liquefaction, differential settlement, and cracking of unconsolidated deposits and artificial fill. The sole structural failure reported in the area was the partial collapse of the main building of the Kadiak Fisheries cannery located on a beach cusp on Shearwater Bay along the north shore of Kiliuda Bay. The structure split in half when it was shifted off its piling foundation according to the cannery watchman, Mr. Sergei Pestrikoff. The piling was driven into beach gravel that was partially liquefied during the earthquake (fig. 6). The fallen section was later washed away by the seismic sea waves.

SURFACE WAVES

Reliable data on the amplitude and period of the ground waves that accompanied the earthquake in the area are unavailable. Long-period surface waves set bodies of surface water, trees, radio antennas, and hanging objects such as lighting fixtures and wall pictures into violent oscillation throughout the islands but caused only minor damage to manmade structures. The period of an oscillating antenna pole about 50 feet high on a bedrock site was timed by one observer as "slightly less than one second."

Visible traveling undulations of the ground surface in areas underlain by unconsolidated deposits were reported at the villages of Uzinki and Afognak. The wavelength at Uzinki was described as 30 feet; estimates of amplitude could not be made. Similar progressive linear earth waves having estimated amplitudes as great as 3 feet were observed at numerous localities underlain by unconsolidated deposits in the part of south-central Alaska where the earthquake was strongly felt. Such waves have been frequently noted in comparable geologic environments during other great earthquakes throughout the world. The waves may correspond to the large amplitude "hydrodynamic" waves discovered by Leet (1946, p. 209–211) on seismograph recordings of underground explosions. It is conceivable that such waves, which have particle orbits comparable to those of water waves, may be propagated in ground that has become semifluid as a result of ground vibration.

Elsewhere in areas underlain by consolidated deposits and in areas of poorly consolidated Ter-tiary rock, there was minor cracking of interior plaster, concrete and concrete-block walls and floors, and a few concrete-block chimneys, and rupture of buried pipelines. In some of these areas slight damage was incurred when heavy objects such as generators, appliances, and furniture were shifted about or overturned. In areas underlain by unconsolidated deposits it was generally difficult or impossible for people to stand or walk during the earthquake.

Ground motion in areas of pre-Tertiary bedrock or bedrock mantled by thin unconsolidated deposits—areas where most communities and canneries of Kodiak and the adjacent islands are located—was not strong enough to cause structural damage. Some small light objects or heavier objects in precarious positions were thrown down, although in most places inanimate objects were not disturbed. People report that, although difficult, it was possible to stand and move about during the earthquake.

Estimates of the Mercalli intensity of ground shaking in the area, based on the reported effects on people and inanimate objects, are shown on figure 5. Ground-water effects, landsliding, and avalanching, which were widely distributed and bore no clearcut relationship to structural damage, were not considered as suitable criteria for intensity estimates. Except as noted, assigned intensity ratings are according to the abridged Modified Mercalli Intensity scale of 1931, in which the violence of ground motion is separated into 12 categories of increasing destructiveness from I to XII (Hodgson, 1964, p.58–59).

With one exception, assigned Mercalli intensities range from VI to VIII throughout the area. They are lowest in areas of pre-Tertiary bedrock or bedrock mantled with thin well-drained unconsolidated deposits and highest in areas of poorly consolidated Tertiary rocks and thick unconsolidated deposits. Significantly, the highest intensity experienced, which is estimated as VIII to IX on the scale, was at the Kadiak Fisheries cannery—the only large structure in the entire area that is founded wholly on unconsolidated, saturated, granular deposits.

AFTERSHOCKS

Many of the numerous aftershocks that followed the main shock were felt as short, sharp, jarring shakes. They reportedly occurred at intervals of a few minutes to an hour throughout the night of the earthquake and at increasingly longer intervals for a period of several weeks thereafter. One aftershock, at 12:55 p.m. on April 14th, was especially noted throughout the islands. Its epicenter was about 20 miles northwest of the city of Kodiak (fig. 4), the magnitude is given as 5.4, and the focal depth as about 19 miles (30 km). Oddly enough, although this aftershock was the strongest one felt in the area, its magnitude was less than many of the other nearby aftershocks. It reportedly hit with a short jarring motion equal to the intensity of the main shock, after which it quickly subsided. Although it caused major consternation, it resulted in no noteworthy damage on Kodiak Island except for three broken pipelines at one cannery on the northwest coast of Kodiak Island, and a cracked roof at another cannery in Alitak Bay on the southwest coast of the island.

SOUNDS

The initial shock was heard as a low-pitched rumble by two individuals in the area. One of them reportedly heard the rumbling an estimated 5 seconds before the tremors were felt. During the weeks after the earthquake, many people heard aftershocks as deep rumbles a second or so before they were felt. Some individuals, both in the area and elsewhere in south-central Alaska, said they heard warning rumbling sounds before every felt aftershock. Richter (1958, p. 128) postulated that such noise may be produced during passage of the body waves, but that the shaking is felt only upon arrival of the slower moving surface waves.

SURFICIAL SUBSIDENCE AND ASSOCIATED GROUND CRACKS

Vibratory loading of noncohesive granular deposits during the earthquake resulted in local surficial subsidence through compaction, flow, and sliding. Areas of greatest subsidence were in thick, unconsolidated, saturated marine or lacustrine deposits and uncompacted manmade fills. Subsidence in some of these areas was accompanied by cracking of the ground and ejection of water or water-sediment mixtures. By the time this reconnaissance study was initiated 4 months after the earthquake, however, much of the evidence of ground cracking was obliterated.

Surficial subsidence of unconsolidated beach and delta deposits along the coast was most clearly manifested in the relatively greater amount of inundation of shoreline areas as compared to nearby rock outcrops. Virtually all areas underlain by such deposits, both in the zone of tectonic subsidence and slight uplift, show some indication of salt water immersion in the form of dead brown terrestrial vegetation (pl. 1).

BEACH DEPOSITS

At the Kadiak Fisheries cannery along the north shore of Kiliuda Bay, local subsidence of beach deposits was 2–10 feet more than that of the adjacent bedrock areas. The cannery is on a broad, roughly triangular cusp that juts out into Shearwater Bay—a small bay on the north side of Kiliuda Bay (figs. 5, 6). Before the earthquake, the buildings shown in the foreground of figure 6 extended on piling slightly beyond the water's edge, as shown in the photograph. Beyond this was a pier 170 feet long. The piling had been driven to refusal, that is, 10–15 feet into the beach deposits. The piles were originally vertical and the tops were level.

After the earthquake, measured subsidence was 5⅓ feet at the shipway piling to the right (north) of the cannery buildings. This subsidence, 2 feet more than that at a bedrock site 1 mile to the south, indicates surficial settlement of about 2 feet relative to bedrock. Furthermore, measurement of the difference in height of the tops of the piling that previously supported the destroyed part of the cannery indicates that an additional 7.8 feet of surficial settlement occurred towards the tip of the cusp (fig. 7).

7. — Timber pile foundation at Kadiak Fisheries cannery site. Pronounced tilting of unbroken piling is indicative of lateral motion of the piling through 10–15 feet of beach gravel. Piling tops formerly level are now 7.8 feet lower at the seaward end of the cannery site than in the foreground owing to local settlement of the distal part of the beach cusp. Bent drift pins in the piling tops indicate that the cannery moved southward (away from the observer) off the piling.

8. — Road near the head of Lake Rose Tead submerged by about 5 feet of surficial subsidence of inlet-stream deltaic deposits. Ugak Bay is visible in the background. Photograph by Alaska Department of Fish and Game.

The site is now submerged at high tides, and the facilities have been replaced by a floating cannery. Ground cracks as much as a foot wide reportedly crisscrossed the cusp after the earthquake. Mr. Edward Pestrikoff, the cannery watchman, saw cracks form in the ground during the earthquake and saw water ejected as high as 6 feet. Reduction of shear strength of the unconsolidated deposits through partial liquefaction is suggested by the manner in which the foundation pilings shown in figure 7 were tilted without being broken when the cannery building collapsed.

Elsewhere, local differential subsidence of unconsolidated beach deposits relative to nearby bedrock amounted to an estimated 1–2 feet at Old Harbor and perhaps 5 feet near the McCord cattle ranch on Sitkalidak Island.

ALLUVIAL AND LACUSTRINE DEPOSITS

Mr. Joe Beaty, a long-time cattle rancher at Narrow Cape, observed that during the earthquake his truck and other heavy machinery settled as much as 2 inches into alluvial deposits on the flood plain of a small stream on the cape. He also noted much cracking at a bog between two lakes near the tip of the cape, and extrusion of gravel that had been buried beneath 20 feet of fine-grained surficial alluvial deposits; thus the cracks evidently extended to at least that depth.

Local subsidence of lacustrine delta deposits was noted at three localities by personnel of the Alaska Department of Fish and Game who carried out studies of the earthquake's effects on salmon spawning and sport fishing (Alaska Dept. Fish and Game,

1965, p. 3–21). Several feet of subsidence occurred on deltas of three streams that enter Buskin Lake near the city of Kodiak and at the inlet stream deltas of two large lakes—Lake Rose Tead and Saltery Lake—along the north shore of Ugak Bay. Surficial subsidence has resulted in local flooding of shoreline vegetation of these lakes and inundation of a segment of road along the shore of Lake Rose Tead (fig. 8). Mr. Ron Hurst, a rancher at Saltery Lake, reports that several acres along the lakeshore sank as much as 3 feet, and large amounts of subsurface pumice was pumped up into Saltery Lake and caused excessive turbidity early in the summer of 1964.

Slumped lake deltas, ground cracks, and spectacular sand-vent deposits were examined and photographed by F. O. Jones, consultant geologist to the Chugach Electric Association, in the upper Terror River drainage, on Kodiak Island between Ugak and Viekoda Bays at about 1,250-1,400 feet altitude. The inlet delta of Terror River at the head of Terror Lake slumped and subsided during the earthquake; near-shore vegetation there was put under 2–3 feet of water (fig. 9, next page). Lateral extension of the slumped delta margin caused it to be cut by a system of rectilinear cracks as much as 1 foot wide (fig. 9). Large volumes of light-colored fine- to medium-grained pumice were ejected to the surface from many of these cracks, and the pumice forms clastic dikes that fill the cracks below the surface (fig. 10 p. D17). Jones noted similar slumped and cracked deltas elsewhere along the margin of Terror Lake and saw from the air an extensive area of reticulate cracks

and sand-vent deposits in a partially filled lake basin 3 miles upstream from Terror Lake.

Drowning of shoreline vegetation was noted from the air along the margins of numerous lakes throughout the area. Undoubtedly shoreline subsidence, cracking of the ground, and extrusion of sediment similar to that noted above also occurred in comparable geologic environments at the numerous other lakes on the island that were not examined in detail.

ARTIFICIAL FILLS AND EMBANKMENTS

In addition to the subsidence of natural unconsolidated deposits, damage was caused to engineering works by surficial subsidence and cracking of filled ground and by settling of engineered fills and breakwaters into underlying unconsolidated natural deposits. Most of these effects, which occurred in the Kodiak area and along the highway east of Kodiak, will be discussed separately in the section of this report that describes effects on highways and in the companion report on damage to communities. The only other noteworthy examples of subsidence of artificial fill occurred at the U.S. Coast Guard Loran facility on Sitkinak Island where measured differential settlement of $4\frac{7}{8}$ inches occurred at one corner of a reinforced-concrete structure that was reportedly built on a 12-foot-thick fill. At Narrow Cape the approach fill of a ranch road on alluvial deposits sank about 2 feet below the level of a bridge deck.

CAUSES OF SURFICIAL SUBSIDENCE

From the foregoing descriptions it should be apparent that surficial subsidence of unconsoli-

9. — Inlet delta at the head of Terror Lake showing inundation of slumped and cracked delta margin and linear cracks defined by light-colored pumiceous ejecta. Photograph by F. O. Jones.

10.— Sectioned extension crack 1 foot wide at head of Terror Lake showing light-colored fine- to medium-grained pumiceous sand ejecta at surface and subsurface clastic dike. Photograph by F. O. Jones.

dated deposits and attendant ground cracking occurred under a variety of geologic conditions over a vast area. Causes of the subsidence are probably diverse and are related to the physical properties of the materials composing each deposit, as well as to the configuration of the deposit.

Subsidence of natural granular materials and uncompacted fills under vibratory loading may result from: (1) compaction, or volume reduction due to closer packing of the grains that compose the deposit; (2) varying

degrees of liquefaction of saturated incoherent material with resultant lateral spreading through flow or sliding; (3) shear failure causing downward and outward movement of the slide mass; and (4) combinations of (1), (2), and (3).

Details of the physical properties and configuration of the affected materials before and after the earthquake are unavailable so that the specific cause, or causes, of subsidence are generally not known. Compaction of some of the deposits is suggested by sur-

face ejection of water and water-sediment mixtures. Reduced shear strength through liquefaction is indicated at the Kadiak Fisheries cannery, where piling embedded 10–15 feet in beach deposits was dragged laterally and tilted to angles of as much as 20° without failure. Reduced bearing strength and compaction of some ground is suggested by the mass sinking of compacted fills, breakwaters, structures, and heavy objects into underlying alluvial deposits and artificially filled ground.

LANDSLIDES

Long-duration horizontal and vertical accelerations during the earthquake triggered numerous landslides and avalanches on the slopes of Kodiak and the adjacent islands. The landslides included a wide variety of falls, slides, and flows involving bedrock, unconsolidated deposits, and snow in varying proportion.[1] Landslides of rock and soil presumably loosened by shaking during the initial shock were unusually abundant in the months after the earthquake. Some of them may have been triggered by the larger aftershocks or by summer thaw of frozen ground. None of the landslides or avalanches in the area caused property damage or human casualties.

The following general descriptions of the distribution and nature of the landslides and avalanches are based almost entirely on aerial observation, interpretation of postearthquake aerial photographs, and accounts by local

[1] The classification and nomenclature for landslides used herein correspond to those of Varnes (1958).

residents. Only a few of these features were examined on the ground.

DISTRIBUTION AND NATURE

Most of the landslides occurred along the southeast coast of Kodiak Island and on the islands offshore from Kodiak Island. A few other landslides—mainly large rockfalls—occurred at widely scattered sites on Kodiak Island and on Afognak and Marmot Islands. The generalized areal distribution of the larger landslides that occurred during or after the earthquake and before August 1964 is shown in figure 11. Many of these slides were reactivated older slides. In some places—most notably along steep coastal bluffs—rockfalls are so closely spaced that a single symbol on figure 11 necessarily represents several slides. No attempt was made to map the smaller rockfalls and soil slips, although, as might be expected, their frequency is roughly proportional to that of the large slides.

Numerous snow avalanches and debris avalanches of snow-rock mixtures are visible on aerial photographs of the steep slopes at higher altitudes along the rugged backbone of Kodiak Island. They are not shown on figure 11 because the postearthquake aerial coverage was inadequate to permit photogeologic mapping of their distribution. Furthermore, most of the avalanches at high altitudes were obscured by new snowfall by the time this study was initiated 3½ months after the earthquake.

In approximate order of abundance, the landslides in the area may be divided into the following general categories: (1) rockslides and rockfalls in areas of consolidated rock, (2) debris slides and avalanches of Tertiary and Quaternary deposits, (3) earthflows and soil slips of unconsolidated surficial materials, and (4) rotational slumps in both consolidated rock and soil. Many of the landslides observed are complex features that probably

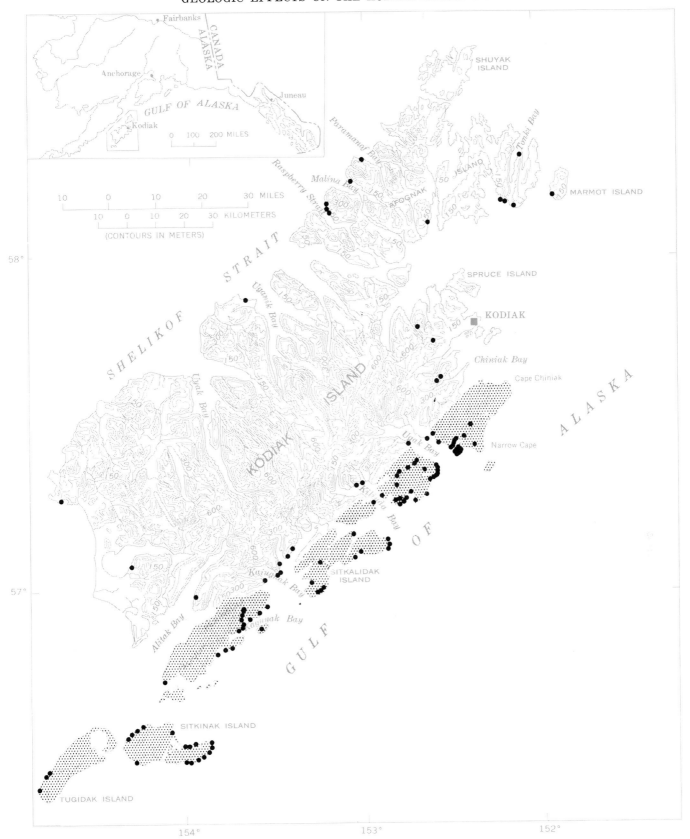

11. — Generalized distribution of the larger landslides and soil slips triggered by the March 27, 1964, earthquake on Kodiak and nearby islands. Areas underlain by rocks of Tertiary or probable Tertiary age are shaded.

12. — Rockslides in tightly folded blocky sandstone along north shore of Ugak Bay, Kodiak Island. Bluff is about 1,000 feet high and is exposed to surf from Gulf of Alaska.

13. — Reactivated large debris slide in sedimentary rocks of middle Tertiary age along the south shore of Sitkinak Island. Note the characteristic steplike transverse scarps, displacing surface vegetation at head of the slide. A small rockfall covers part of the beach in lower left of photograph. Vertical height of slide mass is approximately 300 feet.

Rockfalls and rockslides are locally very numerous along steep coastal bluffs (fig. 12). Commonly, the bluffs are partially undercut by wave erosion and have surf-cut sea caves near the hightide line that lead to precipitous failures of large rock masses. The rock falls and slides are particularly numerous where blocky massive sandstone and basalt of Tertiary age, or older igneous intrusive rocks, form the steep bluffs along the shore. They are relatively rare in areas underlain by the well-indurated bedded and slaty rocks of pre-Tertiary age that compose the central part of Kodiak Island and most of Afognak and Shuyak Islands (fig. 3). Many rockfalls, too small to be plotted on the landslide distribution map, were seen in areas underlain by the blocky granitic rocks that compose much of the rugged drainage divide on Kodiak Island.

Debris slides and debris avalanches were sporadically distributed along the southeastern coast of Kodiak Island, on Sitkalidak Island, and on Sitkinak Island. They apparently occurred mostly in areas underlain by bedded rocks of Tertiary age or by Quaternary deposits. Such slides are especially numerous on deeply weathered, moderately steep slopes underlain by rocks of middle to late Tertiary age. The debris slide shown in figure 13 is typical of many throughout the area.

The slide illustrated on plate 2 is probably the largest that occurred in the area and is anomalous in that it spread as a relatively thin sheet over the valley below the slide source. The areal distribution and irregular surface characteristics of the slide debris suggest that it was emplaced by high-velocity viscous flow.

involve varying combinations of falling, sliding, and flowage, but in the descriptions that follow they have been classified on the basis of their most characteristic features as interpreted mainly from the aerial photographs and from aerial observation.

Earthflows and soil slips of unconsolidated materials occurred throughout the area, but were especially common along the moderately steep slopes that were deeply weathered and mantled with thick deposits of one or more of the following: (1) glacial till, (2) volcanic ash, (3) colluvium. Typically, the flows and slips are manifested at the head as a series of transverse "wrinkles" or scarps stepped downslope, below which is a subtle bulge of debris (fig. 14). All gradations occur between the earthflows and soil slips that involve thin surficial layers of unconsolidated debris and the debris slides that are characterized by relatively coherent slide units.

Rotational slumps were rather rare in the study area. This type of landslide was recognized only at Narrow Cape on Kodiak Island and along the southeast cape of Sitkalidak Island. Pierre St. Amand of the U.S. Naval Ordnance Test Station and George W. Moore of the U.S. Geological Survey directed our attention to these features, which were studied with special care because their long linear scarps bore a superficial resemblance to fault breaks.

The Narrow Cape landslide involved moderately dipping, poorly indurated sedimentary rocks of late Tertiary age. It occurred on slopes of 15°–35° along a structurally controlled northeast-trending linear valley that is incised 125–150 feet into a flat-lying erosion surface. The main scarp of the slide (fig. 15) broke at the top of the southeast valley wall along a distance of roughly 1,400 feet. The slide mass slumped down on the northwest side as much as 15 feet with headward tilting along a surface of rupture that intersected the surface on the valley floor 125–150 feet be-

14. — Earthflow resulting from soil slip or slump in deeply weathered **Tertiary** sedimentary deposits along the north shore of Sitkinak Island. The head of the slide is marked by numerous small scarps; the foot is the hummocky bulbous mass in the lower left corner.

15. — Main scarp at the head of a large rotational slump in Tertiary deposits on Narrow Cape, Kodiak Island. The landslide is approximately 1,400 feet long and 125–150 feet high. The rock mass at the left slid 8–15 feet downslope along a surface of rupture, the main scarp of which trends diagonally across the photograph. Note the headward tilt of the original surface on the upper part of the slide mass and draping of the vegetation mat over the crown of the main slide.

[199]

low. Open tension cracks and shallow grabens are abundant on the erosion surface headward from the main scarp. The slide toe is characterized by transverse pressure ridges and small overthrusts in the surface mat of muskeg vegetation. The brush-covered hummocky topography of the lower part of the slide surface and the chaotic internal structure suggest that earlier gravity movement has taken place.

At the southeast end of Sitkalidak Island, a discontinuous zone of landslides occurs along the base of a moderately steep southeast-facing ridge that fronts on a broad, gently sloping terrace. The landslides have exposed a series of southeast-facing scarps that can be traced along the base of the ridge for about 1½ miles. They die out both to the northeast and the southwest. As seen from the air, the freshly exposed scarps are estimated to be as much as 15 feet high and appear to be largely in unconsolidated deposits. The slide masses consist of both headward-tilted blocks and irregular hummocky earthflows along the downslope sides of the scarps.

The relatively straight and abrupt break in slope along which the sliding occurred on Sitkalidak Island strongly suggests the possibility that the topographic feature is controlled by a preexisting fault and that the line of slumps may have been related to renewed displacement along this inferred fault during the earthquake. Fortunately, it was feasible to check this possibility by measuring vertical displacement of the shore relative to sea level both to the northeast and southwest of the line of landslides. No changes indicative of vertical fault displacement during the earthquake were detected within the limits of precision of the method (estimated to be ±1½ ft in this area). On the contrary, the measurements showed a slight northwest tilting of the island which is opposite in sense to the down-to-the-southeast movement along the landslide scarps.

CAUSES

Elastic ground vibrations during the 1964 earthquake triggered most of the fresh landslides (and avalanches), or so loosened large masses of rock that they slid shortly thereafter. A contributory factor may have been ground accelerations related to the observed permanent vertical displacements, together with possible horizontal displacements, that occurred during the earthquake. The effect of transitory horizontal accelerations is to increase temporarily the shear stress on slope-forming materials; this increase may result in failure (Varnes, 1958, p. 43). In some instances slope failure may have occurred because of loss of shear strength through partial liquefaction of saturated granular materials below the layer of seasonal frost.

Although the earthquake was clearly the trigger, it was not the ultimate cause of the slides. In a topographically rugged and geologically complex area such as Kodiak and the nearby islands, many rock masses are in a state of unstable equilibrium as a result of local topography, lithology, structure, weathering, and water saturation. Even without earth shocks to act as a trigger, numerous landslides continually occur.

Of particular interest is the concentration of earthquake-induced slides along the southeast coast of Kodiak Island and the nearby offshore islands (fig. 11), in contrast to their relative scarcity elsewhere. This distribution appears to be controlled primarily by local lithology and structure but may also be related to proximity to the earthquake focal region. Steepness of slope probably is not an important factor in controlling the overall distribution, inasmuch as maximum slope angles in the area of few slides are, in general, equal to, or greater than, those in the zone of many landslides.

The strong coincidence of maximum landslide frequency and outcrop areas of bedded Tertiary rock is shown in figure 11. It is also noteworthy that the landslides in Tertiary rock are exceedingly diverse and complex in character and include all the types that were described above, whereas those in pre-Tertiary outcrop areas are almost exclusively rockfalls.

The predominance of landsliding in areas underlain by Tertiary rock seems to be largely controlled by the physical properties of the rocks in at least five ways: (1) The Tertiary sequence locally contains inherently weak materials such as clay, siltstone, and tuff along which sliding may occur. ((2) The rocks, as a rule, are complexly folded and are broken by numerous discontinuities such as faults, joints, and bedding planes, which reduce shear strength. (3) The relative ease of weathering has resulted in local thick accumulations of landslide-prone soil and colluvium. (4) More rapid erosion has produced numerous steep-sided stream valleys and wave-cut cliffs, and attendant slope instability has resulted from removal of lateral support. (5) Intensity of the tremors during the earthquake (fig. 5) suggests that the horizontal ground accelerations and amplitudes in some areas underlain by Tertiary rock were greater than in areas underlain by pre-Tertiary rock. Such differences in intensity would result in proportionately larger transient increases in shear stress and attendant reductions in shear strength of slope-forming materials in the Tertiary outcrop belt during the earthquake.

In summary, the distribution of landsliding shown in figure 11 appears to be closely related to local geologic conditions, the slides being most abundant in areas underlain by the least competent Tertiary rocks, and relatively few and widely scattered throughout the remainder of the region. The five factors enumerated above

apply especially to units of middle and late Tertiary age. Rocks of early Tertiary age, as a rule, are well indurated, can be distinguished from pre-Tertiary bedded rocks only with difficulty, and probably have physical properties and susceptibility to sliding that are intermediate between those of the late Tertiary and pre-Tertiary sequences.

Although it appears that landslide frequency is largely controlled by the underlying rock units, the possibility must also be considered that proximity of the southeastern coast to known faults (fig. 3) or to the focal region (as defined by aftershock distribution shown on figs. 1 and 4) may have resulted in a higher intensity of ground motion and attendant susceptibility to slid-

ing. The limited available data, however, do not indicate that either proximity to faults or to the focal region had a discernible influence on landslide distribution. Geologic study of the deformation in the area of highest landslide frequency failed to reveal active faults having significant surface displacement along which landslides might be concentrated. Furthermore, if the landsliding were controlled mainly by proximity to the focal region rather than by lithology and structure, there should be a progressive decrease in landslide frequency northwestward, away from the focal region, instead of the abrupt change that occurs between the belt of Tertiary rocks and the remainder of the area studied.

EFFECTS ON GROUND AND SURFACE WATER

Earthquake-induced fluctuations in level and (or) flow of some wells, lakes, and streams occurred at numerous localities throughout Kodiak and the adjacent islands. Temporary and permanent fluctuations of water level and flow that were recorded after the earthquake throughout much of Alaska, Canada, and conterminous United States, Hawaii, and Puerto Rico (Waller and others, 1965) are to be detailed in a separate volume of this series of reports that deals with earthquake-induced changes in the hydrologic regime and, consequently, will be described only briefly in the following paragraphs.

OBSERVATIONS

Reported effects of the earthquake on the few water-supply wells on the islands varied mark-

edly. Some wells went dry or decreased yield and a few had increased yield, but most reportedly had no perceptible change. Many wells were muddied, and some along the coast became saline. Because none of the wells on the islands were equipped with water-level recorders, all the available data on earthquake-induced changes are, of necessity, based on observations by local residents reported in questionnaires and personal interviews.

The only wells in the area known to have gone completely dry during the earthquake were shallow hand-dug wells on a small island near the Port Bailey cannery on the south side of Kupreanof Strait (fig. 2). A cannery worker, Mr. Rudy Lorenson, reported that after the earthquake the wells were dug 2 feet deeper

without finding water. The wells were still dry 4 months later. Ranch wells at Narrow Cape (fig. 2) became muddy immediately after the earthquake. Although the yield of some wells reportedly increased, it is not known whether this increase was accompanied by a permanent change of level. Wells along the shore at Afognak village were also muddied after the earthquake. These wells, and the school well at Old Harbor, became salty and unusable. There was no change in quality or level of water at the Coast Guard station near Cape Chiniak on Kodiak Island, or at the Federal Aviation Agency radio station at the north end of Shuyak Island.

Observers throughout the area report that ice on virtually all lakes and reservoirs at low altitudes was cracked during the earthquake—particularly around the margins. At higher altitudes pilots noted cracking of ice on some large lakes, but many of the smaller lakes showed no perceptible changes. A small cabin along the shore of a pond near Cape Chiniak was destroyed when seiching drove the ice cake over the bank and into the structure. According to eyewitnesses at Afognak village, ice on the lakes began cracking as soon as the earthquake was felt. Marginal cracking of lake ice probably can be attributed to the inertial effect of the water and ice cakes in resisting horizontal ground oscillations during the earthquake. In other parts of south-central Alaska it was noted that pressure ridges built up in the ice and snow along the shorelines in response to repeated pounding of the ground against the ice cakes. Although similar pressure ridges undoubtedly formed along lakeshores in the area, they were not specifically noted by local residents.

In general, lake levels were either unaffected by the earthquake or were lowered. R. M. Waller has pointed out that erroneous reports of lowered lake levels may have been made in places where earthquake-induced seiching stranded cracked ice along the shore, or where the tremors have caused collapse of peripheral ice and snow bridges that commonly form by normal lowering of lake levels during the winter. Two shallow lakes between 3 and 3½ feet deep on Shuyak Island reportedly went dry during the earthquake. One filled up soon afterward but the other remained dry. Numerous shallow lakes on Kodiak Island that had gone dry during the earthquake were still dry or had lower water levels 4 months

afterward. A cirque lake 2,000 feet long by 1,000 feet wide, at an altitude of 500 feet 5 miles northwest of Narrow Cape, reportedly was lowered 20 feet during the earthquake, although nearby lakes showed no perceptible change of level.

A few local changes in streamflow—involving both decreases and increases in volume—were reported in the area after the earthquake. Abnormally reduced water flow at two important salmon-rearing streams was noted by Dexter Lall of the Alaska Department of Fish and Game.

A particularly interesting sequence of changes was noted by Mr. Rudy Lorensen in a small stream that flows across Mesozoic bedrock near the Port Bailey cannery on northern Kodiak Island. According to Mr. Lorenson, the creek flow was reduced to about half its normal volume after the earthquake. The remaining flow was cut off entirely during the jarring aftershock of April 14th, the epicenter of which was located within 10 miles of the cannery (fig. 4). The stream remained dry for two months until another sharp aftershock in June started the normal volume of flow once again.

The flow of streams at Afognak village and springs at a ranch on the north shore of Ugak Bay on Kodiak Island reportedly increased for a period of one week after the earthquake. Four larger streams on which U.S. Geological Survey water-level recording gages were installed showed no significant flow changes following the earthquake.

CAUSES OF FLUCTUATIONS

Lack of detailed data on the pre- and postearthquake flow records of wells, streams, and springs for which earthquake-in-

duced changes are reported precludes analysis of the origin of these changes.

Elsewhere in the part of Alaska strongly affected by the earthquake, where adequate data are available, the widespread lowered well and lake levels and reduced streamflow in granular materials has been attributed by H. E. Thomas of the U.S. Geological Survey to temporary increases in the porosity of saturated materials (in Grantz and others, 1964, p. 10). This mechanism could be the reason for lowered well levels in the islands, and, in conjunction with increased opportunity for water seepage from lakes and streams into earthquake-cracked frozen banks, and through cracked ice dams at lake outlets, could also explain some of the lowered lake and stream levels.

In many places, however, lowered water levels in wells, streams, and lakes appear to be permanent. The reported sequence of abrupt changes in discharge of the small stream near Port Bailey suggests that, in areas underlain by bedrock, fracture porosity may be abruptly increased or decreased by slight shock-induced adjustments of bedrock blocks. Similar changes may have resulted from tectonic deformation within the area, especially if significant horizontal extension accompanied the vertical subsidence. Retriangulation within the zone of subsidence near Anchorage has revealed horizontal extension roughly normal to the trend of the zone amounting to as much as 8×10^{-5} or roughly one-half foot per mile (U.S. Coast and Geodetic Survey, 1965, p. 17). If comparable extension occurred on Kodiak and the nearby islands, where subsidence is equal to or greater than that of the Anchorage area, near-surface fracture porosity may have increased sufficiently to cause some of the reported changes in water regimen, and particularly in areas of fracture porosity.

The permanently increased salinity of a few wells in highly permeable beach and alluvial deposits at Afognak and the school well at Old Harbor probably was the result of encroachment of sea water into aquifers after tectonic subsidence. Temporarily increased salinity of most of the shallow dug wells, however, resulted from flooding of watershed areas by the seismic sea waves.

VERTICAL TECTONIC DEFORMATION

The March 27 earthquake was accompanied by tectonic deformation that resulted in vertical crustal movements, both upward and downward throughout the report area. Anomalous tide levels soon after the earthquake made coastal residents aware of the vertical displacement of the land.

The isobase contours of figure 16 (next page) show the amount and direction of vertical displacement that accompanied the earthquake. Directions and relative amounts of change were determined at four localities from coupled pre- and postearthquake tide-gage readings, at about 25 localities from estimates made by local residents, and at 95 localities from measurements of the displacement of the upper growth limit of sessile intertidal organisms along the seashore. Data-point locations are shown on figure 16.

Determinations of vertical displacement at tide gages is probably accurate to within a few tenths of a foot. Most of the estimates made by fishermen, mariners, and other coastal residents who have had long experience with the local tides are probably correct to within a foot. The technique used for estimating vertical displacements from the height of the upper growth limit of marine organisms above tidal datum planes has been outlined elsewhere (Plafker, 1965, p. 1675-

1679.) It will also be described in detail in a forthcoming volume on tectonic deformation, to be prepared for this series of publications on the earthquake. Such measurements were carried out in 1964 and 1965 on a reconnaissance basis in the area. Those based on difference in pre- and postearthquake altitudes of upper growth limits of barnacles and algae are thought to be generally accurate to about 1 foot. Most of the measurements, however, are based only on the postearthquake altitude of these organisms above sea level; they contain inherent errors due to (1) deviation of sea level from predicted heights and (2) local variations in the growth limits of the organisms resulting from local factors of exposure, rock type, and water characteristics. They are estimated to be accurate to within 1½ feet in sheltered bays on the eastern side of the islands. Along segments of the coast exposed to heavy surf or swells, and especially in areas of high and erratic tides such as the Shelikof Strait side of the islands (see table 2), the measurements may be in error by as much as 2½ feet. In these areas, more reliance was placed on estimates made by coastal residents and on the measured difference in upper growth limits of pre- and postearthquake organisms than on those measurements that require use of tide level as a datum.

DISTRIBUTION

Almost all of Kodiak Island, and all of Afognak, Shuyak, and Marmot Islands have undergone tectonic subsidence (fig. 16). The zone of subsidence consists of a broad trough that plunges gently northeastward along an axis that approximately coincides with the axis of the Kenai Mountains between Alitak Bay and the city of Kodiak. The limbs of the trough are strongly asymmetric, the steepest limb being southeast of the axis. Subsidence in excess of 6 feet has occurred in the vicinity of northern Kodiak Island, on Afognak Island, and on Shuyak Island. Maximum subsidence of 6½–7 feet was measured on eastern Afognak Island and on Marmot Island.

Uplift has occurred in a narrow zone that includes Narrow Cape on Kodiak Island, the southeastern half of Sitkalidak Island, all or part of Sitkinak Island, and some small islands off the southeastern coast of Kodiak Island. Maximum uplift of 2½ feet was measured on Sitkalidak Island. Mr. Joe Beaty (see p. D15) reports that at the tip of Narrow Cape on Kodiak Island a surf-cut platform about 200 feet wide is now exposed at stages of tide that completely inundated the platform before the earthquake. Uplift of at least 2 feet, and possibly in excess of 3 feet, is suggested near this locality by postearthquake

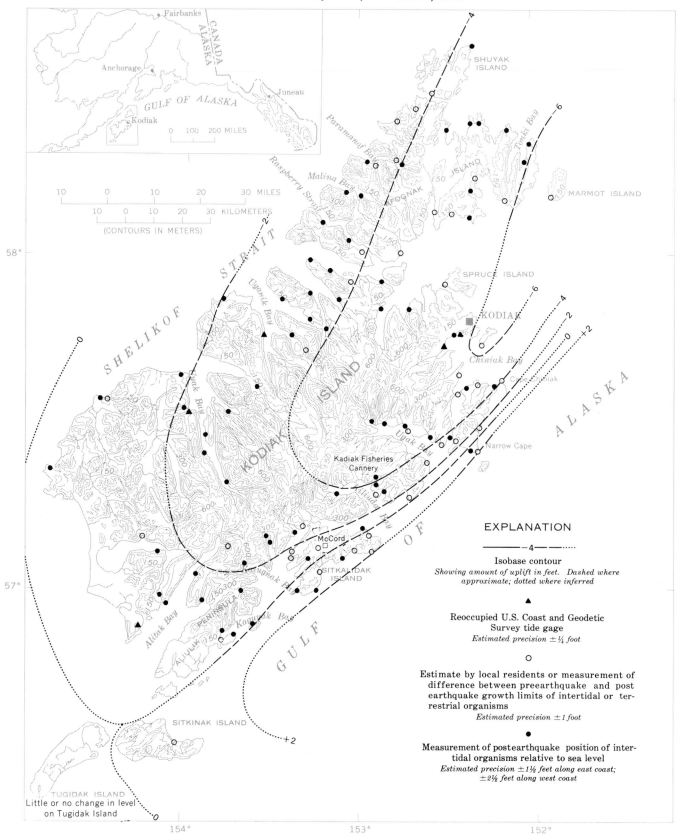

EXPLANATION

——— —4— — — —·······

Isobase contour

Showing amount of uplift in feet. Dashed where approximate; dotted where inferred

▲

Reoccupied U.S. Coast and Geodetic Survey tide gage

Estimated precision ±¼ foot

○

Estimate by local residents or measurement of difference between preearthquake and post earthquake growth limits of intertidal or terrestrial organisms

Estimated precision ±1 foot

●

Measurement of postearthquake position of intertidal organisms relative to sea level

Estimated precision ±1½ feet along east coast; ±2½ feet along west coast

16. — Areas affected by tectonic deformation on Kodiak and nearby islands.

incision of streams and the consequent partial draining of two small beach-barred lakes. However, the outlet streams may have become incised through scouring action of the seismic sea waves that entered the lakes after the earthquake. At Sitkinak Island, another rancher, Mr. Hal Nelson, noted 1–2 feet of shoaling at the entrance to a lagoon immediately after the earthquake—probably the result of a slight crustal uplift. Evidence of as much as 2 feet of uplift in the coastal area and small offshore islands between Narrow Cape, Sitkalidak Island, and Sitkinak Island suggests that the zone of uplift is probably continuous beneath intervening water-covered areas.

As far as could be determined during the brief reconnaissance of the area, changes of land level associated with the earthquake resulted from regional warping rather than faulting. A diligent search was made for surface faults, particularly in the vicinity of the zero isobase between the areas of uplift and subsidence, a zone roughly paralleling numerous known faults (fig. 3). No evidence of significant surface faulting was found, nor were there any anomalous abrupt changes in amounts of uplift or subsidence along the coast suggestive of measurable displacement along concealed faults.

Past movements on the major faults in this zone have been mainly dip slip with the northwest blocks upthrown (fig. 3). Consequently, if any of these faults were reactivated during the earthquake only a reverse displacement could produce the observed pattern of deformation along the southeast coast of the islands.

EFFECTS ON SHORELINES

Tectonic subsidence, augmented locally by surficial subsidence of unconsolidated deposits, has had a profound effect on shoreline morphology, intertidal marine organisms, and terrestrial vegetation. Virtually all shorelines that subsided more than 3 feet show clear physical evidence of the change, and the changes were locally noticeable where the subsidence was as little as 1 foot.

The effects were most pronounced in areas of lowest mean annual tidal range (table 2), inasmuch as both the frequency and duration of shoreline immersion for a given amount of subsidence vary inversely with the tidal range. The conspicuous effect of subsidence is the fringe of dead brown terrestrial vegetation along the shore that has been killed by salt-water inundation at periods of high tides (pls. 1, 3).

Beach berms and stream deltas in subsided areas are shifted landward and are building up to the new higher sea levels. The lower reaches of streams are now inundated by tides for distances of as much as 4,500 feet inland (table 3). The striking effect of subsidence in the estuarine part of Olds River at Kalsin Bay is illustrated by plate 3. Many former beach-barred lakes at stream mouths or bay heads have become tidal lagoons. Wave action at the higher sea levels is rapidly eroding shorelines composed of poorly consolidated deposits that are now brought within reach of the tides (pl. 4). An irreparable loss resulting from accelerated erosion of such deposits is the destruction of many coastal archaeological sites situated on them. Former reefs and low-lying islands along the coast are now submerged, and some tombolo-tied points or capes have become islands.

Effects of the small and localized uplift along the shore are minor compared to those due to subsidence. At Narrow Cape a new surf-cut rock terrace 200 feet wide reportedly is exposed at zero tide, and nearby beach-barred lakes have been partially drained by incision of the outlet

TABLE 3. — *Tidal inundation resulting from tectonic and surficial subsidence*

Stream	Location (fig. 2)	Approximate tectonic subsidence (feet)	Length of stream newly inundated by tides (feet)[1]
	Afognak Island		
Danger Bay Creeks	14 miles northeast of Afognak.	5½	865
Marka Creek	5 miles northeast of Afognak.	4–5	2,600
Back Bay Creeks	5 miles north of Afognak.....	3½–5	605
Afognak River	4½ miles north-northeast of Afognak.	3½–5	825
	Kodiak Island		
Kiliuda Creeks	Kiliuda Bay	4–5	1,900
Eagle Harbor Creek....	Ugak Bay	4	850
Saltery Cove Creek	.... do	5	570
Olds River	Kalsin Bay	4½	4,500

[1] Alaska Department of Fish and Game (1965, p. 5).

streams. Elsewhere a few new reefs are exposed at stages of tide when they formerly were under water. Lowered tide levels in lagoons in the area with attendant reduced volume and velocity of diurnal flow through the outlets may eventually result in the barring of the lagoon outlets and subsequent conversion of the lagoons to fresh-water lakes.

REGIONAL SETTING OF THE CHANGES

The 4,900-square-mile land area of Kodiak and the nearby islands within which vertical displacements were measured is but a part of a regional zone of tectonic deformation associated with the earthquake. An area of at least 70,000 square miles, and possibly 110,000 square miles or more of south-central Alaska, is involved (Plafker, 1965). The zone, which is more than 500 miles long and as much as 200 miles wide, is roughly parallel to the Gulf of Alaska coast from the Kodiak group of islands northeastward to Prince William Sound and thence eastward to about long 143° W. It consists of a major seaward zone of uplift bordered on the northwest and north by a major zone of subsidence (fig. 17). These two zones are separated by a line of zero land-level change that trends northeastward from Sitkinak Island along the seaward sides of Sitkalidak and Kodiak Islands (fig. 16). From Kodiak Island, the line trends northeastward to intersect the mainland between Seward and Prince William Sound. It then curves eastward

through the western part of Prince William Sound to the vicinity of Valdez and crosses the Copper River valley about 50 miles above the mouth.

In addition to most of the Kodiak group of islands, the zone of subsidence includes most of Cook Inlet, the Kenai Mountains, and the Chugach Mountains. The axis of maximum subsidence within this zone trends roughly northeastward along the crest of the Kodiak and Kenai Mountains and then bends eastward in the Chugach Mountains. Maximum recorded downwarping along this axis is 7½ feet.

In the northern part of the deformed area, uplift in excess of 6 feet occurred over a wide area including part of Prince William Sound, the mainland east of the sound, and offshore islands on the continental shelf as far southwest as Middleton Island. Along surface faults on Montague Island, the uplift locally exceeded 30 feet (Plafker, 1965, fig. 7). Southwest of Montague Island the sea bottom may have been uplifted more than 50 feet (Malloy, 1964, p. 1248), where pre- and post-earthquake bottom soundings show seaward continuations of new fault scarps along preexisting fault lines. Large-scale uplift of the continental shelf and slope southwest of Montague Island is inferred from the trend of isobase contours in the northeastern part of the deformed area, and from the presence of the fringe of uplift along the outer coast of the Kodiak Island area (fig. 16). The minimum extent of this inferred offshore zone of uplift is

thought to be roughly outlined by the earthquake focal region, or belt of major aftershocks, shown on figure 1.

The major zones of vertical tectonic displacement and the belt of aftershocks, which lie within and parallel to the Aleutian Trench and the Aleutian volcanic arc, are inferred to have resulted from displacement along a fault or zone of faulting that dips at a moderate angle northward from the Aleutian Trench beneath the continent (Grantz and others, 1964, p. 2). Neither the orientation nor the sense of movement on the primary fault (or faults), along which the earthquake presumably occurred, is certain, inasmuch as the primary fault or zone of faulting is not known to intersect the surface on land.

The two known surface breaks, which occurred on preexisting faults on Montague Island along the axis of maximum uplift, are clearly within and subsidiary to the zone of regional uplift. The faulting on Montague Island is known to extend offshore southwestward at least 15 miles, and comparable fault displacements probably occurred along this trend or elsewhere on the sea floor of the continental shelf within the focal region of the earthquake. Indeed, the direction of travel and reported arrival times of the initial wave crest in the area (p. D30–D39) suggest that the axis of maximum uplift (fig. 17), along which faulting occurred on Montague Island, may extend southwestward perhaps to the latitude of Sitkalidak Island (Plafker, 1965, p. 6; Plafker and Mayo, 1965, fig. 12).

SUBSIDENCE AT MIDDLE BAY

Extensive inundation at the head of Middle Bay resulting from 5 feet of tectonic subsidence and an unknown but substantial amount of surficial subsidence. Arrows indicate the approximate location of remnants of the Kodiak-Chiniak highway. Dashed line shows the approximate preearthquake mean high-water shoreline which has been shifted about half a mile landward.

This photograph is printed in color in the USGS original.

UNDERMINED TREES ON BARRIER BEACH IN IZHUT BAY, AFOGNAK ISLAND

Accelerated wave erosion in an area of about 5 feet of tectonic subsidence caused this damage.   Foliage of trees along shore has turned brown from salt-water immersion of the roots.

This photograph is printed in color in the USGS original.

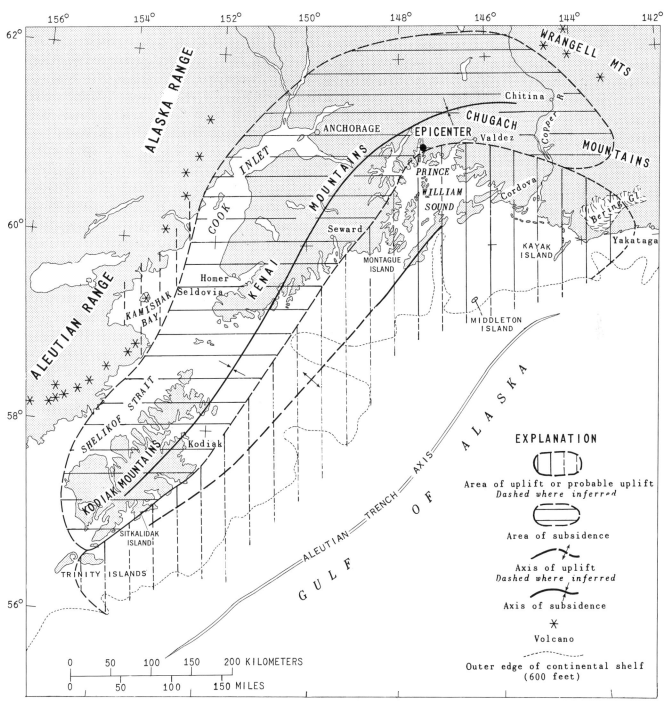

17. — Setting of the observed and inferred vertical displacements of the Kodiak group of islands with respect to regional tectonic deformation in south-central Alaska.

SEISMIC SEA WAVES

By far the most catastrophic effect of the 1964 earthquake on Kodiak and the adjacent islands was the train of destructive seismic sea waves that first struck the coast about 38 minutes after the start of the earth tremors. The waves, repeatedly inundating low-lying coastal areas, caused 18 fatalities and extensive property damage along the southeast coast of the islands. This train of seismic sea waves resulted in the worst natural disaster to befall the islands in historic times. There is no authenticated record of previous destructive seismic sea waves along this same segment of the Alaskan coast.

According to a widely quoted account in the historical novel "Lord of Alaska" (Chevigny, 1942, p. 63), the original Russian settlement on Kodiak Island at the site of a native village in Three Saints Bay was wiped out by a "tidal wave" during a violent earthquake in 1792 after which it was moved to the present location of Kodiak. The historian, Bancroft (1886, p. 324), states, however, that the decision to move the settlement was based solely on sound tactical and economic reasons. The original site continued to be inhabited by natives at least until 1805, at which time the Russian naval captain Lisiansky called at Three Saints Bay in the ship *Neva* (Bancroft, 1886, p. 434-435).

CHRONOLOGY

For a period of about half an hour after the earthquake, most residents were busily assessing the relatively light earthquake-induced damage and discussing the terrifying shaking they had so recently endured. Few people recall having noticed any unusual movements of the sea in that interval of time. The tide was ebbing and nearly at low stage (table 2), the wind was calm, and there was ample daylight for reliable visual observations for about 2 hours after the earthquake, or until about 7:30 p.m.

The only reported noteworthy fluctuation of water level prior to arrival of the first seismic sea wave was a gradual rise and subsequent withdrawal of the sea. This fluctuation was noted by a fisherman, Mr. Jerry Tilley, who was aboard the 75-foot shrimp-fishing boat *Fortress* tied up at the city dock in Kodiak. Mr. Tilley states that the water level rose calmly from about 0 to 13 feet within 10 minutes after the earthquake was initially felt. Water level then receded gradually for an estimated 25 minutes to about —10 feet, after which the first wave moved in from the south as a large swell. This first, calm rise of water level has not been reported elsewhere, and it caused no damage whatever. The origin of this reported sea-level rise at Kodiak is uncertain. It could have been a local seiche generated largely by the tectonic tilting and possible horizontal displacement that occurred during the earthquake. However, the fact that it was not noticed at the nearby Naval station, which underwent approximately the same amount of subsidence, argues against this possibility. In any event, the limited data available on this initial sea-level rise suggest that it was a local phenomenon, rather than part of the train of long-period seismic sea waves that followed.

At 6:14 p.m., 38 minutes after the start of the earthquake, Fleet Weather Central, Kodiak Naval Station, received an ominous report of a "30-foot tsunami" at the Cape Chiniak station of the U.S. Coast Guard 15 miles to the southeast (fig. 18). An immediate "tidal-wave" warning, broadcast over the Armed Forces Radio, resulted in the timely evacuation to high ground of most base and city personnel in the Kodiak area. Many individuals began immediately trying to fly amphibious aircraft from the harbor area, to pilot fishing boats to the relative safety of deep water, or to remove vehicles and other valuable belongings to high ground, but with varying degrees of success.

At about the time that the wave was observed at Cape Chiniak, Mr. Joe Beaty (see p. D15) was on the roof of his ranch home at Narrow Cape repairing a radio antenna broken during the earthquake. Looking seaward, he was astonished to see the sea withdraw a long distance from the shore; the withdrawal was immediately followed by a "wall of water" that moved in from the east and broke off shore. A wave then surged over low-lying parts of the ranch as much as three-quarters of a mile inland from the beach; it deposited vast quantities of driftwood but it stopped just short of the house and outbuildings. Seven head of cattle were drowned, contrary to one journalist's account which claimed that the animals somehow sensed the oncoming wave in time to move to the safety of high ground.

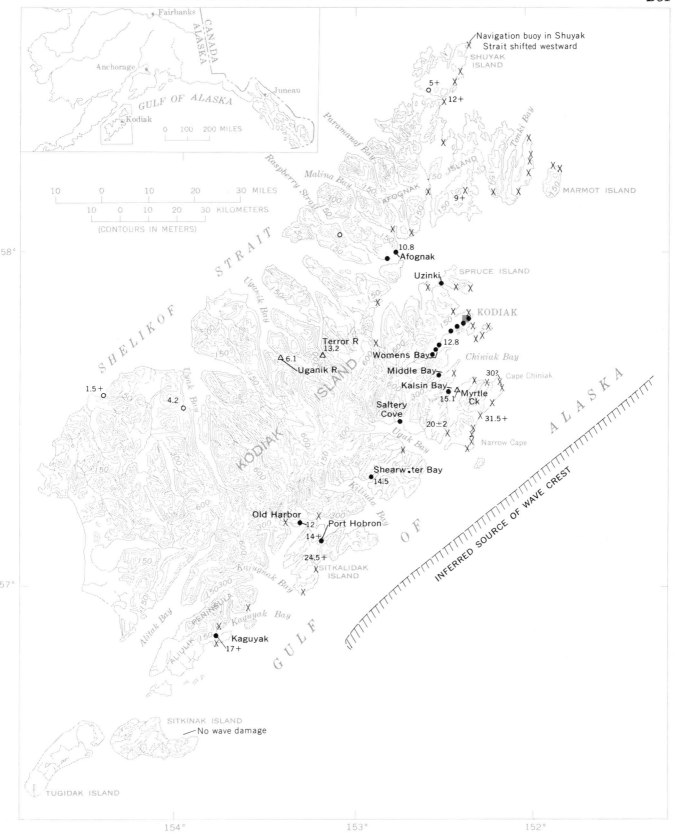

18. — Localities on Kodiak and nearby islands at which waves caused major property damage (black circles), shorelines showing physical evidence of wave damage (x), shorelines reportedly inundated by runup (open circles), and U.S. Geological Survey streamflow gages on which waves were recorded (triangles). Numbers indicate approximate highest runup in feet above existing tide level; plus sign following numeral indicates that tide stage is unknown and maximum runup shown is minimum value assuming coincidence of wave with high tide. Lined pattern offshore indicates inferred position of the northwest and southwest margins of the wave-crest source.

19. — Seaplane ramp at Kodiak Naval Station along shore of Womens Bay showing approximate high-water level reached by first wave. Note calm water surface. Aircraft parked in front of hangar at left center were later moved to high ground and saved. Photograph by U.S. Navy.

Shortly after the initial wave struck the outer coast from Cape Chiniak to Narrow Cape, inhabitants elsewhere along the southeast coast between Kaguyak and Afognak noticed rapid rises of the sea, accompanied in some places by dull rumbling sounds. By 6:35 p.m., 63 minutes after the start of the earthquake, the initial wave was cresting at the city of Kodiak, nearby Kodiak Naval Station, and other points along the shore of Chiniak Bay, and was inundating low-lying coastal areas. Everywhere except at Cape Chiniak and Narrow Cape, the first waves were described as a gentle gradual flood with swirls resembling riverflow that rose at estimated rates of as much as 3 feet per second. Figure 19 shows part of the airport at Kodiak Naval Station as the first wave crested. At Kodiak and Old Harbor, gradual withdrawals of about 10 feet reportedly preceded the initial wave, but no withdrawal in Womens Bay was observed at the Kodiak Naval Station.

The initial wave was followed everywhere by a turbulent swirling retreat of water from the shore, during which segments of the sea floor were bared far below the level of the extreme low tides. Much of the fishing fleet at Kodiak was left grounded, but some boats were swept offshore and caught in whirlpool-like eddies or high-velocity currents that accompanied the withdrawal. The water withdrew to about 10 feet below the postearthquake mean lower low water at the Kodiak Electric Association powerhouse in Kodiak. At the Kodiak Naval Station, the water withdrew to about 11½ feet below the post-earthquake mean lower low water.

Approximately at 7:40 p.m., as darkness was falling and the tide beginning to flood, a second wave that was the largest and most destructive of the train in the Chiniak Bay area struck the coast. It swept away docks, houses, and vehicles along the shore and drove flotsam and fishing vessels inland as battering rams, causing much destruction of property previously undamaged by the high water.

The withdrawal that followed the second wave was extremely turbulent and rapid. Swirling currents with velocities variously estimated at 20–25 knots flowed through the straits near Kodiak. The water was choked with debris, and vessels that were unable to steer against the swirling erratic currents were carried on its flood.

The third wave, which struck the southeast coast of the area between 8:30 and 9:30 p.m., was slightly lower than the second wave in Chiniak Bay, but because it came in on a rising tide it reached almost the same altitude along the shore as the previous wave, adding substantially to the damage. It was the highest and most destructive wave witnessed at the villages of Afognak, Old Harbor, and Uzinki; numerous homes and other structures were washed to sea, and fishing vessels were sunk or beached. At the widely spaced villages of Afognak and Old Harbor, the arrival time of the wave crest was recorded on clocks that were stopped by the inundation almost simultaneously—at 9:27 p.m. and 9:28 p.m., respectively. By this time virtually everyone along the southeast coast except those aboard boats and personnel at Fleet Weather Central had evacuated to higher ground, and it was too dark in most places to permit reliable observations on the nature and sequence of waves.

The instrumental records and the record kept at the Kodiak Naval Station show that waves continued to inundate the shoreline with progressively decreasing amplitude until early the next morning. However, the highest runup in some localities, including Womens Bay near Kodiak Harbor, coincided with high tide shortly after midnight (table 2).

The greatest observed withdrawal of water occurred at the Kodiak Naval Station a few minutes after midnight. At that time, water level fell some 24 feet from a plus 8-foot tide to 16 feet below mean lower low water.

Along the Shelikof Strait side of the group of islands, no wave action or water motions were noted, aside from minor local turbulence, until about 90 minutes after the earthquake. Water fluctuations there consisted of rapid low-amplitude tide changes accompanied by swift and erratic currents. The shoreline was inundated a few feet above normal preearthquake highest tide levels only by the waves that occurred between 11:30 p.m. and 1:00 a.m., within an hour of high tide (table 2). The last recorded anomalous tide rise on the Shelikof Strait side of the island that could be attributed to wave action was at about 5:00 a.m. on the morning after the earthquake.

CREST HEIGHTS

Locations of coastal areas on Kodiak and nearby islands that were affected by the seismic sea waves are shown on figure 18. Also shown are maximum runup heights recorded at shore stations and the inferred source area of the waves.

The sole operative tide gage on Kodiak and the nearby islands was at the Kodiak Naval Station in Womens Bay. It was put out of action by the earthquake tremors and was subsequently inundated by the waves; the marigram for March was lost. Observations of water-level changes at the Naval Station were made by Fleet Weather Central personnel throughout the night of March 27 and the early hours of March 28. It is the most complete record available of the seismic sea waves in the area or elsewhere along the Gulf of Alaska coast in the region strongly affected by the earthquake.

Unique instrumental records of arrival times and maximum runup heights of the higher waves were obtained from three U.S. Geological Survey streamflow gages at localities shown on figure 18. The three gages were situated at sites near stream mouths that subsided sufficiently during the earthquake to bring them within reach of the highest seismic sea waves; the two gages on the Shelikof Strait side of the island are low enough to record the higher astronomical tides since the earthquake. Arrival times, crest heights, and runup altitudes of the waves at Womens Bay and at the three streamflow gages are given in table 4 (next page).

With the exception of the four localities enumerated above, all data on wave-arrival times were obtained through conversations or written communications with eyewitnesses. Most are little more than rough estimates of elapsed time beween start of the tremors and the wave-crest arrivals. Few observers had the opportunity or presence of mind under the prevailing conditions to record the time at which the waves struck, and in any given locality opinions varied considerably.

The maximum heights to which the waves rose along the shore at localities other than Womens Bay and the sites of the streamflow gages could be readily ascertained from the strand lines of seaweed and driftwood, waterstains on buildings, and abraded bark or broken branches in trees and brush along the shore. Heights were measured by hand level and stadia rod above prevailing sea level and later reduced to mean lower low water. At most localities measured heights were substantially lower than those indicated by eyewitnesses or estimated by some investigators who visited the area after the earthquake.

Because much of the land area had been lowered or uplifted by the tectonic deformation that presumably occurred during the earthquake (Plafker, 1965, p. 1680) and because the wave train struck the coast at stages of tide ranging from low to high, appro-

TABLE 4.— *Heights (in feet) and arrival times of seismic sea-wave crests at Womens Bay, Myrtle Creek, Terror River, and Uganik River on Kodiak Island*

[Local (Alaska standard) time. MLLW, postearthquake mean lower low water]

Wave	Womens Bay[1] (Kodiak Naval Station)			Myrtle Creek[2]			Terror River[3]			Uganik River[4]		
	Time	Crest height		Time	Crest height		Time	Crest height		Time	Crest height	
		Above tide level	Above MLLW		Above tide level	Above MLLW		Above tide level	Above MLLW		Above tide level	Above MLLW
March 27												
1	6:35 p.m.	10.8	10.6	6:45 p.m.	15.2	15.0	11:15 p.m.	8.0	18.2	11:00 p.m.	6.2	15.2
March 28 (Terror River, Uganik River)												
2	7:40 p.m.	12.8	12.8	7:40 p.m.	18.6	18.8	1:15 a.m.	1.8	17.0	1:15 a.m.	0.9	16.0
3	8:30–8:44 p.m.	8.6	9.7	8:30 p.m.	17.2	18.4	1:50 a.m.	2.6	17.7	2:32 a.m.	4.9	18.5
4	10:00 p.m.	9.4	13.7	9:45 p.m.	14.3	18.4	3:00 p.m.	8.6	21.1	----------	-------	-------
5	11:16–11:34 p.m.	11.6	18.8	11:15 p.m.	13.2	20.3	4:20 a.m.	9.2	18.2	----------		
March 28 (Womens Bay, Myrtle Creek)												
6	0:47 a.m.	3.2	11.6	2:40 a.m.	7.3	13.9	----------	-------	-------	----------	-------	-------
7	1:54 a.m.	6.4	13.8	----------	-------	-------	----------	-------	-------	----------	-------	-------
8	2:20 a.m.	3.0	10.0	----------	-------	-------	----------	-------	-------	----------	-------	-------
9	2:58 a.m.	2.2	7.2	----------	-------	-------	----------	-------	-------	----------	-------	-------
10	3:20 a.m.	1.6	5.6	----------	-------	-------	----------	-------	-------	----------	-------	-------

[1] Data from Fleet Weather Station, U.S. Navy, Kodiak.
[2] Data recorded on U.S. Geological Survey streamflow gage about 1 mile above preearthquake stream mouth.
[3] Data recorded on U.S. Geological Survey streamflow gage 0.7 mile above preearthquake stream mouth.
[4] Data recorded on U.S. Geological Survey streamflow gage 0.5 mile above preearthquake stream mouth.

priate corrections for vertical displacement and tide stage had to be made at each locality to obtain the actual runup heights shown in figure 18 and table 4. Where wave-crest arrival times were known, corrections were made by subtracting from the measured runup heights (1) the amount of subsidence, if any, at the shore station, and (2) the predicted tide height above lower low water at the time the wave crested. Where runup heights were measured from swash marks or other evidence left along the shore at unknown stages of tide, corrections could be made for vertical displacement but not for tide stage. In these localities,

the height indicated on figure 18 is a minimum value (indicated by a plus sign following the numeral) that assumes coincidence of the highest wave with high tide on the morning of March 28 (table 2). Along the ocean side of the islands the highest waves apparently occurred between low and half tide, so the runup heights of the highest waves most probably were 4–8 feet higher than those shown on figure 18.

RUNUP HEIGHTS

In general, the waves were high and destructive only along the exposed ocean coast. They barely inundated shorelines above normal highest tide levels along

the Shelikof Strait side of the islands and the straits between the larger islands. The waves were too low to flood above the shoreline along the southwest shore of Kodiak Island or at Sitkinak Island.

As indicated by figure 18, maximum runup heights of the waves around the islands ranged from a minimum of 5 feet or less to at least 31½ feet. Large local variations in runup heights occurred around the islands—apparently controlled by the highly irregular configuration of the coastline, differences in offshore bottom topography, and length of wave travel path. The highest recorded runups were along exposed beaches and bluffs on southeastward-facing shores of Kodiak and Sitkalidak Islands, whereas runup heights in adjacent sheltered embayments and segments of coast protected by offshore reefs were substantially lower.

The highest measured runup was at an uninhabited locality between Cape Chiniak and Narrow Cape, where trees were damaged 31½ feet above predicted astronomical high tide on the night of the earthquake; however, the highest wave probably coincided with the first large wave at low tide that was witnessed at Narrow Cape and Cape Chiniak. If it did, runup above existing tide level would have been almost 40 feet. Runup of 24½ feet above the March 28 high-tide level was measured on an eastward-facing beach at Sitkalidak Island, and driftwood deposited on a terrace at the south end of the island is estimated to be at least 15 feet higher. Wave-deposited driftwood was also seen from the air at high altitudes on bluffs along the north coast of Marmot Island.

In sheltered embayments along the ocean coast, runup heights ranged from 12 to 17 feet. The highest runup of 17+ feet occurred at Kaguyak which is situated at the head of a large, deep bay that opens into the Gulf of Alaska. The rather low measured runup of 8 feet at Afognak village and at other localities on Afognak Island that face the open ocean are suggestive of rapid dissipation of wave energy with distance from the inferred offshore-source area, especially in areas of shoal waters and shallow reefs such as extend several miles offshore from Afognak village.

On the Shelikof Strait side of the islands, maximum runup heights generally range from 5 to 6 feet. A lone exception is at the Terror River streamflow gage site, where, as described in the following section, seiching caused anomalous water-level rises of as much as 10 feet above tide level at 3:00 a.m. and 4:00 a.m. on the morning of March 28.

Other than at the Terror River gage site, maximum recorded runups above tide level occurred during the first three waves. The highest runups above predicted postearthquake astronomical tides recorded at Kodiak Naval Station and at the Myrtle Creek streamflow gage (12.8 and 18.4 ft, respectively) occurred during the second wave. At Cape Chiniak and Narrow Cape the first wave (at least 31½ and possibly 40 ft) reportedly was the highest. At Afognak and Old Harbor the third wave (8 and 13 ft above tide level, respectively) was the highest. The maximum runup altitude in these areas, however, did not necessarily coincide with the highest wave, inasmuch as the maximum was the resultant of both wave height and the stage of postearthquake astronomical tide at any given locality. As shown by table 2, the tides on which the seismic sea waves were superimposed ranged from slightly less than 0 to 16.0 feet. Consequently, the highest recorded runup at many localities, including those stations indicated on table 4, coincided with wave arrivals close to midnight at about high tide, rather than with the larger early waves that arrived at lower tide stages.

PERIODS

The first three seismic sea waves as recorded at Womens Bay and the stream gage at Myrtle Creek had periods of 50–55 minutes (table 4). This period probably most nearly approximates that of the waves at their source. Later irregularities in the interval between successive waves at these places and at the two stream gages on the Shelikof Strait side of the islands may reflect superposition of local seiches upon the wave train. Such superposition may in part explain the inconsistencies in the reports by eyewitnesses at different localities on the number and arrival times of wave crests.

The anomalous increase in wave height recorded at the Terror Bay streamflow gage (table 4) is suggestive of a longitudinal seiche excited in Terror Bay through approximate coincidence between the natural oscillation period of the bay and that of the seismic seawave train. That the anomalous high waves in the bay were purely of local origin is clearly demonstrated by the record of successive waves of declining amplitude during the same period on the Uganik River gage and at inhabited areas nearby. The Terror River gage is at the head of a nearly rectangular fiord about 14 miles long, less than 1 mile wide, and with an average depth of roughly 270 feet. The natural period of oscillation for the fundamental mode of open-sided bays, such as Terror Bay, is given by the formula:

$$Tn = \frac{4l}{\sqrt{gd}}$$

where Tn is the natural period in seconds, l is the length of the bay in feet, g is the gravitational constant, and d is the water depth in feet (Ruttner, 1953, p. 43). The fundamental mode of oscillation is that in which the first node is situated at the mouth of the bay. By use of this formula and the dimensions and depth indicated above, the period for the fundamental mode of water in the fiord is about 53 minutes, which coin-

20. — Opening torn by seismic sea waves in the barrier beach of a large lake along the shore of Izhut Bay on Afognak Island. Channel scour and subsidence of at least 6 feet permit sea water to enter the basin at all stages of tide. Note partially submerged trees along inner margins of the beach spits, and small new rockslide along bluff in background. Photograph by Alaska Department of Fish and Game.

cides almost too closely with the period of 50–55 minutes indicated for the initial waves. Consequently, the anomalously high wave recorded at the stream gage may have resulted from resonant amplification of a longitudinal seiche that was excited by the train of seismic sea waves.

EFFECTS ON SHORELINES AND SEA BOTTOMS

High-velocity currents associated with the repeated ebb and flood of the waves resulted in extensive damage through erosion of artificial fills and unconsolidated deposits along the coast. The effect of the surges may be compared to erosion during extreme flood conditions of rivers. At several places, barrier beaches damming coastal lakes were breached by the waves, and the lakes were thereby converted to lagoons, as illustrated in figure 20.

Stream gravel was removed from the bed and banks of Olds River at the head of Kalsin Bay along a length of at least 400 feet of the estuary (Alaska Dept. Fish and Game, 1965, p. 6). Mud was eroded from tidal flats along the shore at Kodiak to a depth of 10 feet. Bottom changes off shore from Kodiak at a depth of 75 feet were reported by a scuba diver, Mr. Jerry Tilley, who noted that the channel had been scoured clean of mud and that thousands of clams were thereby exposed on the sea floor.

The combination of swift currents and the buoyant effect of large-amplitude waves moved several navigation and mooring buoys in the Chiniak Bay area, and dragged the navigation buoy in Shuyak Strait off station. Undoubtedly the 20- to 25-knot currents associated with the waves caused intensive scouring of sediment from shorelines and narrow

21. — Shoreline damage between Narrow Cape and Cape Chiniak caused by driftwood-laden seismic sea wave. Spruce trees as much as 8 inches in diameter were broken off at about 30 feet altitude. Limbs were broken and trunks scarred to a measured altitude of 42 feet above lower low water. Crowns of downed trees point in direction of water movement.

straits and deposition of the eroded material in deeper quieter water. Few such effects, however, have been documented along the shores of Kodiak and the nearby islands because of the general scarcity of preearthquake reference marks in coastal areas and the complicating factor of widespread postearthquake subsidence.

At uninhabited capes and embayments along the ocean coast, wave inundation was evidenced by newly deposited driftwood and seaweed above the level of highest tides and by broken and scarred shoreline vegetation in timbered areas. Figure 21 illustrates the effects on a stand of spruce trees near Narrow Cape of a driftwood-laden surge of water that ran up to an altitude of 42 feet above lower low water.

ORIGIN

The seismic sea waves clearly were generated off shore from the Kodiak group of islands within the Gulf of Alaska, as shown by the arrival times of the initial waves, the distribution of wave damage, and the orientation of damaged shorelines. The distance traveled by the waves can be determined where wave velocity along the propagation path and travel time are known. Because the wave lengths are long, seismic sea waves move as shallow water waves even in the deepest ocean. As such, their velocity is controlled by the depth and conforms closely to LaGrange's equation (in Lamb, 1932, p. 257):

$$V = \sqrt{gh}$$

where g is the gravitational constant, and h is the water depth along the travel path (as determined from nautical charts). The travel time is taken as the elapsed time between arrival of the first wave crest at shore stations and the inferred time at which the waves were generated.

Calculations of the distance travelled by the first waves to the few stations where reliable data are available on arrival times defines a source area that trends northeastward at a minimum distance of 28 miles off Cape Chiniak and 17 miles offshore from Sitkalidak Island—assuming that the waves were generated at the time of the earthquake or shortly thereafter (fig. 18). A time delay between the beginning of the earthquake and generation of the waves would modify the position of the inferred source by shifting it shoreward. Thus, if as much as 5 minutes elapsed between the beginning of the earthquake in Prince William Sound and the generation of the waves offshore from the Kodiak area, the inferred source area would be 4–6 miles shoreward from the position shown on figure 18. The absence of large waves at Sitkinak Island and in Alitak Bay suggests that the wave source did not extend southwest of the general latitude of southern Sitkalidak Island. The anomalous lack of wave effects along the low-lying northeast shore of Sitkinak Island, which is ideally situated to receive heavy damage from northeasterly waves, further suggests that the waves were strongly directional—as might be expected from a linear northeast-trending source area.

Initial upward motion in the source area is suggested by (1) the distribution of measured land-level change along the adjacent coast and offshore islands,

(2) the initial rise recorded on tide gages outside the immediate area affected by the earthquake (Van Dorn, 1964, p. 11), and (3) possibly by the unique atmospheric waves ("seismic air waves") recorded shortly after the earthquakes on microbaragraphs at both the University of California at Berkeley and the Scripps Institution of Oceanography at La Jolla (Van Dorn, 1964, p. 7; Bolt, 1964, p. 1096). The initial direction of water movement within the Kodiak islands area is less clear, however, because there were no operative tide gages, and in many localities water movement during and after the earthquake was complicated by land-level changes along the coast, and perhaps also by local waves generated by the ground tremors or by subaerial and submarine landslides. With a few notable exceptions, however, most observers along the coast of the Kodiak group of islands and elsewhere along the coast of the Kenai Peninsula and Prince William Sound area reported that the first strong surge of waves from the Gulf of Alaska was upward; this report tends to support the inference of vertical displacement in the source area.

The waves recorded on Kodiak and the nearby islands and those that struck the outer coast of the Kenai Peninsula (fig. 17; Plafker and Mayo, 1965, p. 10, fig. 12) appear to have originated along a linear axis of maximum uplift that extends about 350 miles between Sitkalidak Island in the Kodiak group and Montague Island in Prince William Sound. The discrepancy in the position of the inferred axis of maximum uplift offshore from the Kodiak Island area between figure 21 and that of a preliminary report (Plafker and Mayo,

1965, fig. 12) results from a previous error in calculating propagation velocities of the waves.

The axis of the inferred wave source as shown in figure 17 and as computed independently by Van Dorn (1964, figs. 8, 10) are in close agreement. At the north end of this axis near Montague Island there is clear evidence for significant upward displacement in a 6-mile-wide segment of the sea floor. Both extreme crustal warping and large fault dislocation must have taken place. The southwest tip of Montague Island was elevated as much as 33 feet relative to sea level; there was at least 18 feet of vertical offset on land along the Patton Bay fault (Plafker, 1965, p. 1132; Plafker and Mayo, 1965, p. 7). Furthermore, the fault has been traced as a prominent scarp in the ocean floor for at least 15 miles southwest of Montague Island towards the Kodiak group of islands. As much as 50 feet of net uplift of the sea floor along this line has been inferred from comparison of pre- and postearthquake bathymetric surveys made by the U.S. Coast and Geodetic Surveys southwest of Montague Island (Malloy, 1964).

The inferred source area shown on figure 18, from which destructive waves radiated northwestward to batter the coast of the Kodiak group of islands could be a southwestern extension of the axis of uplift and faulting in the Montague Island area. As in that area, it may represent a relatively narrow strip of extreme differential uplift and (or) faulting that is superimposed on the broad regional zone of uplift. The position of the inferred wave source is largely in an area of flat slopes and shoal water on the continental shelf; the possibility is thus virtually precluded that the waves result either from massive submarine landslides along the continental slope or from special resonant oscillations of water in the adjacent Aleutian Trench.

The low-amplitude dipole-type wave that Van Dorn (1964) considered to have been formed by tectonic warping of the broad zones of uplift and subsidence shown on figure 17 apparently did not adversely affect Kodiak or the nearby islands, although it may have contained much of the wave energy radiated out into the Pacific Ocean. No negative wave phase was recorded within the zone of subsidence along the shores of the islands, nor was a positive phase reported at any

locality other than the city of Kodiak prior to the arrival of the initial wave crest. The tectonic warping did result, however, in almost immediate withdrawal of water from some tilted uplifted areas and in complementary rises of water level in depressed areas. The reported initial calm rise of water observed at Kodiak immediately after the earthquake may have been associated with this regional crustal tilting about the axis of zero land-level change.

The amount of uplift at the inferred wave source offshore from the Kodiak group of islands is not known and probably cannot be determined because the area had not been covered by de-

tailed preearthquake bathymetric surveys. That the vertical sea-floor displacements may be of the same order of magnitude as those in the Montague Island area is suggested by the similarity in the maximum runup heights of the seismic sea waves (35–40 ft) along physiographically comparable segments of coast both on the Kenai Peninsula opposite Montague Island (Plafker and Mayo, 1965, p. 10) and on Kodiak Island. Other factors, however, such as rate of uplift, initial slope at the wave source, and energy loss along the propagation path preclude direct correlation of runup heights with displacement at the source.

DAMAGE AND CASUALTIES

The earthquake and attendant subsidence and seismic sea waves severed the main coastal highways on Kodiak Island and caused extensive damage to the fishing, cattle ranching, and logging industries on Kodiak and the nearby islands. These industries constitute the main economic base for the region. The city of Kodiak also receives substantial revenue from the operation and maintenance of the Kodiak Naval Station that is about 6 miles south of the city.

The effects of the earthquake on the highway routes and on the various industries throughout the Kodiak Island region are described in the following section. The nature and cause of the extensive damage to public, private, commercial, and military property at population centers in the Kodiak region is discussed in a separate volume of this series of reports on earthquake effects

on Alaskan communities. The estimated dollar value of damage by the earthquake is shown in table 1.

HIGHWAYS

There are approximately 125 miles of highway on Kodiak and the nearby islands; about 115 miles are on Kodiak Island—85 miles of which are rural routes (fig. 22, next page). This report will consider only the 85 miles of rural highway on Kodiak Island, because the remainder are in communities and will be discussed in the companion chapter in Professional Paper 542.

The earthquake caused approximately $5,036,000 worth of damage to the highway system on Kodiak Island—about $446,000 in the city of Kodiak and $1,677,000 in the Kodiak Naval Station (Tudor, 1964, fig. 3). Chiniak highway on the Naval Station was damaged from the station

complex to Middle Bay, the southern boundary of the station.

Most of the damage occurred on the 47-mile route to Chiniak and Sequel Point. The seismic sea waves destroyed two bridges at Womens Bay, four in Middle Bay, one across Mayflower Creek, one across the Kalsin River at Kalsin Bay, two on Twin Creek, and one at an unnamed creek at mile 33.7, about 0.8 mile east of Twin Creek. (Mile posts are reckoned north and south of the Buskin River—mile 0.0—which flows through the main complex of the Kodiak Naval Station.)

Eyewitness accounts of the seismic sea waves indicate that the bridges were not destroyed by the incoming water of the first wave, but by the outgoing wave and by the more violent incoming and outgoing subsequent waves. Figures 23 and 24 (p. D41) show seismic sea-wave damage to two bridges.

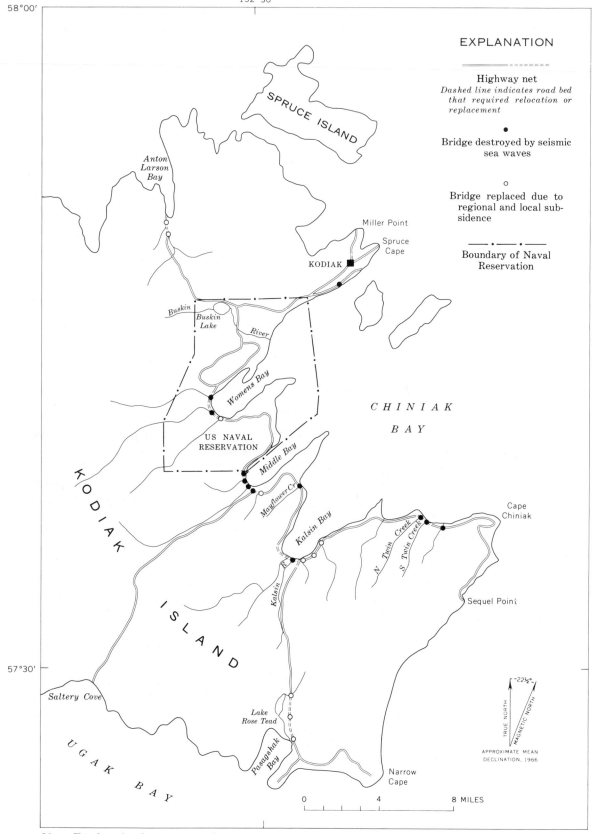

22. — Earthquake damage to major highway routes on Kodiak Island.

23. — Bridge at Womens Bay destroyed by seismic sea waves. Deck of bridge collapsed owing to destruction of piles. Compare with fig. 24. Photograph by U.S. Navy, March 30, 1964.

24. — Deck of highway bridge at Womens Bay washed away by seismic sea waves. Photograph by U.S. Navy, March 30, 1964.

25. — Section of roadway along Chiniak highway at Womens Bay destroyed by seismic sea waves. Photograph by U.S. Navy, March 30, 1964.

In addition to those that were destroyed, five bridges on the Chiniak highway had to be replaced either because they were underwater during high tide or because their approaches needed realinement. The bridges that required replacement (indicated by open circles on fig. 22) are at Womens Bay, Middle Bay, and Kalsin Bay.

The seismic sea waves destroyed at least 13 miles of roadway on the highway to Chiniak. About 3 miles of road was destroyed at Womens Bay (figs. 22 and 25), 3 miles at Middle Bay (pl. 3), 1 mile at Mayflower Creek, and 4 miles at Kalsin Bay. The roads in these areas were not only destroyed but had to be realined because regional and local subsidence was so great that the pre-earthquake alinement left the roadway under water during high tides.

The Anton Larson highway spur, 9 miles long, starts near Buskin Lake on the Naval Reservation and runs west and then north to Anton Larson Bay. Dam-

age occurred near the terminus of the road at the bay. One mile of roadway was destroyed and required replacing. In addition, two bridges near the bay required replacing.

The Saltery Cove spur road originates at the Chiniak highway at Middle Bay. It heads generally southeastward for 14 miles to Saltery Cove on Ugak Bay. Damage on this spur occurred near its point of origin at Middle Bay and at the divide between the Saltery Cove and Middle Bay drainage basins. Two miles of roadway were destroyed and one bridge had to be replaced.

The Narrow Cape spur road is 15 miles long; it originates at Kalsin Bay and heads south, where it skirts the east edge of Lake Rose Tead, then runs on to Pasagshak Bay. At the head of Pasagshak Bay, the road forks. One spur continues south about 2 miles to Pasagshak Point; the other spur heads east for about 5 miles to Narrow Cape.

Two miles of roadway of the Narrow Cape spur was damaged

by the earthquake and attendant subsidence. At Kalsin Bay 1 mile of roadway had to be replaced. Another mile of roadway required replacement at Lake Rose Tead (fig. 8). In addition to 2 miles of roadway that was destroyed, three bridges had to be replaced on the Narrow Cape spur road. Two bridges at Lake Rose Tead and one on a small creek that flows into the head of Pasagshak Bay required replacement.

Along the 85 miles of rural highway on Kodiak Island, 18 miles of roadway, 22 bridges, and 1 culvert were either destroyed by seismic sea waves or had to be replaced because of regional and local subsidence. No bridges were destroyed by seismic shock even though some were on foundations of unconsolidated deposits.

FISHING INDUSTRY

The salmon, king crab, halibut, dungeness crab, shrimp, and clam fishing industry, upon which the economy of the area is almost en-

26. — Chaotic condition of the commercial section of the city of Kodiak following inundation by seismic sea waves. The small-boat harbor, which was in the left background, contained an estimated 160 crab and salmon fishing boats when the waves struck. Photograph by U.S. Navy, March 30, 1964.

tirely dependent, suffered devastating losses of processing facilities, vessels, and gear. Three canneries at Kodiak and one at Uzinki were destroyed by seismic sea waves, and one other cannery and a cold-storage plant at Kodiak were severely damaged. The Kadiak Fisheries cannery at Shearwater Bay was damaged by seismic shock during the earthquake, after which it was virtually destroyed by the waves. Estimated value of the structures and the finished products they contained is $2,610,000.

The total number of lost or damaged fishing boats is not known. In the vicinity of Kodiak alone, 13 vessels were lost and 19 others were swamped or run aground (fig. 26). Vessels underway in deep water were not damaged by the waves. One boat, a 38-foot seiner, went down with its crew of six when it either struck a wave-propelled log or was grounded between waves in shallow water near Spruce Cape, 8 miles northeast of Kodiak. Two other lives were lost on two fishing boats that sank in the Kodiak

small-boat harbor. Replacement cost of vessels that were sunk, grounded, or otherwise damaged throughout the area has been estimated at $2,466,500.

As a result of regional tectonic subsidence, three canneries and their facilities were made unusable by inundation, and four others sustained costly damage. The lost and damaged cannery facilities were valued at $1.3 million (Alaska Dept. Fish and Game, 1965, p. 21).

Studies of salmon habitat by the Alaska Department of Fish

[223]

and Game (1965, p. 3) indicate that, because of subsidence, tides have made many previous intertidal salmon spawning areas nearly useless and have engulfed former fresh-water stream rearing areas. As shown by table 3, tidal inundation of streams extends as much as 4,500 feet farther inland than before the earthquake. According to the Department of Fish and Game, at least two important salmon fishing areas did not produce in 1964, even though it was a bumper salmon year elsewhere. Studies have been initiated to determine whether the poor catch was due to normal seasonal variations in salmon runs, or was in some way related to the earthquake.

Significant changes in currents and the time of tide changes have been reported by fishermen on the Shelikof Strait side of the islands since the earthquake. These changes are probably related to changes in water depth resulting from the tectonic deformation. The difference in tides and currents has required modification of fishing techniques and could have a detrimental long-term effect on the migration pattern of the salmon.

In Sitkalidak and Raspberry Straits (fig. 2) where subsidence amounted to about 1 and 3½ feet, respectively, local residents report not only higher high tides since the earthquake but also lower low tides. In these areas, clamming is reportedly better on minus tides than it was prior to the earthquake. These reports have not been confirmed or explained by the fisheries authorities.

Tectonic uplift and subsidence has changed the appearance of landmarks used by vessel operators along the treacherous rocky coast and has altered water

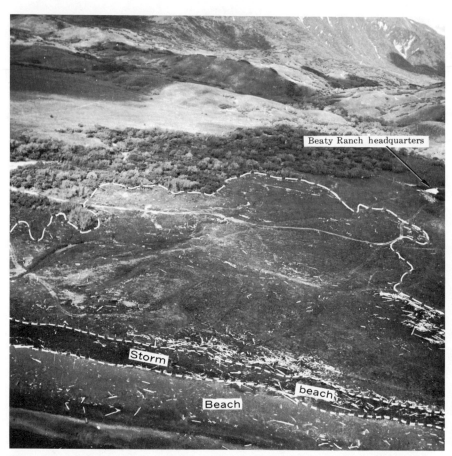

27. — Part of Beaty Ranch showing extent of wave inundation, as indicated by light-colored debris. Ranch buildings are a quarter of a mile from the shoreline.

depths. These changes have reportedly caused several vessels to be damaged or sunk since the earthquake by collision with submerged objects.

CATTLE RANCHES

The earthquake was a near-disaster to several of the small cattle ranchers in the area who were struggling to develop sound and profitable operations.

Inundation by seismic sea waves caused extensive property damage at all the isolated cattle ranches along the southeast coast of Kodiak Island and on Sitkalidak Island. According to a U.S. Department of Agriculture report (Oliver, 1964), 175 cattle were drowned, 3 ranch houses and 20–25 outbuildings with their contents were swept away, and 25 miles of corral and range fencing was lost. In addition, several hundred acres of land used for hay production was littered with wave-borne debris (fig. 27).

Numerous beaches and deltas along the southeast coast of Kodiak and Sitkalidak Islands are now inundated by tides, and salt water has ruined several hundred acres of the best beach rye lands which were used for winter grazing.

LOGGING INDUSTRY

Logging in the area is carried on by small operators and is almost entirely for local consumption. One of the sawmills near Afognak village on southern Afognak Island was abandoned because seismic sea waves washed away most of the docking facilities and caused extensive damage to the mill. A second small mill near Uzinki sustained an unknown amount of wave damage to the dock.

CASUALTIES

In the Kodiak Island area the earthquake caused the loss of 18 lives through drowning, but the extent of wave damage and attendant loss of life would undoubtedly have been much greater had not the largest waves coincided with low, rather than high, stages of tide. Furthermore, the disaster would have been worse had the earthquake occurred during the summer when the population of the islands is substantially increased by large numbers of fishermen and cannery workers, many of whom normally live and fish along shores.

The toll of 18 dead, although relatively light, was to a considerable extent needless and was caused largely by public ignorance concerning the nature and destructive force of seismic sea

waves. Especially serious is the prevailing mistaken belief that the first wave is necessarily the highest. As a consequence some individuals made the disastrous error of returning to low-lying coastal areas after the initial wave, and 10 of them were trapped and drowned by subsequent waves. Furthermore, the first wave did not reach any of the boat harbors until about an hour after the earthquake, and a local warning broadcast was issued half an hour earlier advising of the impending wave, yet few manned vessels were piloted to the safety of nearby deep water. All the vessels that were sunk, including three in which eight lives were lost, went down in shallow water.

Clearly, a better method of disseminating information is required as the key to minimizing loss of life from future seismic sea waves in coastal areas of the Kodiak group of islands, as well as elsewhere along coastal segments of the Gulf of Alaska that may be threatened by similar waves in the future. Evacuation

procedures for the populace and for boats should be carefully worked out in advance, and it should be made clear that the danger from such waves may persist for several hours after the initial wave strikes. The Seismic Sea Wave Warning System operated by the U.S. Coast and Geodetic Survey can provide advance warning where destructive waves are generated by distant earthquakes in the Pacific Ocean basin. The present system, however, cannot assure warnings for locations closer to the wave source than about 1,000 miles because at least an hour may be required to locate the earthquake epicenter, determine its magnitude, and broadcast a warning (Spaeth and Berkman, 1965, p. 4–7). Consequently, in earthquake-prone areas—such as the Gulf of Alaska and Alaska Peninsula— where any strongly felt earthquake of long duration could be accompanied by destructive seismic sea waves, immediate evacuation of low-lying coastal areas is the only prudent course of action.

REFERENCES CITED

Alaska Department of Fish and Game, 1965, Post-earthquake fisheries evaluation; an interim report on the March 1964 earthquake effects on Alaska's fishery resources: Juneau, Alaska, 72 p.

Alaska Department of Health and Welfare, 1964, Preliminary report of earthquake damage to environmental health facilities and services in Alaska: Juneau, Alaska Dept. Health and Welfare, Environmental Health Br., 46 p.

Bancroft, H. H., 1886, The history of Alaska: San Francisco, Calif., A. L. Bancroft and Co., 775 p.

Bolt, B. A., 1964, Seismic air waves from the great 1964 Alaskan

earthquake: Nature, v. 202, no. 4937, p. 1095-1096.

Capps, S. R., 1937, Kodiak and adjacent islands [Alaska]: U.S. Geol. Survey Bull. 880-C, p. 111-184.

Chevigny, Hector, 1942, Lord of Alaska; Baranov and the Russian adventure: New York, The Viking Press, Inc., 320 p.

Grantz, Arthur, Plafker, George, and Kachadoorian, Reuben, 1964, Alaska's Good Friday earthquake, March 27, 1964: U.S. Geol. Survey Circ. 491, 35 p.

Gutenberg, Beno, 1957, Effects of ground on earthquake motion: Seismol. Soc. America Bull., v. 47, no. 3, p. 221-250.

Hodgson, J. H., 1964, Earthquakes and earth structure: New Jersey, Prentice-Hall, Inc., 166 p.

Lamb, Horace, 1932, Hydrodynamics: 6th ed., England, Cambridge Univ. Press, 738 p.

Leet, L. D., 1946, Earth motion from the atomic bomb test [New Mexico, July 16, 1945]: Am. Scientist, v. 34, no. 2, p. 198-211.

Malloy, R. J., 1964, Crustal uplift southwest of Montague Island, Alaska: Science, v. 146, no. 3647, p. 1048-1049.

Moore, G. W., 1964, Magnetic disturbances preceding the Alaska 1964 earthquake: Nature, v. 203, no. 4944, p. 508-509.

Oliver, W. B., 1964, A shock to Alaska agriculture: Soil Conservation, v. 30, no. 2, p. 30-31.

Plafker, George, 1965, Tectonic deformation associated with the 1964 Alaska earthquake: Science, v. 148, no. 3678, p. 1675-1687.

Plafker, George, and Mayo, L. R., 1965, Tectonic deformation, subaqueous slides and destructive waves associated with the Alaskan March 27, 1964, earthquake —an interim geologic evaluation: U.S. Geol. Survey open-file report, 21 p.

Richter, C. F., 1958, Elementary seismology: San Francisco, Calif., W. H. Freeman and Co., 768 p.

Ruttner, Franz, 1953, Fundamentals of limnology: 2nd ed., Toronto, Canada, Toronto Univ. Press, 242 p.

Spaeth, M. G., and Berkman, S. C., 1965, The tsunami of March 28, 1964, as recorded at tide stations: U.S. Coast and Geod. Survey, 59 p.

Tudor, W. J., 1964, Tsunami damage at Kodiak, Alaska, and Crescent City, California, from Alaskan earthquake of 27 March 1964: U.S. Naval Civil Eng. Lab., Tech. Note N-622, 124 p., Port Hueneme, Calif.

U.S. Coast and Geodetic Survey, 1964a, Prince William Sound, Alaskan earthquakes, March-April, 1964: U.S. Coast and Geod. Survey, Seismology Div. Prelim. Rept., 83 p.

———1964b, Tide tables, high and low water predictions, 1964, West Coast North and South America including the Hawaiian Islands: U.S. Coast and Geod. Survey, 224 p.

———1965, Assistance and recovery in Alaska, 1964: U.S. Coast and Geod. Survey, 45 p.

U.S. Weather Bureau, 1964, Climatological data, Alaska, v. 50, no. 3, p. 42-58.

Van Dorn, W. G., 1964, Source mechanism of the tsunami of March 28, 1964, in Alaska: Coastal Eng. Conf., 9th, Lisbon 1964, Proc., p. 166-190.

Varnes, D. J., 1958, Landslide types and processes, in Eckel, E. B., ed., Landslides and engineering: Natl. Acad. Sci.-Natl. Research Council Pub. 544, Highway Research Board Spec. Rept. 29, p. 20-47.

Wahrhaftig, Clyde, 1965, The physiographic provinces of Alaska: U.S. Geol. Survey Prof. Paper 482, 52 p.

Waller, R. M., Thomas, H. E., Vorhis, R. C., 1965, Effects of the Good Friday earthquake on water supplies: Am. Water Works Assoc. Jour., v. 57, no. 2, p. 123-131.

CLARIFICATIONS

Geology Vol. Page	USGS Page	Column	Line	Remarks
178	D 2	3	33, 34	See Kachadoorian and Plafker, USGS PP 542-F, abstract, this volume, p. 539
183	D 7	1	29, 30	Later computed as 61.04°N; 147.73°W
193	D 15	3	30	USGS PP 545-C; also this volume, p. 641
193	D 15	3	32	USGS PP 542-F, abstract, this volume, p. 539
201	D 23	1	38	USGS PP 544; also in *The Great Alaska Earthquake of 1964: Hydrology*, p. 12–308
203	D 25	2	9, 10	USGS PP 543-I; also this volume, p. 47
219	D 39	2	38	See Kachadoorian and Plafker, USGS PP 542-F, abstract, this volume, p. 539
225	D 45	3	7	The Seismic Sea Wave Warning System is now known as the Tsunami Warning System

1.—South-central Alaska showing coastlines affected by the earthquake. Land to left of zero land-level change was generally lowered; land to right was raised.

KIRK W. STANLEY*

GEOLOGIST

ANCHORAGE, ALASKA

Reprinted with minor changes from
U.S. Geological Survey Professional Paper 543-J,
"Effects of the Alaska Earthquake of March 27, 1964, on Shore Processes and Beach Morphology"

Effects on Shore Processes and Beach Morphology

ABSTRACT

Some 10,000 miles of shoreline in south-central Alaska was affected by the subsidence or uplift associated with the great Alaska earthquake of March 27, 1964. The changes in shoreline processes and beach morphology that were suddenly initiated by the earthquake were similar to those ordinarily caused by gradual changes in sea level operating over hundreds of years, while other more readily visible changes were similar to some of the effects of great but short-lived storms. Phenomena became available for observation within a few hours which would otherwise not have been available for many years.

In the subsided areas—including the shorelines of the Kenai Peninsula, Kodiak Island, and Cook Inlet—beaches tended to flatten in gradient and to recede shoreward. Minor beach features were altered or destroyed on submergence but began to reappear and to stabilize in their normal shapes within a few months after the earthquake. Frontal beach ridges migrated shoreward and grew higher and wider than they were before. Along narrow beaches backed by bluffs, the relatively higher sea level led to vigorous erosion of the bluff toes. Stream mouths were drowned and some were altered by seismic sea waves, but they adjusted within a few months to the new conditions.

In the uplifted areas, generally around Prince William Sound, virtually all beaches were stranded out of reach of the sea. New beaches are gradually developing to fit new sea levels, but the processes are slow, in part because the material on the lower parts of the old beaches is predominantly fine grained. Streams were lengthened in the emergent areas, and down cutting and bank erosion have increased.

Except at Homer and a few small villages, where groins, bulkheads, and cobble-filled baskets were installed, there has been little attempt to protect the postearthquake shorelines. The few structures that were built have been only partially successful because there was too little time to study the habits of the new shore features and to design appropriate protection measures. Emergence of large areas that were once below water and permanent submergence of once-useful land areas have led to many problems of land use and ownership in addition to the destruction or relocation of wildfowl, shellfish, and salmon habitats.

INTRODUCTION

One of the strongest earthquakes ever reported occurred in Alaska on March 27, 1964, at 5:36 p.m. Alaska standard time. The epicenter was at Unakwik Inlet in Prince William Sound (fig. 1). The magnitude of the main shock was 8.4–8.6 on the Richter scale (Wood, 1966). The area of land and sea bottom affected by the earthquake is at least 70,000 square miles and may exceed 110,000. Forty thousand square miles was lowered as much as 7½ feet and 25,000 square miles was raised as much as 33 feet (Plafker, 1965, 1967). The coastlines affected by the earthquake are shown by figure 1.

Definite limits of the coastal area of Alaska affected by the earthquake have not been determined. Most authorities, however, agree that it is bounded by Yakataga (just southeast of the area shown in figure 1) on the east and the Kodiak group of islands on the southwest (Plafker, 1965). If all the shoreline irregularities of the mainland and the islands affected by the earthquake are included, the shoreline within the area exceeds 10,000 nautical miles.

Certain changes in beach forms occurred as a result of relative changes in sea level caused by uplift or subsidence of the land during the earthquake. These changes were abrupt and thus cannot be unconditionally compared to a gradual change in sea level, but they did provide much information regarding normal shore processes. Because sea-level changes were not only abrupt but also permanent, months were afforded for observations, which other-

*Formerly Tidelands Supervisor, Division of Lands, Alaska Department of Natural Resources.

[229]

wise—as during storms—would have been limited to hours or at the most several days.

No attempt is made in this paper to present a detailed description of changes in beaches throughout either the submergent or emergent areas. A study of this type might have provided some interesting and descriptive material, but, considering the great distances and the general remoteness of much of the shoreline involved, such a study would have been impractical. This paper is therefore restricted to descriptions of specific areas and problems. These limited observations do not reflect all conditions and processes that occurred within the area affected by the earthquake, but they do provide a basis for understanding the general processes that occurred.

The chief objective of this report is to compare pre- and post-earthquake processes. For this reason, Homer Spit is used as an example for much of the descriptive matter; it happens to be one of the few places for which considerable preearthquake information is available. Descriptions of coastal erosion primarily involve examples along Cook Inlet because (1) much of the shoreline there is eroding and (2) the area is more densely populated than elsewhere.

The earthquake not only caused physical changes which have left their marks upon the beach; it also had certain significant economic and legal consequences. These sociological effects have an interconnection with the physical effects and are considered worthy of mention.

SHORELINES OF THE EARTHQUAKE-AFFECTED REGION

The line of zero land movement, (fig. 1) trends southwest from the epicenter on Unakwik Inlet at the head of Prince William Sound, along the east shore of Kenai Peninsula, to Kodiak Island. West of this line the land subsided; to the east it was uplifted. Anomalous areas of submergence, particularly along deltas and at the heads of bays, occur in both regions and were caused by compaction and settlement of sediments. Compaction of sediments in the uplifted area reduced the overall upward change in some localities; compaction in the subsided areas accentuated submergence.

The landmass bordering the coastal area affected by the earthquake is mountainous, and both it and the shoreline are characterized by glacial or periglacial features. The shoreline from Yakataga northwestward to the Copper River Delta is characterized by long sweeping beaches broken by wide-mouthed rivers and resembles a ria coast (Lobeck, 1939). The shoreline features were formed in part of outwash deposits from the Bering and other large glaciers. Westward from the Copper River Delta the shoreline is glacially carved and is highly irregular, deeply incised, and fringed by numerous offshore rocks and reefs. The offshore area, particularly between the mouth of the Copper River and Cordova, is shallow and has numerous shoals, barrier islands, and spits. Active glaciers occupy the heads of many bays in the region, particularly in Prince William Sound.

Along Kodiak Island the shoreline is characterized by fiords in classic forms. The bays, particularly along the Shelikof Strait side of Kodiak Island, have deep depressions at their heads and submarine threshholds of either rock or unconsolidated material at their mouths—a feature that, according to Guilcher (1958, p. 160), denotes a true fiord. The walls of the bays are usually steep, and many headlands are characterized by cliffs. Beaches are generally poorly developed and are composed of medium to coarse shingle. Sandy beaches and constructional coastal forms occur along the heads of bays, however, and well-developed sand-shingle beaches tens of miles in length are present along the southwesternmost part of the island.

Along the southern Kenai Peninsula and the western part of Prince William Sound, the shoreline resembles that of Kodiak Island in its irregularity, although bayhead depressions and submarine rock ramparts at the bay mouths are less well developed. However, the presence of active glaciers along the shoreline indicates that many of the indentations are true fiords. Here also the walls of many of the bays are steep, and cliffs are more numerous than along Kodiak Island. Narrow, relatively steep beaches consist predominantly of shingle. Sandy beaches occur along the sides and heads of inlets and bays but are less well developed than along the eastern shoreline of Prince William Sound.

Contrasting sharply with the irregular shorelines of Kodiak Island and Prince William Sound is the more uniform one of Cook Inlet. Cook Inlet extends into the mainland more than 175 miles and narrows and shallows towards its head. The backshore, particularly east and north of the inlet, consists of low gently rolling glacial outwash plains. Wave-cut bluffs as high as several hundred feet occur in that area, and the adjacent beaches are generally well developed. At the head of Cook Inlet the waters are shallow, and broad silty tidal flats are common. South of Tuxedni Bay, on the west shore of Cook Inlet, the low coastal plain pinches out, and mountains rise abruptly from the sea.

Much of the shoreline affected by the earthquake presents seemingly contradictory evidence of both uplift and subsidence—a contradiction that perhaps is not surprising when viewed in the light of the complex tectonic history of the region. The high Chugach Mountains, Saint Elias Mountains, and Fairweather Range are obvious manifestations of strong tectonic uplift. Raised beaches along some coasts indicate more recent uplift, also, but the drowned fiordlike character of much of the shoreline, combined with numerous offshore islands, skerries, and reefs, suggest coastal subsidence and submergence.

Reconnaissance studies of the displaced shorelines, paced by numerous radiocarbon dates, have brought out a general similarity between the pattern of earthquake displacements and the long-term trend of Holocene coastal emergence or submergence, as well as a remarkable widespread submergence during the past several centuries over much of the zone that was uplifted during the earthquake, and at least part of the zone that subsided (Plafker and Rubin, 1967; Plafker, 1968, 1969).

Thus, according to Plafker, the tectonic movements that accompanied the earthquake were but one pulse in a long-continuing trend of diastrophic deformation that has resulted in regional emergence of parts of the continental margin, simultaneous submergence of the Kenai-Kodiak Mountains belt, and either relative stability or emergence along the shores of Cook Inlet and parts of Shelikof Strait.

COASTAL FEATURES AND EARTHQUAKE EFFECTS

BEACHES

The beach face is the area between high and low water (fig. 2). It is an ever-changing feature, but normally the changes are subtle and become noticeable only during severe storms.

During the earthquake of 1964, rapid changes in land elevation caused obvious changes in shore processes and beach-face morphology. These changes were comparable in magnitude to changes that normally are caused by centuries-long fluctuations in sea level—or, paradoxically, to sudden changes caused by severe storms. Thus, changes in the beach face following the earthquake are important both to the study of fluctuating sea level as it affects a beach and to the engineering problems that might be met along the beach face as a result of changes caused by storms.

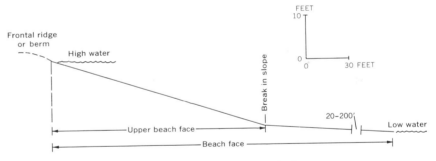

2.—Diagram illustrating beach features.

CHANGES IN PROFILE AND GRADIENT

Obvious changes in profile and gradient occurred along shingle beaches within the submergent areas. In those areas, changes were noticed within 1 week after the earthquake. The most noticeable change was a flattening of the gradient and a recession of the beach face.

Many shingle beaches within the submergent areas range in gradient from 1:8 to 1:30 and are characterized by a break-in-slope 50–200 feet seaward of the high-water line. The break-in-slope marks the location where waves act longest at high tide (King, 1959). The beach face (fig. 2) shoreward of the break (termed the "upper beach face") has a steeper gradient and coarser material than does the lower beach face. The break-in-slope shown in figure 3 is typical of those on many shingle beaches in Alaska.

3.—Sharp break-in-slope between upper and lower beach faces extends from mid-foreground to midcenter of photograph, just to right of man. These features, here seen in Kachemak Bay at low tide, are common to many shingle beaches.

After earthquake-caused subsidence, waves reached higher on the beach face and caused severe scour erosion of the upper face; the break-in-slope g r a d u a l l y shifted shoreward. The upper limit of the swash was also extended at some places, and the frontal ridge, or berm, was overflowed. Part of the material eroded from the beach face was thus carried by the swash over the frontal ridge and was deposited along the landward side.

A good example of profile and gradient changes along a shingle beach within the submergent areas was afforded by beaches along Homer Spit. Adjustment of the Homer Spit beaches to the new high-water level was gradual but can be described as occurring in three stages (fig. 4). The first stage was characterized by severe erosion and planing off of the beach face and crest by wave and swash overwash. Part of the eroded material was carried across the beach crest and onto the spit. The second stage was characterized by

active erosion along the break-in-slope and the development of a new postearthquake frontal ridge. During this stage the beach became noticeably convex upward because material from near the break-in-slope moved toward the upper beach face. The third stage was characterized by development of a well-defined break-in-slope that had gradually shifted landward. Erosion and recession of the beach face continued until the slope approached the preearthquake gradient. During the third stage the new frontal ridge increased noticeably in height and eventually retarded overflow. During this stage also, some of the material carried by the longshore drift began to accumulate along the lower beach face near the break-in-slope. The observed erosional and depositional effects of a relatively raised sea level on the Homer Spit beaches are in agreement with suggestions made originally by Bruun (1962) and partly tested by Schwartz (1965) with small-scale laboratory experiments. Bruun

concluded in part that a raised sea level is followed by shoreward displacement of the beach profile as the upper beach is eroded and that the amount of material eroded from the upper beach is equal in volume to that deposited on the nearshore bottom. Thus the rise of the nearshore bottom that results from this deposition will ultimately equal the original rise in relative sea level.

Along beaches protected from severe storm waves, adjustment to subsidence differed somewhat from that on exposed shingle beaches such as Homer Spit. Within the protected areas, for example those along the south side of Kachemak Bay and certain shores of Kodiak Island, recession of the beach face was more uniform and the convex-upward profiles were less noticeable because wave action was less turbulent. Erosion along the new break-in-slope and swash action along the beach crest were also less severe. Thus, the rate of beach-face recession along the beaches not acted on by large waves was more uniform and less rapid than along exposed beaches.

Even less noticeable changes occurred along sandy beaches, probably because their gradient is usually flatter than that of shingle beaches and because sand is less readily moved by wave action than is shingle.

One area of subsidence where sandy silty beaches predominate is upper Cook Inlet. That region is characterized by an estuarine environment where the beach material consists largely of silt-sized particles derived from glacier-fed streams (Karlstrom, 1964). Storm waves seldom exceed 4 feet in height. The beach gradient is as low as 1:500 and, because the beach is acted upon by a tidal range of 35 feet, silty mud flats several

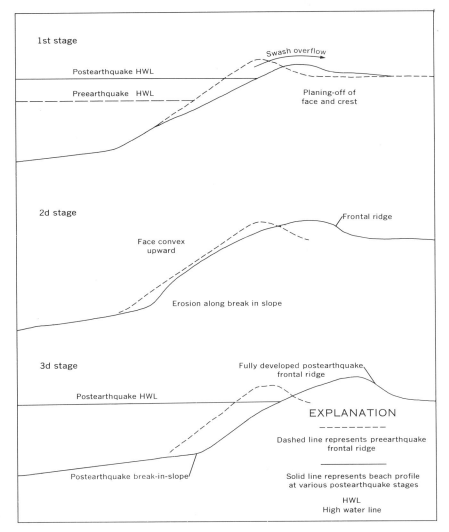

4.—Sketch of three stages that characterized the postearthquake changes of beach configuration in the submergent areas. Sketch is based on behavior of the beach on the Cook Inlet side of Homer Spit, but applies to many other beaches.

MINOR BEACH FEATURES

Minor beach forms including cusps, small beach ridges, and steps began to reappear on all submergent beaches within a few weeks after the earthquake. The new beach cusps were generally poorly developed and irregularly spaced upon the beach. Some of the hollows were overly large—being 30–40 feet wide as compared with preearthquake forms 5–15 feet wide. The outlines of the forms were vague, and at some places one horn was two to three times longer than the other. In all known examples, however, when the beach face itself began to revert to the preearthquake form, the cusps also began to develop gradually into preearthquake forms.

On beaches where the **gradient** was lowered by initial postearthquake processes, cusps did not reappear until the gradient had steepened, possibly because lack of mobility of the materials retarded the formation of the beach cusps. On beaches where the **gradient** was initially steepened after the earthquake, p o o r l y defined cusps formed early, that is, within 3 months after submergence. These cusps were alternately destroyed and rebuilt by large storm waves, however—a process that suggests that beach cusps will not form, or at least will not persist, if the gradient of the beach flattens below a critical gradient. Along Homer Spit, this gradient apparently is about 1:20 for shingle beaches.

Prior to the earthquake, small beach ridges and steps occurred along the upper beach face of most shingle beaches. Submergence destroyed or greatly altered both features. However, the ridges and steps began to develop in approximately the same location on the postearthquake beach face about 3 months after subsidence. Unlike

miles wide are exposed during low water. Subsidence of the region was not uniform but was as much as 2 feet. Some beaches examined shortly after the quake showed no noticeable change in profile or gradient, but by mid-1967, 3 years after the earthquake, subtle changes in profile had occurred.

The action of shore processes following subsidence of the coastal region and the resultant effects on the beaches were similar to the effects of a severe storm. However the changes resulting from subsidence must be measured in years, whereas the maximum destructive action of a storm is usually measured in hours.

Within the emergent areas, as along the Copper River Delta, the profile and gradient of the uplifted beaches remain unaffected with respect to wave action. The changes that have taken place are related to abandonment and stranding of the former beach faces above high water, and to exposure to the normal processes of subaerial erosion. In time, of course, new beaches will develop below the abandoned ones to fit the postearthquake high-water lines.

beach cusps, the ridges and steps became stable within 1 year after submergence.

LOW-WATER FEATURES

The most prominent low-water features on beaches are ridges, runnels, and submarine sandbars. All three forms were modified by the earthquake, and the changes observed give some insight into the movement of material and the development of such forms.

RIDGE AND RUNNEL

Ridges and runnels occur along most beaches of low gradient where sand is available and where the tide range is large enough to expose several hundred feet of beach face at low water. Good examples are found along many beaches of Alaska but they are especially conspicuous at Cook Inlet.

The ridges are composed chiefly of sandy material; the runnels, or troughs, are floored with gravel. The runnels provide channels which drain the beach on the ebbing tide. King (1959) suggests that a correlation can be made between the most persistent ridges and the position at which the tide will stand for the longest period during the tidal cycle. The ridges along the Alaska coast are usually fairly stable, particularly those that are alined parallel to the coast and perpendicular to the direction of the dominant wave approach.

In profile the normal sand ridge is asymmetrical, not unlike a ripple mark, but on a much larger scale; seaward-facing slopes are steeper than shoreward-facing ones. In general, individual ridges near the low-water line are higher than those farther up the beach face.

In the areas of land subsidence, a noticeable scouring of sand

occurred in the runnels within a few weeks after the earthquake, and at numerous places exposed a much coarser bed material. During the same period the ridges became rounded and more symmetrical in profile. The heights of many ridges increased a foot or more. At many places where the preearthquake ridges were hard enough to support the weight of a man without appreciable indentation, the post-subsidence ridges were soft. Approximately 30 days after the earthquake, many of the ridges had widened, some to as much as several hundred feet, from previous widths of a few scores of feet. During the widening process the adjacent runnels were partly filled, and low basins were left in some areas to serve as drainage channels. Ridges and runnels that were particularly conspicuous prior to the earthquake were modified to broad, somewhat undulating sand flats without definitely recognizable features.

The landward shifting of the ridges was not a simple process of individual ridge migration. Instead, the ridges were first rounded then widened, and finally were coalesced—a process which often obscured and obliterated the intervening runnels. No appreciable seaward migration of material occurred. The predominant landward migration seems to bear out King's statements (1959) that seaward of the plunge zone, or break-in-slope of the beach face, there is a definite landward migration of material.

One year after the earthquake, most of the ridges and runnels had stabilized in approximately the same configurations as those before the earthquake.

The landward migration of the ridges apparently is not a simple process of removal from the seaward side of the ridges and deposi-

tion on the landward side, such as that by which a new frontal ridge forms along the crest of a beach. Instead, the process seems to be one of flattening and spreading of the material followed by a landward movement of material en masse. As the landward migration of sand is slowed by its deposition at a higher elevation on the beach, runnels begin to form. Water draining from the beach contributes to the process by eroding sand from the channels. The eroded sand is thereafter transported to the lower beach face where part of it is eventually carried downbeach by littoral currents. For this reason there was a persistent meandering and relocation of the runnel courses during the first year following subsidence, something that had not been observed before the earthquake. The meandering process is a result of the larger quantity of available sand and its increased movement along the low-water areas; part of the sand was deposited by the runnels themselves.

On new beaches within the uplifted areas, particularly along the Copper River Delta, incipient ridges and runnels became noticeable about a year after the earthquake. They were poorly developed, perhaps because the newly formed lower foreshore had not yet stabilized with respect to gradient and profile. In part, material in the ridges was transported landward and deposited on the upper beach face or on frontal ridges along the new high-water line. A few preearthquake sand ridges and runnels were partly stranded above the high-water line and so were altered or destroyed by storm waves.

SUBMARINE SAND BARS

Limited observations indicate some relocation of submarine bars.

This relocation is suggested by previously reported hard bottoms in anchorages that, after the earthquake, were composed of soft sand. This condition was particularly noticeable along Homer Spit where scuba diving showed that preearthquake areas of hard-packed sand were characterized by soft loose sand within a year after the earthquake.

In some areas, particularly in Prince William Sound, submarine sand bars apparently were altered or destroyed by seismic sea waves or by local waves. G D. Hanna (written commun., 1965) states that soft sediments were scoured from many shallow bottom areas. Elsewhere submarine bars were altered even though tsunami effects were not evident along the shoreline.

MODERN BEACH RIDGES

Beach ridges (also referred to as "beach storm berms") occur along many of the beaches of Alaska; in the submergent areas many of these ridges were altered during the earthquake. Observations since the earthquake have provided information on the formation of beach ridges as well as their adjustment to relatively higher sea level.

Beach ridges of south-central Alaska are more perfectly formed along shingle beaches than along sand beaches where most are smaller and less well developed. Most constructional coastal forms, such as cuspate forelands, spits, and tombolos, are formed and enlarged by the development of successive beach ridges along the shoreline.

The usual beach ridge consists of a mound or windrowlike deposit along the beach immediately above the high-water line. King (1959, p. 353) considers the ridges to be the product of steep storm waves which throw debris above the reach of normal waves. The larger

ridges along the Alaska coast are composed of shingle, often with minor amounts of sand. A beach ridge along the present shoreline is generally referred to as a modern or frontal ridge, whereas the ridges farther inshore are referred to as ancient or old ridges.

Most individual ridges are 5–6 feet above high water and 8–10 feet wide, but some are as high as 20 feet and their bases may be as wide as 200 feet. Most ridges eventually become stabilized by vegetation that establishes itself on the landward slope.

Frontal ridges grow gradually in both height and width by the deposition of material carried onto and across the ridge crest by waves and swashes during storms. As the ridges increase in height, the ability of the overwash to carry debris across them decreases. Thereafter material will accumulate along the seaward side of the ridge; as the accumulation of debris progresses, a second ridge, seaward of the earlier one, will begin to form. The entire process may then be repeated.

The time span between development of successive ridges is variable, being about a year or less along certain narrow stable beaches (a "stable" beach being defined as one not enlarging seaward or retreating landward) but several hundred years or more along such large forms as cuspate forelands and spits.

It is generally accepted that coastal forms, such as cuspate forelands and spits, widen seaward by the development of successive parallel and subparallel beach ridges. The landward parts of such coastal forms are usually characterized by a series of old vegetation-covered beach ridges that represent former shorelines that trend parallel or subparallel to the present shoreline.

RESPONSE TO SUBSIDENCE AND UPLIFT

Changes in beach ridges occurred in many submergent areas. The magnitude of the changes depended on (1) the extent to which the land was submerged, (2) the geographic location of the beach with respect to storm waves, (3) the slope of the beach face, and (4) the type of beach material. In sheltered areas where submergence was only about 1–2 feet, changes were minor, but in areas of greater subsidence and exposed sea conditions the changes were often major.

In some areas, such as along Homer Spit, subsidence caused waves to reach as much as 6 feet higher on the beach face than before the earthquake, and swashes overflowed the crest of the frontal ridge. Material along the upper beach face, which was formerly above all but the highest waves and swashes, was scoured and eroded. Part of the eroded material was carried by the swash across the crest of the frontal ridge and deposited along the landward slope (fig. 5).

As overflow of the frontal ridges continued, material eroded from the beach face, including the face of the frontal ridge, was carried onto the backshore and deposited there. Continued overflow and erosion of the preearthquake frontal ridges reduced the crest height and caused the eroded material to spread out along the backshore.

The beaches along Homer Spit (Stanley, in Waller, 1966a) are good examples of postearthquake beach-ridge development. Within approximately 30 days after the earthquake, the beach face in some areas had receded as much as 15 feet, but the frontal ridges had increased as much as 30 feet in width and 2–3 feet in height. As the frontal ridges widened, coarse debris

5.—Overflow of the crests of some beaches caused material to be carried and spread out along the backshore, left half of picture. Gradually the material accumulated into a new and higher frontal ridge. View along Homer Spit, looking southeast.

was deposited near the crest and the finer material was carried toward the backshore. Along the crest and the seaward side of the ridge, the material was poorly sorted because of the severe scour. On the landward slope of the frontal ridges, the sorting was generally better and the grain size decreased. Along the extreme landward edge of the frontal ridge, the overflow material was delicately layered in fanlike forms and consisted of silt, sand, and pea-sized gravel.

Continued overflow and the transfer of material from one side of the frontal ridges to the other caused the ridges to migrate toward the backshore. The transfer of material from one location to the other led to a net loss along the seaward side and a net gain along the landward side. Thus the process of landward ridge migration was accomplished by the transfer of material within the ridge proper.

During overflow of the frontal ridges a greater volume of coarse material was deposited along the crest than along the landward side; the height of the ridges thus gradually increased. When the ridges had increased sufficiently in height to prevent overflow, migration stopped and the ridges stabilized.

Observations of the migration of beach ridges after the earthquake suggest an explanation as to why some ridges appear to migrate even under conditions not necessarily related to a rise in sea level. As stated above, beach ridges along Homer Spit migrated landward under conditions of relatively higher sea level, the migration being brought about by the process of overflow. Migration of the ridges ceased, however, when the width of the ridge was sufficient to further the heightening by deposition of material along the crest. It is concluded, therefore, that a beach ridge will stabilize if there is sufficient backshore area upon which the overflow material can accumulate.

If a barrier beach fronts a lagoon, then there is no platform

for buildup of material, and landward migration of the beach ridge may continue indefinitely. This condition is exemplified by the barrier beach at Breving Lagoon, on the Seward Peninsula, far from the area where shorelines were affected by the earthquake (fig. 6). This barrier beach has a maximum width of 500 feet and is separated from the mainland by a shallow lagoon as much as a mile across. The beach is migrating landward, apparently because of storm-wave action and the resultant process of overflow. Material eroded by storm waves from the seaward side and transferred by overflow to the landward side of the barrier beach is carried into, and spread out on the floor of, the lagoon. Because the lagoon affords no platform on which overflow material can accumulate there can be no appreciable widening of the barrier beach, and therefore, the height of the beach cannot be increased. Hence under normal storm conditions the beach will continue to migrate landward; the landward migration is not dependent on a rise in sea level.

Unlike the large ridges along shingle beaches at such places as Homer Spit, beach ridges along sandy beaches on the east shore of Cook Inlet were destroyed in many areas, particularly along the toes of low bluffs. In such areas the widths of beaches between the high-water line and the bluff toes prior to the earthquake ranged from 25 to 150 feet. After subsidence the beach widths were decreased and the small beach ridges—those from 1 to 4 feet high—were destroyed. The relatively narrow width of such beaches prevented overflow material from accumulating, and thus the beach ridges could not retreat landward when acted on by a sea level as much as 2 feet higher

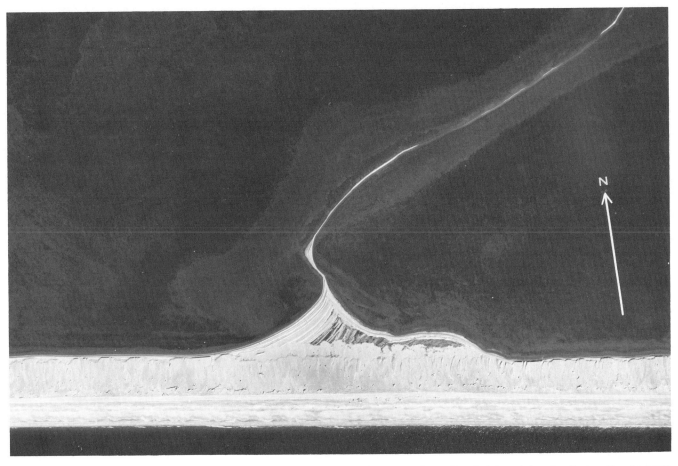

6.—Part of the barrier beach at Breving Lagoon, Seward Peninsula. Lagoon is north of (above) beach; Bering Sea is south of (below) beach. The lagoonward migration of the barrier beach is shown by superposition of the overflow upon the cuspate spit. Most beaches in the earthquake-affected part of Alaska migrated landward only short distances because they were backed by land platforms that allowed overwash material to accumulate. Photograph by Alaska Highway Department.

(fig. 7). Thus, the material, instead of accumulating higher on the beach (as it did along Homer Spit) was dissipated by wave action and was transported away from the site by the longshore drift. As the bluffs in such areas erode and recede, the beaches will eventually regain their preearthquake widths, and new beach ridges similar to those that existed before the earthquake should develop.

In the uplifted areas the old frontal ridges are abandoned and stranded above high water. New ridges have formed in some places, and rather rapidly. In most areas, however, the growth of new ridges has been slow, probably because the predominantly fine material

7.—Submergence caused the high-water line to shift to a higher elevation on this beach on the eastern shore of Cook Inlet. The establishment of a new high-water line caused undercutting and sloughing of bluffs. Note absence of beach ridges.

along the preearthquake lower beach face does not form stable beach ridges as readily as does shingle. The old ridges in the uplifted areas will gradually be covered by vegetation and will then assume the character of the typical old beach ridges of many coastal areas. New ridges along the lower high-water line will begin to develop as material continues to be worked by waves. However, the new ridges probably will require several years to stabilize, mainly because of a lack of coarse source material.

ANCIENT BEACH RIDGES

Postearthquake studies of subsided coastal forms afford an explanation for the fact that the crests of some ancient beach ridges are uniformly lower than the modern or frontal ridge. In some areas this condition is sufficiently pronounced to result in a basin-shaped area between the frontal ridge and the mainland. This habit of Alaska beach ridges has also been noted elsewhere (Bird, 1964; Johnson, 1919).

Johnson (1919), Fisher (1955), and Zenkovitch (1959) attribute the relatively lower crest elevation of the older ridges to a continuous rise in sea level whereby each successive frontal ridge builds higher. This is well illustrated along Homer Spit; as a result of the earthquake-caused rise in relative sea level, the frontal ridge here has been built higher than the older ridges. If a rise in sea level is the only factor at work, however, the profile between the frontal ridge and mainland should have a gentle landward slope rather than the commonly observed basin-shaped profile.

Studies by the author after the earthquake suggest that compaction and settlement of sediments

by seismic shaking may also contribute to a change of coastal forms. The 1964 earthquake caused compaction and settlement of sediments in many parts of south-central Alaska (Kachadoorian, 1965; Coulter and Migliaccio, 1966; Waller, 1966a). Coastal forms must have been subjected to similar compaction processes many times: During the past 50 years that official records have been kept, hundreds of earthquakes have occurred along the Alaska coast (U.S. Coast and Geodetic Survey, 1964, p. 23).

As new beach ridges develop, the coastal form widens seaward with a corresponding increase in thickness of the column of sediment. The coarsest material is usually near the mainland and the smaller particles along the seaward side. If the mass of this sediment is repeatedly subjected to seismic and microseismic shocks, the sediments—particularly the finer particles—will lose bearing capacity and settlement will follow (Terzaghi and Peck, 1948). In some kinds of sediments, vibration can lead to spontaneous liquefaction which would cause additional settlement.

Even though the coastal form nearest the mainland is oldest and hence has been subjected longest to seismic action, the sediment layer there is thinnest and the size of the particles is coarsest. Compaction by seismic shaking, therefore, would be less in such areas than in the seaward part of the landform where the sediment is thicker and the particle size is smaller.

Although the modern frontal ridge has been subjected to fewer earthquakes than have the ancient ridges, sediment compaction does occur there also. However, any decrease in height caused by compaction would perhaps be offset by the addition of new material brought in by waves. Maximum decrease in

height from compaction and settlement, therefore, probably would occur between the modern frontal ridge and the mainland and would lead to the typical basinlike profile that characterizes so many coastal constructional forms along the south-central coast of Alaska.

STREAM-MOUTH CHANGES

Stream mouths were changed throughout the areas of uplift and subsidence. In uplifted areas, streams were lengthened and incised into the elevated beach face. In the submergent areas, streams were shortened and drowned.

SUBMERGENT AREAS

Stream mouths were drowned throughout the submergent areas. Maximum drowning occurred mostly at the mouths of low-gradient streams that flowed across low-flying backshores composed of water-laid sediments. Within such areas, subsidence is attributed both to tectonic movement and compaction of the sediments (Kachadoorian and Plafker, 1967, p. F27; Kachadoorian, 1965, p. B2), and the extent of stream drowning is a function of both.

The most notable examples of stream-mouth drowning are along the shores of Kodiak Island and the southern Kenai Peninsula where subsidence of the land was 5 feet or more in some locations (Alaska Dept. Fish and Game, 1965). Several excellent photographs of drowned streams on Kodiak Island are shown in a report on that area by Plafker and Kachadoorian (1966).

During the earthquake many bays along Kodiak Island were hit by seismic sea waves. Spits, bay-mouth bars, and barrier beaches at or near stream mouths were altered or destroyed. Some of the lower of these landforms were overwashed, eroded, and reduced in height. New outlets formed where the tsunamis tore channels through ridges and spits. In all examples known to the writer, stream mouths that were acted upon by tsunamis were widened by scour and erosion.

Since the earthquake, erosion by normal wave and swash overflow has gradually caused many coastal features such as spits and barrier beaches to flatten in profile and recede landward. Thus, the effect of the tsunami and of normal wave action has reduced many once-conspicuous forms to flattened, poorly defined deltalike features. In some areas of active shore drifting, material eroded by wave action from the stream mouths has replenished the beach along the downdrift side. In areas of weak or inactive shore drifting the eroded material is merely spread out on the lower beach face.

In certain streams of low gradient and velocity, the shores were subjected to strong wave action when the land subsided, and material eroded from the unconsolidated deposits along their banks, such as deltas and outwash fans, was transported by waves into the stream mouths. This process is particularly noticeable along Turnagain Arm in upper Cook Inlet, where mud is accumulating in drowned stream mouths.

In some areas the drowning of streams has decreased the supply of material for natural beach nourishment. By reducing stream gradients, submergence has led to prograding rather than degrading of channels. Stream erosion therefore is less effective than it was before the earthquake, and the reduced quantity of debris carried by the streams diminishes the quantity of material available to the longshore drift. The extent to which the beaches will be affected

8.—Tectonic uplift created new lands permanently above high water, such as this area along the Copper River Delta. View at high tide, several months after the earthquake. The preearthquake high-water line is shown approximately by the dashed line. Photograph by U.S. Forest Service.

by the decreased supply of material is not yet clear; however, because of a decrease in stream-borne material, because wider stream mouths will retard longshore drifting and by-passing of material, and because of continuing wave action, beach erosion probably will characterize many drowned stream-mouth areas for many years to come.

UPLIFTED AREAS

Changes at the mouths of streams in the uplifted areas are related to stream-course lengthening and downcutting (fig. 8). These changes range from minor alterations along shorelines of little uplift to major changes along gently sloping, easily eroded beaches in areas that were appreciably uplifted.

The effects of tsunamis on stream mouths in the uplifted areas varied widely. In many places, sand and silt were scoured

from the mouths and carried with other debris into the upper reaches of the streams. Such deposition caused considerable silting in stream mouths and channels, and in some streams caused a temporary damming or blocking. Spits and barrier ridges at stream mouths were generally altered by the tsunamis. Many of the lower beach forms were appreciably changed, and material was redistributed along the beach into the stream mouth. Such redistribution of the material even obliterated some stream courses.

Along appreciably uplifted shorelines composed of sand and silt, rapid gullying occurred at stream mouths (fig. 9). Along the Copper River Delta, an area of readily eroded sand and silt that was uplifted several feet, gullying commenced within hours after uplift (Reimnitz and Marshall, 1965). Rapid headward erosion produced small waterfalls 1–2 feet high.

9.—Rapid gullying and sloughing caused by headward stream erosion along the uplifted coast on the Copper River Delta. Photograph by U.S. Forest Service.

Along beaches of mixed sand and shingle, stream adjustments were slower. Small riffles formed at stream mouths along such beaches.

Kirkby and Kirkby (1968) described in detail stream-mouth adjustment along elevated intertidal zones composed of sand and shingle at Montague Island, where uplift was as much as 33 feet. As on the Copper River Delta, stream adjustment began immediately after uplift had occurred.

Along some elevated shingle beaches, streams disappeared into the gravel of the uplifted intertidal zone. Generally this condition was temporary, and after several months the streams developed new courses across the intertidal zone.

Most uplifted stream courses showed evidence of degradation and bank erosion within a few days after the earthquake. Slumping of bank material and debris deposited by seismic sea waves also contributed material. In addition, after spring breakup, the normal increase of streamflow made deposition of material all the greater. The

overall result was an increase in material carried by the streams and deposited at their mouths.

Along some stream mouths the newly deposited material has retarded channel development and has led to meandering. Along the larger streams the process has been mainly silting and dissection of newly formed deltas and spits.

Although evidence indicates an increase in sediment carried by the streams, the length of time the increased load was carried probably was short. By the fall of 1964, 6 months after the earthquake, the stream-carried sediment load was normal (Waller, 1966b).

COASTAL EROSION AND MOVEMENT OF MATERIAL

EROSION

Coastal erosion is active along all shorelines within the area affected by the earthquake except on the rocky platforms. The shorelines most affected are those composed of unconsolidated material within the submergent areas.

Of the shorelines modified by

wave erosion, none were affected more than the east shore of Cook Inlet from Kachemak Bay to Turnagain Arm—a distance of more than 170 miles (fig. 1). There the entire shoreline is eroding. As already mentioned, the shoreline is a relatively uniform sandy beach with slopes as low as 1:300. The tidal range is about 22 feet along the southern section but increases to more than 30 feet near Turnagain Arm. Because of the low beach gradient and high tidal range, several thousand feet of tidelands are exposed at low water. The beach is backed by a line of bluffs about 200 feet high in most places, but locally as high as 600 feet in the Homer area. Most of the bluffs are of unsorted glacial material that is easily eroded.

Prior to the earthquake, wave action was undercutting the bluffs in many areas. Most of the sandy fraction of the sloughed material drifted away, but part of the coarser material remained along the high-water line in the form of shingle on beach ridges. The ridges, which were as high as 8 feet, protected the toes of the bluffs from all but the larger storm waves.

During the earthquake the shoreline subsided as much as 3½ feet along the southern section near Homer and as much as 1 foot near Point Possession at the mouth of Turnagain Arm. Prior to submergence the width of beach between the high-water line and the toe of the bluff was generally less than 100 feet, and in some areas less than 20 feet. Submergence decreased these widths and, after the earthquake, storm waves, particularly along the southern section, acted directly upon the toes of the bluffs. Many beach ridges that had previously protected the toes of the bluffs were exposed to waves of even, moderate height (fig. 10).

10.—Undercutting and sloughing of bluffs caused by tectonic subsidence, eastern shore of Cook Inlet. Driftwood along toe of bluff indicates the position of postearthquake high-water line.

11.—Serious bluff erosion caused by subsidence along the waterfront of the town of Kenai. View looking northwestward, about 30 days after the earthquake.

The two communities along this shoreline most seriously affected by bluff erosion were Kenai and Homer. Kenai is at the mouth of the Kenai River, a tidal estuary. During the earthquake the area subsided 12–18 inches. South of the town, bluffs as much as 150 feet high consist of readily eroded glacial material and alluvium. After regional subsidence, the preearthquake accumulation of sloughed debris along the toe of the bluffs was quickly removed. Undercutting by waves and by the river began a few days after the earthquake, and within 3 months the bluffs had receded as much as 20 feet (fig. 11).

In the Homer area the regional subsidence was about 3½ feet. Particularly damaging wave erosion occurred in the Millers Landing area, toward the east end of Homer on Kachemak Bay, along a low line of bluffs composed of peat, sand, and silt. After the earthquake, undercutting caused serious sloughing; within 6 months, the bluff line had receded as much as 8 feet.

SHORE PROTECTION MEASURES

Except at Homer and a few small villages, no serious effort has been made to construct erosion-preventive works anywhere in the earthquake-affected area. Along the Cook Inlet side of Homer Spit, erosion on the lee side of the groin farthest downdrift became critical. Retreat of the beach was jeopardizing the spit highway. In July 1964, a seawall and two additional groins were constructed. Two hundred feet of the wall was constructed to a height of 1–2 feet above the high-water line, and one section was built 5 feet higher above the high-water line. Figure 12 shows the timber bulkhead and the additional groins a short time after construction. Figures 13 and 14 show the same area 6 and 16

By 1967, 3 years after the earthquake, the bluff line in some areas had receded sufficiently to provide a width of beach that afforded protection from all but the larger storm waves. Elsewhere intermediate-size storm waves still (1967) erode the toes of the bluffs. Until the bluff line recedes enough to provide a sufficient beach to prevent wave runup to the toe, erosion and recession will continue.

12.—Timber seawall and new groins along west side of Homer Spit as constructed
3½ months after earthquake-caused subsidence.

13.—Seawall shown in figure 12, approximately 6 months after construction.

14.—Seawall shown in figure 12 some 16 months after construction. Note that the bulkhead and one of the groins were completely destroyed during this period owing to their excessive height.

15.—Cobble-filled wire-mesh fence under construction at Larsen Bay, Kodiak Island, shortly after the earthquake and resultant subsidence of 2 feet. Most of the fence was destroyed by a storm before it could be completed.

anchored in unstable beach gravel.

Elsewhere wire-mesh baskets filled with cobbles were placed along the beach to serve as bulkheads. Such baskets appeared to function well along Homer Spit, even though they were pounded by waves as high as 10 feet. Erosion, moveover, occurred on neither the updrift nor the downdrift side. A similar cobble-filled wire-mesh fence was started at Larsen Bay on Kodiak Island (fig. 15), but most of it was destroyed by storm waves before it could be completed.

Wave erosion of landslides caused by the earthquake was rapid, particularly along Cook Inlet where the frontal edges of the slides were greatly modified within 2 years. Many slides consisted of sandy-silty material. Silty-mud beaches have developed gradually, particularly on the downdrift sides.

Erosion within the uplifted areas is evident along the post-earthquake lower high-water line. Wave erosion along most of the uplifted area is not serious so far as loss of land is concerned; most streams across elevated tidal flats are incising channels.

LONGSHORE MATERIAL MOVEMENT

No significant changes resulting from the earthquake are known or reported for the directional habit of the longshore drift. The changes that have occurred are only in the quantity of material carried. Along most shorelines affected by the earthquake, more material has entered the longshore drift than before.

The additional material began to enter the sea immediately after the earthquake. This fact was made obvious along many shorelines by a broad band of muddy water that was several miles wide

months later, respectively. Sixteen months after construction, the high timber bulkhead between the fifth and sixth groin had been destroyed, as had the last groin (fig. 14). Similar high bulkheads were

constructed in other areas but most were destroyed within several months, or at most within a year, after the earthquake. Failure is attributed to the fact that the bulkheads were too high and were

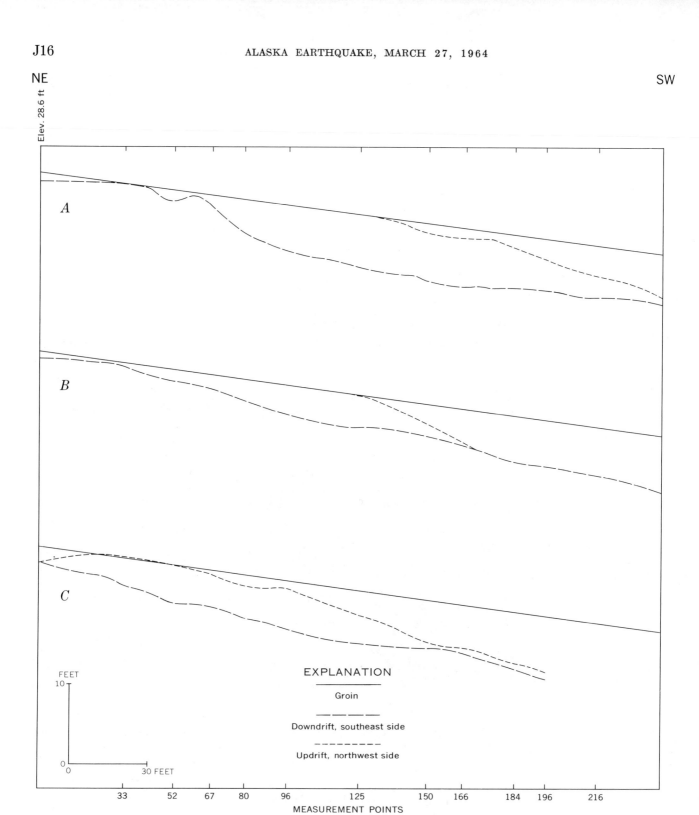

16.—Profiles of updrift and downdrift fill of groin at Homer Spit, measured (*A*) on March 2, 1964, a few weeks prior to the earthquake; (*B*) on August 28, 1964, 4 months after submergence; and (*C*) on September 30, 1965, 18 months after submergence. The change in configuration of the groin fill was caused by submergence and the resultant higher level of water on the fill. Note, however, that the gradient at 18 months approximates the preearthquake gradient.

in some areas, but no direct effect, such as the formation of new berms by the deposition of the material, was observed along beaches until several weeks after the earthquake. A good example of the effect of a delayed longshore drift is described by Stanley (in Waller, 1966a, p. D24). At Homer Spit the additional quantity of material that had entered the longshore drift in the source area, 2–6 miles west of the spit, did not reach the spit until about 30 days after the earthquake.

Accelerated shoreline erosion in the submergent areas caused more material to enter the drift than had been entering before the earthquake. However, in the same areas, material contributed by rivers and streams decreased. The converse was true in the uplifted areas. What effect the change in balance of the source and supply of material will have on the character of the longshore drift is not yet known. In planning future coastal projects the possible changes in source and supply that have occurred since the earthquake must be taken into consideration.

UPSLOPE MATERIAL MOVEMENT

Only one limited study of material movement was made within the first year following the earth-

quake (Stanley, in Waller, 1966a). Significant changes in material movement may therefore have passed unnoticed.

The study was made by the Alaska Division of Lands along the west side of Homer Spit at a system of filled groins that had been studied prior to the earthquake. After submergence the high-water line rose 3.5 feet. Within 5 days after submergence, 1–2 feet of material had accumulated along the landward end of the groins and had spread inland to a width of 30–50 feet. The newly deposited material was first thought to have been carried in by the longshore drift. However, the first profiles made 7 days after submergence indicated that the intergroin fills had actually receded and flattened and all had undergone a net loss of material (fig. 16A). Inasmuch as the material lost from the intergroin fill area about equaled the newly deposited material along the landward end of the groins, the material probably was derived from the adjacent interfill area rather than from some distant source.

Additional profiles were made at about 15-day intervals for the next 60 days (fig. 16B, C). Within the first 30 days the intergroin fills receded as material continued to accumulate along the landward

ends of the groins (fig. 16B), but about 30 days after the earthquake the intergroin fills began to enlarge, and thereafter the enlargement increased noticeably. The material causing the increase probably was brought there by the longshore drift.

Observations indicate that during the 30-day period following the earthquake, the material deposited along the beach crest came from the lower-upper beach face of the groin fills and was carried upslope. Erosion along the lower-upper beach face continued until a new profile of equilibrium had been established. The dominant movement of material during the 30-day period following subsidence was upslope because the waves were reaching higher up the beach face. Waves running higher up the beach face shorten the travel distance of the swash and thus increase its carrying capacity.

The increased shoreline erosion throughout the area unquestionably increased the supply of material to the longshore drift; after about 30 days a noticeably increased quantity of material was drifting alongshore, but during this first 30-day period following submergence the dominant motion of material was up the beach rather than along it.

BIOLOGIC EFFECTS OF SHORELINE CHANGES

FISH

At the time this report was written (1967), the most comprehensive discussion of the effects of the earthquake on the Alaska fisheries was the one compiled by the Alaska Department of Fish and Game (1965). Although a complete analysis and assessment of

damage to this resource has not yet been made, the environment and habitat of the salmon is known to have been drastically changed in some areas.

Part of Prince William Sound was uplifted as much as 33 feet, and great changes in the environment and habitat of pink and chum salmon resulted. Similarly, in the submergent areas, such as

Kodiak Island, important intertidal spawning grounds were inundated.

G. Y. Harry, Jr. (written commun., 1964), reported, 5 months after the earthquake, that the greatest damage to the salmon in Alaska was probably in Prince William Sound; here 75 percent of the pink and chum salmon production comes from the intertidal spawning areas. Thorsteinson (1964) states that within Prince William Sound the runs of pink salmon range from 3.2 to 8.7 million fish and the chum salmon from 0.4 to 0.6 million fish.

Compounding the permanent damage caused by uplift and submergence of the intertidal spawning grounds was the temporary effect of tsunamis and local waves. In parts of Prince William Sound, the waves caused considerable scour, and debris and silt were carried upstream for several hundred feet. Some biologists believe that many salmon eggs were scattered by the movement of debris. When, all contributing factors in Prince William Sound are taken into account, the salmon loss caused by the earthquake and its subsidiary effects is thought to be about one-quarter of a million salmon (Noerenberg and Ossiander, 1964).

In the Kodiak Island area, where submergence was as much as 6 feet, widespread flooding of the intertidal spawning areas occurred. In some places flooding of the intertidal area was helpful to the salmon in that waterfalls which formerly obstructed their upstream migration were eliminated. Along other streams, submergence and flooding increased the size of the intertidal area. Removal of waterfalls in some areas and enlargement of other areas, thus increased the size and availability of certain intertidal salmon-spawning grounds.

W. L. Sheridan (written commun., 1965) stated that the changes in the intertidal spawning habitat and environment have not been fully assessed, but that future production will decrease. Although some intertidal spawning areas have increased in size, Sheridan indicates that many of

the preearthquake lower areas are now characterized by excessive quantities of sediments that decrease the survival rate of salmon eggs and alevins.

SHELLFISH

One of the more important habitats of shellfish, particularly the razor clam, is along the Copper River Delta. The delta was uplifted as much as 8 feet, and, because of the low offshore gradient, extensive intertidal areas were permanently elevated above high water. This area supported a large population of razor clams. The widespread death of these and other bivalves throughout Prince William Sound was evident within a few weeks after the earthquake (S. B. Haven, written commun., 1965). Many of the clam beds are now above high water and are lost, but clam beds formerly below lower low water were elevated and are now accessible to clam diggers. In some areas of Prince William Sound, particularly along the western part, subsidence at the bayheads was caused by local compaction of the sediments. Consequently, clam beds which were once readily accessible are now from 2 to 4 feet below low water and out of reach to conventional methods of harvesting.

There is no general consensus as to what long-term ecological effect either submergence or emergence has had upon the general clam or bivalve population within the affected areas. Certainly the initial mortality rate was high—especially in the uplifted areas—as was proved by the skeletons. In the submergent areas the greater depth of water now present over the outermost clam beds has also resulted in bivalve mortality.

WILDFOWL

Ordinarily submergence or emergence would not be considered to affect waterfowl adversely, but, according to P. E. K. Shepherd (written commun., 1966), there has been an indirect effect. In the feeding ground of the dusky Canada goose in the Copper River Delta, the preferred food of the goose is a type of vegetation referred to as "forb-grass." This grass—actually a combination of herbs and grasses—apparently requires occasional inundation by marine waters and usually grows along the sides of tidal sloughs and other areas regularly inundated by the highest tides. Because of changed tide levels, the forb-grass is dying, and before it is reestablished at a higher elevation, the dusky Canada goose is likely to have changed its habitat. Shepherd indicates that the habitat of the goose may be further changed because its former nesting grounds will become overgrown with conifers or other plants when the salt is leached out of the soil. To some extent these same changes are affecting the habitats of the dabbling and diving ducks and the trumpeter swans.

Brakish-water lagoons and sloughs are particularly favored as nesting or feeding grounds by some wildfowl. Uplift drained some of these areas or made them less brackish because of the inflow of fresh water. Thus, changed environments, whether caused by uplift or submergence, may ultimately contribute to a decrease in the wildfowl population in specific areas. Whether new wildfowl communities will spring up in areas made more favorable by the earthquake will not be known for some years.

EFFECTS ON PROPERTY VALUES AND MANMADE STRUCTURES

Earthquake-caused uplift and subsidence—and the consequent changes in coastal processes—affected the legalities of land ownership, and also led to many changes in property values and necessitated reconstruction or relocation of many coastal installations. A few of the resultant problems are touched on here.

SUBMERGENT AREAS

As already mentioned, coastal erosion is occurring in many of the submergent areas, and in some areas—such as on the Kenai Peninsula—the rate of bluff recession is several feet per year. In other areas, erosion may still become a problem although the process is not yet noticeable. One such area is along upper Cook Inlet where submergence was less than 2 feet. The dramatic effects seen in areas of greater submergence are not present in this area, but there is unquestionably a gradual retreat of the shoreline. This retreat is occurring in some of the more densely populated areas where land values are high.

At Turnagain Arm, wave erosion has damaged road and railroad embankments that were raised after the earthquake. Wave erosion in that area will probably continue, and the embankment will require constant surveillance and maintenance. In Homer, wave action has already damaged sections of the newly constructed Homer Spit highway.

Some shore installations that escaped severe damage at the time of the earthquake were, because of the higher stand of the sea, endangered by flooding a few weeks after the earthquake when tides were high. Several cannery wharves and loading platforms had to be raised. In some places, such as at the Wakefield Cannery at Port Wakefield on Kodiak Island, complete relocation of the cannery was necessary.

In some submergent areas, wave scour has moved large quantities of gravel under or away from canneries and other facilities built over the high-water line. For example, a cannery at Larsen Bay on Kodiak Island, which was built in a seemingly ideal location and was adequately protected before the earthquake has incurred considerable storm damage since the earthquake. Erosion of gravel from the adjoining beach has endangered some of the cannery buildings.

EMERGENT AREAS

Some of the immediate effects of emergence that necessitated economic and engineering consideration were related to small-boat harbors. In the Cordova area the land was elevated about 8 feet. There emergence necessitated dredging and enlarging the small-boat harbor. Some of the channels of the Copper River Delta that had formerly been accessible to fishing boats required considerable redredging in order to afford access after the earthquake. In some uplifted areas, individuals who formerly had access to the sea by shallow channels or tidal sloughs found it necessary to dredge their access routes. In other areas, landing facilities, such as docks and wharves, could no longer accommodate deep-draft vessels and had to be enlarged or relocated.

In Cordova, because of the 8 feet of emergence, it has also been necessary to relocate the installations upon which barges, scows, and fishing boats are stored in off-season months. At the beginning of the 1964 fishing season, following the earthquake, some craft had to be pulled from their storage areas onto the tidal flats by tractors before they could be refloated.

LEGAL PROBLEMS

Because the State of Alaska has jurisdiction over the bottoms of all navigable waters, legal problems have arisen wherever land raised or lowered by the earthquake abuts navigable waters. In Alaska the boundary of tidal waters is the line of mean high tide.

A person whose Alaskan property abuts the line of mean high tide is called an "upland owner." By common-law principles the upland owner enjoys all littoral rights and privileges afforded him by the location of his land. Such rights and privileges include, among others, free and unobstructed ingress and egress to the sea.

The line of mean high tide thus is the legal boundary that separates the upland owner's private property from the State-owned tidelands. The line of mean high tide remains fixed unless the shoreline is altered by accretion or erosion. If these processes result from natural causes and the shoreline changes are gradual and imperceptible, the legal boundary will change location to match the line of mean high tide. However, if the changes are natural but sudden in character and wholly perceptible, the process is termed "avulsion," and the legal boundary remains fixed even though the mean high tide line has been displaced.

Movement of the land during the earthquake was abrupt, certainly occurring within a matter of hours if not of minutes, and flooding or withdrawal of waters from the land was equally abrupt. On September 14, 1964, the attorney general for the State of Alaska described this process as one of avulsion and therefore the legal boundary line—the line of mean high tide—remains fixed as it was the instant before the earthquake

(State of Alaska Attorney Gen. Opinion 6, Sept. 14, 1964).

Along the uplifted coasts many private parcels of land abutted the line of mean high tide before the earthquake; afterwards, however, the natural line of mean high tide was shifted seaward, in some places several hundred feet. Because withdrawal of the water has been defined as avulsion, the private ownership cannot follow the retreating line of mean high tide but must instead remain fixed to the line existing the instant before the earthquake. Thus those persons

who enjoyed all the rights and privileges afforded them as upland owners before the earthquake now find themselves unable to exercise their littoral rights and privileges. The opposite has occurred in the submergent areas. There, owners of land that abutted the line of mean high tide prior to the earthquake now find their boundary line (that is, the preearthquake line of mean high tide) some distance seaward of the natural mean high tide line. These persons in fact own tidelands but the lands are legally described as uplands.

NEED FOR FURTHER STUDIES

One danger in attempting to rectify coastal-erosion problems is that protective measures are often taken without a clear understanding of littoral conditions. This problem has already manifested itself at various localities where installations that were constructed to protect the land have in fact destroyed it.

Some of the later damage to roads and embankments may perhaps be explained by the rather hurried reconstruction effort immediately following the earthquake. The necessity for haste

probably did not allow for full consideration of design methods with respect to unnatural slopes; such slopes can promote wave erosion. Time did not always allow for adequate investigation of nearshore conditions, such as wave runup and current direction; consequently, adequate safeguards to insure maximum protection against coastal erosion were not designed. Certainly, in the submergent areas the sea has encroached upon the land establishing a new profile of equilibrium. When artificial impediments are placed in

such areas, the result more often than not promotes rather than retards wave erosion.

The installation and construction of shore protective works will undoubtedly become necessary long before a profile of equilibrium develops and stabilizes—a profile which will itself eventually retard shoreline erosion. Therefore, the economic ramifications of coastal erosion not now readily noticeable may, within the next few years, become a problem which must be dealt with if valuable areas of land are to be saved.

REFERENCES CITED

Alaska Department of Fish and Game, 1965, Post-earthquake fisheries evaluation; an interim report on the March 1964 earthquake effects on Alaska's fishery resources: Juneau, Alaska, 72 p.

Bird, E. C. F., 1964, Coastal landforms; an introduction to coastal geomorphology with Australian examples: Canberra, Australian Natl. Univ., 193 p.

Bruun, Per, 1962, Sea-level rise as a cause of shore erosion: Am. Soc. Civil Eng. Proc., v. 88, paper 3065, Jour. Waterways and Harbors Div., no. WW 1, p. 117–130.

Coulter, H. W., and Migliaccio, R. R., 1966, Effects of the earthquake of March 27, 1964, at Valdez, Alaska: U.S. Geol. Survey Prof. Paper 542–C, p. C1–C36.

Fisher, R. L., 1955, Cuspate spits of St. Lawrence Island, Alaska: Jour. Geology, v. 63, no. 2, p. 133–142.

Guilcher, André, 1958, Coastal and submarine morphology [translation by B. W. Sparks and R. H. W. Kneese]: New York, John Wiley and Sons, Inc., 274 p.

Johnson, D. W., 1919, Shore processes and shoreline deveolpment: New

York, John Wiley and Sons, Inc., 584 p.

Kachadoorian, Reuben, 1965, Effects of the earthquake of March 27, 1964, at Whittier, Alaska; U.S. Geol. Survey Prof. Paper 542–B, p. B1–B21.

Kachadoorian, Reuben, and Plafker, George, 1967, Effects of the earthquake of March 27, 1964, on the communities of Kodiak and nearby islands: U.S. Geol. Survey Prof. Paper 542–F, p. F1–F41.

Karlstrom, T. N. V., 1964, Quaternary geology of the Kenai Lowland and glacial history of the Cook Inlet region, Alaska: U.S. Geol. Survey Prof. Paper 443, 69 p.

King, C. A. M., 1959, Beaches and coasts: London, Edward Arnold and Co., 403 p.

Kirkby, M. J., and Kirkby, A. V., 1968, Erosion and deposition on a beach raised by the 1964 earthquake, Montague Island, Alaska: U.S. Geol. Survey Prof. Paper 543–H. (In press.)

Lobeck, A. K., 1939, Geomorphology; an introduction to the study of landscapes: New York, McGraw-Hill Book Co., 731 p.

Noerenberg, W. H., and Ossiander, F. J., 1964, Effects of the March 27, 1964, earthquake on pink salmon alevin survival in Prince William Sound spawning streams: Alaska Dept. Fish and Game Inf. Leaflet 43, 10 p.

Plafker, George, 1965, Tectonic deformation associated with the 1964 Alaska earthquake: Science, v. 148, no. 3678, p. 1675–1687.

Plafker, George, 1967, Surface faults on Montague Island associated with the 1964 Alaska earthquake: U.S. Geol. Survey Prof. Paper 543–G, p. G1–G42.

——— 1969, Tectonics of the March 27, 1964, Alaska earthquake: U.S. Geol. Survey Prof. Paper 543–I.

Plafker, George, and Kachadoorian, Reuben, 1966, Geologic effects of the March 1964 earthquake and associated seismic sea waves on Kodiak and nearby islands, Alaska: U.S. Geol. Survey Prof. Paper 543–D, p. D1–D46.

Plafker, George, and Rubin, Meyer, 1967, Vertical tectonic displacements in south-central Alaska during and prior to the great 1964 earthquake: Jour. Geoscience, Osaka City Univ., v. 10, art. 1–7, p. 53–66.

Reimnitz, Erk., and Marshall, N. F., 1965, Effects of the Alaska earthquake and tsunami on recent deltaic sediments: Jour. Geophys. Research, v. 70, no. 10, p. 2363–2376.

Schwartz, Maurice, 1965, Laboratory study of sea-level rise as a cause of shore erosion: Jour. Geology, v. 73, no. 3, p. 528–534.

Stanley, K. W., and Grey, H. J., 1966, Spray-on paint stripes to determine the direction of beach drifting: Jour. Geology, v. 74, no. 3, p. 357–361.

Terzaghi, Karl, and Peck, R. B., 1948, Soil mechanics in engineering practice: New York, John Wiley and Sons, Inc., 566 p.

Thorsteinson, F. V., 1964, Effects of the Alaska earthquake on pink and chum salmon runs in Prince William Sound: U.S. Bur. Commercial Fisheries Biol. Lab., Auke Bay, Alaska, 16 p.

Twenhofel, W. S., 1952, Recent shoreline changes along the Pacific coast of Alaska: Am. Jour. Sci., v. 250, no. 7, p. 523–548.

U.S. Coast and Geodetic Survey, 1964, Prince William Sound, Alaskan earthquakes, March–April 1964: U.S. Coast and Geod. Survey, Seismology Div., Prelim. Rept., 83 p.

Waller, R. M., 1966a, effects of the earthquake of March 27, 1964, in the Homer area, Alaska, *with a section on* Beach changes on Homer Spit, by K. W. Stanley: U.S. Geol. Survey Prof. Paper 542–D, p. D1–D28.

——— 1966b, Effects of the March 1964 Alaska earthquake on the hydrology of south-central Alaska: U.S. Geol. Survey Prof. Paper 544–A, p. A1–A28.

Wood, F. J., ed., 1966–67, The Prince William Sound, Alaska, earthquake of 1964 and aftershocks: U.S. Coast and Geod. Survey Pub. 10–3, v. 1, 1966, 236 p.; v. 2, pt. A, 1967, 391 p.

Zenkovitch, V. P., 1959, On the genesis of cuspate spits along lagoon shores: Jour. Geology, v. 67, no. 3, p. 269–277.

CLARIFICATION

Geology Vol. Page	USGS Page	Column	Line	Remarks
231	J 3	3	10	See USGS PP 543-I, this volume, p. 47

PETER J. BARRETT*

THE OHIO STATE UNIVERSITY

Reprinted with minor changes from
Journal of Sedimentary Petrology,
"Effects of the 1964 Alaskan Earthquake on Some Shallow-Water Sediments
in Prince William Sound, Southeast Alaska" [1,2]

Effects on Some Shallow-Water Sediments in Prince William Sound

ABSTRACT

The effects of the 1964 Alaska earthquake on four shallow subtidal and intertidal areas in Prince William Sound have been recorded by mass movementof pre-quake sediment and changes in the grain-size distribution of post-quake sediment because of uplift. No changes could definitely be attributed to the large waves associated with the earthquake.

Limited mass movement of pre-quake silt on the Rude River delta front has resulted in local warping and rupture of the sediment. Orientation of the associated rectangular cracks appears to be directly related to the geometry of the delta.

Where pre-quake sediment was predominantly silt and thus difficult to erode (Rude River delta and Cordova, uplift 6 feet), post-quake sediment accumulation resulted only from introduced material, and the increase in grain size at the surface of deposition at the time of the earthquake was rapid and large. However,where pre-quake sediment was predominantly sandy and easy to erode (Macleod and Hanning Bays, uplift 29 feet), and where introduction of post-quake sediment was limited, there was only a small increase in the grain size of post-quake sediment, despite the large increase in wave energy due to the change from a subtidal to an intertidal environment of deposition. This is thought to result from absorption of wave energy in eroding and transporting the sand; as the supply of readily available sand decreases, more energy will become available for winnowing, and the grain size will increase as deposition proceeds. Thus, here a sudden increase in energy level of the environment of deposition will be preserved in the geologic record as a gradual increase in grain size.

INTRODUCTION

On March 27, 1964, a major earth movement warped the Prince William Sound area about a northeasterly axis. Land northwest of a line passing through Perry Island (fig. 1) was down-warped as much as 6 feet in the Port Wells area; to the southeast uplift reached about 30 feet at the southwest end of Montague Island (Plafker, 1965). Large waves associated with the earth movement reached heights of at least 40 feet in Prince William Sound.

The earthquake presented an unusual opportunity to examine effects on sediments of an event of known character, in contrast to the more common situation wherein the geologist attempts to determine the nature of unknown events from the sedimentary record. At least two phenomena resulting from the earthquake were thought capable of changing the character of at least shallow water sedimentation: waves resulting directly or indirectly from the earthquake, and the accompanying relative change in sea level. To study the effects of these phenomena on the sediments, a series of samples passing from post-quake to pre-quake sediments was clearly desirable, and the most practical method of obtaining these samples seemed to be by coring. A program was therefore planned for areas in which sand and mud predominated, because fine sediments are easier to core and treat in the laboratory, and they are more sensitive than coarser sediments to energy changes in the environment of deposition.

SETTING

Prince William Sound is in a tectonically active region that has recently undergone, and locally is still experiencing, mountain glaciation. Consequently the topography is rugged, with elevations ranging from about 12,000 feet in the nearby Chugach Mountains to about a minus 3000 feet between Perry and Naked Islands in Prince William Sound (fig. 1). Area with accessible and reasonably fine-grained sediments were found at only 4 of the 15 localities visited: the Rude River delta, the Cordova mudflats, and at MacLeod and Hanning Bays on Montague Island (fig. 1). The bedrock in these four areas consists of severely folded and indurated clastic sediments of Mesozoic (?) age that contain graded bedding, load casts, shale pebble conglomerates and other features characteristic of flysch sediments.

SAMPLE LOCATION AND RECOVERY

The coring apparatus was constructed from a design modified by Paul Colinvaux, of the Department of Zoology and Entomology, Ohio

[1] Manuscript received March 28, 1966.
[2] Contribution 85, Institute of Polar Studies, Ohio State University, Columbus, Ohio.

*Now with Victoria University of Wellington, New Zealand.

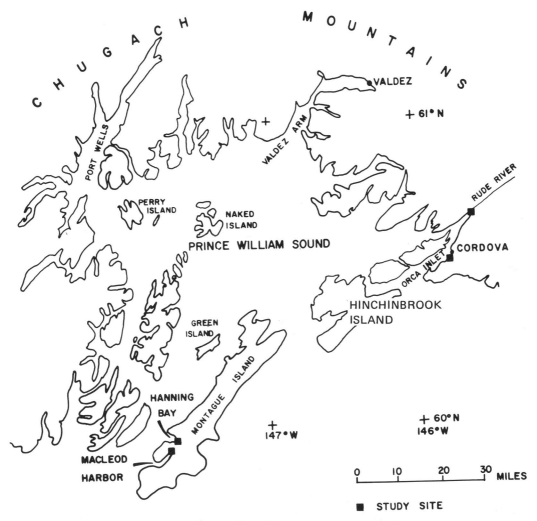

FIG. 1.—Prince William Sound, southeast Alaska.

State University, from a simple, one-man, piston corer designed by Livingstone (1955). The cores were recovered and transported in aluminum tubes 2 inches in diameter, and 3 and 4 feet long. In each of the areas studied a pace-compass map was made from a taped baseline. Core sites were located by intersection on the nearest and most favorably placed survey points. The error in location is estimated from the triangles of intersection to be not more than about 4 percent. Each survey station and the core taken there have the same number—for example, S 12 and C 12. Survey stations used for intersection but which were not core sites are not included in this report. Samples from the cores are designated by letters following the core number, "a" being nearest the surface.

FIELD WORK

Rude River Delta Site

The Rude River delta at the head of Orca Inlet was examined on June 21 and 22, 1965. The delta spreads across a glaciated valley about 1.5 miles wide with walls rising steeply to 2000 feet. The Rude River drains a large area of the central Chugach Mountains, which rise to 7500 feet only 16 miles to the northeast. The river is braided throughout the lower part of its course; at sea level the channel sediments are almost entirely gravel, but the broad interfluves were, prior to the uplift, areas of mud deposition. The area chosen for study (fig. 2) lies on the southeast side of the delta, where a small stream is cutting into pre-quake muds. The mean tidal range is about 12 feet and the uplift resulting from the earthquake about 7 feet, determined from Shepard Point nearby.

The oldest pre-quake sediment recovered was pebbly coarse sand cored from S 1, 3, and 10 (figs. 2 and 3) in the present channel. The pebbly sand extends several hundred feet farther west than the present gravelly bottom of the channel, and is overlain with sharp contact by consolidated mud like that which comprises the entire

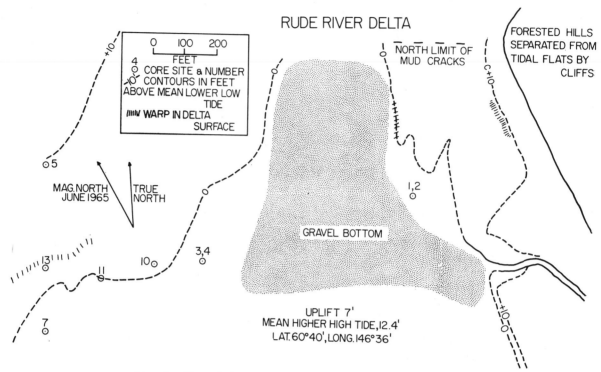

FIG. 2.—Plan of the southeast part of the Rude River Delta.

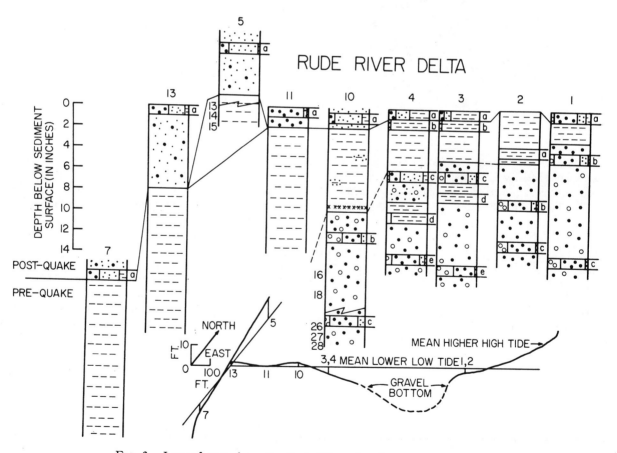

FIG. 3.—Logs of cores from the Rude River site. Legend on figure 16.

core of pre-quake sediments at other stations. Within a few hundred feet of the valley wall the mud commonly contains thin layers of fir leaves and other plant fragments, but on the west side of the stream channel these are uncommon.

Post-quake sediments, identified by their lack of consolidation and a grain size much coarser than the underlying mud, tend to be thinner and less discontinuous below low tide. Four of the five cores from below low tide contain post-quake sand, though it is only 1 or 2 inches thick. Just above low tide, fine-to-medium sand is as much as one foot thick in local depressions (figs. 4, 5.), but large areas of pre-quake mud are also exposed. Near high tide, patches of similar sand, locally as much as 1 foot thick are forming on the pre-quake, mud-flat surface (fig. 6).

Mudcracks in pre-quake mud are quite common in the area covered by figure 2. Between S 5 and the channel, and a few hundred feet north of S 1, they have a polygonal form and are about 3 feet across. The pattern suggests that they formed by dehydration of the mud. However, near S 13 and 300 feet northeast of S 1, strongly developed mudcracks have a rectangular pattern (fig. 4). At S 13 this pattern parallels a sharp, seaward dipping inflexion in the present delta surface, which here drops about 3 feet in 15. Recent erosion has exposed pre-quake sediments whose warping parallels the delta surface inflexion (figs. 2, 4, 5). Northeast of S 1 a regular mudcrack pattern parallels a similar though less obvious inflexion which is aligned with the direction of the cliffs 100 feet farther to the northeast. It is inferred that both sets of rectangular cracks resulted from mass movement of the delta muds which was initiated by the earth-

FIG. 5. Stream margin 200 feet north of S 1 (fig. 2) at low tide. Slightly warped and cracked pre-quake silt (light grey) is stratigraphically overlain by post-quake sand (dark grey).

quake and whose direction was controlled to a large extent by the geometry of the delta.

Cordova Site

Orca Inlet near Cordova is about 3 miles wide and reaches a depth of about 40 feet. Bottom sediments are predominantly mud, and extensive mud flats have formed in bays south of Cordova city. On July 4, 5 and 6, 1965, cores were taken from a bay in which mud flats cover an area of about 0.6 square miles 2.5 miles south of Cordova. The tidal range here is about 12 feet and uplift about 6 feet. The core site plan and logs are shown in figures 7 and 8.

The oldest sediments recovered are muddy, fine sand (C 49) and sandy mud with rare peat laminae (C 51, 52, 54, 55). These are overlain by markedly coarser sediments, pebbly sand in cores near the present stream location (C 54, 55, 52), and fine-to-medium sand offshore (C 48, 49, 50, 51, 56). The youngest pre-quake sediments

FIG. 4.—Looking northeast from S 13 (fig. 2). Post-quake medium sand (dark grey) is accumulating in hollows on the pre-quake delta surface. Rectangular mudcracks in pre-quake silt are attributed to mass movement resulting from the earthquake. Rod is 5 feet long.

FIG. 6.—A bed of small clams (*Mya*) 700 feet north of S 1 (fig. 2), now dead and being eroded as a result of the uplift. Post-quake sand (dark) is accumulating in patches on the old delta surface. Note the sand being blown up-delta (left to right) in the middle distance.

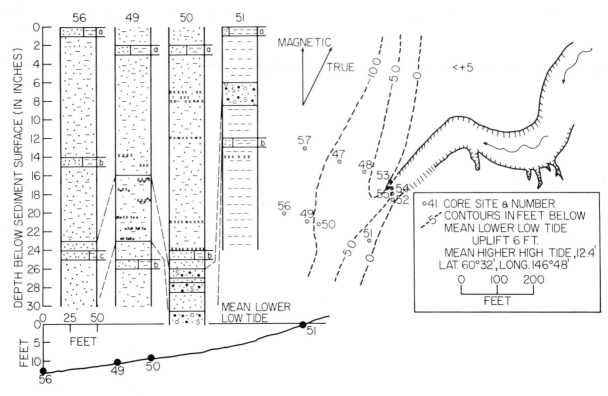

Fig. 7.—Plan of the Cordova site and some core logs. Legend for logs on figure 16.

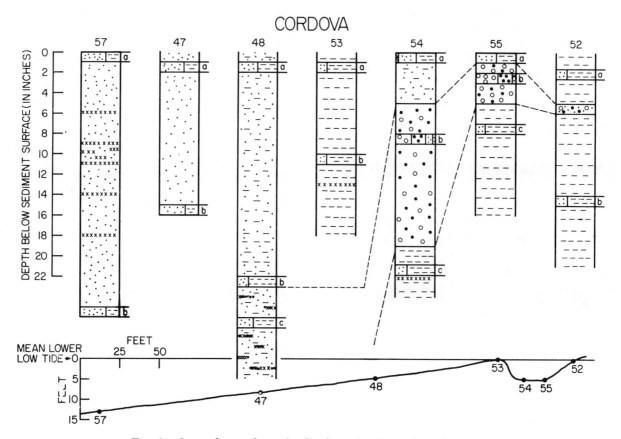

Fig. 8.—Logs of cores from the Cordova site. Legend on figure 16.

FIG. 9.—Clams killed and exposed by the uplift. Erosion has lowered the mudflat surface at least by several inches and possibly by as much as 20 inches. Photo taken during low tide at Cordova site.

are muddy, fine sand and sandy mud with occasional peat laminae, sediments similar to those below the coarse layer. No post-quake sediments were found.

Some idea of the amount of sediment removed since the earthquake is given by the exposure of the large clam shells (*Schizothaeris*), most of which are still in place but whose highest parts are now 2 to 3 inches above the sediment surface (fig. 9). However, as much as 20 inches of sediment may have been removed, since *Schizothaeris* often burrows to a depth of 18 inches (G Dallas

Hanna, personal communication, March 21, 1966).

It was expected that little post-quake sediment would have been introduced because of the small discharge of the streams, but it was surprising to find none at all, not even offshore 13 feet below low tide, or in the stream channel. It seems that the supply of post-quake sediment must have been very small compared with the supply at the Rude River delta. For the Cordova site there are three possible sediment sources: the small meandering streams that have now cut down into the mud flats to a depth of about 6 feet; tidal currents; and earthquake-induced waves, which washed several hundred yards inland in this area. None of these possible sources have been effective in introducing sediment to the site studied.

MacLeod Harbor Site

MacLeod Harbor, visited on June 26 and 27, 1965, lies at the southwest corner of Montague Island, which here is about 6 miles wide and rises to a height of about 2400 feet. The tidal range here is 11 feet and the uplift 29 feet. Two large braided streams with gravelly beds enter the bay near its head. Between these and along the south shore of the bay lies an extensive elevated beach surface. The terrace so formed dips gently seaward and is presently being eroded both by lateral migration of the streams, and by wave

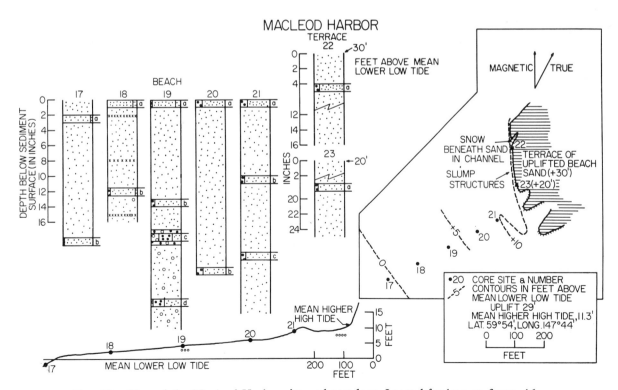

FIG. 10.—Plan of the Macleod Harbor site and core logs. Legend for logs on figure 16.

FIG. 11.—Contorted pre-quake beach sands disturbed by an event before the 1964 earthquake. Rod is 5 feet long.

FIG. 13.—Channel cut and partly filled before the 1964 earthquake. Rod is 5 feet long.

action. The latter has cut cliffs 15 to 20 feet high in beach sand at the head of the bay. The core sites at the head of the bay and the core logs are shown in figure 10.

The oldest sediment cored was a pebbly sand bed no less than a foot thick. It extends seaward at least to S 19, and can be traced about 1000 feet north and 1500 feet west of S 21. This bed is overlain by about 20 feet of well-sorted, stratified sand whose upper surface forms the widespread terrace. Shell material is fragmentary and rare, and peat laminae were seen only in C 18 and 21. Stratification is mostly subhorizontal, but between S 22 and 23 it is extremely contorted (fig. 11). The event causing this contortion pre-dates the 1964 earthquake, because the contorted beds have been truncated and overlaid by as much as one foot of horizontally-stratified sand.

No post-quake, water-laid sediment, apart from gravel in the present stream bed, could be found, although a lag concentrate similar to that

formed by wind erosion on the terrace might have been expected.

The flat terrace near the head of the bay is about 3000 feet wide. It is broken by several channels with inverted bell-shaped cross-sections, and roughly 15 feet wide and 10 feet deep at their seaward ends. They become shallower landward, until after several hundred feet they merge with the terrace surface. One or two seem to have been enlarged by headward erosion caused by resurgent ground water appearing from the gravel bed at the base of the terrace. Other channels are being filled by windblown sand from the terrace surface, where a lag concentrate of small pebbles and some shell material is accumulating. One such channel contains a few inches of sand overlain by a discontinuous layer of snow as much as 15 inches thick which is overlain by sand from a few inches to 2 feet thick (fig. 12). The sand in the channel is loose and structureless, and, therefore, deposition in this channel clearly dates from at least

FIG. 12.—A pre-quake subtidal channel containing the previous winter's (1964–65) snow, overlain by wind-blown sand.

FIG. 14.—The terrace of prequake material on the southeast shore of MacLeod Harbor. Postquake dis-

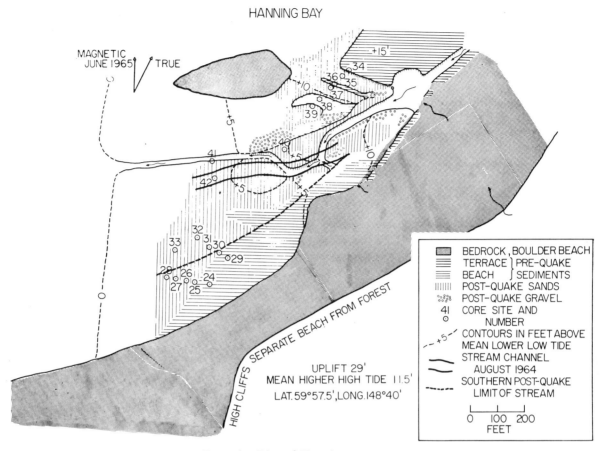

Fig. 15.—Plan of Hanning Bay site.

the previous fall (1964). The channel may well have existed as part of the normal beach topography for some time prior to the uplift, as did the channel shown in figure 13.

On the south shore of the bay, about 2 miles southwest of the cored area, the raised terrace is only about 150 feet wide. The seaward 100 feet of the terrace is fine-grained beach sand with only a few thin layers of small pebbles, whereas the landward 50 feet of the terrace is gravel; the transition takes place over only a few feet (fig. 14). Stratification in the sand dips gently seaward, subparallel to the terrace surface. Cross-stratification, where developed, lies at only a few degrees to the terrace surface.

Hanning Bay Site

Hanning Bay, which was visited on June 28 and 29, 1965, lies 8 miles northeast of MacLeod Harbor and has the same tidal range and amount of uplift. The area studied is a small, sandy beach near the head of the bay. It is flanked to the southeast by a rocky promontory and boulder beach, and to the northwest by a low rocky reef. The beach, and the raised subtidal sands that

now form an extensive terrace at its head, are cut by a small gravelly stream.

Before coring was begun, the beach was mapped and areas of post-quake erosion and deposition were defined (fig. 15). Pre-quake sediments were recognized by their greater compaction, presence of peat layers, and finer grain size. Areas containing numbers of dead clams in place were clearly being eroded; no living clams were found in this part of the bay. Core logs are shown in figure 16.

The oldest sediment cored is silty, fine sand at the base of C 42. This is overlain by a somewhat coarser shelly sand which is correlated with similar coarse sediments comprising the lower parts of C 26, C 38, and C 39. The shelly sand is overlain by silty, fine sand which is typical of pre-quake sediment in most other cores from this beach. These fine sands contain some thin peat laminae and, more rarely, laminae of comminuted shell material. The youngest pre-quake sediment occurs in the raised terrace now 15 feet above low tide. Around S 34 the sand is noncalcareous, but along the eastern margin of the beach, where the terrace has lapped onto the

[257]

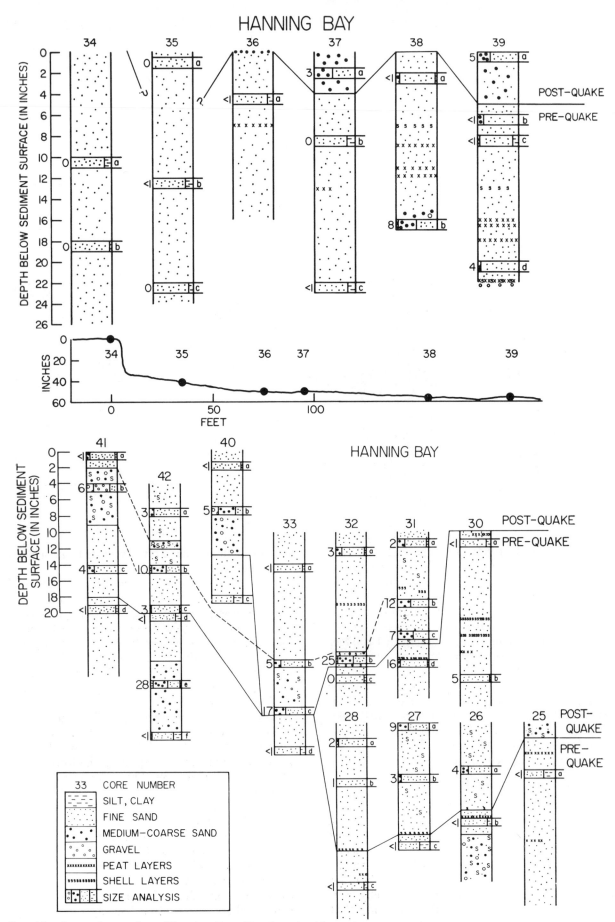

FIG. 16.—Logs of cores from Hanning Bay. Numbers beside analyses are carbonate percentages.

boulders, comminuted shells form a considerable part of the sand.

Post-quake sediment adjacent to the stream and above the mid-tide level is a thin deposit of shells and gravel (fig. 17). Most pebbles around S 40 are between 2 and 14 inches along, and shells are as much as 8 inches long. This deposit extends only 100 feet from the stream, but in at least two places it is overlapped by fine to medium post-quake sand that lies directly on pre-quake sand.

The area of post-quake accumulation in the southeast part of the beach extends seaward from S 25 and S 30. The change from pre-quake to post-quake sedimentation in C 25 to C 28 is marked only by a small concentration of shell material and a slight coarsening in grain size; the change in C 31 to C 33 is marked by a considerably larger change in these properties. The start of post-quake deposition in C 41 and C 42 is marked by a slight coarsening in grain size 18 to 20 inches below the surface; the coarse pebbly sand several inches higher probably has resulted from lateral migration of the adjacent stream.

Post-quake sand in the area crossed by the core line from C 34 to C 39 is fine to medium and a little shelly. The sand has accumulated in elongate patches parallel to the low, wave-cut bank at the head of the beach.

LABORATORY ANALYSES

Results of laboratory analyses of the non-calcareous part of the samples are given elsewhere.[3] In the following discussion, measures involving only the 16th, 50th and 84th percentiles have been used, as a number of the curves did not extend to the 95th percentile. The Inclusive Graphic Mean of Folk and Ward (1957) $(\emptyset16+\emptyset50+\emptyset84)/3$ is used to describe the average grain size, and dispersion is determined from Inman's (1952) sorting measure $(\emptyset84-\emptyset16)/2$, the standard deviation of the distribution. Typical size distributions are plotted in figure 18.

[3] A table listing the results of laboratory analyses has been deposited as Document No. 9083 with the American Documentation Institute, Auxiliary Publications Project, c/o Library of Congress, Washington 25, D.C. Copies may be secured by citing the Document number and remitting $1.25 for photocopies or $1.25 for 35 mm microfilm. Advance payment is required.

FIG. 17.—Looking northeast upstream from near S 41. Pre-quake silty sand is exposed in the stream bank and is overlain by a post-quake shell and gravel deposit. Some clams are still in place. A widespread terrace of pre-quake sand 15 feet above low tide is in the middle distance.

Rude River Delta Site

Grain size distribution.—The older pre-quake sediments are pebbly sands, except for samples from a silt layer a few inches below the top of the coarse sediments in C 3 and C 4, and from the adjacent thin sand. The sands are moderately to poorly sorted and internal sorting is also poor; in only two of the ten samples is there a clear polymodal size distribution in the sand and gravel fraction. This lack of internal sorting indicates lack of reworking. suggesting relatively rapid deposition and burial, probably under fluvial rather than littoral conditions. Sea level then was at least as low as it is now.

The younger pre-quake sediments are predominantly silt, but have a coarse "tail" (fig. 18, sample 2c), which is probably the result of rafting of sand by ice. Sand in small ice blocks on a Rhode Island beach has been suggested by Dillon and Conover (1965). A pebble three-fourths of an inch across is enclosed in pre-quake mud in C 1 and is thought to have been ice-rafted. These younger pre-quake sediments were deposited at least several feet below low tide, for sediment now accumulating at or just below low tide is predominantly sandy. Because the pre-quake silts are found at least 10 feet above present low tide (at S 5), this part of the delta must have risen more than 7 feet, the amount of uplift determined from the displacement of biological zones at Shepard Point, 3 miles to the southeast. Whether this inferred greater uplift is tectonic or the result of mass movement of

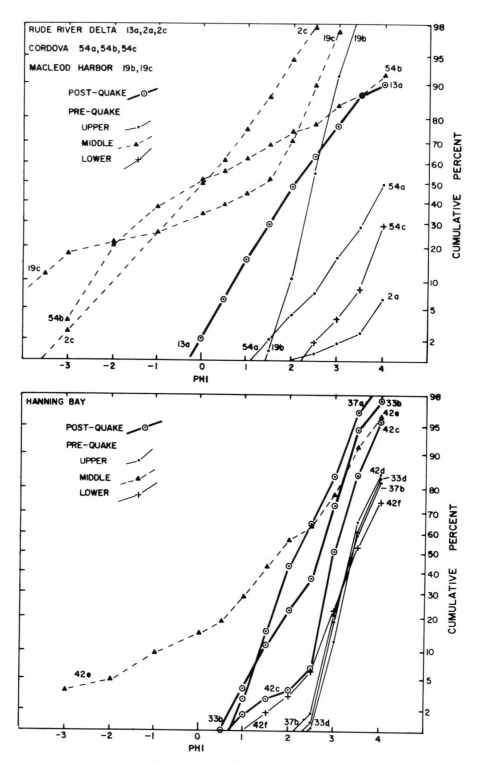

FIG. 18.—Grain-size distribution of selected samples.

delta sediment cannot be determined without a precise topographic survey of the delta.

The post-quake sediments are much coarser than the pre-quake sediments immediately underlying them (table 1, fig. 18). The sampled postquake sediments are finest at S 3 and S 4 where the average grain size is about 5∅; else-where the mean ranges from 1.1 to 3.1∅. The sediments are moderately to well sorted, the most poorly sorted samples coming from below low tide, where comparatively little wave energy is expended. Most post-quake sediment was introduced into the area and was not derived by reworking of local pre-quake silts. Pre-quake silts

TABLE 1.—*Summary of mean grain size and sorting, in phi units. Figure in brackets gives number of samples. The horizontal lines represent approximate time lines.*

		Rude River		Cordova		Macleod Harbor		Hanning Bay (C34–C39)	
		Mean	Sorting	Mean	Sorting	Mean	Sorting	Mean	Sorting
POSTQUAKE		1.1–3.1 (except 3a, 4a)	0.7–1.5(6)					2.3, 2.8 (except 35a)	0.8(2)
PRE-QUAKE	Upper	>5		>3.6	0.6–1.0(10)	2.3–3.3	0.4–0.8(13)	2.6–3.5	0.3–0.6(11)
PRE-QUAKE	Pebbly	−0.3–2.4	0.9–1.7(10)	−1.0, 0.3	2.0, 2.8(2)	0.2, 1.8	2.8, 0.6(2)	2.1	0.8(1)
PRE-QUAKE	Lower			>5					

HANNING BAY

		Cores——41, 42		40		30–33		25–28	
		Mean	Sorting	Mean	Sorting	Mean	Sorting	Mean	Sorting
POST-QUAKE	Upper	2.9, 2.6	0.6, 0.8(2)	? erosion		2.5–3.1	0.3–0.7(3)	2.4–3.0	0.3–0.7(5)
POST-QUAKE	Middle	0.5, 1.7	2.2, 1.5(2)	3.0	0.3(1)				
POST-QUAKE	Lower	2.5, 3.1	0.9, 0.4(2)	0.6	2.3(1)	1.9–2.5	0.7–1.2(5)		
PRE-QUAKE	Upper	3.2, 3.4	0.4, 0.5(2)	3.6	0.8(1)	2.8–3.5	0.5–0.6(5)	3.3–3.8	0.5–0.9(4)
PRE-QUAKE	Pebbly	1.7	1.5(1)						
PRE-QUAKE	Lower	3.6	0.8(1)						

contain only 5 percent sand, most of which is fine-grained; the delta surface would have to have been eroded down at least 20 feet to produce the few inches of post-quake sand now present.

Composition.—There appears to be no significant difference in gross composition of the pre-quake gravel and silt and the post-quake sand. The sediment is dominated by fragments of indurated shale and minor sandstone, which together total about 70 percent. Quartz, with minor altered feldspar, comprises about 15 percent, and opaque minerals make up almost all the remainder of the sediment.

Cordova Site

Grain-size distribution.—Overlying old, moderately sorted silt is much coarser pre-quake sediment. This is coarsest in C 54 and C 55, from the stream channel, and appears to be quite unsorted, indicating rapid deposition by a well-supplied stream. The sand rapidly becomes finer seaward and to the south, indicating that the channel in which the sand was deposited lay in about the same position as the present channel. Sea level then is inferred to have been about the same or slightly lower than it is now. The youngest pre-quake sediments sampled have a mean grain size from 3.6 to 5∅, and are moderately to well sorted (table 1). Only 51a has the coarse "tail" common in the silt samples from the Rude River delta.

No post-quake sediments were identified.

Composition.—There is no significant difference in composition between the coarse sediment and the overlying silt, but lithic fragments

are less common (40 percent), and mica and non-opaque heavy minerals are several times more common (each about 10 percent) than at the other three sites. The lowest silt contains 3 to 5 times as much mica, mainly brown biotite, as the overlying sediment.

MacLeod Harbor Site

Grain-size distribution.—The oldest sediment, from C 19, is pebbly sand, which probably is part of a widespread layer extending landward beneath younger pre-quake sands. Grain size distribution of the two samples may be regarded as a mixture of three near-normal distributions (table 2). The modes are well-defined and similar in both samples suggesting that the sediment was derived from previously well sorted deposits. The pebbly sand was probably deposited in an environment similar to that in the braided gravelly streams now entering the bay. Sea level was then about the same as it is now.

The overlying pre-quake sand samples are similar to each other in grain size and sorting (table 1), though there seems to be a significant coarsening in grain size landward, and in C 17, C 18 and C 19 downward.

No post-quake sediments were identified.

Composition.—No significant compositional differences were found between the pebbly horizon and the overlying sand. Rock fragments, mainly indurated shale, dominate the samples (65 percent), whereas quartz and feldspar comprise about 20 percent of the sand. The remaining 15 percent consists mainly of opaque minerals. Shell material is present in almost all samples but does not exceed one or two percent.

TABLE 2.—*Breakdown of samples 19c and 19d into components indicated by the modes.*

Sample No.	Fine sand	Coarse sand	Gravel	
19c	60%	20%	20%	
19d	90%	3%	7%	Proportions
19c	2.0∅	−0.5∅	−3.6∅	
19d	2.1∅	−0.4∅	−2.5∅	Mean grain size
19c	0.6∅	0.9∅	0.8∅	
19d	0.5∅	0.7∅	1.0∅	Standard deviation

Hanning Bay Site

Grain-size distribution.—The oldest sediment sampled, a moderately sorted fine sand, was reached only in C 42. The overlying pebbly horizon was sampled in C 38 and C 42, and in both samples a polymodal size distribution was apparent, although it is not as well-defined as in the MacLeod Harbor samples. Again, fluvial deposition, when sea level was at least as low as it is now, is indicated.

Most of the exposed pre-quake sediments are the overlying fine sands, which have an average mean grain size of 3.2∅ and an average standard deviation of 0.6. Most of these otherwise well-sorted sands have coarse "tails" (fig. 18), although they form only a few percent of the sample and, thus, do not influence the standard deviation significantly. This coarse material was probably introduced in the same manner as that in the Rude River delta silts, by floating ice. There seems to be no clear relation between mean size or sorting, and between the vertical or areal position of the samples.

The post-quake sediments range in size from gravel to fine sand, and their character varies markedly with location and time at which they were deposited. They are coarsest adjacent to the upper reaches of the stream channel above the +5 foot contour, where a thin shelly gravel lies on pre-quake fine sand. This gravel may have resulted from large waves associated with the earthquake, the large shells and scattered pebbles representing a lage concentrate winnowed by later, more moderate wave action. However,

deposition during post-quake flooding is also possible. The grain-size data (table 1—Hanning Bay) indicate that soon after the uplift the stream established a south-westerly course, passing over S 40 and then S 31, S 32 and S 33. Here mainly medium sand was deposited on the pre-quake sediments, while adjacent to the stream fine sand only slightly coarser than pre-quake sand accumulated. By August 1964, when air photos show the stream to be near S 41 and S 42, the channel had migrated northward, depositing at S 41 and S 42 a coarse, poorly sorted sand on top of the fine basal post-quake sand there. In the vacated channel to the south, fine sand began accumulating again. Finally the stream, after moving farther north, cut its present channel, and fine, well sorted sand began to accumulate over the whole area to the southeast.

As in areas adjacent to the channel just after the earthquake, the mean size of the sand now being deposited south of the present channel is only slightly coarser than that of pre-quake sands here, in spite of the change to an environment in which much more energy is being expended. This can be explained by the abundance of available fine sand, and by the absorption of energy in erosion, leaving little energy to winnow and remove the large fine fraction.

At S 35 the post-quake sand is better sorted than the underlying pre-quake sand, but is almost identical in size distribution to samples from the uplifted terrace at S 34. This thin strip of sand adjacent to the terrace has been

TABLE 3.—*Breakdown of samples 37a and 39a into components indicated by the modes.*

Sample No.	Fine sand	Medium sand	Coarse sand	
37a	45%	55%	—	
39a	73%	25%	2%	Proportion
37a	2.8∅	1.7∅	—	
39a	2.7∅	1.3∅	−0.8∅	Mean (0)
37a	0.4∅	0.4∅	—	
39a	0.4∅	0.5∅	0.6∅	Standard deviation

eroded and deposited with very little change in character. In contrast, thin post-quake sands around S 37 and S 39 are coarser and more poorly sorted than the underlying pre-quake sand (table 1). The size distribution of the post-quake sand is polymodal (table 3), and, although the mean of the finest mode is similar to that of the underlying pre-quake sand, it is markedly coarser than the mean of pre-quake sands higher on the beach (M 3.1 to 3.5∅). It seems then that the post-quake sands at S 37 and S 39 consist mainly of coarser material introduced by the nearby stream since the earthquake, rather than of sand reworked from the nearby terrace.

Composition.—There is no significant areal or vertical variation in gross composition of the non-calcareous fraction. Lithic fragments constitute about 50 percent of the sediment, quartz and feldspar about 40 percent, and opaque minerals most of the remaining 10 percent. The proportion of shell material in the pebbly sands, whether pre-quake or post-quake, ranges from 5 percent to 28 percent of the sample. However, in the finer grained sands a shell content of more than one percent is unusual in pre-quake sand, but is quite common in post-quake sand. This is attributed to erosion and comminution of shells of molluscs killed as a result of the uplift, and also to erosion of shell sand from the adjacent rocky areas.

CONCLUSIONS

The oldest sediment examined is silty, fine sand in the lower part of several cores from Cordova and one from Hanning Bay. It is similar to the fine sediment that was deposited just prior to the earthquake and was probably deposited under similar shallow sub-tidal conditions. The silty sand is overlain by stream-deposited, pre-quake pebble sand and sandy gravel, which were found at the two other sites also. The change is attributed to a relative lowering of sea level to a position as low as or lower than it is now. The submergence that followed the deposition of the pebbly material was rapid, for the contact with overlying silt and fine sand is quite sharp. This submergence, which was terminated by the 1964 earthquake, may have been responsible for the killing of trees by the sea, observed by Grant and Higgins (1910) at eight localities in Prince William Sound.

Only in the Rude River delta were pre-quake sediments directly affected by the earthquake. Here, rectangular mudcrack patterns and inflections in the pre-quake silts clearly indicate mass movement, whose direction was closely controlled by the attitude of the delta front and the valley wall. Because pre-quake silts are now

found 10 feet above low tide, though the uplift determined from biological zones at Shepard Point was only seven feet, it appears that local doming resulted from the mass movement.

Although it is known that, following the earthquake, large waves swept several parts of the Sound, a possible record of this exists at only one site, Hanning Bay. Even here the evidence is not conclusive; flood conditions not long after the earthquake could also have deposited the shelly gravel.

The most widespread effect of the earthquake on the shallow water sediments has been the associated uplift, which raised considerable areas of the sediment surface into an intertidal environment. The change in grain size from pre-quake to post-quake sediments appears to have been controlled mainly by two factors:

(1) The amount of local pre-quake sediment readily available. This must obviously depend on the grain size of the sediment, because sand is much more easily eroded than silt.

(2) The amount of sandy sediment introduced since the earthquake.

Four combinations of these two factors are apparent at the four sites that were studied.

At the Rude River delta site, derivation from the consolidated pre-quake silt appears minimal but a fair range of grain sizes is readily available from the Rude River. Current and wave action have been sufficient to sort the material at least moderately well, and it is likely, therefore, that the change from deposition under subtidal to intertidal conditions is fairly represented by the change here from fine silt to fine to medium sand.

At the Cordova site, where no post-quake sediment could be identified, the absence of introduced, sandy material is consistent with the lack of effective transporting agents in the area. The dominantly fine-grained character of the pre-quake sediment appears to have effectively inhibited its erosion and redeposition.

At the MacLeod Harbor site the well-sorted, pre-quake sands have been removed in great quantity, but no post-quake sediment was positively identified. The active cliffing requires a seaward movement of sand, though the presence of peat laminae only a few inches below the surface in C 18 and C 21 limits the possible thickness of the layer of transient sand. Grain-size analyses show that the topmost sediments are actually finer than those below, which were deposited before the earthquake. It appears that no further sorting accompanies the removal of the sand to the subtidal site of deposition.

At the Hanning Bay site, well sorted, pre-quake fine sand and coarse silt has been available since the earthquake, and some coarser sediment has been introduced by the stream. The small change in mean size from pre-quake to post-quake sediment in most cores indicates an energy balance similar to that at MacLeod Harbor, where wave and current energy has been dissipated almost entirely by erosion and removal of the readily available sediment, leaving little or none for winnowing and sorting. The larger change in C 37 and C 39 can be reasonably attributed to introduction of coarse material by the adjacent stream.

The most significant point gained from the studies at MacLeod Harbor and Hanning Bay is that a rapid change from a low to a high energy environment of deposition need not necessarily cause a rapid change in the character of the sediment, if there is a large supply of readily available sediment. This sediment affects the system rather like a dashpot in a physical model. As the supply of readily available sediment decreases, more energy will become available to be expended on sorting and reworking. Thus there will be a gradual increase in the mean grain size with time, though since the sediment supply here is already well sorted, the sorting may not change significantly.

ACKNOWLEDGMENTS

The field work was carried out in June and July, 1965, in conjunction with a California Academy of Sciences biology program financed by the National Science Foundation and the Atomic Energy Commission. The writer is indebted to Dr. G. Dallas Hanna, the program supervisor, for the opportunity to participate in it, and to the members of the biological party and the crew of the "Harmony" for their invaluable assistance with coring with boat handling. Thanks are also expressed to the Institute of Polar Studies, Ohio State University, for supplying field equipment and working facilities, to Dr. Arthur Mirsky, Institute of Polar Studies, and Dr. Malcolm P. Weiss, Department of Geology, for reviewing the manuscript, and to Dr. Richard P. Goldthwait for his help in setting up the program.

REFERENCES

DILLON, W. P., CONOVER, J. T., 1965, Formation of ice-cemented sand blocks on a beach and lithologic implications: Jour. Sedimentary Petrology, v. 35, p. 364–367.

FOLK, R. L., AND WARD, W. V., 1957, Brazos River bar: a study in the significance of grain size parameters: Jour. Sedimentary Petrology, v. 27, p. 255–292.

GRANT, U. S., AND HIGGINS, D. F., 1910, Reconnaissance of the geology and mineral resources of Prince William Sound, Alaska: U. S. Geol. Survey Bull. 443, 89 p.

INMAN, D. L., 1952, Measures for describing the size distribution of sediments: Jour. Sedimentary Petrology, v. 22., p. 125–145.

LIVINGSTONE, D. A., 1955, A light-weight piston sampler for lake deposits: Ecology, v. 36, p. 137–139.

PLAFKER, GEORGE, 1965, Tectonic deformation associated with the 1964 Alaska earthquake: Science, v. 148, p. 1675–1687.

ERK REIMNITZ*
SCRIPPS INSTITUTION OF OCEANOGRAPHY

NEIL F. MARSHALL
SCRIPPS INSTITUTION OF OCEANOGRAPHY

Reprinted with minor changes from
Journal of Geophysical Research,
"Effects of the Alaska Earthquake and
Tsunami on Recent Deltaic Sediments" [1]

Effects of the Earthquake and Tsunami on Recent Deltaic Sediments

Abstract. The Alaska Good Friday earthquake (its epicenter about 80 mi from the Copper River delta) and the events associated with the quake left indelible marks on the recent sediments of the delta. A relatively dense pattern of earthquake shock structures is found in the upper part of the section. These include sand dikes, sand pipes, slumps, faults, and joints. The structures increase in abundance toward the central part of the delta, where sediments are thickest, and become rare along its fringes, where sediments are thinnest. The 6-ft uplift of the region was responsible for some erosion and other immediate changes. But the establishment of a new equilibrium, biologically as well as geologically, for barrier islands, tidal flats, and marshes, will advance only gradually over the next few years. Seiches, brought about by the earthquake, with current velocities of up to 20 or 30 knots, regionally planed off the upper 2 or 3 ft of the tidal flats. These areas often are marked by accumulations of clam shells. The eroded materials were dumped into deep channels and troughs.

INTRODUCTION

In the summer of 1963 a sedimentation study of the Copper River delta in the Gulf of Alaska was initiated. This study was interrupted by the 1964 Good Friday earthquake, which had its epicenter in Prince William Sound, about 80 mi from the center of the delta. Owing to the infrequent and unpredictable nature of earthquakes and tsunamis, the understanding of their effects on geologic environments is limited. The purpose of this paper is to point out some of the geologically important phenomena which resulted.

The Copper River delta extends about 60 mi along the north coast of the Gulf of Alaska (Figure 1). It hugs the steep flanks of the Chugach Mountains, is bordered on the east by a southward extension of that range, and has its western fringes in Prince William Sound. The delta is divided into three parallel east-west zones, which, from the gulf toward the mountains, include: (a) the barrier islands, (b) the tidal flats or wadden, and (c) the marsh. A fourth zone, transverse to the others, is the river flood plain and dune area directly outside the mouth of the Copper River valley. The part of the delta which lies in the eastern section of

Prince William Sound is included in the tidal flats.

THE EARTHQUAKE AND TSUNAMI

We arrived in the area about three weeks after the earthquake. Consequently, a part of our information is of second-hand nature. During the earthquake and the consequent tsunamis people had little time and inclination for accurate observations. Such second-hand information is therefore not always completely reliable.

The main shock of the March 27 earthquake occurred at 1735, Alaska time. This was shortly before low tide, and large parts of the tidal flats were exposed. According to present calculations (personal communications with Capt. Richards of the U. S. Coast and Geodetic Survey), the uplift for the Cordova area amounts to 6.3 ft. Most of this was apparently associated with the main shock [*Van Dorn,* 1964]. On a regional scale, maximum uplift occurred along a zone trending from Hinchinbrook Island, Prince William Sound, in a southwesterly direction toward the southern edge of Kodiak Island. Water waves, generated by the tilting of the crust, traveled in a northwesterly direction into the coastal regions and in a southwesterly direction across the Pacific Ocean. The waters in Prince William Sound were set into a rocking

---

[1] Contribution from the Scripps Institution of Oceanography, University of California, San Diego.

*Now with the U.S. Geological Survey.

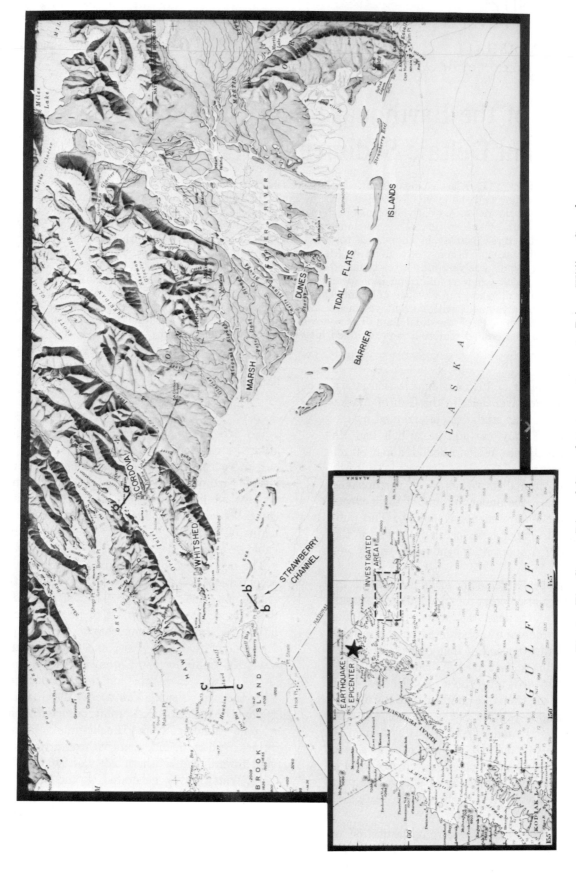

Fig. 1. The Copper River delta and eastern entrance to Prince William Sound.

motion. The amplitude and period of this rocking varied at different places, depending on the configuration and size of the fjords.

In Orca inlet, which is partially filled with deltaic sediments, the water was oscillating past the town of Cordova with a period of perhaps one half hour. At about 2020 the Coast Guard Cutter *Sedge* ran aground in a channel near Cordova, where, according to charts, the water should have been 43 ft deep. The ship draws 13 ft of water. Assuming the channels had not yet filled with sediment, the sea level during the seiches apparently dropped to about −30 ft. At this time during the peaks, the tide in the inlet was not covering the bars which were near MLLW. Thus an amplitude of perhaps 30 ft is suggested for the seiches. With the rising tide the crests of successive seiches got higher, causing a major 'wave' at Cordova at 0007 on March 28, the time of high tide. This wave, measured on a tide staff, reached a high mark of 21.5 ft. Considering the previous uplift, an absolute wave height of 28 ft is suggested.

Emil Rautio, a fisherman living at Point Whitshed (see Figure 1), stated that the approaching 'major wave' could be heard on the northwest side of Hawkins Island about 1 hr before its arrival. It approached from two sides simultaneously (from Hawkins Cutoff and from Cordova), and the two waves met near the point. The wave coming from Cordova appeared to be about 25 ft high and was breaking all across the 3-mile-wide inlet. A rush of air was said to have preceded the wave.

Observers estimated the current velocities associated with the seiches at 40 knots. The Coast Guard channel buoys, moored with more than 1 ton of ballast, were moved for miles. From the 23-min time delay of the peaks between Cordova (0007 hr) and Whitshed (0030 hr), and the distance of 7.5 mi, a current velocity of 19.5 knots can be calculated.

According to *Keulegan* [1949], the velocity of propagation for a surge on a dry bed is roughly approximated by

$$V \approx 2(gh)^{1/2}$$

where $g = 32$ ft/sec² and h is the height of the wave. Using 25 ft for the wave height, one gets a velocity of 56.5 ft/sec, or about 33 knots, for the velocity of propagation of the wave front over the exposed tidal flats in Orca inlet.

For several days afterward the sea level fluctuated with an amplitude of several feet superimposed on the new normal tidal cycle.

The effects of the previously discussed events will be dealt with in three cause-related sections: (*a*) effects of the earthquake shock, (*b*) effects of the uplift, and (*c*) effects of the tsunami.

EARTHQUAKE SHOCK EFFECTS

During the earthquake, Cordova, being built on bed rock, suffered little damage, although shock intensities were high. The direction of ground motion in the bed rock area could not be ascertained, but earthquake waves distinguished by wet and dry zones were seen traveling across the exposed tidal flats around Cordova in a northwesterly direction. The Copper River highway was rippled by waves 3 ft in amplitude, the crests of which were trending north-south. The ripples that were partially preserved in the road bed may possibly be correlated with underlying coarse-grained deposits of old glacier streams that trend north-south. These were compacted less by the earthquake shock waves than the intervening finer grained materials. While the bridges remained high, the average road bed seems to have settled by as much as 2 ft into the deltaic sediments. Numerous landslides were observed in the mountains surrounding the Copper River delta.

Sandspouts. During the major shock and for 5 to 10 min afterward, people in certain areas of the tidal flat region observed spouts of 'mud and water,' some of them yellowish to rusty in color, shooting into the air as high as 30 to 40 ft. These spouts were so closely spaced that several people at first thought they were seeing herds of sea lions or other animals. Except in one instance, where the gushers were spaced about 100 ft apart along the edge of a channel, no apparent trends could be observed. According to one eye witness, individual spouts were active intermittently. This was not corroborated by another person watching from the same spot. *Grantz et al.* [1964] reported that eyewitnesses from Portage said that sheets of mud spouted about 75 to 100 ft high along a width of 100 ft.

In the field the effects of these spouts were readily observed where not affected by the tides or on tidal flats composed of fine-grained,

Fig. 2. Crater left by a mudspout on a former tidal flat surface no longer affected by the tides. Note the sandy materials on this side of the spout and the 'desiccation' cracks washed out by rain.

compacted surfaces. They usually were circular depressions, commonly 10 to 15 in. deep and from 0.5 to 20 ft or more in diameter (Figures 2 and 3). A rim of sediment, coarser grained than the indigenous surface sediment, frequently surrounded the depression and extended away from it as a tongue-like feature.

No definite structures could be ascertained from trenches because of the problems involved with digging in soft silt and clay. However, it is reasonable to assume that they represent long necked funnels with wide mouths. Layering cut by these features may at times be up-curved around the blow holes.

Since the surface in the Copper River delta region was severely fractured by a different mechanism, described in the next section, the sheetlike mud spouts mentioned above did not leave such obvious features. However, John Mathes from the U. S. Forest Service, who flew over the area on the day after the earthquake, observed sheetlike deposits of sediment on top of the snow, extending from long fissures for perhaps ¼ mile in a downwind direction.

Similar phenomena have been reported in numerous cases where recent water saturated sediments were disturbed by severe earthquake shocks [*Dutton*, 1889; *Lawson et al.*, 1908; *Fuller*, 1912; *Davis and Sanders*, 1960; *Swenson*, 1964].

Housner [1958] has postulated a mechanism for the sand spouts in terms of the principles of soil mechanics. He believes that two conditions must be fulfilled: (*a*) a readjustment of grain-to-grain relationships in a zone that eventually approaches the surface and (*b*) a shallow water table. An impermeable layer overlying the water-saturated materials is not required. Our findings agree with this, as craters were found both on the marsh and on the tidal flats, whereas only the marsh has such an impermeable surface layer. However, it seems that the disturbed zone supplying water and sand need not approach the ground surface but may

Fig. 3. Twenty- to thirty-foot-diameter crater in an east-west trending, very soft zone, which appears to be a fracture zone.

be overlain by at least 20 ft of undisturbed materials. If the sources for the sand spouts were confined to their immediate vicinity, depressions should be found surrounding the rim of the craters. Such depressions were not observed.

A hole drilled near one of the spout craters that had produced sand showed that the source was over 20 ft deep, as no sandy layers were encountered down to that depth. In the marsh, where steep cut banks expose the section, it was frequently established that the materials came from depths in excess of 13 ft.

Cracks and faults. Cracks and faults developed in all regions of the delta. Since, except on the tidal flats, the ground surface was frozen at the time of the quake, many cracks were very sharply defined (Figure 4). A great majority were mere open fractures, with the opposite walls separated by as much as 3 ft. Most types of faulting were also displayed with lateral displacements of up to 3 ft and vertical displacements of up to 6 ft. When viewed from the air

the cracks on the marsh as well as on the barrier islands commonly showed a polygonal pattern. The following trends were observed: (a) on the barrier islands, cracks parallel to the outline of the islands, especially on the seaward side, were dominant; (b) in the dune area of the delta, cracks along the trend of the crests were pronounced, and random patterns were superimposed (Figure 5); (c) slump cracks following the slough banks in the marsh and the channel edges on the tidal flats were very common (Figure 6). The reason for these trends lies either in the topography or the local geology. Steep slopes or cutbanks gave way to form slump cracks while bodies of sediments with different grain size, reacting differently to violent shocks, formed tension cracks in the coarser materials, in this case barrier islands or dunes.

Not much can be said about the cracks on the tidal flats because the surface is intermittently reworked by relatively strong currents. But it was noted that along some linear fea-

Fig. 4. Earthquake cracks in the marsh of the central Copper River delta. Note the sharp edges due to frozen ground.

tures which we suspected were cracks, the sediments had changed markedly. Approaching these features, one would suddenly sink 2 to 3 ft into materials which, on the previous step, easily supported a person. This condition was not encountered in previous years.

In the marshes and on the flat parts of the barrier islands almost all cracks were open, suggesting a shrinking or compression of the crust. Some cracks were only partially filled with sediments. Others, however, were over-filled, so that the surface expression is a ridge of sediment occasionally over 2 ft high (Figure 7).

The cracks on the delta extended through the thick cover of snow found over large regions at the time of the quake. Since wind is an important agent for sediment transport in the region of the Copper River delta, it is possible that some of these cracks, especially those on the barrier islands, may have been filled with

eolian materials. Then, as the snow melted, ridges of sediment conceivably could have formed on top of the cracks. We believe, however, that the sediments filling the open fractures issued from below and that this mechanism, supplying sediment to the surface, is different from that associated with the sand spouts. The cracks in the ground alternately opened and closed as the shock waves traveled through the sediments. In this manner unconsolidated materials that were not water saturated were pumped to the surface at the same time that sections between the cracks were compressed.

In only one region of the marsh, which at that particular place is at least 14 ft thick, parallel elongate depressions were noted with the cracks and ridges. These swales were spaced about 100 to 200 ft apart and were 1 to 2 ft deep. It is believed that here the sandy ma-

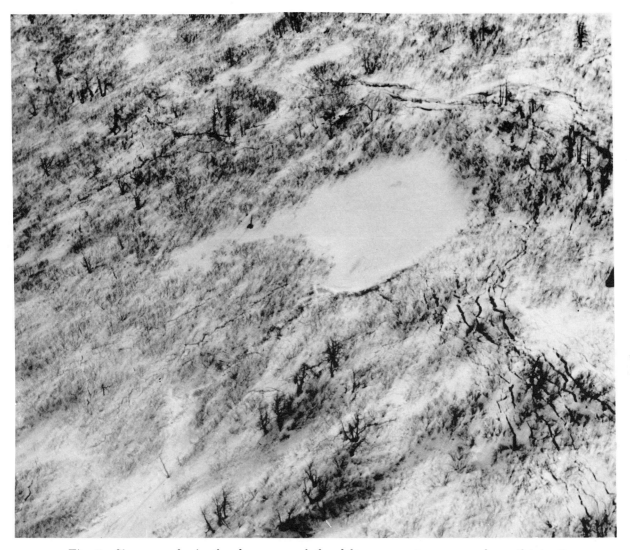

Fig. 5. Slump cracks in the dune area of the delta are most pronounced parallel to the crests, with other patterns superimposed. Photograph through the courtesy of R. von Huene of the Naval Ordnance Test Station at China Lake, California.

terials issued from a narrow zone immediately adjacent to the cracks, causing the ground surface above this zone to sag.

When the area was revisited in August, 4 months after the earthquake, the sand dikes were still very evident on the flat parts of the barrier islands. Although the surface irregularities were largely leveled off by wind action, the fractures could be traced because of the different material filling them (Figure 8). In areas of dense vegetation on the tidal flats the features were hidden and not noticeable.

Upheaval of slough banks. In places along the sloughs in the marsh large masses of material had been thrust upward and away from the banks (Figure 9). It is believed that unsup-

ported ice crust, during the quake, dropped into the water at the bottom of the slough. Sections of the slough banks were consequently overturned by the uprush of water.

All of the above-described earthquake shock effects showed a notable increase in abundance toward the central part of the delta, where the recent sediments are thickest. This agrees with the findings of the State Earthquake Investigation Commission on the 1906 earthquake in California [*Lawson et al.,* 1908]; in the alluvium-filled valleys of the Coast Ranges, and in the central valley, isoseismals were parallel to the valley bottoms and a diminution of intensity with thinning of alluvium was apparent.

Fig. 6. Slumping along the sloughs in the marsh.

Fig. 7. Ridges of sediment supplied from depth along cracks in the ground.

Fig. 8. Sand dike on flat part of barrier island 4 months after quake.

EFFECTS OF THE UPLIFT

While the uplift of the western part of the delta has been established at 6.3 ft, in other parts only rough measurements, made by our- selves, are presently available. These seem to indicate an average upheaval of 6 ft, with local variations of from 6 to 11 ft. Although these measurements are in no way conclusive, the pattern indicates maximum uplift along the

Fig. 9. Upheaval of marsh banks along sloughs, caused by the dropping of ice crust into the water.

mountains, where the sediments are thinnest, and minimum uplift in the central regions of the delta, where the sediments are thickest and where compaction compensated for uplift. The immediate effects of this uplift, when compared with those changes that will presumably take place over the next ten years or more, are relatively unimportant for the delta as such.

Formation of new drainage channels or gullies on the tidal flats started right after the earthquake, but was most active during the spring break-up and during the summer, when runoff from the land reached its peak. Incipient gullies, showing very rapid headward erosion, were commonly observed with waterfalls of 1- to 2-ft height. Waterfalls with heights of 5 ft were reportedly observed in the Controller Bay region within days after the earthquake (Jerry Thornton, seal hunter and fisherman, personal communication). Drainage channels with little runoff were filled by slumping from the channel banks within a very short time.

Along the sloughs of the marsh, as well as along the beaches of the barrier islands, new

berms were developing at lower levels. In these places the old berms are being obliterated by wind action, whereas along stable slough banks the old berm should be preserved for a long time.

Seaward of, and adjacent to, the marshes, as well as on the lee side of the barrier islands, are large areas of mud flats which now either are above high tide or at most are only reached by spring tides. It is in these areas that a curious phenomenon was observed: during the time interval between the earthquake and our arrival typical mud cracks had formed (Figure 2) almost everywhere on the flats. Since it had been raining and snowing daily during that time, these mud cracks are not necessarily desiccation cracks. Possibly a combination of the following factors is responsible for their formation: (a) change of salt content in the interstitial waters, brought about by the flushing of the sediments through melt and rain waters, (b) reorientation of the grains and consequent denser packing of the sediments, caused by the earthquake shock waves, and (c) a change in the degree of water saturation due to the uplift beyond the normal tidal range.

Large areas of mud flats in the central regions of the delta, where channels are shallow and pre-uplift tidal currents were rather slow, will probably silt up since the tidal prism has been further reduced. It is possible that within a few years marshes will start to form here, connecting the barrier islands with the grass bank and thereby pushing the shoreline seaward for many miles. In other areas, however, it appears that tidal currents are strong enough to cut the channels, if not the mudflats, down to the old level relative to the sea. Whether offshore bars outside the barrier islands will build up above sea level remains to be seen. So far there is no indication of this action.

No major changes in the drainage pattern of the distributaries on the Copper River delta could be observed.

Large parts of the marsh that before the earthquake were within range of spring tides are now above that range. Biological changes in this zone should become very important, and

they are being studied by Peter Shepherd of the Alaska Department of Fish and Game.

Four months after the uplift, in the western part of the delta where salinities are higher, green algae had started to grow on high mudflats. In the eastern low salinity part of the delta, traces of vegetation were observed along mudcracks at the hightide line (P. Shepherd, personal communication).

EFFECTS OF THE TSUNAMI AND SEICHES

In Orca Inlet the obvious effects of the seiches were the washed out and damaged cabins and other structures along the waterfront. In a few isolated places the water had topped sea cliffs, deposited drift wood and other debris, and had broken down trees. In places the marsh was overwashed for short distances inland by 2 to 5 ft of water, indicating a wave height of up to 19 ft in these areas. Only occasionally did the barrier islands show much drift wood at elevations of up to 20 ft. Since the dunes on these islands migrate, this wood will eventually be deposited at the level where it normally ac-

Fig. 10. Dead clams, in patches up to hundreds of feet in diameter, littered the surface of the bars.

cumulates. Therefore, these effects are not geologically important.

The tidal flats at ebb, however, did show extreme erosional effects. In areas populated by clams, elongate current scours, gaping slump cracks along channel banks, and small depressions were filled with empty shells. Dead clams, in patches up to hundreds of feet in diameter, littered the surface of the bars (Figure 10). The most common shell in these accumulations was that of the cockle *Clinocardium nuttalli* (Con-

rad), which lives just below the sediment surface. Also present in large numbers were horse-clam shells *Schizothaerus capax* (Gould), which, according to Rae Baxter, Shellfish Biologist for the Alaska Department of Fish and Game, live at a depth of about 30 in. This accumulation of clams indicates that in relatively large areas the upper 30 in. or more of the surface was planed off by strong currents.

Off Cottonwood Point in an area of many square miles of tidal flats, large numbers of old

Fig. 11. Post-earthquake soundings of the U. S. Coast and Geodetic Survey superimposed on old chart show approximate pattern of deposition. Almost all dotted areas show at least 10 ft of deposition; some show up to 30 ft of deposition. The black spot in center indicates 26 ft of erosion.

tree stumps were exposed as much as 2 ft or more. The stumps apparently were brought down by the river years ago and had been silted over. In 1963 the area was found completely free of stumps. This indicates that here a layer at least 2 ft thick has been eroded away.

The materials eroded from the tidal flats during the seiches and since then, owing to the uplift, probably are deposited in deep parts of channels, on the seaward side of the barrier islands, and in Prince William Sound.

Soundings of the entrance to Cordova harbor by the Coast and Geodetic Survey a few days after the earthquake, when compared with old charts, show that in some places channels have shoaled by 30 ft (Figure 11). This is after taking into consideration the uplift of 6 ft. Comparative sounding lines that we made in the same area in 1963 and again in 1964 about three weeks after the earthquake confirm this, but they also show that the tidal currents were able to again deepen the channels between the time of the U. S. Coast and Geodetic Survey work and our work (Figure 12). A survey of the tidal inlet connecting the Gulf of Alaska with the tidal flat region at Strawberry Point also shows a shoaling of 33 ft. However, sounding lines in Hawkins Cutoff did not show any major changes.

The erosion of the flats and deposition in deeper areas probably did not take place with one sweep of a current surge, but instead during a number of such surges, producing currents in opposite directions. Between these surges of opposite sense were periods of slack water. We speculate that the deposits of the seiches, which decreased in intensity over a period of several days, may not only be graded but may show many features commonly associated with 'turbidity current deposits' and that possibly a number of such units make up a channel fill.

Conclusion

The marks left by the 1964 Alaska earthquake and associated events on the recent sediments of the Copper River delta are significant. Sedimentary structures related to these extend to a depth of at least 20 ft, and probably much deeper. Among the structures are sand dikes, sandpipes (formed by sand spouts) with funnel-shaped orifices, faults, and joints. Because of the erosion brought about by seiching action and the uplift, in many areas these structures are terminated by an unconformity. In the tidal flat deposits this unconformity is marked in places by accumulations of burrowing clams of mixed species. In deep channels and troughs

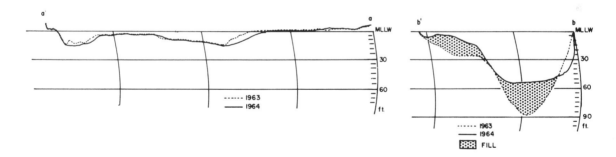

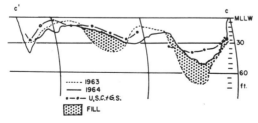

Fig. 12. Comparative profiles before and after earthquake showing erosion and deposition. Note 10 to 15 ft erosion of channel fill in profile c–c', comparing post-earthquake soundings made about two weeks apart. For location of profiles refer to Figure 1.

on or around the delta large volumes of sediment accumulated.

Since earthquakes have been common in the area in the past, it seems likely that underlying sediments have been affected in a manner similar to the way in which the surface layers were affected.

A study of secondary structures of the types we observed in stratigraphic sections is necessary for a better understanding of the behavior of recent deposits under extreme stresses.

Acknowledgments. This study was made possible through a grant from the U. S. Steel Foundation and funds from the Office of Naval Research under contract NONR 2216 (23). We are indebted to many people in the Cordova area, who, through their assistance, enabled us to reconstruct the sequence of events. Among these, special thanks are due Emil and Dorothy Rautio and Edward A. Haltness, Sr. Drs. F. P. Shepard, J. R. Curray, and E. Winterer critically read the manuscript and offered suggestions. The illustrations were prepared by Dawn Carey and James Moriarty.

References

Davis, T. N., and N. K. Sanders, Alaska earthquake of July 10, 1958: Intensity distribution and field investigation of northern epicentral region, *Bull. Seismol. Soc. Am., 50*, 221–252, 1960.

Dutton, C. E., The Charleston earthquake of August 31, 1886, *U. S. Geol. Surv. 9th Ann. Rept.,* 203–528, 1889.

Fuller, Myron L., The New Madrid earthquakes, *U. S. Geol. Surv. Bull. 494,* 1–119, 1912.

Grantz, A., G. Plafker, and R. Kachadoorian, Alaska's Good Friday earthquake, March 27, 1964—A preliminary geologic evaluation, *U. S. Geol. Surv. Circ. 491,* pp. 1–35, 1964.

Housner, G. W., The mechanism of sandblows, *Bull. Seismol. Soc. Am., 48,* 155–161, 1958.

Keulegan, G. H., Wave motion, in *Engineering Hydraulics,* edited by H. Rouse, Proceedings of the Fourth Hydraulics Conference, Iowa Institute of Hydraulic Research, June 12–15, 1949, chap. 11, pp. 711–756, 1949.

Lawson, A. C., et al., The California earthquake of April 18, 1906, *Report of the State Earthquake Investigation Commission, Carnegie Inst. Wash. Publ. 87,* 1908.

Swenson, F. A., Ground-water phenomena associated with the Hebgen Lake earthquake: The Hebgen Lake, Montana, earthquake of August 17, 1959, *U. S. Geol. Surv. Profess. Paper 435,* 159–165, 1964.

Van Dorn, Wm. G., Source mechanism of the tsunami of March 28, 1964 in Alaska, *Proceedings of the 9th Conference on Coastal Engineering,* American Society of Civil Engineers, 166–190, 1964.

(Manuscript received January 21, 1965.)

DAVID S. McCULLOCH
U.S. GEOLOGICAL SURVEY

Abstract reprinted with minor changes from
U.S. Geological Survey Professional Paper 543-A,
"Slide-Induced Waves, Seiching, and Ground Fracturing Caused by the
Earthquake of March 27, 1964, at Kenai Lake, Alaska"

Slide-Induced Waves, Seiching, and Ground Fracturing at Kenai Lake

ABSTRACT*

The March 27, 1964, earthquake dislodged slides from nine deltas in Kenai Lake, south central Alaska. Sliding removed protruding parts of deltas—often the youngest parts—and steepened delta fronts, increasing the chances of further sliding. Fathograms show that debris from large slides spread widely over the lake floor, some reaching the toe of the opposite shore; at one place, debris traveled 5,000 feet over the horizontal lake floor.

Slides generated two kinds of local waves: backfill and far-shore waves. Backfill waves were formed by water that rushed toward the delta to fill the void left by the sinking slide mass, overtopped the slide scarp, and came ashore over the delta. Some backfill waves had runup heights of 30 feet and ran inland more than 300 feet, uprooting and breaking off large trees. Far-shore waves hit the shore opposite the slides. They were formed by slide debris that crossed the lake floor and forced water ahead of it, which then ran up the opposite slope, burst above the lake surface, and struck the shore. One far-shore wave had a runup height of 72 feet.

Kenai Lake was tilted and seiched; a power-spectrum analysis of a limnogram shows a wave having the period of the calculated uninodal seiche (36 minutes) and several shorter period waves. In constricted and shallow reaches, waves caused by seiching had 20- and 30-foot runup heights.

Deep lateral spreading of sediments toward delta margins displaced deeply driven railroad-bridge piles and set up stress fields in the surface sediments which resulted in the formation of many shear and some tension fractures on the surfaces of two deltas.

---

*USGS Professional Paper 543-A has been reprinted in its entirety with minor changes, beginning on p. 47 in *The Great Alaska Earthquake of 1964: Hydrology*; the 41-page original version, published in 1966, is also for sale by the Superintendent of Documents, U.S. Government Printing Office, Washington, D.C. 20402.

HELEN L. FOSTER
U.S. GEOLOGICAL SURVEY

THOR N. V. KARLSTROM
U.S. GEOLOGICAL SURVEY

Abstract reprinted with minor changes from
U.S. Geological Survey Professional Paper 543-F,
"Ground Breakage and Associated Effects in the Cook Inlet Area, Alaska,
Resulting from the March 27, 1964, Earthquake"

Ground Breakage and Associated Effects in the Cook Inlet Area

ABSTRACT*

The great 1964 Alaska earthquake caused considerable ground breakage in the Cook Inlet area of south central Alaska. The breakage occurred largely in thick deposits of unconsolidated sediments. The most important types of ground breakage were (1) fracturing or cracking and the extrusion of sand and gravel with ground water along fractures in various types of landforms, and (2) slumping and lateral extension of unconfined faces, particularly along delta fronts.

The principal concentration of ground breakage within the area covered by this report was in a northeast-trending zone about 60 miles long and 6 miles wide in the northern part of the Kenai Lowland. The zone cut across diverse topography and stratigraphy. Cracks were as much as 30 feet across and 25 feet deep. Sand, gravel, and pieces of coal and lignite were extruded along many fissures. It is suggested that the disruption in this zone may be due to movement along a fault in the underlying Tertiary rocks.

The outwash deltas of Tustumena and Skilak Lakes in the Kenai Lowland, of Eklutna Lake and Lake George in the Chugach Mountains, of Bradley Lake in the Kenai Mountains, and at the outlet of upper Beluga Lake at the base of the Alaska Range showed much slumping, as did the delta of the Susitna River. Parts of the floodplains of the Skilak River, Fox River, and Eagle River were extensively cracked.

A few avalanches and slumps occurred along the coast of Cook Inlet in scattered localities. Some tidal flats were cracked. However, in view of the many thick sections of unconsolidated sediments and the abundance of steep slopes, the cracking was perhaps less than might have been expected.

Observations along the coasts indicated changes in sea level that, although caused partly by compaction of unconsolidated sediments, may largely be attributed to crustal deformation accompanying the earthquake. Most of the Cook Inlet area was downwarped, although the northwest side of Cook Inlet may have been slightly upwarped. Maximum change in the Cook Inlet area was probably less than 6 feet. Little or no regional tilting was detected in the lake basins of Tustumena and Skilak lakes.

*USGS Professional Paper 543-F is on file at the NAS–NAE Library, 2101 Constitution Avenue, Washington, D.C. 20418; the 28-page original version published in 1967 is also for sale by the Superintendent of Documents, U.S. Government Printing Office, Washington, D.C. 20402.

M. J. KIRKBY*
THE JOHNS HOPKINS UNIVERSITY

ANNE V. KIRKBY*
THE JOHNS HOPKINS UNIVERSITY

Abstract reprinted with minor changes from
U.S. Geological Survey Professional Paper 543-H,
"Erosion and Deposition on a Beach Raised by the 1964 Earthquake, Montague Island, Alaska"

Erosion and Deposition on a Raised Montague Island Beach

ABSTRACT†

During the 1964 Alaska earthquake, tectonic deformation uplifted the southern end of Montague Island as much as 33 feet or more. The uplifted shoreline is rapidly being modified by subaerial and marine processes. The new raised beach is formed in bedrock, sand, gravel, and deltaic bay-head deposits, and the effect of each erosional process was measured in each material. Fieldwork was concentrated in two areas—MacLeod Harbor on the northwest side and Patton Bay on the southeast side of Montague Island. In the unconsolidated deltaic deposits of MacLeod Harbor, 97 percent of the erosion by June 1965, 15 months after the earthquake, was fluvial, 2.2 percent was by rainwash, and only 0.8 percent was marine; 52 percent of the total available raised-beach material had already been removed. The volume removed by stream erosion was proportional to low-flow discharge raised to the power of 0.75 to 0.95, and this volume increased as the bed material became finer. Stream response to the relative fall in base level was very rapid, most of the downcutting in unconsolidated materials occurring within 48 hours of the uplift for streams with low flows greater than 10 cubic feet per second. Since

then, erosion by these streams has been predominantly lateral. Streams with lower discharges, in unconsolidated materials, still had knickpoints after 15 months. No response to uplift could be detected in stream courses above the former preearthquake sea level.

Where the raised beach is in bedrock, it is being destroyed principally by marine action but at such a low rate that no appreciable erosion of bedrock was found 15 months after the earthquake. A dated rock platform raised earlier has eroded at a mean rate of 0.49 foot per year. In this area the factor limiting the rate of erosion was rock resistance rather than the transporting capacity of the waves.

The break in slope between the top of the raised beach and the former sea-cliff is being obliterated by debris which is accumulating at the base of the cliffs and which is no longer being removed by the sea. Current cliff retreat by rockfall, mudflows, and landslides was estimated at 0.7 to 2.0 feet per year, and in parts of Patton Bay the accumulation of debris has obliterated 78 percent of the original break in slope in 15 months.

Evidence of two relative sea-level changes before 1964 was found in Pat-

ton Bay. At a high stand of sea level lasting until about 2000 B.P. (before present), an older raised beach was formed which, over a distance of 5 miles, shows 40 feet of deformation relative to the present sea level. Peat deposits exposed by the 1964 uplift also record a low sea level that lasted until at least 600 B.P.

The 1964 raised beach was used to test the accuracy of identification of former sea-level elevations from raised beach features. The pre-1964 sea level could be accurately determined from the height of the former barnacle line, so an independent check on high-water level was available. The most reliable topographic indicator was the elevation of the break in slope at the top of a beach between a bedrock platform and a cliff. Even here, the former sea level could only be identified within 5 feet. The breaks in slope at the top of gravel beaches were found to be poor indicators of former sea level.

On Montague Island, evidence of former high sea levels appeared to be best preserved (1) as raised bedrock platforms on rocks of moderate resistance in slightly sheltered locations and (2) as raised storm beaches where the relief immediately inland was very low.

---

*Now with the University of Bristol, England.

†USGS Professional Paper 543-H is on file at the NAS–NAE Library, 2101 Constitution Avenue, Washington, D.C. 20418; the 41-page original version, published in 1969, is also for sale by the Superintendent of Documents, U.S. Government Printing Office, Washington, D.C. 20402.

[281]

OSCAR J. FERRIANS, JR.
U.S. GEOLOGICAL SURVEY

Abstract reprinted with minor changes from
U.S. Geological Survey Professional Paper 543-E,
"Effects of the Earthquake of March 27, 1964, in the Copper River Basin Area, Alaska"

Effects in the Copper River Basin Area

ABSTRACT*

The Copper River Basin area is in south central Alaska and covers 17,600 square miles. It includes most of the Copper River Basin and parts of the surrounding Alaska Range and the Talkeetna, Chugach, and Wrangell Mountains.

On March 27, 1964, shortly after 5:36 p.m. Alaska standard time, a great earthquake having a Richter magnitude of about 8.5 struck south central Alaska. Computations by the U.S. Coast and Geodetic Survey place the epicenter of the main shock at lat. 61.1°N and long. 147.7°W,† and the hypocenter, or actual point of origin, from 20 to 50 kilometers below the surface. The epicenter is near the western shore of Unakwik Inlet in northern Prince William Sound; it is 30 miles from the closest point within the area of study and 180 miles from the farthest point.

Releveling data obtained in 1964 after the earthquake indicates that broad areas of south central Alaska were warped by uplift and subsidence. The configuration of these areas generally parallels the trend of the major tectonic elements of the region. Presumably a large part of this change took place during and immediately after the 1964 earthquake.

The water level in several wells in the area lowered appreciably, and the water in many became turbid; generally, however, within a few days after the earthquake the water level returned to normal and the suspended sediment settled out. Newspaper reports that the Copper River was completely dammed and Tazlina Lake drained proved erroneous.

The ice on most lakes was cracked, especially around the margins of the lakes where floating ice broke free from the ice frozen to the shore. Ice on Tazlina, Klutina, and Tonsina lakes was intensely fractured by waves generated by sublacustrine landslides off the fronts of deltas. These waves stranded large blocks of ice above water level along the shores. River ice was generally cracked in the southern half of the area and was locally cracked in the northern half.

In the area of study, the majority of the ground cracks occurred within a radius of 100 miles from the epicenter of the earthquake. Ground cracks formed in flood plains of rivers, in deltas, and along the toes of alluvial fans. They also occurred locally in low terraces adjacent to flood plains, in highway and other fill material, along the margins of lakes, along the faces of steep slopes of river bluffs and hillsides, and in areas cleared of vegetation for several years.

The ground cracks were restricted to areas underlain by unconsolidated deposits where one or more of the following conditions existed: (1) permafrost was absent or deep lying, (2) the ground-water table was near the surface, (3) bedrock was relatively deep lying, and (4) slopes were steep. Because the earthquake occurred in March, seasonal frost was present throughout the area.

Despite the diversity of local conditions, the origin of most of the ground cracks can be explained by the following mechanisms: (1) lateral extension, caused by materials moving toward an unconfined face such as a lakeshore, river bluff, hillside, or terrace escarpment; (2) horizontal compaction, caused by repeated alternate compression and dilation (in the horizontal direction) of materials in flat-lying areas where there are no unconfined

---

*USGS Professional Paper 543-E is on file at the NAS–NAE Library, 2101 Constitution Avenue, Washington, D.C. 20418; the 28-page original version, published in 1966, is also for sale by the Superintendent of Documents, U.S. Government Printing Office, Washington, D.C. 20402.
†Later computed at 61.04°N; 147.73°W.

faces; (3) differential vertical compaction, caused by the shaking of materials that vary laterally in thickness or character; and (4) combinations of the above.

Snowslides, avalanches, and rockslides were restricted to the mountainous areas surrounding the Copper River Basin. They were especially numerous in the Chugach Mountains which are closest to the epicenter of the earthquake. The large amount of snow and rock debris that has cascaded onto the icefield and glaciers of these mountains, and, probably even more important, the overall disturbance to the icefield will affect the regimen of the glaciers.

Most of the damage to man-made structures occurred in the southern half of the area, and, primarily because of the sparsity of population and man-made structures, property damage was not great and no lives were lost.

SAMUEL J. TUTHILL*
MUSKINGUM COLLEGE

WILSON M. LAIRD†
UNIVERSITY OF NORTH DAKOTA

Abstract reprinted with minor changes from
U.S. Geological Survey Professional Paper 543-B,
"Geomorphic Effects of the Earthquake of March 27, 1964,
in the Martin-Bering Rivers Area, Alaska"

Geomorphic Effects in the Martin-Bering Rivers Area

ABSTRACT‡

The Alaska earthquake of March 27, 1964, caused widespread geomorphic changes in the Martin-Bering Rivers area—900 square miles of uninhabited mountains, alluvial flatlands, and marshes north of the Gulf of Alaska and east of the Copper River. This area is at lat. 60°30′ N and long. 144°22′ W 32 miles east of Cordova, and approximately 130 miles east-southeast of the epicenter of the earthquake.

The geomorphic effects observed were: (1) earthquake-induced ground fractures, (2) mudvent deposits, (3) "earthquake-fountain" craters, (4) subsidence, (5) mudcones, (6) avalanches, (7) subaqueous landslides, (8) turbidity changes in ice-basined lakes on the Martin River glacier, (9) filling of ice-walled sinkholes, (10) gravel-coated snow cones, (11) lake ice fractures, and (12) uplift accompanying the earthquake.

In addition to geomorphic effects, the earthquake affected the animal populations of the area. These include migratory fish, terrestrial mollusks, fur-bearing animals, and man.

The Alaska earthquake clearly delineated areas of alluvial fill, snow and rock avalanche corridors, and deltas of the deeper lakes as unsuitable for future construction.

---

*Now with the Iowa Geological Survey.
†Now with the American Petroleum Institute.
‡USGS Professional Paper 543-B is on file at the NAS–NAE Library, 2101 Constitution Avenue, Washington, D.C. 20418; the 29-page original version, published in 1966, is also for sale by the Superintendent of Documents, U.S. Government Printing Office, Washington, D.C. 20402.

MARCUS C. HOYER*

ARIZONA STATE UNIVERSITY

Abstract reprinted with minor changes from
Geological Society of America Bulletin
"Puget Peak Avalanche, Alaska"

The Puget Peak Avalanche

ABSTRACT†

The Alaska earthquake of March 27, 1964, caused four phenomena at the head of Puget Bay in south central Alaska. A large rock–snow avalanche fell from Puget Peak and slid into the bay. Sea waves struck the coast, transporting debris inland to elevations of 7 m. Tectonic warping uplifted Puget Bay 1.7 m, and earth cracks formed in the surficial valley alluvium.

The Puget Peak avalanche transported $1.8 \times 10^6 \, m^3$ of rock, snow, soil, and plant debris downslope. The avalanche began as a large rockfall of jointed and fractured bedrock from Puget Peak. The rockfall reached the cirque traveling at a speed of more than 100 kph; there it set in motion a large volume of snow. Most of the debris was deposited on the beach and in the bay.

Undisturbed 1963–1964 snow in the cirque, areas of undisturbed vegetation and soil, many fresh grooves and scars on bedrock surfaces, and large areas stripped of surficial vegetation and soil along the avalanche track indicate that the avalanche mass slid on snow, soil, and rock from the cirque to the bay. Evidence along the avalanche track indicates that the avalanche mass traveled at high speed along its entire extent.

Similar avalanches have occurred at Puget Bay in the past and will occur again, because shattered bedrock and steep slopes remain on Puget Peak.

*Now with The Ohio State University.

†*Geological Society of America Bulletin*, 82 (May 1971), 1267-1284, is on file at the NAS–NAE Library, 2101 Constitution Avenue, Washington, D.C. 20418.

II
EFFECTS
ON
COMMUNITIES

WALLACE R. HANSEN
U.S. GEOLOGICAL SURVEY

Reprinted with minor changes from
U.S. Geological Survey Professional Paper 542-A,
"Effects of the Earthquake of March 27, 1964, at Anchorage, Alaska"

Effects at Anchorage

ABSTRACT

Anchorage, Alaska's largest city, is about 80 miles west-northwest of the epicenter of the March 27 earthquake. Because of its size, Anchorage bore the brunt of property damage from the quake; it sustained greater losses than all the rest of Alaska combined. Damage was caused by direct seismic vibration, by ground cracks, and by landslides. Direct seismic vibration affected chiefly multistory buildings and buildings having large floor areas, probably because of the long period and large amplitude of the seismic waves reaching Anchorage. Most small buildings were spared. Ground cracks caused capricious damage throughout the Anchorage Lowland. Cracking was most prevalent near the heads or within landslides but was also widespread elsewhere. Landslides themselves caused the most devastating damage.

Triggering of landslides by the earthquake was related to the physical-engineering properties of the Bootlegger Cove Clay, a glacial estuarine-marine deposit that underlies much of the Anchorage area. The Bootlegger Cove Clay contains zones of low shear strength, high water content, and high sensitivity that failed under the vibratory stress of the earthquake. Shear strength in sensitive zones ranged from less than 0.2 tsf to about 0.5 tsf; sensitivity ranged from about 10 to more than 40. Sensitive zones generally are centered about 10 to 20 feet above sea level, between zones of stiff insensitive clay. Many physical tests by the U.S. Army Corps of Engineers were directed toward analyzing the causes of failure in the Bootlegger Cove Clay and finding possible remedies. Strengths and sensitivities were measured directly in the field by means of vane shear apparatus. Atterberg limits, natural water contents, triaxial shear, sensitivity, dynamic modulus, consolidation strength, and other properties were measured in the laboratory. Pulsating-load tests simulated earthquake loading.

Most of the destructive landslides in the Anchorage area moved primarily by translation rather than by rotation. Thus, all the highly damaging slides were of a single structural dynamic family despite wide variations in size, appearance, and complexity. They slid on nearly horizontal slip surfaces after loss of strength in the Bootlegger Cove Clay. Some failures are attributed to spontaneous liquefaction of sand layers. All translatory slides surmounted flat-topped bluffs bounded marginally by steep slopes facing lower ground. Destructive translatory slides occurred in the downtown area (Fourth Avenue slide and L Street slide), at Government Hill, and at Turnagain Heights. Less destructive slides occurred in many other places—mostly uninhabited or undeveloped areas.

In most translatory slides, damage was greatest in graben areas at the head and in pressure-ridge areas at the toe. Many buildings inside the perimeters of slide blocks were little damaged despite horizontal translations of several feet. The large Turnagain Heights slide, however, was characterized by a complete disintegration and drastic lowering of the prequake land surface. Extensive damage back from the slide, moreover, was caused by countless tension cracks.

An approximation of the depth of failure in the Bootlegger Cove Clay in the various slides may be obtained by using a geometric relationship herein called the "graben rule." Because the cross-sectional area of the graben at the head of the slide approximated the cross-sectional area of the space voided behind the slide block as the block moved outward, the depth of failure was equal to the area of the graben divided by the lateral displacement. This approximation supplements and accords with test data obtained from borings. The graben rule should apply to any translatory slide in which flowage of material from the zone of failure has not been excessive.

Geologic evidence indicates that landslides similar to those triggered by the March 27 earthquake have occurred in the Anchorage area at various times in the past.

INTRODUCTION

Anchorage, "metropolis of the north" and Alaska's largest city, is the rapidly expanding commercial center of the 49th State. Anchorage is about 80 miles west-northwest of the epicenter of the March 27 earthquake (fig. 1).

The Anchorage Lowland, a broad, undulatory glacial plain on which the greater Anchorage area is situated, is roughly triangular. It is bounded on the northwest by Knik Arm of Cook Inlet, on the southwest by Turnagain Arm, and on the east by the abrupt west front of the Chugach Mountains. Anchorage itself is crowded close to Knik Arm, but its perimeter is moving east and south because of suburban growth and soon, no doubt, will reach Turnagain Arm. Expansion north and northeast toward the Eagle River, along the narrow corridor between the mountains and Knik Arm, is largely checked by the military reservations of Fort Richardson and Elmendorf Air Force Base.

ACKNOWLEDGMENTS

Many ideas and conclusions presented in this report were reached in concert with R. D. Miller and C. A. Kaye, both of whom shortly after the March 27 earthquake joined the author in field investigations at Anchorage. Most of the credit for devising the "graben rule" (see p. A41) must go to Kaye. Discussions with M. G. Bonilla, Ernest Dobrovolny, E. B. Eckel, Reuben Kachadoorian, D. S. McCulloch, and Roger M. Waller consciously or unconsciously led to thoughts incorporated into this report. J. R. Helm, A. B. Dodd, and Arthur Gervais of the Topographic Division, U.S. Geological Survey, ran control for profiles of the various landslides. Helm also prepared the topographic maps of the Native Hospital, Government Hill, and Turnagain Heights slides, using a Wild B–8 plotter. Special thanks are due the U.S. Army Corps of Engineers for the materials and information that they supplied. A report prepared for the Corps by Shannon and Wilson, Inc. (1964) has been freely utilized, and several of its illustrations are reproduced herein. The Engineering Geology Evaluation Group (see p. A10), an ad hoc organization that carried out early investigations at Anchorage at a critical time immediately after the earthquake, is also thanked for its free release of otherwise unobtainable information.

THE EARTHQUAKE AND ITS IMMEDIATE AFTERMATH

At 5:36 p.m. on Good Friday, March 27, 1964, Anchorage and all southern Alaska within a radius of about 400 miles of Prince William Sound were struck by perhaps the strongest earthquake to have hit North America within historic time. The magnitude of this great quake has been computed by the U.S. Coast and Geodetic Survey at 8.5 on the revised Richter scale. Its epicenter was about 80 miles east-southeast of Anchorage near the head of Prince William Sound. Reportedly, the quake was felt throughout most of Alaska, including such remote points as Cape Lisburne, Point Hope, Barrow, and Umiat, 600 to 800 miles north of the epicenter on the Arctic Slope of Alaska, and at Fort Randell, 800 miles southwest at the tip of the Alaska peninsula.

Eyewitness accounts of happenings at Anchorage during and immediately after the earthquake have been reported in many publications, both technical and popular. Much valuable information has thus been gained from the objective observations of individuals who were equal to the task. Calm detachment under such trying circumstances plainly is a rare and admired virtue. Some confusion and contradiction did appear in early accounts, not surprisingly, in view of the distressing conditions under which the observations were made.

The duration of the earthquake at Anchorage can only be surmised owing to the lack of strong-motion seismograph records. Although seismographs have since been installed, none was present in Southern Alaska at the time of the quake. Intense seismic motions seem to have lasted 3 to 4 minutes, possibly longer. Where localized ground displacements occurred, as in or near landslides, strong motions may have lasted appreciably longer, after strong seismic shaking had ceased. According to Shannon and Wilson Inc. (1964, p. 11), the durations at Anchorage, timed on wrist or pocket watches, by several eyewitnesses whom they consider reliable, ranged from 4 minutes 25 seconds to 7 minutes. Even longer durations were reported outside the Anchorage area. Steinbrugge (1964, p. 62) noted that persons at Anchorage were able to accomplish several time-consuming tasks during the shaking, including such things as leaving and reentering buildings more than once, or helping other individuals to escape, despite much difficulty in standing and walking. In some areas, however, people reportedly were thrown to the ground by the force

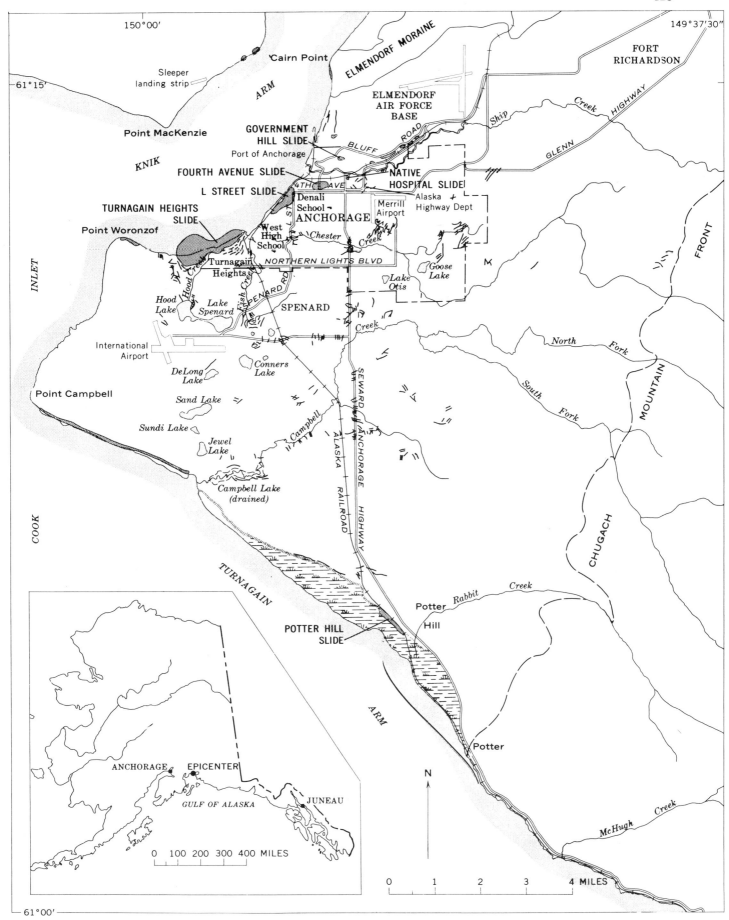

1.—Map of Anchorage, Alaska, and vicinity showing locations of major landslides and ground cracks, much generalized.

of the acceleration and were unable to regain their footing.

There seems to be general agreement that the first waves to arrive at Anchorage had strong east-west components of movement. Objects reportedly were thrown from shelves and cupboards on east and west sides of rooms, and some individuals were said to have been propelled bodily across rooms in those directions. Figure 2 shows the trace on an asphalt tile floor made by a dresser leg. Because the epicenter was east of Anchorage, an east-west ground motion was expectable. As the shaking continued, however, the motion is said to have shifted to north-south, and tall buildings that had first rocked to-and-fro east and west began to rock north and south as well, in a complex combination of movements. Strain-fracture patterns in the walls of multistory buildings at Anchorage seem to bear out such observations. North-south components of motion, moreover, are theoretically plausible, especially in view of the severe tectonic readjustments southeast and south of Anchorage in the Prince William Sound and Kodiak Island areas. The earthquake seems to have resulted from the rupture of rock at depth beneath a very broad area, extending from some point near the epicenter southwest to the south tip of Kodiak Island (U.S. Coast and Geodetic Survey, 1964, p. 31; Grantz and others, 1964, p. 2); the arrival of seismic waves at Anchorage from such a broad source must have caused a very complex ground motion (fig. 2).

Total earthquake damage to property in the Anchorage area has not been fully evaluated and perhaps will never be fully known. Nine lives are reported to have been lost—five in the downtown area, three at Turnagain Heights,

and one at the International Airport. In less than 5 minutes, more than 2,000 people, including apartment dwellers, were made homeless, according to press estimates. The loss of life was less in Anchorage than in some of the small coastal towns, where many people were killed by sea waves. But Anchorage, because of its much greater size, bore the brunt of the property damage and property losses reportedly were greater there than in all the rest of Alaska combined.

Early estimates by the Office of Emergency Planning indicated that about 75 percent of the City's total developed worth was measurably damaged. Early estimates of total damage, however, tended to be larger than later ones. According to the Anchorage Daily Times of April 9, 1964, 215 homes were destroyed in Anchorage and 157 commercial buildings were destroyed or damaged beyond repair (Grantz, Plafker, and Kachadoorian, 1964, p. 14). At Turnagain Heights alone, 75 or more dwellings were destroyed. Estimates by the Daily Times placed the damage at about $200 million. Later, the Office of Emergency Planning estimated the total damage to Alaska at about $537,600,-000, of which about 60 percent was sustained by the Anchorage area (National Board of Fire Underwriters and Pacific Fire Rating Bureau, 1964, p. 5). The final total damage estimate for Alaska, exclusive of personal property and loss of income, was about $311 million (Federal Reconstruction and Development Planning Commission for Alaska, 1964, p. 11). Scores of buildings throughout Anchorage sustained damage requiring repairs costing many thousands of dollars.

The school system was hard hit. Early estimates of damage came to

about $3.86 million. Classes were not in session, fortunately, so the buildings were empty. Twenty of the 26 schools in Anchorage were soon back in operation. West Anchorage High School, however, was severely damaged by seismic vibration. Government Hill Grade School, astride a landslide (fig. 3), was nearly a total loss, although plans have been made to salvage an intact part of the building outside the slide for use other than as a school. Denali Grade School was damaged by ground cracks and was closed indefinitely, pending damage evaluation and repair.

In downtown Anchorage (the L Street and Fourth Avenue landslide areas), about 30 blocks of dwellings and commercial buildings were destroyed or severely damaged (fig. 4). A new six-story apartment building, the Four Seasons, was razed. A new five-story department store (J. C. Penney Co.) was damaged beyond repair by seismic shaking and had to be torn down (fig. 5). Many automobiles in the downtown area were struck by falling debris. Twin 14-story apartment buildings, though a mile apart, sustained massive, nearly identical vibratory damage, much of it in response to vertical shearing forces caused by oscillation. Many other multistory or large-area buildings were severely damaged.

Water mains and gas, sewer, telephone, and electric systems were disrupted (Waller, Thomas, and Vorhis, 1965, p. 126). Total damage to utilities has been estimated at about $15 million (Alaskan Construction Consultants Committee, 1964, p. 11). Providentially, electric power failed at the very onset of the quake. Although the loss of power might seem to be an added hardship to the stricken city, untold numbers of fires were

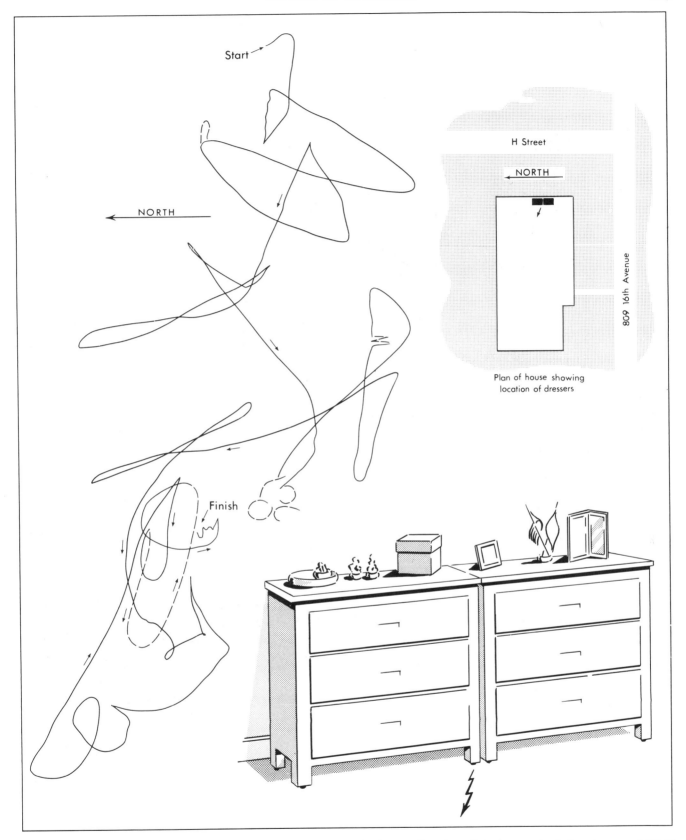

2.—Horizontal trace on asphalt tile flooring left by dresser leg during earthquake. Net movement of dresser was about N. 75° W. Other legs left nearly identical traces. Sundry items on dresser tops were little disturbed. Trace reproduced by Oliver V. Kola, published by permission of Dr. M. A. Sozen. Scale of trace, ×½.

3.—Wreckage of Government Hill School. The south wing of the building, shown here, collapsed into a graben at t

d of the slide. Net slip of the graben block is shown by the displacement of the roofline. Photograph by M. G. Bonilla.

4.—View west along Fourth Avenue at head of landslide. North (right) side of street has collapsed into a graben. Vertical displacement is about 10 feet. Photograph by Mac's Foto, Anchorage, Alaska.

probably avoided because of the lack of electric current in all the severed wires—and at a time, too, when water was unavailable for fighting fire. The destruction of San Francisco by fire on the heels of the earthquake of 1906 is forcefully recalled. Fukui, Japan, was similarly destroyed in 1948. Anchorage spent the night of March 27 in total darkness, but the city had no fires and was prepared to deal with the many disrupted electric circuits when service was restored.

Roads and railroad facilities were badly damaged. In the downtown area, many streets were blocked by debris, and in landslide areas, streets and roads were completely disrupted. Differential settlement caused marginal cracking along scores of highway fills throughout the Anchorage Lowland. In The Alaska Railroad yards where landslide debris spread across trackage and damaged or destroyed maintenance sheds (fig. 6), an estimated $2,370,700 damage was sustained (Alaskan Construction Consultants Committee, 1964, p. 74). Cars and equipment were overturned, and car shops were damaged by vibra-tion. Along the main line of the railroad, bridges failed, fills settled, and tracks were bent or buckled; at Potter, near the south margin of the Anchorage Lowland, several hundred feet of track was carried away in an area that has had a long history of repeated sliding.

At the Anchorage International Airport, the control tower failed under seismic vibration and collapsed to the ground (fig. 7), killing one occupant and injuring another. The airport terminal building, although tied structurally to the tower, was only slightly

5.—Wreckage of Penney's department store, Fifth Avenue and D Street, Anchorage. Building failed after sustained seismic shaking. Most of rubble has been cleared from streets. Photograph by George Plafker.

damaged except where it adjoined the tower. A nearby Post Office building was damaged a moderate amount (Berg and Stratta, 1964, p. 14). Almost 20,000 barrels of aviation fuel was lost from a ruptured storage tank. Runways and taxiways were slightly damaged but not put out of commission; air traffic was temporarily controlled first from a parked aircraft and then from a tower at the nearby Hood Lake landing strip (Federal Reconstruction and Development Planning Commission for Alaska, 1964, p. 25).

Facilities at the Port of Anchorage were damaged by seismic vibration and ground cracks. Four cranes jumped their tracks and in so doing, damaged their undercarriages and counterweight arms (Berg and Stratta, 1964, p. 44 and 47). Two steel storage tanks were

toppled and destroyed. Nearby oil-storage tanks were damaged superficially, but large quantities of fuel oil were lost. An expected seismic sea wave fortunately did not materialize.

Landslides caused the greatest devastation in the Anchorage area. Great slides occurred in the downtown business section (Fourth Avenue slide), in the lower downtown business and residential area (L Street slide), at Government Hill, and at Turnagain Heights. Less devastating slides occurred in undeveloped or unpopulated areas near the Alaskan Native Service Hospital, at Romig Hill, at the Alaska Highway Department garage, at Bluff Road near the U.S. Army Corps of Engineers Headquarters Building, on the west bluff of Government Hill, at Point Woronzof, Point Campbell,

Cairn Point, and on the west side of Knik Arm near Sleeper landing strip in an uninhabited area recently opened to homesteading. The slide at Potter has already been mentioned.

Capricious damage was caused by ground cracks. Such damage was mostly localized, and many areas were spared. Cracking was most common behind the heads of landslides, but it was also prevalent throughout the lowland in areas underlain by clay or silt or artificial fills on muskeg. Differential compaction was a common cause. Cracking was minimal in areas of thick ground moraine.

The flow of streams, such as Ship Creek and Chester Creek, was greatly reduced, temporarily, by percolation of water into cracks. Gages in water wells recorded

6.—Damage to yards of The Alaska Railroad, looking northwest, caused by earthflow at toe of Government Hill slide. Note undamaged water tank in background.

marked fluctuations, not just in Anchorage and southeast Alaska, but at places as distant as Georgia, Florida, and Puerto Rico (Waller and others, 1965, p. 126, 131).

For a city of its size, Anchorage has in residence a large contingent of geologists and other earth scien-tists. Within hours after the quake, many of these individuals had begun independent investiga-tions of the location, severity, na-ture, and causes of earthquake damage. On March 29, 2 days after the earthquake, a small group of geologists under the leadership of Dr. Lidia Selkregg of the Alaska State Housing Authority was commissioned by the housing authority and the city of Anchor-age to outline "necessary and im-mediate courses of action" to be taken by the city. This group be-came known as the Engineer-

7.—Wreckage of control tower at Anchorage International Airport. Six-story tower failed under sustained seismic shaking. Photograph by George Plafker.

ing Geology Evaluation Group (Schmidt, 1964, p. 13). Its membership rose to 40 after a call was made for technical help.

The group immediately began a program of mapping and data gathering. They contracted for aerial photography, started a drilling program in the major slide areas in cooperation with the Alaska Department of Highways, and ran standard laboratory tests on the various soil zones involved in the land failures. Drilling and soil testing were subsequently taken over and greatly expanded by the office of the U.S. Army District Engineer at the request of the city of Anchorage, under a contract dated 25 April 1964 between the District Engineer and Shannon and Wilson, Inc., soil mechanics and foundation engineers, Seattle, Wash. The Corps of Engineers meanwhile had immediately begun disaster relief.

The work of the Engineering Geology Evaluation Group deserves high praise. Its preliminary findings and recommendations were completed on April 12, 1964, 2 weeks after the earthquake, and a final report was completed on May 8, 1964. The findings and conclusions of the group provided the basis for many subsequent investigations by other agencies. Much of the information presented by this paper has been derived from the work of this group.

GEOLOGIC SETTING

Anchorage is near the east border of a deep structural trough filled with moderately consolidated Tertiary rocks that underlie Cook Inlet and extend northeastward toward Mount McKinley at the head of the Susitna Lowland (Capps, 1916, 1940). At Anchorage, Tertiary rocks are covered by Pleistocene deposits, but they have been penetrated by drill holes.

The Chugach Mountains just east of Anchorage consist chiefly of Mesozoic argillite and graywacke, variably deformed and metamorphosed, and intruded by small bodies of igneous rock (Capps, 1916, p. 153). The nature of the contact between the soft Tertiary rocks of the lowland and the harder Mesozoic rocks of the mountains has not been ascertained, owing partly to a lack of exposures and partly to a lack of study, but the very straight trace of the mountain front and the seeming truncation of structural trends by the mountain front suggest that the contact is a fault. On similar evidence, Karlstrom (1964, p. 21) inferred that the Kenai Mountains—a southward structural and topographic extension of the Chugach Mountains—are also bounded by a fault on the west. If these inferences are correct, a major structural displacement separates the Cook Inlet

Lowland from the bordering mountains.

Cook Inlet and the Anchorage Lowland were occupied repeatedly by large piedmont glaciers in Pleistocene time (Karlstrom, 1957, 1964; Miller and Dobrovolny, 1959). Karlstrom has distinguished five major Pleistocene glacial advances in Cook Inlet, although not all reached the Anchorage area. At the site of Anchorage, Pleistocene deposits accumulated to a thickness of 600 feet or more. In general, these deposits seem to thicken westward from the mountain front toward Cook Inlet. They exerted a vital influence on the location and the extent of earthquake damage in the Anchorage area.

Because the Pleistocene deposits of the Anchorage area have been described previously in considerable detail (Miller and Dobrovolny, 1959; Karlstrom, 1964; Cederstrom, Trainer, and Waller, 1964), they will be described but briefly here. They consist chiefly of three categories of material: glacial till, deposited as ground moraine; proglacial silty clays (including the Bootlegger Cove Clay) deposited in estuarine-marine or lacustrine-estuarine environments; and fluvioglacial deposits of several types, but chiefly outwash sand and gravel.

Most of Anchorage lies on late glacial (Naptowne-Wisconsin) outwash deposited in front of the youngest Pleistocene glacier that entered the area. This glacier constructed a large end moraine north of the city at Elmendorf Air Force Base (Miller and Dobrovolny, 1959, p. 59). Remnants of the moraine are also preserved west of Knik Arm about 2½ to 3 miles northeast of Point MacKenzie. Outwash sand and gravel from this glacier spread southward across the Anchorage Lowland and buried ground moraine and Bootlegger Cove Clay alike to depths as great as 60 feet. In general, the outwash thins toward the west and south away from its source. It wedges out completely between Turnagain Heights and Point Woronzof.

East of Anchorage along the foot of the Chugach Mountains, a massive lateral moraine was deposited by one or more of the pre-Wisconsin glaciers that occupied the area (Miller and Dobrovolny, 1959, p. 21). This moraine stands generally 1,000 to 1,200 feet above sea level and has a maximum altitude of about 1,400 feet. Because the area commands impressive views across Cook Inlet toward the snow-swept Alaska Range and Mount McKinley, it has experienced a mild real estate boom, and the next few years should see extensive urbanization of its heights. The moraine fared well in the March 27 earthquake; structures built on it were little, if at all, disturbed.

BOOTLEGGER COVE CLAY

The Bootlegger Cove Clay has become renowned, since the March 27 earthquake, for its part in the devastation. Most of the severe damage in the Anchorage area is traceable to failure within this formation, and an understanding of the mechanisms of landsliding in the Anchorage area requires some knowledge of its character and physical properties. Because of its critical relationship to the landsliding, it has been studied intensively since the earthquake, by the Corps of Engineers and by consultants to the corps.

The Bootlegger Cove Clay was named and first described by Miller and Dobrovolny (1959, p. 35–48). In general the formation consists of three physically distinct but gradational zones—an upper and a lower stiff competent zone and a central weak sensitive zone. Failures occurred chiefly in the central zone. Waves generated by the earthquake led to a drastic loss of strength, a consequent failure of dynamically sensitive saturated sand, silt, and silty clay, and a resultant disruption of the ground surface by landsliding (Shannon and Wilson, Inc., 1964, p. 1–3).

The Bootlegger Cove Clay underlies most of Anchorage and much of the adjacent area (Miller and Dobrovolny, 1959, pls. 3 and 6; Trainer and Waller, 1965). Along Knik Arm, it is exposed almost continuously from a point about three-quarters of a mile east of Point Woronzof northward at least to the Eagle River. Just north of Anchorage, it passes beneath the Elmendorf Moraine. Toward the east and southeast, it laps across older glacial deposits and thins out against higher ground in the morainal belt at the base of the Chugach Mountains. South of Anchorage, it is continuous beneath a cover of sand and muskeg west from the Seward-Anchorage Highway to the east base of the Point Woronzof-Point Campbell highland area and south to Turnagain Arm. It laps up and thins out against the deltal sand and gravel of the Point

Woronzof-Point Campbell highland area.

As described by Miller and Dobrovolny (1959, p. 39), the Bootlegger Cove Clay consists chiefly of silty clay, light gray (N7)[1] when dry and dark greenish gray (5GY 4/1) when wet. Very commonly the upper several inches to several feet immediately beneath the overlying outwash is oxidized to yellowish gray. The clay generally is delicately laminated in layers a fraction of a millimeter to several centimeters thick, although some intervals several feet thick are free of visible bedding. Throughout the clay are scattered layers of sand, some mere partings but others 25 feet or more thick. Such layers are lenticular and can only be traced short distances. In at least one landslide (Fourth Avenue), liquefaction of a sand layer is believed to have been the chief immediate cause of failure (Shannon and Wilson, Inc., 1964, p. 41).

Scattered pebbles are present throughout the Bootlegger Cove Clay. Cobbles and boulders are present also but are rare. These stones contributed nothing to the failure of the clay and had no part in the landsliding, but they do indicate the periglacial environment in which the clay was deposited. Only ice rafting could have emplaced the larger boulders. Pebbles are most numerous in the lower part of the formation. On the west side of Knik Arm opposite Cairn Point, where the base of the formation is above tide water, the clay grades downward into stony till, seemingly without a clear-cut contact.

PHYSICAL PROPERTIES

Soon after the earthquake, work started by the Engineering Geology Evaluation Group (1964) and later taken over by the U.S. Army Corps of Engineers (Shannon and Wilson, Inc., 1964) showed that the physical properties of the Bootlegger Cove Clay are far from uniform. Rather, a medial zone of low static shear strength and high sensitivity grades upward and downward into stiffer nonsensitive zones. Sensitivity is defined as the ratio of undisturbed shear strength of a soil sample to remolded (kneaded or squeezed) shear strength of the same sample, regardless of the cause (Terzaghi and Peck, 1948, p. 33).

Numerous physical tests by the Corps of Engineers—both in the field and in the laboratory—were made to analyze the causes of failure in the Bootlegger Cove Clay and find possible remedies. These tests are described in detail by Shannon and Wilson, Inc. (1964, p. 13–30); most of the information in the following paragraphs was abstracted from their report. About 150 borings were drilled within and adjacent to the several landslide areas, either into or through the sensitive zone of the Bootlegger Cove Clay. Most borings were sampled at 5-foot intervals, and continuous samples were obtained at selected locations. Undisturbed samples were collected in 3- by 36- or 3- by 37-inch steel Shelby tubes. Five large-diameter "bucket auger" holes were drilled by the Corps for visual inspection of critical zones in the clay, for in-place shear-strength tests, and for carving out undisturbed samples by hand. Vane-shear tests in standard 3-inch holes were made at 12 locations in the Fourth Avenue, L Street, and Turnagain Heights slide areas to measure in-place strengths and sensitivities of the clay. Similar tests were made on undisturbed samples both in the field and in the laboratory. In the laboratory, samples were also analyzed for Atterberg limits (see p. A14), natural-water content, triaxial shear, sensitivity, dynamic modulus, and consolidation strength.

SHEAR STRENGTH

Shear strength was measured in torsional-vane-shear tests, undrained triaxial tests, consolidated-undrained triaxial tests, and consolidated-drained triaxial tests; strain, stress, volume change, and pore-water pressure were recorded throughout the tests (Shannon and Wilson, Inc., 1964, p. 28). The results of vane-shear tests for the Fourth Avenue and Turnagain Heights slide areas are shown in figure 8. Triaxial tests performed on the clay generally correlated well with the vane-shear tests within the ranges of strengths at which failure was prevalent. Tests correlated well in the range 0.4 to 0.5 tsf (tons per square foot), but for clays of higher strength, the triaxial tests generally yielded somewhat higher values than the vane tests. Most of the samples of clay from critical depths in the landslides had initial shear strengths between 0.2 and 0.7 tsf, and in this range the ratio of torsional-vane-shear-test results to triaxial-compression-test results is generally between 0.7 and 1.5 (Shannon and Wilson, Inc., 1964, p. B8). This ratio indicates a fairly good correlation between test methods. In any event, the vane-shear-test results shown by the graphs of figure 8 clearly demonstrate the generally lower shear strength of the clay at intermediate depths as compared with shallower and deeper layers.

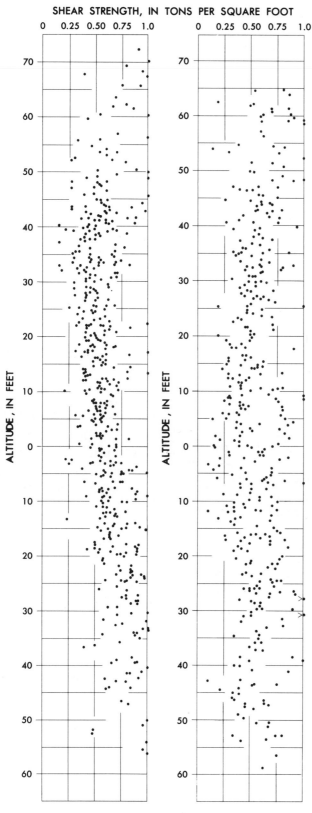

SHEAR STRENGTH, IN TONS PER SQUARE FOOT

8.—Summary of torsional-vane-shear strengths of selected borings, Bootlegger Cove Clay, from Fourth Avenue slide area (left) and Turnagain Heights slide area (right). Simplified from Shannon and Wilson, Inc. (1964, pl. B15).

Torsional-vane-shear apparatus was also used to measure the strength of the Bootlegger Cove Clay under sustained stress, because it was recognized that the duration of stress influences the resulting shear strength shown by the tested specimen (Shannon and Wilson, Inc., 1964, p. B7). At a given level (0.1 tsf), shear stress was applied for varying lengths of time. These tests showed that the Bootlegger Cove Clay loses shear strength as stress application is prolonged. In other words, the longer the stress is sustained, the lower the shear strengths.

SENSITIVITY

Sensitivity has previously been defined as the ratio of undisturbed shear strength to remolded shear strength. For example, a clay having an undisturbed shear strength of 0.4 tsf and a remolded shear strength of 0.02 tsf has a sensitivity of 20. Sensitivies were measured by the Corps of Engineers on about 2,100 selected samples of the Bootlegger Cove Clay by means of field and laboratory vane-shear devices (Shannon and Wilson, Inc., 1964, p. 27), and a record of sensitivities was plotted on the boring logs. Of the 2,100 samples tested, 302, or 14 percent, had sensitivities greater than 10; 125, or 6 percent, had sensitivities greater than 20; 40, or 1.9 percent, had sensitivities greater than 30; and 11, or 0.5 percent, had sensitivities greater than 40. The highest sensitivity measured was 60.

The sensitive zone generally ranges in thickness from about 20 to 30 feet, but it is as much as 40 feet thick in some places and is nonexistent in others. In most places the center of the sensitive zone is above sea level, generally 10 to 20 feet above, but in parts of the Turnagain Heights area it is below sea level. At no place has sensitive clay been observed higher than about 50 feet above sea level or lower than about 30 feet below sea level. Laboratory tests by the Corps indicate that the shear strength of the sensitive clay ranges from less than 0.15 to about 0.40 tsf, and the sensitivity ranges from about 25 to as high as 60. The maximum shear strengths of the stiffer clays exceed 1 tsf.

ATTERBERG LIMITS

In a laboratory analysis of fine-grained cohesive soils, it is customary to perform tests that yield information on the plasticity of the soils. These tests include measurements of natural water content (Wn) liquid limit (LL) and plastic limit (PL). The liquid limit is the water content in percentage of dry weight at which the soil passes from the liquid state into the plastic state. Similarly, the plastic limit is the water content of the soil at the boundary between the plastic state and the solid state. These limits of consistency are defined by standardized test procedures and are known as the Atterberg limits (Terzaghi and Peck, 1948, p. 32–36). The numerical difference between the liquid limit and the plastic limit is called the plasticity index (PI). The plasticity index represents the range of moisture content within which the soil is plastic. Clayey soils thus have higher plasticity indices than nonclayey or silty soils because they remain plastic through a wider range of moisture content (Stokes and Varnes, 1955, p. 85, 110; U.S. Bureau of Reclamation, 1960, p. 8, 28).

The plasticity charts (fig. 9) show the statistical relationship of liquid limit to plasticity index of the Bootlegger Cove Clay in the Fourth Avenue and Turnagain Heights slide areas, as measured for the Corps of Engineers by

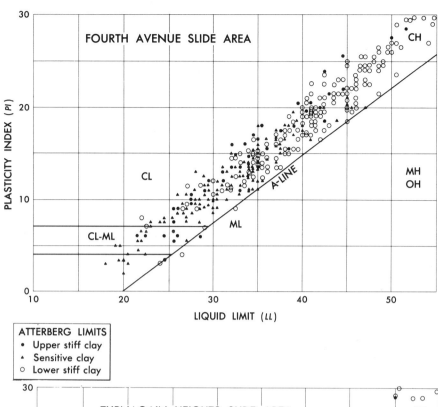

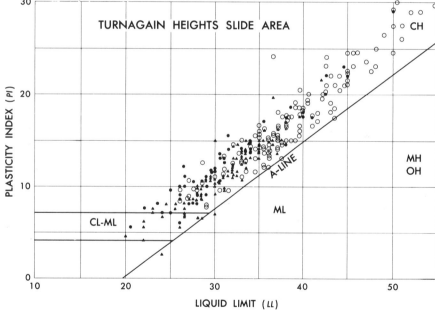

9.—Plasticity charts from selected borings, Bootlegger Cove Clay, Fourth Avenue and Turnagain Heights slide area. Reprinted from Shannon and Wilson, Inc. (1964, pl. B16). CL, inorganic clay of low to medium plasticity; ML, inorganic silts and very fine sand; CH, inorganic clay of high plasticity; MH, inorganic silt; OH, organic clay.

Shannon and Wilson, Inc. (1964). These charts show generally higher plasticity indices and liquid limits for the lower stiff clay than for the upper stiff clay or the sensitive clay. Differences between the upper stiff clay and the sensitive clay are not obvious on these charts, but they are quite apparent on statistical liquid-limit distribution curves (fig. 10). Nearly all points plotted on the plasticity charts lie above the "A" line—the line which separates soils of high cohesion and low permeability above from soils of low cohesion and high permeability below (Casagrande, 1947, p. 801).

The statistical liquid-limit distribution curves (fig. 10) show the distinctions between the three zones of the Bootlegger Cove Clay in the Fourth Avenue and Turnagain Heights areas. These curves bring out the differences between the upper stiff zone and the sensitive zone, and also the higher liquid limit of the lower stiff zone. The statistical relationship of sensitivity to liquid limit is shown by figure 11. In general, about 80 percent of the soil samples tested had liquid limits within the range of 22 to 48 percent, regardless of their vertical position in the formation. About 80 percent of the liquid limits of the sensitive clay range from 22 to 38 percent, and about 80 percent from the lower stiff clay range from 32 to 50 percent. As sensitivity increases, the upper limit of the liquid limit decreases. Most clay samples of sensitivities greater than 10 had liquid limits in the range of 20 to 40 percent, and no sensitive-clay sample had a liquid limit above 45 percent. For sensitivities greater than 40, the range of liquid limits was only 22 to 28 percent (Shannon and Wilson, Inc., 1964, p. B11). Several samples analyzed had a natural-water content greater than their liquid limits.

To relate the limit values of a soil to its natural-water content, the water-plasticity ratio, or liquidity index, is sometimes used (Casagrande and Fadum, 1944, p. 341). This ratio is equal to the natural-water content of the soil minus the plastic limit divided by

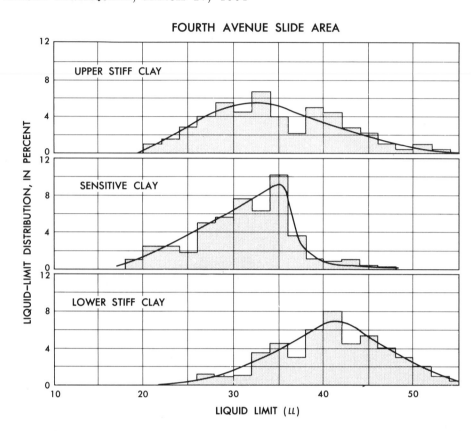

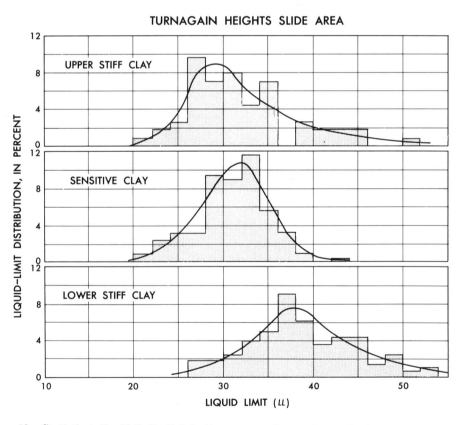

10.—Statistical liquid-limit distribution curves from selected borings, Bootlegger Cove Clay. Reprinted from Shannon and Wilson, Inc. (1964, pl. B16).

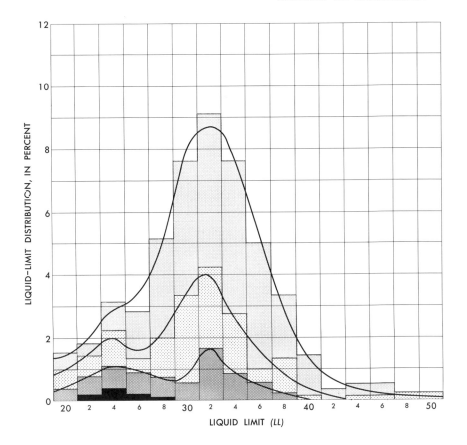

LIQUID-LIMIT DISTRIBUTION FOR SAMPLES HAVING SENSITIVITY (S)

             >10
             >20
             >30
             >40

Sum of all samples having sensitivity (S) >10 equals 100 percent

11.—Liquid-limit sensitivity distribution curves, Bootlegger Cove Clay. Reprinted from Shannon and Wilson, Inc. (1965, pl. B17).

the liquid limit minus the plastic limit; that is $(Wn-PL)/(LL-PL)$. For the Bootlegger Cove Clay, it was found that in most soils having a water-plasticity ratio greater than 1.0 the liquid limit ranged from 20 to 40 percent, and in soils having a water-plasticity ratio greater than 2.0 the liquid limit lay in the range 19 to 27 percent. A direct correlation also was found between sensitivity and the water-plasticity ratio (Shannon and Wilson, Inc., 1964, p. B11, pl. B17; see fig. 12, next page). Thus in the Bootlegger Cove Clay a high water-plasticity ratio is related to low shear strength, high sensitivity, and high susceptibility to failure.

VIBRATION TESTS

Representative samples of sand and clay from the various slides were subjected to vibration tests from which the dynamic Young's modulus and the dynamic shear modulus of elasticity could be computed. These tests were designed to simulate in part the vibratory effects of the earthquake on the sand and clay. The vibration apparatus, developed by Shannon and Wilson, Inc. (1964, p. E3), subjected a cylindrical specimen to a sinusoidal vibration in a longitudinal or torsional mode in such a way that the frequency corresponded to a state of resonance. Both longitudinal and torsional resonance frequencies increased as straight-line functions of increased confining pressure.

The shear modulus of the sands was found to be dependent on the confining pressure. The shear modulus of the stiff clay was about 5,000 psi (pounds per square inch), and that of the soft sensitive clay was about 1,500 psi (Shannon and Wilson, Inc., 1964, p. 28). In nearly all tests, the value of the shear modulus and of Young's modulus increased as straight-line functions of increased confining pressure.

PULSATING-LOAD TESTS

Pulsating-load tests on saturated fine silty sand and on undisturbed samples of silty clay and clayey silt were run for the Corps of Engineers by H. B. Seed and K. L. Lee of the University of California at Berkeley (*in* Shannon and Wilson, Inc., 1964). These tests demonstrated the susceptibility of the Bootlegger Cove Clay and associated sands to loss of strength under pulsating-load conditions such as would be induced by an earthquake. In other words, the shear strength of the samples was markedly less under pulsating-load conditions (simulating an earthquake), than under static load.

Seed's apparatus was so designed that applied deviator (axial) stress could be increased and decreased in one direction or could be changed from vertical to horizontal during each stress cycle, and thus the direction of shear stress in the specimen could be reversed. The latter test is called a "stress-reversing test."

Because it is not feasible to collect undisturbed sand samples, sand specimens were artificially deposited in water in the laboratory under conditions that simulated natural sedimentation. The sand was then subjected to pressures comparable to the in-place overburden pressures of the natural environment, about 1.8 kg per cm². Under stress-reversing conditions, sand specimens showed negligible strains, but they did show progressive increases in pore-water pressures with increasing numbers of stress cycles. Failure abruptly followed a sudden increase in pore-water pressure equal in magnitude to the applied confining pressure, accompanied by large strains and complete liquefaction. Liquefaction followed 50 cycles of pulsating deviator stress of about 0.5 kg per cm² applied at a frequency of about 2 cycles per second. This stress level is only about 10 percent of the strength of an identical specimen tested under static-loading conditions.

Clay samples were found to fail at levels of pulsating deviator stress substantially lower than the undrained compressive strength. Undrained compressive strengths of the specimens tested ranged from about 0.4 to 1.8 kg per cm², and sensitivities ranged from about 15 to 60. Moreover, under stress-reversing conditions, the level of failure was substantially lower than under non-stress-reversing conditions. Thus, under a non-stress-reversing p u l s a t i n g load at a frequency of 2 cycles per second, failure generally followed 50 cycles of maximum stress of 80 to 100 percent of the static undrained strength, after a gradual buildup of strain, whereas under stress-reversing conditions, failure occurred abruptly without prior significant strain after a maximum stress of only about 55 percent of the static undrained strength. The natural vibration of an earth-

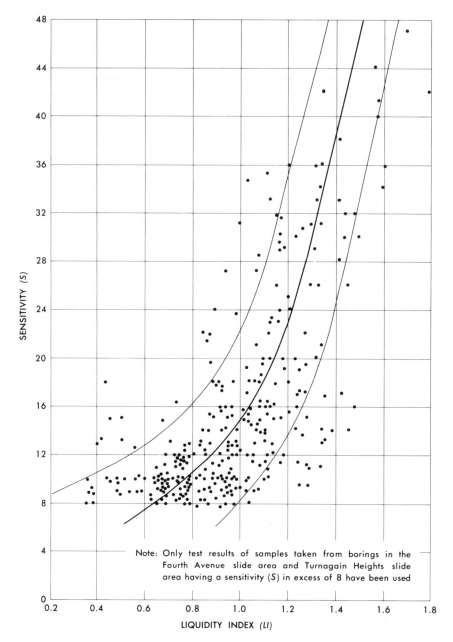

12.—Relation between sensitivity and liquidity index (water-plasticity ratio), Bootlegger Cove Clay. Reprinted from Shannon and Wilson, Inc. (1964, pl. B17).

quake, according to Seed, probably has a pulse form somewhere between the two types used in these laboratory tests. It is concluded, therefore, that under earthquake conditions, failure would occur at a stress level below the static undrained strength of the clay, that is, somewhere between the limits indicated by the two types of

pulsating stress applied in the laboratory.

SPECIFIC GRAVITY

Specific gravity was measured by Shannon and Wilson, Inc. (1964, p. B11–B12) on 26 test specimens from various depths at seven different slide areas. Of the specimens tested, 1 had a specific gravity of 2.67, but the other 25 ranged from 2.71 to 2.82, the average being 2.78. No correlation between specific gravity and shear strength or sensitivity was apparent.

PHYSICO-CHEMICAL TESTS

Physico-chemical analyses of six samples were made for the Corps of Engineers by J. K. Mitchell (*in* Shannon and Wilson, Inc., 1964, p. I3). Four of the samples—two from Turnagain Heights and two from the Fourth Avenue area—were cuts from core intervals that also were analyzed mineralogically. The other two samples came from the L Street slide. Each sample was tested for pH, salt content, conductivity, and base-exchange capacity. Values of pH ranged from 8.2 to 10.3. These relatively high base values, according to Mitchell, are "consistent with high sensitivity because of the tendency of a high pH to promote dispersion of remolded samples" (*in* Shannon and Wilson, Inc., 1964, p. I3).

The salt content of the samples, expressed in terms of equivalent NaCl, ranged from 1.03 grams per liter to somewhat less than 6 grams per liter. "By way of comparison," Mitchell points out, "the salt content of sea water is about 34 grams per liter. Thus if the Anchorage clays are of marine origin then the results of these tests would suggest that they have been leached of salt since their original deposition. Such leaching could be important in generating a high sensitivity and stable suspensions after remolding." In support of this view, a marine depositional environment of near normal salinity, at sample depths spanning the zone of landslide failure, is indicated by the microfaunal assemblages in the clay (Patsy J. Smith, written commun., 1964). The

paleontology of the clay is discussed on page A20.

In measuring electrical conductivity, Mitchell (*in* Shannon and Wilson, Inc., 1964, p. I4) found that remolded clay had consistently greater conductivity at all frequencies than undisturbed clay. Remolded clay generally also had a greater variation in conductivity as frequency was varied. Mitchell attributed these differences to greater dispersion (parallelism of clay particles) and smaller average effective particle size in the remolded samples.

Base-exchange capacities of the six samples studied by Mitchell ranged from 4.6 to 10.9 milliequivalents per 100 g of dry clay. Of the three cations determined—sodium, calcium, and magnesium—Mitchell found that calcium was the most abundant in solution in all but one sample. Sodium was next and magnesium was least abundant. This ratio also suggests that authigenic brine was leached from the clay by the action of ground water; hence that leaching may have been a cause of the sensitivity.

MINERALOGY

Not much mineralogic work has been done on the Bootlegger Cove Clay. Seven samples collected by Miller and Dobrovolny (1959, p. 42–43) from four localities and from seven different parts of the section were analyzed by X-ray diffraction in two fractions each—clay (<2μ) and silt (2 to 74μ). Both fractions of each sample contained quartz, feldspar, mica, and chlorite as the chief constituents. Some contained montmorillonite, mixed layered chlorite-montmorillonite, or mixed layered chlorite-montmorillonite-hornblende (Mil-

ler and Dobrovolny, 1959, p. 42). Quartz predominated in most silt fractions, followed by feldspar, but it was subordinate in the clay fractions, in which chlorite predominated. These seven samples resembled, in composition and general proportions of minerals, samples of other silty clay collected from lake, estuarine, and till deposits of the same general vicinity but of different ages. Their compositions, therefore, probably reflect parent material more than diagenesis.

A single clay sample collected at Turnagain Heights after the earthquake was found to contain chlorite, illite, quartz, and feldspar in its clay fraction (Grantz, Plafker, and Kachadoorian, 1964, p. 26). Its composition by size was 25 percent clay, 61 percent silt, and 14 percent fine sand.

Samples of Bootlegger Cove Clay from four drill holes, two from the Fourth Avenue area and two from Turnagain Heights, were analyzed by X-ray, differential thermal, thermogravimetric, and petrographic means by T. S. Shevlin for the Corps of Engineers (Shannon and Wilson, Inc., 1964, p. H3). Two of the samples were sensitive; two were stiff. Shevlin found that quartz predominated in all samples; its peak intensities (X-ray) were greater than any other mineral in all size fractions analyzed. Feldspar was present in finely divided form in all samples, and kaolinite, illite, and chlorite were also present. One of the stiff samples was gritty and much siltier than the others, but there was no consistent variation either in size or mineral content between the sensitive and the stiff samples. Shevlin's table 1 is reproduced in part at top of page 20 to show the distribution of particle sizes.

Sample [1]	Depth (feet)	Classification	Percent finer than particle size (microns)					
			38	10	8	4	2	1
A117AX	77.6– 78.3	Sensitive	99.6	81.5	78.9	64.7	49.0	36.0
A117AX	124.5–125.2	Stiff	96.9	96.7	92.2	73.4	52.7	38.5
C108B	73.2– 73.9	Sensitive	96.8	64.0	60.3	46.6	33.3	24.4
C117	116.7–117.4	Stiff	81.8	26.7	22.3	12.9	8.1	5.5

[1] Samples prefixed with A are from Fourth Avenue area; samples prefixed with C are from Turnagain Heights

DEPOSITIONAL ENVIRON-MENT

Recent paleontologic studies by Patsy J. Smith (written commun., 1964) indicate that the Bootlegger Cove Clay is of marine origin throughout but that it was deposited in environments of variable salinity. The depositional environment bears on the origin and distribution of sensitivity in the clay. Clay deposited in saline waters tends to flocculate. Flocculation occurs when negative particle surfaces are attracted to positive particle edges by electrostatic forces (Lambe, 1958, p. 8; Rosenqvist, 1962, pl. 5; Meade, 1964, p. B4–B5); flocculated clay in turn acquires sensitivity when the interparticle bond is destroyed, as when ground water leaches the cation and thereby diminishes the electrolyte concentration (Mitchell, 1956, p. 693). Such leaching is promoted when marine clay beds are elevated above sea level. According to Bjerrum (1954, p. 49; 1955, p. 108), the reduced electrolyte concentration, by decreasing the activity of the clay minerals, leads to a lowering of the Atterberg limits, which in turn reduces the shear strength of the clay by as much as 30 percent.

Until recently the depositional environment of the Bootlegger Cove Clay was in serious doubt, if not dispute (Miller and Dobrovolny, 1959, p. 44; Schmidt, 1963, p. 350; Karlstrom, 1964, p. 35; Cederstrom, Trainer, and Waller, 1964, p. 30). A brief review of past thinking, therefore, seems warranted. The environment has been considered to have been lacustrine, estuarine, or marine, or some combination thereof. Marine organisms had been noted in the Bootlegger Cove Clay by several investigators, although some doubt had existed as to whether the specimens noted were in place or had been cast ashore by storm waves (Miller and Dobrovolny, 1959, p. 45). Trainer (*in* Miller and Dobrovolny, 1959, p. 45) found estuarine mollusks that he was convinced were in place. Schmidt (1963, p. 350) verified Trainer's find and added an abundant microfauna in confirmation. Miller and Dobrovolny (1959, p. 46) reasoned that varvelike beds and laminations high in the clay near Cairn Point indicated probable fresh-water deposition, a view subsequently shared by Cederstrom, Trainer, and Waller (1964, p. 32) but on slightly different evidence—the presence of well-sorted interbedded sands. Karlstrom

(1964, p. 38) expressed the opinion that "the Bootlegger Cove Clay records proglacial-lake sedimentation * * * with an intervening interval of marine deposition"—in other words, fresh-water deposits separated by salt-water deposits.

Smith's conclusions (written commun., 1964) are based on studies of microfossils from drill samples collected by the Corps of Engineers. These continuously cored samples afforded a chance not provided by surface exposures to examine the depositional environment of the clay from the top of the formation down through and below the sensitive zone. Smith concluded that the formation was marine throughout the interval studied but that the upper part was deposited in a deltaic environment of low variable salinity such as now exists in the Yukon and Koskokwim deltas. Fossils from the lower part of the formation, including the sensitive zone, indicated a shallow (25± meters) marine environment probably of near-normal salinity. Vertical variations in the depositional environment, as indicated by fossils, thus may provide an explanation for the zonal character of the sensitivity: the stiffer clays accumulated in water of low salinity and the more sensitive clays accumulated in waters of near-normal salinity. Since deposition, reduction of the brine concentration by leaching probably has altered the plasticity of the clay and increased the sensitivity.

Fossils identified by Smith, and their relative abundance, are shown in tables 1 and 2.

TABLE 1.—*Foraminifera from Bootlegger Cove Clay, Anchorage, Alaska, Shannon and Wilson, Inc. (1964) boring A120 A*

[Abundances estimated: A, abundant; C, common; F, few; R, rare]

Species	Sample interval (feet)																					
	29.9-32.0	34.9-37.0	39.7-42.0	44.7-46.0	54.7-56.5	64.0-66.5	69.0-71.5	71.5-74.0	79.0-81.5	80.0-86.5	89.9-90.5	92.3-93.9	96.4-08.9	101.6-103.8	106.3-108.8	115.9-118.4	120.9-122.5	125.0-127.5	130.0-132.5	136.8-137.9	137.5-142.0	142.2-144.3
Protelphidium cf. orbiculare (Brady)	F	F		F	R	F	R	R	A		F	F	R	C	A	A	F	F	F		C	F
Elphidium clavatum Cushman						F								R		A						
frigidum Cushman			R													F						
bartletti Cushman														R								
Pateoris hauerinoides Loeblich and Tappan														F	F	F						
														F	F	R						
Polymorphina sp									R										R			
Fissurina sp	R													R	R							
Buliminella curta Cushman																				R		
Ostracodes									R	R			F			A	R					

TABLE 2.—*Foraminifera from Bootlegger Cove Clay, Anchorage, Alaska, Shannon and Wilson, Inc. (1964) borings A 110 A and B*

[Abundances estimated: AA, very abundant; A, abundant; C, common; F, few; R, rare]

Species	Sample interval (feet) and boring letter																		
	27-38 (B)	28-28.7 (B)	28.7-29.5 (B)	29.1-30 (B)	30-30.9 (B)	30.9-31.8 (B)	32-32.8 (B)	32.8-33.6 (B)	33.6-34.4 (B)	38.3-39 (A)	44.6-45.5 (A)	45.5-46.5 (A)	48.5-49.5 (A)	49.5-50.5 (A)	50.5-51.5 (A)	51.5-52.5 (A)	53.3-54.5 (A)	54.5-55.5 (B)	54.9-56 (A)
Protelphidium cf. orbiculare (Brady)	R			R	F	R	AA	C		C	AA	B	AA	A	A	A	A	A	A
orbiculare (Brady)														F	C				
Elphidium clavatum Cushman		F		F			R												
subarcticum Cushman									C										
bartletti Cushman													F		F	C	C	C	C
incertum (Williamson)															R				
Elphidiella groenlandica (Cushman)							R		C		F		F	C	C				
Quinqueloculina cf. seminula (Linné)						R						C	C	C	C				
Pateoris hauerinoides Loeblich and Tappan									C				C	C	C	C	F		F
Polymorphina sp									F				C						
Fissurina sp				R			R				R	R	R	C	F	A	C	F	F
Dentalina sp													R	F	F		R	R	R
Cassidulina islandica Nørvang			R						R			R							
Buliminella curta Cushman									R			R							
Bolivina pseudopunctata Höglund												R							
												R				R			
Buccella frigida (Cushman)				R															
inusitata Anderson								R										R	
Rosalina sp																C		R	
Globigerina bulloides d'Orbigny				R								R				R		R	
pachyderma (Ehrenberg)								R				F							
Ostracodes	R	R	R		R	R	C	F		F			C	C	C	C	C	C	C
Mollusk fragments													R						

EARTHQUAKE EFFECTS

DIRECT SEISMIC EFFECTS

Most of the more spectacular structural damage in the Anchorage area resulted from secondary causes such as landslides and ground cracks, themselves triggered by seismic vibration. Structural damage due directly to seismic vibration was subordinate in terms of total property damage and financial loss and, for the most part, was relatively unspectacular. Nevertheless, the extent of such effects must not be underestimated. The cumulative damage was impressive, and had there been no landslides at Anchorage, vibratory effects of the earthquake undoubtedly would have received more attention by investigators and by the press.

Vibratory damage to buildings and other structures is not strictly a geologic effect, but the extent and amplitude of vibration is dependent partly on geologic factors such as foundation and subfoundation conditions. Other things being equal, vibration is more intense and damage is greater in areas of thick unconsolidated deposits than in areas of bedrock. Examples of this rule are too numerous and too widely recognized to need documentation. All the severe vibratory damage in the Anchorage Lowland was in areas underlain at some depth by Bootlegger Cove Clay. Design and construction practices, on the other hand, are critical nongeologic factors that influence building performance and vibratory damage. As pointed out by Berg and Stratta (1964, p. 58), structural weaknesses are quickly ferreted out by earthquakes.

Inasmuch as this report emphasizes primarily the geologic effects of the March 27 earthquake in the Anchorage area, only the highlights of the vibratory effects are summarized here. Detailed analyses of structural response to vibratory stress have been presented by several authors (Berg and Stratta, 1964; McMinn, 1964; National Board of Fire Underwriters and Pacific Fire Rating Bureau, 1964; Steinbrugge, 1964), and the following summary is based largely on their findings.

The distribution and character of direct seismic damage were unusual to say the least. Probably few buildings in the Anchorage area were totally undamaged, but many blocks of homes and small commercial buildings received cursory damage at most and sustained virtually no damage to structural members, frameworks, or foundations. Many chimneys toppled, and quite a few fireplaces separated from adjoining exterior walls. Indoors, plaster cracked and objects were thrown to the floors of many homes. On many buildings however, fragile decorative facings, pillars, and cornices were unscathed. Church steeples remained standing. Headstones in cemeteries—long used as indicators of earthquake intensity—stood untoppled throughout the area. Large elevated well-guyed water tanks were undamaged (fig. 6), although trees whiplashing back and forth touched the ground on either side according to eyewitnesses. On the other hand, multistory buildings and buildings having large floor areas commonly sustained significant structural damage; several such buildings were total losses (figs. 5 and 13), and many required major repairs.

Thus, direct seismic damage was highly selective. Aside from variations in design, construction practice, and workmanship, large buildings were more severely damaged than small ones. Inertia was a factor, of course; other things being equal, heavy structures are more susceptible to vibratory damage than light ones.

Steinbrugge (1964, p. 58–72) has described vibratory damage effects in the Anchorage area in terms of engineering seismology. He ascribed (p. 59) the selectivity of the effects to the great magnitude of the quake and the distance of Anchorage from the epicenter: "The ground motion at Anchorage did not appear to contain significant short period motion which has been commonly observed in epicentral regions of destructive shocks." He added (p. 71): "The earthquake damage in Anchorage was selective * * *. This damage pattern appears to be attributable to the distance that Anchorage was from the epicenter, with the longer period ground motion having a dominant effect at this distance." According to White (1965, p. 91), attenuation of sinusoidal seismic waves at low frequencies should vary as the square of the frequency. Where seismic vibrations have long periods and large amplitudes, distortion and strain are far more severe in large structures than in small ones. The reason for the selectivity of the March 27 earthquake at Anchorage is thus apparent. The prolonged duration of the shaking must also have heightened all other effects; as mentioned before, strong motion lasted 3 to 4 minutes, possibly longer.

In general, most buildings outside of landslide areas withstood well the effects of the earthquake. The low loss of life is, in some measure, a tribute to the structural soundness of most of the larger buildings but in part also is the result of the low susceptibility of smaller structures to the long-period vibrations that racked the area. All the high-rise structures in Anchorage (10 stories or more) sustained moderate to heavy damage without collapse or loss of life. Four structures of medium height—four to nine stories—collapsed or were damaged beyond repair. Several low buildings of less than four stories were totally destroyed, but most such structures were damaged little or not at all.

In the general downtown area, outside the Fourth Avenue and L Street slides, a 5-story department store (J. C. Penney Co.) was a total loss, 4 buildings 1 or 2 stories high were heavily damaged, 9 buildings 1 to 14 stories high sustained moderate damage, and about 22 buildings received light damage (National Board of Fire

Underwriters and Pacific Fire Rating Bureau, 1964, p. 26). In the same area, however, many single family dwellings, stores, and small commercial buildings were damaged little if at all. Steinbrugge (1964, p. 71) found no evidence to indicate that one construction material was superior to another, given comparable attention to design and construction.

A few buildings seem to have been designed without regard to earthquake stresses. The Hillside Apartments and various warehouses that collapsed were examples. In other buildings, inadequate connections between structural parts were the most common causes of failure; improperly welded joints, inadequate ties in reinforced-concrete members, and improperly spliced reinforcing rods all were loci of failure. Welded precast- and prestressed-concrete structural members seemed to be particularly susceptible to joint failure, although some buildings so framed were undamaged. In some buildings, construction joints were inadequately keyed. Poured nonmonolithic concrete joints were sites of shear failures, and some concrete appeared to be substandard. Most poured-in-place concrete structures, however, fared well. In some multistory buildings, provisions for vertical shear were inadequate to withstand a stress of the intensity generated by the March 27 earthquake (Berg and Stratta, 1964, p. 58).

Small wood-frame buildings outside areas of ground displacement were generally little damaged (Steinbrugge, 1964, p. 63–64). Unreinforced masonry walls and chimneys were usually intact, and most interior wooden stud walls sustained nothing more than minor nonstructural cracking. Foundations of poured concrete or hollow concrete block (some apparently unreinforced) generally were intact. Usually windows were unbroken, and objects remained on shelves indoors.

Of the many buildings damaged or destroyed by direct seismic vibration in Anchorage, several structures described briefly below are most significant for the damage or lack of damage they sustained, relative to design and construction practice. These structures, therefore, have received the most attention from investigators. The following synopsis is based mostly on the reports of Berg and Stratta, Steinbrugge, and the National Board of Fire Underwriters and Pacific Fire Rating Bureau.

ALASKA PSYCHIATRIC INSTITUTE

The three-story steel-framed Alaska Psychiatric Institute, southeast of the main part of Anchorage, is notable because it sustained so little damage. There were minor cracks in stair wells and broken pipe hangers and machinery mounts in the penthouse. The nearby new Providence Hospital and the Alaska Methodist University also were little damaged. Significantly, perhaps, these three buildings are outside the area underlain by Bootlegger Cove Clay.

THE ALASKA RAILROAD MARSHALLING YARDS

Several buildings in the Alaska Railroad marshalling yards were damaged. Warehouses collapsed and shops were slightly damaged. The steel-framed wheel-shop building partly collapsed and has since been torn down. Some buildings were in or near the toe area of the Fourth Avenue landslide and, hence, may have been subjected to ground displacements as well as to seismic vibration.

ALASKA SALES AND SERVICE BUILDING

The one-story Alaska Sales and Service Building on East Fifth Avenue at Medfra Street was under construction but was structurally almost complete at the time of the earthquake; it was a total loss. Collapse is attributed chiefly to failure of welded connections between T-shaped precast-concrete columns and roof beams, caused either by the breaking of welds or tearing out of bar inserts. The exterior precast-concrete walls of the building partly collapsed when the roof gave way.

ANCHORAGE INTERNATIONAL AIRPORT

The Anchorage International Airport control tower, a reinforced-concrete structure, collapsed to the ground (fig. 7), killing one occupant and injuring another and damaging the connecting walls of the adjacent terminal building. The terminal building was otherwise little damaged. At the airport post office building, a rear wall pulled away from the roof trusses and leaned outward; moderate nonstructural damage was sustained indoors.

ANCHORAGE WESTWARD HOTEL

The steel-framed Anchorage Westward Hotel complex is just west of the Fourth Avenue landslide area facing Third Avenue between E and F Streets and is within the area of peripheral cracking. Several cracks passed through the building foundations and first floors. Some cracks had vertical offsets. There was little visible damage to the flexible exterior metal skin of the 14-story tower, but there was significant structural damage (since repaired) to the more rigid interior structural elements. Reinforced-concrete columns were buckled, and reinforced-concrete shear walls were damaged. An interior east-west shear wall had failures above all door openings in every story. At the eight-story level there was shear-wall damage along a horizontal joint between older and newer sections of the building. Considerable damage was caused by pounding between the 14-story tower and the adjacent 3- and 6-story wings.

CORDOVA BUILDING

The Cordova Building is a six-story structure at the northeast corner of Sixth Avenue and Cordova Street. The damage was mostly light and was caused chiefly by an east-west movement of the building. This direction is parallel to the shorter dimension of the floor plan and also is the direction of greatest strength in the steel support columns (Berg and Stratta, 1964, p. 37). Damage was mainly in the first story. The southeast-corner support column failed below the second-floor beam, and the exterior reinforced-concrete curtain walls sheared at the top of the basement; the corner broke away at the first and second stories. The center column in the south wall buckled. The reinforced-concrete stair and elevator shaft sheared at the base of the first story. The penthouse collapsed. Repairs have since been completed.

ELMENDORF AIR FORCE BASE

At Elmendorf Air Force Base the reinforced-concrete control tower was damaged by cracks extending from its base to a height of about 15 feet. A warehouse (No. 21–884) partly collapsed when roof-beam anchor bolts pulled away from poured-in-place concrete piers. The Elmendorf Field House was slightly damaged at the roof corners and at the junctions of the side walls with the steel frame. Elmendorf Hospital was damaged by X-shaped shear fractures in block-panel walls at the second- through the fifth-story levels, by interior failures at a few reinforced-concrete columns and at the elevator shaft, and by some movement between different sections of the building. Damage has since been repaired, reportedly at a cost of more than $1 million (R. M. Waller, written commun., 1965).

FIFTH AVENUE CHRYSLER CENTER

The one-story Fifth Avenue Chrysler Center just north of Merrill Field was a total loss. It had a precast- and prestressed-concrete T-beam roof supported by concrete-block walls. The front of the building collapsed and the T-beam roof fell in on the showroom. The hollow-core concrete-block side walls failed at the rear corners of the building.

FIRST FEDERAL SAVINGS AND LOAN BUILDING

The three-story First Federal Savings and Loan Building is located at the northwest corner of Fifth Avenue and C Street. Ground cracks opened parallel to its east and south walls evidently in back fill. Even though the east and south faces of the building are mainly glass, there was little glass breakage. The west and north walls and the brick panels in the east wall sheared horizontally through the second story. The building has been repaired.

FOUR SEASONS APARTMENT BUILDING

The Four Seasons Apartment Building at West Ninth Avenue and M Street was a spectacular total loss (fig. 13). It was designed for year-round luxury living, but didn't survive its first sea-

son. The building was nearing completion at the time of the earthquake, but fortunately it was not yet occupied—it collapsed in a pile of rubble. It was a six-story lift-slab reinforced-concrete building with two central poured-in-place cores, one for a stairwell and one for an elevator. The floor slabs were torn loose from shear heads on the structural-steel columns and pulled away from keyways in the stairwell and elevator cores. Some dowels connecting the slabs to the cores broke; others were pulled free.

The collapse of the Four Seasons Apartment Building was witnessed from 1000 Tenth Avenue by Glen L. Faulkner, a consulting geologist, who reported (oral commun., 1964) that the building collapsed just before the end of the quake, after shaking violently for perhaps 2 to 3 minutes. Just before it fell, it seemed to start crumbling near the second-floor level in the area of its northeast corner. Then with a slight tilt northward it collapsed vertically in a great cloud of dust. The two central cores were left leaning sharply northward. The steel support columns fell to the north also, and the slab floors were stacked one on another like pancakes.

The effects of seismic vibration in areas of cracked ground cannot always be separated from the effects of ground displacement. The collapse of the Four Seasons Apartment Building (fig. 13), a case in point, has been attributed to seismic vibration. Perhaps vibration was the dominant factor in the building's failure. The building, however, was close to the L Street graben at West Ninth Avenue and M Street, and a large subsidiary fracture, trending about west-southwest, passed directly under the building. In the chaotic pile of rubble left after the

13.—Wreckage of six-story Four Seasons Apartment Building, Anchorage, Alaska. Canted elevator shaft at center. Large crack in foreground, filled in on M Street to restore traffic, passed beneath building.

quake, the fracture may have been overlooked by early investigators. Furthermore, part of the fracture was quickly bulldozed over to restore traffic along M Street. In any event, the fracture was mapped by the Engineering Geology Evaluation Group, and its extensions east and west were still well preserved 2 months or more after the quake. Near the building the fracture had a vertical displacement of about 2 feet; the north side dropped down—a displacement that few manmade structures could be expected to withstand. The actual displacement beneath the building, however, is uncertain. The fact that the elevator shaft and stair well of the building fell northward suggests that they tilted in that direction in response to the northward displacement along the fracture. Support pillars collapsed in the same direction.

The building reportedly withstood most of the earthquake, although it shook violently, but it collapsed suddenly shortly before the end of the quake. Eyewitness accounts of the L Street slide (Shannon and Wilson, Inc., 1964, p. 53) indicate that sliding there occurred in the latter part of the quake. The timing seems more than coincidental; the crack beneath the Four Seasons Apartment Building must have attained offset at about the same time. It could not have had offset until the slide itself had begun.

HILL BUILDING

The Hill Building, an eight-story office building at the southeast corner of Sixth Avenue and G Street, was slightly damaged. There apparently was no damage to the steel frame, and there was little exterior damage. A reinforced-concrete column failed at

its junction with the canopy roof of the service entrance. The center cores, which were intended to resist horizontal forces, dropped as much as 5 inches at one point and 3 inches at another where they were partly shattered at their connections with the footings. The core walls were cracked also, and the beams between the cores were sheared by vertical stresses.

HILLSIDE APARTMENTS

The Hillside Apartments were on the south side of Sixteenth Avenue between G and H Streets on a bluff overlooking Chester Creek. They were damaged beyond repair and have since been dismantled. This was a split-level building, five stories high on the south side and three stories high on the street side. It had a post-and-lintel frame with steel-pipe columns, rolled-steel beams and concrete floor slabs on steel joists.

Walls were unreinforced hollow concrete block. The building was sheared in an east-west direction at the third-story level on the south side and in the lower two stories on the north side—the upper stories lurched west relative to the lower stories. Seemingly, no provision had been made for resistance to strong lateral seismic stress.

KNIK ARMS APARTMENT BUILDING

The six-story Knik Arms Apartment Building, of poured-in-place reinforced-concrete framing, is on the west side of L Street between Sixth and Seventh Avenues, on the L Street landslide block between the headward graben and the bluff overlooking Knik Arm. It is especially noteworthy for its apparent lack of damage, despite a lateral displacement of about 10 feet west-northwest as it was carried along with the underlying slide block. Many smaller residential buildings on the slide block were also undamaged or little damaged.

MOUNT McKINLEY BUILDING AND 1200 L STREET APARTMENT BUILDING

The Mount McKinley Building and the 1200 L Street Apartment Building are twin 14-story reinforced-concrete apartment buildings about a mile apart and facing in opposite directions. They sustained similar damage, almost matching crack for crack, although damage in general was somewhat more severe in the Mount McKinley Building. The Mount McKinley Building is on Denali Street between Third and Fourth Avenues; the 1200 L Street Apartment Building is across town near Inlet View School.

The most obvious damage to both buildings was X-shaped shear cracks in spandrel beams, caused by vertical shear between exterior support piers as a result of lateral swaying. Spandrels in general were most heavily damaged in the middle third of the floor levels. Interior walls were less damaged than exterior ones.

In the Mount McKinley Building, vertical piers sheared horizontally at the third-story level on the north side of the building (at a construction joint) and at the second story on the south side. An exterior column fractured diagonally at the first-story level. A television-antenna tower on top of the building was undamaged.

Failures similar to those in the Mount McKinley Building occurred in the 1200 L Street Apartment Building in piers at the south face of the building at the second- and third-story levels. Corner spandrels were more heavily damaged than those in the Mount McKinley Building.

An account of the earthquake as related by an occupant of the 12th story of the 1200 L Street Apartment Building was provided by William G. Binkley (written commun., 1964). Mr. Binkley, a geologist, noted wryly that he was living in a sort of oversized seismograph. The quake was first felt in the building as a light tremor that intensified rapidly until objects began to fall to the floor. About 30 seconds of trembling motion was followed by perhaps 2 minutes of violent jarring, in which the building seemed to sway 8 to 10 feet horizontally and 1 to 2 feet vertically. Bookcases were overturned, and fallen books and furniture were thrown back and forth across the room. Violent shaking was accompanied by a deep rumble and by higher pitched sounds of shattering plaster and falling dishes and furniture. In the kitchen, everything from the cabinets and refrigerator crashed to the floor, where it was "churned into a melange of broken dishes and glass, catsup and syrup, flour, beans, pots and pans, eggs, lettuce, and pickles." Mr. Binkley was able to crawl from the living room to a hall where he braced his feet against one wall and his back against another. Then the building stopped "jumping," the noise stopped abruptly, and the motion of the building diminished gradually with a subsiding, weaving tremble.

Most people at ground level experienced far less violent shaking than those in tall buildings. Many individuals were unaware of the catastrophic proportions of the quake until much later when the reports began to come in. In the heights of the 1200 L Street Apartments, however, the accelerations undoubtedly were greatly magnified.

PENNEY'S DEPARTMENT STORE BUILDING

The Penney's Department Store Building (fig. 5) was a total loss and has since been dismantled. Photographs of its wreckage have been widely distributed in magazines and newspapers. Penney's was a five-story reinforced-concrete structure having shear walls on three sides and a curtain wall of precast panels on the north. Failure is attributed to torsion caused by rotational displacements, in turn caused by an eccentric position of the center of rigidity of the structure. This rotational motion sheared off the west support wall at the second-story level, causing the wall and all overlying floors to collapse. The floor slabs also sheared at their connections to the next adjacent column wall to the east. The northeast corner of the building collapsed (fig. 4), and most of the precast panels on the north face fell to the street. Berg and Stratta (1964, p. 35) reconstructed the sequence of events as follows: The northeast corner of the building collapsed following failure of the east shear wall at that point; the west shear wall then failed at the second-story level at the north end of the building. The east shear wall failed at the south end of the building, and the precast curtain-wall panels collapsed at the north face of the building.

The north-facing curtain wall must have fallen rather late in the quake. Some motorists reportedly were able to start their parked cars and move them away from below the wall before it fell. One motorist who ran to her car in an attempt to move it, however, was trapped and killed (R. M. Waller, written commun., 1965).

PORT OF ANCHORAGE AREA

Much of the damage in the Port of Anchorage area was caused by ground displacements along fractures, but some damage is attributable to direct seismic shaking. The main pier lurched laterally 5 to 19 inches. Large longitudinal cracks and several transverse ones opened up, and the walls of several buildings were cracked. All four gantry cranes were damaged. Steel piles penetrated the deck of a subordinate pier. Approach roads and railroads settled as much as 18 inches. Two cement-storage tanks were toppled, one at the property of the Permanente Cement Co. at the entrance to the U.S. Army Dock and one at the Alaska Aggregate Corp. facility just north of Ship Creek. Oil-storage tanks

in the dock area were mostly superficially damaged, but some tanks were bulged outward at the bottom, probably by rocking and pounding back and forth as the contents sloshed to and fro.

WEST ANCHORAGE HIGH SCHOOL

West Anchorage High School is on the south side of Hillcrest Drive a few blocks west of Spenard Road and just south of a bluff overlooking Chester Creek. Structurally separate parts of the school building reacted differently to the vibrations. The two-story classroom section of the building was heavily damaged, especially the second story. Exterior columns failed at connections with the roof and with the second-floor spandrels. Extensive damage was caused by pounding between the gymnasium section and the classroom section. There was extensive ground cracking along the bluff above Chester Creek and a small rotational slump formed due north of the school.

GROUND DISPLACEMENTS OTHER THAN LAND-SLIDES

GROUND CRACKS AND COMPACTION

The distribution of ground cracks in the Anchorage area (generalized in fig. 1) was mapped by the Engineering Geology Evaluation Group (1964, pl. 1) shortly after the earthquake. Most of the observations on which this map is based were made on traverses adjacent to streets and highways but some were obtained from a scrutiny of aerial photographs. Many unobserved cracks probably formed in the less-accessible snow-covered undeveloped areas. Frozen muskeg in and bordering swamps, for example, was very susceptible to cracking. The map, nevertheless, shows clearly the widespread

distribution of cracking, and it emphasizes the high susceptibility to cracking of lowland areas underlain by silty clay and outwash, as opposed to highland areas underlain by ground moraine. Made land in former muskeg areas, reclaimed either by draining or by filling directly over muskeg, was also very susceptible to cracking.

Reportedly, many ground cracks opened and closed with the rhythm of the earthquake. Such action may help explain the extensive damage some cracks caused. A pulsating fracture would cause more damage to a superencumbent structure than a fracture that merely opened.

The most severely cracked ground was adjacent to landslides (fig. 40) where cracks were caused by tension directly related to sliding. The cracks in turn caused much structural damage in built-up areas. Some cracked ground undoubtedly would have developed into landslides had the earthquake lasted longer, as for example at Turnagain Heights, back of the landslide (pl. 1). Here, the pattern of fracturing was concentric to the head of the slide, and many crescentic tension cracks extended as far as 2,200 feet from the slide proper, to the vicinity of Northern Lights Boulevard. In the downtown area, many streets and buildings were damaged by cracks behind the periphery of the Fourth Avenue slide. Major cracking and ground adjustments extended a city block or more back from the slide. In contrast, the L Street and Government Hill slides broke away clean; they were much cracked themselves, but few cracks extended behind them.

Preexisting zones of weakness in the ground were particularly susceptible to cracking. Some cracks followed backfilled utility trenches, for example, or backfills around building foundations. Old frost cracks in pavement—caused by contraction at low temperatures—were reopened by the earthquake; at Turnagain Heights, the pattern of cracking was very striking—ground cracks veered along concrete curbings, crossed streets at right angles along old contraction cracks, and then resumed direction on the other side. In filled areas, cracks commonly formed near the contact between filled and preexisting ground. Some buildings unfortunately constructed partly on fill were sundered by cracking between the fill and the adjacent ground.

Trees were split by cracks that passed through their root systems (fig. 40), their roots being held fast by the frozen ground.

On sloping ground, cracks generally formed parallel to the slope, owing to differential compaction, lateral shifting (lurching) under the influence of gravity, tension, and rupture.

Alternate cuts and fills along streets, highways, and railroads demonstrated a predictable pattern of fractures. Fills that compacted under the vibratory stress of the quake were cracked adjacent to the fill-cut contact. Many cracks of this sort crossed the Seward-Anchorage Highway, some fills dropping several inches. One in particular formed a very sharp pavement break on the north approach to the Rabbit Creek crossing near the south margin of the Anchorage Lowland. Similarly, an Alaska Railroad embankment across Fish Creek east of Turnagain Heights cracked to pieces and collapsed.

Extensive ground cracks formed in the Port of Anchorage area on the flats extending north from the mouth of Ship Creek to and beyond City Dock between the bluff on the east and the shore of Knik

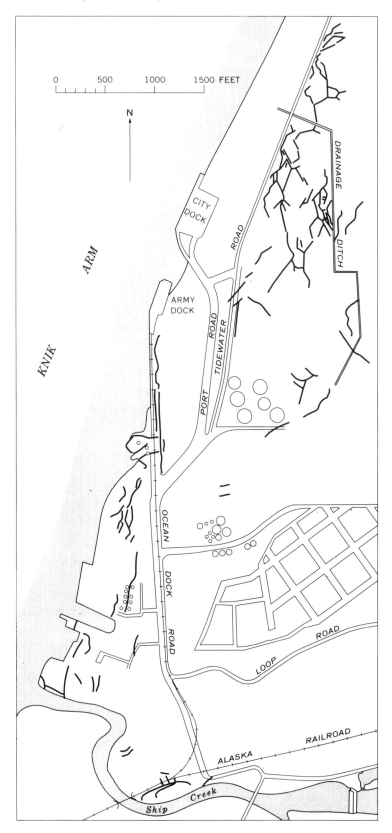

14.—Ground cracks, Port of Anchorage and vicinity. Anchorage, Alaska. Many of these cracks spouted mud, particularly those east of City Dock. Base by city of Anchorage, Office of City Engineer.

Arm on the west (fig. 14). This area is underlain by estuarine silt, peat, muskeg, and artificial fill (Engineering Geology Evaluation Group, 1964, p. 22), all highly susceptible to cracking under the stresses of prolonged vibration and compaction. Great quantities of mud were extruded from large polygonal fractures in the flats northeast of City Dock. To the south, longitudinal cracks 300 feet or more long extended the full length of the Army Dock embankment. At the south end of the embankment, in an area of transverse cracks, a steel cement-storage tank was overturned. Collapse of the tank, however, may have been caused by inadequate anchoring of base plates to support columns (Berg and Stratta, 1964, p. 46).

Facilities south of the Army Dock to the west of Ocean Dock Road were also damaged by ground cracks. Cracks extended through the tank farm of the Union Oil Co. of California and damaged the adjacent Alaska Fish and Farm Products lease and the Cook Inlet Tug and Barge lease. There was ground cracking in the dock area at the mouth of Ship Creek, where another cement storage tank toppled and where the right abutment of the adjacent Alaska Railroad bridge across Ship Creek was damaged by subsidence and cracking.

Incipient and minor slumping along the bluff east of the dock area also produced many cracks, some of them large. All these, however, were in undeveloped woodland areas, mostly on military land.

SAND BOILS AND MUD FOUNTAINS

Sand boils and mud fountains are transient or short-lived features commonly produced by

15.—Part of a sand boil, Turnagain Heights slide area. Ridges 2 to 3 feet high and 100 feet long or more were formed as fountains of water were ejected through frozen outwash.

strong earthquakes where ground breakage occurs. They were widespread in the damage zone of the March 27 Alaskan earthquake (Grantz, Plafker, and Kachadoorian, 1964, p. 6). At Anchorage they have been reported at several localities and probably occurred in many others.

Mud fountains were produced where the water table was shallow and frozen ground overlying saturated, unconsolidated sand or silt was cracked by the earthquake. Intense shaking possibly accompanied by settlement and compaction forced muddy water out through the cracks.

At the Port of Anchorage, mud was ejected from many cracks east and northeast of the City Dock and from a few cracks between the Army Dock and Ship Creek. The ground was snow covered at the time, and consequently the ejected mud shows plainly on aerial photographs taken shortly after the earthquake.

A mile above the mouth of Chester Creek, where Spenard

Road crosses it, large mud fountains were reported by a motorist whose passage was blocked by cracks in the road. The fountains reached higher than his car (R. D. Miller, oral commun., 1964).

At Turnagain Heights, large sand boils, unlike any others in the area, resulted from agitation and settlement of slump blocks within the landslide (fig. 15). These boils built ridges of sand 2 to 3 feet high, 3 to 6 feet wide, and about 100 feet long. Some ridges had hollow cores. The sand generally was finer grained than the subjacent outwash, from which it must have come, and it may, therefore, have been sorted by natural elutriation in a pulsating water column.

A large kidney-shaped boil near Turnagain Heights, but outside the landslide area, spread over an area of about 3,200 square feet. This boil was just west of a collapsed Alaska Railroad embankment across Fish Creek one-fourth mile north of Northern Lights Boulevard (Engineering Geology

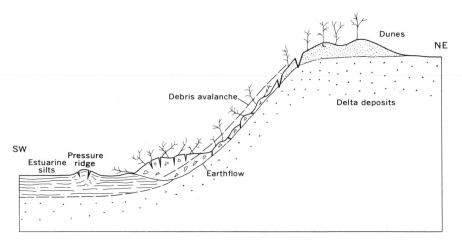

16.—Diagrammatic section near Point Campbell, showing mode of failure along bluff line overlooking Turnagain Arm.

strength to resist the accelerations of the quake in potentially unstable topographic settings. A landslide occurs where the ratio of shearing resistance of the ground to the shearing stress on the potential slide surface decreases from a value greater than one to unity. An earthquake can cause an almost instantaneous decrease in this ratio (Terzaghi, 1950, p. 110).

SLIDES ALONG TURNAGAIN ARM

Structurally, the simplest slides were in the bluffs facing Turnagain Arm southeast of Point Campbell (fig. 16). There, a thin cover of wind-blown sand and slope wash had been loosely anchored to the steep face of the bluff by an overgrowth of trees, shrubs, and grasses. The entire superficial mat, probably frozen at the time, slumped downward a few inches to several feet along the full length of the bluff from Point Campbell to Campbell Creek, a distance of about 4 miles. Locally the slumping was more intense, and the face of the bluff was laid bare from top to bottom. Southeast of Campbell Creek, minor or incipient slumping and cracking extended along the bluff to the tracks of The Alaska Railroad near Potter, where slides destroyed trackage and embankments.

Between Point Campbell and Campbell Creek, the earth slid either in a mass, as a shallow nonrotational glide, or it disintegrated into blocks and fragments, as a debris slide or avalanche (Varnes, 1958, pl. 1). All intermediate steps are represented. The velocity of motion has not been ascertained, but it probably was rapid because of the height and steepness of the slope and the granular incoherent character of the material.

Evaluation Group, 1964, pl. 8). Two other large boils poured out of the opposite side of the same embankment. They may have been caused by spontaneous liquefaction of subjacent silty sand, that was pumped to the surface when the embankment fill collapsed. Several similar but smaller boils formed in the downtown area in the toe of the Fourth Avenue slide, east and just below the intersection of E Street and West Second Avenue (Engineering Geology Evaluation Group, 1964, pl. 5).

Most of the lakes in the Anchorage area—solidly frozen over at the time of the quake—developed distinctive patterns of peripheral ice cracks extending generally 50 to 100 feet out from shore but in places much farther. The fracture zones in the larger lakes were wider than those in the smaller ones, and some small lakes had no cracks at all. Most of the cracks ejected fountains of water during the quake, and where the bottom was shallow enough they ejected mud, particularly in toward shore. Large mud fountains formed at Lake Otis (on the northeast

shore), Lake Spenard, Hood Lake, and Connors Lake, to name a few.

The earth dam impounding Campbell Lake, near Turnagain Arm, broke during the earthquake. As the water level fell, ice on the lake broke into blocks, and fountains of muddy water squirted up through the cracks. Reportedly, these fountains reached heights of 20 feet or more.

LANDSLIDES

DEBRIS SLIDES, AVALANCHES, AND ROTATIONAL SLIDES

Landslides precipitated along the bluffs of Knik and Turnagain Arms and along the benches above Ship Creek were the most spectacular and awesome manifestations of earthquake damage in the area. The slides took several forms and occurred in several types of earth material. The most destructive slides, in terms of property damage, resulted from failures in the Bootlegger Cove Clay. Serious failures, however, also occurred in glacial till, delta deposits, and dune sands—the only criteria being unconsolidated surficial deposits having insufficient shear

Trees carried along in the slides were tilted at all angles of disarray, many were rotated outward, some inward, and some were overridden by surging at the base of the slope. In some places the debris surged out into lobate forms on the estuarine muds and swamps at the foot of the bluff, and in many places one, two, or three pressure ridges were formed at the foot of the slope or out on the flats. Some ridges were more than a thousand feet from the bluff. The flats below the bluff were snow covered at the time and probably frozen. Pressure probably was transmitted directly from the slide through the frozen layer to the points of failure on the flats.

The high, steep part of the bluff nearest Point Campbell consists chiefly of loose deltaic sand and gravel veneered with dune sand. The bluff supported little or no vegetation prior to the earthquake because of more or less continuous buffeting by storm waves. It had, therefore, practically no cohesion with the slope and failed chiefly by avalanching.

Many gaping cracks remained along the edge of the bluff between Point Campbell and Campbell Creek after the temblor ceased. The sliding, however, was entirely superficial and did little to alter the firmness of the land surface back from the bluff. Nevertheless, by partial removal of the stabilizing vegetative mantle, the vulnerability of the slope to continued sapping has been heightened, and intermittent sluffing will probably take place for a long time to come. Slow, gradual backwasting, in fact, should be regarded as normal.

What effect tectonic subsidence—about 2 feet in the Anchor-age area—will have on the stability of the bluff line is still undetermined. Certainly the part of the bluff near Point Campbell will be even more exposed to the attacks of tide and wave than it was before the quake. Other points along the bluff farther southeast probably will be attacked by occasional storm waves also, especially when strong winds coincide with highest tides. It seems likely that, wherever the foot of the bluff is accessible to storm waves, new slope profiles will have to be established before equilibrium can be fully regained.

POTTER HILL SLIDES

Destructive slides carried away several hundred feet of track and right-of-way along The Alaska Railroad between mile posts 103 and 104 about 2½ miles northeast of Potter (fig. 17). These slides, known as the Potter Hill slides, were mapped and examined in detail after the earthquake, on April 20, 1964, by D. S. McCulloch and M. G. Bonilla of the U.S. Geological Survey on behalf of The Alaska Railroad. The following summary is based on their findings.

The Potter Hill area has a history of landsliding that extends back at least 35 years. Bert Wennerstrom, chief accountant of The Alaska Railroad recalled that "in the late twenties and early thirties, heavy rains caused sliding along this section (mile 103–104). The largest slide took out about 1,000 feet of track." Wennerstrom remembered that the failures involved cuts in the natural bank material (McCulloch and Bonilla, written commun., 1964).

On October 3, 1954, landslides caused by an earthquake again destroyed trackage in the same area. One slump left 140 feet of track suspended 15 to 20 feet in the air (Miller and Dobrovolny, 1959, p. 105). Although it is not clear just what materials were involved, failure probably occurred in natural bank material as well as in fill.

The slides of March 27, 1964, affected cuts in both natural bank material and fill. The ground was frozen at the time of the earthquake and, presumably, there was little surface runoff. Sand boils, however, indicate that the material in the slides had a high water content.

Several kinds of material were involved. Glacial till forms the top of the bluff back of the slides and most of the exposed face of the bluff in the northern part of the slide area. The till rests on outwash with a contact that dips gently north. The outwash in turn lies on a sequence of blue clay, silt, and fine sand, which perhaps is equivalent to the Bootlegger Cove Clay. This sequence forms the lower part of the slope. At the south end of the slide area, a coarse gravel overlies the till. The materials in the bluff abut against and probably pass beneath intertidal silts in the flats at the base of the bluff.

The bluff is saturated at its base, and, at several levels above its base, ground water escapes laterally through permeable beds in the outwash. In wells east of the slide area, ground-water levels reportedly are 30 to 240 feet above sea level. During the earthquake, sand spouts issued from cracks 400 feet east of the edge of the bluff.

All the slides along Potter Hill had a similar form. They con-

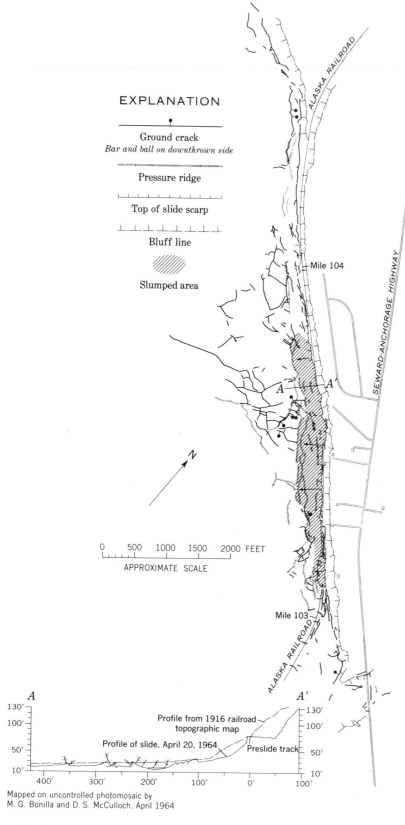

EXPLANATION

Ground crack
Bar and ball on downthrown side

Pressure ridge

Top of slide scarp

Bluff line

Slumped area

Mile 104

Mile 103

ALASKA RAILROAD

SEWARD-ANCHORAGE HIGHWAY

0   500   1000   1500   2000 FEET
APPROXIMATE SCALE

A

| 130' |
| 100' |
| 50' |
| 10' |

Profile from 1916 railroad
topographic map

Profile of slide, April 20, 1964

Preslide track

A'

130'
100'
50'
10'

400'   300'   200'   100'   0'   100'

Mapped on uncontrolled photomosaic by
M. G. Bonilla and D. S. McCulloch, April 1964

17.—Map and profile of Potter Hill landslide area near Anchorage, Alaska.

sisted of elongate fragmented slump blocks rotated backward and broken into many pieces toward the base of the slope. In places at the toe, they turned into earth and mudflows derived partly from the intertidal silt of Turnagain Arm and partly, perhaps, from the clay-silt-sand sequence in the lower part of the bluff.

Many pressure ridges formed on the flats below the slides; some smaller ones were as far as a third of a mile beyond the toe, but most of the larger ones were within 400 feet. They were formed by compressive stresses probably transmitted horizontally from the toe of the slides through the frozen upper layers of the estuarine silt.

Marginal fractures bounded the slides roughly parallel to the face of the bluff. They cut across natural bank material and fill alike as high as the level of the tracks, in the roadbed itself, and in the drainage ditch beside the tracks. Near Rabbit Creek, where the tracks turn southward across the flats, cracks reached nearly to the top of the bluff. At one point they extended as far back as 400 feet from the edge of the bluff. Sand that was ejected from these cracks during the quake spread out onto the surface of the snow. But in general, cracking was confined to the face of the bluff itself.

The mechanics of sliding has been investigated by D. S. McCulloch and M. G. Bonilla (written commun., 1964). They concluded that sliding was initiated by failure and flowage of material from the base of the slope. Higher parts of the slope slumped and disintegrated as a consequence. Flowage may have occurred in the modern estuarine silt at the base

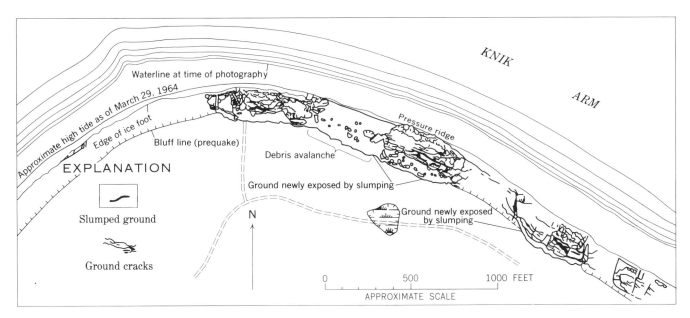

18.—Photogeologic sketch map of Point Woronzof landslide area, Alaska.

of the slope, which carried part of the weight of the roadbed, or in the fine silt and sand in the lower part of the bluff. Perhaps it occurred in both.

Measurements by McCulloch and Bonilla indicate that the volume of the slide material that accumulated at the base of the slope and on the adjacent flats was less than that of the material removed from the slope by sliding. They concluded, therefore, that this difference in volume was compensated partly by flowage in the estuarine silt and partly by lateral translation through the silt to pressure ridges on the flats.

SLIDES AT POINT WORONZOF

Point Woronzof is underlain by loose unconsolidated sand and gravel. Because it projects north into Knik Arm, the point is exposed continuously to the ebb and flow of the strong tidal currents and to the pounding of storm waves propelled across the arm by northerly winds sweeping down across the Susitna Lowland. The maximum tidal range at Anchor-

age is about 38 feet. Point Woronzof, therefore, has been subjected to more or less continuous and vigorous shoreline erosion, and, since 1909 at least, has retreated southward at a mean rate of about 2 feet per year (Miller and Dobrovolny, 1959, p. 89).

Waves and tides, by periodically removing sluffed increments of sand and gravel from the foot of the point, have kept the slopes above in a state of precarious repose. It is not surprising, therefore, that on March 27 large volumes of material slumped down the face of Point Woronzof under the driving force of the earthquake. As shown by figure 18, the bluff caved away in three separate parts, mostly by modified rotational slumping. The largest mass, directly beneath Point Woronzof, extended about 1,500 feet along the bluff and about 50 to 100 feet back behind the old bluff line. Part of the slumped mass disintegrated into a debris avalanche, but most of it slid down as an intact though much fractured block. It probably moved very rapidly.

The next smaller slide was 300 feet east. It extended about 500 feet along the bluff and caved back about 30 to 40 feet behind the old bluff line. It, too, was a much fractured but basically intact slump. The smallest slide, 150 feet farther east, was about 200 feet wide. It broke away from the slope entirely below the old bluff line.

SLIDES NEAR CAIRN POINT

Several small landslides were generated by the earthquake along Knik Arm just south of Cairn Point at the west end of Elmendorf Air Force Base. Cairn Point, like Point Woronzof, projects out into Knik Arm and is subject to vigorous erosion by waves and tidal currents. It, too, therefore, has a past history of instability and slumping.

At Cairn Point an exceptionally thick sequence of Bootlegger Cove Clay is overlain by silty till of the Elmendorf Moraine. The clay is at least 126 feet thick, and the till is at least 110 feet thick (Miller and Dobrovolny, 1959, p. 39). The quake-induced landslides probably

19.—Rotational slump near Sleeper landing strip, on the west side of Knik Arm opposite Cairn Point. At its foot, the slump passed into an earthflow. Tidewater in foreground. Scarp to left of upper center is about 80 feet high.

involved both materials, but they broke away mostly from the lower half of the slope and, hence, were mostly in the Bootlegger Cove Clay. Morphologically, the slides were rotational slumps, modified by disruption and flowage.

The largest slide was about 450 feet wide at beach line, and it surged out at least 200 feet onto the tidal mudflat. From its appearance after the quake, it must have disintegrated into many blocks as it moved downslope, the parts that moved farthest disintegrating most completely. At its toe, it passed into an earthflow. The several other slides, although smaller, were identical to the largest in form.

SLIDES ON WEST SIDE OF KNIK ARM

Two large rotational slumps were generated by the earthquake on the west side of Knik Arm about a mile northeast of Sleeper landing strip. The larger of the two (fig. 19) was just below hill

204 in sec. 35, T. 14 N., R. 4 W. (This hill is shown on the U.S. Geological Survey 1962 map of Anchorage and vicinity.) The smaller slide was about a quarter of a mile southwest. The Bootlegger Cove Clay rests on glacial till at about the level of mean high tide, with a contact that appears to be gradational. The clay contains scattered pebbles throughout, especially near the base; some are as large as 4 inches across.

Bootlegger Cove Clay extends nearly the full height of the bluff, to an altitude of about 190 to 195 feet, where it is topped by a veneer of sand, silt, and peat. Sliding, therefore, was largely in the clay. Till may have been involved near the foot of the slides, but if so, it was pushed out into Knik Arm below tidewater. Both slides surged out onto the tidal mudflat in broad earthflow lobes that reached an undetermined distance into the water below low tide.

Before the earthquake, the top and slope of the bluff supported a forest of birch and cottonwood in the slide areas. These trees were rotated backward in an arc of about 30° to 60°, the angle of tilt being progressively greater farther downslope. In the earthflow lobes, many of the trees lay flat, their crowns pointed toward the bluff and their roots toward Knik Arm.

Detailed land measurements have not been made of either slide. Estimates based on air and ground reconnaissance and on photographs indicate that the larger slide was about 700 feet wide along the bluff line. It worked headward about 200 feet into the bluff, and it surged out perhaps 500 feet onto the mudflat for a total length of at least 700 feet from crown to

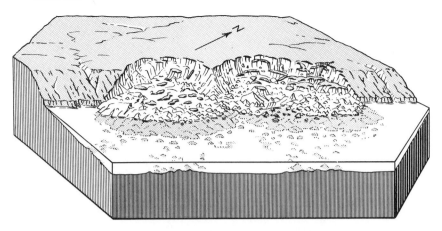

20.—Block diagram of compound slump near Sleeper landing strip. Two lobes of slide surged out onto mudflat below high tide.

toe. It was a compound slide in that it extended back into the bluff in two large joined arcuate alcoves (fig. 20). The slide was complex in that the slumped mass broke into several slices below the crown and into countless jumbled blocks toward the foot, where it passed into an earthflow. Its main scarp had a pronounced concave-outward profile and a maximum height of about 80 feet from the crown to the jumbled blocks below.

The smaller slide was similar to the larger one in morphology and habit, but its main scarp formed a simple arcuate alcove about 90 feet high. Gouging and slickensides on the face of the scarp indicate that the slumped mass slid diagonally downward from upper left to lower right (as viewed from the crown) rather than directly down the fall line; the reason for the diagonal slipping is unclear, unless the mass slumped almost instantaneously and at the same time lurched laterally in response to the ground motion of the quake. The slumped mass itself was rotated backward toward the bluff, but it was broken into helter-skelter blocks in various attitudes of disarray, particularly out toward the toe.

Near the foot of the smaller slide there were sand boils 3 to 4 feet high. Because the bluff had only a thin veneer of sand at the top, the boils presumably were derived from the subjacent beach.

The slip plane of an older slide was exposed in section on the south side of the main scarp of the smaller slide. The older slide—no longer preserved as a topographic form—was truncated by the slip plane of the younger one.

Further slumping at a gradually diminished rate is forecast for both slides. The toes of both slides project far out into Knik Arm where they are under relentless attack by tidal currents and waves and where removal of material will reduce whatever buttressing effect may have existed immediately after the quake. Loss of buttress support, in turn, will encourage further rotation of the main slide masses; this rotation will remove support from the main scarps. These scarps already are precarious, and will remain so until headward slumping has reduced their height and pitch to a more stable configuration. In brief, therefore, erosion at the toes and slumping at the heads will continue indefinitely at a gradually diminishing rate until something approaching the prequake profile of the bluff has been restored.

21.—Chaotic pressure ridge at toe of rotational slide, Bluff Road.. In part, toe surged forward as an earthflow. Compare with figure 22.

ROTATIONAL SLIDES ALONG BLUFF ROAD

Several rotational slides gave way along the south-facing bluff line of Ship Creek, between Bluff Road and the tracks of The Alaska Railroad (fig. 1). The most widespread failure in that area extended east along the bluff between the district offices of the Corps of Engineers and the steam generating plant of Elmendorf Air Force Base. About 1,300 feet of bluff gave way in a compound displacement consisting of four separate but connected slumps. Collapse at the heads of the slumps extended back horizontally into the bluff as much as 120 feet. An additional 400 feet of bluff line east and west of the main slide mass cracked and began to slump. Altogether, about 650 feet of Bluff Road was destroyed, dropping as much as 40 feet below the prequake gradeline and rotating backward 15° to 30°.

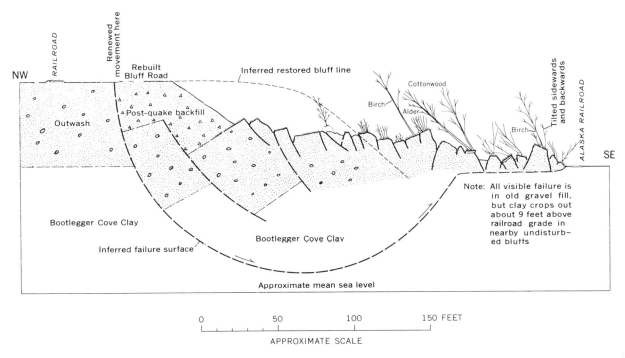

22.—Sketch section through rotational slide at Bluff Road.

All four slumps were modified by multiple cracking, internal breakup, and flowage. None moved as a simple block. Within each slump, slices rotated on individual slip surfaces, their motions modified by interference or shoving of one slice against another. There was evidence, moreover, of flowage beneath each slump, as well as of extrusion of material at the toe.

At the toe, each of the four slumps bulged out into a chaotic lobe of jumbled blocks (fig. 21). These lobes were transitional in form between pressure ridges and earthflows. Three of them stopped short of The Alaska Railroad tracks; the most easterly lobe, however, advanced across two sets of tracks, but without damaging the tracks or the roadbed. Each slump had a length of about 300 feet from crown to toe.

In general, the rotation of blocks within the slides diminished downslope from the head of each slide toward a position about halfway down, below which rota-

tion either increased again or the attitude of the blocks became chaotic (fig. 22). In other words, the old ground surface was tilted most near the head and least about halfway to the toe. This differential tilting (in addition to rotation) seems to have been in response to a withdrawal of material from beneath the headward parts of the slumps, either by flowage and extrusion, by lateral spreading, or by a combination of the two. If by a combination, these slides represent a transitional form between the simple slumps of the Point Woronzof and Cairn Point areas and the block-glide displacements in the downtown Anchorage area.

Most of the visible landslide material was coarse o u t w a s h gravel. Some of it had been disturbed prior to the quake, and some plainly had been backfilled artificially. Bootlegger Cove Clay, however, was exposed along a line of springs 9 feet above the base of the slope of the bluff just west of the slides, and it must have

extended into the slide area. Its loss of strength under the vibratory motion of the quake very likely contributed to the failure of the slope and to the flowage at the toes and beneath the heads of the slumps.

East from the steam generating plant, cracks and smaller separate slumps extended along the bluff a total distance of about 3,000 feet. The bluff beyond was appreciably lower and presumably more stable. Some of these slumps showed clear evidence of movement prior to the March 27 earthquake, particularly the slump just east of the steam plant and the one in the next bend of Bluff Road farther east. Old settlement cracks in the road at these places had been filled and patched before the quake.

Emergency repairs along Bluff Road did little to stabilize the sliding triggered by the quake. These repairs consisted simply of backfilling collapsed areas with gravel to reestablish the grade profile, without regard for the unbalancing effect that the backfilling might have on the slide itself. At several points along the bluff, fill material dumped onto the slides probably caused continued movement by overweighting the head and altering whatever balance had been achieved naturally. By mid-May of 1964, new cracks with small vertical displacements had already formed in the repaired fills. Unless remedial procedures are altered, therefore, continued slow movements at the heads of the slumps seem inevitable. A comprehensive stabilization program for these slides, on the other hand, may be less feasible economically than intermittent road repair and maintenance.

TRANSLATORY SLIDES

All the highly destructive landslides in the built-up parts of Anchorage were of a single structural-dynamic family, despite wide variations from slide to slide in size, appearance, and complexity. All moved chiefly by translation rather than rotation. They slid laterally on nearly horizontal slip surfaces following drastic loss of strength in previously weak sensitive zones of the Bootlegger Cove Clay. Slides in which the slid mass was practically intact are classed as block glides; those in which the slid mass underwent appreciable disruption are probably best classed as failures by lateral spreading (Varnes, 1958, pl. 1). Between these limits, all gradations of form were represented—not only from place to place but also in time. Structurally, the Fourth Avenue slide was the simplest and the Turnagain Heights slide was the most complex. The Turnagain Heights slide, however, must have begun as a simple though highly transient block glide, or perhaps as several such block glides, arising independently along the bluff line. As sliding progressed, the Turnagain Heights slide deteriorated rapidly into a complex failure involving simultaneous motions in several directions. Its predominant motion, however, remained translatory. Destruction to property in the several slides was caused by tilting, wrenching, warping, and disruption of structures over the cracked, collapsed, and compressed zones of the slides. Structures in undistorted parts of some slides were little damaged despite horizontal ground translations of several feet.

Translatory slides are less common than rotational slides. They have, therefore, received less attention in the literature. Examples similar in many respects to those at Anchorage, however, have been reported and described from Scandinavia where the Pleistocene history has been comparable in some ways to that at Anchorage. Notable translatory slides occurred at Skottorp, Sweden, in 1946 (Odenstad, 1951) and at Bekkelaget, Norway, in 1953 (Eide and Bjerrum, 1955, p. 88–100; Rosenqvist, 1960, p. 10). The Skottorp slide, particularly, resembled the Turnagain Heights slide, except that it was smaller; the Bekkelaget slide was similar to the Fourth Avenue slide. Translatory slides in the conterminous United States somewhat like those in Anchorage have been described by Crandell (1952, p. 552; 1958, p. 73) and by Varnes (1958, p. 26–32). All these slides—in Scandinavia and in the United States—moved in response to gravitational stress, without the intervention of earthquakes.

Earthquake-triggered landslides accompanying the great New Madrid, Mo., earthquakes of 1811 seem to have been very similar to the slides at Anchorage. The physical setting of the slides was analogous to that at Anchorage. Fissures, sand blows, and various other features related to sliding are described by Fuller (1912, p. 48, 59–61) on the basis of early accounts and on observations made nearly 100 years after the quakes. Fuller's descriptions might well apply to the Turnagain Heights slide. Grabens and tension cracks, for example, were formed where clayey alluvium, afloat on quicksand, glided laterally.

The Chilean earthquake of May 22, 1960, triggered three large landslides at Lago Riñihue, 65 kilometers east of Valdivia in central Chile. The descriptions of Davis and Karzulovíc (1963, p. 1407) indicate that these slides resembled the Turnagain Heights slide in form, size, and mode of failure. Translatory movement predominated; rotational movement was subordinate. Significantly, these slides occurred in an area of previous landsliding and were partly superimposed on pre-existing landslides.

GEOLOGIC SETTING

All areas of translatory sliding in Anchorage had the same general geologic environment. All were underlain at various depths by Bootlegger Cove Clay that had zones of low shear strength, high water content, and high sensitivity. All surmounted flat-topped bluffs bounded on one side by steep slopes. In all areas, except the westernmost part of the Turnagain Heights slide, the Bootlegger Cove Clay was overlain by outwash sand and gravel. These deposits thinned markedly over a distance of a few miles from north to south and from east to west; grain size diminished concomitantly from gravel to sand. Near the Alaska Native Service Hospital the outwash is about 55 feet thick, near Government Hill

School about 40 feet, in the downtown area about 30 to 40 feet, and at Turnagain Heights from about 25 feet to zero.

Outwash deposits had no critical part in the sliding. Failure was confined to thin zones of sensitive clay, silt, and sand within the Bootlegger Cove Clay.

Several geologic factors acting in concert with earthquake shaking probably caused failure in the several slide areas. All these factors are themselves variables at each site. They include: (1) the topographic elements of bluff configuration—the height of the bluff above its base, the slope angle or declivity of its face, and perhaps the ground-plan configuration, (2) the soil-strength profile, including consistency, dynamic shear strength, and sensitivity, and (3) water content and liquid limit of the soil at the critical depth below the ground surface. Some of these factors seem to be interdependent—the height, slope, and ground-plan configuration, for example, may have influenced the water content of the soil, which in turn influenced the consistency.

The influence of topography, particularly the bluff profile, on failure susceptibility seems obvious. The ultimate driving force of landsliding was gravity, operating on a nearly horizontal shear surface in the direction of least shear resistance (the free face of the bluff) and acting on a dynamically sensitive soil that had undergone a severe loss of strength by earthquake shaking. Other factors being equal, the higher and steeper the bluff profile, the greater is the shearing stress, the less effective is the shear resistance of the clay, and the greater is the susceptibility of the bluff to failure.

The full significance of ground-plan configuration is uncertain

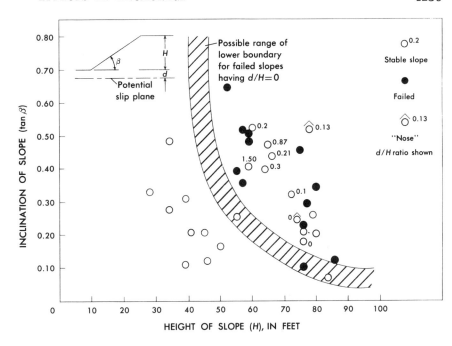

23.—Slope stability chart. Reprinted from Shannon and Wilson, Inc. (1964, pl. 7.1).

and may involve several variables difficult to evaluate. Most failures took place along fairly straight or recessed bluff lines, for reasons not entirely clear, although possibly because such places are apt to be well watered (Shannon and Wilson, Inc., 1964, p. 33). Saliants or cuspate areas ("noses") generally were spared failure, again possibly because they are apt to be well drained, although the slide at the Native Hospital failed precisely at just such a salient.

Using factors of height and slope, only, Shannon and Wilson, Inc. (1964, pl. 7.1), constructed a slope stability chart that grouped failed and stable slopes and showed lower limits of slope-to-height ratios below which failure is improbable (fig. 23). The higher the slope, the flatter the angle at which the slope is susceptible to failure, other variable factors such as soil strength and water content being equal. The fact that several stable slopes, including salients or "noses," have

slope-to-height ratios within the same area of the chart as slopes that failed seems to point up the modifying influences of other factors such as soil-strength profile and water content. A low slope underlain by soil having a high water-plasticity ratio, for example, may be more susceptible to failure—may have a lower safety factor—than a high slope underlain by soil having a low water-plasticity ratio. In a unit of time, other factors being equal, a salient should drain and desiccate more rapidly than a recess; hence it should be more stable.

The length of time a bluff has been stationary and unmodified by erosion may perhaps influence its dynamic stability by affecting the water content of the underlying Bootlegger Cove Clay. Far more information on the water content of the clay at critical localities than is now available would be needed to test this hypothesis, but presumably a long-stationary bluff line would have a better chance of desiccation, and hence of

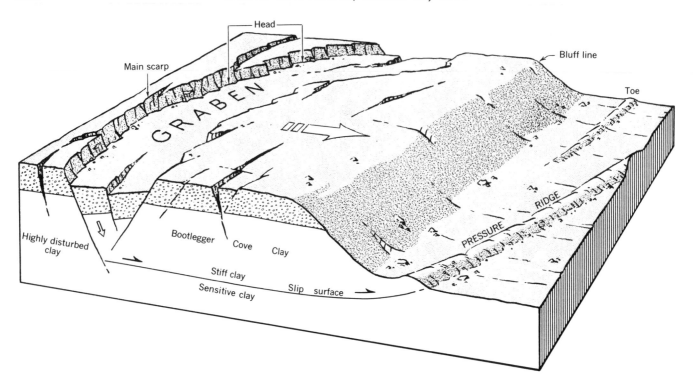

24.—Block diagram of a translatory slide.

dynamic stability, than an actively retreating one. Permeability is extremely low in most of the Bootlegger Cove Clay, and a long period of immobility would be required to promote even a low degree of drainage and desiccation. At Turnagain Heights, for example, the bluff line facing Knik Arm, which failed so dramatically during the earthquake, was in a state of relatively rapid regression owing to active shoreline processes prior to the quake, whereas the bluff line facing Fish Creek was relatively stationary before the quake and did not fail during the quake.

GEOMETRY AND MODE OF FAILURE

Translatory slides of the Anchorage area varied widely in size, shape, and internal complexity, but they all conformed to a single basic geometric format. Figure 24 is a simplified block diagram showing the essential structural elements, including the head, toe,

bluff line, slip surface, graben, and pressure ridge. Sections through both the Fourth Avenue and the L Street slides closely approximate the idealized section at the front of the block diagram. The so-called slip surface probably is not generally a surface at all, at least at the onset of sliding, but rather is a narrow planar zone of failure.

Geometric development of the translatory slide is reconstructed in the following sequence: Earthquake shaking drastically reduces the shear strength of saturated sensitive zones in the Bootlegger Cove Clay. The strength of the clay falls below the level of shear stress caused by the weight of material in the bluff and the accelerations of the quake. Under the influence of gravity, therefore, a prismatic block of earth begins to move laterally on a nearly horizontal slide surface toward the free face of the bluff. In effect, the block is afloat

on a zone of disturbed clay whose strength properties are those of a confined viscous liquid. As the block starts to move, tension fractures form at the head of the slide and widen as movement progresses. These tension fractures dip toward the slide block at commonly observed angles of about 60° to 70°. As the fractures widen, their hanging wall (on the moving block) loses support and collapses along one or more antithetical fractures to form a graben.

The term "graben," since the earthquake, has become a household word to the populace of Anchorage. The downward piston-like movement of the graben is synchronous with the lateral slippage of the slide block. Continued slippage places more ground under tension behind the slide, and additional fractures form as the slide retrogresses headward. In the more complex slides such as the Government Hill slide, and, especially, the Turnagain Heights slide, this process occurred repeatedly, and a series of alternate horsts and grabens developed regressively, parallel to the direction of slippage. (See figs. 37, 44, and pl. 2).

As the block moves outward, tension at the head of the slide is partly countered by compression at the toe, and pressure ridges form in the flats below. This step may be transient, because continued compression leads to rupture and overthrusting. Both steps occurred in each of the translatory slides and caused extensive local damage. The Turnagain Heights slide not only sheared off at the toe, but it slid under gravity down the mudflat into Knik Arm—at one point it slid more than half a mile. But if resistance in the toe builds up to a level equal to the thrust of the moving block plus the shear resistance of the clay at the slip surface, motion will stop. A modification of this principle was utilized by the Corps of Engineers in designing remedial buttresses. The Corps, however, visualized the driving mechanism of the slide as the "active earth pressure" of the earth mass behind the head of the slide (Shannon and Wilson, Inc., 1964, p. 32) plus the acceleration of earthquake ground motion. But inasmuch as the head of the slide block is plainly under tension during sliding, there obviously can be no "active earth pressure" from the mass behind it. Furthermore, inasmuch as regression and sliding continued after earthquake ground motion had ceased (p. A64), the accelerations of the quake cannot be the driving mechanism either. Rather, sliding was precipitated by gravity as soon as the accelerations of the quake had reduced the shear resistance of the soil to the point of failure. The earthquake was the "trigger"; gravity was the "propellant." Sliding continued as long as the gravitational component on the sliding surface exceeded the shear resistance of the soil. At Turnagain Heights, sliding probably continued a full minute or more after earth shaking had stopped (see page A64).

In plan, each slide was bounded laterally by a series of crescentic tension fractures, which also marked the outer wall of the outermost graben. Subordinate crescentic tension fractures— bounding potential slide blocks— commonly extended headward, outside the slide proper, scores or hundreds of feet beyond the bounding fractures. At Turnagain Heights, numerous crescentic tension fractures extended back through the subdivision as much as 2,200 feet beyond the head of the slide (pl. 1); had the earthquake lasted longer, sliding undoubtedly would have retrogressed back into that area. "Retrogression," as applied to landslides, means a headward expansion of the slide. (See Varnes, 1958, p. 31.)

Extensive internal fracturing also characterized all slides, although internal fracturing was minimal in the L Street slide. The Native Hospital slide contained abundant radial fractures; as noted before, this slide occupied a salient or "nose" on the bluff line, and the radial fractures undoubtedly were tensional responses to lateral spreading.

THE GRABEN RULE

A close approximation of the depth of failure is prerequisite to planning remedial or stabilization procedures. A significant geometric relationship, here called the "graben rule," affords a rapid, yet reliable, estimate. The graben rule should apply to any translatory slide in which flowage of material from the zone of failure has not been excessive. Because the cross-sectional area of the graben trough approximates the cross-sectional area of the space voided behind the block as the block moves outward, the depth of failure can be estimated from the simple relationship $D=A/l$ where D is the depth of failure, A is the cross-sectional area of the graben, and l is the lateral displacement of the block. For example, the Fourth Avenue graben, on the average, was about 11 feet deep, 100 feet across, and had an area (A) of about 1,100 square feet. Its maximum lateral displacement (l) was about 17½ feet, as determined by postquake resurveys. The calculated depth of failure (D) was about 63 feet, or about 43 feet above mean sea level. Subsurface exploration, though somewhat indecisive in its results, yielded a nearly identical figure.

INDIVIDUAL TRANSLATORY LANDSLIDES
Fourth Avenue Slide

The Fourth Avenue slide involved all or parts of 14 city blocks in a roughly oval area of about 36 acres, containing perhaps 2 million cubic yards of earth, centered at the north side of downtown Anchorage (fig. 25). It was bounded headward on the south by Fourth Avenue, on the west by E Street, on the north approximately by First Avenue, and on the east somewhat indefinitely by Barrow Street. Its length north to south in the direction of slippage was about 1,050 feet; east to west it was about 1,800 feet across. Strong fracturing and related ground displacements extended 1½ blocks (about 450 feet) or so south of the slide proper, where considerable damage was inflicted on buildings,

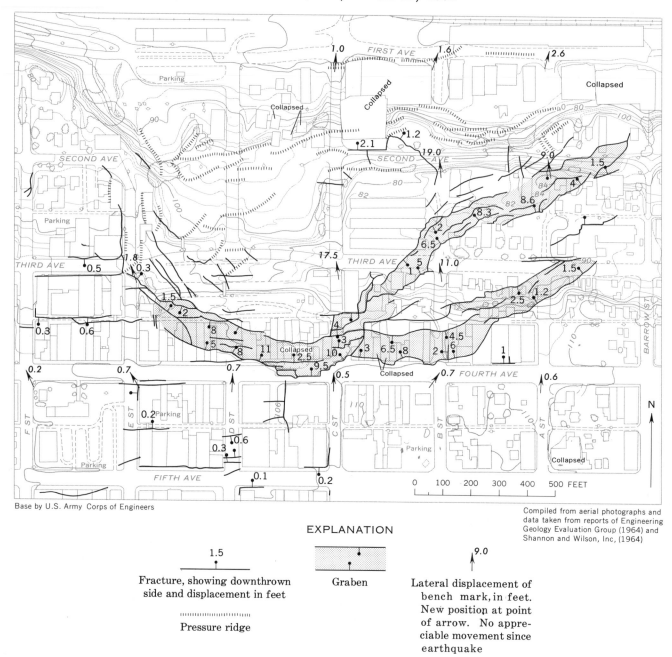

Base by U.S. Army Corps of Engineers

Compiled from aerial photographs and data taken from reports of Engineering Geology Evaluation Group (1964) and Shannon and Wilson, Inc, (1964)

EXPLANATION

1.5 ─────•─────
Fracture, showing downthrown side and displacement in feet

Graben

9.0
Lateral displacement of bench mark, in feet. New position at point of arrow. No appreciable movement since earthquake

Pressure ridge

25.—Fourth Avenue landslide area, Anchorage, Alaska.

streets, and sidewalks. Minor displacements extended as far south as 600 feet. Eyewitnesses reported that sliding began about 2 minutes after the earthquake started and stopped about the same time as the earthquake (Grantz, Plafker, and Kachadoorian, 1964, p. 15).

Most of the damaging tensional fractures within the slide mass were between Second and Fourth Avenues in the east part of the slide and between Third and Fourth Avenues in the west part. North from those areas, downslope, compressional movements in the foot of the slide caused numerous pressure ridges.

Ground dislocations were most severe in the graben areas at the head of the slide along the north side of Fourth Avenue (fig. 4). Ironically, these areas also had the highest property evaluations. Many small business and commercial buildings, apartment houses, and residences were destroyed or badly damaged. Vacant lots and parking spaces within the slide block to the north were little disturbed. Just east of C Street the main graben bifurcated, and two long belts of severe damage extended northeast toward Barrow Street.

Between B and D Streets, where the destruction was total, the main graben had a width of 100 to 150 feet and a depth of as much as 11 feet. Lateral displacements near the center of the slide just north of the graben were as much as 17½ feet toward the north, according to surveys by the City Engineer's office. Near the foot of the bluff on Second Avenue a block east of B Street, a complex of pressure ridges was pushed up by 19 feet of lateral displacement—apparently the greatest local slippage in the slide. Although several days elapsed after the quake before resurveys were started, there appears to have been no movement since the main quake. None of the strong aftershocks caused measurable movement.

Subsurface exploration of the Fourth Avenue slide was started by the Engineering Geology Evaluation Group soon after the earthquake, and was expanded and concluded by the Corps of Engineers. The findings of these groups indicate that failure occurred at the top of the sensitive zone of the Bootlegger Cove Clay at a depth of about 60 feet (48 feet above mean sea level). Additional failures may have occurred at greater depths, inasmuch as many pressure ridges formed at the surface in the toe of the

slide at altitudes below 48 feet, unless, as suggested by their sharply peaked crests and steep sides (fig. 26), the ridges were caused by simple surface translations of the rigid frozen surface layer of the soil.

Shear-strength profiles measured near the head of the slide by Shannon and Wilson, Inc. (1964, p. 41) show that the clay decreases in strength from about 1.0 tsf at altitude 70 (top of clay) to as low as 0.25 tsf between altitudes 45 and 20, then increases in strength to about 0.75 tsf at 15 feet below sea level. The zone of maximum sensitivity coincides with the zone of minimum strength, and failure appears to have followed spontaneous liquefaction of sand layers as well as loss of strength in silty clay.

L Street Slide

The L Street slide involved all or parts of about 30 city blocks in the northwest part of Anchorage adjacent to Knik Arm (fig. 27). It extended northeast about 4,800 feet along the bluff and had a maximum breadth northwest across the bluff of about 1,200 feet, parallel to the direction of slippage. It reached about a block and a half back from the bluff line into thickly settled residential and commercial neighborhoods of Anchorage. In all, about 72 acres were included between the graben at the head of the slide and the outermost pressure ridges at the toe. The total volume probably approached 6 million cubic yards though an accurate estimate is difficult. Much of the 72-acre area, however, was little if at all damaged, despite lateral shifting of as much as 14 feet. Most of the damage was concentrated along the graben, which with marginal fractures covered about 14 acres, and along the pressure ridges, which were mainly linear features

but which involved properties of a total area of perhaps 7 to 8 acres. There was very little fracturing much beyond the bounding fractures of the graben, and there was not much fracturing within the slide mass itself except for the graben area. Eyewitness reports indicate that slippage began during the latter part of the earthquake (Shannon and Wilson, Inc., 1964, p. 53).

The whimsical pattern of destruction in Anchorage was perhaps best exemplified by the L Street slide; here wrecked buildings inside or astride the graben faced almost undamaged adjacent properties on either side (fig. 28). The irregular trends of the bounding fractures further compounded the fateful selectivity of the slide. Damage was equally capricious, moreover, in the compressed areas at the toe of the slide; here individual dwellings were buckled or shoved by pressure ridges that as often as not left adjoining buildings undisturbed (fig. 29).

The graben itself formed a broad arc in plan, concave toward the slide block. It extended south from West Third Avenue between K and L Streets and curved westward to R Street between Ninth and Tenth Avenues. It was about 3,600 feet long and had a maximum width of about 250 feet; generally, its width was between 150 and 200 feet (fig. 30). Its depth—that is, the displacement of the down-dropped block—reached a maximum of about 10 feet; the displacement was greater south of Sixth Avenue than north. Overall, the graben looked like a dry canal or a streambed, and, when contrasted with the lack of damage on either side, it stirred considerable speculation in the minds of early viewers. One popular magazine account stated that it resulted from collapse of an old

26.—Sharp-crested pressure ridge at Second Avenue and C Street, Anchorage. Probably caused by shallow translation of frozen surface layer. Note smaller pressure ridge in street part way up block and toppled chimney of building behind car. Photograph by Mac's Foto, Anchorage.

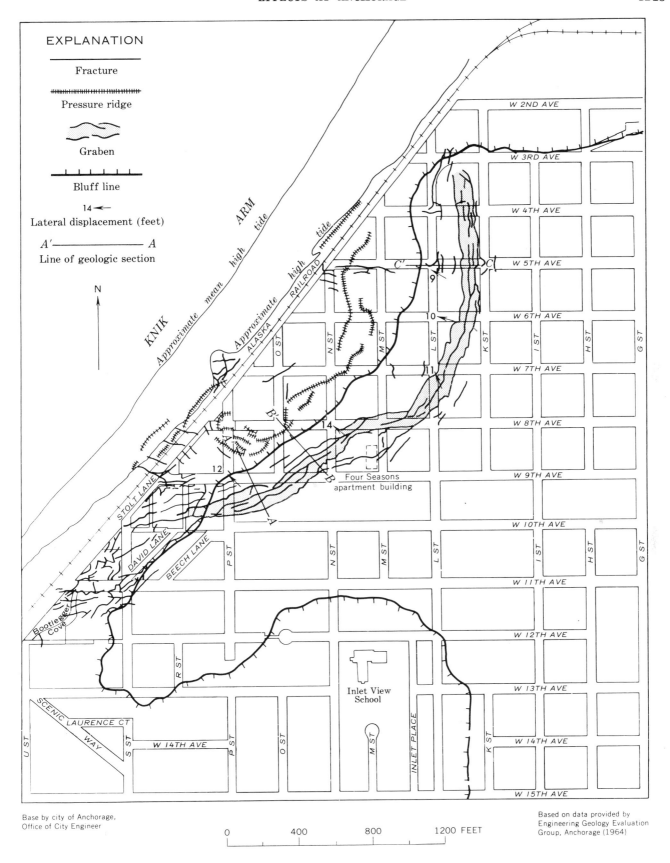

Based on data provided by
Engineering Geology Evaluation
Group, Anchorage (1964)

27.—L Street slide area, Anchorage, Alaska.   Geologic cross sections are shown in figure 30.

28.—Wrecked dwelling astride boundling fracture, L Street graben at Eighth Avenue and N Street. Damage caused entirely by ground displacement along fracture.

29.—House pushed off foundation by pressure ridge at toe of L Street slide. Well-framed house not otherwise visibly damaged. Push must have been shallow and nearly horizontal.

buried but melted-out ice-filled channel!

Many buildings on the slide block, including a six-story apartment building carried 10 feet laterally, sustained little or no damage, but utility service to the slide block was curtailed. Overhead wires and buried water, gas, and sewer lines all were disrupted where they crossed the graben. In most places, entirely new emergency connections had to be made before service could be restored. Many buildings, therefore, which were not themselves damaged were nevertheless evacuated.

Pressure ridges below the slide block were concentrated mostly in

a zone about 200 feet wide close to the foot of the bluff at 40 to 55 feet above sea level (figs. 27, 30). A few extended beyond The Alaska Railroad tracks, which were damaged by lateral shove, and even onto the tidal flat of Knik Arm about 500 feet from the foot of the bluff and only about 15 feet above mean sea level. Individual ridges ranged in length from a few tens of feet to more than 600 feet. They ranged in width from sharply peaked ridges 10 to 15 feet across to broad gentle bulges several tens of feet across. Most were less than 3 feet high, but a few were as high as 7 feet. Many were ruptured and overthrust toward Knik Arm.

The available evidence, both surface and subsurface, favors the view that the pressure ridges were caused chiefly by shallow compressional translations of the frozen superficial soil mantle, which in turn was shoved laterally by the sliding block behind. This mantle was only a few feet thick, but it was highly competent in its frozen state. Some indication of its strength was provided at one point where a small chunk of partly buried concrete caught in a surface fracture was so firmly held in place that it parted in half instead of breaking free from the frozen soil. In further support of the shallow depth concept, the altitude of the

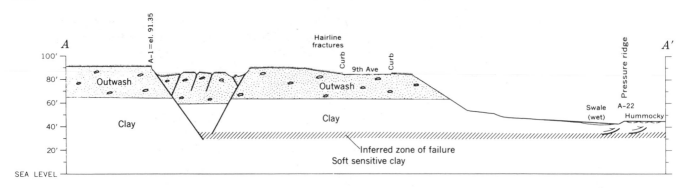

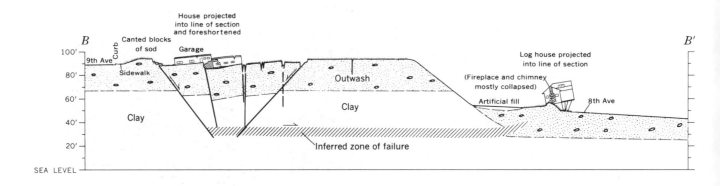

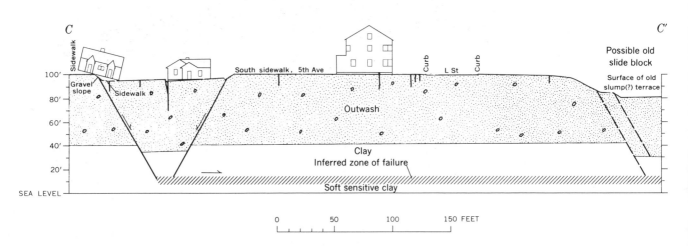

30.—Geologic section through the L Street slide. In section C–C′ the toe of the slide is to the right of C′.

pressure ridges above sea level was very close to the inferred altitude of failure beneath the main slide block.

Damage caused by pressure ridges was extensive in the L Street slide although it was generally less devastating and less spectacular than that caused by tensional cracking and displace-ment in the graben area. Even so, losses to many small dwellings to-taled thousands of dollars; more expensive losses were sustained by larger structures. Some buildings that showed little evidence of dam-age on the outside sustained severe structural damage within. Utili-ties were badly damaged also.

Subsurface exploration of the L Street slide, as of the Fourth Ave-nue slide, was started by the Engi-neering Geology Evaluation Group soon after the earthquake, to learn the causes of sliding, to predict future behavior of the slide, and to recommend courses of action to be taken by the city. Subsequently, this work was trans-ferred to the Corps of Engineers.

Extensive drilling and sampling by the Corps, augmented by surface studies, indicated a complex and varied stratigraphy, modified by erosion downslope from the bluff line and by prior landsliding of undetermined age. Shannon and Wilson, Inc., (1964, p. 54) reported the following general sequence of stratigraphy:

1. At the top, outwash sand and gravel, generally 40 to 60 feet thick.
2. Stiff, silty clay, about 30 to 50 feet thick, and interbedded layers of sand and silt. This clay had a static shear strength generally greater than 0.5 tsf.
3. Silty clay, sensitive, 20 to 30 feet thick, having very sensitive layers of clayey silt, silt, and fine sand. Static shear strengths ranged from about 0.2 tsf to more than 0.5 tsf, and sensitivity ranged from about 5 to 30.
4. Stiff silty clay containing scattered sand grains, pebbles, and lenses of sand; thickness undetermined but greater than 50 feet. Static shear strength in this unit generally exceeded 0.5 tsf and increased with depth.

Despite numerous borings, the position of the zone of failure in the L Street slide was not definitely established, although zones of very low strength and high sensitivity were clearly indicated. Presumably, slippage occurred at the top of the sensitive zone, where the strength was lowest and the shearing stress was highest (Shannon and Wilson, Inc., 1964, p. 55). This position varied appreciably—from about 55 to 85 feet below ground surface (45 to 15 feet above sea level)—in different drilling locations. Estimates based on the graben rule place the zone of failure within that range also. Pres-

sure ridges at the foot of the slide lie within the same range of altitudes. Therefore, if failure beneath the block was within that range, the pressure ridges—as noted above—must have been caused by shallow translations of the relatively thin frozen surface layer—a sort of shove effect—rather than by deeper surfaceward shear. If so, some of the remedial buttresses proposed by the Corps of Engineers (Shannon and Wilson, Inc., 1964, pl. 9.6) would require design changes to be effective in the event of future movement.

Failure by liquefaction may also have occurred in saturated sand layers within the clay because several such layers were penetrated during the drilling program. Remolding would not necessarily lead to strengthening of these sand layers, unless repacking led to consolidation accompanied by escape of excess pore water. Unless these strengthening conditions have been met, the sand could fail again under similar circumstances as before.

Native Hospital Slide

The Native Hospital slide, or First Avenue slide [2] as it has occasionally been called, disrupted part of the grounds of the Alaska Native Service Hospital and wrecked a fuel-storage tank at the foot of the bluff (figs. 31, 32). Although it was a small slide and not a very destructive one, it was of unusual scientific interest because of its clear portrayal of repeated translatory landsliding in the same area. The slide of March 27, 1964, transected an earlier slide of identical habit and exposed the older graben in full cross section (fig. 32) in the headward scarp of the present graben. This site of failure, therefore, seems to answer the question

[2] Inasmuch as First Avenue does not extend into this part of Anchorage, the name "First Avenue slide" is misleading.

as to whether natural remolding and consolidation of the clay after sliding is sufficient in itself to forestall further sliding—it obviously was not, in the Native Hospital slide. Most other slide areas at Anchorage and vicinity also presented evidence of multiple sliding, but none did it as clearly as the Native Hospital slide. Multiple sliding is discussed further on pages A66–A67.

The Native Hospital slide involved only slightly more than 4 acres of ground and perhaps 360,000 cubic yards of earth. From flank to flank—northwest to southeast—it was about 650 feet across; from head to toe it was about 350 feet. Most of the disruption was in the slopes of a cuspate salient on the bluff line behind the hospital, but about three-fourths of an acre of upland behind the hospital collapsed into the graben as the main headward fracture opened up 120 feet or so back from the rim. Part of the parking lot of the hospital and an area of lawn-covered grounds were destroyed. Fractures that extended back from the slide damaged the hospital building itself.

The graben was exceptionally large for the size of the slide. Its disproportionate size is attributed to the large apparent lateral slippage of the slide. Arcuate in plan, it was about 600 feet long; it had a mean width of about 120 feet and a downthrow (depth) of as much as 25 feet which averaged about 20 feet. Its depth diminished rapidly toward the south, where horizontal slippage died out also.

Near the center of the slide, the downdropped graben wedge broke off precisely at the bluff line and tilted headward as it collapsed, so that the displacement at the headwall of the graben was greater than at the front wall and gave

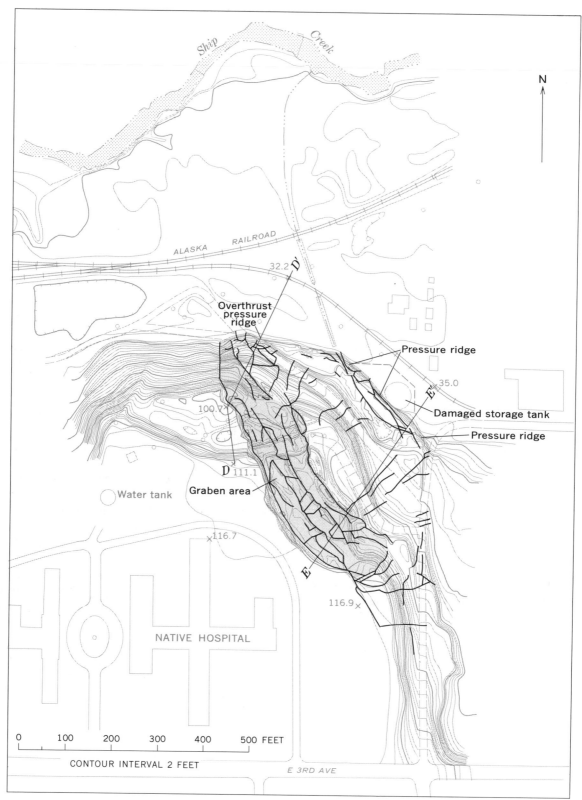

31.—Native Hospital slide area, Anchorage, Alaska.   Graben indicated by shading.

32.—Air view (looking south) of Native Hospital slide showing graben and pressure ridge. The scar of an older landslide is transected by the slide of March 27, 1964. Photograph by U.S. Army.

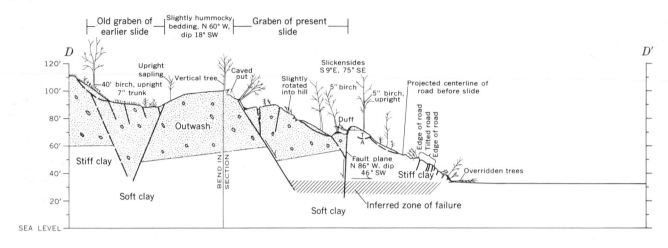

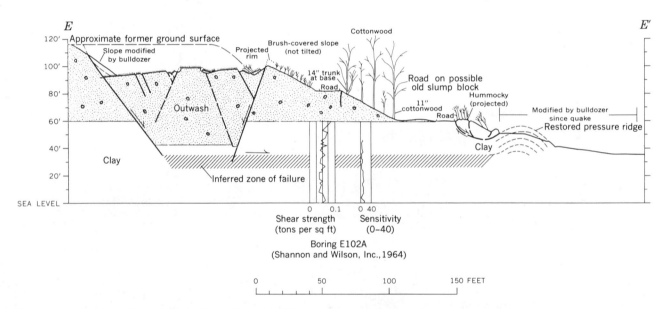

33.—Geologic sections through the Native Hospital slide, Anchorage, Alaska. Section D–D' transects the graben of an earlier landslide (upper left). Boring data from Shannon and Wilson, Inc. (1964).

the slide a pseudorotational appearance; however, the causative failure and dominant movements were horizontal, as verified by the perfectly upright attitude of trees in the main slide block. Longitudinally, the graben wedge was rent by great gaping tension cracks. The total relations are well illustrated by the aerial view (fig. 32) and by the cross sections (fig. 33).

Inasmuch as the slide moved outward from a salient, it was un-

confined laterally. Accordingly, it spread as it moved outward, and tension cracks opened in a fanlike arrangement at the periphery. Some of these tension cracks are visible in figure 32. They have been plotted in figure 31.

A large shallow-rooted pressure ridge about 500 feet long at the toe of the slide absorbed much of the thrust of the slide. At its greatest development the ridge was about 15 feet high and 40 to 50 feet wide. It wrecked the fuel-storage

tank at the foot of the bluff (fig. 32) and overrode overturned trees where it thrust forward as much as 12 feet (fig. 34).

Exactly how much the Native Hospital slide block was displaced laterally has not been determined, owing to a lack of good prequake horizontal control. Lateral offsets in roads and trails that crossed the block, however, afford a basis for reasonable estimates. These estimates range from 17 feet of slippage near the north flank of

34.—Overthrust toe of Native Hospital slide. Road is bulged up and displaced about 12 feet laterally. Note overridden trees at left.

the slide to 25 feet near the center. Furthermore, at least 15 feet of slippage can be accounted for in the pressure ridge at the toe of the slide. Projections to the theoretical slip surface of the slide, based on these figures and using the graben rule, place the slip surface at a depth of 85 to 95 feet or 25 to 35 feet above sea level. This altitude is very close to the height of the flat on which the pressure ridge formed at the foot of the slide and to the top of the sensitive zone of the Bootlegger Cove Clay beneath the bluff. It is a probable altitude, therefore, for the zone of failure. Thus lat-

eral slippage of 17 to 25 feet within the slide block is geometrically reasonable. Any appreciably smaller slippage would require an inordinately deep slip surface to compensate for the relatively large sectional area of the graben.

Figure 33 shows cross-sectional reconstructions of the Native Hospital slide based on both surface and subsurface data. Although subsurface exploration by the Corps of Engineers did not disclose the surface of rupture, it did clearly define zones of stiff clay above and below a zone of weaker clay. Most of the clay sampled had sensitivities below 10, but the

sensitivity of some of it exceeded 30. Several thin sand layers may have contributed to failure by liquefaction.

Government Hill Slide

The Government Hill slide caused severe dislocations in the south-facing bluff on the north side of Ship Creek (fig. 35). Altogether, about 11 acres of land was involved, including about 2¼ acres of bottomland below the bluff where the slide passed into an earthflow and spread out in the yards of The Alaska Railroad. The volume of earth involved was about 900,000 cubic yards.

From flank to flank the slide

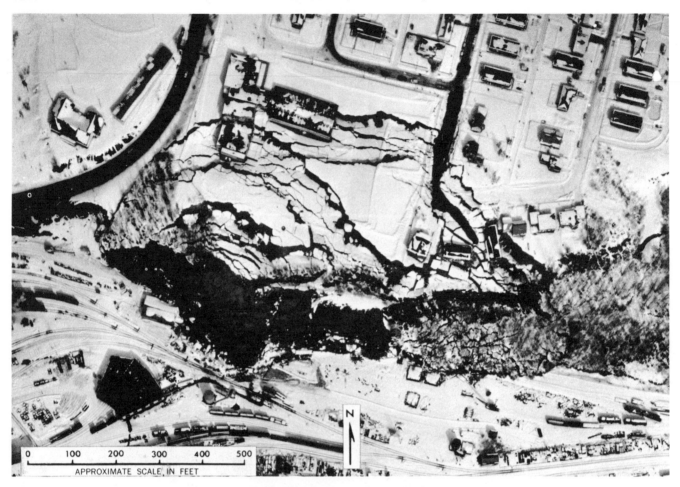

35.—Air view of Government Hill slide, Anchorage, Alaska. Graben plainly discernible. Compare with figure 38. Photograph by Air Photo Tech, Anchorage, Alaska.

had a width of 1,180 feet. From head to toe its greatest length, in the direction of slippage, was about 600 feet. The head of the slide regressed back about 400 feet behind the prequake bluff line, where it intersected the Government Hill Grade School. The slide devastated all but one wing of the school, destroyed two houses, damaged a third, left a fourth (since removed) perched precariously above a cliff, wrecked a shed in the railroad yards at the foot of the bluff, and did extensive damage to railroad equipment and trackage.

If any good fortune accompanied the March 27 earthquake, it was its timing; had school been in session, the disaster would have

been unthinkable. The south wing of the school dropped as much as 20 feet vertically into a graben after being sheared cleanly in half (fig. 3). Electric wall clocks stopped at 5:36 p.m. The east wing, also astride a graben, collapsed after being split longitudinally. The playground was a mass of chaotic blocks and open fissures (fig. 36).

The slide was more complex than the Fourth Avenue, L Street, or Native Hospital slides. Its complexity was a step further toward the total disruption shown by the Turnagain Heights slide (fig. 37). As shown by the map (fig. 38), a complex of arcuate horsts and grabens, more or less concentrically disposed, retrogressed head-

ward as the slide pulled away from the bluff. Two or three partly integrated grabens formed side by side along the crown of the bluff; these were complicated by internal collapses, cracking, and slumping along the face of the bluff. Two additional grabens formed behind the crown on the upland surface. The head of the slide broke away clean; back from the head there was very little cracking and virtually no damage to property.

Each graben was about 100 feet across. The two upland grabens, however, merged laterally, and at their junction the downdropped block was 200 feet across. The outer grabens were deepest—they exceeded 20 feet in depth; the

36.—Wreckage of Government Hill School as viewed from the playground, looking west. Graben in foreground is about 12 feet deep. Note undamaged water tower.

medial graben was 14 to 16 feet deep, and the inner graben averaged 12 to 14 feet deep. The intervening horsts glided laterally with slight vertical displacement.

Lateral displacements on the slide varied greatly from place to place inasmuch as the movement of the outermost horst block must have equalled the sum of movements of all blocks behind it plus its own differential movement.

Although precise figures for displacement are unavailable, careful comparisons of prequake and postquake aerial photographs give reasonable approximations. The south wing of the elementary school shifted laterally 6 to 7 feet to the southwest. A house at the end of Birch Street, on a horst detached from the main bluff, but otherwise little disturbed, moved about 35 feet southwestward. On

the playground south of the school building and across a graben from the building, a children's slide and whirligig moved about 35 feet southwestward. South of the whirligig across another graben, an old concrete blockhouse moved about 65 feet. The outermost points on the toe of the slide moved as much as 150 feet; these points, however, moved partly by flowage.

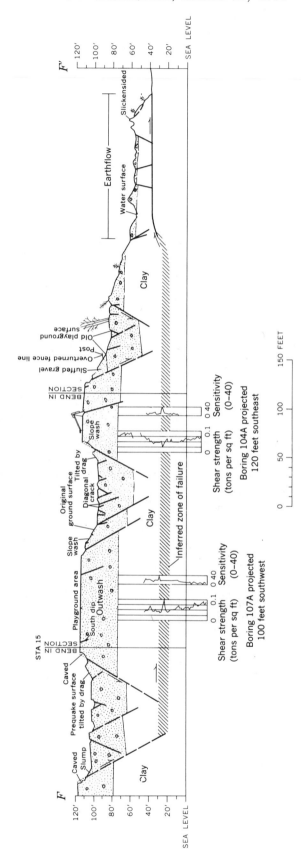

37.—Geologic section through Government Hill slide. Boring data from Shannon and Wilson, Inc. (1964).

Topography stereocompiled by J. R. Helm and
Gaylord Johansen, U.S. Geological Survey

38.—**Map of Government Hill slide, Anchorage, Alaska.** Many small fractures have been omitted. Graben areas indicated by shading. Compare with aerial photograph, figure 35.

39.—Homes devastated by Turnagain Heights slide; deep within slide area, upper; at main scarp, lower. About 75 homes were destroyed.

Surface inspection of the bluff line and subsurface studies by the Corps of Engineers indicate that the top of the Bootlegger Cove Clay is somewhat uneven in the Government Hill slide area but averages about 70 feet above sea level (40 to 55 feet below the original ground surface of the bluff). Overlying the clay is outwash sand and pebble gravel.

Shear strength profiles of the Bootlegger Cove Clay measured by Shannon and Wilson, Inc. (1964, p. 94) show the characteristic weak zone, in which static strength ranges from about 0.35 to 0.5 tsf, separated by stiffer clay zones above and below. Scattered throughout the section are lenses of sand and silt. In general, the strength profiles show a gradual

decrease in strength to a depth of 85 to 90 feet (altitude 25 to 30 feet) followed by a gradual increase in strength down to the lowest depth tested. The top of the weak zone (shear strength less than 0.5 tsf) generally lay at an altitude of about 40 feet. Most sensitivities were relatively low, perhaps owing partly to consolidation of the clay after remolding, but some were within the range of 20 to 40.

Most of the clay contained a percentage of water less than the liquid limit, but some clay—particularly at critical depths near the indicated depth of failure—had natural water contents equal to or greater than the liquid limit. Thus, the zone of lowest strength and highest sensitivity in the clay coincided with a zone of critically high water-plasticity ratios.

Failure appears to have occurred somewhere between altitudes of about 20 to 40 feet—depths somewhere between 70 and 90 feet below the prequake bluff line. This depth is very close to the top of the weak zone of the clay, and is near the altitude (40 feet) of the flat at the base of the bluff in The Alaska Railroad yards. It also coincides closely with the minimum depth of failure estimated according to the graben rule by using a horizontal translation of 35 feet divided into a graben sectional area of 2,500 square feet.

Several independent factors operating in concert helped precipitate failure. These factors included low shear strength, high sensitivity, and water contents exceeding liquid limits, combined at a depth where static shear stress was critically high, and where added stress conditions were introduced by the accelerations of the earthquake. An additional factor—artificial modification of the toe of the bluff by excavations at the base of the slope—may have contributed to failure by increasing the static shear stress on the slope. Aerial photographs taken in 1962 show plainly that the slope had been modified artificially prior to the earthquake. Shannon and Wilson, Inc. (1964, pl. 13.3), also presented clear evidence that the face of the slope had been modified by removal of material from the toe.

Turnagain Heights Slide

The Turnagain Heights slide was the largest, most complex, and physiographically most devastating landslide in the Anchorage area (figs. 39, 40; pl. 1). It extended west to east along the bluff line about 8,600 feet. Its maximum headward retrogression from the bluff was about 1,200 feet; its average retrogression into the heavily populated residential section of Turnagain Heights, where 75 homes reportedly were destroyed (fig. 39), was about 500 feet. A total area of about 130 acres was completely devastated by displacements that broke the ground into countless deranged blocks, collapsed and tilted at all odd angles. The ground surface within the slide area behind the prequake bluff line was lowered an average of about 35 feet below the old prequake level. The volume of earth within the slide was about 12½ million cubic yards.

Lateral spreading extended the slide seaward, as the leading edge glided down the mudflat into Knik Arm beyond the low tide line. The leading edge of the slide extended farther out beyond the old bluff line than the head of the slide regressed behind; in most places it reached much farther, even twice as far, before passing below tidewater. Maximum lateral slippage exceeded 2,000 feet. Thus, the

40.—Tree trunk split by tension fracture, Turnagain Heights slide. Many trees were similarly damaged because their roots were firmly embedded in the frozen ground.

landslide, on coming to rest, occupied an area considerably more than twice as large as the original undisturbed area.

As seen in plan, the Turnagain Heights slide was composite. It consisted of two main lobes: a West Turnagain lobe and an East Turnagain lobe, each in front of a separate headwall. Each lobe probably started as a separate landslide, but the two lobes merged laterally at a northward-projecting salient that was spared of sliding on the new bluff line. This salient centered on the mouth of

41.—Furrowed, slickensided clay ridge, Turnagain Heights slide. Ridge is about 20 feet high. Tilted collapsed block at left. Compare with figure 42.

Hood Creek and extended southward along the Hood Creek ravine. For a distance of 150 to 300 feet from the creek this shallow ravine formed an immobile, apparently stable, crack-free buttress that projected into the heart of the slide and divided the slide into east and west counterparts (pl. 1).

Each lobe removed about 4,300 feet of bluff line. The West Turnagain lobe, however, retrogressed headward much farther and extended farther seaward than the East Turnagain lobe, but the fractured area behind the East Turnagain lobe was much broader and more intensely broken than the area behind the West Turnagain lobe. If the East Turnagain lobe had retrogressed to the limit of intensive fracturing, it would have become a nearly exact counterpart of the West Turnagain lobe. Apparently the West Turnagain lobe had approached a state of dynamic stability by the time shaking stopped. In other words, the lobe probably had retrogressed to a point of near equilibrium under the dynamic conditions of

the time; it probably would not have reached much farther back if shaking had continued. The ground behind the East Turnagain lobe, on the other hand, was left in a state of precarious equilibrium when shaking ceased; it undoubtedly would have retrogressed much farther—possibly as far as Northern Lights Boulevard—if shaking had continued.

In addition to the slide proper, hundreds of tension fractures (fig. 40; pl. 1) opened behind the head of the slide—as far away as 2,200 feet from the main scarp of the East Turnagain lobe (Engineering Geology Evaluation Group, 1964, pl. 8b). These fractures were disposed concentrically about the two main centers of regression—one south of the East Turnagain lobe between Fish Creek and Hood Creek, and one south of the West Turnagain lobe west of Hood Creek. Besides causing g r e a t structural damage to housing in the Turnagain Heights subdivision, these fractures totally disrupted all underground utilities and seriously damaged streets and

curbings. Even more ominous, they outlined a potential headward expansion of the landslide that was forestalled only by the cessation of ground shaking. Continued shaking undoubtedly would have involved much more property in the landslide.

The ground behind the East Turnagain lobe had in fact begun to move, and the displacement increased toward the new bluff line. Preliminary studies reported by the Engineering Geology Evaluation Group (1964, p. 17) indicated that the area along Turnagain Parkway between the head of the slide and Northern Lights Boulevard was lengthened by more than 3 feet. Differential movement in this distance was taken up by the opening of tension cracks. There also was subsidence of 6 inches or more within a city block of the new bluff line. Detailed measurements by Dickinson Oswald and Associates, Anchorage, for the Engineering Department, City of Anchorage (summarized by Shannon and Wilson, Inc., 1964, p. 64) indicate that movement occurred chiefly before resurveying began—probably during the strong-motion period of the quake—and that no appreciable movement occurred during a 3-month period following the quake when detailed measurements were still being made.

It thus appears that the weak zone in the Bootlegger Cove Clay under the intensely fractured area between the slide proper and Northern Lights Boulevard did indeed fail, but sufficient shear resistance remained in the block after shaking stopped to prevent further sliding. The area at that time was buttressed, of course, by the passive pressure of the slide debris in front of it.

At the east margin of the slide, the bluff line facing Fish Creek held firm despite a sharp local re-

42.—Sharp-crested clay ridge, Turnagain Heights slide. Collapsed blocks tilted toward ridge on both flanks. Note horizontal stratification in ridge. Compare with figure 41.

lief of 40 feet or more. The slide, in fact, moved northwest almost diametrically away from Fish Creek, leaving behind a somewhat cracked but otherwise little-damaged salient or riblike buttress 70 to 400 feet wide projecting north along Loussac Drive. Conditions at Fish Creek, thus, were comparable to those at Hood Creek at the far side of the East Turnagain lobe.

One can but conclude that the shallow valleys of Fish Creek and Hood Creek were instrumental in limiting ground failure in the Turnagain Heights slide. Their function is unclear, but they may have acted as natural sumps that partly dewatered, and hence stabilized, the adjacent ground in the slopes of the ravines and in the bordering uplands some distance back from the ravines. This sup-

position gains support from subsurface data at Fish Creek where a boring by the Corps of Engineers penetrated clay of high strength, low sensitivity, and low water-plasticity ratios at the critical depths where failure had occurred nearby. The boring nearest Hood Creek (200 feet southeast of the creek) showed high sensitivity and low shear strength at the critical depth, but it showed high strength and low sensitivity immediately above. Fish Creek (altitude near mean sea level) had eroded its channel to the depth of the sensitive zone, but Hood Creek—a smaller stream—had not. But by cutting through the overlying clays, Hood Creek must have effectively lowered the water table in the adjacent ground, and in so doing further stiffened the upper clays. A drill hole closer to Hood

Creek might have provided more conclusive data.

Hundreds of sharp-crested clay ridges alternating with collapsed troughs, and oriented normal to the direction of slippage, distinguished the disruption pattern of the Turnagain Heights slide from all other slides at Anchorage. The ridges, however, were exact homologs of the horsts of the Government Hill slide; the troughs were exact homologs of the grabens. The chief distinction of the Turnagain Heights slide, therefore, other than its size, was the utter totality of its disruption. Its pattern is well portrayed by the topographic map (pl. 1) and by the strip map and section (pl. 2).

Most of the clay ridges ranged in height from about 10 to 15 feet, but a few were more than 20 feet high. They were as much as 300 feet long and were spaced 50 to 150 feet apart. Their steep sides, which sloped 60° to 70°, were furrowed and grooved by slippage of one surface against another (figs. 41, 42). On the average, the ridges were sharper crested and more closely spaced in the West Turnagain lobe than in the East Turnagain lobe.

Stratification was greatly disturbed in the collapsed areas between ridges, but it was little disturbed in the ridges themselves; the ridges were displaced virtually without rotation. There was, moreover, little vertical displacement as the ridges glided toward Knik Arm. Detailed studies along the disrupted seaward projection of Turnagain Parkway (pl. 2) indicated that clay ridges which were displaced as much as 300 feet laterally were reduced only about 12 feet vertically. Some of this reduction may have been due to attrition at the slip surface or to flowage in the sensitized clay below, but most of it probably was due to a seaward slope on the slip surface itself. This slope, then, must have had an inclination of about 4 percent.

The complete disruption of the ground surface within the Turnagain Heights slide may have been due to several factors in combination—including the shallow depth to the zone of failure—but the unhindered movement of the slide down the wet mudflat toward Knik Arm certainly was paramount. In every other translatory slide at Anchorage, slippage was resisted by dry or frozen ground at the toe and by an abrupt flattening of the ground slope at the foot of the slide below the bluff line. At Turnagain Heights, however, the slide broke away from the bluff within the intertidal zone and slid out directly onto the sloping tidal muds, which themselves were wet and sensitive. At the flanks of the slide, the tidal flat slopes about 3°, or 5 to 6 percent; before failure it probably had a comparable slope in front of the slide also.

Shear resistance of dry or frozen ground in front of a given slide must have had a natural buttressing effect that in turn must have been a factor in the resistance of the slide to slippage. All the translatory slides at Anchorage possessed such natural buttresses except the Turnagain Heights slide. The ground at the top of the intertidal zone, where the Turnagain Heights slide sheared to the surface, had previously had little opportunity to desiccate, and the thickness of the frozen layer must have been minimal—if indeed, the ground there was frozen at all. Reconnaissance along the foot of the bluff several years prior to the earthquake, moreover, disclosed a prevalence of saturation, slumpage, and flowage in the clay at the foot of

the bluff. More or less continuous slumpage, abetted by wave and tidal action which constantly removed the accumulated debris, prevented drying of the naturally wet clay and kept the bluff line in a precarious state of repose.

Part of the slip surface of the slide was left as a window near the west end of the slide, where the overlying debris slid free out to tidewater (fig. 43). Sliding, however, was not confined to this one surface. On the contrary, there is every indication that blocks slid out one on another at higher levels in the same vicinity. In other places, failure may have occurred mainly at some other level. But this surface was plainly an important locus of shearing in this particular part of the landslide.

Altogether, about a quarter of an acre of the slip surface was uncovered. The surface was mantled here and there by small pyramidal mounds and blobs of clay. Long furrows and welts, oriented in the direction of slippage (N. 3° W.) and extending the length of the exposure, were well preserved 6 weeks after the earthquake, despite desiccation and cracking.

The surface itself passed below highest tide at its seaward margin. It sloped about 15 feet per 100 feet, on the average, but it was convex; the outer edge was steeper than the inner edge. The exposed surface was precisely on the projection of the old prequake shoreline, so there is no doubt as to where the slide sheared off with reference to the prequake topography; it must have sheared to the ground surface at tidewater at the very foot of the bluff.

Mounds of clay left on the slip surface, showing evidence of having been overridden themselves, were grooved and slickensided on their tops and flanks. Their sides sloped steeply down to the slip sur-

face on which they rested, angles of 40° to 60°.

In places the slip surface was overlain by blocks of peat and forest duff. Frozen at the time of the quake, these blocks must have been lowered onto the slip surface as the intervening incompetent clay slid and flowed out from under them. The conclusion seems inescapable that the clay overlying the slip surface glided seaward primarily under the influence of gravity; a window to the slip surface could have been exposed in no other way.

At the extreme east end of the slide the slip surface did not break through to the ground surface. Instead, it died out laterally, as the thrust of the sliding mass was taken up by a large pressure ridge in the tidal silts just below the foot of the bluff (fig. 44). This ridge cut dramatically at an oblique angle across an old riprap embankment placed along the beach at the foot of the bluff—years before the earthquake—to retard marine erosion. The embankment was arched up into an anticline where the pressure ridge passed beneath it. The ridge was about 700 feet long, as much as 50 feet wide, and 10 to 15 feet high on the landward side. On the seaward side it was higher and was modified by subsidiary slumping on its oversteepened flank. Just west of the pressure ridge the translatory movement of the landslide was greater, and the slide itself was correspondingly more complex. The tidal silts failed, and the overriding slide blocks glided far out into the Knik Arm.

Subsurface explorations of the Turnagain Heights slide were made by the Corps of Engineers after an initial investigation was started by the Engineering Geology Evaluation Group. Undisturbed samples for field and labo-

43.—Slip surface of Turnagain Heights slide exposed near west margin of slide. Furrows and welts still well preserved despite desiccation and weathering. Point Woronzof and Knik Arm in distance.

ratory tests were collected from borings at 42 localities within the slide and adjacent to it. In some places the low strength of the clay made it difficult to collect undisturbed samples; some of this clay may have lost strength by remolding.

Surface and subsurface observations showed that the Bootlegger Cove Clay is mantled by outwash sand of somewhat varied thickness; the sand is about 20 feet thick at the east end of the slide and tapers nearly to zero at the west end. The clay is as much as 100 feet thick. Shear-strength profiles showed that the clay diminished gradually in strength from about 1 tsf at the top of the clay to about 0.25 tsf at an altitude of 15 to 20 feet above sea level; it then increased gradually in strength to about 0.6 tsf at some depth (generally about 30 feet) below sea level. Values of minimum strength in some borings were much less than 0.25 tsf, again perhaps because of partial remolding of disturbed sensitive clay.

The depth of lowest strength commonly coincided with the depth of highest sensitivity and highest water-plasticity ratios. Throughout much of the Turnagain Heights area the clay at lowest shear strength contained water in excess of its liquid limit and had sensitivities greater than 40. Remolded, this clay had a shear strength of about 0.02 tsf (Shannon and Wilson, Inc., 1964, p. 65).

Thus, the depth of failure probably was 15 to 20 feet above sea level, at or near the top of the zone of lowest shear strength. This altitude also was the height of the knick point or slope break at the base of the bluff before the earthquake—the position at which the slide evidently broke to the surface and glided seaward down the mudflat.

The mode of failure of the Turnagain Heights slide differs in degree rather than in kind from the other translatory slides of the Anchorage area. Some idea of the sequence of failure can be had by examining different parts of the slide where movements had gone to different stages of completion by the time the earthquake stopped. At the extreme east end of the slide near the mouth of Fish Creek, for example, the failure compared morphologically with failure at the Native Hospital slide and near the east flank of the Fourth Avenue slide. A little farther west where the deterioration was somewhat greater, the failure was comparable to that in the Government Hill slide.

As stated previously, the slide was composite in that it was formed by the lateral merger of two main lobes. Within each of the main lobes there were subsidiary lobes that apparently formed independently at the bluff line, then merged laterally as they retrogressed, and finally slid in unison toward Knik Arm. They moved different distances, and the leading edge of their combined mass at tidewater therefore had a scalloped outline after motion ceased. (See map, pl. 1.) In the East Turnagain lobe, they also retrogressed unevenly into the bluff, making the new bluff line very irregular.

Interference or crowding between subsidiary lobes was accompanied by complex shifting and wrenching of blocks. Such movements may have caused lateral components of displacement of as much as 150 feet in a direction parallel to the old bluff line—as

indicated by the postquake positions of objects such as houses transported on the slide toward Knik Arm (Engineering Geology Evaluation Group, 1964, pl. 1). As the blocks pushed and shoved in response to the overall motion of the landslide, they also were lurched sharply from side to side by the vibratory motion of the earthquake. This lurching was mirrored by abrupt deflections in furrows and slickensides preserved on the sides of clay ridges.

Some time after the onset of the earthquake, the bluff line is visualized as having begun to fail along a broad front, but mainly from one or more centers in each main lobe of the slide. Blocks then began to break off headward and to the flanks of each center. Eyewitness accounts indicated that 2 minutes or more elapsed from the start of the quake before the bluff began to give way (Shannon and Wilson, Inc., 1964, p. 64) and that movement continued for some time after the earthquake had subsided. A particularly lucid and informative report was given by Mr. Brooke Marston to Mr. E. R. Bush (Grantz, Plafker, and Kachadoorian, 1964, p. 14) :

I was driving my automobile westward on McCollie Avenue when the earthquake occurred. I immediately stopped my automobile and waited until the quake subsided. It appeared to me that the car was rocking from north to south. It rocked so violently that I nearly became seasick. From my car I could observe an earth crack alined north-south and opening and closing from east to west. As soon as the quake subsided I proceeded to drive westward to the corner of McCollie Avenue and Turnagain Parkway. After turning right on Turnagain Parkway and driving approximately 180 feet north, I realized the bluff was gone north of my driveway, which paralleled the bluff in an east-west direction. I got out of the car, ran northward toward my driveway, and then saw that the bluff had

broken back approximately 300 feet southward from its original edge. Additional slumping of the bluff caused me to return to my car and back southward approximately 180 feet to the corner of McCollie and Turnagain Parkway. After I stopped at this point, the bluff continued to slowly slide northward as I continued to back my auto southward on Turnagain Parkway. The bluff slowly broke away until the corner of Turnagain Parkway and McCollie had slumped northward.

It is my impression that the Turnagain Bluff area slumped northward in segments and that much of the southward receding of the bluff occurred after the major earthquake had subsided.

From Mr. Marston's account, it is clear that large-scale ground displacements were still in progress after the earthquake had stopped. After the quake, during the time that Mr. Marston drove down McCollie Avenue, turned north down Turnagain Parkway, got out of his car and returned, then backed south along Turnagain Parkway, stopped, and resumed backing—all this after the shaking had stopped—the bluff continued to regress southward. It regressed at least 200 feet, and the elapsed time must have been a full minute or more. If Mr. Marston had been driving 5 miles per hour, for example, including backing but not counting stops, he would have needed about 55 seconds to go 400 feet. He probably drove appreciably farther than 400 feet, however, and his stops must have taken several seconds each.

Small-scale slumping continued for several days after the quake as oversteepened slopes along the new bluff line continued to sluff away and frozen blocks of sand and forest duff began to thaw. One house, left precariously balanced, but not severely damaged on the rim of the bluff at Chilligan Drive, toppled and collapsed several days later. So far as is

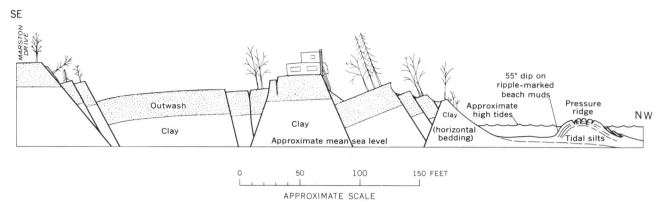

SE

MARSTON DRIVE

Outwash

Clay

Clay

Approximate mean sea level

Clay

(horizontal bedding)

Approximate high tides

55° dip on ripple-marked beach muds

Pressure ridge

NW

Tidal silts

0   50   100   150 FEET

APPROXIMATE SCALE

44.—Sketch section through eastern part of Turnagain Heights slide. Note pressure ridge, upright blocks at center and to left of pressure ridge, and tilted collapsed blocks between.

known, aftershocks did not cause any additional sliding.

Failure at Turnagain Heights probably occurred near the top of the lowest-strength zone of the Bootlegger Cove Clay, at an altitude of 15 to 20 feet above sea level. Inasmuch as the top of this zone was a subhorizontal surface, the failure itself must have been along a subhorizontal surface also, and the initial movements of the slide must have been translatory. Because the clay contained water in excess of its liquid limit, because the strength of the clay under pulsating or vibratory stress was appreciably less than under static stress, and because the zone of lowest strength coincided with the zone of highest sensitivity, the face and crown of the bluff were—in effect—afloat on a liquefied layer of viscous clay. The bluff then began to glide slowly seaward under the influence of gravity, leaving a gaping crack in its wake. The presence of open cracks—denoting release of tension—is significant; nearly all eyewitness reports allude to them.

Earth materials strained under horizontally directed tension commonly have two sets of tension fractures: one set antithetical to the other such that alternate fractures dip toward and away from one another and both sets are oriented normal to the direction of

maximum tension. As the slide began to spread, countless tension fractures disrupted its surface and the surface of the ground behind the slide; after movement stopped, incipient grabens were preserved in the subdivision behind the slide.

Along antithetical fractures dipping south, the unsupported hanging wall generally collapsed toward the north; along fractures dipping north, the hanging wall collapsed toward the south. At a given clay ridge bounded by opposed fractures dipping away from the ridge, adjacent collapsed blocks commonly were tilted toward the ridge on both flanks (figs. 41, 42). Farther from the ridge in the bottom of the adjoining trough or graben, collapsed blocks were tilted into helter-skelter attitudes.

As each new block pulled away from the bluff, the new bluff line was left unsupported on the seaward side. Tension fractures reduced support on the landward side. Blocks were pulled away successively by gravity as long as the shear resistance at the slip surface was exceeded by the force of gravity plus the accelerations of the earthquake. When the earthquake stopped, the force of gravity alone was sufficient to cause large-scale failure for some time afterward. And in the hanging wall of each tension fracture, subordinate

blocks collapsed and toppled under their own weight—the entire mass at the same time gliding slowly toward Knik Arm.

After the earthquake, the outermost slide block of the original bluff line was preserved to view only at the extreme east end of the slide (fig. 44) where the thrust of the toe was countered by a pressure ridge. Elsewhere along the front of the slide, where movement was much greater, the toe of the slide and the old bluff line passed beneath the waves of Knik Arm. Only at the east end of the slide, therefore, where the movement did not go to completion, is it possible to visualize what happened at the outset when the bluff first began to fail. Rotational movement at the east end of the slide is ruled out; stratification in the Bootlegger Cove Clay was undisturbed despite lateral shifting of several feet, and trees on the slide block remained perfectly upright. Rotational effects came into play behind the block, however, where the overhanging trailing edge of the block, lacking support, tilted backward and collapsed.

Some idea of the complexity of the disruption is presented in plates 1 and 2 and in a restored section through the slide prepared for the Corps of Engineers

[353]

(*in* Shannon and Wilson, Inc., 1964, pl. 10.8). This restoration is in general agreement with figure 43 and with the steps previously outlined, although it emphasizes the part played by rotation in the process and minimizes the effects of translatory motion. This res-

toration also contains minor geometric inconsistencies. Contrary to this view, translatory motion under gravity is here envisaged as the primary operative mechanism of landsliding, not only at Turnagain Heights but at the other major slides in Anchorage as well.

Rotation, as well as flowage, must have occurred in some degree in all the slides, but rotation is viewed as a subordinate process not germane to the failure of the ground, even though it certainly was significant in the disruption of the ground surface.

LANDSLIDING PRIOR TO THE MARCH 27 EARTHQUAKE

Geologic evidence indicates that landslides similar to those set off by the March 27 earthquake have occurred previously in the Anchorage area. Most of these slides predated the settlement of Anchorage, and it is not known, therefore, whether or not most of them were triggered by earthquakes; the morphology of some, by analogy with the March 27 slides, suggests that earthquakes have had a part. Some inferences as to timing suggest the same. The earthquake of October 3, 1954, clearly triggered slides along The Alaska Railroad near Potter Hill.

Evidence of old landslides in certain areas of Anchorage has been cited elsewhere in this report (p. A31, A49). The evidence is here reiterated, together with evidence of sliding elsewhere. Miller and Dobrovolny (1959) recognized many areas of past landsliding, showing them on their map (pl. 1) as "areas covered by landslides, slumps, or flows," with the prognosis that "shocks, such as those associated with earthquakes, will start moving material that under most conditions is stable" (p. 104).

Old landslides, like recent ones, were concentrated along bluff lines where topographic relief caused high static-shearing stress on the underlying soil. Most old slides have the form of recessed alcoves with uneven terracelike floors. Small slides may have the form of

steplike breaks on the sides of the bluffs. Some slumps have left lobate accumulations of earth at the foot of the bluffs. The fact that an area has slid previously apparently is no basis for predicting that it will or will not slide again. Many former landslides were stable during the March 27 earthquake, but in some places new slides were superimposed directly on old ones.

Compelling evidence of previous translatory sliding was found at the site of the Native Hospital slide, where a well-preserved graben was truncated by the slide of March 27. The old slide block and its graben are shown well in figure 32. Birch trees growing on the scarp of the old graben average about 7 inches in trunk diameter at breast height. Trees of that size on well-drained ground in the Anchorage area average about 60 years in age (Reed and Harms, 1956, p. 241). Five years or more may have been required after sliding to establish forest growth on the raw gravel. About 65 years, therefore, is the probable minimum age of the slide, an age which dates to about the turn of the century. Many earthquakes, some of them severe, occurred at about that time in southern Alaska (Davis and Echols, 1962), and one of them might have triggered landslides at Anchorage. The great Yakutat earthquake of 1899 was felt in

much of southern Alaska, including points more distant that Anchorage (Tarr and Martin, 1912, p. 68 and pl. 33), but whether the quake's intensity was sufficient to trigger landslides as far away as Anchorage is uncertain.

Remnants of old slides are abundant elsewhere along the bluffs of Ship Creek. Between the Native Hospital slide area and the Fourth Avenue slide area, the Alaska State Highway Department facilities are located in an old slide area that was partly reactivated on March 27. The alcovelike area centered at the city parking lot north of Fourth Avenue, between C and E Streets, probably also is the scar of an old landslide (Shannon and Wilson, Inc., 1964, p. 39; R. M. Waller, written commun., 1965). The area coincides almost exactly with the Fourth Avenue slide of March 27, except that the Fourth Avenue slide retrogressed farther into the bluff. The salient west of this slide partly bounded by Christensen Drive and Second Avenue appears to be a lowered slump block.

On the north side of Ship Creek, the recess just west of the destroyed Government Hill School may be an old slide scar. Points farther west along the bluff and north around the bend above the Port of Anchorage have many of the topographic markings of landslides, including alcoves, step terraces, and grabenlike depressions. The bluff at Cairn Point below the Elmendorf Moraine has a long history of minor slumping. Evidence of prior slumping along Bluff Road east of Government Hill School has been noted previously.

Along the bluff above Knik Arm between L Street and O Street, scallop-shaped recesses and terracelike benches below the crown of the bluff probably are old slide blocks. A remarkable channellike trench that trends diagonally southwest from the vicinity of R Street and Tenth Avenue toward S Street and Eleventh Avenue probably is a remnant of an old graben. Trees in this trench are comparable in size to those in the old graben near the Alaska Native Hospital.

Farther southwest near the mouth of Chester Creek, the bench along Bootlegger Cove Drive probably is an old slide block, and due east from there the broad recess centered near Inlet View School probably is an old slide area also (fig. 27). This feature is very subdued and probably is very old.

The bluff line along the south side of Chester Creek from the mouth of the creek discontinuously as far east as Rogers Park shows evidence of past slumping. Terracelike features lacking continuity along the valley margin, especially those deeply recessed into alcovelike niches, or those having irregular floors—particularly back-sloping floors, probably are slump blocks. On March 27 a small slump occurred in the bluff just north of West High School. Forest Park Golf Course between the mouths of Chester and Fish Creeks appears to be situated in an area of old landslides.

West from Fish Creek to Point Woronzof the bluff line has had a long history of slumping. There is no indication of previous sliding comparable to the disastrous Turnagain Heights slide, but small-scale sluffing away and localized slumping were continuing problems; the long-range effect was a slow but relentless sapping away of the bluff line.

The long bluff line south of Anchorage facing Turnagain Arm showed little evidence of landsliding prior to the March 27 earthquake except at Potter Hill and Point Campbell. Slumping at Potter Hill has been a recurrent problem, only in part caused by earthquakes. At Point Campbell, intermittent debris slides and sand runs have been caused by ordinary wave and current erosion at the foot of the bluff—processes unrelated to earthquakes.

REFERENCES

Alaskan Construction Consultants Committee [1964], Reconstruction and development survey of earthquake damage in Alaska: Prepared for and published by Federal Reconstruction and Development Planning Commission for Alaska; Honorable Clinton P. Anderson, U.S. Senator, Chairman, 98 p.

Berg, G. V., and Stratta, J. L., 1964, Anchorage and the Alaska earthquake of March 27, 1964: New York, Am. Iron and Steel Inst., 83 p.

Bjerrum, Laurits, 1954, Geotechnical properties of Norwegian marine clays: Geotechnique, v. 4, no. 2, p. 49–69.

——— 1955, Stability of natural slopes in quick clay: Geotechnique, v. 5, no. 1, p. 101–119.

Capps, S. R., 1916, The Turnagain-Knik region: U.S. Geol. Survey Bull. 642–E, p. 147–194.

——— 1940, Geology of The Alaska Railroad region: U.S. Geol. Survey Bull. 907, 201 p.

Casagrande, Arthur, 1947, Classification and identification of soils: Am. Soc. Civil Engineers Proc., v. 73, no. 6, pt. 1, p. 783–810.

Casagrande, Arthur, and Fadum, R. E., 1944, Application of soil mechanics in designing building foundations: Am. Soc. Civil Engineers Trans., v. 109, Paper 2213, p. 383–490.

Cederstrom, D. J., Trainer, F. W., and Waller, R. M., 1964, Geology and ground-water resources of the Anchorage area, Alaska: U.S. Geol. Survey-Water Supply Paper 1773, 108 p.

Crandell, D. R., 1952, Landslides and rapid-flowage phenomena near Pierre, South Dakota; Econ. Geology, v. 47, no. 5, p. 548–568.

——— 1958, Geology of the Pierre area, South Dakota: U.S. Geol. Survey Prof. Paper 307, 83 p.

Davis, T. N., and Echols, Carol, 1962, A table of Alaskan earthquakes, 1788–1961: Alaska Univ. Geophys. Inst. Geophys. Research Rept. 8 [UAG–R131], 43 p.

Davis, S. T., and Juan Karzulovíc K., 1963, Landslides at Lago Riñihue, Chile: Seismol. Soc. America Bull., v. 53, no. 6, p. 1403–1414.

Eide, Ove, and Bjerrum, L., 1955, The slide at Bekkelaget: Norges Geotek. Inst. Pub. 10; Geotechnique, v. 5, no. 1, p. 88–100.

Engineering Geology Evaluation Group, 1964, Geologic report—27 March 1964 earthquake in Greater Anchorage area: Prepared for and published by Alaska State Housing Authority and the City of Anchorage, Anchorage, Alaska, 34, p., 12 figs., 17 pls.

Federal Reconstruction and Development Planning Commission for Alaska, 1964, Response to disaster, Alaskan earthquake, March 27, 1964: Washington, U.S. Govt. Printing Office, 84 p.

Fuller, M. L., 1912, The New Madrid earthquake: U.S. Geol. Survey Bull. 494, 119 p.

Goddard, E. N., chm., and others, 1948, Rock-color chart: Washington, Natl. Research Council (repub. by Geol. Soc. America, 1951), 6 p.

Grantz, Arthur, Plafker, George, and Kachadoordian, Reuben, 1964, Alaska's Good Friday earthquake. March 27, 1964, a preliminary geologic evaluation: U.S. Geol. Survey Circ. 491, 35 p.

Karlstrom, T. N. V., 1957, Tentative correlation of Alaskan glacial sequences, 1956: Science, v. 125, no. 3237, p. 73–74.

Karlstrom, T. N. V., 1964, Quaternary geology of the Kenai Lowland and glacial history of the Cook Inlet region, Alaska: U.S. Geol. Survey Prof. Paper 443, 69 p.

Lambe, T. W., 1958, The structure of compacted clay: Am. Soc. Civil Engineers Proc., v. 84, SM2 Paper 1654, 34 p.; reprinted, 1960, in Am. Soc. Civil Engineers Trans., v. 125, pt. 1, p. 682–706.

McMinn, J. H., 1964, The verdict of Anchorage—good structural design survived: Eng. News-Record, v. 172, no. 15, p. 23–25.

Meade, R. H., 1964, Removal of water and rearrangement of particles during compaction of clayey sediments—review: U.S. Geol. Survey Prof. Paper 497–B, p. B1–B23.

Miller, R. D., and Dobrovolny, Ernest, 1959, Surficial geology of Anchorage and vicinity, Alaska: U.S. Geol. Survey Bull. 1093, 128 p.

Mitchell, J. K., 1956, The fabric of natural clays and its relation to engineering properties: Highway Research Board Proc., v. 35, p. 693–713.

National Board of Fire Underwriters and Pacific Fire Rating Bureau,
1964, The Alaska earthquake, March 27, 1964: San Francisco, Calif., 35 p.

Odenstad, Sten, 1951, The landslide at Sköttorp on the Lidan river, February 2, 1946: [Royal] Swedish Geotech. Inst. Proc., no. 4, 40 p.

Reed, J. C., Jr., and Harms, J. C., 1956. Rates of tree growth and forest succession in the Anchorage-Matanuska Valley area, Alaska: Arctic, v. 9, no. 4, p. 239–248.

Rosenqvist, I. T., 1960, Marine clays and quick clay slides in south and central Norway: Internat. Geol. Cong., 21st, Oslo, Norway, 1960, Guide to Excursion C13, 27 p.

———— 1962, The influence of physico-chemical factors upon the mechanical properties of clays, in Swineford, Ada, ed., Clays and clay minerals: Natl. Conf. on Clays and Clay Minerals, 9th, Lafayette, Ind., 1960, p. 12–27.

Schmidt, Ruth A. M., 1963, Pleistocene marine microfauna in the Bootlegger Cove Clay, Anchorage, Alaska: Science, v. 141, no. 3578, p. 350–351.

———— 1964, Geology in a hurry: Geotimes, v. 9, no. 3, p. 13–15.

Shannon and Wilson, Inc., 1964, Report on Anchorage area soil studies, Alaska, to U.S. Army Engineer District, Anchorage, Alaska: Seattle, Wash., 109 p., app. A–K, pls., illus.

Steinbrugge, K. V., 1964, Engineering seismology aspects, in Prince William Sound, Alaskan earthquakes, March–April 1964: U.S. Coast and Geod. Survey, Seismology Div., Prelim. Rept., p. 58–72.

Stokes, W. L., and Varnes, D. J., 1955, Glossary of selected geologic terms with special reference to their use
in engineering: Colorado Sci. Soc. Proc., v. 16, 165 p.

Tarr, R. S., and Martin, Lawrence, 1912, The earthquakes at Yakutat Bay, Alaska, in September 1899: U.S. Geol. Survey Prof. Paper 69, 135 p.

Terzaghi, Karl, 1950, Mechanism of landslides, in Application of geology to engineering practice (Berkey volume): New York, Geol. Soc. America, p. 83–123.

Terzaghi, Karl, and Peck, R. B., 1948, Soil mechanics in engineering practice: New York, John Wiley & Sons, Inc., 566 p.

Trainer, F. W., and Waller, R. M., 1965, Subsurface stratigraphy of drift at Anchorage, Alaska: U.S. Geol. Survey Prof. Paper 525–C, 1965.

U.S. Bureau of Reclamation, 1960, Earth manual—A guide to the use of soils as foundations and as construction materials for hydraulic structure, 1st ed.: U.S. Bur. of Reclamation, Denver, Colo., 751 p.

U.S. Geological Survey, 1962, Anchorage and vicinity, Alaska: U.S. Geol. Survey topographic map series, scale 1 : 24,000.

Varnes, D. J., 1958, Landslide types and processes, in Eckel, E. B., ed., Landslides and engineering practice: Natl. Research Council, Highway Research Board Spec. Rept. 29, p. 20–47.

Waller, R. M., Thomas, H. E., and Vorhis, R. C., 1965, Effects of the Good Friday earthquake on water supplies: Am. Water Works Assoc. Jour., v. 57, no. 2, p. 123–131.

White, J. E., 1965, Seismic waves—radiation, transmission, and attenuation: New York, McGraw Hill Book Co., 302 p.

CLARIFICATIONS

Geology Vol. Page	USGS Page	Column	Line	Remarks
347	A 59	1	19	Plate 1 is Plate E in Part B, the accompanying map case
349	A 61	3	20	Plate 2 is Plate F in Part B, the accompanying map case

The town of Valdez, part of the Valdez outwash delta, the Valdez Glacier, and the Chugach Mountains.   Photograph by
Bradford Washburn, 1937.

[358]

HENRY W. COULTER
U.S. GEOLOGICAL SURVEY

RALPH R. MIGLIACCIO*
ALASKA DEPARTMENT OF HIGHWAYS

Reprinted with minor changes from
U.S. Geological Survey Professional Paper 542-C,
"Effects of the Earthquake of March 27, 1964, at Valdez, Alaska"

Effects at Valdez

ABSTRACT

Valdez is situated on the seaward edge of a large outwash delta composed of a thick section of saturated silty sand and gravel. The earthquake of March 27, 1964, triggered a massive submarine slide, involving approximately 98 million cubic yards of material, that destroyed the harbor facilities and nearshore installations. Waves generated by the slide and subsequent strong seiches did additional damage in the downtown area. Stresses generated by the seismic shocks and the slide developed an extensive system of fissures throughout the unconsolidated deposits at the head of the fiord. These fissures plus the shocks caused structural damage to many of the buildings in Valdez and destroyed the sewer and water systems. Removal of support from the face of the delta by submarine sliding allowed some of the material to move seaward and caused parts of the shore area to subside below high-tide level.

A site for relocating the town of Valdez has been designated. It is situated on the Mineral Creek fan—an area underlain by coarse alluvial gravel. This relocation site is protected from sea waves by a series of bedrock ridges and islands that also provide a resistant buttress retaining and protecting the toe of the fan from danger of sliding or slumping. The absence of evidence of ground breakage on the Mineral Creek fan indicates that the coarse subsoils at the relocation site react favorably under seismic conditions.

INTRODUCTION

At 5:36 p.m., March 27, 1964 (Alaska standard time), a great earthquake of magnitude 8.4 to 8.6 on the Richter scale, centered at lat 61.05° N. and long 147.50° W. approximately 45 miles west of Valdez, rocked south-central Alaska (Grantz, Plafker, and Kachadoorian, 1964). The loss of life and damage at Valdez resulting from submarine slides, sea waves, and ground breakage (pl. 1) coincident upon this event were so great, and the prognosis of recurrence of such effects during possible future seismic activity so forbidding, that the decision was made to move the entire community to a safer location. The results of the geologic investigations which supplied background information for this decision are presented here. The new site chosen is about 4 miles northwest, on Mineral Creek fan—a more stable area that also has natural protection from sea waves.

Port Valdez, the northeasternmost extension of Prince William Sound, is a narrow steep-walled glaciated reentrant or fiord in the Chugach Mountains (fig. 1). The fiord trends east-west and is approximately 14 miles long and 3 miles wide. The axial alinement of Port Valdez is controlled by a strongly developed, steeply dipping foliation in the metasedimentary rocks of the Valdez Group of Late Cretaceous(?) age. Alinement of the tributary valleys is controlled by a prominent north-south joint set. The Port Valdez depression extends laterally into four subsidiary valleys—Valdez Narrows to the southwest, Shoup Bay to the northwest, Valdez Glacier valley to the northeast, and Lowe River valley and Heiden Canyon to the east (frontispiece and fig. 20.) Elsewhere Port Valdez is hemmed in by steep mountain walls rising to altitudes of 3,000 to more than 5,000 feet. Soundings in Port Valdez indicate that the high-angle subaerial slopes continue beneath the water and form a steep-sided flat-bottomed trough with maximum depths of more than 800 feet. The submarine topography shows irregularities similar to the subaerial glaciated landforms of Port Valdez, many elongate ridges displaying prominent stoss and lee morphology.

*Now with R&M Engineering and Geological Consultants, Fairbanks.

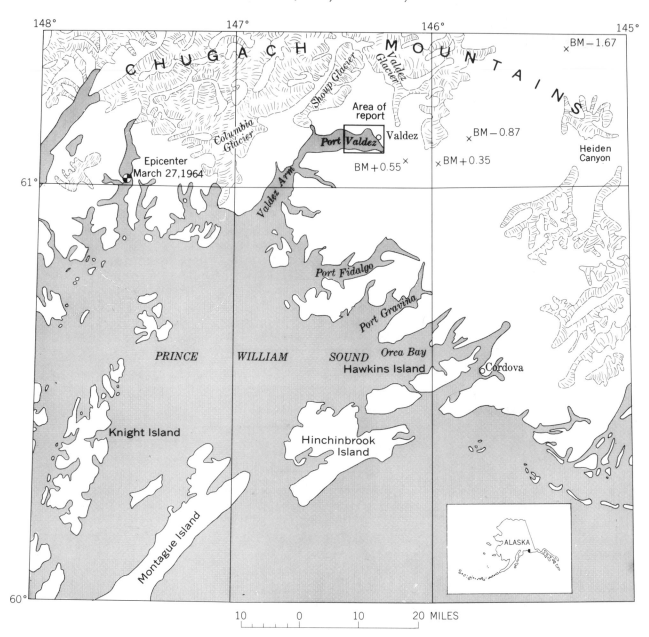

1.—Index map, Valdez area.   Bench marks show change in altitude, in feet.

The eastern end of Port Valdez is being filled rapidly by an outwash delta supplied by material carried by the Lowe River, the Robe River, and the stream from Valdez Glacier.   The subaerial part of this delta slopes westward from approximately 300 feet at the toe of Valdez Glacier to sea level in a distance of approximately 4 miles.   The town of Valdez is situated on the seaward edge of this outwash delta.

The geographic importance of Valdez stems from the fact that it is the farthest north ice-free seaport in Alaska and is the southern terminus of the Richardson Highway—the shortest and most direct route from tidewater to Fairbanks and interior Alaska.   The principal industry is shipping, and Valdez is the home port of a modest commercial and sport fishing fleet.   The population given for Valdez in the 1960 census is 555,

but during the heaviest shipping season a maximum population of 1,000 is estimated by the Alaska Department of Health and Welfare (1964).

ACKNOWLEDGMENTS

Many individuals and organizations contributed time, effort, and information in support of this investigation.   Mayor Bruce Woodford and the people of Valdez extended all possible assistance to us, as did the Fairbanks Committee for Alaska Earthquake Recovery through the agency of their representative, Acting Valdez City Manager, Ed Martin. Ralph Taylor, American Institute of Architects, of the Fairbanks Committee, supplied valuable data on the nature and extent of damage to buildings. District Engineer Nels Kjelstad, Assistant District Engineer William Whitnal, and the Valdez District staff of the Alaska Department of Highways were most cooperative. Charles H. Clark, geologist, Alaska Department of Highways, prepared a detailed map of the fissure distribution within the city and supervised the waterfront drilling program, and Robert Felland and Gordon Brunton, geologists, Alaska Department of Highways, supervised the drilling program at the Mineral Creek townsite. Charles H. Blake, U.S. Army Corps of Engineers, supplied detailed information on the damage to sewer and water supply systems. The late Capt. F. J. Bryant, U.S. Coast and Geodetic Survey, supplied preliminary data on altitudes and harbor soundings, and R. M. Chapman, U.S. Geological Survey, made preliminary observations in Valdez on April 1 and 2, 1964, and supplied pertinent information.

GEOLOGIC SETTING

The distribution and nature of the deposits in the vicinity of Valdez are shown on figure 2. For purposes of this discussion, they are most conveniently subdivided into one bedrock unit and three depositional complexes of unconsolidated sediments.

Port Valdez lies within the outcrop belt of the Valdez Group of Late Cretaceous(?) age. These rocks have been described by Moffit (1954) as: "Interbedded slate and graywacke prevailingly in thick beds. Includes minor amounts of argillite, arkosic sandstone, and conglomerate. Closely folded and subschistose to schistose."

In the vicinity of Valdez, the rocks of the Valdez Group have a well-developed foliation which strikes east-west and dips steeply to the north. They are also strongly jointed, the most prominent joint set being oriented perpendicular to the foliation. These two structural trends in the bedrock determine the topographic grain in the region. The southern flank of the Chugach Range, underlain by rocks of the Valdez Group, has been subjected to repeated episodes of intense glacial erosion, which has imposed a topography characteristic of ice-scoured areas on the entire region. It is into and against these glaciated bedrock landforms that the recent sediments have been, and are being, deposited.

At the eastern end of the Port Valdez fiord, the outwash plains of the Robe River, the Lowe River, and the stream from Valdez Glacier coalesce to form a broad delta, the surface of the delta slopes westward from about 300 feet above msl at the toe of Valdez Glacier to sea level in a distance of approximately 4 miles. Although the deepest well in this outwash delta penetrates only to a depth of 250 feet, the configuration of the bedrock valley and the depth of water in Port Valdez suggest that this section of unconsolidated deposits may be as much as 600 feet thick near the shoreline.

The prequake and postquake configurations of the seaward face of this deltaic complex are shown on plate 2. Subsurface investigations by the Alaska Department of Highways indicate that the delta is composed of a thick section of poorly consolidated silt, fine sand, and gravel (pl. 3 and table 1). The silt and fine sand occur as beds and stringers within the section and also are widely disseminated throughout the coarser fractions. The surficial beds of stream-deposited outwash gravels dip gently to the southwest, but more steeply dipping deltaic foreset beds probably occur at depth. The water table lies within a few feet of the surface throughout this outwash delta complex, so the entire section is saturated.

The Mineral Creek alluvial fan lies approximately 4 miles northwest of the town of Valdez. It was deposited in an elongate depression between the main valley wall and a parallel outlying bedrock ridge that forms a series of ribs and islands along the north shore of Port Valdez (see figs. 20 and 21, p. C34). This bedrock ridge serves to confine and contain the Mineral Creek fan on the seaward side. The fan slopes from approximately 60 feet above msl at the mountain front to sea level. The braided flood plain of Mineral Creek occupies the western margin of the fan, and the eastern margin and a short segment along the southwest shore are covered by tidal-flat deposits.

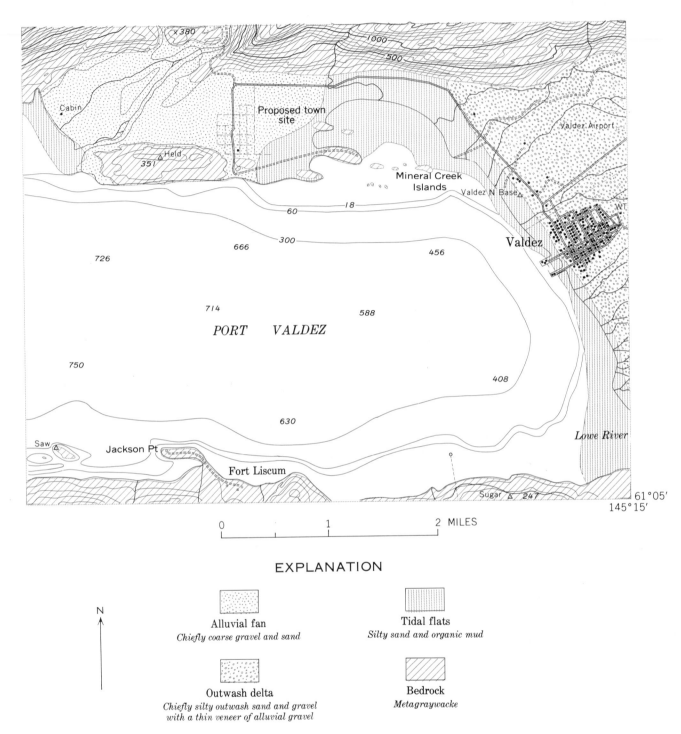

EXPLANATION

Alluvial fan
Chiefly coarse gravel and sand

Tidal flats
Silty sand and organic mud

Outwash delta
*Chiefly silty outwash sand and gravel
with a thin veneer of alluvial gravel*

Bedrock
Metagraywacke

2.—Ground conditions at Valdez.

TABLE 1.—*Grain-size analyses of test-boring samples from the Valdez delta*

[*LL*, liquid limit; *PL*, plastic limit; NV, no value; NP, nonplastic]

Boring	Sample	Sieve analysis, percent passing—												Atterberg limits		Moisture content (percent)	Specific gravity
		3 in.	2 in.	1¼ in.	1 in.	¾ in.	½ in.	No. 4	No. 10	No. 40	No. 200	0.02 mm	0.005 mm	LL	PL		
1	1	100	100	100	100	100	100	100	94	64	36.2	0	0	16	NP	9.7	----------
	2	100	100	100	100	100	100	100	100	100	96.1	0	0	21	NP	17.7	----------
	3	100	100	100	100	100	100	100	24	12	4.5	0	0	NV	NP	12.6	----------
	4	100	100	100	100	100	100	100	56	19	6.0	0	0	NV	NP	12.4	----------
	5	100	100	100	100	100	100	100	65	27	7.2	0	0	NV	NP	12.7	----------
	6	100	100	100	100	100	100	100	63	29	7.7	0	0	NV	NP	13.4	----------
	7	100	100	100	100	100	100	100	75	40	14.0	0	0	NV	NP	14.0	2.80
	8	100	100	100	100	100	100	100	78	46	14.3	0	0	NV	NP	16.3	2.73
	9	100	100	100	100	100	100	100	79	54	19.2	0	0	NV	NP	17.5	2.74
	10	100	100	100	100	100	100	100	74	36	8.4	0	0	NV	NP	14.1	2.73
	11	100	100	100	100	100	100	100	74	34	8.9	0	0	NV	NP	14.7	2.73
	12	100	100	100	100	100	100	100	77	23	5.6	0	0	NV	NP	17.5	----------
	13	100	100	100	100	100	100	100	71	27	7.0	0	0	NV	NP	13.8	----------
	14	100	100	100	100	100	100	100	51	26	9.6	0	0	NV	NP	11.2	----------
	15	100	100	100	100	100	100	100	4.0	3.0	1.8	0	0	--------	--------	19.6	----------
	16	100	100	100	100	100	100	100	17	8	3.3	0	0	--------	--------	7.9	----------
2	1	100	100	100	100	100	100	100	44	21	10.1	0	0	NV	NP	8.4	----------
	2	100	100	100	100	100	100	100	41	20	9.3	0	0	NV	NP	12.2	----------
	3	100	100	100	100	100	100	100	2.0	1.0	.8	0	0	--------	--------	15.0	----------
	4	100	100	100	100	100	100	100	42	18	6.7	0	0	NV	NP	14.4	----------
	5	100	100	100	100	100	100	100	76	17	3.4	0	0	NV	NP	21.3	----------
	6	100	100	100	100	100	100	100	77	37	6.8	0	0	NV	NP	16.7	----------
	7	100	100	100	100	100	100	100	61	25	8.5	0	0	NV	NP	12.1	----------
	8	100	100	100	100	100	100	100	80	43	7.9	0	0	NV	NP	16.9	2.74
	9	100	100	100	100	100	100	100	77	41	7.4	0	0	NV	NP	18.0	2.73
	10	100	100	100	100	100	100	100	83	55	14.0	0	0	NV	NP	18.7	2.73
	11	100	100	100	100	100	100	100	81	58	19.0	0	0	25	NP	14.6	2.75
	12	100	100	100	100	100	100	100	63	28	7.7	0	0	NV	NP	12.2	2.71
	13	100	100	100	100	100	100	100	75	39	7.7	0	0	NV	NP	14.5	----------
	14	100	100	100	100	100	100	100	71	33	6.7	0	0	NV	NP	14.5	----------
3	1	100	100	100	100	100	100	100	46	18	6.4	0	0	NV	NP	10.7	----------
	2	100	100	100	100	100	100	100	45	15	7.6	0	0	NV	NP	13.9	----------
	3	100	100	100	100	100	100	100	37	17	7.5	0	0	--------	--------	12.9	----------
	4	100	100	100	100	100	100	100	54	24	7.2	0	0	NV	NP	11.2	----------
	5	100	100	100	100	100	100	100	50	15	4.6	0	0	NV	NP	11.6	----------
	6	100	100	100	100	100	100	100	64	26	7.0	0	0	NV	NP	13.5	----------
	7	100	100	100	100	100	100	100	92	66	11.2	0	0	--------	--------	24.4	----------
	8	100	100	100	100	100	100	100	68	29	6.3	0	0	NV	NP	13.9	----------
	9	100	100	100	100	100	100	100	70	36	9.8	0	0	NV	NP	12.9	----------
	10	100	100	100	100	100	100	100	58	28	8.6	0	0	NV	NP	13.8	----------
	11	100	100	100	100	100	100	100	75	36	7.1	0	0	NV	NP	15.0	----------
	12	100	100	100	100	100	100	100	78	45	14.2	0	0	NV	NP	12.3	----------
	13	100	100	100	100	100	100	100	54	27	9.9	0	0	NV	NP	13.4	----------
	14	100	100	100	100	100	100	100	73	42	12.1	0	0	NV	NP	12.1	----------
	15	100	100	100	100	100	100	100	62	46	18.1	0	0	NV	NP	9.2	----------
	16	100	100	100	100	100	100	100	88	60	39.2	0	0	17	NP	15.0	----------
	17	100	100	100	100	100	100	100	80	43	14.2	0	0	NV	NP	11.6	----------
	18	100	100	100	100	100	100	100	73	32	5.6	0	0	NV	NP	14.3	----------
	19	100	100	100	100	100	100	100	99.7	99.4	84.2	36.8	18.5	18	18	23.0	----------
	20	100	100	100	100	100	100	100	80	51	16	8.1	3.6	NV	NP	11.3	----------
4	1	100	100	100	95	82	72	51	47	23	7.2	0	0	--------	--------	----------	2.76
	2	100	100	100	95	93	84	61	40	14	5.1	0	0	--------	--------	----------	2.73
	3	100	100	100	100	86	78	51	35	23	7.0	0	0	--------	--------	----------	----------
	4	100	100	100	100	81	74	59	37	11	3.3	0	0	--------	--------	----------	----------
5	1	100	100	100	100	73	71	62	54	30	8.0	0	0	--------	--------	----------	2.64
	2	100	100	100	100	80	67	42	26	12	5.6	0	0	--------	--------	----------	----------
	3	100	100	100	96	91	76	57	42	21	8.4	0	0	NV	NP	----------	2.68
	4	100	100	100	100	86	65	45	29	11	3.7	0	0	--------	--------	----------	----------
	5	100	100	100	84	82	72	55	39	18	8.0	0	0	--------	--------	----------	2.76
	6	100	100	100	100	97	83	61	42	19	8.2	0	0	NV	NP	----------	2.61
	7	100	100	100	100	97	88	67	50	22	4.3	0	0	NV	NP	----------	2.71
	8	100	100	100	100	100	100	95	90	56	26.1	0	0	NV	NP	----------	2.75
	9	100	100	100	100	100	99	91	83	57	14.4	0	0	NV	NP	----------	2.70
	10	100	100	100	96	96	91	77	63	28	2.6	0	0	NV	NP	----------	2.69
6	2	100	100	100	100	100	100	93	82	55	16	0	0	NV	NP	----------	2.68
	3	100	100	100	100	92	90	78	68	41	9.6	0	0	--------	--------	----------	2.74
	4	100	100	100	100	92	81	60	43	18	6.1	0	0	--------	--------	----------	2.68
	5	100	100	100	100	93	89	77	64	45	8.8	0	0	--------	--------	----------	2.70
	6	100	100	100	96	93	88	72	50	22	4.1	0	0	NV	NP	----------	2.68
	7	100	100	100	92	83	79	61	42	32	25.9	0	0	NV	NP	----------	2.63
	8	100	100	100	100	85	77	59	44	17	6.0	0	0	NV	NP	----------	2.80
	9	100	100	69	66	64	59	44	34	18	9.3	0	0	NV	NP	----------	2.65
7	1	100	100	100	100	100	100	100	84	72	42.4	24.6	10.2	NV	NP	18.0	2.69
	2	100	100	100	100	100	100	100	63	40	16.0	9.0	5.0	NV	NP	12.5	2.73
8	1	100	100	100	100	100	100	100	36	20	8.7	6.6	3.4	NV	NP	2.8	2.73
	2	100	100	100	100	100	100	100	56	31	15.7	11.0	5.6	NV	NP	13.2	2.67
	3	100	100	100	100	100	100	100	54	40	22.1	13.5	6.1	NV	NP	13.4	2.69
9	1	100	100	100	100	100	100	100	83	66	34.5	18.5	7.4	NV	NP	25.3	2.68
	2	100	100	100	100	100	100	100	95.4	86	52.7	23.6	8.8	NV	NP	26.2	2.73
	3	100	100	100	100	100	100	100	90.3	77	38.6	19.0	8.0	NV	NP	24.0	2.71
10	1	100	100	100	100	100	100	100	71	32	12.4	9.0	5.3	NV	NP	7.4	2.73

A comprehensive subsurface investigation was made of the central part of the Mineral Creek fan—the area selected for the new location of the town of Valdez. The investigation was initiated by the U.S. Geological Survey and the Alaska Department of Highways under the sponsorship of the Alaska State Housing Authority and the U.S. Army Corps of Engineers. Responsibility for the final phases of the investigation was assumed by Shannon and Wilson, Inc., of Seattle, Wash., under contract to the U.S. Army Engineer District, Anchorage, Alaska. Studies were made of 27 test pits ranging in depth from 7 to 12 feet, of 7 solid auger borings ranging in depth from 20 to 33 feet, and of 8 rotary borings ranging in depth from 37 to 121 feet.

The subsurface data show that the Mineral Creek alluvial fan is underlain by more than 100 feet of medium dense to very dense cobble gravel in a matrix of medium to coarse sand. Where exposed in the test pits, this gravel consists primarily of elongate tabular pebbles and cobbles of graywacke and some quartz showing a pronounced interlocking texture. The gravel is overlain by a thin layer of sand and silt and an organic mat 6 to 8 inches thick. In some places, along abandoned stream channels, the sand and silt may be as much as 4 feet thick, but the average thickness is about 1 foot. The complete results of the subsurface investigations are included in a report prepared by Shannon and Wilson, Inc. (1964).

Because of the relatively high tidal range (about 17 feet) and the large volume of finely comminuted rock particles carried by the glacial streams, broad tidal flats composed of silt, fine sand, and organic muds are being deposited at the seaward edge of the Valdez outwash delta and at the seaward edge of the Mineral Creek alluvial fan. These deposits are probably quite similar to, and in fact coextensive with, those being deposited as foreset beds along the face of the Valdez outwash delta.

At the time of the earthquake the ground at Valdez was frozen down to the water table, that is, to depths ranging from 4 to 6 feet below the surface; approximately 5 feet of snow lay on the ground. The predicted low tide for March 27, 1964, was −0.6 feet at 6:19 p.m., and the predicted high tide for March 28 was +12.4 feet at 12:42 a.m.

DRAINAGE

The town of Valdez has always been subject to intermittent flooding by the stream from Valdez Glacier (frontispiece). The first appraisal of this problem on record was made by Edward Gillete, an engineer in the party, led by Capt. W. R. Abercrombie, that surveyed the route from Valdez to Copper Center in 1899. Mr. Gillete wrote (in Abercrombie, 1900):

Where the small town of Valdez has been hastily built there is danger at any time of having the buildings swept into the Bay by swift and quickly changing channels formed by the numerous streams flowing from uncertain and everchanging parts of the immense Valdez Glacier situated some 4 miles north of town.

At present the channel of the stream from Valdez Glacier is artificially confined by levees, and the town itself is protected by a dike. The continued retreat of the terminus of Valdez Glacier over the past 50 years (fig. 3) into the mouth of its bedrock canyon has made the problem of channel control progressively less difficult. However, an unusual advance of Valdez Glacier, such as occurred along the coast after the 1899 Yakutat earthquake (Tarr and Martin, 1914, p. 168–194), could change the present drainage system enough to bypass the levees and cause damage to the highway and town.

Three large and several smaller ice-dammed lakes along the flanks of Valdez Glacier constitute another potential flooding hazard to the highway and town. Possible development of new crevasse systems in the glacier, such as might be caused by an earthquake, could result in a sudden release of large volumes of water from one or more of these lakes and consequent flooding in the lower drainage system.

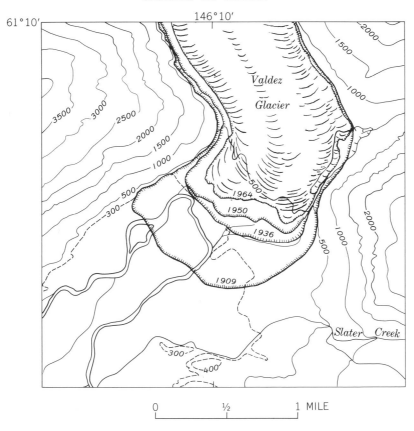

3.—Recorded positions of the terminus of Valdez Glacier since 1909.

SEISMIC HISTORY

Approximately 70 earthquakes of recorded or estimated magnitudes of 5 or greater have been reported from Valdez since 1898 (Davis and Echols, 1962; Heck, 1958). Of these, five in particular warrant special attention here because reinterpretation of the historical accounts suggests that these quakes were in fact accompanied by submarine landslides similar to the one triggered by the March 27th earthquake.

At the time of the Yakutat earthquake (Sept. 3, 1899), at Valdez the shaking was reportedly so strong "that men were made dizzy and could not stand, houses and forests were disturbed, and there were earthquake water waves in Port Valdez" (Tarr and Martin, 1912, p. 66).

There is also a fugitive report that a ship which had anchored off the mouth of the Lowe River in 40 feet of water in 1898 was unable to reach bottom with 200 feet of cable in the same spot late in the fall of 1899.

The second of the five relevant earthquakes took place on February 14, 1908, at 1:41 a.m. local time. It was variously reported by eyewitnesses to have lasted anywhere from 3 seconds to about 2 minutes. Several witnesses who were former residents of San Francisco stated that it seemed to be as violent as any of the shocks felt there April 18, 1906. The most interesting aspect of this quake, however, is the record of submarine cable breaks. These breaks were described and interpreted by Tarr and Martin (1912, p. 98):

* * * both the Valdez-Sitka and Valdez-Seward cables were interrupted close to the city of Valdez, and well inside Valdez Narrows * * *. A short length of the cable was covered by the upheaval of the sea bottom, so that it had to be abandoned.

A map by Lt. Paul Hurst, of the United States cableship *Burnside* (Pl. XXVII), shows the places where the cables were broken. The Valdez-Seward cable was broken in four places three-eighths to 1½ miles apart, while the Valdez-Sitka cable was broken in seven places five-eighths to seven-eighths mile apart. This later report shows that the cables were buried not in one place but in three, the outermost being 1½ to 3 miles from shore in 700 feet of water.

The United States Geological Survey party, under the direction of U. S. Grant, which worked in the region in 1908, did not discover actual faults running ashore nor changes of level of the land; one stretch of coast, however, along Valdez Inlet near the cable breaks, was not examined by them. Prof. Grant says:

"While at Valdez I went out to the Valdez Glacier and also walked westward from the town for about a mile and a half. On both of these trips I had in mind the possibility of earthquake cracks but saw no evidence of such. I think that cracks of any size made in February ought still to be visible the following summer. I also examined the south shore of Valdez Inlet from Fort Liscum westward to Entrance Island. This examination was done from a small gasoline launch which was practically everywhere within a few rods of the shore. When farther away I used a field glass. I saw no evidence of earthquake cracks along the shore, and I think that any displacements of a foot or so could easily be recognized. Neither did I see any evidence of elevated or depressed shore lines, although of course the shore was not examined in great detail.

"There was fire in the cable office at Valdez on the night of my arrival there and the maps and records of the earthquake of February 1908, were destroyed. I did not get [the] map showing the breaks in the cable until almost time to start home and so had no opportunity to study carefully the shore opposite the breaks."

The hypothesis that the pairs of breaks in parallel cables three-eighths to three-fourths of a mile apart are caused by faulting is of decided interest. The Coast Survey chart shows that this cable lies in soft mud under 280 to 800 feet of water where the breaks occurred. At these depths the alternate hypothesis of breaking of the cables by masses of silt sliding down the steep submerged delta front near Valdez does not seem plausible, for the soundings show no slopes down which the mud could slide to cause several of the breaks. Nor does a hypothesis of breaks a mile or more apart caused by jellylike shaking of the fiord-bottom deposits during the earthquakes seem applicable. It is far more likely that the cables were broken at the points shown (Pl. XXVII) by actual fault movements during the earthquakes.

It was further stated that the steamer *Northwestern*, which was approaching the dock at Valdez, encountered a "tidal wave" and "felt as though the ship struck on the bottom."

In a subsequent report, Grant and Higgins (1913, p. 12), made the following statement concerning the 1908 quake:

* * * It seems quite probable that the slumping is taking place occasionally along the seaward edge of the delta. On February 14, 1908, an earthquake of considerable magnitude visited this district and broke in several places both the Seattle-Valdez and the Valdez-Seward cables, which run east and west through Port Valdez. Accompanying the earthquake there seems to have been a slumping of the delta front which buried sections of the cables. The cause of the earthquake is not known, but it is thought to have been minor faulting, for one of the cables was broken in deep water on the flat bottom of the fiord 11 miles from Valdez. The slumping of the delta front at this time was therefore probably a result rather than a cause of the earthquake.

The third of these five relevant earthquakes took place on September 21, 1911, and was described by Tarr and Martin (1912, p. 100):

A. H. Brooks, geologist in charge of the division of Alaskan mineral resources of the United States Geological Survey, has given one of the best accounts of the earthquake as follows:

"The record in my notebook shows that on September 21 I noted four earthquakes between 7 and 8:30 p.m. I was at that time at the camp of the Ibex Mining Co., on the west side of Valdez Glacier, about 8 miles from the town of Valdez. I corrected my time observations in accordance with the clock at the Signal Corps station at Valdez upon my return. The correction shows the shocks to have been as follows:

"The first one was at 7:01 p.m. This lasted 20 seconds by my observation. As, however, I was sitting across the tent from the candle and as I did not recognize it as an earthquake at once, I think it safe to add 5 or 6 seconds to this observation.

"The second shock came at 7:13 and lasted between 5 and 10 seconds. The third shock came at 7:28 and lasted 3 to 5 seconds. The fourth shock came at 8:38 and lasted about 2 seconds. The earth movement seemed to be from west to east. I had no means of measuring the intensity of the shock, but it did not seem to have been sufficient to upset anything on the shelves where I was. I was told that at Valdez some articles were thrown from shelves and that a heavy glass bowl was moved, so that it was in danger of falling from a sideboard. The clock at the Signal Corps station at Valdez stopped at two minutes past 7.

"So far as I know, there was no perceptible earthquake wave at Valdez, but of this I have no definite information. It would seem that there should have been a wave there when the cable was broken. Curiously enough, the operator at Valdez told me that the cable was not broken immediately, but that communication was kept up with Sitka some seconds after the earthquake shock. He was telegraphing to Sitka at the time of the shock. The shock at Valdez was sufficient to frighten the people very badly. Nearly everyone rushed out on the street. I did not learn, though, that it had done any damage whatsoever.

"As I had never before felt an earthquake shock I had no basis for comparison. The tent in which I was sitting was located on a little spur jutting out from a steep slope about 1,000 feet above the Valdez Glacier, and the rumbling of the earthquake was confused with heavy falls of boulders down the talus slopes. The talus slopes on both sides showed considerable movement after the earthquake shocks."

During this earthquake the submarine cable from Valdez to Sitka was broken just north of Fort Liscum, at a point 3³⁄₁₆ miles west of the dock at Valdez, near latitude 61°06'08'' N., and longitude 146°19'23'' W., and was buried for 1,650 feet. This is almost exactly at one of the points (Pl. XXVII) where the cable was broken during the earthquake of February 14, 1908, when twice as great a length of cable was buried near this break. The water here is 700 to 750 feet deep and the slope of the fiord bottom is less than 50 feet to the mile. The break at this same point in 1911 seems to verify our suggestion made in 1908 (p. 98), that a fault exists there. Mr. Brooks' statement that cable communication was not interrupted until several seconds after the shock may tend to show that there was slight flowage of fiord-bottom mud along a fault scarp, resulting in the burial of a great length of cable. We do not think that the earthquake shaking alone, without actual displacement by faulting, could have caused sufficient flowage on the flat fiord bottom to break the cable.

A. J. Burr, a former Valdez resident states: "* * * that was the first time that we had ever observed Valdez Bay so literally covered with dead fish as a result of the concussions in the water so that in most of the patches the dead fish were so thick it was difficult to see much of the water" (written commun., July 29, 1964).

Records of the fourth of this series of relevant earthquakes, with which submarine slides appear to haxe been associated, are less detailed than for those of 1908 and 1911. The fourth earthquake took place on January 31, 1912, at 8:11 p.m. local time. The epicenter was recorded as lat 61° N., long 147½° W.; the focal depth was 80 km and the magnitude 7¼. The submarine cables were again broken in Port Valdez.

The fifth of these quakes occurred on February 23, 1925, at 1:55 p. m. local time and is remembered by many present residents of Valdez. Many electric lines were broken, and the front wall of the vacant Valdez Brewery collapsed. More significantly a part of the dock collapsed; an unusual wave accompanying the tremors tore up a section of the boardwalk along Water Street, and the submarine cables were again broken (Gov. William A. Egan, oral commun., August, 1964).

Thus, the record shows that on at least five occasions in the past 70 years, submarine slides—and associated turbidity currents—have accompanied earthquakes at Valdez. To this extent, the combined effects of the earthquake of March 27 were in no way abnormal. Instead, they typify a reaction pattern under seismic conditions that may be expected in the prism of saturated fine-grained deposits that make up the Valdez delta.

SUMMARY OF EVENTS OF THE 1964 EARTHQUAKE

The following description of the events of the March 27 earthquake at Valdez has been constructed from interviews with eyewitnesses, responses to questionnaires, and unpublished reports submitted to various agencies.

The first tremors were felt in Valdez at approximately 5:36 p.m. The shocks lasted from 3 to 5 minutes and were reported to have been accompanied by a low-pitched rumbling sound. The one observation on which there is any semblance of unanimity was that the ground had a rapid rolling motion. Jarring also was reported by many. The ground surface was reported to have been "heaving in much the same manner as a ground swell in the open ocean, except that the swells were much more rapid and frequent." Large fissures could be seen opening and closing along the streets and in areas cleared of snow. Water and sus-

pended silt and sand spurted from many of the fissures. Ground water augmented by water from broken mains and sewers was ejected from the fissures and was trapped between snow berms along the streets; in many places the water attained a depth of 18–24 inches. Trees pitched wildly as if buffeted by a strong wind; several were split but none was broken across. Cars parked in gear or with brakes set moved back and forth, and drivers of moving cars were forced to stop to avoid losing control.

Within buildings, bric-a-brac and lamps were overturned, large heavy objects were shifted, and cans and bottles were thrown down from tables and shelves.

Structural damage to buildings is described in another section of this report (see p. C30).

The most detailed report of the effects of the earthquake in town

was made by Charles H. Clark of Valdez. Mr. Clark is a geologist with the Alaska Department of Highways and an experienced aircraft pilot. Hence, he is not only a trained observer of natural phenomena but also possesses the proven ability to judge distances and depths quickly and accurately. His observations are as follows:

The writer was in Valdez at the time of the quake and the following is an attempt to describe the earthquake as it occurred.

The first tremors were hard enough to stop a moving person and shock waves were immediately noticeable on the surface of the ground. These shock waves continued with a rather long frequency which gave the observer an impression of a rolling feeling rather than abrupt hard jolts. After about one minute the amplitude or strength of the shock waves increased in intensity and failures in buildings as well as the frozen ground surface began to occur. Cracks in the roadway surface opened and closed again as the troughs and crests passed the failure. These cracks opened as much as three feet but the most frequent failures were only opened several inches. As these cracks closed due to passing of a shock wave trough, water from both ground water sources and broken sewers and water pipes squirted in a spray about twenty feet into the air. These occurred at intervals several seconds between sprays, but no other timing of the waves was attempted by the writer. The amplitude of waves was estimated by observance of a boy standing about 410 feet away. This boy is the writer's son, stands 6 feet tall and was in plain sight during most of the earthquake. As a crest would pass him, he would appear in full sight with one depression between himself and the writer. As he entered a trough, he would appear to sink out of sight up to about one foot below belt line. This would indicate that he rose and fell about 3 to 4 feet, and that the waves had a fairly large amplitude. Other features in the vicinity viewed by other qualified observers seem to substantiate this sort of estimation.

After about 2 to 2½ minutes, failures of buildings became apparent and power poles began going down. After about 3½ minutes the severe shock waves ended and people began to react as could be expected.

Many things occurred during the brief few minutes of the severe earthquake. Buildings of a wooden frame construction swayed and rocked as if on a high sea. The frame structures evidently were flexible enough to give and sway with very little structural damage. Damages to foundations occurred under these structures, but in general they held together very well for a shock of this intensity and duration. Structures of concrete block or other masonry construction suffered severe damage to both bearing walls and foundations. Glass breakage was very limited. Also, it should be noted that the cracks mentioned previously extended under almost every building in town and caused damage to plumbing as well as foundations.

The single most disastrous event caused by the earthquake at Valdez was the submarine landslide which occurred on the waterfront (fig. 4). This slide and its concomitant waves were responsible for the loss of 30 lives. The slide also caused much of the property damage in the city as well as the destruction of all docks and associated facilities (figs. 5 and 6).

The slide occurred so rapidly and with such violence that eyewitnesses on the shore were overwhelmed. Most of them have very little recollection of what actually occurred directly beneath their feet. The SS *Chena*, a converted liberty ship some 400 feet long, was discharging freight at the Valdez dock when the quake struck. The *Chena* first rose 20–30 feet, then bottomed, rose, bottomed, shot forward, bottomed again, and was lifted clear. Men on the ship say it heeled over at least 50° before being righted by waves. Witnesses on shore state that the bow rose until it could be seen well above the dock warehouses, then fell and the stern rose until the ship's propellers were exposed. Two men on the ship were killed by falling cargo, and another died of a heart attack. By this time the ship was under way and moved to deep water and safety.

As the *Chena* was rising, the Valdez dock was in violent motion. Within seconds of the first tremors, the dock broke in two and the warehouses flipped forward and vanished into an extremely turbulent sea. *Chena* crewmen watched men, women, and children on the dock struggling desperately to get off or to find something to hold on to. None had time to escape.

The following account of events as seen from the deck of the SS *Chena* was recorded by Capt. M. D. Stewart, master of the vessel.

The *Chena* arrived at Valdez at 1612 hours, March 27. About 1731 o'clock, while discharging cargo, we felt a severe earthquake—followed almost immediately by tidal waves. There were very heavy shocks about every half a minute. Mounds of water were hitting at us from all directions.

I was in the dining room. I made it to the bridge (three decks up) by climbing a vertical ladder. God knows how I got there.

The Valdez piers started to collapse right away. There was a tremendous noise. The ship was laying over to port. I had been in earthquakes before, but I knew right away that this was the worst one yet. The *Chena* raised about 30 feet on an oncoming wave. The whole ship lifted and heeled to port about 50°. Then it was slammed down heavily on the spot where the docks had disintegrated moments before. I saw people running—with no place to run to. It was just ghastly. They were just engulfed by buildings, water, mud, and everything. The *Chena* dropped where the people had been. That is what has kept me awake for days. There was no sight of them. The ship stayed there momentarily. Then there was an ungodly backroll to starboard. Then she came upright. Then we took another heavy roll to port.

I could see the land (at Valdez) jumping and leaping in a terrible turmoil. We were inside of where the dock had been. We had been washed into where the small boat harbor used to be. There was no water under the *Chena* for a brief interval. I realized we had to get out quickly if we were ever going to get out at all. There was water under us again. The stern was sitting in broken piling, rocks, and mud.

I signaled to the engine room for power and got it very rapidly. I called for "slow ahead," then "half ahead" and finally for "full." In about four minutes, I would guess, we were moving appreciably, scraping on and off the mud (bottom) as the waves went up and down. People ashore said they saw us slide sideways off a mat of willow trees (placed as part of the fill material in the harbor) and that helped put our bow out. We couldn't turn. We were moving along the shore, with the stern in the mud. Big mounds of water came up and flattened out. Water inshore was rushing out. A big gush of water came off the beach, hit the bow, and swung her out about 10 degrees. If that hadn't happened, we would have stayed there with the bow jammed in a mud bank and provided a new dock for the town of Valdez!! We broke free. The bow pushed through the wreckage of a cannery. We went out into the bay and had to stop. The condensers were plugged with mud and

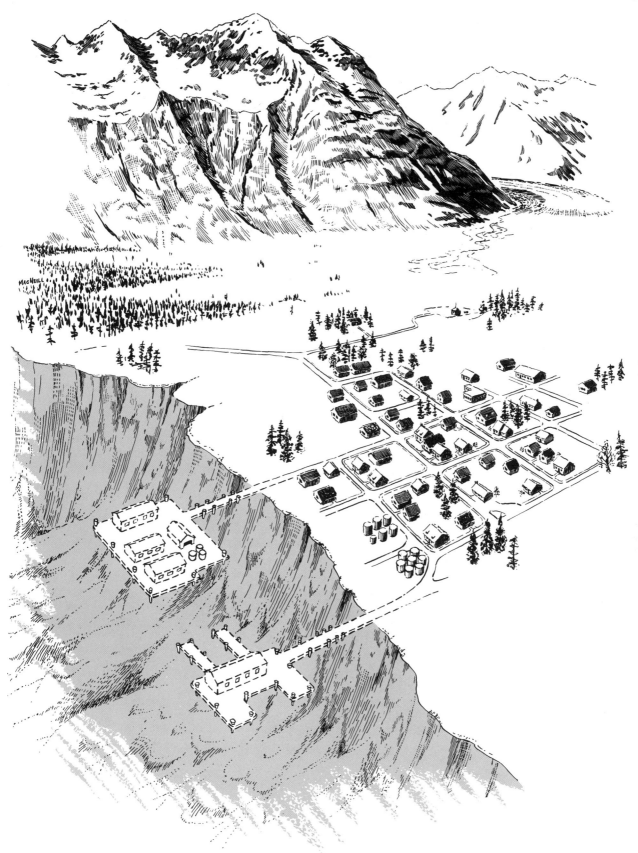

4.—Submerged slide area at Valdez. Dashed lines indicate dock area destroyed in earthquake. Sketch by David Laneville, Alaska Department of Highways.

5.—Valdez dock area, September 23, 1963. Photograph by U.S. Bureau of Land Management.

6.—Valdez dock area, June 13, 1964.   Photograph by Air Photo Tech, Inc.

pieces of the dock. The chief mate, Neal L. Larsen, checked to see then if we were taking water. We were taking none. It was unbelievable after what the ship had been through. We had the lifeboats all manned and ready. I didn't think she would float in deep water. Maybe the soft mud bottom made the difference.

Exact details of the wave sequence at Valdez have been difficult to determine; however, four major waves have been distinguished. During the first two waves, most eyewitnesses state, the turbulence in the harbor area generated a mist or haze that obscured the bay beyond the shoreline. In addition, the gyrations and maneuvers of the SS *Chena* during the first wave were so remarkable that few recall seeing anything else at that time. Later in the evening, general apprehension concerning the possibility of a tsunami was sufficient cause for the absence of observers in the waterfront area.

Apparently there was no major surge of water from Prince William Sound through Valdez Narrows into Port Valdez. The reason for this conclusion is the dearth of evidence of wave or high-water effects in Sawmill Bay, a reentrant at the mouth of Valdez Narrows whose alinement and

configuration are such that damage there from an incoming surge would have been extreme. Furthermore, the high-water marks and runup effects at the north end of Valdez Narrows (see fig. 20) indicate outward flow of water only. This conclusion is in agreement with Van Dorn's analysis (1964, p. 166) that "the tsunami source was somewhat directional radiating energy preferentially to the southeast." He believed that wave effects in the fiords in northern Prince William Sound were the results of slumping of deltas and strong seiching action.

The first major wave at Valdez closely followed the submarine slide. Without doubt, it was caused by the sudden transfer of approximately 98 million cubic yards of unconsolidated deposits from the face of the delta out into the bay. This wave, estimated to have been from 30 to 40 feet high, surged onto the Valdez waterfront with destructive violence. A component of this slide-generated wave seems to have been propagated westward down the bay and to have caused the extreme runup to 170 feet above sea level at Cliff Mine. It probably caused the outward surge of water through Valdez Narrows that was reported by Mr. Red Ferrier, a

Valdez fisherman who rode out the wave on his boat in the Narrows. This down-bay wave may have been reinforced by subsidiary slumps off small deltas along the flanks of Port Valdez.

The second major wave to strike the waterfront at Valdez arrived approximately 10 minutes after the strong ground motion ceased; it has been described as a violent surging wave only slightly smaller than the first. Presumably, this wave was the return surge from the first wave reflected back from the opposite end of the bay.

The seismic energy plus the submarine landslides seem to have generated a complex multinodal seiche in Port Valdez that persisted until early the following morning.

At approximately 11:45 p.m. and 1:45 a.m., just before and just after high tide, waves three and four, described as rapidly moving tidal bores, advanced into the town. These two waves are presumed to have been the result of the coincidence of long-period seiche waves with the high tide.

The late evening seiches may have been reinforced by the effects of one or more of the strong aftershocks, or possibly by the arrival of greatly attenuated tsunami.

SUBMARINE LANDSLIDE

DIMENSIONS

Precise dimensions of the submarine slide are impossible to obtain because measurements depend upon a comparison of prequake and postquake soundings, and the prequake soundings were taken in 1959, nearly 5 years before the earthquake. Accurate modern prequake soundings below 360 feet are not available, and

there is no way in which the interim changes in bottom topography can be determined. However, the total volume of material transferred between 1959 and 1964 is more than 100 million cubic yards (pl. 2). It is probable that some of this transfer took place before the earthquake and that additional material was carried down by waves flowing over the

newly formed scarp. The entire face of the delta was affected, and the volume of material directly involved in the March 27 slide is estimated to be approximately 98 million cubic yards.

SUBSURFACE CONDITIONS

The sediments underlying the eastern end of Port Valdez have not been studied enough to warrant a detailed description of the entire submarine slide area. Insofar as is known, three exploratory borings put down by the Department of Highways are the only deep borings ever made on the Valdez waterfront or, for that matter, along the entire eastern shore of Port Valdez. Several deep water wells have been drilled in the city of Valdez, but they are approximately 1 mile from the waterfront area. The records of these early wells are not considered to be of great value because the samples were not tested, and apparently no geologist or soils engineer was present during the drilling. The records are much too general for identifying accurately the stratigraphic units.

The drilling by the Department of Highways was done with a truck-mounted rotary drill, using water and bentonite as the circulation medium. Samples were taken at 5-foot intervals or wherever a change of lithology occurred. The borings were all in the Valdez dock area, and thus the information obtained applies only to that area.

These three borings, which reached depths of 105, 82, and 132 feet, show a remarkable degree of horizontal continuity and vertical uniformity (see pl. 3, logs 1, 2, and 3). There are two distinct layers. The first, or surface layer, is a loose to medium-dense sandy gravel with cobbles and silt. This layer is 20 to 30 feet thick. Conversations with local residents and examination of old photographs indicate that this material is fill moved in during the development of the harbor facilities.

The gravel layer is underlain by an undetermined thickness of loose to medium-dense gravelly sand containing thin lenses of silt. This zone persists to the maximum depths drilled.

Standard penetration resistance (relative density), particle-size distribution, and natural-moisture content are fairly uniform throughout both layers.

The shape of individual particles varies from subangular to rounded. The majority of sand-size particles are subangular, whereas the gravels and cobbles are rounded. The original faces and edges of the coarser fractions have been almost completely destroyed, but most of the particles show at least one flat surface.

Ground-water levels were measured in all borings after a 24-hour period to allow for equalization of drilling fluid and ground water. All measurements showed ground water within 6 feet of the ground surface in the locations drilled.

The geologic environment suggests that sediments from the northern extremity of the delta to some point between the stream from the Valdez Glacier and the Lowe River should be similar in composition and particle-size distribution to those in the dock area, except, naturally, the layer of coarse fill material in the dock area. Inasmuch as materials carried by the Lowe River have been transported much farther than those on the rest of the delta, presumably they would generally have a finer grain or particle size. This finer material represents the only probable departure from overall uniformity of sediments in the upper 100 feet in the Valdez delta.

MECHANICS OF THE SLIDE

That certain soils, particularly loose water-saturated sand, may suffer a loss of bearing capacity when subjected to seismic shock has long been recognized (Terzaghi and Peck, 1948, p. 100). The geologic environment at Valdez provides optimum conditions for this phenomenon and bears many similarities to other liquefaction flow sites described by Terzaghi (1956, p. 23–34).

During the earthquake, several factors apparently combined to produce the slide. First, the actual shocks or ground vibrations were of the critical intensity and duration required to create a condition of spontaneous liquefaction in the loose to medium-dense saturated sand. During liquefaction an increase in pore-water pressure, in effect, transformed a normal sediment into a concentrated suspension with a minimal shear strength. Second, the water withdrew from the beaches almost simultaneously with the initial shocks, according to eye witnesses. The withdrawal may have been accompanied by a sudden decrease in hydrostatic head. The net result would have been an immediate increase in the weight of the upper soil layers and a corresponding decrease in support at the toe of the slide due to the sudden drop in sea level. The situation was further aggravated by the fact that the slide occurred at low tide. All these factors, together with the seepage pressures that existed in the area, presumably combined to produce a slide of large proportions.

The slide was probably very similar in shape to the classic sandflows common in subaerial sediments. This shape cannot be accurately determined because receding waves removed enough material from the root of the slide to mask its original configuration. In addition, the mound normally located at the toe of a slide is absent. However, once the sand particles had been placed in a state of suspension and had begun flowing downslope, they probably would not have come to rest in a large pile or mound. The tendency would be to spread laterally, with a consequent thinning of the sliding mass. Movement would probably continue until the suspension reached an area which was nearly flat, where gravity and friction would slow and ultimately stop the rapidly moving soil suspension. If this interpretation is correct, the soil suspension could accurately be described as a turbidity current, a theory that seems to be borne out by the description of the earthquake which struck the Valdez area on September 21, 1911. Of particular interest is the fact that some 1,650 feet of cable was buried. The breaks and cable burial apparently occurred several seconds after the tremor some 3 miles west of the Valdez waterfront. During the February 19, 1908, earthquake, the Valdez to Sitka submarine cable was broken at a point identical to that just described, and the length of buried cable was nearly twice as great.

The 1908 and 1911 cable breaks were considered, at that time, to have been caused by faulting on the floor of Port Valdez. This mechanism is now considered unlikely for several reasons. First, there was no evidence of any faulting visible along the shores of Port Valdez after either the 1908 or the 1911 earthquake. Second, it seems unlikely that any faulting would have occurred after the earthquake. The fact that communication was maintained during the entire 1911 earthquake and was not disrupted until several seconds after the tremors stopped argues strongly against t h e faulting theory. More probably, the tremors triggered a submarine slide that began moving during the tremors and took several seconds to reach and break the submarine cables.

The fact that numerous cable breaks occurred during or im-mediately after the 1908, 1911, and 1925 earthquakes adds support to the theory that submarine landslides caused the cable breaking. Even though the breaks occurred at many points, sliding cannot be ruled out as the cause.

In addition to the Valdez outwash delta, there are at least five other locations in Port Valdez where streams have built relatively large deltas: (1) Mineral Creek, (2) Gold Creek, (3) the stream from Shoup Glacier, (4) Sawmill Creek, and (5) Allison Creek. All these streams enter Port Valdez from the north or south. Thus, any slides which occurred on their respective deltas would most likely move in a north-south direction. The magnitude of the turbulence which would be created by five or six masses of liquefied soil moving in different directions, particularly when two or more crossed paths, would break any cable within range.

Cable service to Valdez has long been discontinued, and consequently this means of comparison between previous earthquakes and the 1964 earthquake no longer exists.

PRESENT STABILITY OF THE VALDEZ WATER-FRONT

The Valdez waterfront has proven to be unstable under seismic conditions. Records of slides which have occurred during previous earthquakes make any additional elaboration unnecessary. It is important, however, that an attempt to assess the static stability of the Valdez waterfront be made. This assessment is important not only for the Valdez area, but for all harbor facilities located on the numerous deltas throughout south-central Alaska.

Slides have occurred on the Valdez waterfront without any acceleration caused by earth tremors. Because the damage caused by these slides was relatively light and no lives were lost, the events received little, if any, attention from the general public and were not described in the scientific literature. Three separate incidents of slides on the waterfront were related to us by Valdez residents.

The first slide occurred in the early 1920's. A cargo of large spools of cable had been off loaded onto the north dock. At some time during the night, the section of dock upon which the cable was resting sheared away from the rest of the dock, carrying the cable with it. The cable was never recovered. Reportedly the piling supporting the failed section was not broken but was carried out by a sliding mass of soil. A diver reported that he had difficulty working on the delta face after the slide because of the steepness of the slope. In this case, apparently the subsoils simply did not have sufficient strength to support the concentrated weight of the dock and cable. The slide was localized, and the other sections of the dock were not damaged.

The second dock failure occurred in the late 1920's and is illustrated by figure 7. In this failure there is no record of heavy loads on the dock at the time of failure. Note that the failed section is tipped shoreward.

Sometime between 1942 and 1945, a third slide occurred beneath the cannery dock. Although its exact dimensions are unknown, the slide affected the entire dock and was estimated to have been at least 100 feet wide. Oddly enough, the dock, although badly damaged, was not carried away, probably because it was tied together rather rigidly.

7.—Dock failure in late 1920's. Note that failed section has tipped shoreward. Photograph courtesy of James Dieringer.

The reason for these two later slides is not as clearly understood as the first slide described. The dock was empty when the last two slides occurred, and there was no noticeable seismic action. Because both seismic action and heavy loads can be ruled out, other factors were undoubtedly responsible. It should be emphasized that these slumps were small localized features.

The most probable cause of these local slides would appear to be oversteepening of the delta face during the natural processes of deposition and erosion. Terzaghi (1956) described two prevalent causes of oversteepening in this type of environment, either or both of which may be applicable to these slides: (1) the intercalation of cohesive strata within the deltaic

sequence and (2) artificial interference with the natural depositional and erosional patterns.

Clayey silts have been found in the Valdez waterfront borings (see pl. 3, log. 3), in the Mineral Creek townsite borings (Shannon and Wilson, Inc., 1964, borings No. B–5A, B–6), and in the deep well at Valdez (see Waller and Tolen, 1962, table 2, well 1). Hence, local oversteepening from intercalation of cohesive strata is a possibility.

Artificial interference with the natural environment along the Valdez waterfront, however, is a more probable cause of local oversteepening. Since the construction of the dike around Valdez in the early 1900's, distributary channels across the delta have been denied access to the Valdez waterfront

area, and since construction of the levee system, beginning in the 1930's, the distributaries have been entirely restricted to the southern half of the delta. Construction of the docks and the breakwater system has also seriously disrupted the natural-wave and longshore-current pattern across the northern part of the delta face. This situation appears to be similar to that described by Terzaghi (1956) as contributing to the submarine slope failure at Howe Sound, British Columbia. There, interference with the natural processes allowed accumulation of a perched body of fine-grained concentrates to a point where the critical slope value was exceeded and failure in the dock area ensued.

The absence of evidence of past large-scale slides occurring along the face of the Valdez delta under static conditions indicates that massive slides along the relatively stable delta are not likely to occur under ordinary circumstances. The evidence that the postquake slope of the delta face is practically parallel to the prequake slope lends support to this conclusion.

Calculations were made in an attempt to assess the static slope stability of the delta face. Because shear-test data were not available, assumed angles of internal friction derived from the angle of repose of the materials involved and from the standard penetration indices recorded during the waterfront drilling program were used in the computations. In view of the assumptions involved, the computed safety fac-

tors can be considered relative only; consequently no attempt is made to state them in numerical terms.

If the present average slope of the delta face of 16° is used in the calculations, the delta face appears to be relatively stable against massive failure under static conditions. If the slope angles of 20°, 33° and 45°, which represent the locally oversteepened condition on the upper part of the delta only, are used in the calculations, the stability against slumping on the upper part of the delta ranges from marginal to critical.

All available evidence indicates that the face of the Valdez delta is fairly stable under static conditions, insofar as massive slides involving large sections of the waterfront are concerned. Small

slumps occurring at frequent intervals involving the upper part of the delta face only are considered highly probable. Neither of these conclusions takes earthquake acceleration into consideration.

Under seismic conditions, the subsoils underlying the Valdez waterfront are susceptible to spontaneous liquefaction and subsequent failure. Because the Valdez area lies in a zone of high seismic activity, numerous quakes with a wide range of intensities will occur. If the intensity and duration of a shock are sufficient, large blocks of the Valdez delta will liquefy and slide. This fact looms over all considerations which suggest that an incipient failure condition under the local oversteepened case exists even without earthquakes.

GROUND DISPLACEMENT

VERTICAL DISPLACEMENT

Valdez appears to lie on the hinge line—or line of zero tectonic altitude change—separating the zone of regional uplift to the south and east from the zone of regional subsidence to the north and west. The two closest bench marks set in bedrock, on the Coast and Geodetic Survey first-order level line [1] south of the town at mile 5 and mile 10 on the Richardson Highway show displacements of +0.55 feet and +0.35 feet, respectively. The first two bench marks, set in bedrock on the first-order line north of the town at mile 19 and mile 46 on the Richardson Highway, show displacements of −0.87 feet and −1.67 feet, respectively. The

[1] Preliminary Coast and Geodetic Survey first-order level data released November 9, 1964.

distribution of these changes in altitude strongly suggests that the Port Valdez valley—and its continuation into Heiden Canyon—lies on the dividing line between the area of tectonic uplift and subsidence (see fig. 1).

Because of the direct evidence of differential displacements resulting from landsliding, fissuring, sand ejection, and possibly compaction within the unconsolidated sediments of the Valdez delta, the changes in level of individual bench marks there apparently do not adequately reflect the nearshore develeling. These movements within the unconsolidated deposits are strictly local readjustments in contrast to the regional develeling indicated by changes in altitude of bench marks set in bedrock.

An index of the amount of subsidence in the waterfront area can

be gained from a comparison of the prequake and postquake highway profiles along Alaska Avenue measured by the Alaska Department of Highways (pl. 1). These profiles are comparable as far west as Hobart Street and diverge progressively from there to Water Street where the indicated subsidence is 9 feet. An estimate of subsidence west of Water Street to the remaining end of the ramp of the main dock suggests an additional 10 feet of develeling. This estimate is based on the present submergence at high tide of the dock gatepost, which formerly stood at approximately 18 feet above high water.

The nature and extent of flooding of areas formerly above high tide confirm the observations that develeling as just estimated above has in fact taken place. Furthermore, continued progressive encroachment of high tides suggests that some component of the factors that caused the initial rapid subsidence has continued to affect the area for as long as a year after the earthquake.

No detailed prequake measurements are available in the shore area south of the town; however, study of prequake and postquake photographs indicates a comparable steepening of the beach profile and drowning of drainage channels across the entire face of the delta.

Apparently the major component of the deleveling in the waterfront area was a response to submarine sliding which removed support from the face of the delta and thereby allowed some of the material to move seaward and caused parts of the shore area to subside. The observation that some of the pile-supported structures near the waterfront have subsided less than the surrounding ground surface suggests that some compaction of the subsoils has taken place. The generally poor consolidation of the subsurface materials indicated by the low penetration resistances recorded in the waterfront exploratory borings (pl. 3, Nos. 1–3) suggests that compaction cannot have been extensive.

LATERAL DISPLACEMENT

Observations of horizontal separation across fissures in the unconsolidated deposits throughout the town indicated that seaward lateral displacement of considerable magnitude coincided with the submarine slide and resultant removal of support from the delta face. Prequake horizontal control networks were not sufficiently detailed to establish the amount of movement. Measurements of the separations across fissures along

Alaska Avenue from the waterfront to the east end of town totaled more than 80 feet. However, because some differential displacement and tilting of the blocks were obviously involved, this figure is not an true indication of the amount of lateral displacement.

Measurements that do appear to

reflect actual lateral displacement became available during the reconstruction work; accurate records were kept of the horizontal separations of waterlines throughout the town. Separations on the four main lines were measured between 7th Street and McKinley Street (table 2 and pl. 1).

TABLE 2.—*Water-line separations*

[C. H. Blake, U.S. Corps of Engineers, written commun., 1964]

Street	Separation between Sherman and 4th	Separation between Hobart and McKinley	Minimum individual separation	Maximum individual separation	Total separation between McKinley and 7th
Wickersham Avenue			3 in.	1 ft	10 ft 3 in.
Alaska Avenue			3 in.	1 ft 4 in.	12 ft 6 in.
Broadway	5 ft 3 in.				13 ft 1 in.
Keystone Avenue		6 ft 4 in.		1 ft 10 in.	16 ft 2 in.

Besides the measurements of these displacements, accurate measurements of the distance between the prequake and postquake positions of the bulkhead at the small-boat harbor at the foot of Keystone Avenue indicate a lateral displacement of 25 feet, as shown on a postquake map made by the Corps of Engineers. The total measurable seaward displacement along Keystone Avenue from 7th Street to the waterfront is 41 feet 2 inches.

Other measurements of lateral displacement were reported by M. L. Wilson of the Alaska Department of Highways (written commun., 1964):

Some lateral movement was noted in the stretch of road going southeasterly out of Valdez, with the movement being associated with the earthquake of March 27, 1964. The most severe shift was located about 1,100 feet past the concrete bridge over Glacier Stream #3, towards Glennallen.

As-built plans and a survey made in 1962 for the City Streets project tied the original centerline of the roadway to U.S.C. & G.S. triangulation station Knife. The same triangulation was repeated in June 1964 in connection with project ER–13(1).

Assuming that station Knife has remained fixed in the same location, the horizontal distances from the road to

Knife before and after the quake indicate the following:

That a shift of about 1.5 feet towards the bay has occurred on the road near the ball park. The shift continues and increases to an apparent maximum deflection of 5.3 feet at the point 1,100 feet past the bridge. The deflection then decreases to nil around 2.2 mile. Isolated segments of displacement of smaller magnitude were noted past 3 Mile.

Visual examination of the movement past the bridge tends to verify our calculations, and we should be fairly close in the order of magnitude.

Further evidence of lateral displacement was found in the rupture and offset of the casings in water wells.

Beneath the powerplant building at 5th and Broadway, a 6-inch well casing was broken during the quake at a depth of 15 feet 8 inches below the surface, and the upper part of the casing was offset to the west (shoreward). The well point was also bent at a depth of 20 feet 8 inches below the surface, but this damage may have occurred during removal of the point from the ruptured casing.

The casing of the auxiliary water-supply well at the northeast end of town was also damaged during the earthquake. However, the main well there appeared to have been undamaged and the internal pipe and well point moved freely inside the casing on March 27. During a strong aftershock on June 16, 1964, the casing of the main well was bent at a depth of 28 feet below the surface and the casing of the auxiliary well was ruptured at a depth of 48 feet. The casing of the main well was bent again at an undetermined depth during an aftershock on

September 22, 1964, and the well had to be abandoned. In each of these wells the direction of movement of the bends and breaks in the well casings was westward (shoreward).

The postquake condition of powerlines throughout the town supplied additional confirmation of seaward lateral extension. West of McKinley Street, most lines were broken and many utility poles were down. East of McKinley Street along streets at right

angles to the waterfront, powerlines were stretched tightly and lines on many blocks had to be slacked off to prevent breakage. In general, along streets parallel to the waterfront the lines maintained a normal amount of sag.

Without doubt, lateral displacements comparable to those described above took place in the shore area south and west of the town, but there are no fixed reference points in that area to indicate such displacements.

GROUND BREAKAGE

The theory of formation of earth fissures, sand vents, and allied phenomena has been elucidated by several authors (Oldham and Mallet, 1872, p. 264–268; Thomas Oldham, 1882; R. D. Oldham, 1899; Davis and Sanders, 1960, p. 248–250; and Imamura, 1937, p. 70–77). These phenomena characteristically occur in areas where thick sections of saturated, incompetent, predominantly fine-grained deposits overlain by more coherent surficial strata have been subjected to stresses generated by a high-magnitude earthquake. The following are the better known of the historic documented earthquakes from which the particular set of physical circumstances necessary to produce the widespread broken-ground phenomena have been described:

New Madrid (Fuller, 1912)
Cachar (Thomas Oldham, 1882)
Charleston (Dutton, 1889)
The Great Indian Earthquake of June 12, 1897 (R. D. Oldham, 1899)
California (Lawson and others, 1908)
Bihar-Nepal (Roy, 1939)
Fukui (Tsuya, 1950)

Alaska, April 7, 1958 (Davis, 1960)
Alaska July 10, 1958 (Davis and Sanders, 1960).

Oldham (1899, p. 86) makes a clear distinction between fissures which "start at the surface and penetrate down to the depths," and fractures which "may be taken to have been propagated upward from below." Fissures are considered to be "a result more or less indirect of the wave motion which has been set up elsewhere and traveled to the place where the fissures are formed." Fractures on the other hand "must be regarded as a cause and as surface manifestations of the deeper seated fracture by whose formation the wave motion was originated." Fissures are subdivided by Oldham (1899, p. 87–90) into two genetically distinct categories. Those of the first category are attributed to lateral spreading toward an unconfined face. This type of fissure has often been attributed to a rather loosely defined phenomenon termed "lurching" (see Richter, 1958, p. 124). Fissures of the second category are formed on level ground where the unconfined-face effect does not ob-

tain. They are attributed to "visible undulations of the ground induced by the earthquake which traveled as independent quasi-elastic or purely gravitational waves. Such waves traversing the alluvium would throw each part into alternate compression and extension as the surface was bent into a concave or convex curve and in a compressible material decidedly lacking in elasticity this might easily lead to the formation of fissures" (Oldham, 1899, p. 89). Ejection of water, silt, sand, and even coarser particles may accompany the formation of either of these types of fissures.

The occurrence during earthquakes of low-velocity, short-wavelength, high-amplitude surface waves—variously called "earthquake waves" (Freeman, 1932, p. 769), "visible waves" (Richter, 1958, p. 129), "visible undulations of the ground" (Oldham, 1899, p. 89), and "gravity waves" (Imamura, 1937, p. 28)— has been accepted by many seismologists and has been questioned by others. Such waves have been observed and recorded from dynamite and nuclear blasts (Leet and Leet, 1964, p. 181). The major arguments against occurrence of such waves associated with earthquakes are: (1) that they are characteristically not recorded on instruments (Heck 1936, p. 22; Eiby, 1957, p. 26), and (2) that there is a stated disparity between the damage such waves would be expected to do and the damage actually done in areas where the waves have been reported (Freeman, 1932, p. 770). Insofar as the seismic records are concerned, apparently neither the normal calibration of the instrumentation nor the normal geologic environment of instrumentation is such that waves of this nature would be recorded. In this context, Swain's (1962, p. 240) reports of Gutenberg's observations that lead to the "rule of thumb under which the multiplication of displacement from rock to alluvium or fill could be expected to be two to ten times" and Gutenberg's (1957, p. 221) further assessment that "at sites on alluvium, relatively strong shaking lasts several times as long as at those on crystalline rock" seem particularly pertinent. Insofar as the damage is concerned, until instrumental records become available for analysis, the damage potential from such waves cannot be adequately assessed. Doubtless, as pointed out by Richter (1958, p. 130–132), many erroneous and mistakenly exaggerated reports have been made about this phenomenon; however, judgments concerning these visible ground waves must still rest on the purely qualitative information from eyewitnesses and from secondary analysis of effects.

FISSURES

At the time of the quake, the ground at Valdez was frozen down to the water table at depths of from 4 to 6 feet, and hence it could be expected to react some-

what like a rigid pad suspended on saturated granular subsoils. A snow cover approximately 5 feet deep also lay on the ground.

During the earthquake and while the slide was taking place along the waterfront, an extensive system of fissures developed across the Valdez delta. Some of these fissures reportedly were opening and closing during the tremors, and considerable volumes of water and suspended silt and sand were pumped from many of them. Within the town the pattern of this fissure system is complicated by refraction of fissures across deeply frozen zones under plowed streets and by the tendency of individual fissures to follow thawed zones over pipelines, sewers, and into foundation pits and cellars. On the open flood plain southeast of town, however, two distinct fissure sets could be recognized (figs. 8 and 9).

TRANSVERSE FISSURES

The first of the two sets of fissures on the flood plain, hereafter called the transverse set or transverse fissures, has a general trend of N. 30° W., approximately parallel to the waterfront. The width of the transverse fissures ranges from a few inches to more than 2 feet. No accurate appraisal of the original depth of the fissures could be gained although they probably lost their identity as discrete voids at the water table. The maximum length of any individual segment of the transverse set is approximately 1,000 feet although a broad zone of subparallel segments, which overlap in plan, extends across the entire breadth of the delta from north of Airport Road to the mouth of Robe River. In general, both the width of individual fissures in this set and their number per unit area decreases away from the shore. Aerial

photographs taken within a few days of the quake show that minor quantities of silt and sand were ejected from some of the transverse fissures near the shore. Evidence of this ejected material was obliterated by the effects of subsequent high tides. Elsewhere, evidence of pumping along transverse fissures is uncommon. Only four of the transverse fissures observed showed much vertical displacement. The maximum displacement recorded was 6 inches, and in all four fissures the relative movement was west side down. No suggestion could be discerned in the pattern of these transverse fissures of the stepped, tilted, tread-and-riser arrangement typical at the heads of block-gliding-type landslides nor of the concentric, crescentic fractures typical of arcuate slip failures. Instead, the physical characteristics and the spatial arrangement of the transverse fissures suggest that they originated as tension breaks in response to the lateral displacement and the imposition of a seaward camber on the distal part of the frozen delta surface coincident upon removal of support from the delta face by seismically triggered submarine landsliding. Thus, the transverse fissures belong to Oldham's first category (lateral spreading toward an unconfined face).

LONGITUDINAL FISSURES

The second prominent set of fissures on the flood plain, hereafter called the longitudinal set or longitudinal fissures, displays more complexity and diversity than the transverse set. In general, the trend of the longitudinal set is oriented at right angles to the transverse set and to the waterfront, although many individual fissures depart from this orientation. The longitudinal fissures

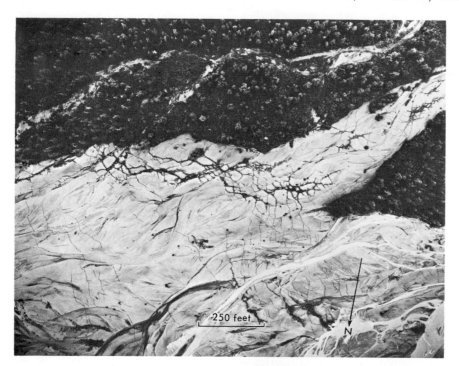

250 feet

N

8.—Vertical aerial photograph showing fissures on the flood plain of the stream from the Valdez Glacier. Photograph by Air Photo Tech, Inc.

9.—Transverse fissures (foreground) and longitudinal fissures (in the middle distance). Ridges of ejected material (silt and sand) border the longitudinal fissures.

are concentrated in, but not confined to, swales and depressions in the flood plain of the delta where the thickness of the frozen layer and the depth to the water table were least. Only transverse fissures were found on the higher and older surface of the low terrace remnants although the thick brush cover on the terrace remnants hindered accurate observations and precluded accurate plotting there.

The largest individual longitudinal-fissure segment observed was located 1,500 feet east of Dike Road and 800 feet north of Richardson Highway. It was 6 feet wide, 4 feet deep, and approximately 250 feet long (see fig. 10). Although some parts of the walls of the fissure apparently had collapsed during the spring thaw, the overall width does not appear to have been increased appreciably. A large volume of fine sand and silt was ejected from this fissure.

10.—Large longitudinal fissure. Surrounding area covered by ejected sand and silt. Carpenter's rule across fissure is 6 feet long; vertical scale below it is 1 foot high.

Figure 11 shows the fissure wall and approximately 2 feet of ejected material overlying the original surface. The thickness of this blanket of ejecta decreases away from the fissure on both sides to a featheredge approximately 100 feet from the centerline of the fissure. The volume of material ejected is roughly estimated as 2,000 cubic yards.

The distribution of ejected material from this fissure on the Valdez flood plain differs in several respects from that of similar features elsewhere. Commonly a steeper lip or ridge borders this type of fissure, and circular scour pits, attributed to the rapid return flow of water at the cessation of seismic shaking, occur along the fissures (Davis and Sanders, 1960;

Oldham, 1899). On the Valdez flood plain, however, the thick blanket of snow covering the surface at the time of the quake apparently exercised a strong control on the somewhat atypical distribution of the ejecta. It also impeded the return flow of water enough that circular scour pits were not formed nor was much ejected material washed back down into the fissures.

In several areas, the largest of which measured approximately 300 by 900 feet, the entire surface was blanketed by a layer of silt and fine sand as much as 3 feet thick which completely obscured the fissure complex from which it was ejected.

Trenches were dug across several of the longitudinal fissures in an attempt to determine their subsurface configuration and relationships. In each trench, fines were concentrated at the bottom of the fissure, but the identity of the fissure was lost completely at the water table from 1½ to 3 feet below the bottom of the void. Examination of these trenches suggests that features comparable to the discrete sand dikes described by Fuller (1912, p. 52) will not be preserved here. As stated earlier, the physical relationships required for the formation of these features comprise a thick section of poorly consolidated, predominately fine-grained, saturated deposits overlain by a more competent stratum. In the examples cited in the literature, the stratigraphy of the area has included a pronounced lithologic break—for example, sandy alluvium overlain by a well-developed soil, sand overlain by clay, or a similar lithologic break—and the material of the underlying saturated unit was carried up into and through the overlying competent unit. On the flood plain at Valdez, the lithology

11.—Longitudinal-fissure wall showing concentration of fines in ejected material.   Original surface at pencil top.

is relatively homogeneous (see pl. 3 and table 1), and the break was between units having different physical states (that is, between frozen and unfrozen strata) rather than between units having different lithologies. Thus, at Valdez, the finer fractions were elutriated from the underlying unfrozen deposits and carried up into and through the overlying frozen deposits, but the transported material is indistinguishable from the fine-grained beds and interstitial material of the frozen deposits.

RELATIONSHIP BETWEEN TRANSVERSE AND LONGITUDINAL FISSURES

An area, at the zone of intersection of a transverse-fissure complex and a longitudinal-fissure complex, which illustrates many of the commonly developed characteristics of the fissures at Valdez is shown on figures 12 and 13. This area lies along the zone of swales and abandoned channels parallel to and west of the low terrace remnant south of Dike Road. The transverse fissures furthest away from the longitudinal pattern are clean but, as they approach the longitudinal fissures, more and more ejected material appears along them (see fig. 14). At the point of intersection, the exact relationships become obscured by the large volume of ejecta, but in general the trends of the transverse fissures are deflected or terminate at longitudinal fissures. Within the longitudinal pattern itself, there is a general linear trend, but many segments intersect complexly. Some of these segments display a roughly conjugate arrangement, whereas others anastomose without any apparent systematic alinement. Large volumes of ejected silt, sand, and in some places pebbles characterize the central part of the longitudinal complex.

On each flank of the longitudinal complex, and parallel to it, are a series of clean fissure segments which show vertical displacement and which cut both the longitudinal- and transverse-fissure segments. The displacement ranges from 2 to 8 inches and the down-dropped side is always interior, forming a graben with the longitudinal-fissure complex on the down-dropped block. Late-stage collapse pits are associated with these border faults (figs. 15 and 16). Collapse pits were still forming as late as August 1964.

ORIGIN OF LONGITUDINAL FISSURES

The process whereby the longitudinal fissures originated is visualized as follows, and the fissures correspond closely to Oldham's second category: As seismic energy was transmitted from the surrounding bedrock walls into the thick alluvial fill at the head of the fiord, the displacements were augmented until large-amplitude slow-moving visible surface waves were being excited in the alluvium. These waves increased in size until the strength of the frozen surface layer was exceeded, characteristically in areas where that layer was the thinnest, and rupture occurred. Continued wave action subjected the underlying saturated materials to alternate compression and tension, and water containing suspended silt and sand was pumped up through the zones of rupture and out onto the surface. Removal of relatively large volumes of subsurface materials in this manner allowed subsidence to take place along the flanks of the longitudinal fissure zones, and the border faults and, ultimately, the late-stage collapse pits were formed. Because the transverse fissures are deflected by or terminate at longitudinal fissures, many

of the transverse fissures must have formed later than the longitudinal fissures. However, the evidence of pumping of material along transverse fissures at localities where they approach longitudinal fissures indicates that the formation of the transverse fissures must have taken place prior to the cessation of strong ground motion.

Two minor features associated with the fissures are discussed below.

Tabular ridges of silt and sand stand in relief along some of the narrower fissures (fig. 14). These ridges were at first interpreted as extrusions indicating final compressive stress along these particular fissures. However, the fact that many of these ridges intersect almost at right angles argues against their origin by compression. The absolute lack of plasticity of the granular materials comprising these ridges also militates against this explanation; it appears that the ridges are not extrusions but are accumulations of ejected material deposited in fissures that were propagated up into the snow cover; and that the ejecta were left standing in relief after the snow melted.

An early interpretation on the height to which water and suspended silt and sand squirted into the air was later proven incorrect. Eyewitnesses reported that individual jets of water reached as high as 20 feet. These jets were observed only along plowed streets and cleared areas within the town in places where an increased hydrostatic head from broken water mains could be expected. Elsewhere in a few localities the water broke through the snow cover but did not go much above the cover. In an area of heavy brush north of the airport road, however, where little ground was broken, mud splashes and clots

12.—Flood plain of the stream from the Valdez Glacier showing the intersection of a set of transverse fissures with a set of longitudinal fissures. The longitudinal set appears darker because of ejected silt and sand.

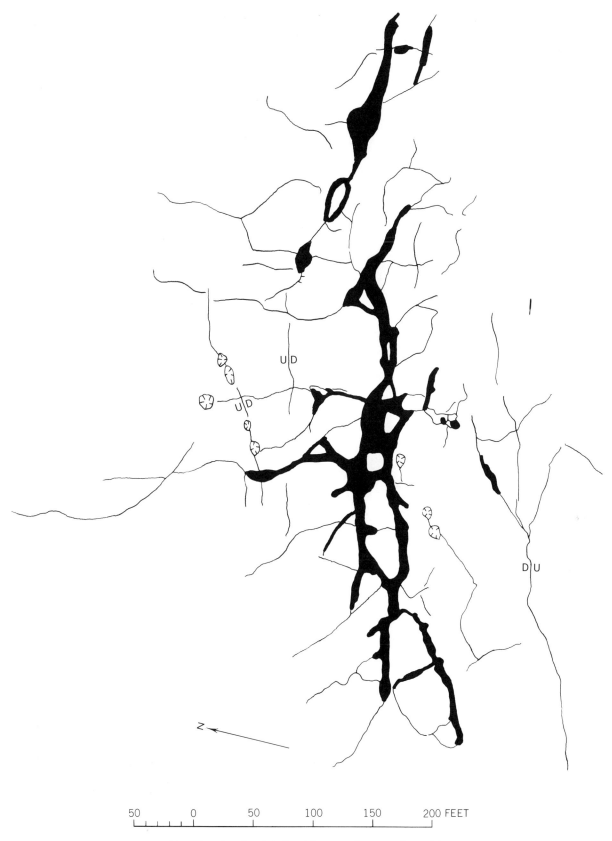

13.—Map showing details of fissures shown on figure 12.

14.—Zone of intersection between longitudinal fissures (foreground) and transverse fissure (background). Note increasing evidence of sand ejection along transverse fissure as it approaches longitudinal-fissure complex. Scale is 1 foot.

15.—Collapse pit in a graben on the flank of a set of longitudinal fissures. Scale is 1 foot.

16.—Collapse pit on the flank of a set of longitudinal fissures.   Scale is 1 foot.

were observed on alder branches 25 to 30 feet above the ground, but it was eventually recognized that the mud spots were only on the ends of branches which had been weighted down to the ground by the heavy snow cover and, hence, were not related in any way to the height of water jet.

DAMAGE TO STRUCTURES

To facilitate the discussion of the effects of the earthquake on manmade structures, four somewhat arbitrary categories will be used. The cause-and-effect relationships among the various categories are generally complexly interrelated. The four categories are:

1. Effects to structures on or near the waterfront resulting from the submarine slide.
2. Effects to structures resulting from waves and (or) high water.
3. Effects to structures resulting from ground breakage under or near them.
4. Effects to structures resulting from strong ground motion.

The damage to structures resulting from the submarine slide are so graphically illustrated by figures 4, 5, and 6 that little elaboration of this category is necessary, other than the enumeration of some salient dimensions to portray the scale of the effects.

Approximately 500 feet were lost off the end of the north dock. The ship berth on the north and the west face of this dock each measured 325 feet. The dock held six large buildings, each approximately 50 feet wide, having an aggregate length of nearly 700 feet, and numerous smaller sheds, platforms, and related structures. Almost 400 feet were lost off the end of the south dock, including a berth at the west face 200 feet long. The dock held one large building 200 by 50 feet, one smaller building, and an extensive bank

of freezer units. Several large trucks and semitrailers, cars, and numerous pieces of heavy-cargo-handling equipment were lost with the docks. A 500-foot L-shaped bulkhead between the two docks and 900 linear feet of floats in the small-boat harbor were also destroyed.

Wave and water damage (category 2) was areally restricted but severe. The violent surging wave which struck the shore within minutes of the slide did additional damage to the dock ramps and destroyed three of the four buildings at the head of the small-boat harbor and another building along the north-dock ramp. This wave also completed the wrecking of the small boats and the fishing fleet. One fishing boat was carried approximately 150 feet inland, and wave-carried debris damaged the installations in the Standard Oil Co. tank farm. One of the asphalt storage tanks was presumably punctured at this time. The runup from this first wave reached beyond McKinley Street at several points.

Apparently the down-bay component of this first slide-generated wave caused the extensive damage at the western end of Port Valdez. In the bight between Shoup Spit and the steep north wall of the fiord, the wave attained its maximum runup height and completely obliterated the abandoned installations at Cliff mine. Small submarine slumps off Shoup Spit and elsewhere probably augmented the wave in this vicinity. On the steep

valley wall above Cliff mine, the high-water marks on the snow reached 170 feet above msl. Slopes were stripped of vegetation up to altitudes as high as 70 feet along parts of the west wall of the fiord, and the navigation light standing on a concrete pylon approximately 25 feet above msl in Valdez Narrows was carried away. On the south side of the fiord, the cannery building at Jackson Point was torn from its foundations and drifted several miles down the bay; the runup in Anderson Bay reached 70 feet and destroyed an occupied dwelling.

The second wave, presumably the return surge from the first wave, crossed the waterfront at Valdez approximtaely 10 minutes after the first wave, carrying much debris. Water from this wave is reported to have reached a depth of 18 inches in the Valdez Hotel on McKinley Street, but elsewhere its effects cannot be differentiated from those of subsequent higher waves.

At approximately 11:45 p.m. and again at 1:45 a.m., respectively, the third and fourth waves advanced. The third reached as far as Hobart Street and was reported to have been 2½ feet deep in the Valdez Hotel. Water from the fourth and final wave was 5–6 feet deep in buildings along McKinley Street and 2 feet deep on Hobart Street (see fig. 17) and was responsible for most of the water damage to buildings, homes, and merchandise and supplies in the commercial establishments

17.—High-water mark from the early-morning wave, about 1:45 a.m., March 28, 1964, on a building on the east side of North Front Street between Rudolph Alley and Dike Street.

along McKinley Street and west of it. Large volumes of silt were deposited in and around buildings by the wave. Some of the wooden structures floated free during the high water, and an empty storage tank in the Standard Oil Co. tank farm was toppled. The final wave evidently advanced and receded with considerable speed because the high-water marks left by it on building exteriors are in most places several inches higher than the interior high-water marks. Furthermore, much wreckage and many damaged boats were swept off the waterfront, and consider-able scour and gullying around buildings and other obstructions occurred during the recession of the final wave.

The apparent sporadic distribution and the many anomalous effects of the final wave can be explained in large part by the existence in the town of high snow berms and a deep snow cover which channeled the water and restricted its distribution.

The principal cause of damage to manmade structures away from the waterfront was ground breakage. Approximately 40 percent of the homes and most of the larger commercial buildings in Valdez were seriously damaged by fissures extending under or near them. The effects to wooden buildings—the predominant type—are not readily apparent from the outside, but extensive foundation damage, which completely destroyed the structural integrity of the building, occurred in every unit intersected by fissures. The breakage of the foundations in most houses was accompanied by fracturing of floor joists, buckling of floors, and warping and cracking of interior walls. In many houses, intersec-

18.—Damage to the Alaskan Hotel on McKinley Street between Alaska Avenue and Broadway. The foundation of this building was intersected by four fissures. Photograph by T. L. Péwé.

tion of the foundations by fissures resulted in the pumping of large volumes of silt and sand into the cellars and crawl spaces. The effects on the commercial cinder-block structures are more apparent (fig. 18).

Simple rectangular buildings having heavily reinforced-concrete pad foundations—such as the Highway Department maintenance shop at North Front Street and Rudolph Alley, the power-plant at Broadway and 5th Street, and the Post Office at Alaska Avenue and Hobart Street—were not affected by fissures, although some differential settlement of the Post Office building appears to have taken place. Foundations of multicomponent structures having less heavily reinforced-concrete pad foundations—such as the hospital at Hobart Street and Wickersham Avenue, the high school at Empire Avenue and Sherman Street, and the Harborview complex at 6th and Wickersham Avenue—were damaged owing to intersection by fissures (fig. 19); these buildings also showed evidence of differential movement between their various elements.

The west abutment of the concrete bridge that crosses the stream from Valdez Glacier at 0.8 mile from Valdez was fractured, had dropped about 16 inches, and showed evidence of rotation toward the stream channel. There was partial failure of all three bridge approaches between town and mile 3, leaving steps between the approaches and the bridge decks. The characteristic damage to road embankments, particularly where the road is flanked by deep borrow pits, in the section between town and mile 3 included wide fissures along the flanks of the embankment and concomitant sags in the pavement; this damage sug-

19.—Transverse fissure through the concrete foundation slab of the Valdez High School, Sherman Street and Empire Avenue.

gests lateral spreading of the embankment.

Waterlines were broken by fissuring in at least 150 places throughout the town, and service was disrupted within one block of the water tower (Waller, Thomas, and Vorhis, 1965, p. 126). Comparable damage was done to the sewerage system.

Damage to structures that can be directly attributed to strong ground motion was not wide-spread. Many brick, fieldstone, and cinder-block chimneys were damaged or destroyed. Loose items on tables and shelves were upset, tumbled, and thrown down. The riveted steel tanks in the Union Oil Co. yard, unlike the welded tanks in the Standard Oil Co. yard, ruptured, but the subsequent fire and explosions obscured any evidence of the exact cause of rupture. At the power-plant the heavy 200-kw generators

System station at Alaska Avenue and McKinley Street were bent, but the tower was prevented from falling by heavy steel-cable guys.

The financial losses to the Valdez community are summarized in detail in the reports of the Federal Reconstruction and Development Planning Commission (1964).

The absence of evidence of wave damage, of ground breakage and fissures, and of vibration damage to the single dwelling on the Mineral Creek Fan (figs. 20 and 21) indicates a more stable environment there under seismic conditions than exists on the Valdez Delta.

20 (above).—Oblique aerial photograph showing Mineral Creek fan and Mineral Creek islands (foreground), the western end of Port Valdez, Shoup Spit, and Valdez Narrows (background). Photograph by U.S. Air Force.

21 (below).—Vertical aerial photograph showing the new location for Valdez on the Mineral Creek fan. Photograph by U.S. Bureau of Land Management.

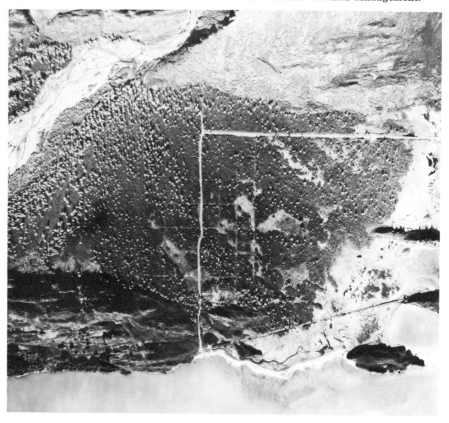

were rocked out of alinement and approximately three-fourths of the water from two cylindrical 3,500-gallon water tanks was sloshed out. No damage or loss of water from strong ground motion occurred at the 200,000-gallon city water tank, which is supported by a heavily cross-braced wooden tower, although the tank drained rapidly through watermain breaks. The exact contents of the tank at the time of the quake cannot be established. The legs of the 60-foot steel radio mast at the Alaska Communications

CONCLUSIONS

Valdez is located on the seaward edge of a large outwash delta composed of saturated silty sand containing some gravel. The March 27, 1964, earthquake triggered a massive submarine slide, involving approximately 98 million cubic yards of material, which destroyed the harbor facilities and nearshore installations. Waves generated by the slide and subsequent strong seiches did additional damage in the downtown area. Stresses generated by the seismic shocks and the slide developed an extensive system of fissures throughout the fine-grained saturated deposits of the delta. These fissures plus the shocks caused structural damage to most of the buildings in Valdez and destroyed the sewer and water systems. Removal of support from the face of the delta allowed some parts of the delta to move seaward and caused parts of the shore area to subside below high-tide level. Continued progressive encroachment of high tides and fracturing of well casings strongly suggest that subsidence and lateral movement were still active many months after the quake. Furthermore, the drainage from Valdez Glacier continuously threatens the artificial dike and levee system protecting the town and the access road.

In summary, Valdez is unsuitable as a habitation site or port facility in the following respects:
1. Poor foundation conditions on saturated fine-grained materials which are unstable under seismic conditions.
2. Exposure to slide or seismically generated sea waves.
3. Exposure to serious floods.

In contrast with the unfavorable geologic conditions at the present site of Valdez, the conditions at the new Mineral Creek townsite are very suitable for habitation and port facilities. The Mineral Creek site is situated on an alluvial fan confined on the seaward side by a series of bedrock ridges and islands (figs. 20 and 21). It is underlain by coarse tabular cobble gravel having an interlocking bedded texture which will provide excellent foundation conditions. The bedrock configuration at the mouth of Mineral Creek effectively prevents the stream from swinging eastward into or near the townsite.

In summary, the Mineral Creek townsite has the following advantages:
1. A series of bedrock ridges and islands which act as a resistant buttress retaining and protecting the toe of the alluvial fan from danger of sliding or slumping. This bedrock buttress plus the higher elevation of the Mineral Creek site also provides protection from slide or seismically generated sea waves.
2. A stable foundation anchor on bedrock for a major dock facility, favorable offshore conditions, and a protected locality for a small-boat harbor.
3. Good foundations conditions. On the basis of the absence of ground breakage and fissures, and of vibration damage to the single dwelling there, the coarse alluvium of the Mineral Creek site appears to be relatively stable under seismic conditions.
4. Excellent natural protection from floods.

REFERENCES CITED

Abercrombie, W. R., 1900, Copper River exploring expedition, in U.S. Congress Senate Committee on Military Affairs, Narratives of explorations in Alaska: Washington, U.S. Govt. Printing Off., p. 561–709, 755–825.

Alaska Department of Health and Welfare, 1964, Preliminary report of earthquake damage to environmental health facilities and services in Alaska: Juneau, Alaska Dept. Health and Welfare, Environmental Health Br., 46 p.

Davis, T. N., 1960, A field report on the Alaska earthquakes of April 7, 1958: Seismol. Soc. America Bull., v. 60, no. 4, p. 489–510.

Davis, T. N., and Echols, Carol, 1962, A table of Alaskan earthquakes 1788–1961: Alaska Univ., Geophys. Inst., Geophys. Research Rept. 8 [UAG–R131], 43 p.

Davis, T. N., and Sanders, N. K., 1960, Alaska earthquake of July 10, 1958—Intensity distribution and field investigation of northern epi-central region: Seismol. Soc. America Bull., v. 50, no. 2, p. 221–252.

Dutton, C. E., 1889, The Charleston earthquake of August 31, 1886: U.S. Geol. Survey 9th Ann. Rept., p. 203–528.

Eiby, G. A., 1957, About earthquakes: New York, Harper and Bros., 168 p.

Federal Reconstruction and Development Planning Commission for Alaska, 1964, Response to disaster, Alaskan Earthquake, March 27, 1964: Washington, U.S. Govt. Printing Off., 84 p.

Freeman, J. R., 1932, Earthquake damage and earthquake insurance: New York, McGraw-Hill Co., 903 p.

Fuller, M. L., 1912, The New Madrid earthquake: U.S. Geol. Survey Bull. 494, 119 p.

Grant, U. S., and Higgins, D. F., 1913, Coastal glaciers of Prince William Sound and Kenai Peninsula, Alaska: U.S. Geol. Survey Bull. 526, 72 p.

Grantz, Arthur, Plafker, George, and Kachadoorian, Reuben, 1964, Alaska's Good Friday earthquake, March 27, 1964, a preliminary geologic evaluation: U.S. Geol. Survey Circ. 491, 35 p.

Gutenberg, Beno, 1957, Effects of ground on earthquake motion: Seismol. Soc. America Bull., v. 47, no. 3, p. 221–250.

Heck, N. H., 1936, Earthquakes: Princeton, N.J., Princeton Univ. Press, 222 p.

———— 1958, Earthquake history of the United States: U.S. Coast and Geod. Survey Pub. 41–1, 80 p.

Imamura, Akitune, 1937, Theoretical and applied siesmology: Tokyo, Maruzen Co., 358 p.

Lawson, A. C., and others, 1908, The California earthquake of April 18, 1906: Carnegie Inst. Washington Pub. 87, 451 p.

Leet, D. L., and Leet, Florence, 1964, Earthquake—discoveries in seismology: New York, Dell Publishing Co., 224 p.

Moffit, F. H., 1954, Geology of the Prince William Sound region, Alaska: U.S. Geol. Survey Bull. 989–E, p. 225–310.

Oldham, R. D., 1899, Report on the great earthquake of 12th June 1897: India Geol. Survey Mem., v. 49, 379 p.

Oldham, Thomas, ed., 1882, The Cachar earthquake of 10th January 1869: India Geol. Survey Mem., v. 19, 98 p.

Oldham, Thomas, and Mallet, Robert, 1872, Notice of some of the secondary effects of the earthquake of 10th January 1869, in Cachar: Geol. Soc. [London] Quart. Jour., v. 28, p. 255–270.

Richter, C. F., 1958, Elementary seismology: San Francisco, Calif., W. H. Freeman and Co., 768 p.

Roy, S. C., 1939, The Bihar-Nepal earthquake of 1934, Seismometric study: India Geol. Survey Mem., v. 73, 391 p.

Shannon and Wilson, Inc., 1964, Report on subsurface investigations for Mineral Creek townsite, City of Valdez, Alaska, to U.S. Army Engineer District, Anchorage, Alaska: Seattle, Wash., Shannon and Wilson, Inc., 12 p.

Swain, R. J., 1962, Recent techniques for determination of "in situ" elastic properties and measurement of motion amplification in layered media: Geophysics, v. 27, no. 2, p. 237–241.

Tarr, R. S., and Martin, Lawrence, 1912, The earthquakes at Yakutat Bay, Alaska, in September, 1899: U.S. Geol. Survey Prof. Paper 69, 135 p.

———— 1914, Alaskan glacier studies of the National Geographic Society in the Yakutat Bay, Prince William Sound and lower Copper River regions: Washington, D.C., Natl. Geog. Soc., 498 p.

Terzaghi, Karl, 1956, Varieties of submarine slope failures: Texas Conf. Soil Mechanics and Found. Eng., 8th, 1956, Proc., art. 3, 41 p.

Terzaghi, Karl, and Peck, R. B., 1948, Soil mechanics in engineering practice: New York, John Wiley & Sons, Inc., 566 p.

Tsuya, H., ed., 1950, The Fukui earthquake of June 28, 1948: Tokyo, Japan Sci. Council, Spec. Comm. Study Fukui Earthquake, 197 p.

Van Dorn, W. G., 1964, Source mechanism of the tsunami of March 28, 1964, in Alaska: Conf. Coastal Eng., 9th, Lisbon, 1964, Proc., p. 166–190.

Waller, R. M., Thomas, H. E., and Vorhis, R. C., 1965, Effects of the Good Friday earthquake on water supplies: Am. Water Works Assoc. Jour., v. 57, no. 2, p. 123–131.

Waller, R. M., and Tolen, D.A., 1962, Hydrological data: Alaska Dept. Health and Welfare Rept. 16, 32 p.

CLARIFICATIONS

Geology Vol. Page	USGS Page	Column	Line	Remarks
359	C 1	1	27, 28	Plate 1 is Plate G in Part B, the accompanying map case
361	C 3	2	43	Plate 2 is Plate H in Part B, the accompanying map case
361	C 3	2	48	Plate 3 is Plate I in Part B, the accompanying map case

RICHARD W. LEMKE
U.S. GEOLOGICAL SURVEY

Reprinted with minor changes from
U.S. Geological Survey Professional Paper 542-E,
"Effects of the Earthquake of March 27, 1964, at Seward, Alaska"

Effects at Seward

ABSTRACT

Seward, in south-central Alaska, was one of the towns most devastated by the Alaska earthquake of March 27, 1964. The greater part of Seward is built on an alluvial fan-delta near the head of Resurrection Bay on the southeast coast of the Kenai Peninsula. It is one of the few ports in south-central Alaska that is ice free all year, and the town's economy is almost entirely dependent upon its port facilities.

The Alaska earthquake of March 27, 1964, magnitude approximately 8.3–8.4, began at 5:36 p.m. Its epicenter was in the northern part of the Prince William Sound area; focal depth was 20–50 km.

Strong ground motion at Seward lasted 3–4 minutes. During the shaking, a strip of land 50–400 feet wide along the Seward waterfront, together with docks and other harbor facilities, slid into Resurrection Bay as a result of large-scale submarine landsliding. Fractures ruptured the ground for several hundred feet back from the landslide scarps. Additional ground was fractured in the Forest Acres subdivision and on the alluvial floor of the Resurrection River valley; fountaining and sand boils accompanied the ground fracturing. Slide-generated waves, possibly seiche waves, and seismic sea waves crashed onto shore; wave runup was as much as 30 feet above mean lower low water and caused tremendous damage; fire from burning oil tanks added to the destruction. Damage from strong ground motion itself was comparatively minor. Tectonic subsidence of about 3.5 feet resulted in low areas being inundated at high tide.

Thirteen people were killed and five were injured as a result of the earthquake. Eighty-six houses were totally destroyed and 269 were heavily damaged. The harbor facilities were almost completely destroyed, and the entire economic base of the town was wiped out. The total cost to replace the destroyed public and private facilities was estimated at $22 million.

Seward lies on the axis of the Chugach Mountains geosyncline. The main structural trend in the mapped area, where the rocks consist almost entirely of graywacke and phyllite, is from near north to N. 20° E. Beds and cleavage of the rocks commonly dip 70° W. or NW. to near vertical. Locally, the rocks are complexly folded or contorted. No major faults were found in the mapped area, but small faults, shear zones, and joints are common.

Surficial deposits of the area have been divided for mapping into the following units: drift deposits, alluvial fan deposits, valley alluvium, intertidal deposits, landslide deposits, and artificial fill. Most of these units intergrade and were deposited more or less contemporaneously.

The drift deposits consist chiefly of till that forms moraines along the lower flanks of the Resurrection River valley and up tributary valleys. The till is predominantly silt and sand and lesser amounts of clay-size particles, gravel, cobbles, and boulders. Glacial outwash and stratified ice-contact deposits constitute the remainder of the drift deposits.

Fans and fan-deltas have been deposited at the valley mouths of tributary streams. Some, including the one upon which Seward is built, project into Ressurrection Bay, and deltaic-type deposits form their distal edges. The larger fans—composed chiefly of loosely compacted and poorly sorted silt, sand, and gravel—form broad aprons having low gradients. The fan deposits range in thickness from about 100 feet to possibly several hundred feet and, at least in some places, lie on a platform of compact drift. Smaller fans at the mouths of several canyons have steep gradients and considerable local relief.

Valley alluvium, deposited chiefly by the Resurrection River, consists mostly of coarse sand and fine to medium gravel. In the axial part of the valley it is probably more than 100 feet thick. Near the head of Resurrection Bay, the alluvium is underlain by at least 75 feet of marine deltaic sediments, which are in turn underlain by 600 or more feet of drift in the deepest part of the bedrock valley.

Beach, deltaic, and estuarine sediments, deposited on intertidal flats at the head of the bay and along fan margins that extend into the bay, are mapped as intertidal deposits. They consist mostly of silt, sand, and fine gravel, and lesser amounts of clay-size particles.

The earthquake reactivated old slides and trigged new ones in the mountains. Rock and snow avalanches, debris flows, and creep of talus deposits characterized slide activity on the steeper slopes.

The Seward waterfront had been extended before the earthquake by adding artificial fill consisting of loose sand and gravel; part of the lagoon area had been filled with refuse. After the earthquake, fill, consisting of silt and sand dredged from the head of the bay, was pumped onto part of the lagoon area and also on land at the northwest corner of the bay.

Response to the disaster was immediate and decisive. City, State, and Federal agencies, as well as other organizations and individuals, gave unstintingly of their time and facilities. Within a few days, there was temporary restoration of water, sewerage, and electrical facilities.

The U.S. Army Corps of Engineers was authorized to select sites and construct a new dock for the Alaska Railroad, a new small-boat basin, and related facilities. The firm of Shannon and Wilson, Inc., under contract to the Corps of Engineers, investigated subsurface soils extensively to determine the factors responsible for the sliding along the Seward waterfront and to assist in site selection for reconstruction of the destroyed harbor facilities. Borings were made along the Seward waterfront and at the head of the bay, and laboratory tests were conducted on pertinent samples. These studies were augmented by geophysical studies both on land and in the bay. In addition, the Corps of Engineers made shallow borings on the intertidal flats at the head of the bay and performed piledriving and load tests. Borings also were drilled and test pits were dug in the subdivision of Forest Acres.

Sliding along the Seward waterfront markedly deepened the water along the former shoreline. Postearthquake slopes of the bay floor immediately offshore also are steeper in places than before the earthquake. The strong ground motion of the earthquake triggered the landsliding, but several factors may have contributed to the magnitude and characteristics of the slides. These factors are: (1) the long duration of strong ground motion, (2) the grain size and texture of the material involved in the sliding, (3) the probability that the finer grained materials liquefied and flowed seaward, and (4) the added load of manmade facilities

built on the edge of the shore. Secondary effects of the slides themselves—sudden drawdown of water, followed by the weight of returning waves—also may have contributed to the destruction.

Submarine sliding at the northwest corner of the bay occurred in fine-grained deltaic deposits whose frontal slopes probably were in metastable equilibrium under static conditions. Uplift pressures from aquifers under hydrostatic head, combined with the probable liquefaction characteristics of the sediments when vibrated by strong ground motion, probably caused the material to slide and flow seaward as a heavy slurry.

Under static conditions, no major shoreline or submarine landsliding is expected in the Seward area; in the event of another severe earthquake, however, additional sliding is likely along the Seward waterfront and also in the deltaic deposits at the northwest corner of the bay. Fractured ground in back of the present shoreline along the Seward waterfront is an area of incipient landslides that would be unstable under strong shaking. For this reason the Scientific and Engineering Task Force placed the area in a high-risk classification and recommended no repair, rehabilitation, or new construction in this area involving use of Federal funds; it was further recommended that the area should be reserved for park or other uses that do not involve large congregations of people. The deltaic deposits at the head of the bay probably also would be susceptible to sliding during another large earthquake. This sliding would result in further landward retreat of the present shoreline toward the new railroad dock. Specifications for the new dock, whose seaward end is now approximately 1,100

feet from the back scarp of the subaqueous landslide, require design provisions to withstand seismic shock up to certain limits.

Earthquake-induced fracturing of the ground in the subdivision of Forest Acres was confined to the lower part of a broad alluvial fan. There, sewer and water lines were ruptured and the foundations of some homes were heavily damaged. Landsliding, such as occurred along the shoreline of the bay, was not a contributing cause of the fracturing. Two hypotheses are offered to explain the fracturing:

1. Seismic energy was transformed into visible surface waves of such amplitude that the strength of surface layer was exceeded and rupturing occurred; tensional and compressional stresses alternately opened and closed the fractures and forced out water and mud.

2. Compaction by vibration of the fine-grained deposits of the fan caused ground settlement and fracturing; ground water under temporary hydrostatic head was forced to the surface as fountains and carried the finer material with it.

Water waves that crashed onto shore, while shaking was still continuing, were generated chiefly by onshore and offshore landsliding. Waves that overran the shores about 25 minutes after shaking stopped and that continued to arrive for the next several hours are believed to be seismic sea waves (tsunamis) that originated in an uplifted area in the Gulf of Alaska. During the time of seismic sea-wave activity and perhaps preceding it, seiche waves also may have been generated within Resurrection Bay and complicated the wave effects along the shoreline.

INTRODUCTION AND ACKNOWLEDGMENTS

Seward was one of the cities most heavily damaged by the great Alaska earthquake of March 27, 1964. The city is near the head of Resurrection Bay, on the southeast coast of the Kenai Peninsula, and about 75 airline miles south of Anchorage (fig. 1; pl. 1). The climate is mild and humid because

of the influence of the Gulf of Alaska, and Seward is one of the few ports in south-central Alaska that is ice free the entire year. It therefore provides year-round access from the coast by railroad and highway to Anchorage and the interior of Alaska.

Before the earthquake of March 27, 1964, the economy of Seward was based mostly on shipping. Freighters, barges, tankers, and fishing boats docked regularly in the harbor. Most of the freight was transhipped to other communities by road or rail. Texaco, Inc., and the Standard Oil Co. of

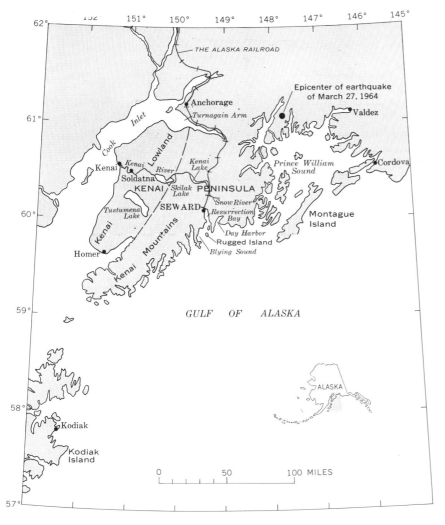

1.—Index map, Seward and the Kenai Peninsula.

California had established large tank farms on the waterfront. Fishing boats unloaded their catch, and at least one cannery was in operation.

The entire economic base of the town was wiped out by the near-total destruction of harbor facilities during the earthquake. Damage was caused chiefly by shoreline and offshore landsliding and by locally generated waves, seismic sea waves, and fire. A tectonic downdrop of approximately 3.5 feet caused formerly dry low areas to be covered by water at high tide.

This paper describes the effects of the earthquake at Seward and relates them to engineering geologic applications. The physical properties of the geologic units, as they affect manmade structures, are emphasized. The aim of the paper, therefore, is not only to describe the geologic conditions that caused structures to fail during the earthquake but also to record other geologic conditions in the area so that future facilities can be so planned and located that they will undergo minimal damage in the event of another severe earthquake.

The writer gratefully acknowledges many sources of informa-

tion. Federal, State, and City organizations, contractors, and many local individuals gave complete cooperation. One of the most helpful single sources of information was the consulting firm of Shannon and Wilson, Inc., (of Seattle, Wash.), which was under contract to the Corps of Engineers. Their report (Shannon and Wilson, Inc., 1964) on the subsurface investigation for the city of Seward and vicinity contains valuable data derived from borings, samplings, soil testing, test pits, and seismic surveys. The writer worked closely with representatives of this firm during their field investigations. Information and ideas, freely interchanged, permitted maximum and timely use of the information.

Information was also interchanged between representatives of the Corps of Engineers and the writer. The outstanding cooperation of John A. Spangler, Resident Engineer at Seward for the Corps of Engineers and of his staff is particularly acknowledged. Mr. Spangler provided office space and generous assistance in many other ways.

City officials of Seward, especially Perry Stockton, Mayor, J. W. Harrison, City Manager, and his successor, Fred Waltz, also cooperated in every way possible. In spite of extremely heavy demands upon their time, they willingly lent assistance whenever asked.

Many individuals provided their own observations of the earthquake. Without these accounts, the sequence of events during and after the earthquake could not have been reconstructed.

Robert D. Miller of the U.S. Geological Survey assisted the writer for a week when ephemeral earthquake-produced features were being mapped.

THE EARTHQUAKE AND ITS EFFECTS

The Alaska earthquake of March 27, 1964, began at 5:36 p.m., local time. The epicenter of the main shock was determined as lat 61.1° N. and long 147.7° W. ±15 km (U.S. Coast and Geodetic Survey, written commun., 1965), near Unakwik Inlet in the northern part of Prince William Sound, and approximately 95 airline miles northeast of Seward (fig. 1). A Richter magnitude of approximately 8.3–8.4 has been assigned, and the focal depth has been calculated as 20–50 km.

The events that took place during and immediately after the main shock at Seward were reconstructed from eyewitness reports. The writer interviewed more than 100 individuals and studied written accounts that had already been obtained by others; the report by Lantz and Kirkpatrick (1964) was especially useful. The chronology of events, however, must be regarded as approximate because few individuals looked at their watches until late that night or the following day. In an attempt to determine this chronology as accurately as possible, the writer estimated how long it would take an individual to complete various actions, such as running three blocks or driving a car a certain distance, that observers did between the occurrences of reported events.

Strong ground motion at Seward, which was in a north-south direction at least part of the time, lasted 3–4 minutes. Nearly all accounts indicate that the shaking started gently but increased markedly in a few seconds and continued to grow in violence until

people could hardly stand without support. Reportedly the ground rose and fell like waves, trees bent in unison, and buildings swayed back and forth. Two gantry cranes at The Alaska Railroad dock bounced off their tracks and into Resurrection Bay, and automobiles rocked from side to side. Several chimneys fell, windows were broken, and foundations were cracked in various parts of the city. The Seward city hall was damaged beyond repair by shaking, but the building is said to have been in poor condition before the earthquake. Some other public buildings were damaged to some extent by shaking. Material on shelves tumbled to the floor, and glassware breakage, in such places as bars and liquor stores, was heavy. Water and sewer lines were ruptured in several parts of the city and in Forest Acres subdivision.

Almost as soon as shaking started, rocks began falling from some of the steeper valley walls. As shaking continued, rock slides were triggered in Jap Creek canyon and Box Creek canyon. Snow avalanched down the walls of Lowell Creek canyon and of several tributary valleys.

The more extensive and spectacular effects of the earthquake, however, were along the Seward waterfront. Between 30 and 45 seconds after violent shaking began, the distal part of the Seward fan, an area extending from the Standard Oil Co. dock to beyond the San Juan dock, began sliding seaward as a result of large-scale offshore landsliding. Slice after slice of ground along the shore slid pro-

gressively as shaking continued, until a strip of harbor area 50–500 feet wide had disappeared into the bay (fig. 2, p. E6). Large fractures broke the ground surface behind the slide area and extended several hundred feet inland as shaking continued (figs. 3, 4, p. E8, E10). Some fractures near the Texaco tanks reportedly opened and closed repeatedly during the shaking; some were at least 20 feet deep. They filled quickly with water and, as the shaking continued, spewed muddy water at intervals. When the shaking ceased, fracturing had reached its maximum extent and the shoreline had receded to the position shown in figure 2 (bottom).

Pipes and valves of the tanks at the Standard Oil Co. dock began rupturing 30–45 seconds after shaking started, and fuel poured from the tanks. As the tanks began to overturn and slide into the bay, they exploded with a roar, and flames leaped 200 feet into the air. Water, displaced by landsliding, receded rapidly from the shore carrying burning fuel on its surface. A tanker unloading at the Standard Oil Co. dock reportedly hit bottom when the water level suddenly dropped 15–20 feet. In the small-boat harbor north of San Juan dock, the *Unga* also hit bottom; from the known former depth of water in the harbor and the draft, the withdrawal there must have been at least 7 feet vertically.

As the water was displaced suddenly from the shore, a large mound of water formed several hundred yards out in the bay and in line between the Standard Oil Co. tanks and Fourth of July

Point. Waves radiated in all directions from this mound, but predominantly in two directions: one toward the Seward waterfront and Lowell Point, the other toward the head of the bay. Both caused much damage.

The wave moving toward Lowell Point overran the northeast corner of that fan approximately 1 minute and 15 seconds after shaking started, or about half a minute after the landsliding started in the Standard Oil Co. dock area. It was estimated to be 30 feet high, as it approached Lowell Point, and was free of debris until it hit the shore, where it churned up much sand and silt; burning oil covered its surface halfway to Lowell Point. The wave swept several hundred feet inland and caused much destruction, totally demolishing a nearly completed marineway and smashing heavy earthmoving equipment, trucks, and other objects against trees or twisting them into wreckage.

The water surged back from the mound toward the southwest part of the Seward waterfront also. A large swell broke over The Alaska Railroad dock area (fig. 5, p. E12), lifting flat cars off the tracks and picking up several vehicles. Its crestline at Railroad Avenue was nearly as high as that of any later wave. As this wave hit the shoreline at the Standard Oil Co. tanks, burning oil was carried back onto shore. An 80-car freight train on the tracks between the Standard and Texaco tanks was just ready to start moving north. Its last 40 cars were filled oil tankers and as the fire swept onto shore, the tankers caught fire in a chain reaction of exploding cars down the track toward the Texaco yard. Reportedly several minutes elapsed before the Texaco tanks caught fire, even though oil from ruptured

tanks had already spread over the surrounding area.

While this large wave was moving toward the Seward waterfront and Lowell Point, the other large wave from the mound of water offshore from the Standard Oil Co. tanks swept toward the head of the bay, swirling and boiling as it moved. As it neared shore, it broke up into several secondary waves, and much sand and silt were churned to the surface. This complex wave pattern was presumably due not only to the sliding along the edge of the Seward fan but also to sliding of deltaic deposits at the head of the bay. As wave crests reached the small-boat harbor, moored boats were lifted over the breakwater. A few were carried over the railroad embankment into the lagoon area, but most were first driven wildly to-and-fro in the northwest corner of the bay and then beached at the head of the bay. At about the time the first returning wave hit the small-boat harbor, the Army dock was lifted by a wave and then dumped into the bay. Although these early waves caused heavy damage, they did not attain the heights reached by later waves that arrived after the shaking stopped. Many people, who left the downtown area as soon as the shaking ceased, were able to travel on the highway across the lagoon and they noted only small amounts of debris on and adjacent to the road. Later the road was completely blocked by houses, boats, railroad cars, and other debris carried in by subsequent waves.

After strong ground motion had ceased and before the first seismic sea wave arrived, at least two additional waves swept the Seward waterfront. Water continued to slosh back and forth in the bay for at least 15 minutes following the quake. Near the head of the

bay, swirling and boiling continued, actuated either by continued submarine sliding of deltaic deposits or possibly by seiche action. Some boats, which had been lifted out of the small-boat harbor by the first waves, are reported to have been quiet for as long as a minute as the water calmed, only to be driven wildly about as the water again began to churn. This pattern was repeated many times before the boats were finally driven onto land.

Fires ignited during the shaking continued to burn intensely after shaking had ceased, and new ones were started as explosions periodically ripped the waterfront. Burning oil and combustible debris covered most of the water surface from beyond the south end of Seward to the head of the bay. Without water (because of broken mains), the efforts of firemen and volunteers were largely futile. Had not a gentle wind been blowing eastward across the bay, the entire town probably would have burned. Most people thought the town was doomed either by fire or by expectable "tidal" waves. Some rushed in cars across the lagoon area, but most made their way to the hospital, which was at the head of the fan, on the highest ground they could reach.

The arrival time of the first seismic sea wave from outside the Seward area is conjectural. Several people witnessed the wave's arrival, but none noted the time. By estimating the time that it would take these observers to perform a series of activities after shaking stopped and before the wave hit, it is concluded that the wave arrived between 20 and 30 minutes after shaking stopped; 25 minutes is the closest approximation that can be made.

The first seismic sea wave is reported to have spanned the width

The Alaska Railroad dock

Diversion tunnel

RAILROAD

WASHINGTON STREET

AVENUE

ADAMS STREET

JEFFERSON STREET

MADISON STREET

MONROE STREET

FIRST AVENUE

SECOND AVENUE

THIRD AVENUE

FOURTH AVENUE

FIFTH AVENUE

SIXTH AVENUE

SEVENTH AVENUE

A ST

Standard Oil Co dock

Standard Oil Co tanks

Army dock

San Juan dock

2. Seward before and after the earthquake. Top, before the earthquake of March 27, 1964. Bottom, 1 day after the earthqu

WASHINGTON STREET

RAILROAD

ADAMS STREET

JEFFERSON STREET

MADISON STREET

MONROE STREET

SECOND AVENUE

THIRD

FOURTH AVENUE

FIFTH AVENUE

SIXTH AVENUE

SEVENTH AVENUE

Maximum height reached by waves

Standard Oil Co tanks

Lagoon

Clearview

VAN BUREN STREET

BAY (AIRPORT) ROAD

NORTH

Small-boat harbor

Inc tanks

500   0   500   1000   1500

APPROXIMATE SCALE IN FEET

March 27, 1964. Photographs by the U.S. Army, Corps of Engineers; mosaicked by the U.S. Geological Survey.

VAN BUREN STREET

Lagoon

Clearview

NORTH

tanks

500   0   500   1000   1500

APPROXIMATE SCALE IN FEET

Apparent curvature of streets caused by photographic distortion

3. Aerial view of the southern part of the Seward waterfront showing extent of ground fracture and earthquake damage.   Photog

Army; mosaicked by U.S. Geological Survey. See figure 4 (next page) for view of northern waterfront and index map.

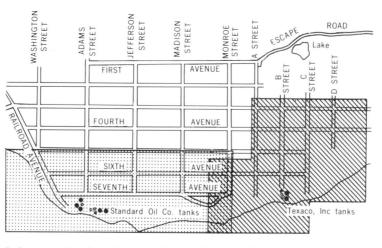

Index map showing relation of figures 3 and 4. Stippled area is figure 3, hachured area figure 4.

4. Aerial view of the northern part of the Seward waterfront showing extent of fractured ground and earthquake damage. Photograph by U.S. Army; mosaicked by U.S. Geological Survey. Index map (upper left) shows relation of figures 3 and 4.

of the bay as it entered the Seward area and to have been 30–40 feet high as it neared the head of the bay. Burning oil covered much of its surface. Carrying boats, houses, and railroad cars collected from the Seward waterfront area, the wave crashed over the railroad embankment into the lagoon area and moved inland at the head of the bay. Debris was piled so high on the road across the lagoon that it blocked all motorized exit from town. At the airport, a wall of water rushed part way up the airstrip at an estimated speed of 50–60 miles per hour. The wave was reportedly accompanied by a rumbling sound like the noise of a fast-moving freight train and by a terrific rush of air at its front as it overran the land. There is general agreement that this wave extended farther inland at Seward and at the head of the bay than any of the earlier locally generated waves; it also inundated a larger part of Lowell Point than earlier waves. Its maximum runup, however, apparently was not as great as that of at least one of the later waves.

Several other large waves followed the first seismic sea wave. Information on the number, height, and periodicity of these waves is fragmentary. There are accounts of waves arriving at about half-hour intervals until 11:00 p.m.; the last wave in the Seward area, however, was reported to have arrived at about 4:20 a.m., March 28. The third seismic sea wave was probably the largest, but most of the destruction had already been done by he earlier waves. Fires burning on the surface of the bay were extinguished several times by incoming waves, only to start anew as burning oil poured out along the waterfront.

Water apparently withdrew from the shores in the intervals be-

5.—Damage caused by water waves to old Alaska Railroad dock and facilities. Photograph by U.S. Army.

tween the seismic sea waves, but there is no indication that the water receded immediately before the first wave. According to one report, at approximately 9:45 p.m. the surface of the bay near the site of a former cannery (on the road to Lowell Point just south of the railroad dock) was 40 feet below mean lower low water. The floor of the bay at the end of the cannery dock was reported to have been exposed.

The maximum extent of the waves in Seward and at the head of the bay shown in figure 2 and on plate 1 represent the maximum runup reached by one or more waves and, therefore, represent the composite pattern of the wave action. Eyewitnesses agree generally that the third seismic sea wave was the highest, but other waves may have been locally higher.

Heights of wave runup in different parts of Seward are shown

below. The altitudes, based upon a detailed topographic map made after the earthquake, are in feet above mean lower low water; however, the preearthquake datum, approximately 3.5 feet higher than present land level, was used on plate 1.

Wave runup (feet)	Location
24	First St., south end.
25	Depot, Railroad Ave.
26	Fifth St., south end.
28	Adams St., east end.
31	Jefferson St., east end.
31	Madison St., east end.
29	Monroe St., east end.
28	A St., east end.
28	B St., east end.
29	C St., east end.
26	D St., east end.
30	Second St., north end.

At Lowell Point the position of scars on trees and the directions in which debris was carried inland indicate that at least three waves from three different directions ran up onshore. The first wave, generated by landsliding offshore from the Standard Oil dock, hit the northeast corner of Lowell Point. Debris carried by this wave was lodged several hundred feet inland and approximately 30 feet above mean lower low water. A second wave hit the southern end of Lowell Point and carried debris in a northerly direction to approximately the same altitude. A third wave overran the shore at the eastern end of Lowell Point and moved westward. It apparently did not move inland as far as the other two waves, but heavy tree growth may have dissipated the wave's energy. Whether more than one wave hit the shore in each direction cannot be ascertained. One eyewitness account states that a larger second wave hit Lowell Point less than an hour after the first wave, but exactly where is not made clear.

Debris lines several hundred feet or more inland marked the limit reached by waves on Fourth of July Point. The number of waves and the direction they traveled onto this fan are difficult to reconstruct. Manmade structures or other points of reference are largely lacking. Debris brought in by waves was found, however, at a height of 25 feet above mean lower low water, and in places waves may have reached greater heights.

LOSS OF LIFE AND DAMAGE TO MANMADE STRUCTURES

Thirteen people were killed and five injured in and near Seward as a result of the earthquake. Most of the 13 were killed by wave action. One man was killed by an incoming wave about 10:30 p.m. as he was helping to clear debris off the highway in the lagoon area to open an escape route out of town. Three bodies were never found.

6.—Earthquake damage along Seward waterfront in area of Texaco, Inc., tanks. Photograph by U.S. Army.

Harbor facilities in the waterfront area between the Standard Oil and Texaco tanks were almost completely destroyed, and other parts of the waterfront were heavily damaged (fig. 6). The Standard Oil dock, 13 oil tanks, the Army dock, and the San Juan dock, on which a cannery was located, disappeared completely into the bay. Several Texaco tanks were destroyed by fire.

The Alaska Railroad dock at the south end of town was almost totally destroyed by wave action and shaking (fig. 5). Sheet piling cells, upon which the main dock was constructed, split open and dropped the front of the dock into the bay. Much of the adjacent auxiliary dock and the warehouse on it were also destroyed, chiefly by waves. A cannery and small dock just to the south along the road to Lowell Point were crushed by one of the first waves and disappeared into the bay.

The railroad marshalling yards were left a tangled mass of wreckage by wave action and fire (fig. 7, next page). Railroad cars, many of them filled with cargo, were moved at least 100 feet and heaped in windrows by the waves. Twisted rails and overturned loco-

motives attested to the energy of the waves.

Eighty-six houses were totally destroyed and 269 were heavily damaged (James W. Harrison, Mayor, oral commun., 1964); water waves caused nearly all the destruction. Homes in the area between the Texaco tanks and the lagoon were swept completely off their foundations, and most were washed into the lagoon (fig. 8, p. E15).

Earthquake damage in the outlying areas was less severe. There was little damage in the Clearview subdivision except at the Jesse Lee Home where shaking toppled a chimney and damaged a large building reported to have been in poor structural condition before the quake. In Forest Acres, sewer and water mains were broken by ground fracturing. Foundations and floor joists of several homes were heavily damaged, but most of the structural elements were repairable. At Lowell Point, a nearly completed marineway and its construction equipment were totally destroyed. The few houses that were in the path of the water waves on that fan also were completely demolished. The old freight-line dock and warehouse

7.—Wave damage in the area of railroad marshalling yards.

on the east side of the bay across from Seward were heavily damaged. A lumber mill at the northeast end of the bay was heavily damaged by wave action, as were all the houses in the Crawford subdivision just north of the old Signal Corps building (still largely intact). Several ground fractures cut the airstrip, but it was used immediately even though one end, lowered by tectonic subsidence, was washed by high tides. Damage was fairly heavy to railroad embankments, highway bridges,

and areas of road fill outside the town.

Total damage in Seward and vicinity to public and private facilities, based upon cost of restoration, was estimated at $22,363,349 (Alaskan Construction Consultant Comm., 1964, p. 44).

SLIDES AND OTHER CHANGES IN NATURAL FEATURES

Snow avalanches were the most conspicuous type of slides triggered by the earthquake in Lowell

canyon. Two of three snow avalanches in the lowermost mile of Lowell canyon reached the creekbed and piled up snow, rock fragments, and broken trees as high as 30 feet. Several talus deposits were also activated by the shaking. There was a general creep of material downslope, and in places small debris flows formed near the bottom of the slopes.

A fairly large rock and debris slide was triggered by the earthquake near the mouth of Jap Creek canyon. A projecting ledge of

8.—Houses and other debris carried by waves into the lagoon area at the north end of Seward. Main road leading north out of town shown in right-hand part of photograph. Photograph by U.S. Army.

bedrock 200–300 feet above the floor of Jap Creek was dislodged, and a near vertical back scarp about 80 feet high was left. The slide toe extended across Jap Creek and was 15–25 feet thick in the creekbed.

A small rock slide also was triggered by the earthquake a short distance upstream from the large slide. A snow avalanche, which contained some rocks and other debris, moved downslope across Jap Creek a few hundred feet downstream from the major rock slide

and continued a short distance up the opposite valley wall. In both places, Jap Creek continued to flow under the slide masses and no water was impounded.

Rock and debris slides were activated by the earthquake in Box Creek canyon. The largest slide extended entirely across the valley front and blocked the creek channel. Small-scale sliding occurred intermittently during the summer, apparently triggered at least in part by aftershocks.

On part of the Jap Creek fan, as well as on much of the valley bottom of Resurrection River, the frozen ground was conspicuously fractured during shaking. Water spouted from many of the fractures. The ejected water pulsated in height and volume as the fractures opened and closed and commonly fountained to heights of 3–6 feet. Some early phases of fountaining were clear and were muddied later when much silt and sand was ejected; other fountains were muddy from the beginning.

Effects of the earthquake on water wells in and near Seward were moderate. Seward's main source of water is Lowell Creek, and neither this supply nor the storage tank in Lowell canyon was adversely affected. However, casings and pump collars were bent or broken to such a degree in three supplemental wells between Clearview and Forest Acres that it was necessary to drill two new wells (Waller and others, 1965). A circular pattern of fractured ground, downthrown about 6 inches, around one of the wells suggested that there was considerable differential subsidence of material around the hole. A well 47 feet deep in alluvium, 4.5 miles north of Seward, was flowing before the earthquake, but no water was obtainable from it after the quake, perhaps owing to a broken casing. The water surface in a second nearby well, which was 22 feet deep, was about 6 feet from the top of the well before the earthquake. Immediately after the quake, the well became artesian and gushed 2 feet into the air. It was still bubbling at the surface a week later, but by August 22, 1964, the well was at its preearthquake level. Additional information on earthquake effects on the hydrologic regimen is discussed by Waller (1966).

TECTONIC LAND CHANGES

Regional tectonic deformation that accompanied the 1964 Alaska earthquake has been described by Grantz, Plafker, and Kachadorian (1964), U.S. Coast and Geodetic Survey (1964), Plafker (1965), and others. During the summer of 1964 the U.S. Coast and Geodetic Survey reestablished vertical and horizontal control and added new controls designed to link the earthquake-disrupted geodetic net with the undisturbed portion of the net near Fairbanks. The surveys furnished much valuable information on the amount of vertical and horizontal land movements.

On the basis of first-order leveling by the U.S. Coast and Geodetic Survey (1965, p. 29), the landmass in the Seward area subsided approximately 3.5 feet. Low areas which were above higher high tide (10.6 feet above lower low tide) before the earthquake are now covered by water. High tides now advance several hundred feet to nearly half a mile farther inland at the head of the bay. Likewise, part of the lagoon area, the distal edge of Lowell Point (where residential development was underway), and a strip of land at Fourth of July Point are now covered by water during high tides. The airstrip must be reconstructed, the road around the head of the bay must be relocated, and other land has lost its private-use potential.

As part of the geodetic surveys conducted by the U.S. Coast and Geodetic Survey after the earthquake, a horizontal control survey was extended southward from Anchorage to Seward. The results of this survey, when compared with the original third-order survey made by the U.S. Army Corps of Engineers in 1942, indicate that the landmass on the west side of the Resurrection River valley north of Seward moved 5 feet north with respect to the landmass on the east side of the valley (U.S. Coast and Geod. Survey, 1965, p. 18). This indicated 5-foot shift extends northward past Kenai Lake to Turnagain Arm south of Anchorage.

It is not clear whether the translation between opposite sides of the valley reflects tectonic displacement or instrumental differences in the two survey nets used for comparison. In the mapped area at Seward the writer found no surface evidence of ground breakage related to faulting; the intricate fracturing in surficial deposits is attributed to landsliding and other nontectonic causes. On the other hand, Rusnak (oral commun., 1965; and in Corwin and Bradley, 1965) believes that large-scale rock movements along preexisting faults and folds that parallel the configuration of the bay contributed to submarine sliding of the overlying sediments. This interpretation is based on data he obtained from geologic samples and subbottom profiles of Resurrection Bay.

GEOLOGIC SETTING

Seward lies on the axis of the Chugach Mountains geosyncline (Payne, 1955). Sedimentary rocks of Jurassic and late Cretaceous age were highly deformed and partly metamorphosed during post-Paleocene time (Payne, 1955). Graywacke and phyllite predominate in the Seward area. Extrusive igneous rocks are interstratified with the sedimentary rocks in some places and some granitic rocks are also present; these rocks are outside the mapped area of plate 1. During the Tertiary Period and continuing into the Quaternary Period, the area was uplifted and eroded several times.

Unconsolidated glacial and fluvial deposits now overlie the bedrock in most places except on the steep higher slopes.

The business district and most of the residential district of the city are on the alluvial fan of Lowell Creek near the northwest corner of Resurrection Bay. The area of about 8 square miles north of the bay that was annexed to Seward shortly after the earthquake includes the Forest Acres subdivision on the distal edge of the alluvial fan of Jap Creek, and the sites of scattered homes in part of the valley of Resurrection River and some of its tributaries. The population of Seward at the time of the earthquake was slightly more than 1,900.

Most of the surrounding region is very rugged and is characterized by numerous glaciers (pl. 1). The Kenai Mountains rise steeply above Resurrection Bay and the valley of Resurrection River. Iron Mountain, Marathon Mountain, and Bear Mountain—the highest peaks on the west side of the bay and the valley—attain altitudes of 4,274, 4,603, and 4,003 feet, respectively.

Jap Creek, Lowell Creek, and Spruce Creek are the chief streams on the west side of the Resurrection River valley; all three are fed by cirque glaciers at their heads. The large Harding Icefield lies only a few miles to the west of the bay, but its drainage flows to Resurrection River.

Resurrection Bay is a deep fiord about 25 miles long and 3–5 miles wide. Its maximum depth is 978 feet, in the vicinity of Thumb Cove approximately 8 miles south of the head of the bay. Near Seward, the bay is 2–3 miles wide and about 500 feet deep. Except at the head of the bay and near some alluvial fans, the water is deep immediately offshore.

Engineering properties of graywacke

[Data provided by the U.S. Army Corps of Engineers (written commun., 1964)]

Location	Specific gravity (CRD-107-60)	Los Angeles abrasion (CRD-117-56) (percent)	Soundness, magnesium sulphate (CRD-137-62) (percent)
1. Old quarry near high school, Seward_____	2. 71	15. 6	-----------
2. West end of lagoon area, Seward_____	2. 69	16. 7	-----------
3. North end of Lowell Point_____	2. 73	17. 2	-----------
4. Lowell canyon, about ½ mile west of Seward_____	2. 74	24. 2	0. 69

BEDROCK

Alternating units of graywacke and phyllite constitute virtually all of the bedrock in the immediate vicinity of Seward (pl. 1). Each unit is commonly tens to hundreds of feet thick. In places, however, the graywacke and phyllite are in thin interbeds only 1–4 inches thick. In still other places, all gradations in composition and texture exist between the two rock types.

On the west side of Resurrection Bay, from the northern end of Seward to Lowell Point, nearly all the bedrock below an altitude of about 1,000 feet consists of graywacke, whereas phyllite predominates above this altitude. On the east side of the bay, phyllite is almost continuously exposed in sea cliffs from near the head of the bay to Fourth of July Point. Phyllite predominates over graywacke in the higher parts of the mountains on the east side of the bay and along the valley walls north of the head of the bay.

The graywacke is medium to dark gray, fine to medium grained, generally massive, and indistinctly bedded. It commonly forms ledges that have slopes ranging from about 45° to more than 70°. It is well indurated and slightly metamorphosed.

Engineering properties of the graywacke, based upon analyses from four locations, are shown in the table above. The tests were made by the U.S. Army Corps of Engineers, during a postearthquake search for armor rock to construct breakwaters for new harbor facilities; the rock chosen for the breakwaters was from location 3 at the north end of Lowell Point where a large quarry was opened. The data obtained are believed to be fairly representative of the more massive graywacke of the area.

The phyllite originally was a shale that has been subjected to low-grade metamorphism. It is dark gray to nearly black and fine grained and has a well-developed cleavage parallel to the bedding in most places. On steep weathered slopes, it commonly splits into sheets from less than an inch to several inches thick and from less than a foot to several feet across. The cleavage surfaces have a lustrous sheen produced by flakes of mica and chlorite. Some less metamorphosed rocks, more nearly slate, are also present, and shale that has undergone little or no metamorphism has been found in a few outcrops.

The main structural trend of the rocks in the Seward area is from near north to approximately N. 20°

E. Beds and cleavage commonly dip 70° W. or NW. to near vertical. Locally the rocks are complexly folded and contorted, and Moffit (1906, p. 18) reported that about 2 miles east of Resurrection Bay near Godwin Glacier (pl. 1) the beds lie in immense folds slightly overturned to the east. Smaller folds in the vicinity of Seward also appear to be slightly overturned to the east.

No major faults have been identified in the mapped area, but the rectilinear pattern of the major valley system extending northward from Seward into the central part of the Kenai Peninsula strongly suggests that this valley system is at least in part fault controlled. If so, the trough extending south from Kenai Lake and continuing along the long axis of Resurrection Bay may reflect a fault valley scoured by glacial erosion. Rusnak (oral commun., 1965; and in Corwin and Bradley, 1965) believes that during the earthquake of 1964 there was large-scale rock movement in Resurrection Bay along preexisting faults and folds that parallel the configuration of the bay. The writer, however, has found no evidence to support this view.

Small faults, shear zones, and joints are common in the mapped area. The rocks are commonly offset vertically a few inches to several feet along these faults. The shear zones, mostly less than 5 feet wide, commonly are made up of angular pieces of graywacke or phyllite a few inches to a few feet long, though some are composed of finely ground rock fragments or a bluish-gray clayey gouge. The more massive graywacke is characterized in many places by a major and a secondary joint system. North of Lowell Point, where the joints are well exposed, the major set strikes N. 60°–70° W.

and dips approximately 85° NE., and the secondary set trends northeastward. Most of the joints are filled with quartz but some are filled with calcite.

SURFICIAL DEPOSITS

Surficial deposits in the Seward area are both glacial and nonglacial in origin and generally are intermixed in the valley of Resurrection River.

The surficial deposits, of Pleistocene and Recent age, are divided on the basis of land form and origin into six units: glacial deposits, alluvial fan and fan-delta deposits, valley alluvium, intertidal deposits, landslide deposits, and artificial fill. Most of the units are gradational and were deposited more or less contemporaneously. Marine deposits are known only from the subsurface (pl. 1) and are not discussed separately.

GLACIAL DEPOSITS

Remnants of lateral moraines flank the main valley of Resurrection River and extend up the sides of the tributary valleys to a maximum altitude of about 1,500 feet. In a few places, as directly west of Seward, the original form is still well preserved, and the ridges are 25–75 feet high and fairly sharp crested. Many ridge crests slope downvalley rather steeply from individual tributary valleys; these steep slopes suggest that the ridges are lateral moraines of tributary glaciers. The tributary glaciers, which flowed from large icefields in the higher mountains, probably coalesced in the main valley to form a large trunk glacier whose terminus is not known, although it must have been some miles or tens of miles south of the present head of Resurrection Bay.

The lateral moraines are heavily vegetated in most places. In the few places exposed, however, they consist chiefly of rather loose gray

till, which oxidizes to a yellowish gray. The till consists predominantly of silt, sand, and gravel, and smaller amounts of clay-size particles, cobbles, and boulders. A sample from a roadcut just west of the lagoon area at the north end of Seward consists of about 10 percent clay-size particles, 20 percent silt, 40 percent sand, and 30 percent gravel. The finer material is derived largely from phyllite bedrock, and the material of gravel size and larger is mostly graywacke. The cobbles and boulders are generally sharply angular.

About 50 feet of loose sand, gravel, and cobbles is exposed along the road about 4 miles northeast of Seward in what may be a kame terrace. Bedding in the lower part of the deposit dips as much as 20° SE.; the upper part is more lenticular and consists chiefly of poorly sorted gravel with boulders as much as 1.5 feet long.

ALLUVIAL FANS AND FAN-DELTA DEPOSITS

Alluvial fans and fan-deltas have been deposited at the mouths of several tributary valleys. Some fans extend into Resurrection Bay and deltaic deposits form their distal edges. Most of the others have spread out onto the alluvial floor of the Resurrection River valley. The four largest fans, composed chiefly of silt, sand, and gravel, form broad aprons having low gradients.

SEWARD FAN-DELTA

The fan-delta on which the town of Seward is built is at the mouth of Lowell Creek canyon and projects into Resurrection Bay. It is approximately 1¼ miles long in a north-south direction and half a mile wide, and rises from sea level to an altitude of 130 feet at the mouth of the canyon—an average gradient of about 3°, or about 275 feet per mile.

Data from drill holes, backhoe

Lowell Creek Canyon

Lowell Creek flume —

ADAMS ST

SEVENTH AVENUE

rmer ad dock

Standard Oil Co. tanks

9.—Seward alluvial fan in 1939 showing torrential-type deposition from Lowell Creek after a flood. Photograph by Robert Zentmire.

trenches, and excavations for sewer and water lines indicate that the fan-delta deposits are predominantly very loosely compacted and nearly unstratified sand and gravel together with smaller amounts of clay-size particles, silt, cobbles, and boulders. The sand is mostly medium to coarse and consists chiefly of flat chips of phyllite; the gravel is generally subangular to subrounded and is mostly graywacke.

Light-gray silt is rather evenly disseminated throughout the deposits. Cobbles and boulders, nearly all subangular to angular pieces of graywacke, generally are locally concentrated. They are most abundant toward the head of the fan and along the former channel of Lowell Creek where the boulders are as much as 2.5 feet long. Before construction of a diversion tunnel (2,000 feet long and 10 feet in diameter) from Lowell

canyon a quarter of a mile west of Second Street to the bay at the southern end of Seward, Lowell Creek flowed in a channel approximately coincident with the present Jefferson Street (pl. 2). Floods pouring down this channel periodically spread deposits of sand and gravel over much of the fan during historic time. One such flood in 1939 dumped considerable debris at and near the mouth of the creek (fig. 9).

The thicknesses of the fan deposits were determined from three holes (S–100, S–105, and S–106) drilled after the earthquake along the Seward waterfront (pl. 2), from the log of a water well drilled near the hospital at the west end of Jefferson Street, and from seismic studies across the fan along Jefferson Street and offshore from the fan (pl. 2).

These data indicate that the fan deposits generally are approximately 100 feet thick but are considerably thicker along the distal edge. The deposits can be divided into three subunits on the basis of seismic velocities (pl. 2): (1) an upper unit, approximately 25 feet thick, having a seismic velocity of 1,600 fps (feet per second); (2) an intermediate unit, 10–90 feet thick, having a seismic velocity of 2,800 fps; and (3) a wedge-shaped unit underlying the others along the distal edge of the fan and extending beneath the bay, which has a seismic velocity of 6,100 fps. The log of drill hole S–100 indicates that the velocity differences in the three subunits are primarily due to the degree of compaction rather than grain size or composition. The uppermost unit is very loose material, deposited partly in historic time, and includes some loose artificial fill. The two more compact underlying units may represent deposits laid down during two distinct phases of glaciation in the mountains to the west.

The fan deposits intertongue with marine sediments along the frontal scarp of the fan from the vicinity of the Standard Oil Co. tanks to somewhat north of the Texaco, Inc., tanks. Drill hole S–100, at the eastern end of Adams Street (pl. 2), penetrated 292 feet of fluvial deposits and then about 15 feet of marine sediments before passing into a probable till. Drill

hole S–105, near the former Army dock, penetrated several layers or stringers of marine sediments interbedded with fluvial deposits in the upper 312 feet of hole. In drill hole S–106, just north of the Texaco tanks, much of the material penetrated between depths of 80 and 313 feet is marine sediments.

The fan deposits are believed to lie on a platform of till and associated compact glaciofluvial deposits. Seismic studies (pl. 2, SL–1 and SL–2) show that the drift has a velocity of 7,200–7,500 fps. In drill hole S–100, which penetrated this unit from 306 feet to the bottom of the hole at 333.4 feet, the material is a compact mixture of sand and gravel and minor silt—probably a till partly reworked by water. A more silty or clayey till containing large boulders was penetrated b e t w e e n depths of 25 and 78 feet (bottom of the hole) in a water well dug before the earthquake at the apex of the fan near the hospital (Tryck, Nyman, and associates, 1961, app.). After the earthquake this hole was deepened to 118 feet; bedrock was penetrated at about 113 feet (J. C. Ireton, Corps of Engineers, written commun., 1966) and till presumably was penetrated between 78 feet and 113 feet.

The bedrock that forms the valley walls along the western margin of the fan probably extends beneath the fan deposits at about the same slope as above the fan, 30°–45°, and beneath most of the fan is probably more than 1,000 feet deep. Bedrock was not detected in seismic surveys in which depth of penetration ranged from 600 to 1,200 feet.

JAP CREEK FAN

At the mouth of Jap Creek canyon, a broad fan, 1½ miles long (north-south) and 1 mile wide, extends onto the alluvial floor of the

Resurrection River valley. It rises from an altitude of about 25 feet along its outer margin to approximately 300 feet at the mouth of the canyon—an average gradient of 3.3°, or about 285 feet per mile. Most of the surface of the fan, however, is below an altitude of 100 feet.

The composition and thickness of the fan deposits have been determined primarily from logs of water wells and test holes and exposures in test pits and water and sewer lines, mostly in the subdivision of Forest Acres. The fan deposits are chiefly sand and gravel, in general progressively finer grained from the head of the fan to its outer margin. In a few exposures along the creek banks where Jap Creek emerges from its canyon, the deposits are mostly medium to coarse gravel, cobbles, and boulders of graywacke as much as 5 feet long; near the outer margin of the fan, they are chiefly silt, sand, and fine gravel. Most of the fine-grained material has been derived from phyllite. Considerable fossil wood was exposed in waterline trenches along Diamond Boulevard and Evergreen Street in Forest Acres. Fossil tree trunks as much as 1 foot in diameter were fairly abundant at a depth of 7–8 feet. Most were embedded horizontally in a slightly plastic silty layer, but others, which also had their roots in the silty layer, were upright and extended in some places to the surface soil—conditions that indicate rapid deposition of the upper sand and gravel.

The Jap Creek fan deposits in the Forest Acres area are generally more distinctly bedded than the Seward fan deposits. Lenses or beds of clean sand, 1–5 feet thick, commonly intertongue with units of poorly sorted sand and gravel. Here and there, lenses of silt, generally less than 2 feet thick, are intercalated in the sand layers. The mixed sand and gravel units are very loose and tend to slump on near vertical slopes. All the deposits slump when excavated below the water table on steep slopes.

The thickness of the fan deposits is not known, but it is probably more than 200 feet in most places. A water well near the outer margin of the fan between the Forest Acres and Clearview subdivisions penetrated 310 feet of sand and gravel (Tryck, Wyman, and Associates, 1961, app.). Whether all the sand and gravel are part of the fan deposits or whether all or some of the lower part of the section are alluvial deposits of Resurrection River cannot be determined. Morainal deposits probably underlie the fan deposits, at least near the head of the fan, as they do the Seward fan. Bedrock probably lies from several hundred feet to possibly more than 1,000 feet beneath the fan, except immediately adjacent to the valley wall.

LOWELL POINT FAN-DELTA

The Lowell Point fan-delta, 1½ miles south of Seward at the mouth of Spruce Creek canyon, extends into Resurrection Bay for nearly half a mile. All the fan is below an altitude of 100 feet and much of it is below 50 feet. By local usage, the entire fan area is known as Lowell Point, the official designation of the easternmost point of the fan (pl. 1).

The fan deposits have been laid down by Spruce Creek, which is fed in part by glacial melt waters. From late May until October, Spruce Creek is a fast-flowing stream about 50 feet wide and 3–4 feet deep. The stream, which in the past has migrated across the fan, will cut new channels during

large floods. Cobbles and boulders, as much as 2 feet long, form the channel floor.

In most places the fan deposits appear to consist chiefly of fine gravel and coarse sand, minor amounts of coarser gravel, and cobbles, and a few boulders mostly about 1 foot in maximum dimension; from the vicinity of Spruce Creek to the southern end of the fan, they consist mostly of coarse sand. The sand contains little or no intermixed silt or clay-size material and consists almost entirely of flat chips of phyllite.

Depth to bedrock beneath the fan is unknown. Projection of the bedrock profile from the slope of the adjacent mountains would place it several hundred feet below the surface of most of the fan and perhaps more than 1,000 feet beneath the distal edge. No data are available to indicate if there are morainal deposits between the fan deposits and bedrock.

FOURTH OF JULY FAN-DELTA

On the east side of Resurrection Bay, Fourth of July Creek has built a triangular-shaped fan about 2½ miles long in an east-west direction and 1½ miles wide along its distal edge. Unlike the three fans previously described, it projects into the bay only a short distance beyond the mountain front and most of it forms the valley floor of the lower reaches of Fourth of July Creek. The fan in most places is nearly flat with a gradient of only about 1°, or 90 feet per mile. Fourth of July Creek, which is fed in part by melt water from Godwin Glacier, flows in several bifurcating channels across the fan.

Sand and gravel constitute most of the fan deposits in the vicinity of the bay. Toward the head of the fan, the deposits are coarser, and cobbles and boulders are more

abundant. Thicknesses of the fan deposits are not known but probably exceed several hundred feet along the edge of the bay.

OTHER FANS

Small fans also are present at the mouths of several canyons. Most have fairly steep gradients and considerable local relief. Exposures are rare because of a heavy tree cover, but the presence of large isolated boulders and a general hummocky topography on many of the fans, especially those along the valley wall between the northeast corner of Resurrection Bay and Bear Lake, suggest that morainal deposits underlie the surfaces at shallow depth. It is likely that the morainal deposits are being partly reworked by stream action and that the fluvial deposits themselves are thin and patchy. Some mudflow and other types of mass-wasting deposits probably constitute parts of some of the fans.

VALLEY ALLUVIUM

Resurrection River is a wide, braided, and low-banked stream. During alternate accretion and erosion the channel has migrated laterally across a wide flood plain. The flood-plain deposits of this stream and those of tributary streams are described as valley alluvium.

The flood-plain deposits of Resurrection River consist mostly of coarse sand and fine to medium gravel. Medium to coarse gravel and small cobbles form lag concentrates along some of the abandoned stream courses. Like the fan deposits, the gravel-size material is predominantly graywacke, and the sand is chiefly flat chips of phyllite. However, the larger size fractions are somewhat more rounded probably because of a greater transport distance, than those of similar size in the fan deposits. The alluvium deposited along the lower reaches of Salmon Creek consists chiefly of medium to coarse sand and fine gravel. The deposits that underlie the north-trending valleylike trough south of Bear Lake (pl. 1) are of composite origin and, therefore, differ considerably in grain size from place to place. No stream flows the entire length of this trough at the present time although it probably was used as a melt-water channel during one phase of deglaciation. Streams at the north and south ends of this trough have deposited sand, gravel, cobbles, and some boulders on their flood plains. Swamp deposits in the SE¼ sec. 24, T. 1 N., R. 1 W., consist largely of organic debris and sand.

In the main part of the Resurrection River Valley, the alluvium probably is more than 100 feet thick in most places. At the head of the bay, at least 75 feet of deltaic sand and gravel overlies about 100 feet of marine sand and silt (pl. 1). It is not known how far upvalley the marine deposits extend. However (as shown on pl. 1) 600 feet or more of till and other glacial drift have been deposited in a deep bedrock valley that entered the northwest corner of the bay and probably extended for some miles northwestward under the recent alluvial deposits of Resurrection River. The continuation of this deep bedrock valley beneath Resurrection Bay is reflected as a trough on the bay floor offshore from Seward (pl. 2).

INTERTIDAL DEPOSITS

Beach, deltaic, and estuarine sediments, deposited on intertidal flats at the head of the bay and along the margins of fans extending into the bay, are referred to here as intertidal deposits. The deposits mapped (pl. 1) are those

that were exposed between mean lower low water and mean higher high water before the earthquake. Some of the tidal flats formerly exposed at lower low water are now inundated because of tectonic subsidence of approximately 3.5 feet, probable compaction of the sediments, and some sliding along the front of the deltaic deposits during the earthquake. Furthermore, low areas bordering the shore that formerly were above tidal range are now covered by water at high tide.

Borings near the new railroad dock (pl. 2) show that the grain size of the intertidal deposits decreases with depth. The upper 5–20 feet consists chiefly of silty sandy gravel in which most of the pebbles are less than 1 inch long. Underlying this unit to a depth of about 60 feet are beds that consist chiefly of gravelly silty sand, which in turn is underlain by silty sand to sandy silt. Between 85 and 100 feet, clay-size material predominates in some beds.

Holes drilled near the outlet of the lagoon in the small-boat harbor show that the intertidal deposits are somewhat finer grained there than in the vicinity of the new railroad dock. Silty sand and minor quantities of fine gravel predominate in approximately the upper 25 feet of the sediments. Below, to a depth of at least 40 feet, sandy silt is more abundant.

In holes drilled on the intertidal flats near the northeast corner of the bay, the sediments, ranging in grain size from silty sand to silty gravel, are approximately 60 feet thick and are underlain by compact till. Small cobbles, gravel, and coarse sand form a beach shingle on the higher parts of the intertidal area.

Intertidal deposits form comparatively narrow bands, in most places not more than 500 feet wide,

around the distal edges of the alluvial fans at Lowell Point and Fourth of July Point. The washed surfaces are characterized by a thin veneer of cobbles, gravel, and sand, except at the south end of Lowell Point where sand predominates. Underlying the washed surfaces to an unknown depth are deposits chiefly of coarse sand and fine gravel. The surfaces generally are firm even when covered with water and can support heavy loads such as large tractors.

LANDSLIDE DEPOSITS

The earthquake reactivated some old landslides and triggered new ones. Rock and snow avalanches, debris flows, and talus creep characterized slide activity on steep mountain slopes. The large-scale shoreline and submarine sliding, which occurred in places along the bay, are described on page E26.

In Lowell Canyon, several talus deposits, whose unvegetated slopes were at the angle of repose (about 32°), were activated during the earthquake, and in places small debris flows formed near the bottoms of the slopes. Open fractures at the heads of a few talus deposits, some present before the earthquake and some formed by the earthquake, attest to the present instability of these steep talus slopes. Talus deposits having slopes of less than 32° generally are covered by grass, shrubs, or trees that show no evidence of recent disturbance and appear to be fairly stable.

Rock and debris slides also were actuated by the earthquake in Box canyon, a steep-walled valley just north of sec. 22, T. 1 N., R. 1 W. In the largest slide area, boulder- and cobble-size material extended entirely across the valley floor to a height of 10–15 feet and blocked the creek channel. A channel was bulldozed through the slide mass to allow the stream to resume its former course and to prevent impoundment so that large discharges would not flow down Clear Creek, which heads at this point. Excessive flows down Clear Creek would inundate residential areas downstream.

A fairly large rock and debris slide was triggered by the earthquake near the mouth of Jap Creek canyon (see p. E14). Cobbles and boulders as much as 5 feet long form the slide material in the Jap Creek area. Because of the coarseness of the material, Jap Creek was not impounded behind the slide but flowed through it during the period observed (April–September 1964). There appears to be little or no danger that the slide mass will suddenly break and release large quantities of water downstream. The available impoundment area above the slide is small and, should the stream top the slide, the rate of downcutting to its original bed will probably be slow. Small-scale sliding of this mass continued intermittently during the summer of 1964. A second but smaller rock slide also was triggered by the earthquake a short distance farther upstream; there was no impoundment of water.

Talus deposits form steep slopes on the east flank of Iron Mountain about one-third mile north of the mouth of Jap Creek canyon, and have been shown on the map as landslide deposits. Although there apparently was little movement of the deposits as a result of the earthquake, the upper slopes are mostly unvegetated and slow creep is indicated. Adjacent talus deposits are vegetated and appear to be fairly stable.

Several small landslides are present on steep slopes bordering the bay between Seward and the Lowell Point fan. These occupy V-shaped drainage courses whose slopes generally exceed 40°. Boulders, as much as 6 feet long, and cobbles constitute most of the slide material. In general, the slides are fairly stable and only minor quantities of material moved downslope during the earthquake. However, considerable material was removed from the toes of the slides during road construction after the earthquake, and some sliding can be expected in the future whether or not strong ground motion occurs.

An inactive rock slide is present along the base of the mountain front at the north edge of the Lowell Point fan and about 500 feet back from the shoreline. It is about 200 feet across its outer margin and probably about 30 feet thick. A bedrock outcrop approximately 200 feet upslope from the toe of the slide indicates that little or no slide material is present above this exposure. The slide material consists chiefly of graywacke in blocks as much as 5 feet long and 3 feet wide. A surface cover of vegetation, including unbent trees 1 foot in diameter, indicates that the slide is inactive. The slide material is a small potential source of large-size riprap.

ARTIFICIAL FILL

The chief areas underlain by artificial fill (not shown on geologic map) are along the Seward waterfront, in the abandoned part of the channel of Lowell Creek, in the lagoon area, and in the area at the northwest corner of Resurrection Bay.

During the years prior to the earthquake, additional space for the Seward waterfront facilities was provided by artificial fill along the shoreline. In places, such as in the area of the old railroad docks at the south end of town, a strip of fill 200–300 feet wide and as much as 15 feet thick (seaward edge) was emplaced. Fill also was used to extend the shoreline between the former Standard Oil Co. dock and the San Juan dock to afford additional space for railroad tracks and other facilities. Comparison of a 1939 photograph (fig. 9) with a mosaic of photographs (fig. 2, top) made a few years before the 1964 earthquake shows the extent of fill. Poorly sorted sand and gravel, taken chiefly from overflow deposits of Lowell Creek during flooding (fig. 9), constitute most of the fill material. However, wood cribbing, which helped support the railroad tracks near the water's edge before the tracks were raised, also is incorporated in the sand and gravel.

After Lowell Creek was diverted through a diversion tunnel and no longer flowed across the Seward alluvial fan, the abandoned channel (pl. 2) was filled with sand and gravel. The width of the fill probably does not exceed 150 feet in most places and its maximum thickness in the bottom of the channel is probably less than 10 feet. Water and sewer trenches dug across the fill indicate that the fill material is nearly identical in grain size and other characteristics to the deposits of the adjacent alluvial fan.

Early maps show that the lagoon at the north end of town formerly was larger than it was at the time of the earthquake. Reportedly, the south end of the lagoon, in the vicinity of Van Buren Street and east of Third Avenue, was used as a garbage dump for a number of years and then was cov-

ered with soil. After the earthquake, the lagoon area east of
Third Avenue was filled to a height
of several feet with sand and silt
dredged from the new small-boat
basin (pl. 2).

During construction of the new
railroad dock and marshalling
yards after the earthquake. sand
and silt was dredged from the area
in front of the dock and pumped
onto the intertidal flats and land at

the head of the bay (pl. 2). This
fill, which is 500–600 feet wide,
ranges in thickness from about 15
feet near the shoreline to less than
5 feet about 3,000 feet inland from
the shore.

ENGINEERING GEOLOGY AND THE RECONSTRUCTION EFFORT

Response to the earthquake disaster at Seward was immediate
and effective. The townspeople,
together with city, State, and Federal officials swung into action at
once. For many individuals and
groups the arduous work continued for several months or more.

Preservation of life and property was the first order of business.
All night after the earthquake the
search went on for the dead and
injured. Volunteer g u a r d s
blocked off streets leading to the
waterfront to keep people out of
the area imperiled by incoming sea
waves and the oil tank explosions.
The city was fortunate in having
a highly trained Civil Defense
organization, which had been established to cope with emergencies.
Large stockpiles of food, clothing,
and medicine thus were available
for immediate use. On the evening of the earthquake, an Alaskan
Air Command plane from Elmendorf Air Force Base at Anchorage
delivered an additional 10,400
pounds of relief cargo (U.S. Army
Alaskan Command, 1964, p. 51).

Army personnel already on special duty at Seward, together with
women and girl volunteers, set up
and operated messhalls in the high
school and at the Jesse Lee Home.
Nearly all the citizens of Seward
were fed at these messhalls during
the first few days after the quake.
Much of the frozen and refrig-
erated food supplies in town had to

be cooked immediately to prevent
spoilage.

Saturday morning, March 28,
the first mail (no stamps required)
left Seward on a military plane.
As soon as weather permitted on
Saturday, Army Mohawk aircraft
from Anchorage flew photorecon-
naissance missions. The high-
quality photographs vividly portray the destruction at Seward
(fig. 2, bottom). Later, the Stra-
tegic Air Command photographed
several additional areas. Also on
Saturday 175 Army officers and
men arrived at Seward. Their
equipment included a radio tele-
type, which gave Seward its first
fast communications link with the
outside world (U.S. Army Alaskan Command, 1964, p. 50).
Guard posts were established along
the waterfront and in the business
district, and a patrol was detailed
to assist city police. A water pur-
ification system that treated 10,000
gallons of water daily was set up
by Army personnel at a small lake
at the edge of town; water was distributed by six water trailers.
Army and Civil Air Patrol personnel established a field control
center at the airport to unload the
many supplies coming into the
city. In a 24-hour period, March
30–31, 168 passengers and 59,120
pounds of cargo were delivered to
Seward; in the following 24 hours,
127,700 pounds of cargo and 198
passengers were unloaded (U.S.

Army Alaskan Command, 1964).
City officials worked "around
the clock" to cope with the emergency. At the time of the quake,
Perry Stockton, Mayor, and James
W. Harrison, City Manager, were
in Anchorage to plan the forthcoming celebration of Seward's All
America City Award for 1963.
Acting Mayor Delmar Zentmeyer
thus had the responsibility of making the many decisions for the city
during the next 24 hours. For
many months, problems arrived in
endless succession. The sustained
efforts of individuals and the team-
work of groups produced results
far beyond what might have been
predicted.

The Corps of Engineers partici-
pated fully both in the temporary
restoration of public facilities and
in the permanent reconstruction
program. Demolition experts
razed dangerous buildings, blasted
pits for sanitary use, and did other
jobs that required the use of explosives. In less than a week, temporary water and sewer services
were restored and, with the help
of the Chugach Electric Association, electric power was brought
back into the city.

One of the first large programs
started by the Corps of Engineers
after the earthquake was the massive cleanup job along the Seward
waterfront, at the head of the bay
(fig. 10), and in the bay itself. Onshore, what was salvageable was

10.—Wrecked boats and other debris beached by waves at the northwest corner of Resurrection Bay. Photograph by U.S. Army.

saved; the rest of the debris was burned or otherwise disposed of. In the bay, hazards to navigation, such as boxcars, tankers, oil tanks, piling, rails, and remains of buildings, were removed to a minimum depth of 40 feet; this work was done in two stages: (1) cleanup of the lagoon area and the land area at the head of the bay and (2) cleanup of the railroad area and the bay. Not long after the initial cleanup was completed, reconstruction of public facilities was undertaken by the Corps of Engineers (George and Lyle, 1966).

On April 13 and 14, the U.S. Coast and Geodetic Survey, using the ship *Pathfinder*, made soundings and tidal measurements in Resurrection Bay. This work was augmented by detailed soundings along the Seward waterfront by the Corps of Engineers. The combined data provided bathymetry for navigational purposes, for locating and studying submarine landslides, and for underwater cleanup work. Tidal observations permitted an estimate of the amount of tectonic subsidence. During the summer, a first-order

level line run into the city from Fairbanks gave additional data on land-level changes.

The Urban Renewal Administration of the U.S. Housing and Home Finance Agency, acting through the Alaska State Housing Authority, authorized a city plan and an urban renewal study. The plan was developed by City Planning Associates, of Mishawaka, Ind. In order to plan for best land use and to attempt to minimize damage from future earthquakes in connection with ground stability, this firm based its plan in large part on geologic information supplied by the U.S. Geological Survey, the Scientific and Engineering Task Force, and the Corps of Engineers. Private individuals were assisted through disaster loans from the Small Business Administration.

Many nongovernmental organizations and groups provided assistance. The American Red Cross and the Salvation Army gave food, clothing, household necessities, and money. Church groups, the American Legion, and other organizations contributed in many ways. A large van of furniture was sent from Allentown, Pa., to replace furnishings destroyed by the sea waves. A shipload of lumber donated from the Portland, Oreg., area was unloaded at Seward and distributed to people who had lost their homes. These responses are only a few examples.

It was early recognized that to be sound the reconstruction plan must be based on a thorough understanding of what had happened during the earthquake.

METHODS OF STUDY

Geologic investigations were conducted by the writer at Seward from April to October 1964. Early emphasis was directed toward assessing and mapping the surface geologic effects of the earthquake. During the summer, subsurface studies were coordinated with an extensive program of subsurface exploration by the U.S. Army Corps of Engineers and by Shannon and Wilson, Inc., who performed most of the soil analyses. In addition, consulting advice was given to the Field Team, Scientific and Engineering Task Force of the Reconstruction Commission, in regard to designating high-risk

areas along the waterfront area of Seward and in part of Forest Acres (see Eckel and Schaem, 1966). In late summer and fall the writer mapped the geology of Seward and adjacent areas and collected and analyzed additional information made available during reconstruction.

High-quality low-altitude post-earthquake aerial photographs were used for detailed mapping. Where aerial photographs were not available, mapping was done on an enlarged topographic sheet of the Seward A–7 quadrangle, published scale 1:63,360.

Pre- and postearthquake hydrographic charts prepared by the U.S. Coast and Geodetic Survey were used for offshore studies. In addition, a detailed hydrographic chart, prepared by the Corps of Engineers after the earthquake, was most helpful in the study of landslides in the harbor area.

The Alaska District, Corps of Engineers, undertook a comprehensive study of subsurface conditions, in part by contract with Shannon and Wilson, Inc., of Seattle, Wash., that included test drilling, field and laboratory studies of soil samples, seismic surveys, and pile-driving tests. The soils investigation by Shannon and Wilson was undertaken primarily to determine the factors probably responsible for the submarine landslide along the Seward waterfront and to evaluate the stability of the area under static and dynamic (earthquake) conditions. Test borings and seismic surveys were also made at the head of Resurrection Bay to evaluate the stability of that area for possible new harbor facilities. This phase of the work was supplemented by offshore borings made by the Corps of Engineers. The

heavily damaged part of Forest Acres subdivision also was studied.

During field investigations that were made between May 11 and July 25, 1964, 10 holes were drilled (locations shown on fig. 15, p. E36; pls. 1, 2): 3 along the Seward waterfront, 5 at the head of Resurrection Bay, and 2 in Forest Acres. Those along the Seward waterfront and at the head of the bay ranged in depth from 165 to 481 feet except the hole at the northeast corner of the bay which reached a depth of only 83 feet after penetrating 14 feet of bedrock.

The first six holes were drilled with a rotary rig. Drilling fluid, a thick mixture of bentonite and water, was used to remove cuttings and granular material and to maintain the uncased hole. Below the depth of 100 feet, drilling was continuous to minimize collapse of the hole. Drive samples were obtained at 5- or 10-foot intervals using a standard 2-inch sampler driven by a 140-lb hammer. Selected undisturbed samples were taken in 3-inch Shelby tubes pushed into the soil by a mechanical chain drive on the drill.

Because rotary drilling made it difficult to obtain representative samples, and because the mud masked artesian conditions, a churn drill was used to drill the last four holes. These holes were cased. Drive samples were obtained at 10-foot intervals using a 4-inch split barrel sampler. All samples were classified in the field before being sealed in glass jars and sent to the Shannon and Wilson, Inc., laboratory in Seattle for testing.

Five test pits were dug with a tractor-mounted backhoe: three along the Seward waterfront (pl. 2) and two in Forest Acres (fig.

15, p. E36). All were in areas of fractured ground and were intended to provide information on depositional and structural relations not obtainable from drill holes.

Ground-water levels and artesian pressures were measured or approximated in most borings and test pits. The first confirmation that artesian pressures existed at the northwest corner of the bay was found in hole S–101 when water began flowing at the surface a day after completion of the hole. The rate of flow was measured and related to tide levels. Direct readings of artesian pressure in the rotary-drilled holes could not be made because the holes were uncased and drilling mud was used. Large artesian flows developed in some of the churn-drill holes. Artesian conditions were observed as the holes were advanced; measurements were made using a Bourdon-type pressure gage. After completion of the holes, attempts were made to locate artesian zones that had been sealed off by the casing. The bottoms of the holes were sealed with grout, and the casing was perforated at points where considerable heaving, noted during drilling, indicated probable artesian pressures.

Selected samples from the onshore drilling program were subjected to standard laboratory tests by Shannon and Wilson, Inc. (1964). Most of the samples were necessarily of the finer grained materials; both disturbed split-spoon drive samples and relatively undisturbed Shelby-tube samples were taken. The laboratory test program by Shannon and Wilson included visual classifications of split-spoon samples and visual classification, mechanical and hydrometer analyses, water content, Atterburg limits, organic content, density, and triaxial strength determinations for the Shelby-tube samples.

Two types of soil predominated in the Shelby-tube samples. One was black uniform medium to fine sand, composed of black phyllite particles, usually of medium density, and having wet unit strengths of about 130 lbs per cu ft. Triaxial tests on the sand showed an effective (drained) θ (angle of friction) of approximately 35°–39° and a total (undrained) θ of 32°–40°. Pore pressures at failure were low. The other predominant soil material tested was organic sandy to slightly clayey silt, which had an organic content of less than 5 percent. The plasticity index ranged from nonplastic to 13, and liquid limits from 21 to 34. Natural water contents ranged from 20 to 32 percent, and clay-sized particles made up 10–30 percent of the material. Drained triaxial tests showed positive pore-water pressure at failure. Effective (drained) θ's ranged from 35°–38°. The undrained θ's were lower, ranging upward from 21° for a consolidation pressure greater than the effective overburden pressure and averaging 26° for consolidation pressures equal to the effective overburden pressure.

To supplement the data obtained from the holes drilled on land and to obtain needed offshore information, 15 refraction seismic traverses (see pls. 1 and 2 for locations) were made by Geo-Recon., Inc., under subcontract to Shannon and Wilson, Inc. Profiles (pl. 2) indicated the nature and thicknesses of geologic units at depths considerably greater than were penetrated by the drill holes.

Seventy-one borings, mostly on the intertidal flats at the head of the bay, were made by the Seattle District, Corps of Engineers, to provide information on the subsurface conditions needed for planning restoration of harbor and railroad facilities. Offshore in the area of the new small-boat basin, 21 borings were made: 12 in the vicinity of the new Alaska Railroad dock and 9 near the northeast corner of the bay; on land north of the railroad dock, 27 borings were made.

None of the bore holes were more than 100 feet deep and most were less than 50 feet deep. Those on land were 4–9 feet deep. The borings were water-jet holes made by using a pump that developed 450 psi (pounds per square inch) at approximately 20 gallons a minute (Robert H. Moran, U.S. Army, Corps of Engineers, written commun., 1964). The sampler was a 1-inch split spoon on a 2-inch drill rod inside a 4-inch casing. All work was done at the higher stages of the tide when the tidal flats were covered by water. Samples were classified in the field. According to Moran, this method of investigation is both economical and time proven and gives sufficiently accurate information for assessment of dredging character and design of structures. Logs and test data from four offshore borings (fig. 11, next page) show subsurface conditions in the area of the new Alaska Railroad dock.

Pile tests were conducted offshore from the new railroad dock by the Corps of Engineers. Several steel H-piles were driven into the bay sediments to determine the rate of penetration and bearing strength. One pile, driven 64.25 feet into the ground near the offshore end of the planned dock, also

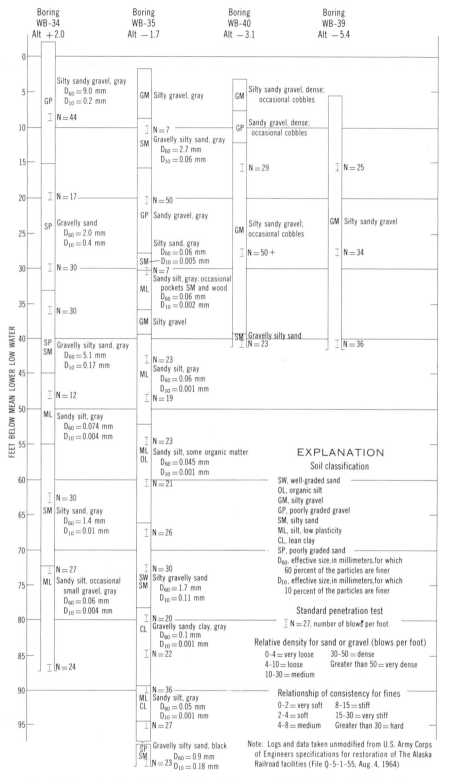

11.—Offshore borings in the vicinity of the new Alaska Railroad dock. See plate 2 for locations.

underwent a static loading test. Results of these tests have not been published but are available in the files of the Corps of Engineers.

LANDSLIDES

SEWARD WATERFRONT AND HEAD OF RESURRECTION BAY

Both onshore and offshore deposits slid into the bay along the Seward waterfront. Near the northwestern and central parts of the head of the bay, sliding was mostly submarine.

Along the Seward waterfront, a strip of land approximately 4,000 feet long and 50–500 feet wide slid into the bay concomitantly with offshore submarine landsliding. Behind the scarp marking this large submarine slide, the ground was intricately fractured for distances of 100–800 feet (figs. 3, 4). Near the northern end of the landslide scarp, some of the fractured ground subsided several feet and rotated as landslide slump blocks (fig. 12).

The submarine sliding along the Seward waterfront resulted in marked deepening of the water in the vicinity of the former shoreline. Cross sections *B–B′* and *C–C′* of plate 2 show the pre- and postearthquake profiles of the bay floor in the vicinity of the former Standard Oil Co. dock and the San Juan dock.   Water that before the earthquake was 35 feet deep (mean lower low water) off the end of the Standard Oil Co. dock is now 160–180 feet deep; water that was approximately 35 feet deep off the end of the San Juan dock is now 140–150 feet deep.   Immediately offshore from the Standard Oil Co. dock area, the average slope of the preearthquake profile to a depth of about 160 feet was about 20°, though locally the slope exceeded 35°.   The slope of the postearthquake profile is 25°–30° to a depth of about 180 feet.   Between 500

12.—Incipient landsliding along northern part of Seward waterfront. Fractured ground has subsided and rotated as landslide slump blocks.

and 600 feet from the present shoreline, both pre- and postearthquake profiles flatten rather abruptly to slopes of less than 5° and continue as nearly coincident surfaces for 2,300 feet. Beyond this point the profiles again steepen for a few hundred feet before reaching the relatively flat trough of the bay bottom. However, even there at a depth of about 500 feet, the bay floor appears to be lower than before the earthquake in spite of a layer of landslide debris. Near the former San Juan dock, the upper parts of the pre- and postearthquake profiles both slope about 10°, much flatter than near the former Standard Oil Co. dock.

There was little or no recession of the shoreline by landsliding in the area of the former Alaska Railroad docks at the southern end of town. Comparison, however, of pre- and postearthquake soundings indicates that submarine sliding deepened the bay floor a maximum of about 40 feet between present depths of 100 and 250 feet, but that the

postearthquake deepening probably diminishes to zero at the shoreward end of the dock. According to J. C. Ireton, U.S. Army Corps of Engineers (written commun., 1966), sliding probably did not contribute to the dock failure. The material that did slide was probably in large part fine-grained marine sediments deposited on the steep frontal slope of the fan deposits. A sample of the marine sediments from this area, collected on the bay bottom at a depth of 75 feet by divers, comprised nearly 50 percent clay-size sediments, 40 percent silt size, and nearly all the remainder, sand size.

Large-scale landsliding of deltaic deposits offshore from the northwest corner of the bay shifted bathymetric contours several hundred feet landward. Water that was 20 feet deep before the earthquake is now about 130 feet deep. In both pre- and postearthquake profiles across a typical part of the slide area (pl. 2, section A—A') the underwater face of the delta slopes approximately 15°, though

after sliding the average slope steepens locally to approximately 20°.

Submarine landsliding of the deltaic deposits extended at least as far east as the mouth of Resurrection River. The extent of sliding east of that point cannot be detemined because of insufficient preearthquake bathymetric control. However, if there was submarine sliding, it probably was of smaller magnitude.

Submarine landsliding also occurred offshore from Lowell Point and Fourth of July Point (G. A. Rusnak, written commun., 1965) although there was no sliding of the land above water. Rusnak noted that offshore material at Lowell Point slid in large masses and is now at the toe of the point. Investigations made from the research vessel, the *Don J. Miller*, by G. A. Rusnak and others (1966, written commun.) provide additional information on submarine slides in Resurrection Bay.

MECHANICS AND CAUSES OF LANDSLIDING

Strong ground motion during the earthquake triggered the sliding along the Seward waterfront and elsewhere in the bay, but several factors contributed to its magnitude.

The long duration of strong ground motion was a major factor. All evidence indicates that sliding took place progressively throughout the approximately 4 minutes of heavy shaking. Eyewitnesses state that strip after strip of land disappeared into the bay until the earthquake ceased. A strip of land marginal to the present slide scarp is heavily fractured into incipient landslide blocks, and divers reported that the underwater slope in the area of the San Juan dock was also deeply fissured. Because much of the sliding at the head of the bay took place underwater, no one saw the progressive sliding in that area, but the intermittent churning and boiling of the waves indicate that sliding there also continued throughout the earthquake and perhaps even for several minutes afterwards.

The configuration of the preearthquake underwater slopes and the nature of the materials forming these slopes also favored largescale sliding. Data from borings and from geophysical profiles show that loose, generally finegrained materials were involved in the sliding. These materials, laid down as deltaic deposits and forming steep underwater slopes, probably were metastable under static conditions; under dynamic conditions of continued seismic shock, they failed readily.

In choosing the location for the new railroad dock and facilities, sites at both the northwest and northeast corners of the bay were considered. On the basis of offshore and onshore borings and geophysical data, the subsurface conditions at the northeast corner appeared to be superior to those at the northwest corner. As stated by Shannon and Wilson, Inc. (1964, p. 25), "In the northeast corner the subsurface conditions are considered to improve with bedrock exposed on shore [east valley wall] and at depths of the order of 100 feet over a substantial area. There are indications that dense glacial till may be present at relatively shallow depth over some of the area. Subaqueous landslides apparently did not occur. Hence it would appear that portions of the northeast corner, on the basis of limited data, are more stable and offer foundation conditions superior to those which may be obtained elsewhere." The writer fully agrees with these conclusions.

In final selection of the dock site at the northwest corner of the bay, however, economic and logistical considerations overrode the indicated differences in geologic suitability. A site at the northeast corner of the bay would have been approximately 7 miles from downtown Seward by the present road system. In addition to time and cost of travel, accessibility would be difficult in winter. Furthermore, The Alaska Railroad would have had to extend its trackage and acquire additional land for marshalling yards. Other facilities, now in Seward, would also have required relocation.

Conditions for failure probably were nearly optimum along the Seward waterfront, where, as shown diagrammatically in cross sections C–C' and B–B' of plate 2, loose sand and gravel in the distal edge of the alluvial fan intertongue and interlense with marine clay, silt, and sand. Torrential flooding from Lowell Creek canyon has periodically dumped sand and gravel off the distal edge of the fan (fig. 9); during the relatively long intervening periods when only minor quantities of fluvial deposits reached the bay, finegrained marine sediments were deposited along the steep underwater face of the fan. Drill-hole data indicate that some of the foreset beds along the distal edge of the fan dip as steeply as 30° and that the chips of phyllite constituting nearly all the sand-size particles are oriented with their flat sides parallel to the bedding.

Vibration of the ground during the earthquake may well have been of sufficient duration and critical frequency to produce liquefaction of the finer grained sediments, particularly the sand, silt, and clay constituting the intertongued marine sediments. If so, there was a

sudden but temporary increase in pore water pressure, and the saturated sediments were transformed into a concentrated suspension with minimal shear strength (Terzaghi and Peck, 1948, p. 100–101). The seaward-dipping tongues of sand, silt, and clay, as well as fine-grained lenses intercalated with the coarser fan materials, would furnish optimum conditions for seaward flowage of material as sliding advanced progressively landward. The structure of the deposits, particularly those deposits forming steep slopes, would collapse, and part of the material would be transformed into a slurry. This suspended material would tend to travel toward the deeper part of the bay and would be dispersed in turbidity currents. Where material was less susceptible to liquefaction and slopes were flatter, discrete blocks consisting of coarser disaggregated particles would tend to slide. In support of this supposition, G. A. Rusnak (written commun., 1965) concluded from his work, done in the fall of 1964 on the research vessel *Don J. Miller*, that landslide debris was deposited in part by mass movement and in part by turbidity currents. Thickness of slide debris, as shown on the cross sections of plate 2, is largely conjectural. Further studies of the bay floor in 1965 by G. A. Rusnak and others have provided much additional data on the thickness of the slide debris and on the total extent of submarine sliding. On the basis of preliminary analyses of these data, Rusnak (oral commun., 1965; and in Corwin and Bradley, 1965) believes that large-scale rock movement along preexisting faults and folds in Resurrection Bay contributed to the sliding of the overlying sediments. As stated previously, however, the writer has found no evidence on the adjacent land to support the supposition that there was fault movement in the Seward area that was related to the earthquake.

According to eyewitnesses, there was a sudden drawdown in water level along the waterfront shoreline during the early part of the strong ground motion. In places, such as near the Standard Oil dock, the water level may have been lowered as much as 20–25 feet. In addition, the water was nearly at low tide. The combined conditions would tend to increase markedly the shearing stresses in the saturated deposits owing to loss of support of the water along the free face of the fan. Slide activity, which initially caused the drawdown, would be increased.

Another factor probably contributing to sliding is the effect of added load of manmade facilities. The docks, which extended out to the steep slopes of the fan, in addition to their own weight, were heavily loaded with filled oil tanks, warehouses, and heavy equipment. Numerous other filled oil tanks, as well as the railroad marshalling yards and associated facilities, were close to the shore. Many of these facilities had been extended seaward by adding artificial fill, as much as 15 feet thick, to the distal edge of the fan. At the time of the earthquake, a fully loaded freight train of 80 cars and a locomotive, stood on the tracks between the Standard Oil dock and the Texaco, Inc., tanks. The combined weight of all these objects must have been considerable. Slopes, which had been built out at the natural angle of repose, may well have been unable to accommodate this additional surcharge under seismic conditions.

Closely related to the manmade surcharge is the possible effect of the added weight of water from the wave that overran the Seward waterfront area after the drawdown of water but while the ground was still in motion. The limit of ground fracturing, which is believed to represent the limit of incipient landsliding, is nearly coincident with the maximum runup of the waves. It seems reasonable to assume that the added weight of water from the first wave, plus the seaward pulling effect as it receded rapidly from the land, was a contributing factor during the later stages of the landsliding. So far as can be determined, however, no further sliding continued during runups of the later seismic sea waves when ground shaking had subsided.

Onshore drilling at the northwest corner of the bay and near the mouth of Resurrection River shows that several aquifers under hydrostatic head intersect the slides in that area. These artesian conditions probably contributed to the sliding in the deltaic deposits. Uplift pressures would tend to create a buoyant effect upon the fine-grained material when vibrated and to decrease the stability and bearing capacity of the slope. This factor, when combined with the probable liquefaction characteristics of the sediments, probably would cause the material to flow seaward as a suspended sediment.

FUTURE SLOPE STABILITY

STATIC CONDITIONS

Under static conditions there seems little likelihood of major shoreline or submarine sliding in the Seward area. In the year after the earthquake, no recession of the shoreline occurred along the Seward waterfront other than local minor slumping and erosion from wave action. During the first few months apparently minor offshore adjustments of slopes took

place; tank cars, railroad ties, and other debris that had been entrapped on the bay floor floated to the surface.

The average underwater slope to a depth of about 180 feet in the vicinity of the former Standard Oil Co. dock is now somewhat steeper than the average preearthquake slope. However, the preearthquake slope exceeded the present slope in places. The present slope will not be further steepened by deposition of alluvium off the edge of the fan, as happened periodically before Lowell Creek was diverted through the diversion tunnel. Moreover, the absence of docks will lessen the possibility that these slopes will become catchments for large accumulations of littoral sediments, which would oversteepen the slopes. Probably even more significant, the landsliding stripped the more slide-prone material from the face of the fan. Subsurface data indicate that the tongues of marine sediments wedge out landward into the more stable fan deposits.

One small area where some submarine landsliding or slumping may occur during static conditions is the cove near the old railroad dock at the southwest end of town. Here a considerable volume of alluvium debouches from the diversion tunnel during times of high streamflow and is deposited on an already steep slope (pl. 2). Conceivably, the underwater slope can be oversteepened to the point of failure. Before construction of any docks in the area, this possibility should be investigated. Farther south, the west shoreline is mostly bedrock and sliding is unlikely.

Offshore slopes at the northwest corner of the bay are approximately the same as they were before the earthquake, and it is unlikely that large-scale sliding will occur under static conditions. The same statement probably holds true for the area to the east. Deltaic and marine deposits will gradually accumulate to establish profiles similar to those that existed b e f o r e the earthquake. Whether the 3 : 1 slope formed by dredging at the end of the new railroad dock (pl. 2) will be stable under static conditions is unknown. There is little doubt, however, that periodic dredging will be necessary in the area in front of the dock and at the entrance to the small-boat basin. Sediment brought in by the Resurrection River and by creeks will continue to accumulate in this area as it has in the past. Tides and offshore currents will tend to spread this material into the dredged areas.

DYNAMIC CONDITIONS

In the event of another large earthquake, additional onshore and submarine landsliding can be expected along that part of the Seward waterfront that slid during the earthquake of 1964. As discussed previously (p. E29) the area of fractured ground back of the present shoreline (figs. 3, 4) is believed to represent incipient landslides. Had shaking continued longer during the 1964 earthquake, a large part of this area would have slid into the bay. Thus, sliding of similar extent can be expected during a future large earthquake.

Because of the potential instability of the Seward waterfront area, the Scientific and Engineering Task Force of the Reconstruction Commission, which based its decision upon the investigations of Shannon and Wilson, Inc., the Corps of Engineers, and the U.S. Geological Survey, placed a large part of this area in a high-risk classification. A map depicting the extent of this area is shown by Eckel and Schaem (1966). In general, the limits of the area shown as high risk include the area of fractured ground (figs. 3, 4). The Task Force recommended that the high-risk part of the waterfront area should be reserved for park or other uses that do not involve large congregations of people. Shannon and Wilson (1964, p. 23) further stated that "The stability of the waterfront could be improved by flattening the underwater slopes and buttressing the toe of the slide with fill. However, due to the great depth we doubt that slope flattening and toe buttressing are practicable." The writer concurs in both statements.

The remaining part of downtown Seward was classified by the Task Force as nominal risk—risk no greater than is normally expected in the construction industry. However, one must consider whether fracturing would extend into the eastern part of the nominal-risk area if an additional strip of shoreline should slide into the bay. This possibility cannot be discounted, but the geologic environment indicates that it would, at most, be of small extent. The thickest part of the fan deposits and probably all the intertongued marine sediments lie between Seventh Avenue and the bay (section C-C', pl. 2). West from Seventh Avenue toward the business district, the fan deposits become progressively coarser, are probably only 100–150 feet thick, are nearly horizontally bedded, and lie on a fairly flat platform of compact stable till. It is therefore probable that fracturing, at least west of Sixth Avenue, would be minor.

The earthquake triggered small-scale landsliding offshore from the old railroad dock, and another severe earthquake could cause additional sliding. The relatively shallow depth to bedrock and the possibility that only thin deposits of fluvial material rest on a stable platform of till probably explain why this area was less susceptible to sliding than other parts of the waterfront.

Additional submarine landsliding can be expected along the present face of the deltaic deposits in the northwest corner of the bay in the event of another large earthquake. The present landslide scarp has about the same slope as the preearthquake foreset bedding. The material back of the scarp has virtually the same physical properties as that involved in the sliding, and landward retreat of the landslide scarp can be expected. Shannon and Wilson, Inc. (1964, p. 25), estimated that "additional sliding may be expected to envelop an area to the north of the present scarp for a distance of some 600 feet." They further stated that "It would be prudent in our opinion to site the proposed improvements [new Alaska Railroad dock] so that an adequate set-back from this zone of potential sliding is maintained." The end of the new railroad dock is approximately 1,100 feet from the edge of the scarp (pl. 2). In the writer's opinion, the amount of scarp retreat will depend in part on the intensity of shaking, but even more on the duration of future shaking. Strong ground motion during the 1964 earthquake lasted approximately 4 minutes. During this period, there was a landward retreat of the delta face of 400–500 feet. If the materials are liquefied during shaking, as believed, then the accumulation of debris at the toe of the slide will not be a deterrent to further sliding. Provided there is no change in the characteristics of the materials involved, slumping will continue landward at about the same slope angle for as long as strong ground motion continues.

In order to provide sufficient depth for ocean-going ships to reach the new railroad dock, it was necessary to dredge a swath, 35 feet deep, 1,700 feet long, and 500–900 feet wide. The sides of the dredged area were constructed on 3:1 slopes, largely in loose fine gravel and sand. A future earthquake as severe as the one of 1964 will probably cause some failure of these slopes and partial filling of the dredged area. Shannon and Wilson, Inc. (1964, p. 24–25), stated "Dredging for ocean ships probably will remove the sand and gravel which overlies the marine sediments, thus structures will obtain their support in these [marine] sediments. Notwithstanding the removal of weight by dredging, significant area subsidence should be anticipated in the event of another great earthquake. Heavy structures, such as earthfills will experience subsidence of the order of several feet and perhaps as much as 10 feet or more whereas lighter structures are expected to subside significantly less. It is possible that piles imbedded in the marine sediments may lose their support in localized areas due to liquefaction during an earthquake." Later, offshore pile-driving tests by the Corps of Engineers showed negligible pile settlement under static loads. However, no dynamic (vibratory) load tests were conducted to simulate the effect of strong ground motion.

To minimize future earthquake damage to the new railroad dock and related facilities, the structures were designed by the Corps of Engineers to withstand seismic shock up to certain limits. In instructions (Warren George, Chief,

Engineering Division, written commun., July 14, 1964) to those responsible for design, it was specified that "Your analysis specifically must consider earthquake dynamic effects on the soils such as liquefaction of sands and silts and inertia forces on the soils and structures thereon. Use a strong motion design for an earthquake of the order of a Richter magnitude of 7.5, a maximum horizontal ground acceleration of 0.15 to 0.20 gravity and a duration above two percent gravity of 3 minutes and an epicenter within 30 miles. Select a group of response spectra reflecting the interrelation of local stratigraphy and formation densities on the structure vibrations and motions."

POTENTIAL LANDSLIDES AND AVALANCHES IN ADJACENT MOUNTAIN AREAS

The earthquake of 1964 triggered several landslides and snow avalanches in steep-walled tributary valleys in the mountains flanking Seward; if there is another large earthquake, additional landsliding and avalanching can be expected.

Future earthquake-induced snow avalanches and rock and debris slides along Lowell canyon could impound sufficient water to flood Seward if there were a sudden rupture of the slide dam. This possibility would be markedly increased if tree trunks and other debris were washed into the diversion tunnel and plugged the intake. To help obviate this last possibility, as well as the possibility of large rocks being stream-carried into the tunnel, at any time, a trash rack could be constructed upstream from the tunnel intake to catch any large material washed downstream.

Additional earthquake-induced rock slides and snow avalanches also can be expected in Jap Creek

canyon, but unless the slides are very large, little damage from flooding is likely downstream if the dams formed by slides are suddenly breached. Additional slides can also be expected in other scattered areas. Further slides in Box canyon, similar to those triggered by the earthquake of 1964, could divert a large discharge of water down Clear Creek that would inundate residential areas downstream. Some talus slopes, already weakened by the 1964 earthquake, may become even less stable. Rock talus slopes, whose toes have been excavated during road construction along the steep cliffs between Seward and Lowell Point, are particularly susceptible to sliding whether an earthquake occurs or not.

FRACTURED GROUND

SEWARD WATERFRONT AREA

Ground fracturing along the Seward waterfront (figs. 3, 4) is believed to be closely related to onshore and offshore landsliding in that area. Horizontal translation and vertical displacement of the ground seaward, as sliding progressed, apparently was the dominant cause of fracturing.

The total amount of horizontal and vertical displacement in the area of fractured ground could not be determined accurately. It undoubtedly was greatest in the area of the Texaco tanks and became progressively less toward the Standard Oil Co. tanks. Two weeks after the earthquake, the fractures in the area of the Texaco tanks were commonly 0.5–2 feet wide, and a few were as wide as 4 feet. In general, the dominant fracture systems were roughly parallel to the shore. Intersecting transverse fracturing commonly produced a roughly polygonal pattern (fig. 4). In most places, the decreasing width of the fractures

13.—Ground fracture near east end of A Street, about 100 feet from present shoreline, showing vertical displacement of about 4 feet.   Downthrown side is toward Resurrection Bay.

away from the shore reflected a decrease of lateral spread of the ground in that direction. Where the fractures were offset vertically, the downthrown side was generally toward the bay (fig. 13). Vertical offsets were confined largely to the near-shore area and to the fractures paralleling the shore. Along the shore at the eastern extension of Monroe Street, vertical offsets of as much as 5 feet marked margins of blocks tilted with their surfaces sloping landward. In most places, however, there was no evidence of rotation of the ground between fractures. Vertical offset decreased southward so that in the vicinity of the Standard Oil tanks little or no vertical displacement was discernible. The sharpness and linearity of fracturing probably can be attributed to the fact that the ground was frozen to a depth of about 0.5 foot. Such a

rigid blanket would tend to fail along sharp, straight fractures.

Near the Texaco tanks and northwest toward the lagoon area, sand was ejected from some of the fractures and deposited as a thin skim on the surface, generally less than 1 inch thick and less than 6 inches wide, bordering the fractures. No conspicuous sand boils or vents, such as characterize the Forest Acres subdivision, were apparent. Eyewitnesses reported that the fractures opened and closed and ejected muddy water during the shaking.

Probably other factors beside lateral translation of the landmass were involved in the area where the sand was pumped from the fractures. In the area of pumping, the near-surface material is generally loose fine-grained silt, sand, and gravel and the water table is within a few feet of the

surface. Such materials are susceptible to compaction when vibrated. During compaction of these saturated deposits, water would be forced from the voids to the ground surface, carrying fine material with it. Whether or not other factors, such as seismic waves reaching critical amplitudes, rupturing the surface, and pumping out sand contributed cannot be properly evaluated for this area. These factors are considered in more detail in the following discussion of Forest Acres and adjacent areas where pumping of water and sand was prevalent.

FOREST ACRES AND ADJACENT AREAS

The conspicuous fracturing of the Jap Creek alluvial fan and of much of the alluvial floor of the Resurrection River valley cannot be directly related to major landsliding. Limited lateral movement of the ground may have been involved in the process, but the area of fracturing is relatively flat and there are no large free faces toward which the materials could be laterally translated except near the head of the bay itself; therefore, the fracturing must be attributed largely to other causes.

Fracturing on the Jap Creek alluvial fan was confined to the distal part of the fan. A fairly distinct scarp, 10–15 feet high, marks the northern margin of the fan, but the much wider eastern margin slopes gradually down to the valley alluvium without a clearly defined boundary. Figure 14 shows the upslope limits of fracturing in this area, and figure 15 (next page) depicts the pattern of fracturing of an area in Forest Acres where there was greatest damage to manmade structures.

In many places the relatively flat alluvial floor of the Resurrection River valley was more intensely fractured than was the outer margin of the Jap Creek fan. Particularly in the lower lying swampy areas and along river bars, fractures were so closely spaced and sand ejected from the fractures was so abundant that individual fractures were commonly obscured. A heavy tree and brush cover over much of the area severely limited detailed ground study and interpretation from aerial photographs. In general, the fracture pattern and geologic environment appear to be similar to that in Forest Acres except along the streams where many of the larger fractures roughly parallel the banks of the drainage courses. There lateral spreading toward a free face is indicated.

The fracture pattern in Forest Acres is different from that along the Seward waterfront in several respects, as can be seen on figure 15,

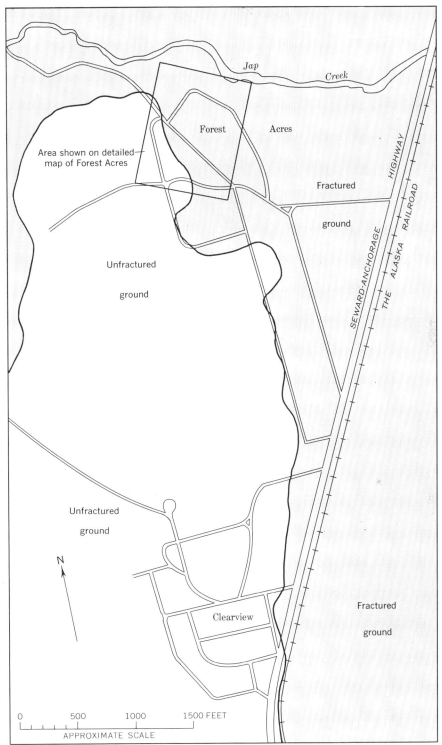

Culture adapted from an aerial mosaic photograph

14.—Map of general area of Forest Acres and Clearview subdivisions of Seward showing extent of ground fractured as a result of the earthquake of March 27, 1964.

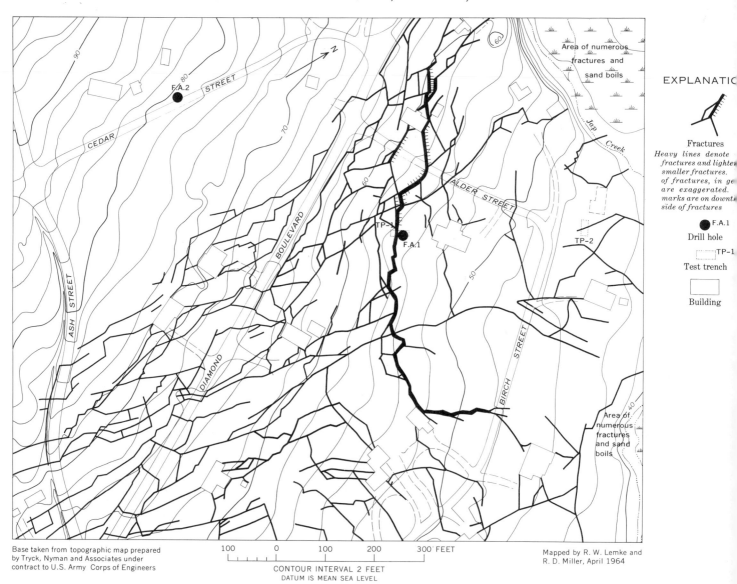

15.—Map of the Forest Acres subdivision showing fractures induced by the earthquake of March 27, 1964.

although in both places the major fracture system (heavy line on fig. 15) and many other long linear fractures roughly parallel the contours. In general, the fracture-bounded areas in Forest Acres are more elongate in plan. Many fractures die out along their extensions (fig. 16). Several fractures intersect at right angles to each other, and otherwise remarkably linear fractures commonly make right-angle turns. Only a few are arcuate in plan. Many fractures

extend diagonally from corners of buildings and die out in a short distance; most of these do not extend under the buildings. Fractures commonly follow the bottoms of the shallow ditches bordering the streets and other manmade excavations where the depth of frozen ground was less than elsewhere.

Along the main fracture system shown on figure 15, the fractures commonly were 2–3 feet wide at the surface at the time of mapping

(Apr. 20–24, 1964). The greatest width was 4.2 feet. Some caving beneath the frozen surface layer, a peaty gravelly soil about 1.5 feet thick, had already occurred, but the frozen layer itself remained intact; hence the dimensions at the time of mapping closely approximated the width of the fractures immediately after the earthquake. Loose sand and gravel, caved from the walls, has filled the fractures so that most were 3–5 feet deep at the time of mapping; the greatest

16.—Ground fracture in Forest Acres area. Fracture is about 2 feet wide in the foreground. Photograph by R. D. Miller, April 1964.

depth observed was 11 feet. The widths of the fractures in general decrease upslope toward Diamond Boulevard from the main fracture system. Widths of 3–4 inches were common, and many fractures were only hairline cracks that broke the hard-packed snow, which covered much of the area to depths of 1–3 feet. West (upslope) from Dia-

mond Boulevard, the fractures became progressively narrower and finally died out entirely. No fractures were found above the 80-foot contour line in this area.

Some fractures, particularly those along the major system, are offset vertically as much as 1.5 feet, but the displacement is generally only a few inches. In places, the

downthrown side of a fracture may be on one side along part of the length and on the other side along another segment. In a few places, small grabens were formed where parallel fractures were downthrown in opposite directions.

In places where the ground was fractured beneath large trees, the tree trunks were cracked. In one place on the alluvial floor of the Resurrection River valley, two trees were split to a width of 1 foot at their bases and to a height of 30–40 feet. If the trees were frozen at the time of the earthquake, as they may have been, splitting would have been facilitated.

Sand boils were formed along part of the major fracture system, particularly in the downslope area. Only a few small sand boils were formed southwest of the major fracture system, and none west of Diamond Boulevard in the area shown on figure 15. Where only a small quantity of water and sand was ejected to the surface, the sand spread out on the snow-covered surface as subcircular or oval patches, 10–30 feet in diameter and 1–4 inches thick. Where fountaining was more pronounced and the volume of pumped sand was greater, as in the low area east of Birch Street, sand from individual vents coalesced and formed aprons as much as 1 foot thick. Many of these larger sand areas nearly obscured the underlying fractures. Here and there tabular ridges of sand 3–6 inches wide reflected the location of the underlying fractures. These ridges were accumulations of sand ejected into the fractured overlying snow and left standing in relief after the snow melted.

The ejected material was everywhere remarkably uniform in size and consisted of a dark-gray, very fine sand (0.0625–0.125 mm),

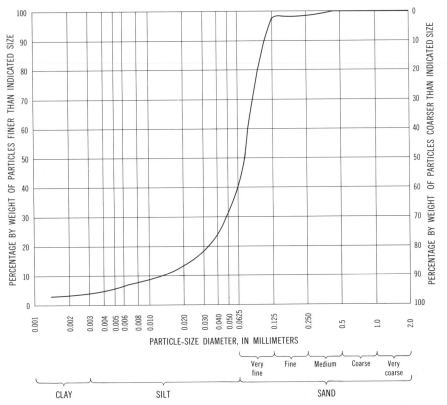

17.—Grain-size analysis of material from a sand boil, Forest Acres area. Analyst George S. Erickson; sample 4–346.

lesser quantities of silt, and minor clay. Figure 17 shows a grain-size analysis of a typical sample taken near trench TP–2.

No well-developed cones of sand surrounding exit vents, such as have been described from other earthquake-affected areas (Fuller, 1912, p. 79–80; Segerstrom and others, 1963), were found. Presumably the ejected material had sufficient fluidity to spread out everywhere as a thin blanket. Only a few surface vents were detectable, and these consisted for the most part of a slight circular enlargement of the fracture walls, open at the time of mapping to a depth only slightly deeper than that of the fracture. In several places, venting appears to have taken place simultaneously along a 25- to 75-foot segment of a fracture.

COORDINATE CAUSES OF FRACTURING

In order to determine the causes and mechanics of the ground fracturing and of the associated sand-boil activity, the subsurface conditions under the fractured area were studied extensively and compared with the sediments underlying the nearby unfractured area (fig. 15). Drill holes F.A. 1 and F.A. 2, bored to depths of 50.0 feet and 69.5 feet through fractured and unfractured ground, respectively, furnished a comparison of the composition and characteristics of the materials. Trench TP–1, dug to a depth of 12.5 feet across the major fracture system, furnished information on bedding and sorting, depth of fracturing, material found in the fractures, and depth to the water table. Trench TP–2, dug farther down-

slope and to a depth of 7.3 feet, supplemented this information.

All subsurface data indicate that the fan deposits, in general, become progressively finer grained downslope. Drill hole F.A. 2 penetrated poorly sorted sand and gravel to a depth of approximately 60 feet and then bottomed in silt and sand. In drill hole F.A. 1, poorly sorted sand and gravel also were penetrated to a depth of 50 feet, but intercalated sand and silt layers were fairly abundant, particularly in the upper part of the section. Hammer blow counts, taken at both holes, also showed generally much more difficult penetration of materials in drill hole F.A. 2 and doubtless reflected larger size fractions. In trench TP–2, as well as in sewer and water trenches along Birch Street, the near-surface deposits were chiefly sand and silt. Gravel, where present, was fine grained.

The water table also comes progressively closer to the surface in a downslope direction. The depth to the water table in drill hole F.A. 2 could not be determined at the time of drilling because of drilling mud. However, 2 weeks later the water level in the hole was at a depth of 22.0 feet; whether the water was under hydrostatic head is not known. The surface of this hole is 25 feet higher than the surface of TP–1, where water entered the trench at a depth of 12.5 feet. In TP–2, downslope from TP–1, a copious volume of water entered the trench from the northeast at a depth of 6.3 feet, approximately the same elevation as the surface of the water in nearby Jap Creek.

Caved material filling the fractures was so nearly identical in appearance to the loose material forming the walls of the fractures that, generally, a well-defined fracture on the surface could not be recognized more than 2–3 feet below the caved material. A notable exception to this, however, was found in TP–1. Here, a fracture 1–2 feet wide at the surface, at a point where a sand boil had formed, was open to depth of 2 feet. Between depths of 2 and 7.7 feet, the fracture was filled with loose sand and gravel that had caved from the adjacent walls. Between 7.7 feet and the bottom of the trench (12.5 feet), the fracture, which was vertical and approximately 1 foot wide, was filled with sand identical in appearance to the sand forming the sand boil at the surface. This sand dike was obviously part of the ejecta that did not reach the surface and, therefore, the bottom of the trench (12.5 feet) provides a minimum depth of sand source for the boil.

The mechanism of ground fracturing on the outer margin of the Jap Creek fan and on the alluvial floor of the Resurrection River valley is not clear. Evidence is strong that differences in the properties of materials and the heights of the water table determined to a large degree the areal extent and magnitude of fracturing and the related sand-boil activity. Two hypotheses present what seem to be the most plausible causes of the fracturing; it is conceivable that both are correct.

In one hypothesis, which Coulter and Migliaccio (1966) favored for explaining the longitudinal fractures that formed in alluvial fill at the head of the fiord at Valdez, seismic energy itself is the contributing cause for the fracturing. This hypothesis was first proposed by Oldham (1899, p. 89). According to Coulter and Migliaccio, seismic energy, transmitted into the thick unconsolidated deposits, is transformed into visible surface waves whose amplitude increases to the point where the

strength of the surface layer is exceeded and rupture occurs. Furthermore, they believed that the ground was broken in areas where the frozen surface layer was the thinnest and that continued seismic-wave action subjected the underlying saturated materials to alternate compression and extension so that water containing suspended silt and sand was pumped up through the fissures onto the surface. A similar interpretation was made by Macelwane (1947, p. 17) who stated that "Another secondary effect of the earthquake motion is extrusion of sand or mud. The alternation tension and compression which is applied to the ground during the passage of earthquake waves opens fissures and sucks down the ground water, then closes them, violently forcing out the water and with it large quantities of sand or mud that lay in its path."

In several ways this mechanism is consistent with the physical conditions and the associated effects of fracturing noted in Forest Acres and adjacent areas. First, although ground waves of large amplitude were not reported in the Seward area, there were accounts of the ground moving in places like ocean waves. These ground waves may have been of sufficient size to break the ground where other conditions, such as the presence of a thick section of loose surficial deposits, favored breakage during alternate compression and extension. Secondly, the fact that the fountains accompanying the sand-boil activity pulsated in height during the shaking argues strongly that the fractures alternately opened and closed during the shaking. This alternation also was confirmed by eyewitnesses.

Finally, the surface layer, frozen to a depth of approximately 1.5 feet in the area of fracturing

in Forest Acres, would act like a rigid, brittle pad; that is, it would break in a well-defined fracture pattern when subjected to compression or extension. The unfractured condition of ground above the 80-foot contour line in Forest Acres might be explained by the presence of a thicker frozen layer sufficiently competent to preclude breakage. The areal extent of fracturing might also have been limited by the characteristics of the materials underlying the frozen layer. Seismic energy tends to generate ground waves of larger amplitude and greater rupture strength in fine-grained deposits, particularly saturated deposits, than in coarser unsaturated material. Both types of materials are present in the Forest Acres area, and the effects of the earthquake on the two types can be explained by the hypothesis. The even greater amount of fracturing along the alluvial floor of the Resurrection River valley also would be explained because there the water table is generally within 5 feet of the surface and in places intersects the surface, and the area is underlain almost entirely by loose silt, sand, and fine gravel.

Coulter and Migliaccio (1966) stated that the depth of fracturing in the Valdez area could not be determined but that the fissures probably lost their identity as discrete voids at the water table. They also emphasize the fact that the ground at the time of the quake was frozen down to the water table at depths of 4–6 feet. In these respects, conditions at Forest Acres were not analogous to those at Valdez. In all places observed in Forest Acres the water table was well below the depth of frozen ground, and, as indicated by the sand dike which extends at least to the water table in trench TP–1, fracturing, at least in places, extended to and possibly below the water table. Whether fractures could be formed to this depth by compression and extension of the ground cannot be evaluated by the writer.

The second explanation of the fracturing and attendant effects in Forest Acres and vicinity involves compaction of the loose deposits under the frozen surface layer and consequent fracturing not only of the surface layer but also of the underlying deposits. The compaction of fine-grained materials during earthquakes has been well documented. As pointed out by Seed (1964, p. 37), "Earthquakes are a good source of vibrations and consequently we can get a great deal of compaction resulting from earthquakes. The decrease in volume of a soil due to compaction will cause settlement of the ground surface * * *. If the sediments which compact during an earthquake are saturated, then water from the voids is forced to the ground surface where it emerges in the form of sand spouts or sand boils."

The actual amount of vertical and horizontal compaction that may have taken place in the surficial materials in the Forest Acres area during the earthquake is not known, but the earthquake did produce substantial amounts of compaction in fine-grained sediments in other parts of Alaska. For example, at Homer, 2.5 feet of subsidence, presumably in near-surface fine-grained material, can be attributed to compaction (Grantz and others, 1964, p. 26). In the vicinity of Portage where there is a great thickness of silt and sand, 4–5 feet of subsidence is attributed to compaction (Seed, 1964, p. 37). Pre- and postearthquake vertical control across the Snow River valley, 18 miles north of Seward, where there was con-

spicuous bridge and highway failure, showed that the alluvial valley floor subsided 2–3 feet relative to the bedrock walls (M. Dickinson, Alaska State Highway Dept., written commun., 1964). The alluvium, at least to a depth of 100 feet, consists chiefly of sand and silt and has a high void ratio; the water table is within 2 feet of the surface. The alluvial surface is heavily fractured for a distance of several miles up the valley, and sand boils are very abundant. It should be pointed out that there was some lateral spreading toward the open face of the nearby delta of Kenai Lake and, therefore, the total amount of subsidence probably cannot be attributed solely to compaction. However, compaction probably was the main factor. The State of Alaska Department of Highways (written commun., 1965) stated that penetrometer logs indicate an increase in density after the earthquake, and it is their conclusion that the granular sediments at Snow River bridge now are more compact than before the earthquake.

Presumably, the deposits in Forest Acres and adjacent areas were also compacted to some extent. If so, the fracturing and associated effects might be explained as follows:

1. Thick loosely consolidated deposits, surficially nearly flat, resting on an irregular bedrock surface (see cross section A–A', pl. 1) would be differentially compacted; that is, the thickest deposits would show the greatest amount of subsidence at the surface. The stretching effect from such differential compaction would tend to produce open tension fractures. This tensional effect also would explain the small

grabens between some of the parallel fractures.

2. Concomitant with the differential compaction of the unfrozen deposits and the formation of tension fractures, the rigid frozen surface layer would also break in response to the tension and the loss of underlying support.

3. Fracturing would tend to die out upslope because of decreased compaction owing to increased grain size and perhaps to decreased depth to bedrock in the direction of the bedrock valley wall.

4. During compaction, water would be forced from the voids of the saturated sediments and, momentarily under considerable hydrostatic head, would spurt to the surface along the fractures. Sand, derived from the finer grained lenses and layers, would also be forced to the surface to form sand boils. The closer the water table to the surface and the finer the material, the greater the amount of fountaining and sand-boil activity one could expect. Both factors fit the geologic environment at Forest Acres.

STABILITY OF FRACTURED GROUND

The ground between the fractures appears to possess chiefly the same degree of static stability as before the earthquake. No collapse pits or other indications of further subsidence were noted in the months after the earthquake. Considerable sand was forced from the underlying deposits, but it apparently came from a large enough mass and from sufficient depth that it did not cause subsidence of the areas between the fractures.

Where the walls of the fractures were offset vertically, as in the graben areas, there was slight subsidence of the downthrown sides for a period of about 1 month after the quake. This movement was not detected after the frozen layer had thawed, and after the initial subsidence it did not exceed 3 inches. Apparently, the subsidence was confined to the frozen layer which adjusted to the configuration of the underlying material. Slumping of the walls of the fractures, of course, continued as the frozen layer melted, and by the fall of 1964 only the larger fractures could be detected on the surface.

What would happen in the fractured area in the event of another large earthquake is difficult to evaluate. Presumably the p r e s e n t fractures represent planes of weakness that could be reactivated by strong ground motion and, therefore, houses or other manmade facilities again would be susceptible to damage where intersected by fractures. However, unless the dynamic conditions were more severe than during the 1964 earthquake, fracturing probably would not extend into the presently unfractured area.

The Scientific and Engineering Task Force of the Federal Reconstruction and Planning Commission classified the area shown in figure 14 in two risk categories as reported in a news release of July 20, 1964. The classification "nominal risk" was applied to the unfractured area and "limited risk" to the fractured part. The limited-risk classification was defined as "ground susceptible to minor fracturing and differential subsidence in response to strong earthquake induced motion." It was further stated that "For this reason, risks are slightly greater than nominal. For construction of residential buildings the following construction practices are recommended: (1) all foundations must be reinforced concrete, and (2) all concrete and unit masonry must be reinforced and interconnected." Although these recommendations were confined to the subdivisions of Forest Acres and Clearview, they could be applied equally to other areas of fractured ground in the vicinity of Seward.

WATER WAVES IN THE SEWARD AREA

TYPES AND INTERPRETATION OF ORIGIN

Slide-generated waves, seismic sea waves, and possibly seiche waves overran the shores in the Seward area. Some were generated locally, others arrived from outside the bay. Whether this multiple wave source formed composite-type waves in the Seward area is not clear. If this condition did occur, then not only could a highly complex wave pattern be expected, but also the wave-arrival times would be erratic and anomalous. Unfortunately this aspect cannot be evaluated because the arrival times of the waves are known only in the most general way.

There is little doubt that the waves that hit the Seward waterfront, the head of the bay, and Lowell Point while strong shaking continued were generated chiefly by landsliding. Other than minor secondary slumping, sliding appears to have terminated at the end of the shaking and, therefore, this source of wave generation also ceased at that time. There are accounts of two local waves, occuring in the interval between the cessation of the shaking and the arrival of the first seismic sea wave about 25 minutes later, that might have been oscillation waves resulting from the first wave. They might, however, have been seiche waves formed as a response to vibratory action during the earthquake or caused by tilting of the bay floor.

The first large wave that arrived in the Seward area approximately 25 minutes after shaking stopped is believed to have been a seismic sea wave (tsunami). It is generally agreed that the seismic sea waves were generated by uplift of the sea floor in the Gulf of Alaska and that the wave crest was generated along one or more line sources within an elongate belt that extends southwestward from the axis of maximum uplift on Montague Island (Van Dorn, 1964; Plafker, 1965). The first seismic sea wave traveling from this source area toward the Kenai Peninsula arrived at Whidbey Bay and Puget Bay (25–30 miles northwest of the line source) approximately 20 minutes after shaking started (Plafker, oral commun., 1965) or approximately 16 minutes after shaking stopped. Arrival time of the seismic sea wave at the mouth of Resurrection Bay probably would be only slightly later than at Whidbey and Puget Bays, which are approximately 15 and 30 miles, respectively, to the east. Allowing for the additional 20 miles of travel up Resurrection Bay and the probable refraction of the wave off the shoreline and islands at the mouth of the bay, the expected arrival time of the wave at Seward would coincide closely with the reported arrival there of the first large wave after shaking stopped.

Other large waves continued to arrive fairly regularly in the Seward area until at least 11:30 p.m. on the night of the quake. The time intervals between waves can be estimated only very roughly on the basis of eyewitness accounts, which indicate that the waves had a periodicity of perhaps half an hour. According to Plafker (oral commun., 1965), the periodicity of the seismic sea waves in the Gulf of Alaska was about 55 minutes. Whether this periodicity would change substantially within the confines of the bay is not known. Also, if seiching developed in the bay, as indicated by Van Dorn (1964), the periodicity of the composite wave effect would be different. Complicated seiching in Kenai Lake about 20 miles north of Seward, due at least in part to westward tilt of that lake basin, has been well documented by Mc-Culloch (1966). It seems reasonable that Resurrection Bay would act almost as a confined basin and that seiche waves could be formed by tilting of the surface in a manner similar to that at Kenai Lake. That the bay was tilted northwestward during the earthquake seems evident from the studies of

Plafker (1965, p. 1677). This tilt would cause the first seiche wave to travel northwestward toward the head of the bay. Coincidence of a seiche wave along its travel path with a seismic sea wave might explain why the third seismic sea wave reaching Seward was reported to be one of the highest. Such a coincidence might also explain the reported high wave at 11:30 p.m. However, 11:30 p.m. was also the time of nearly high tide (10.5-foot tidal range), and wave runup would be correspondingly higher.

POTENTIAL WAVE DAMAGE

If a major earthquake in the future produces water waves of the size and energy induced by the earthquake of 1964, additional damage can be expected in the Seward area. Considerably less damage to manmade structures will occur, however, in the Seward

fan area, if the area inundated by waves induced by the 1964 earthquake is reserved for parks or other uses requiring no major structures. The new railroad dock and associated facilities, on the other hand, as well as the new small-boat basin, are constructed in areas swept by earthquake-induced waves in 1964 and, therefore, are susceptible to damage from future waves of equal magnitude. Likewise, damage to the new marineway on Lowell Point as well as any other facilities built along the shores of this fan can be expected. However, because the docks and related harbor facilities must be built at the water's edge, the risk must be taken. Seward has few suitable sites for these facilities, and it is not feasible to locate them in more sheltered areas or to provide protection, such as breakwaters, to minimize the effects of the waves.

REFERENCES CITED

Alaskan Construction Consultant Committee [1964], Reconstruction and development survey of earthquake damages in Alaska: Prepared for and published by Federal Reconstruction and Development Planning Commission for Alaska; Honorable Clinton P. Anderson, U.S. Senator, Chairman, 98 p.

Corwin, Gilbert, and Bradley, Edward, 1965, Geological Survey's marine program: Undersea Technology, v. 6, no. 9, p. 35–37.

Coulter, H. W., and Migliaccio, R. R., 1966, Effects of the earthquake of March 27, 1964, at Valdez, Alaska: U.S. Geol. Survey Prof. Paper 542–C, 36 p.

Eckel, E. B., and Schaem, W. E., 1966, Work of the Scientific and Engineering Task Force, in The Alaska earthquake, March 27, 1964—Field investigations and reconstruction

effort: U.S. Geol. Survey Prof. Paper 541. (In press.)

Fuller, M. L., 1912, The New Madrid earthquake: U.S. Geol. Survey Bull. 494, 119 p.

George, Warren, and Lyle, R. E., 1966, Reconstruction by the Corps of Engineers, in The Alaska earthquake, March 27, 1964—Field investigations and reconstruction effort: U.S. Geol. Survey Prof. Paper 541. (In press.)

Grantz, Arthur, Plafker, George, and Kachadoorian, Reuben, 1964, Alaska's Good Friday earthquake, March 27, 1964, a preliminary geologic evaluation: U.S. Geol. Survey Circ. 491, 35 p.

Lantz, Bill, and Kirkpatrick, Mildred, 1964, Seward quake; Good Friday 1964: Seward, Alaska, Kirkpatrick Printing Co., 56 p.

McCulloch, D. S., 1966, Slide-induced waves, seiching, and ground frac-

turing caused by the earthquake of March 27, 1964, at Kenai Lake, Alaska: U.S. Geol. Survey Prof. Paper 543–A, 41 p.

Macelwane, J. B., 1947, When the earth quakes: Milwaukee, Wis., Bruce Pub. Co., 288 p.

Moffit, F. H., 1906, Mineral resources of Kenai Peninsula; Gold fields of the Turnagain Arm region [Alaska]: U.S. Geol. Survey Bull. 277, p. 7–52.

Oldham, R. D., 1899, Report on the great earthquake of 12th June 1897: India Geol. Survey Mem., v. 49, 379 p.

Payne, T. G., 1955, Mesozoic and Cenozoic tectonic elements of Alaska: U.S. Geol. Survey Misc. Geol. Inv. Map I–84, scale 1:5,000,000.

Plafker, George, 1965, Tectonic deformation associated with 1964 Alaska earthquake: Science, v. 148, no. 3678, p. 1675–1687.

Seed, H. B., 1964, Soil engineering problems: California Resources Agency, Earthquake and Geologic Hazards Conf., San Francisco, Calif., Dec. 7–8, 1964, p. 37–43.

Segerstrom, Kenneth, Casertano, Lorenzo, and Galli O., Carlos, 1963, Eruptions of water and sand resulting from an earthquake near Concepción, Chile *in* Short papers in geology and hydrology: U.S. Geol. Survey Prof. Paper 475–B, p. B131–B134.

Shannon and Wilson, Inc., 1964, Report on subsurface investigation for city of Seward, Alaska, and vicinity, to U.S. Army Engineer District, Anchorage, Alaska: Seattle, Wash. [29 p.].

Terzaghi, Karl, and Peck, R. B., 1948, Soil mechanics in engineering practice: New York, John Wiley & Sons, Inc., 566 p.

Tryck, Nyman, and associates, 1961, City of Seward municipal water facilities: Anchorage, Alaska, 41 p., app.

[U.S. Army] Alaskan Command, 1964, Operation Helping Hand—The Armed Forces react to earthquake disaster: Seattle, Wash., Alaskan Command Headquarters, 83 p.

U.S. Coast and Geodetic Survey, 1964, Prince William Sound Alaskan earthquakes, March–April 1964: U.S. Coast and Geod. Survey, Seismology Div., Prelim. Rept., 83 p.

———— 1965, Assistance and recovery, Alaska, 1964; A report covering the activities of the U.S. Coast and Geodetic Survey in conjunction with the Prince William Sound, Alaska, earthquake of 1964 for the period March 27–December 31, 1964: U.S. Coast and Geod. Survey, 45 p.

Van Dorn, W. S., 1964, Source mechanism of the tsunami of March 28, 1964, in Alaska: Coastal Eng. Conf., 9th, Lisbon 1964, Proc., chap. 10, p. 166–190.

Waller, R. M., 1966, Effects of the March 1964 Alaska earthquake on the hydrology of south-central Alaska: U.S. Geol. Survey Prof. Paper 544–A, 28 p.

Waller, R. M., Thomas, H. E., and Vorhis, R. C., 1965, Effects of the Good Friday earthquake on water supplies: Am. Water Works Assoc. Jour., v. 57, no. 2, p. 123–131.

CLARIFICATIONS

Geology Vol. Page	USGS Page	Column	Line	Remarks
396	E 2	1	55	Plate 1 is Plate J in Part B, the accompanying map case
413	E 19	3	6	Plate 2 is Plate K in Part B, the accompanying map case

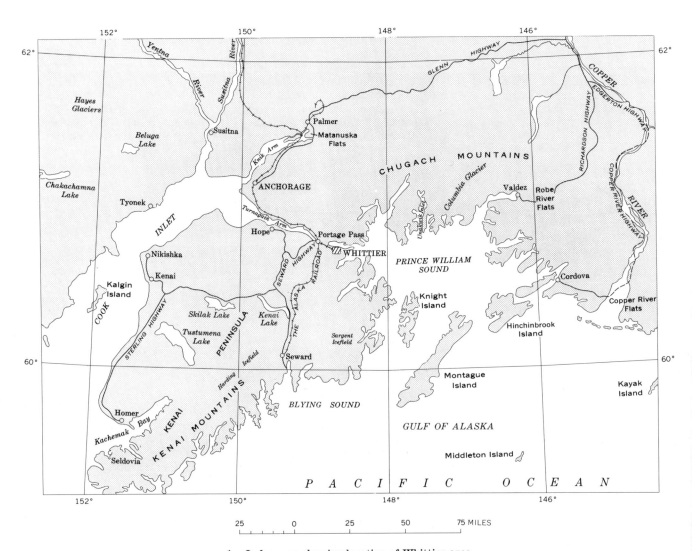

1.—Index map showing location of Whittier area.

REUBEN KACHADOORIAN
U.S. GEOLOGICAL SURVEY

Reprinted with minor changes from
U.S. Geological Survey Professional Paper 542-B,
"Effects of the Earthquake of March 27, 1964, at Whittier, Alaska"

Effects at Whittier

ABSTRACT

Whittier, Alaska, lying at the western end of Passage Canal, is an ocean terminal of The Alaska Railroad. The earthquake that shook south-central Alaska at 5:36 p.m. (Alaska Standard Time) on March 27, 1964, took the lives of 13 persons and caused more than $5 million worth of damage to Government and private property at Whittier.

Seismic motion lasted only 2½–3 minutes, but when it stopped the Whittier waterfront was in shambles and the port facilities were inoperable. Damage was caused by (1) a 5.3-foot subsidence of the landmass, sufficient to put some of the developed land under water during high tides, (2) seismic shock, (3) fracturing of fill and unconsolidated sediments, (4) compaction of fill and unconsolidated deposits, (5) submarine landslides which generated waves that destroyed part of The Alaska Railroad roadbed and other property, (6) at least two, but probably three, waves generated by landslides, which completely wrecked the buildings of two lumber companies, the stub pier, the small-boat harbor, the car-barge slip dock, and several homes, and (7) fire that destroyed the fuel-storage tanks at the Whittier waterfront.

Many buildings and other facilities were totally wrecked, others were damaged to lesser degrees. For example, the 14-story reinforced-concrete Hodge Building, which rests upon at least 44 feet of sandy gravel, was moderately damaged by seismic shock, but the six-story reinforced-concrete Buckner Building, which rests upon bedrock, was only slightly damaged.

INTRODUCTION

The port of Whittier (fig. 1) was constructed under the supervision of the Corps of Engineers in 1942–43 to provide an all-weather terminal for The Alaska Railroad. During World War II, Whittier and Seward served as the two all-weather railroad ports that safeguarded the flow of military supplies, equipment, and personnel from tidewater to Anchorage and Fairbanks. The town of Whittier is owned and operated by the U.S. Government—specifically by The Alaska Railroad of the Department of the Interior and by the U.S. Army of the Department of Defense. Some of the land has been leased to private enterprise.

Whittier was hard hit by the earthquake of March 27, 1964. Tragically, 13 persons were lost during the earthquake. At the time, only 70 people were living at Whittier. The official 1960 census lists a population of 800; however, this figure included military personnel who were subsequently transferred when the Army closed its Whittier operation. Only one body was recovered; the remaining 12 persons were presumed dead. In addition, the earthquake destroyed or made inoperable a major part of the port facilities. Total damage to the Federal and privately owned facilities at Whittier was in excess of $5 million.

The loss of the Whittier port facilities, coupled with destruction of those at both Seward and Valdez, left Alaska without any all-weather port for unloading supplies for movement either by rail or highway to the metropolitan areas of Anchorage and Fairbanks.

FIELDWORK

This report is based on data collected by U.S. Geological Survey personnel during visits to Whittier, and supplemented by data supplied by The Alaska Railroad, the U.S. Army-Alaska, the U.S. Coast and Geodetic Survey, and many citizens of Alaska, particularly those of Whittier. A 10-day study of south-central Alaska was made by the Geological Survey immediately after the earthquake, and the results were published on April 27, 1964 (Grantz, Plafker, and Kachadoorian, 1964). During the summer of 1964, Whittier was again visited by the author and by George Plafker, D. S. McCulloch, and L. R. Mayo—all of the U.S. Geological Survey. Plafker collected additional data on the onshore effects of the earthquake; McCulloch and Mayo made offshore submarine geologic investigations.

ACKNOWLEDGMENTS

Most of the logistic support for the initial study by the Geological Survey between March 29 and April 9, 1964, was provided by the U.S. Army-Alaska (USARAL); this support was provided under the difficult conditions that existed in Alaska immediately after the earthquake. During the followup studies in the summer of 1964, the U.S. Army again provided support. The author appreciates the efficient and enthusiastic support of Col. M. L. Fallwell and Lt. Col. H. E. Nolde, their staffs, and the officers and men of the USARAL Aviation Company of the 19th Aviation Battalion at Fort Richardson, Alaska.

Officials of The Alaska Railroad also cooperated with the Survey by providing preearthquake maps and photographs of the Whittier area as well as post-earthquake information. Among the officials who generously supported the investigation were I. P. Cook, C. L. Griffith, T. C. Fugelstad, B. E. Cannon, and J. A. Morrison.

The author also thanks the many residents of the State of Alaska, especially of Whittier, who supplied eyewitness descriptions and other firsthand information about the earthquake.

CLIMATE

Whittier lies in the coastal rain belt, but is surrounded by high mountains. Thus, the climate is intermediate between that of coastal mountains and open coast. Residents and The Alaska Railroad personnel state that Whittier is frequently buffeted by high westerly winds blowing off Portage Pass. Mr. Jack Farnsworth (oral commun., 1965) stated that winds locally have been so strong that house trailers were blown over by them. The high winds are not restricted to the winter months, as one might expect, but occur the year-round. Climatological data for Whittier are shown on table 1.

TABLE 1.—*Climatological data for Whittier, Alaska*

[U.S. Weather Bureau, 1964]

Month	Average temperature [1] (°F)	Average total precipitation [2] (inches)
January	25. 7	9. 45
February	28. 3	21. 40
March	24. 5	8. 18
April	31. 3	11. 05
May	43. 7	14. 72
June	46. 3	16. 17
July	53. 8	8. 84
August	53. 8	6. 45
September	48. 1	16. 40
October	38. 4	[3] 24. 40
November	22. 8	[3] 6. 13
December	22. 9	[3] 15. 00
Annual average	37. 2	[3] 157. 89

[1] Based on 14-year record.
[2] Based on 9-year record.
[3] Amount is wholly or partly estimated.

GEOGRAPHIC SETTING

Whittier is at the head of Passage Canal on the northeast side of the Kenai Peninsula in south-central Alaska (fig. 1). It is at lat 60°47′ N., long 148°40′ W., about 50 miles southeast of Anchorage and 40 miles southwest of the epicenter of the March 27 earthquake. Passage Canal, a west-southwest-trending fiord, is a western arm of Prince William Sound and is about 11 miles long and 1½ miles in average width.

The Kenai Mountains form the backbone of the Kenai Peninsula and rise sharply from tidewater to an altitude of more than 3,500 feet within 2 miles of Whittier. The large Harding icefield and much smaller Sargent icefield cover much of the higher part of the mountains. The Chugach Mountains to the east do not have a large icefield, but do have several large glaciers. North of Passage Canal the mountains rise abruptly to 4,600 feet, 1.5 miles from the shore.

The boundary between the Chugach and Kenai Mountains is Portage Pass west of Whittier. The pass is 800 feet above sea level; it was used extensively by prospectors during the gold rush as a route from Passage Canal west to Turnagain Arm. The pass is in part occupied by Portage Glacier and Portage Lake.

The main port facilities of Whittier are on the south shore of Passage Canal about 1 mile east of its western end. The town is built on a fan-shaped delta formed by Whittier Creek—a creek fed by Whittier Glacier. The delta has a maximum width of approximately 2 miles, is about 1½ miles long, and rises from sea level to an altitude of 90 feet with a fairly uniform slope of 60 feet per mile.

At the head of Passage Canal is a low-lying deltaic area about 2.3 miles wide and 2.3 miles long having an average seaward slope of 140 feet per mile. The southern part of this lowland consists of coalescing deltas of creeks flowing from Portage Pass, Shakespeare Glacier, and Learnard Glacier. The northern part of the lowland was overridden by a minor advance of Learnard Glacier. When the glacier retreated, it left behind a semicircular moraine with irregular hummocky topography. The margin of the moraine is 10–15 feet high, and the surface of the interior part contains depressions as much as 5 feet deep and small hillocks as much as 10 feet high.

After the ice that sculptured Passage Canal had retreated, the canal remained as a steep-walled U-shaped fiord locally more than 1,000 feet deep. However, immediately after the retreat of the ice, melt water began to construct deltas at the margins of the fiords— Whittier delta and the delta at the west end of Passage Canal being the largest. Another large delta was formed by Billings Creek on the north side of the canal about 3 miles northeast of Whittier.

Prior to the earthquake, Passage Canal was approximately 300 feet deep 0.1 mile from shore at its western end. Along the north shore, the depth within 1.5 miles of the head of the canal and within 0.7 mile of shore was 600 feet. Submarine slopes in front of the unconsolidated delta deposits were steeper than the average slope of the Whittier delta which was about 30° at the time of the earthquake.

GEOLOGY

The rocks in the Whittier area are slate and graywacke of probable Cretaceous age, locally overlain by unconsolidated Quaternary deposits consisting of glacial moraine, reworked outwash and stream gravel, and artificial fill (pl. 1). The slate and graywacke were intruded by quartz diorite and diorite during Cretaceous or Tertiary time. Barnes (1943) has given a more detailed description of the geology of the Whittier area.

BEDROCK

The Cretaceous(?) rocks that underlie the Whittier area are predominantly slate containing minor amounts of graywacke locally interbedded. Commonly the slate grades into the graywacke. Barnes (unpub. data, 1939) stated that locally, along the shore of Passage Canal, graywacke that appears massive above high-tide level actually has a platy structure below. This structure is apparently emphasized by the weathering of the graywacke in the intertidal zone.

The slate and, to a lesser extent, the graywacke have a pronounced cleavage generally parallel to the bedding. The attitude of the cleavage planes ranges from N. 20° E. to N. 30° E., the dips from N. 65° W. to N. 80° W. The strike of the bedding is from N. 20° E. to N. 30° E., and the dips are from N. 60° W. to N. 65° W.

Along the south shore of Passage Canal the slate and graywacke have been intruded by four quartz diorite or diorite dikes or sills, 3, 4, 7, and 100 feet thick, that are approximately parallel to the bedding of the host rock.

UNCONSOLIDATED DEPOSITS

Unconsolidated deposits consisting of outwash and stream gravels form the delta upon which Whittier rests and also the southern part of the delta at the head of Passage Canal.

The Whittier delta is composed predominantly of coarse, subangular to subrounded gravel in a matrix of coarse sand. The maximum thickness of the gravel is unknown but is at least 44 feet beneath the Hodge Building (figs. 2 and 3).

The sediments composing the delta at the head of Passage Canal are generally similar to those of the Whittier delta. However, the outwash and stream deposits in the northern part of the delta are overlain by a moraine of the Learnard Glacier. The thickness of the gravel deposits is unknown.

The moraine that overlies the delta deposits at the head of Passage Canal consists primarily of jumbled heaps and ridges of coarse angular blocks of slate and graywacke. Locally, patches of sand and gravel are interspersed with coarse blocks.

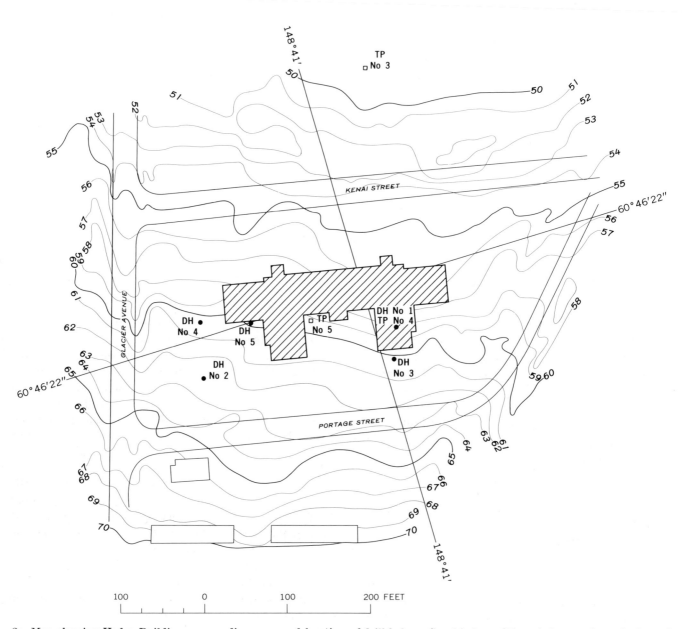

2.—Map showing Hodge Building, surrounding area, and location of drill holes.   Graphic logs of these holes are shown in figure 3.

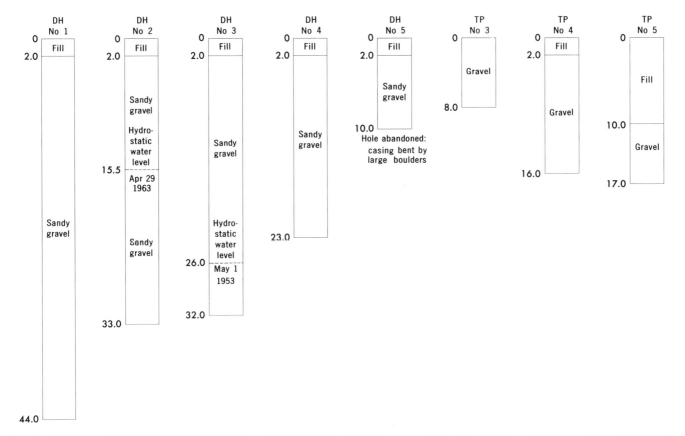

3.—Graphic logs of drill holes (DH) and test pits (TP) in the Hodges Building area. Location of holes and pits are shown in figure 2.

ARTIFICIAL FILL

Areas of artificial fill are shown on plate 1. The easternmost 500 feet of the airstrip, an area near the Union Oil Co. fuel tanks, and an extensive area by the marginal wharf are the largest of these areas. The fill was obtained locally and thus consists predominantly of delta deposits, or glacial outwash and stream deposits.

DESCRIPTIONS OF THE EARTHQUAKE

On Good Friday, March 27, 1964, at 5:36 p.m. (Alaska Standard Time) the earthquake struck Whittier. A light snow was falling, the surface of Passage Canal was "glassy," and the tide was at 1 foot above mean lower low water. Seismic motion accelerated to its maximum intensity in about one-half minute, maintained this intensity for 1–1½ minutes, and then gradually subsided. Thus, seismic motion lasted for a total of approximately 2½–3 minutes. The eyewitness estimates of the time agree closely with charts from automatic recording devices in the powerhouse and salt-water pumphouse at Whittier. The most reliable time record—a chart from the outside air-temperature recording gage in the salt-water pumphouse—shows that seismic shaking lasted for about 4 minutes (fig. 4).

Residents of Whittier said that the motion was generally east-west. However, Mr. W. P. La-Rue, powerhouse superintendent, stated that the motion was generally north-northwest–south-southeast. People who were on bedrock at the time of the earthquake said that the motion was of a jarring nature; those on fill or unconsolidated deposits reported more of a rolling or "round-and-round" motion. Most people felt no vertical motion. Mrs. D. Keat-

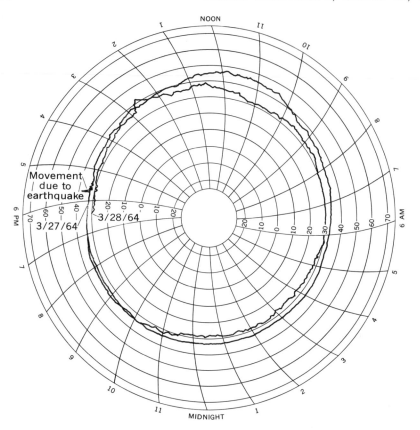

4.—Chart of outside-air temperature from automatic recording device in salt-water pumphouse in Whittier.

ing, who was in the Hodge Building during the earthquake, said, however, that midway through the violent phase of the shaking, the Hodge Building seemed to have been lifted up and set down.

At least three waves were observed during and immediately after the earthquake. Mr. M. J. Dixon and Mr. Farrian Kolb reported that about 1 minute after the earthquake started, the water in Passage Canal rose rapidly to a maximum altitude of 25–26 feet [1] in the vicinity of the town. The water was still glassy and did not contain any debris.

The water immediately receded, and 1–1½ minutes later a large breaking wave came in. This wave was muddy, contained much debris, and was about 40 feet high

when it reached The Alaska Railroad depot (pl. 1). Mrs. Farrian Kolb, who observed the wave from the second story of the depot, described it as a wall of water 30–50 feet high that rose near the center of Passage Canal. She stated that something seemed to be exploding underneath the water. Mr. L. McDonough said that the water in Passage Canal about 50 yards from shore appeared to be boiling. This wave struck the railroad depot 8–10 feet above the ground surface, or at an altitude of 34–36 feet.

From ½ to 1 minute after the first breaking wave (second rise of sea level), another wave struck Whittier. This wave was similar in nature to the first breaking wave. It reached an altitude of

about 30 feet near The Alaska Railroad depot.

There were no eyewitnesses to the waves that struck the shore in other parts of the area, but high-water marks on snow and trees and deposition of debris indicate that waves in Passage Canal reached their maximum altitude not at Whittier but along the shore to the northwest (as measured by Plafker and Mayo). There the waves reached as high as 104 feet. At the extreme north end of the delta at the head of Passage Canal, a wave reached an altitude of 82 feet.

During the earthquake a fire started in the Union Oil Co. and U.S. Army tank-farm area (fig. 5) and burned until March 31; it completely destroyed the fuel-storage tanks.

Thirteen lives were lost at Whittier as the result of wave action. Eyewitnesses state that 10 of the persons lost and presumed dead had gone into the home of one of the Columbia Lumber Co. workers a few minutes before the earthquake struck. The waves totally destroyed both the company's industrial buildings and the homes of the workers (figs. 6 and 7). Two other persons associated with the company are missing and presumed dead. None of the 12

[1] Unless otherwise indicated, altitudes given in this report are based on a pre-earthquake datum and do not reflect the 5.3-foot regional subsidence of the Whittier area during the earthquake because it is not known when the subsidence occurred.

Datum for subaerial contours on all plates is mean sea level; datum for submarine soundings and contours is mean lower low water (MLLW) or 6.3 feet below mean sea level. Height of waves is the actual distance between trough and crest. For example, a 40-foot wave would have an altitude of 34.7 feet because the earthquake occurred at a 1-foot tide or 5.3 feet below mean sea level.

The tide range at Whittier is from a low of −3.8 feet to a high of 15.4 feet (datum is MLLW).

5.—Aerial view, looking northeast, of Union Oil Co. and U.S. Army fuel-storage tanks burning. Note high-water mark where waves washed away snow cover. Photograph by U.S. Army, March 28, 1964.

6.—Preearthquake aerial view, looking south, of Union Oil Co. fuel-storage tanks and Columbia Lumber Co. Photograph by U.S. Army, June 7, 1963.

7.—Postearthquake aerial view, looking north, of destruction of Columbia Lumber Co. Photograph by U.S. Army, March 28, 1964.

bodies was recovered from the wreckage; the only traces found of the missing persons were pieces of children's clothing. It is presumed that all were washed out into Passage Canal. The 13th victim, and the only one whose body was recovered, was a child who lost her life near The Alaska Railroad depot.

Several residents of Whittier commented that on the morning after the earthquake, red snapper fish, which normally inhabit waters deeper than 400 feet, were floating on the surface of Passage Canal and were also strewn along parts of the shoreline. Everyone who saw the fish remarked that they were larger than those normally caught by local fishermen. Dr. N. J. Wilimovsky, a marine biologist from the University of British Columbia, stated that 26 genera of red snappers are caught commercially in Prince William Sound. Two of these—*Seabastolobus* and *Sebastodes*—increase in abundance with depth. Most of the red snappers found dead along the shore and on the surface of Passage Canal were probably fish of these two genera. The fish apparently were killed by a rapid change of pressure in the water and were then brought to the surface by upwelling of the water or by turbidity currents triggered by the seismic shaking.

EFFECTS OF THE EARTHQUAKE

Seven different factors related to the earthquake were responsible for the extensive damage in the Whittier area. These include (1) a change in land level, (2) seismic shock, (3) fracturing of fill and unconsolidated deposits, (4) differential subsidence due to compaction, (5) landslides, (6) waves generated by submarine landslides, and (7) fire. A large avalanche fell on the moraine at the head of Passage Canal; it consisted chiefly of snow debris and did no harm. Plate 1 indicates the nature and extent of damage by seismic shock, compaction, landslides, waves, and fire. Figures 8 and 9 are prequake and postquake aerial photographs of much of the Whittier area.

LAND-LEVEL CHANGES

Studies by the U.S. Geological Survey and the U.S. Coast and Geodetic Survey determined that tectonic subsidence of the landmass at Whittier was 5.3 feet during the earthquake. Residents of Whittier estimate that only 20 percent of the prequake tidal zone is now exposed during low tides (compare pls. 2 and 3). High tides now inundate some of the delta area at the head of Passage Canal, much land leased by the Two Brothers Lumber Co., and about 350 feet of the eastern end of the airstrip (fig. 10). The 5.3-foot subsidence is not wholly responsible for the change in exposure of the tidal zone; landslides

8.—Vertical aerial photographs of Whittier. Top, Prequake; composite of photographs by Bureau of Land Management, September 23, 1963. Bottom, Postquake; photograph by U.S. Army, March 28, 1964.

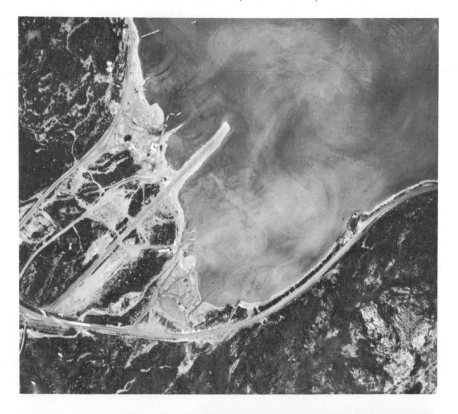

9.—Vertical aerial photographs of delta at west end of Passage Canal. Top, Pre-quake; photograph by Bureau of Land Management, September 23, 1963. Bottom, Postquake; photograph by Air Photo Tech, Anchorage, April 1, 1964.

and compaction (p. B15) also were, in part, responsible.

The most pressing problem at Whittier was to put back into service the port and railroad facilities that were destroyed or damaged by land subsidence. Much of the reconstruction in Alaska depended on immediate use of the car-barge slip dock, which was the only connecting link for transferring supplies and equipment from ships to The Alaska Railroad after the earthquake. To permit maximum use of the dock, which is stationary at the

10.—Aerial photograph, looking south, of delta at head of Passage Canal. Remains of Two Brothers Lumber Co. in right foreground. Projecting into the water is the airstrip. Note high-water mark indicated by snow. Photograph by U.S. Army, March 28, 1964.

——→

land end and free to rise and fall with the tide at the sea end, it was necessary to know the actual amount of subsidence at Whittier. Once the amount of subsidence was determined, the dock was reconstructed and railroad traffic to Anchorage was reestablished in a remarkably short time.

SEISMIC DAMAGE

In the downtown area of Whittier away from the waterfront, most of the damage was caused by seismic shock. Within the area inundated by waves (pl. 1), seismic shock severely damaged one of the slip towers of the car-barge slip dock (fig. 11), part of the marginal wharf, one of the storage tanks at the U.S. Army tank farm, and the highway and rail-

11.—View, looking west, of remains of car-barge slip dock. Slip tower only part of structure left. Photograph by The Alaska Railroad, 1964.

——→

12.—View, looking southeast, of Hodge Building.   Photograph taken April 4, 1964.

13.—Aerial view, looking south-southeast, of part of postquake Whittier.   1 Hodge Building, 2 gymnasium, 3 composite shop, 4 fire station, 5 station storage warehouse, 6 telephone building, 7 ACS building, 8 intransit storage shed, 9 marginal wharf, 10 The Alaska Railroad depot, 11 FHA housing, and 12 Buckner Building.

road bridges crossing Whittier Creek. Beyond the inundated zone there was moderate damage to the Hodge Building (fig. 12), the composite shop, and part of the station storage warehouse (fig. 13). The Buckner Building (fig. 14), gymnasium, fire station, telephone building, ACS (Alaska Communication System) building, powerhouse, and the railroad bridge near the airstrip were slightly damaged.

The Hodge Building, a reinforced-concrete 14-story structure 265 feet long and 50 and 110 feet wide (figs. 2 and 3), rests on at least 44 feet of unconsolidated sand and gravel. The building was constructed as three structural monolithic units connected by 8-inch expansion joints. In the corridors, metal jumper plates spanned the 8-inch joints; on the exterior, the joints were secured by a weather seal. The long dimension of the building was parallel to the predominant east-west direction of the seismic motion;

the expansion joints were perpendicular to the motion. During the earthquake the individual units banged against each other, the weather seals popped out, and the jumper plates were curled. Damage to the structural connections (weather seals, jumper plates, and spandels) was progressively more intense upward in the structure owing to the larger horizontal component of movement. Jumpers on the top floor were shortened 4 inches by curling, whereas on the third floor they curled only a quarter of an inch.

The interior partition walls of the Hodge Building were constructed of concrete block. Damage to the walls was also greater in the upper floors. The walls on the 13th and 14th floors either collapsed or were cracked. On the fourth floor the blocks were loosened, except near the expansion joints where some of the blocks were dislodged. The exterior of the building was not substantially damaged, even where the units

banged against each other.

The interior and roof of the composite shop were moderately damaged by seismic shaking. Most of the interior blocks and some of the concrete posts and beams were cracked; in numerous places the roof purlins were twisted or separated from the beams. Much of the internal bracing in the building was either broken or strained.

The largest building in Whittier, probably the largest in Alaska, is the Buckner Building (figs. 14, 15, and 16). It is a six-story reinforced-concrete structure about 500 feet long and 50–150 feet wide. The long dimension of the structure runs northeast-southwest, oblique to the seismic motion of the earthquake. The building rests on bedrock and did not receive any significant structural damage. The steam powerhouse near The Alaska Railroad depot also rests on bedrock and was not damaged by seismic motion.

Several small structures on un-

14.—Aerial view, looking southeast, of Buckner Building; building in foreground is intransit storage shed; long structure at left of photograph is FHA housing; structure north of FHA housing is depot. Note high-water mark of wave on snow. Photograph taken April 4, 1964.

15.—Map showing Buckner Building, surrounding area, and location of test pits (Pt). Graphic logs of these pits are shown in fig. 16.

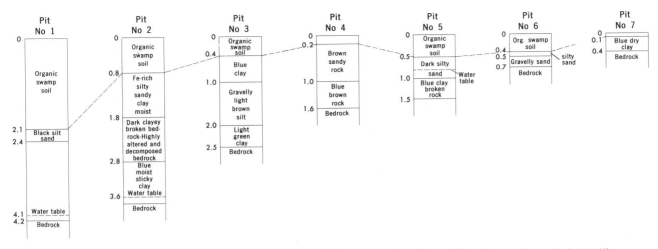

16.—Graphic logs of test pits (Pt) in the Buckner Building area.   Locations of the pits are shown in figure 15.

consolidated sandy gravel which were only slightly damaged by seismic activity include (1) the fire station, (2) the telephone building, which cracked at its corners, (3) the ACS building, (4) the gymnasium, which had some cracks at the top of the structure, and (5) the tunnel between the Hodge Building and the school.

The intransit storage shed, which rests upon several feet of fill on top of delta sediments, was slightly to moderately damaged by the combined effects of seismic shaking, subsidence, and wave action. In places the walls of the structure moved as much as 7 inches; subsequently, the building appeared to have been stretched by the earthquake effects.

In addition to surficial damage, seismic shock broke two 10-inch pipelines from the water-storage reservoir. In order to operate the steam powerplant, water was pumped from the salt-water pumphouse through a firehose.

FRACTURING

Only a few fractures occurred in the fill and the unconsolidated sediments and these caused no damage. A ground fracture formed during the earthquake near The Alaska Railroad depot. This fracture extends beneath the structure and appears to follow the contact between the cut and fill made during the construction of the depot. Minor fracturing in fill occurred near the intransit storage shed. Near the FAA station, a series of cracks parallel to the shore extends about 100 feet inland.

COMPACTION

Compaction of unconsolidated sediments and differential subsidence of the land damaged four structures: the pumphouse near the FAA station, the DeLong Dock, the intransit storage shed, and the marginal wharf. These structures were also damaged by waves. In addition, the pumphouse is now inundated by high tides.

The marginal wharf and the intransit storage shed were constructed on fill overlying delta sediments. The station storage warehouse and the pumphouse near the FAA station are underlain by delta sediments. How much fill, if any, underlies the DeLong Dock is not known.

The maximum recorded subsidence (about 1½ feet) was measured in the area near the marginal wharf and intransit storage shed. Subsidence may have been greater (an estimated 2–3 feet) in the delta area at the head of Passage Canal. The pumphouse here is a concrete structure enclosing two 40-foot wells. The concrete floor subsided 6 inches relative to the well casings during the earthquake.

LANDSLIDES

The landslides triggered by the earthquake (pl. 3) formed in delta sediments at the head of Passage Canal, in delta sediments and fill at Whittier waterfront, and possibly in submarine talus or in a submarine lateral moraine along the north shore of Passage Canal. It is not known if any of the slip surfaces of the landslides are in bedrock.

The profiles of the slides and submarine slopes are shown on plate 3, and the changes in degree of slope are shown in table 2 (next page). The landslides occurred on slopes ranging from 20° offshore of the airstrip to 31° at the marginal wharf. The largest change of sub-

[453]

TABLE 2.—*Effect of landslides on average submarine slopes at Whittier, Alaska*

Landslide	Submarine slopes (degrees)	
	Pre-landslide	Post-landslide
Marginal wharf_____	21	23
Airstrip_____	25	15
Tank-farm area_____	25	24
FAA station_____	20	20
Passage Canal, north shore_____	31	27

marine slope, 10°, was produced by the airstrip landslide. The marginal-wharf landslide effected the only increase in slope. The only landslide scarp exposed is at the FAA station landslide.

The only structures damaged by landslides (pl. 1) were the FAA station (fig. 17), a section of the railroad, a small pier near the FAA station, and the extreme eastern end of the airstrip (fig. 10). The slip tower at the car-barge slip dock may have been destroyed by the landslide at the marginal wharf.

The landslides in the Whittier area did not all occur simultaneously. There were two, and possibly three, different periods of sliding during the earthquake.

LANDSLIDE-GENERATED WAVES

Submarine landslides in Passage Canal generated at least two, and probably three, waves. Plate 1 shows the area inundated and destroyed by waves. The direction and altitude of the highest waves are indicated on plate 3. Only the direction of the highest wave in a particular area can be indicated, because a higher wave would destroy any evidence of an earlier lower wave. A lower wave that followed a higher wave would merely rearrange debris.

The maximum altitude of the waves was 104 feet along the north shore of Passage Canal (pl. 3). About a quarter of a mile north of the FAA station, the wave reached an altitude of 82 feet. Near the airstrip the wave reached 20 feet, and at the extreme south shore of Passage Canal the wave topped the railroad, reaching an altitude of 52 feet. In Whittier the maximum altitude reached by a wave was 43 feet at

the small-boat harbor northeast of The Alaska Railroad depot. On the waterfront area the altitude was 26 feet.

At the Whittier waterfront, submarine landslides apparently generated two different types of waves. Figure 18 illustrates schematically the sequential formation of the waves.

The first wave formed in the scarp area of the submarine landslide. As the landmass slid, a wave was generated by the water rushing in to fill the void formed behind the sliding mass, and a drawdown of water occurred. This wave was directional and its form was chiefly a function of (1) the size and shape of the landslide, (2) the distance of the landslide scarp offshore, (3) the velocity of the sliding mass, and (4) the configuration of the coastline.

17.—View, looking north, of FAA station. Track destroyed by landslide. Bow of boat resting on scarp. Photograph by G D. Hanna, 1964.

The second type of submarine landslide wave was generated when the landslide came to rest at the bottom of Passage Canal. The volume of the landmass displaced the water and created an upwelling near the margins of the depositional area (fig. 18). When the upwelling water surfaced at Passage Canal, it generated a wave system. This wave system was not as directional as the wave generated at the scarp of the landslide. However, water moved primarily in two directions: (1) toward the scarp area, and (2) toward the landslide movement.

The size and force of the second wave were controlled chiefly by (1) the size and shape of the sliding landmass, (2) the velocity of the sliding mass, (3) the submarine configuration of Passage Canal, (4) the distance offshore at which upwelling occurred, (5) the depth of water in which the slide came to rest, and (6) the configuration of the coastline. The character of the waves may also have been influenced by other landslide-generated waves in nearby areas.

Eyewitness accounts indicate that probably both types of waves inundated parts of Whittier. There were no witnesses to the waves that struck the delta at the west end of Passage Canal or its north shore. The apparent submarine explosion described by Mr. Kolb and the "boiling out" of water in Passage Canal described by Mr. McDonough no doubt, preceded waves of the second type. Eyewitnesses reported that one of the slip towers of the car-barge slip dock collapsed before any wave struck the dock. The author believes that the tower was at the head of the marginal-wharf slide (pl. 3) and that the tower col-

lapsed as the land slid during the early violent phase of seismic shaking.

There are several possible explanations of the glassy wave reported by witnesses. If the sliding mass moved with sufficient velocity, the

volume of drawdown could be large enough to form a wave that would reach an altitude of 25 to 26 feet when water rushed into the vacated area yet which probably would not be highly turbulent.

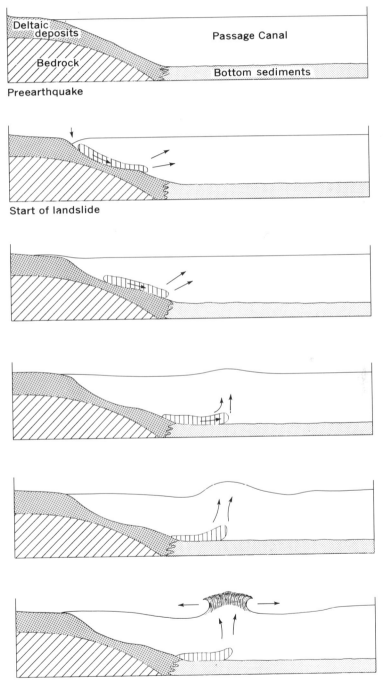

18.—Schematic sections showing generation of waves associated with submarine landslides.

[455]

Another possible explanation for the glassy wave is that it was caused by seiching in Passage Canal. Inasmuch as Passage Canal is in open communication with a large body of water, the period (T) of seiching would occur according to the formula

$$T = \frac{4l}{\sqrt{(gh)}}$$

where T is period in seconds, l is length of Passage Canal in meters, h is the average depth of Passage Canal in meters, and g is the acceleration of gravity. Assuming l is 15,000 meters and h is 300 meters, the period of seiche waves in Passage Canal would be 1,110 seconds or about 18.5 minutes. The earthquake occurred when the tide was at 1 foot and the land subsided 5.3 feet; thus the seiche waves would have to be at least 18.7 feet high to reach the 25-foot altitude (preearthquake datum) attained by the glassy wave. If such seiching occurred, evidence of a high-water level would be found near this altitude in the cove into which Cove Creek drains. Such evidence was not found in the cove. If seiche waves in Passage Canal had been generated by the earthquake, they would have continued at an 18.5-minute interval throughout the night of March 27, 1964. However, residents of Whittier who worked all night after the earthquake did not report any unusual waves in Passage Canal other than the three waves that struck Whittier during or immediately after the earthquake. Therefore, the glassy wave and the following two breaking waves must have been generated by submarine landslides. The absence of waves throughout the night as reported by the eyewitnesses also rules out the possibility that small seiche

19.—View, looking south, of The Alaska Railroad depot. Wave destroyed waiting room of the depot. Photograph taken April 7, 1964.

waves occurred but did no damage at Whittier.

It is remotely possible that submarine landsliding near Billings Creek was responsible for the glassy wave. However, any landmass failure there would have had to be immediate—within 45 seconds of the earthquake—to allow sufficient time for the wave to reach Whittier by the time the glassy wave was observed. The area was not included in the study for the present report.

Wave damage in the Whittier area is shown on plate 1. The wave completely destroyed (1) the small-boat harbor, (2) the stub pier, (3) the car-barge slip dock, (4) the waiting room of The Alaska Railroad depot (fig. 19), and (5) the Columbia Lumber Co. structures (fig. 5 and 7). Many facilities were damaged by a combination of destructive forces: (1) the Army tank farm by fire, seismic shaking, and waves, (2) the Union Oil Co. fuel tanks by fire

and waves, (3) the DeLong Dock and part of the marginal wharf by wave action and subsidence, and (4) the intransit storage shed by waves, subsidence, and seismic shaking.

The waves that struck Whittier had sufficient force to carry heavy objects many feet inland. A 4-cubic-yard barnacle-covered boulder was carried about 125 feet and deposited on The Alaska Railroad track near the depot at an altitude of about 26 feet. Boulders as much as 6 feet across were strewn on the road between the small-boat harbor and the Union Oil Co. fuel tanks. One of the Union Oil Co. fuel tanks containing ballast was moved at least 40 feet south by waves, and another tank containing 1 million gallons of fuel was moved 15 feet south (fig. 5).

The waves that struck the shoreline at the head of Passage Canal damaged practically all the structures near the shore. The waves completely destroyed three unoc-

20.—Photograph of 2- by 6-inch plank driven through a 10-ply tire by wave.

cupied homes on the shore, 200–400 feet south of the FAA station, and the buildings of the Two Brothers Lumber Co. The homes were washed away, and the nearby FAA station was partially inundated by the waves but not significantly damaged. The Two Brothers Lumber Co. buildings were carried inland in a southwest direction; the company's trimmer and conveyor chain were moved 200 feet, the bucking machine 40–50 feet, and the 2,300-pound mill about 100 feet to the southwest. The waves struck the Two Brothers Lumber Co. installation with such force that a 2- by 6-inch plank was driven through a 10-ply forklift tire (fig. 20).

The waves (or single wave) that damaged the west coastline of Passage Canal originated along the north coastline of the canal and traveled southwest. The wave (or waves) was apparently diverted by the eastern end of the airstrip—the structure about 300 feet south of the airstrip was only moderately damaged (pl. 1).

The southwest- and south-traveling wave struck the point along the south shore, about 4,000 feet west of Whittier Creek, with tremendous force. The wave reached an altitude of more than 50 feet. It carried a 1-ton winch and a boulder weighing 2–3 tons 120 feet south and deposited them on The Alaska Railroad tracks, which are about 30 feet in altitude.

FIRE

Fire was chiefly responsible for destruction of the Union Oil Co. and the U.S. Army fuel-storage tanks at the Whittier waterfront. Fire, together with damage by wave and seismic action, completely destroyed the tanks. The cause of the fire is not known, but there are at least two possible explanations: (1) seismic motion may have snapped a live powerline in the area, or (2) fuel from a damaged tank may have flowed into a boiler that was operating in the area.

CONCLUSIONS

The chief conclusion that can be drawn from the Geological Survey's investigation of the effects of the Alaska earthquake of March 27, 1964, on the Whittier area is that damage can be correlated with the local geology.

At Whittier all facilities built on the slate and graywacke bedrock were damaged slightly, or not at all, by seismic shaking. These structures include (1) the six-story Buckner Building, (2) the three-story FHA building, (3) the 1½-million-gallon water tank, (4) the powerhouse, and (5) the salt-water pumphouse. All are concrete except the FHA building, which is a wood frame structure.

In contrast to the facilities on bedrock, most of the buildings on unconsolidated sediments or fill were damaged significantly by seismic activity. These buildings include (1) the 14-story Hodge Building, (2) the gymnasium, (3) the composite shop, (4) the school, (5) the station storage warehouse, (6) the intransit storage shed, (7) the telephone building, (8) the ACS building, (9) the pipe shed, and (10) the fire station. All of the 10 buildings are of concrete construction except the composite shop, intransit storage shed, station storage warehouse, and the pipe shed, which are of various types of construction.

In any earthquake the structural response of a building to a seismic wave is a function of (1) the amplitude, acceleration, and frequency of the seismic wave, (2) the duration of shaking of the building, (3) the shape, height, and width of the building, (4) the type of construction used in the building, and (5) the orientation of the building to the seismic-wave direction.

Richter (1958) stated that there is an elementary relation between amplitude, acceleration, and frequency. He further stated that "Duration of shaking is the single most important factor in producing excessive damage. It takes time to break buildings up once damage starts. Long duration, reasonably high acceleration, and considerable amplitudes are the combination which does most damage in buildings."

Gutenberg (1957) reported that strong seismic shaking may last several times longer in unconsolidated deposits than in bedrock. He also stated that seismic amplitudes in unconsolidated deposits may be as much as 10 times the amplitudes in bedrock. Therefore, because there is a relation between amplitude, acceleration, and frequency and because of the longer duration of shaking, buildings on unconsolidated sediments are subjected to greater damaging forces than buildings on bedrock. The structural damage at Whittier clearly reflected this relationship.

Not only is there a correlation between damage and the underlying bedrock or unconsolidated deposits, but damage appears to be controlled also by the type, size, and thickness of the unconsolidated sediments. The Hodge Building, a 14-story reinforced-concrete structure which rests on coarse sandy gravel, was just moderately damaged by seismic activity. The Whittier delta at this point is only 1,200 feet wide, and the east end of the building is within 300 feet of bedrock. Therefore, the thickness of the sandy gravel that underlies the structure is probably not more than 150 feet.

The Hodge Building received substantially less damage than buildings of comparable height at Anchorage—a city about twice as far from the epicenter as Whittier. At least three geologic factors are responsible for this marked difference of damage: (1) the Hodge Building rests on a small area of unconsolidated deposits as compared to the structures at Anchorage, where a plain several miles wide is underlain by at least several hundred feet of clay, silt, sand, and gravel; (2) the deep fine-grained sediments that underlie Anchorage magnified the seismic amplitudes substantially more than the shallow coarse-grained sediments that underlie Whittier; (3) because the higher frequency components of ground motion attenuate with distance more rapidly than the lower frequency components, the tall structures at Anchorage were more nearly attuned to long-period ground motion. Thus, these structures suffered a proportionately greater degree of damage than the 14-story Hodge Building at Whittier.

The duration of ground motion differs not only between bedrock and unconsolidated deposits, but also with the type of unconsolidated deposits. For example, the longest duration of motion reported was at Portage, where ground shaking lasted about 15 minutes. Portage (fig. 1) is on the eastern shore of Turnagain Arm about 10 miles west of Whittier and approximately 40 miles southeast of Anchorage. The longer duration of ground motion at Portage than at either Anchorage or Whittier can be attributed to the finer grained sediments underlying the area, the shallow water table, and the greater size, shape, and depth of the sedimentary basin.

Ground fractures in the coarse-grained unconsolidated delta and moraine deposits at Whittier are uncommon, especially in the Whittier delta. Although the sediments were laterally extended toward free faces during the earth-

quake, the movement of material was not expressed as surface fractures. Extensive ground fracturing occurred at (1) Valdez, (2) Robe River flats, (3) Copper River flats, (4) Matanuska flats, (5) Anchorage, (6) Seward, and (7) the Portage area. In these places, the unconsolidated deposits are finer grained and thicker, and they cover a more extensive area than the unconsolidated sediments at Whittier. Apparently, the coarse-grained texture and, in part, the thinness of the sediments were responsible for the lack of extensive ground fractures at Whittier.

Even the coarse unconsolidated deposits at Whittier were compacted by the seismic shaking. Compaction and subsequent subsidence should be expected in most unconsolidated sediments during an earthquake of large magnitude.

Landslides formed on submarine slopes in unconsolidated material inclined 20° to 25°. The three submarine landslide-generated waves that struck Whittier were of two types. The first type of wave was generated in the scarp area of the submarine landslide, was unidirectional, and damaged only the area behind the

landslide scarp. The glassy rise of water may have been associated with this wave.

The second type of wave was formed by the volume displacement of water offshore. The upwelling water moved primarily in two opposing directions: (1) toward the scarp area, and (2) in the direction of the landslide movement. These waves were not as directional as the waves generated at the scarp of the landslide, but they were far more destructive.

The landslide-generated waves were responsible for the loss of life and were the chief instrument of damage in the Whittier area. Because the submarine slopes in Passage Canal were not significantly decreased by the landsliding during the earthquake, another earthquake of comparable magnitude would probably trigger more submarine landslides. Destructive waves would inevitably follow.

The hazard of fire is always associated with earthquakes. The towns of Seward, Valdez, and Whittier had fires that originated at the fuel-storage tanks in the waterfront area. An immediate power failure spared Anchorage from electrically ignited fires.

REFERENCES CITED

Barnes, F. F., 1943, Geology of the Portage Pass area, Alaska: U.S. Geol. Survey Bull. 926–D, p. 211–235.
Grantz, Arthur, Plafker, George, and Kachadoorian, Reuben, 1964, Alaskas' Good Friday earthquake,

March 27, 1964, a preliminary evaluation: U.S. Geol. Survey Circ. 491, 35 p.
Gutenberg, Beno, 1957, Effects of ground on earthquake motion: Seismol. Soc. America Bull., v. 47, no. 3, p. 221–250.

Richter, C. F., 1958, Elementary seismology: San Francisco, Calif., W. H. Freeman and Co., 768 p.
U.S. Weather Bureau, 1964, Climatological data, Alaska, in Annual Summary, 1963: v. 49, no. 13, p. 219–230.

CLARIFICATIONS

Geology Vol. Page	USGS Page	Column	Line	Remarks
441	B 3	1	24	Plate 1 is Plate L in Part B, the accompanying map case
447	B 9	1	33	Plates 2 and 3 are Plates M and N, respectively, in Part B, the accompanying map case

Base map from U.S. Army Map Service,
1:1 000,000 series; Anchorage, 1951–53
and Kodiak, 1952

1.—Maps of Alaska showing Homer area.

ROGER M. WALLER
U.S. GEOLOGICAL SURVEY

Reprinted with minor changes from
U.S. Geological Survey Professional Paper 542-D,
"Effects of the Earthquake of March 27, 1964, in the Homer Area, Alaska"

Effects in the Homer Area*

ABSTRACT

The March 27, 1964, earthquake shook the Homer area for about 3 minutes. Land effects consisted of a 2- to 6-foot subsidence of the mainland and Homer Spit, one earthflow at the mouth of a canyon, several landslides on the Homer escarpment and along the sea bluffs, and minor fissuring of the ground, principally at the edges of bluffs and on Homer Spit. Hydrologic effects consisted of at least one and possibly two submarine landslides at the end of the spit, seiche waves in Kachemak Bay, ice breakage on Beluga Lake, sanding of wells, and a temporary loss of water in some wells.

Seismic damage to the community was light in comparison with that of other communities closer to the epicenter. One submarine landslide, however, took out most of the harbor breakwater. The greatest damage was due to the subsidence of the spit, both tectonically (2–3 ft) and by differential compaction or lateral spreading (an additional 1–4 ft). Higher tides now flood much of the spit. The harbor and dock had to be replaced, and buildings on the end of the spit had to be elevated.

Protection works for other buildings and the highway were needed. These works included application of fill to raise the highway and parts of the spit above high tides. Reconstruction costs and disaster loans totaled about $2½ million, but this amount includes added improvement costs over preexisting values.

Homer Spit in particular and the Homer area in general rank as areas where precautions must be taken in selecting building sites. The hazards of landslides, earthflows, compaction and submarine slumping—all of which might be triggered by an earthquake—should be considered in site selection.

In plan, Homer Spit resembles a scimitar with its curving blade pointed seaward. It is about 4 miles long and as much as 1,500 feet wide. The spit is composed largely of gravel intermixed with some sand.

After the earthquake and the resulting tectonic subsidence and compaction, much of the spit was below high-tide levels and consequently flooded periodically. The entire beach face has retreated. Much of the material eroded from the beach has been redeposited to form a new storm or frontal berm, locally migrating around buildings and covering roads. Beach recession of 10–15 feet is probably the overall average; maximum recession 1 year after the earthquake was 56 feet along one limited section of the distal end of the spit.

Subsidence of the mainland has caused accelerated erosion of the beaches and headlands that have been—and are—source areas for the material deposited on Homer Spit. The resulting increased supply of gravel and sand probably will cause the spit to widen gradually on the Cook Inlet side. Similarly, the new frontal berm will probably grow to a height sufficient to prevent overtopping by all but the larger storm swashes. The nature of shore processes on the spit has not been materially altered by subsidence, but the rates of erosion and deposition have been accelerated. The lasting effect of subsidence (excluding flooding) will be enlargement of the beach on the Cook Inlet side and gradual wasting of the beach on the bay side of the spit.

INTRODUCTION

Homer is located at the southern tip of the lowland part of the Kenai Peninsula in south-central Alaska (fig. 1). The lowland lies west of the Kenai Mountains and east of Cook Inlet. This paper deals with the earthquake effects in the general area along the shore of Kachemak Bay from Diamond Creek on the west to Fritz Creek, about 6 miles east of Homer. Homer is about 160 miles southwest of the epicenter of the earthquake of March 1964.

Immediate field observations were limited because the writer's primary assignment was to Anchorage. Early observations in the Homer area were made by U.S. Geological Survey colleagues Reuben Kachadoorian and George Plafker. Special thanks are due to the numerous people at Homer who provided their observations of the earthquake and to Mr. Al Billings, project engineer, U.S. Army Corps of Engineers, Homer, who helped make the offshore fathometer traverses.

*With a section on Beach Changes on Homer Spit by Kirk W. Stanley.

[461]

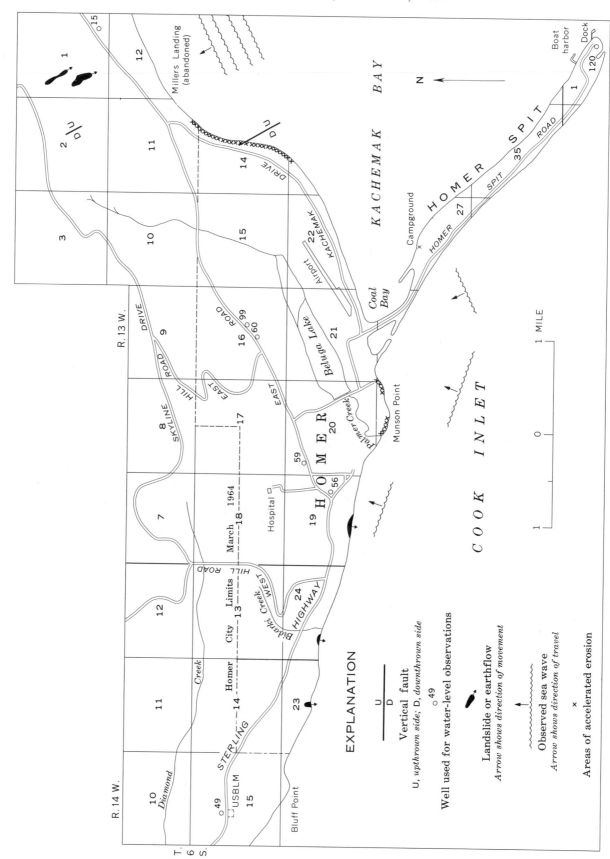

2.—Map of the Homer area showing slide areas, beach erosion points, and locations of wells.

EXPLANATION

U
—
D

Vertical fault
U, upthrown side; D, downthrown side

○ 49
Well used for water-level observations

Landslide or earthflow
Arrow shows direction of movement

Observed sea wave
Arrow shows direction of travel

× Areas of accelerated erosion

PERSONAL OBSERVATIONS

Most of the residents of the small town of Homer were settling down for the evening meal at 5:36 p.m. (Alaska standard time) on Good Friday, March 27, 1964. Several people were still out at the end of the Homer Spit which extends 4 miles into Kachemak Bay (fig. 2). The weather was mild; there was an overcast and near-freezing temperatures and light snow was falling. A thin snow cover lay over most of the land. A high tide of 19.4 feet was ebbing to a low which would occur at about 7:30 p.m.

To some people the first indication of something happening was the loss of electric power, but most persons realized that there was an earthquake when they felt the initial shock at about 5:37 p.m. As the shock waves continued, they realized this was an exceptionally severe earthquake. Estimates of the length of time of earth movement ranged from 1 to 5 minutes. Mr. Ralph Cowles, the mayor of Homer, stated (Grantz and others, 1964, p. 24) "that the total time of the tremor was from 2 to 2½ minutes and that its motion was 'wavy' and east-west." Mr. Paul Gardiner reported 2- to 3-foot ground waves moving east-west near the airport, and Mr. and Mrs. D. P. Lowcock sensed east-west motion on Munson Point. Many people stated, however, that the principal direction of movement was north-south and that the movement was so violent that standing unsupported was impossible. Mr. and Mrs. Albert Greer reported ground waves coming two at a time downhill from north to south. In general, the ground movement was reported to be a gradual buildup of a rolling motion to a peak intensity, then a lull, and then another buildup to a peak

before suddenly stopping. Mrs. Leo Rhodes, Mr. and Mrs. Vic Nelson, and Mrs. Gus Weber remarked on the great silence that prevailed during lulls in the earthquake, in contrast with the rumbling, cracking, and popping noises reported by Mr. Karl Baier, Mrs. Rhodes, the Nelsons, and others as prevalent during the violent-motion phases of the quake.

The violence of earth movement was noted by several witnesses. Mr. Tex Sharp, in his apartment when the quake occurred and the power failed, tried to cross the 10 feet from his apartment door to his place of business, the Waterfront Bar and Dining Establishment. He was unable to cross for about 4 minutes. When the shaking stopped, he entered the bar, in his bare feet, and found his stock of bottled goods and glassware almost totally destroyed. On East Road near Fritz Creek, Mr. Karl Baier was thrown to the ground and was unable to rise for some time. Near the airport, Mrs. Leo Rhodes and Mrs. Vic Nelson were unable to walk without support during the violent phases of the quake; Mr. and Mrs. D. P. Lowcock reported that they and their dog were thrown to the ground by the force of the motion on Munson Point.

Animals, too, were affected. Dogs, sheep, and geese were thrown to the ground. Mrs. Gus Weber reported that two moose ran from the woods into a clearing where they "jumped, bucked up and down like horses, reared up on their hind legs and ran back and forth as the earth moved in all directions." These experiences suggest that the quake had an in-

tensity of between VII and VIII on the Modified Mercalli scale.

At the height of the quake, earth fissures formed and closed in many parts of Homer and the vicinity. Near the airport, according to Mrs. Vic Nelson, the ground and snow cover "cracked like lightning," opening and closing. Mr. and Mrs. Albert Greer reported that fissures formed in the ground "with a cracking noise." Mr. Karl Baier saw a field crack in a checkerboard pattern and a 6-inch fissure traverse the ground and split a spruce tree. On Homer Spit, Mr. Glen Sewell (Grantz and others, 1964, p. 24) watched a fissure form on the oceanside of the spit and travel toward him. The ground split under his truck and between his legs, opening up to about 12 inches and allowing gravel to roll in. The fissure extended, splitting the concrete floor of the Porpoise Room. Paved roads were fissured in various places throughout the Homer area, but significant patterns and extensions of fissures into adjacent unpaved areas have not been recorded.

Exceptional sea waves, both in Cook Inlet and in Kachemak Bay, were seen by various observers. Inasmuch as the waves were observed within 5–10 minutes after the quake, the waves clearly did not originate near the epicenter, 160 miles distant. On the other hand, some reported waves apparently came in from the open ocean; hence it cannot be assumed that all of the waves were seiches although waves that traveled approximately at right angles to the shores of Cook Inlet may have been seiches. Submarine slumping occurred off the tip of Homer Spit. The possibility of larger scale slumping or landsliding, or both, in uninhabited parts of Cook Inlet cannot be disregarded; however, there is no direct evidence that such sliding and slumping occurred to cause the sea waves. In short, the origin of the waves remains unexplained. The reported wave patterns are shown diagrammatically on figure 2.

Eyewitnesses reported that wave heights and patterns were markedly different in Cook Inlet and in Kachemak Bay. For example, while returning to Homer from the spit, shortly after the earthquake, Mr. Glen Sewell noticed a wave "rolling in from the ocean" about a mile offshore. Mr. and Mrs. D. P. Lowcock also saw a wave which probably was the same one seen by Mr. Sewell. After the ground motion stopped, the Lowcocks looked offshore and saw a wave "rolling in from Seldovia." It was perhaps a mile long, cresting, and alined approximately northwest to southeast. They also observed another wave coming directly northwestward toward them. It was shorter and did not appear as high, but it was cresting also. The two waves gave the appearance of an "inverted V," but they were not joined (fig. 2).

The wave coming from the ocean was probably the same one observed also from downtown Homer. It reportedly (Mr. Velton Cason, oral commun., 1964) came in as a 9-foot swell about 5 minutes after the beginning of the earthquake motion, and there was a withdrawal of water on the beach before it struck.

Within Kachemak Bay, wave action developed also. Mrs. Fitzgerald, on East Road, reported that it looked as if "the land was being shoved under the bay" because of the curious breaking and surging of the waves on the tidal flats. Her family had counted seven waves rolling in when their attention was diverted due to a "harder part of the shock." She reported that others counted 14 waves in the bay.

The U.S. Coast and Geodetic Survey (1964a, p. 82) reported from news excerpts that "Ten-foot waves at 2-minute intervals occurred at about the same time the ground shock was felt." This report agrees with Stanley's (1965) statement that the waves immediately after the earthquake were 9 feet high in Cook Inlet and 4 feet high in Kachemak Bay.

Evidently a series of waves was immediately generated in the bay. All except one of the observed waves were parallel to the north shore. Probably the same waves were noted by J. M. Moss (written commun., 1964) on the south shore at Peterson Bay (fig. 1) as the "Tide came and went for at least 15 hrs."

Kachadoorian (unpub. data, Apr. 1, 1964) recorded a fisherman's report of an estimated 50-foot wave seen after dark off the south tip of Kenai Peninsula (lat. 59°07′, long. 151°35′); the wave appeared to emit geysers or smoke. A 28-foot wave hit Perl Island, 35 miles south of Seldovia (fig. 1) at 8:40 p.m. (H. D. Hess, written commun., 1964). Wave action in the general area was also recorded by Jim Reardon, Alaska Department of Fish and Game at Homer, in his radio log (written commun., 1964) as follows: At 10:25 p.m. March 27 Seldovia radio reported the "tide slowly coming in." This rise was 3 hours before the high tide was due at 1:39 a.m. At the same time the radio station at Kasitsna Bay (first bay east of Seldovia, fig. 1) reported that water came in at 40 miles per hour. At 10:28 p.m. Seldovia radio reported "tide coming in fast," and at 10:37 p.m. "water going back out." At 11:15 p.m. Seldovia radio reported "harbor damaged," and at 11:17 p.m. "water coming up fast, estimate 18 feet, going to higher ground." At 11:21 p.m. Seldovia radio said "Water receding" and at 11:55 p.m., "Water down to 12 feet, starting up." Meanwhile Perl Island radio reported a second wave (30 feet) at 11:40 p.m. At 1:40 a.m. March 28 Seldovia radio noted the "tide reached normal high, receding normally." Perl Island radio reported a third wave (30 feet) at 2:30 a.m. At 2:48 a.m. Seldovia radio again reported "water up to 25 feet and receding."

These records of wave action suggest that a tsunami could have arrived about 10:30 p.m. at Seldovia, a second at 11:18 p.m. before the normal high tide arrived, and a third at 2:48 a.m. after the high tide. Halibut Cove (wide bay almost due east of the end of Homer Spit, fig. 1) also reported a tide of 24 feet at 11:35 p.m. which could have been the same one that hit Seldovia at 11:18 p.m. If these waves were tsunamis, Homer would have been hit by them also.

There is some evidence that Homer did indeed experience tsunamis. A. G. Green reported (written commun., 1964) that a 20-foot wave arrived about 9:30 p.m. at Homer. Mr. Jim Reardon reported (H. S. Thompson, oral commun., 1964) overwash at the base of the spit in the late evening. The Inlet Courier [Homer] (Mar. 30, 1964) also reported that at the end of the Homer Spit "Water rose in surges beyond the normal tide heights and covered the floor in the new Porpoise Room. It rose to a height of 4 feet in the Salty Dawg * * * and also covered the floor * * *" of the Land's End Hotel.

The long single wave that was seen to approach Homer from the southwest on the oceanside of the spit may have originated from submarine slumping, p o s s i b l y along the coastline near Seldovia; it may have been an oscillatory wave (seiche); or it may have been the response of the ocean to sudden lowering of the Kenai Peninsula and the floor of Kachemak Bay.

The complex pattern of smaller waves seen in Kachemak Bay perhaps had no relation to tsunamis. More probably these waves were generated by horizontal and vertical movement of the land during the earthquake. Tectonic subsid-

ence also doubtless contributed to the development of the waves in the bay. Alternatively—or additionally—submarine landslides may have contributed to the Kachemak Bay waves. Slumping along the front of the delta lying off Grewingk Glacier (fig. 1) is a likely source of energy for these waves. Tectonic movement probably was the cause of many or even all of the wave phenomena observed at Homer. Furthermore, the larger waves that appeared at intervals probably resulted when the oscillating waves reinforced one another, as is known to happen. It is noteworthy also that most waves be-

came visible only when they traversed the shoals that extend far out from the north shore of Kachemak Bay and Cook Inlet. But the alternative possibilities must be considered as well.

In any event, damage from waves was negligible at Homer for two reasons: (1) the incident waves were small, and (2) the larger waves impinged on the land when the tide was low and an 18-foot tidal freeboard protected the town. If larger waves occur when the tide is high during an earthquake in the future, the damage may be appreciable—especially on Homer Spit.

EFFECTS OF THE EARTHQUAKE

The effects of the earthquake in the Homer area were light compared to the catastrophic effects experienced elsewhere in Alaska. These effects will be considered in four classes: (1) general effects and damage to structures, (2) geologic effects on the mainland, (3) effects on Homer Spit, and (4) hydrologic effects. There is necessarily some overlap and repetition in the discussion.

GENERAL EFFECTS AND DAMAGES

One of the first effects of the shock noticed in Homer was loss of electric power. It was, however, restored in 17 minutes when a standby diesel plant went into operation. Long-distance telephone service was temporarily disrupted, but local service continued. The U.S. Federal Aviation Agency communications cable under Beluga Lake (fig. 2) was broken. Buildings throughout the area were severely shaken but survived, in general, with no damage

or only minor damage. At least five chimneys were knocked down, a few plate-glass windows were broken, and several foundations

3.—Damage to foundation walls of the Inlet Inn Hotel. Unreinforced concrete-block construction.

(fig. 3) and concrete-slab floors were cracked or fissured. Dishes and glassware were broken in many homes and business estab-

4.—Postearthquake erosion at Munson Point as of April 13, 1964. About 5 feet of the overhanging vegetal mat attests to recent erosion of the underlying glacial till as a result of higher water levels relative to land.

lishments. The most severe damage, however, was to the small-boat harbor near the end of Homer Spit. There the outer seawall largely disappeared as a submarine slide removed its foundations. A few small buildings at the distal end of the spit were overturned by falling into another slumped area. Private individuals experienced property losses of about $1,040,000, the sum of 40 applications for Small Business Administration disaster loans (Inlet Courier, June 19, 1964). Total reconstruction costs for Homer are about $2½ million. That sum, however, includes improvement of facilities—especially the small-boat harbor—and is not a reflection of actual damage alone.

Potential suffering and losses that might have resulted from food shortages because of destruction of highway bridges between Anchorage and Homer were averted by airlifts. In particular, airlifted fodder tided over the needs of cat-tlemen caught by the earthquake with a short supply of feed for their animals.

GEOLOGIC EFFECTS ON THE MAINLAND

Changes brought about by the earthquake on the mainland at Homer are of interest principally because they illustrate the types of disruption that under other circumstances have been damaging in other areas. The most far-reaching effect was tectonic subsidence that lowered most of the Kenai Peninsula a few feet relative to sea level (Grantz and others, 1964, fig. 3). This subsidence proved to be most damaging on Homer Spit (p. D7) but had little effect on the mainland other than to expose fresh areas to wave erosion along sea cliffs in the Homer area (fig. 4).

Only one landslide and one earthflow of any consequence occurred near Homer, both in sec. 1, T. 6 S., R. 13 W. (fig. 2). This fact is surprising in view of the incompetent nature of the bedrock and of the thin layer of soil that overlies the rock. The bedrock is described by Barnes and Cobb (1959, p. 224) as "* * * moderately indurated sand, silt and clay in generally thin and intergraded beds and lenses * * *," material that might readily yield to gravity when disturbed by seismic shocks.

The landslide (easternmost in sec. 1, fig. 2) debris covers an area about 600 feet long and 100 feet wide. The material that slid stood previously as a promontory along a bluff eroded into the Kenai Formation. The slide area is near a fault in sec. 2 mapped by Barnes and Cobb (1959, pl. 18), but there is no evidence that this fault moved in 1964. Landslide hazards exist in comparable situations near Homer—and indeed anywhere that promontories extend out from precipitous bluffs and cliffs. Bluff Point, north of Homer (fig. 2) is an example. A field station of the U.S. Bureau of Land Management is situated about 50 feet from the edge of a 700-foot bluff. Numerous fissures (fig. 5) developed during the

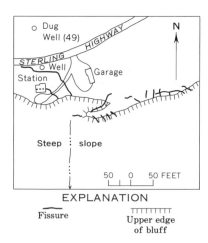

EXPLANATION

Fissure   Upper edge
                   of bluff

5.—Sketch map of the ground-fissure pattern at the U.S. Bureau of Land Management field station near Homer. Traced from field compilation on aerial photograph by K. A. Roddy, U.S. Bureau of Land Management, May 1, 1964.

earthquake on the surface above the bluff, some of them several inches wide. A few could be traced about 20 feet down the bluff face. One earth fissure extended across the area of a field-station building and cracked the basement floor of the structure. Areas above and close below promontories where earthslides might occur must remain suspect as sites for any building.

An earthflow occurred in the first canyon southwest of the landslide (fig. 2); it created a jumbled mass of uprooted trees, mudflows, rafts of soil and vegetation, and collapsed ground. The area of disturbed ground is about 1,000 feet long and has a maximum width of about 400 feet. Horizontal displacement of material within the flow, however, probably did not exceed 200 feet. The material involved consists mainly of silt, some fine sand, and occasional layers of flat pebbles. The head of the flow is near the apex of an alluvial fan at the mouth of a small canyon occupied by an intermittent stream. Water was seeping from both disturbed and undisturbed material on June 21, 1964, and may have contributed to causing the flow.

Two large landslides in the Anchor River valley north of Homer (fig. 1) were seen from the air, and other fresh-looking scars appear on aerial photographs of the north shore of Kachemak Bay, taken after the quake. But whether the slides that caused these features were the result of the earthquake is not known.

The entire Homer area appears to be one where steep slopes, the fine texture and weak consolidation of the rocks of the Kenai Formation, and the common condition of saturation with water favor landslides and earthflows. These hazards should be considered when

locating sites for building, especially because the shaking incidental to earthquakes tends to weaken the cohesion of the rock materials and to cause them to move under the influence of gravity.

Ground fissuring occurred in the Homer area, but as in most other parts of south-central Alaska it was probably not caused by deep bedrock faulting. In general, the fissuring was of minor importance in the Homer area, except for the fissures occurring at the U.S. Bureau of Land Management station and on Homer Spit. Most of the fissures formed on the spit probably were caused by the submarine landslides or compaction. Other fissures were reported at the mouth of Thurston Canyon just west of Fritz Creek in the northeast corner of the study area, but were not checked in the field. These fissures were reportedly so large that a Shetland pony fell into one several days after the earthquake and could not get out.

No fissures formed on the mudflats of the Palmer Creek tidal area near Munson Point (fig. 2) although elsewhere in south-central Alaska such sites were characterized by extensive fissuring. Perhaps the depth of alluvium, estimated at about 200 feet, was not sufficient or the distance from the epicenter was too great for fissuring to develop during the earthquake. Fissuring of unconsolidated material from a seismic wave is a function of distance, topography, and geologic conditions, but thickness of the material probably is important also.

EFFECTS ON HOMER SPIT

The commercial and industrial center of the community is on Homer Spit. The port for both large vessels and small boats is there, and the spit is occupied by a hotel, food-processing plants,

restaurants and bars, and other places of business. The entire spit subsided as a result of the earthquake. Part of the subsidence was tectonic and part—especially at the seaward end—was probably the result of compaction of the unconsolidated gravel that makes up most of the spit. Total subsidence at the end of the spit by June 1965 is reported by the U.S. Coast and Geodetic Survey (oral commun., 1965) to be 5.9 feet. In addition to extensive damage by flooding caused by subsidence, a submarine slide removed most of the seaward side of the small-boat harbor. The heaviest financial losses at Homer, therefore, occurred as a result of earthquake effects on the spit.

In addition to damage to manmade structures, the subsidence caused a change in the physical relations between the spit and the water surrounding it. As a result, the shape of the spit changed and beach stability was disrupted. The phenomena relating to beach changes on Homer Spit are the subject of the section by K. M. Stanley (p. D20). The extent of high-tide flooding of the spit is shown by Stanley (see fig. 15) in a pair of maps that contrast dryland exposure on the spit before and after the earthquake. The devastating flooding on the spit immediately after the quake is further illustrated by figures 6 and 7 (on next page), aerial photographs of the spit taken before and after the earthquake.

Some of the specific damage to structures caused by the flooding may be seen in figure 8 (on next page), which shows the Land's End Hotel elevated on jacks to raise it above the postearthquake high-tide level. Figure 9 (p. D10) shows other scenes of the effects of the high tides. During the high tide of about 19 feet that occurred the night following the earth-

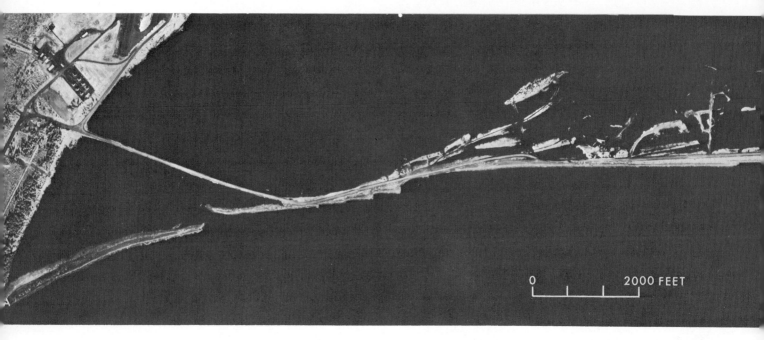

6.—Photomosaic of Homer Spit at high tide on August 8,

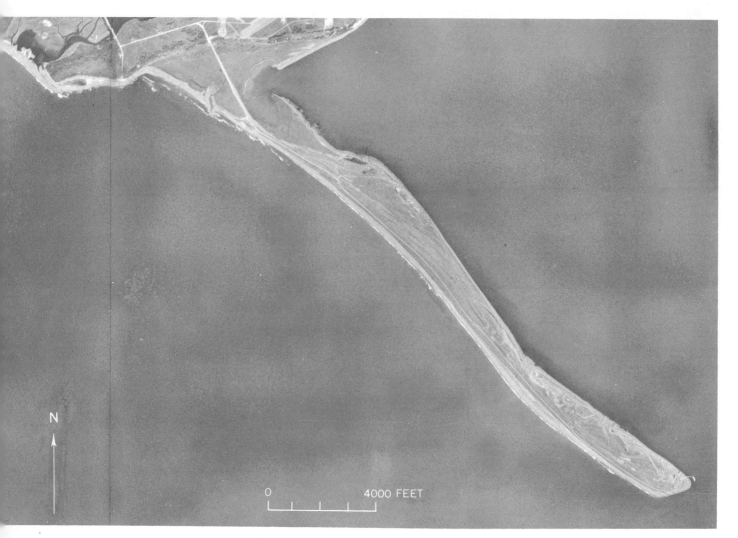

7.—Preearthquake aerial photograph of Homer Spit.

[468]

quake, material salt-water damage was done to the hotel, to the Porpoise Room, the Salty Dawg Saloon, two seafood-processing plants, and the Standard Oil Co. tank farm.

Fortunately the mid-April high tides were not accompanied by strong winds, and most of the facilities survived the first onslaught with only salt-water damage. Some structures that could not be raised on jacks were protected against further flooding by hurriedly built embankments. The only land not inundated at the end of the spit was the storm berm around the perimeter of the spit, older storm berms of the beach, and the spoil pile from the original dredging of the small-boat harbor (fig. 6). The asphalt-covered highway was eroded away near the base of the spit by normal wave action at high tide. The dock had only about 1 foot of freeboard, the oil tanks were in water as much as 6 feet deep, water flowed through the windows of the Salty Dawg, one small warehouse building broke up, and the oil-tank farm warehouse tilted; all this indicated differential subsidence.

It was apparent that, in addition to repairs, remedial measures were needed to avoid future storm-wave damage as well as damage from normal high tides. Such measures were started immediately by some concerns, whereas others awaited aid from the Government, through the Federal Disaster Act, authorized under Public Law 81–875. As of August 30, 1964, the Office of Emergency Planning had authorized reconstruction projects totaling $1,565,000 to replace or rehabilitate public facilities damaged by the earthquake and tides

(Federal Reconstruction and Development Planning Commission for Alaska, 1964, p. 80). The replacement of the Homer dock ($195,000) and a small-boat harbor ($964,200), with more than double the capacity of the old 80-boat harbor, were the principal costs, and construction of both was underway by November 1964. Adverse wind and tide conditions did not occur until late 1964, when wind-driven ice "* * * knocked out part of the new pier now under construction and did further damage to the * * * old pier * * *."

8.—Land's End Hotel jacked up 8 feet to avoid inundation by high tides. View from Homer dock looking west. View during first 20-foot tide. Middle part of hotel not yet raised.

[469]

A   B

C   D

9.—Effects of the high tides submerging the end of Homer Spit on April 12, 1964. *A*, Standard Oil Co. tank farm awash in as as much as 6 feet of water. *B*, Lands End Hotel raised on jacks. *C*, Water rose high enough to flow through the windows of the Salty Dawg Saloon. *D*, New storm berm encroaching on spit southwest of the Land's End Hotel.

(Anchorage Daily Times, Jan. 2, 1965). A subsequent storm with winds of as much as 50 knots from the southwest created heavy surf which churned under Land's End Hotel, but the only damage reported was to the road (Anchorage Daily Times, Feb. 16, 1965). By June 1965 the berm at the end of the spit had migrated about 80 feet.

SUBMARINE LANDSLIDE

Available evidence indicates that one and possibly two submarine landslides occurred at the dis-

tal end of Homer Spit. The loss of the small-boat harbor breakwater was, of course, obvious, but whether only the breakwater slid or whether substantial material from the spit slid with it was not immediately apparent. Indications of another slide were contained in a report that "The area on the shore west of the Salty Dawg collapsed approximately 10 feet." (The Inlet Courier, Mar. 30, 1964, p. 1). An accompanying picture showed this "collapse" and several buildings slumped into it. The area was

covered in a matter of days by a new berm (fig. 9D) that prevented observation.

The writer noticed fissures in the area at the end of the spit on April 12, 1964, during observation of one of the first tidal inundations. The sound of air escaping from the ground was heard and bubbles were seen as the tidewaters overran the spit. The air bubbles occurred in linear patterns near the dock (pl. 1). After the tide receded close examinations of the surface showed three large fissures southwest of Land's End Hotel.

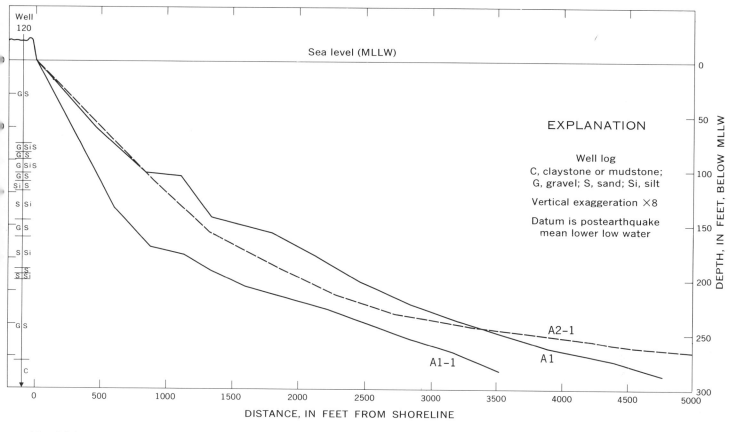

10.—Offshore profiles showing the slope off the end of the Homer Spit.   Lines of profiles plotted on plate 1.   Data from U.S. Army Corps of Engineers.   Profile A1 is the easternmost of the two shown on plate 1.

Other fissures were noted near the Alaskan Seafood plant, along the road, and near the west shore.

The fissures on Homer Spit were plotted (pl. 1) in their approximate locations. Many fissures were somewhat obscured by repeated inundation but, surprisingly, those in vegetated (dune grass) areas were still noticeable several months later. Grantz and others (1964, p. 24) reported that "Many of the fractures had vertical displacement, some as much as 8 inches, with the downdropped side toward the coast," presumably meaning both the bay and the ocean shoreline; hence the material was displaced downward between the fissures and the closest shoreline, a fact which suggests lateral spreading.

The fissures at the end of the spit were possibly related to the known

slip of the breakwater and the collapse of land west of the Salty Dawg Saloon. Offshore bathymetry that might indicate slides also became available. The U.S. Army Corps of Engineers made a bathymetric survey in July 1964 at and adjacent to the small-boat harbor to determine the bottom topography and the displacement of the breakwater remains. The bathymetry (pl. 1) does not extend far enough seaward to show the full extent of the slide nor far enough around the end of the spit to show the supposed second slide. It does, however, show the position of some of the remains of the breakwater. In addition, four lines (pl. 1) were run offshore, each about 5,000 feet long. Three of these profiles are shown on figure 10. The log of test well 120

is also shown (fig. 10) to indicate the seeming coincidence of silty zones beneath the spit with offshore bulges or plateaus on the bathymetric profiles.

Rehabilitation of the Land's End Hotel and other facilities by the expenditure of Federal funds required that the Scientific and Engineering Task Force, established by the Federal Reconstruction and Development Planning Commission, evaluate the risk involved in reconstruction on the spit. The writer supplied data (Federal Reconstruction and Development Planning Commission for Alaska, 1964, p. 53) for the task force on earthquake effects at Homer and pointed out the potential slide danger. Further study of this hazard was requested. Extension of the Corps of Engineers'

[471]

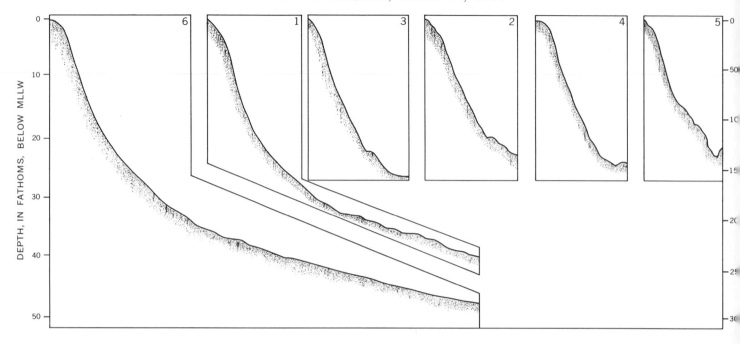

11.—Fathometer profiles showing the slope off the end of Homer Spit. Lines of profiles plotted on plate 1. Line 6 approximates line A2–1 of figure 10.

bathymetric survey was not feasible at the time, so a portable fathometer (used successfully by other Survey geologists in determining subaqueous slides in Kenai Lake and elsewhere) was used to run a few continuous profiles offshore to try to determine slide areas (locations on plate 1). Although the runs were hampered by the writer's inexperience with the instrument, the results are believed to confirm the presence of another slide west of the Land's End Hotel.

The instrument, which measures and continually records the water depths on paper, was carried in a small metal boat powered by an outboard motor. The transducer was set on the floor of the boat in a puddle of water. Experience of previous Survey investigators had indicated that this is convenient and satisfactory for obtaining accurate depth soundings.

The depth soundings were made on August 18, 1964, during low tide and a calm sea. Relative tide-gage readings on the U.S. Coast and Geodetic Survey gage on the Homer dock were 23 feet at the

start of the first traverse and 21.5 feet at the end of the sixth traverse. The predicted low tide preearthquake level of 7.3 feet) occurred just at the end of the last traverse. Hence, a relative sea level of 22 feet was used as an average. The boat was run out an estimated one-half mile, and a line bearing was taken on two prominent shore landmarks. The fathometer was turned on when the boat reached a preset throttle speed of about 3 miles per hour. The recording of each profile was stopped just as the boat touched shore. Although the traverses were run in a straight line, the lengths of the traverses could not be determined with much accuracy. The profiles made by the Corps (pl. 1) were not continuous, so detailed correlation with the writer's profiles (fig. 11) was not possible. The profiles in figure 11 show various irregularities in configuration of the bottom. Humps that are especially prominent on the steeper (profiles 2–5, fig. 11) are interpreted either as recently deposited loose material that has slid down

the slope or as the toes of incipient slides represented by the down-dropped and fissured land on the shore (pl. 1).

Lack of horizontal control precluded contouring the offshore slope in detail, so the Corps of Engineers profile data (pl. 1) was used. The upper foreshore has a slope of about 22 percent, whereas the offshore slopes range from 6 to 12 percent. The contours show part of a scarp extending north-northeast and south-southwest transversely to the spit. The scarp terminates the relatively shallow platform of the Archimandritof Shoals (see fig. 14). The spit has been built onto this platform and extends out into the deep entrance of the bay.

Slope failures off the end of the spit apparently may have occurred, or started to occur, as a downward and outward adjustment—including lateral spreading —controlled by the platform scarp and the slope of the foreset bedding. Terzaghi (1956) indicates that subaqueous slides start by liquefaction of a water-bearing silt layer. Internal hydrostatic pressure can be built up by shock waves until relief occurs by lateral movement of the water and silt. Subsidence and slope failure follows, causing a slump or slide. The breakwater slide had the added factor of a heavy artificial load which contributed to the extended movement of the slide. The possible relation of slide planes to subsurface silt zones has already been mentioned.

SUBSIDENCE

An understanding of the cause of the subsidence of Homer Spit is very important as a guide to future construction. If the geologic conditions of areas that become compacted during high-magnitude earthquakes can be determined, an informed decision can be made on whether or not to build in such areas.

Compaction on Homer Spit is indicated by evidence already mentioned. Further evidence confirming that compaction or lateral spreading, or both, occurred was provided by a resurvey of a highway profile. The Alaska Department of Highways had surveyed

the spit for a new road shortly before the earthquake. They resurveyed the line within a week after the earthquake and found that the spit was lower, principally on the outer end. A plot of the two surveys is shown on figure 12. The line of the profile is along the east side of the Spit road except near the outer end where it angles toward the dock (pl. 1).

The profiles were tied to a bench mark near the airport, which is considered to have been unaffected by compaction. The resurveyed profile shows little change at the landward end and thus supports this conclusion. The tectonic subsidence, of course, lowered the bench-mark area as well as the spit by about 2 feet. The regional tectonic subsidence increases southeastward toward the hinge zone (Plafker, 1965). The subsidence on bedrock at Seldovia is 3.7 feet (U.S. Coast and Geodetic Survey, 1964b, p. 3); hence the tectonic subsidence at Homer should increase toward the end of the spit, possibly by as much as 1 foot.

The total amount of subsidence, including that resulting from compaction or lateral spreading as well as that from tectonic move-

TABLE 1.—*U.S. Coast and Geodetic Survey preliminary bench-mark altitudes on Homer Spit (based on April 1964 tide series)*

Bench mark	Altitude above mean lower low water (feet)		Subsidence (feet)
	Pre-quake	Post-quake	
1	21.81	16.97	4.84
2	22.17	17.25	4.92
3	21.74	[1] 15.16	[1] 6.58
4	22.50	17.71	4.79
5	23.29	[1] 17.53	[1] 5.76
Homer East Base	24.37	[1] 19.48	[1] 4.89

[1] Calculations based on U.S. Coast and Geodetic Survey adjustment factor used on other Homer Spit bench marks.

ments, has been determined at tidal bench marks (table 1) by the U.S. Coast and Geodetic Survey (1964b) and the Alaska Highway Department resurvey. The area of greatest subsidence, about 10 feet, is in the vicinity of the spoil pile formed by excavation of the small-boat harbor. Undoubtedly this material became compacted much more than the natural spit material. However, this area is adjacent to the breakwater slide, and the subsidence may be related to differential compaction or lateral spreading behind the submarine landslide. Release of pore pressure in a compacting silt accompanied the slide, and "progressive liquefaction" could have

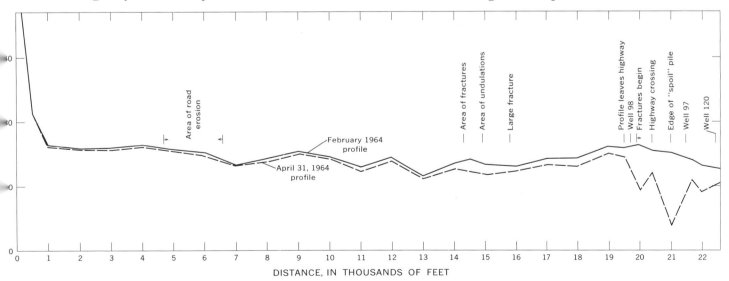

12.—Profiles of Homer Spit surveys by the Alaska Highway Department. Datum is U.S. Bureau of Public Roads temporary bench mark 20, 70.25 feet above (preearthquake) datum. Vertical exaggeration × 200.

extended landward (Terzaghi, 1956).

The conditions indicating differential compaction near the end of the spit may also be related to a submarine landslide. Apparently liquefaction of a water-bearing silt in the material underlying the end of the spit could provide an explanation for the compaction or lateral spreading. The log of well 120 (table 2) shows silty layers at 96–104, 110–123, 130–138, and 140–165 feet which can be correlated with the depths of the anomalous features on the profiles (fig. 11). The earthquake shocks probably liquefied the silt; the liquefaction in turn caused the slope failure and subsidence beyond the scarps. Fortunately, the offshore slopes are not very steep; otherwise an even greater subsidence of the land near shore might have occurred.

An area of the spit about halfway from the mainland (fig. 12) apparently subsided more than adjacent areas. A possible reason for this local difference is suggested by the presence of the adjacent barge harbor. The harbor was recently excavated to a shallow depth to permit barge unloading. The excavation may have provided for the release of water pressure in a metastable formation during the earthquake that caused compaction by progressive liquefaction of some of the silty sediments. Stanley reported postearthquake subsidence in an area south of the groin-protected shore (p. D25). Even the lower high tides flood this area now. Possible causes of postquake subsidence are: (1) the additional diurnal loading of the material in the spit by the high tides, and (2) the gradual release of pore pressure that may have been built up in fine-grained material during the earthquake, and a resultant compression of the material.

TABLE 2.—*Log of well 120. Kachemak Water Co.*

[Drilled and logged by A. H. Thorn]

Material	Thickness (feet)	Depth (feet)
Deposits of Quaternary age:		
Gravel and sand	16	16
Gravel and sand (salt water from here on)	40	56
Sand, coal float, and gravel	6	62
Gravel, large, and sand	5	67
Gravel, small and medium, and sand	25	92
Gravel, large and medium, and sand	4	96
Silt, sand, gravel, and sea shells	8	104
Sand, coarse, and some gravel	6	110
Silt, sand, small gravel, and coal float	13	123
Gravel, large, and sand	2	125
Gravel and sand; some clay	3	128
Sand, coarse, and some gravel	2	130
Sand, fine, and silt	8	138
Gravel and sand	2	140
Silt, fine sand, and coal float	25	165
Gravel, large, and sand	6	171
Sand, medium	3	174
Gravel, large, and sand	8	182
Silt, sand, coal float, and some gravel	15	197
Silt, sand, coal float, and clay "glacial" (hit hard at about 200 ft)	13	210
Sand, fine, and some gravel; solid	3	213
Sandstone, fine	1	214
Silt and sand, fine, blue	6	220
Sand, fine; hard packed	2	222
Sand and some clay; drilled 5 ft ahead	21	243
Sandstone	4	247
Sand, loose, medium; shells	5	252
Silt, sand, and clay chunks	5	257
Sand, clay, and coal float	6	263
Sand and blue clay; increasing clay to 289 (water shut off at 273 ft)	26	289
Silt, sand, coal, and soft clay	4	293
Sand, fine (salt water ends)	1	294
Sand and clay	3	297
Clay, blue, sand and gravel; unit gradually increasing in clay content	24	321
Clay, blue	6	327
Clay, blue; some gravel and gas (flammable)	15	342
Clay, blue, and sand	1	343
Clay, blue, and semiliquid paste sand (salty water rises to 150 ft)	6	349
Clay, soft (drilled ahead, still water)	2	351
Gravel and clay (no water)	15	366
Clay, "marine" (water slow)	18	384
Clay, soft "marine"; gradually getting harder (no water)	33	417
Clay, blue, hard	8	425
Clay, soft, semiliquid	4	429
Sandstone, fine; contains small shells and coal bits	2	431
Clay, soft	31	462
Clay, hard	6	468
Kenai Formation(?)	9	477

NOTE.—The Kenai Formation may have been encountered at 289 ft. The presence of gas below 327 ft suggests the presence of the Kenai Formation.

HYDROLOGIC EFFECTS

Earthquake shock waves affect water bodies at great distances from the epicenters. Surface-water bodies act like inverted pendulums and are set in motion as the land moves under them. Oscillating waves, called seiches, are formed and can, under some circumstances, develop into large waves that may be destructive. Seiches presumably were developed in Kachemak Bay, Beluga Lake, other smaller lakes, in free pools of water in the creeks, and in water tanks in the Homer area. Most of the lakes and streams were ice covered on March 27. Seiches develop in water standing in wells also, but generally they are not noticeable in artesian wells because the seismic waves are compressing and dilating the confined aquifers and are thus causing a much greater effect on the water in the casing. These surges in artesian wells are usually not noted unless water is forced out of the well or the motion is recorded instrumentally.

At Homer, most of the observed hydrologic effects of the March 1964 earthquake were neglible. Many possible effects cannot be ascertained because few hydrologic data had been collected in the area before the quake.

IMMEDIATE EFFECTS

The most noticeable effect of the earthquake on the hydrology of Homer was the breaking of ice and seiching of water in Beluga Lake. Presumably the other small lakes and ponds in the area reacted similarly. At Beluga Lake, nearshore ice was broken by compression and overriding, and the rest of the ice was broken in random patterns. The north and south shores apparently had the most overridden ice. The ice was not broken as much along the west shore, which is formed by the highway (fig. 2). However, this western section of the lake is probably the deepest part or has the steepest nearshore lake-bottom gradient; either characteristic would tend to reduce the overriding effect. Natural and artificial lakes in other areas appeared to show preferred directions of ice breakage related to the direction of the earthquake-wave propagation (Grantz and others, 1964, p. 6).

Streams were near their lowest annual flow and had their thickest cover of ice at the time of the earthquake. All streams in this area are small and have narrow flood plains. Hence, very few effects on streams were noted by residents.

Increased or decreased stream discharge could not be determined because of lack of appropriate records. The only evidence that might indicate a greater discharge is the level of Beluga Lake. Four measurements made at the lake outlet in the May–August 1964 period showed that the lake level was averaging 2–3 feet higher than comparable periods in 1962 and 1963. This higher level may have been due to increased discharge of the escarpment streams feeding the lake.

A temporary increase in sediment load probably resulted from landslides and rockfalls in the canyons along the escarpment; in May extremely silt-laden flows of the streams occurred. Precipitation in April and May was about average. Analogy with daily observations on a stream near Palmer (Waller, 1966) indicates that the increased sediment load probably lasted about a month. As soon as all the finer material of the slide debris was washed away, the streams resumed their normal erosive pattern. The sediment load presumably was carried to the lower reaches of the streams. Bear Creek and five lesser streams deposit their sediment loads in Beluga Lake.

The immediate effects on the ground water included a few failures of domestic water-well systems and muddied or turbid well or spring water. There were no water-level recorders on wells in the Homer area, but the observed movement of the land, the effects noted above, and observations elsewhere (Plafker, 1965; Waller and others, 1965) indicate with certainty that ground water in the Homer area was affected by the earth tremors. These effects are shown by residual changes of water levels in wells which had records of water-level measurements extending back to 1962 (fig. 13, next page).

The failures of some of the well systems resulted from sanding or silting of the pump due to agitation of the wells and differential movement of well casings and the surrounding rock. Most of the wells are unscreened and have 1 to several feet of uncased hole (Waller, 1963, table 1). These conditions readily lend themselves to caving or slumping of the walls under earthquake stress. Hence, pumps turned on or automatically activated when electric power was restored pumped this material into the system and caused turbid water or malfunction of the pump. Other wells that have pumps requiring a full pipe of water for a prime probably lost their prime owing to surging in the well. Thus, reports of dry wells were common, as they usually are after most earthquakes.

Water quality is and has been a serious problem at Homer. The various aquifers differ from one another in chemical quality of the water. Gas is present in the water at many places. Temporary changes in water quality at Homer are probably related to turbidity, whereas any permanent changes that might be noticed later may be due to leakage between aquifers along loosened well casings. The stresses may also have caused local increases in fractures or permeability

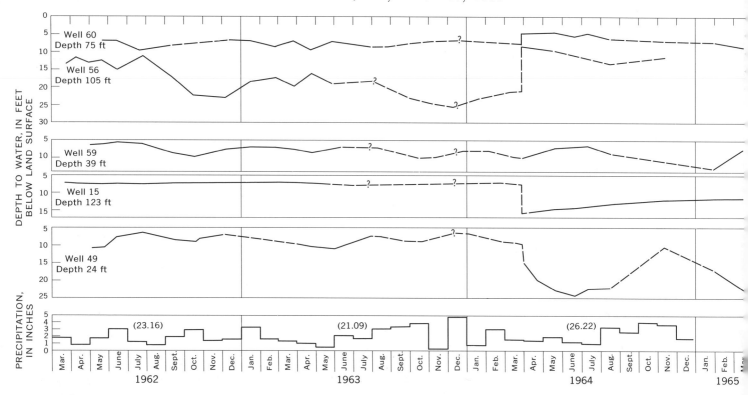

13.—Hydrographs of five Homer wells showing long-term effects of the earthquake.   Locations of wells shown on figure 2.

which would allow interchange of aquifer waters.

Many wells were reported to have become dry because of the earthquake, but only two of these reports were verified. One well (No. 99, fig. 2) was checked by the local driller who reported (A. H. Thorn, oral commun., July 11, 1964) that the well was "bone dry" and when he poured two pails of water in the well "they drained right out." Mr. Thorn also reported that other wells had sanded up and that one near Bluff Point lost most of its yield. This location is near the bluff, and the water level probably fell because of increased discharge from the aquifer through a fracture in the bluff. All the affected wells obtain water from sand in the Kenai Formation. The gradual loss of water in the other well verified dry is discussed on page D17.

LONG-TERM EFFECTS

Long-term hydrologic effects of earthquakes include increased or decreased stream discharge, increased sediment loads of streams, aggradation or buildup of stream channels resulting from lowered land surfaces, changes in water quality, and residual changes in water levels in wells. The only quantitative data available at Homer relate to water-level changes in wells. An observation-well network was maintained from March 1962 until August 1963 to aid in studying the ground-water hydrology of the area. Data on stream flow consisted of only a few random discharge measurements, and data on sediment load of streams were nonexistent. Data on the quality of ground water, on the other hand, were available for many places (Waller, 1963, table 3), but no long-term changes in

water quality appear to have occurred except in a shallow aquifer on Homer Spit.

GROUND WATER

Long-term changes in water levels in wells at Homer were indicated by residual changes from prequake levels. These residuals, whether permanent or semipermanent, indicate changes in the physical structure of the aquifers. Such residual changes in artesian pressure as a result of other earthquakes have been reported (Piper, 1933; Leggette and Taylor, 1935; Piper and others, 1939; Thomas, 1940; LaRocque, 1941; Brown and Ayer, 1948; Tsuya, 1950; Davis and others, 1955; Ferris and others, 1955; Swenson, 1964.) Many of the authors cited also discussed the mechanisms involved in causing the changes. In brief, residual changes are caused by a change in aquifer-pore space created by rearrangement of grains or fractures as a result of the release or development of stress or strain imposed by an earthquake.

Of the 19 Homer wells for which previous periodic water-level observations were made, 15 were remeasured during 1964. The first two rounds of postearthquake measurements showed three wells in which water levels were unchanged, four in which water levels were higher, and eight in which water levels were lower than before the quake. These residual changes, some of which may be permanent, show no apparent correlation with location on the upland, bench, or lowland, nor with Tertiary versus Quaternary aquifers. Because the first measurements were not made until 9 days after the earthquake, the extremes of change are not known.

The hydrographs of the five wells previously used for observation that showed the largest residual changes in water levels are plotted in figure 13. The hydrograph for the 8-month period before March 27, when no water levels were determined, is estimated on the basis of the earlier records and depends on the writer's knowledge of hydrologic conditions at Homer and on correlative seasonal control by measurements in wells in the Matanuska Valley and Anchorage.

The record for well 49, dug on the escarpment near Bluff Point (fig. 2), is of special interest. The well is 24 feet deep and is unused; it taps an unconfined aquifer. The water level in the well dropped steadily for about 3 months after the earthquake. The June measurement found only moist mud at the bottom of the well; thus the water level dropped at least 9 feet and possibly as much as 14 feet. In July the water level made a recovery, and a complete recovery

was finally shown, nearly 8 months after the quake, by the November measurement. However, the 1965 winter measurements showed a decline that did not occur in preceding winter periods, but one that is comparable to the postearthquake decline.

Well 49 probably taps a local water body perched on virtually impermeable Tertiary rock. This impermeable layer fractured, probably minutely from surface fissures, and allowed the perched water to drain slowly downward or laterally toward a nearby topographic low. Recharge from summer and fall precipitaton exceeded the percolation rate and allowed the water to accumulate to its former level. As winter frost developed and inhibited recharge, the water table again fell, but to a lower level than previously, attesting to an increase in permeability of at least a nearby part of the Tertiary rocks. Surface fissures were not noticed in the heavily grass-covered area, but numerous fissures were seen nearby (fig. 5). The behavior of this well and the local conditions are similar to those of a well described by Brown and Ayer (1948).

Well 15 on the lowland bench (fig. 2) also shows a change that is obviously due to the earthquake. It is a 123-foot drilled unused well tapping an artesian aquifer in sand of Tertiary age (Waller, 1963). The casing reportedly extends to 123 feet and is open ended. The water level in this well had not varied more than 0.6 foot in the 2 years of measurements before the earthquake. The water level in this well was displaced downward more than 8 feet when measured on April 5, 9 days after the earthquake. Subsequent measurements show a steady rise, and full recovery to

preearthquake levels may be achieved in time.

The hydrograph for well 56 shows an immediate residual rise of about 12½ feet, perhaps because compaction of the aquifer caused decreased permeability and a higher static head. The persistence of the higher water level may be a result of decreased use during the summer of 1964. The well is normally used to supply water by tank truck to the Land's End Hotel during the summer tourist season, but the hotel's "face lifting" during the 1964 season cancelled the need for a fresh-water supply. Well 60 also shows a rise that may be due to seismic causes, such as a decrease in porosity of the sand aquifer. Well 59, as indicated by the hydrograph, showed little or no effect from the earthquake.

One well on East Hill Road near East Road should be mentioned for the record. Measurements, started soon after the well was drilled in 1963, showed a water level of about 30 feet in this 121-foot drilled well which taps an artesian aquifer in rocks of Tertiary age. Three measurements in the period from June 1964 to March 1965 show a water level of about 61 feet. The well owner reported that he had installed an automatic clothes washer and used it heavily in the interim between the 1963 and 1964 measurements. The lower water level in 1964 probably reflects the new conditions imposed on the well by relatively continuous withdrawals and not a 30-foot drop resulting from the earthquake.

In summary, some aquifers in the Homer area apparently were disturbed by the earthquake, but most show a gradual return to preearthquake conditions, insofar as these conditions are reflected by water levels in the wells.

QUALITY OF WATER

Changes in quality of water obtained from wells were not noticed by residents of the area, so no water samples were taken for chemical analysis.

A change in quality of the ground water on the spit was made apparent, however, by the death of the evergreen trees at the campground (fig. 2). The low knoll at the campground is probably inundated by extreme high tides that contaminate the thin lens of fresh water available for the trees prior to the earthquake. A thinning of the lens because of subsidence is also a possibility. A dug well at Munson Point reportedly was also salty after the earthquake but the water became fresh by late summer.

SEISMIC HISTORY AND CONCLUSIONS

Homer residents are quite used to earthquake shocks; however, no written history is known of the earthquakes recorded or felt in the area since it was settled about 1888. Heck and Eppley (1958) and Davis and Echols (1962) have compiled lists of Alaskan earthquakes from which the writer has excerpted data on the location, date, and time of earthquakes of magnitude 5 or greater that had a reported effect at Homer or that occurred within a radius of about 100 miles of Homer (table 3). It is hoped that this compilation may encourage a more complete recording of such events, possibly by local residents from local archives. The table shows that the earliest known major earthquake near the Homer area occurred in 1883 at nearby Augustine Island.

There have been four earthquakes of magnitude 6.75–7.75 within a radius of 100 miles of Homer. Two earthquakes at or near Homer had intensities of V to VI on the Modified Mercalli scale.

There is evidence of a large landslide at Bluff Point which may have been set off by a prehistoric earthquake. Barnes and Cobb (1959, pl. 2) mapped the low bench beneath the bluff as a landslide deposit. Karlstrom (1964), however, mapped the same bench as a moraine of Naptowne age, but noted (p. 47) that the moraine is covered by landslide debris during a "sudden impulse" of deposition. In previous fieldwork (U.S. Geological Survey unpub. data) the writer noted the material as landslide debris also but followed Karlstrom's mapping scheme. The discussion above seems warranted to point out the potential of the bluffs—particularly the 700-foot Bluff Point—to slide if a major earthquake occurs close to Homer in the future (fig. 16).

Perhaps of greatest importance to Homer is the potential of future tsunamis acting upon Homer Spit. The 1883 volcanic eruption and(?) earthquake (Dall, 1884) created a wave that undoubtedly hit and probably overtopped the Homer Spit. The reports from Port Graham (fig. 1) observers stated (Dall, 1884, p. 92–93) that an estimated 30-foot wave rolled in at 8:30 a.m. after they had seen and heard the volcano on Augustine Island erupt. The wave deluged houses on the lowland and washed boats and canoes away, even though the tide was "extremely low." Other waves of lesser height followed the first one. It seems certain that these waves were tsunamis and that they struck the Homer Spit also. Evidently, tsunamis that would hit Homer could only be generated from a seismic disturbance in the lower Cook Inlet area because of Homer's somewhat sheltered location from the open sea. Seiches, however, can develop with any major earthquake in the region and can be destructive if they coincide with high tide.

Submarine landslides, usually, but not always, generated by earthquakes, are another potential hazard at the distal end of Homer Spit. Thus extensive building on the outer end of the spit seems very unwise.

TABLE 3.—*Summary of larger earthquakes occurring within about 100 miles of the Homer area in the period 1788–1961*

Date	Local time	Approximate location (lat. N.; long. W.)	Estimated magnitude (Richter scale)	Remarks
Oct. 6, 1883	0800	Augustine Island (59°, 154°).	----------	Volcanic activity; seismic wave struck Port Graham.
Aug. 1898	------	South-central Alaska-----	----------	Trees swayed violently at Susitna Station.
July 11, 1899	------	Tyonek (61°, 152°)------	----------	Severe.
Oct. 7, 1900	------	-----do------------------	----------	Severe. Probably is same as following one.
Oct. 9, 1900	0216	South-central Alaska-----	----------	Severe, felt at Seldovia.
Dec. 30–31, 1901.	------	Kenai--------------------	----------	Volcanic eruption and several sea waves.
Sept. 19, 1909	1000	Kenai Peninsula---------	----------	Strong at Seward.
Sept. 21, 1911	0701	Prince William Sound and Kenai Peninsula (60.5°, 149°).	6. 9	Severe, felt at Kenai Lake.
Dec. 9, 1927	------	South-central Alaska-----	----------	Kenai Lake severely shaken by three quakes.
Jan. 27, 1931	0429	-----do------------------	5–6	Cracked walls in Seward.
Oct. 6, 1932	0705	Homer--------------------	----------	Awakened all.
Apr. 26, 1933	1703	Susitna Flats (61.25°, 150.5°).	----------	At Homer, worst shock in 15 years.
May 13, 1933	------	Old Tyonek--------------	----------	Severe, some damage.
June 13, 1933	0219	Northeast of Nikishki (61°, 151°).	6. 25	
June 17, 1934	2314	Soldatna (60.5°, 151°)----	6. 75	
Oct. 10, 1940	2153	Mouth of Kachemak Bay (59.5°, 152°).	6	
July 29, 1941	1551	Northeast of Nikishki (61°, 151°).	6. 25	Damage at Anchorage.
Dec. 5, 1942	0428	Mouth of Kachemak Bay (59.5°, 152°).	6. 25	
Sept. 27, 1949	0530	Blying Sound (59.75°, 149°).	7	Strong aftershock also. Damage at Seward and Anchorage.
June 25, 1951	0612	Chickaloon Bay (61°, 150°).	6. 25	Damage at Anchorage.
Oct. 3, 1954	0118	Caribou Hills (60°, 151°)-	6. 5–7	Damage at Homer.
Jan. 24, 1958	1317	North-northwest of Anchor Point (60°, 152°).	6. 25–6. 5	
Mar. 19, 1959	0503	South of Perl Island (58.6°, 152°).	6. 25	
June 4, 1959	0231	50 miles W of Homer (59.5°, 153°).	5. 5	
Dec. 26, 1959	0819	Stariski Creek (59.9°, 151.7°).	6. 25	
Sept. 5, 1961	0134	Bradley Lake (59.8°, 150.6°).	6–6. 25	Felt. Anchorage rocked.
Sept. 24, 1961	1627	North of Mount Iliamna (60.3°, 153°).	5. 75–6	

BEACH CHANGES ON HOMER SPIT

By Kirk W. Stanley, Alaska Department of Natural Resources

INTRODUCTION

Homer Spit is a well-known landmark on the Kenai Peninsula along the east shore of lower Cook Inlet (fig. 14). Along with its growing popularity as a recreational area, the spit provides one of the few deep-water ice-free ports along the east side of Cook Inlet. During the earthquake of March 27, 1964, the general area subsided tectonically, and the spit is now lower by 4.26–5.70 feet and is nearly 70 percent covered during the higher tides (fig. 15). The relatively higher stand of the sea upon the spit has caused changes in shore processes and beach morphology which are still in progress.

GENERAL SETTING

Homer Spit, about 4 miles long and as wide as 1,500 feet, lies partially athwart the entrance of Kachemak Bay on a shallow shelf called Archimandritof Shoals. In plan the spit resembles a scimitar, with its curved blade pointing seaward and its narrow hilt attached to the mainland (fig. 15). The spit is composed largely of medium gravel, or shingle, intermixed with some sand. Although Homer Spit is considered by Karlstrom (1964, p. 20) to be a relic glacial feature, the old lateral beach ridges upon the surface clearly illustrate that the spit is, at least in its present form, a product of littoral processes. The old beach ridges, moreover, indicate that the spit widened from east to west. During the past few decades, however, the west side of the spit has receded slightly eastward near the base.

The source area of material composing the Homer Spit is probably the mainland to the west. The shoreline there is characterized by wave-cut bluffs composed of partially consolidated coal-bearing shale and sandstone (fig. 16). After the earthquake and subsidence, shoreline erosion in the source area increased and much new material has entered the sea and the littoral drift.

The net direction of the littoral drift along the Cook Inlet side of the spit is southeast, whereas along the bay side it is probably northwest. The maximum calculated wave height along the outside beach is about 10 feet, and along the bay side, about 4 feet. The tides are of the mixed type; two lows and two highs occur

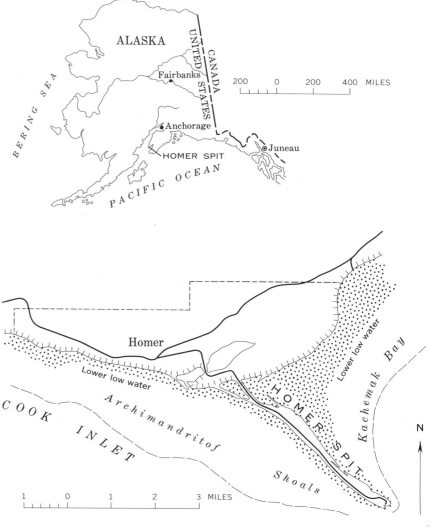

14.—Index map of Homer Spit.

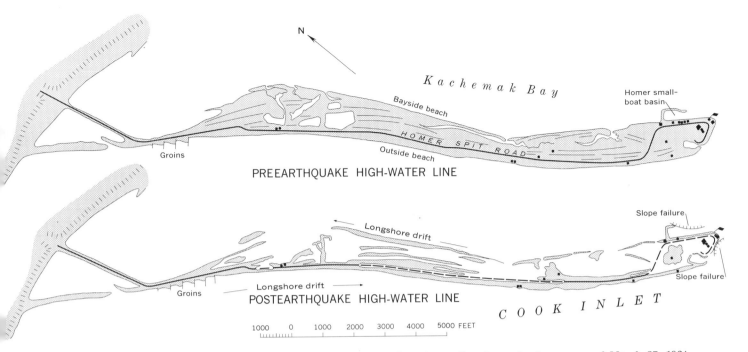

15. Comparison of the high-water line along Homer Spit before and after the earthquake and submergence of March 27, 1964. Light lines on Spit represent old beach berms. High-water line traced from U.S. Army Corps of Engineers aerial photographs, September 1959, and from U.S. Bureau of Land Management infrared photographs, August 1964.

16.—Shoreline west of Homer Spit, probably the source area of material composing the spit.

daily. The maximum tidal range is about 23 feet.

The beach along the spit can be conveniently subdivided into an upper and a lower foreshore. The upper foreshore along both sides of the spit slopes from 1:00 to 1:20, but it steepens to about 1:8 at the seaward, or distal, end. A storm, or frontal, berm forms the beach crest, but because the berm is higher than the old beach ridges along the interior, the spit is slightly basin shaped.

The plunge zone separating the upper and lower foreshore is 100–300 feet seaward of the beach crest and is generally marked along the outside beach by a conspicuous accumulation of cobbles at about the 10-foot level. Seaward of the plunge zone the lower foreshore is characterized by broad sandbars along the outside beach, and by wide silty mudflats along the bay side. The lower foreshore slopes as little as 1:150, but along both sides the slope gradually steepens and the width narrows toward the distal end of the spit where the slope of the lower foreshore steepens to as much as 1:10.

SUBSIDENCE AND POST-EARTHQUAKE CHANGES

The Homer area, including Homer Spit, subsided during the earthquake, as did other regions of south-central Alaska. However, the U.S. Coast and Geodetic Survey has not published final figures confirming the actual drop. The figures released to date are based on short-term tide gage readings and first-order leveling from Anchorage. These data show that the total subsidence, including regional subsidence, measured at the end of Homer Spit, ranges from 4.26 to 5.70 feet.

The spit in subsiding apparently underwent progressive, but not

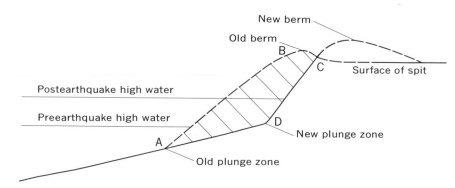

17.—Beach-face recession diagram showing the preearthquake upper foreshore slope (line *AB*) and the postearthquake slope (line *CD*). After subsidence, material within *ABCD*, as a result of the higher water level, was scoured and in part carried onto the spit where it formed a new frontal berm.

18.—Storm berm developed along spit within 6 months after subsidence. Berm before subsidence was less than 3 feet high and 4–5 feet wide at the base.

uniform, consolidation and compaction of sediments from the landward to the distal end. To determine how much the spit proper had subsided, the Alaska Department of Highways (1964, p. 8) made a resurvey of the spit soon after the earthquake. The control used for the survey was an existing U.S. Coast and Geodetic Survey bench mark on the mainland. The survey showed the distal end of the spit to be 2.5 feet lower, rela-

tive to this bench mark, than it was prior to the earthquake. Early evidence indicated that the spit subsided progressively from the landward to the distal end, however, much of the subsidence due to compaction apparently occurred at the distal end (see p. D13).

At least one beach slope failure, or submarine landslide, and possibly others (p. D10), occurred at the distal end of the spit (fig. 15). There is no direct evidence of slope failures elsewhere. Instead, the changes and alterations of the beach along the Homer Spit are related to slow shore processes that can be attributed to: (1) the ability of storm waves to act higher upon the beach face and (2) the increased quantity of material carried to and deposited along the spit by the littoral drift.

BERM DEVELOPMENT AND BEACH-FACE RECESSION

Immediately after subsidence the relative higher stand of the sea resulted in erosion and the consequent recession of the upper beach face. A large part of the material eroded from the face was carried onto the spit where it formed a new storm or frontal berm. The most conspicuous berm development is along sections of the outside beach. The process of berm development and beach-face recession is shown by figure 17. The relative higher water level has shifted the plunge zone shoreward and caused material within area ABCD of figure 17 to be scoured by wave action. Part of the scoured material is transported onto the spit by the swash and accumulates as a new berm.

As an illustration of berm growth, the preearthquake berm at the distal end of the spit was less than 3 feet high, and 4–5 feet wide at the base. Six months after the earthquake, the berm, as shown by figure 18, had built up to 6 feet in height and had widened to nearly 60 feet. The same berm after another 6-month period had widened an additional 20 feet. Elsewhere the berm has migrated around buildings and covered and blocked roads.

The size of the new berm is not in proportion to material lost from, nor to the recession of, the adjacent beach face. Figure 19

19.—Photographs taken 6 months after subsidence (top) and a year after subsidence (bottom) show that the size of frontal berm is not proportional to the recession of the beach face.

shows an example of this disparity. Such examples show that a large part of the material scoured from the beach face was was not carried onto the spit and deposited as part of the berm. According to King (1959, p.

280), most of the scoured material is carried seaward and is lost. To what extent this is true along Homer Spit is not known. However, the absence of noticeable new shingle along the lower foreshore fails to support the conten-

[483]

tion that any appreciable material is migrating toward the sea. More likely, the bulk of material scoured from any one section of the beach has merely drifted farther along the beach. Material drifted to the distal end and not deposited on the beach there is probably lost to the sea.

The entire beach face along the spit has retreated, but not uniformly so. The most noticeable recession is along the outside beach where local areas show a loss of nearly 30 feet, but 10–15 feet probably approximates the overall average. The maximum beach-face recession was about 56 feet and occurred along one limited section at the distal end of the spit.

MATERIAL SUPPLY AND TRANSPORT

Subsidence has ushered in what can be loosely described as a new cycle of shoreline erosion. As a result of accelerated erosion in the source area, much additional material has entered the littoral drift and migrated to the spit. The quantity of material now being transported by the littoral drift can only be estimated, but it clearly exceeds the quantity carried before the earthquake. For example, observations of groins along the spit (fig. 15) indicate that about 1 month after subsidence the fill behind the groins began to enlarge noticeably. The 1-month lag apparently represents the time required for material to enter the drift and migrate from the source area to the spit.

As more material is eroded from the source area and migrates to the spit, it replaces and augments that lost by scour from the beach face. Moreover, the frontal berm has grown in height and width to the extent that after 1 year it is overtopped by only the stronger storm swashes. Thus, although

20.—Section removed from seaward end of groin to allow bypassing of material.

21.—Erosion on the lee side of the last of a series of four groins, a few days after the earthquake.

more material has become available to the spit, less is carried onto the frontal berm and a larger amount remains upon the beach face. As a result, the outside beach is beginning to build, particularly along the outer two-thirds of its length.

Only a minor quantity of material migrates from the outside beach around the end of the spit to the bay side. Moreover, since sub-

22.—The same area as shown in figure 21, 1 year later, after construction of two new groins (right background).

23.—Cobble-filled baskets placed on beach face to prevent erosion.

SHORE PROTECTION WORKS

Erosion, always a problem along the exposed side of the spit near its base, was controlled in one area prior to the earthquake by four timber groins (fig. 15). Shortly after the earthquake the fill between the groins was eroded and the face receded, but after 1 month additional material accumulated and the fill exceeded the preearthquake level. Because the groins were adequately protecting the shoreline, additionally entrapped material served only to deplete the amount moving along the beach. Therefore, to allow bypassing but still preserve the existing fill, a 50-foot section near the end of the last two groins was removed (fig. 20). Some loss of fill occurred, but in general the slope of the fill adjusted to the new conditions. However, erosion on the downdrift or lee side of the last groin became critical. The eroding area on the lee side of the groin is shown by figure 21, taken a few days after the earthquake. To protect the lee side, two additional groins were constructed. Figure 22, taken 1 year after the earthquake, shows the extent of accretion in that area.

Prior to the earthquake, old car bodies were placed along one eroding section on the exposed side of the spit, and they provided some protection. Within a few weeks after subsidence, however, the larger waves scattered the car bodies about the beach.

At one location a small cannery was endangered by undermining. Specially manufactured and prefabricated wire baskets were filled with cobbles and placed along the beach face (fig. 23). After 1 year the beach has built up and has shown no tendency to scour in front of the cobble-filled baskets.

sidence the flooding of the low areas along the bay side at high tide separates the beach into relatively short sections. Material that does find its way around the spit or is scoured from the bay-side beach face is obstructed in its longshore migration by these numerous inlets. The bay-side beach therefore is gradually wasting (Stanley and Grey, 1963, p. 5), a condition also evident before the earthquake.

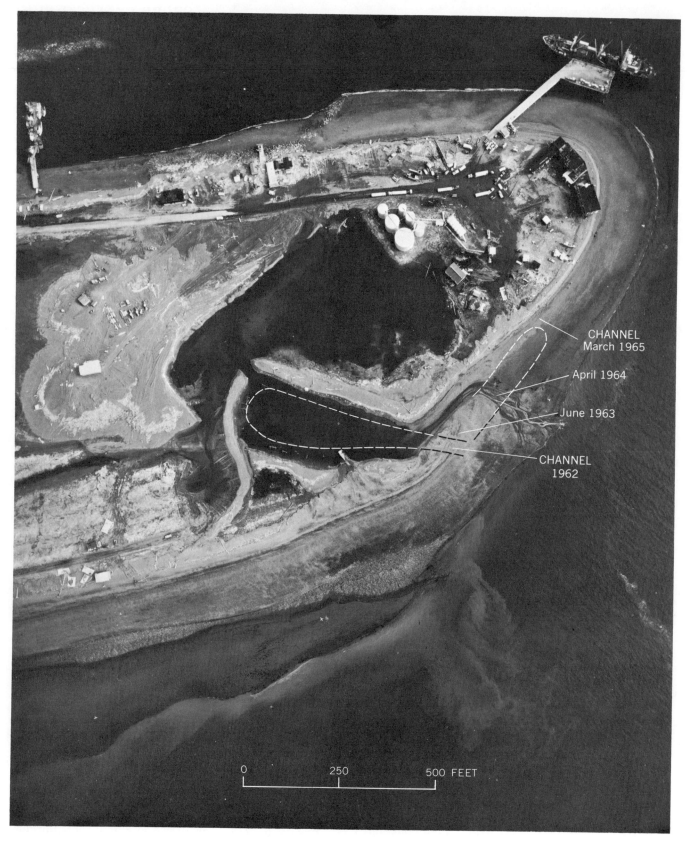

24.—Bar being built across the entrance of a tidal inlet at distal end of Homer Spit.   Photograph by U.S. Army Corps of Engineers, April 30, 1964.

TIDAL INLETS

Since the earthquake and subsidence, more water enters and leaves the tidal inlets on each tidal change. During the flood tide, material drifting along the beach is deflected inward toward the basin, whereas on the ebb tide the outflow tends to deflect the material seaward. As a result, the tidal entrances tend to interrupt longshore drifting.

Some of the finer material migrates into the tidal entrances, and considerable sand and silt are being deposited in each basin. The coarser material tends to be deposited near the entrances where it forms deltalike features. As the delta features enlarge, they tend to further obstruct material drifting along the beach by promoting additional deposition or by deflecting the drift seaward.

A somewhat different situation has developed at the tidal entrance on the distal end of the spit (fig. 24). There the increased rate of deposition brought about by the added load of material in the littoral drift has caused a bar to build outward from the updrift side across the original tidal entrance. As the bar has enlarged, the entrance channel has gradually shifted toward the downdrift side. Deprived of natural increase by the bar, the downdrift side of the channel is gradually wasting.

SUMMARY

Prior to the earthquake, Homer Spit had probably attained a stage of maturity. Active erosion along the landward third of the spit on the Cook Inlet side reflected an absence or scarcity of nourishment from the source area. Material, while accreting along the outer two-thirds of the spit, was partially derived from the landward third. The growth rate of the spit may therefore have been declining through a lack of adequate material supply.

Following subsidence the upper beach face along the spit was eroded and receded. But regional subsidence also accelerated erosion in the source area—the mainland adjacent to the spit. More material thus began to enter the littoral drift and migrate to the spit. This added material has tended to offset the loss of material eroded from the beach face along the spit following subsidence.

The increased supply of material is not likely to decline appreciably for many years, and eventually the frontal berm will, if not artificially disturbed, achieve a height sufficient to prevent overtopping by all but the larger storm swashes. As the process of deposition continues, the beach along the Cook Inlet side, especially along the outer two-thirds of the spit, will gradually widen. Along the bay side, the beach face will probably recede further, and its stability will depend, in part, on the type and location of artificial improvements that may obstruct longshore drifting.

Subsidence has not materially altered the nature of shore processes along the spit; instead it has merely accelerated their rate. Therefore, the lasting effect of subsidence upon the spit (excluding flooding) will be the accentuation of deposition along the beach on the Cook Inlet side and continued erosion and gradual wasting of the beach along the bay side of the spit.

REFERENCES CITED

Alaska Department of Highways, 1964, Homer Spit: Alaska Dept. Highways Reconn. Rept. Proj. F–021–(14), 16 p.

Barnes, F. F., and Cobb, E. H., 1959, Geology and coal resources of the Homer district, Kenai coal field, Alaska: U.S. Geol. Survey Bull. 1058–F, p. 217–260.

Brown, R. H., and Ayre, G. R., 1948, Upstate New York in Water levels and artesian pressure in observation wells in the United States in 1945, pt 1, Northeastern States: U.S. Geol. Survey Water-Supply Paper 1023, p. 191–195.

Dall, W. H., 1884, A new volcano island in Alaska: Science, v. 3, no. 51, p. 89–93.

Davis, G. H., Worts, G. F., Jr., and Wilson, H. D., Jr., 1955, Water-level fluctuations in wells, in Earthquakes in Kern County, California, during 1952: California Div. Mines Bull. 171, p. 99–106.

Davis, T. N., and Echols, Carol, 1962, A table of Alaskan earthquakes, 1788–1961: Alaska Univ. Geophys. Inst. Geophys. Research Rept. 8 [UAG–R113], 43 p.

Federal Reconstruction and Development Planning Commission for Alaska, 1964, Response to disaster, Alaskan earthquake, March 27, 1964: Washington, U.S. Govt. Printing Office, 84 p.

Ferris, J. G., Knowles, D. B., Brown, R. H., and Stallman, R. W., 1962, Ground-water hydraulics—Theory of aquifer tests: U.S. Geol. Survey Water-Supply Paper 1536–E, p. 69–174.

Grantz, Arthur, Plafker, George, and Kachadoorian, Reuben, 1964, Alaska's Good Friday earthquake, March 27, 1964, a preliminary geologic evaluation: U.S. Geol. Survey Circ. 491, 35 p.

Heck, N. H., and Eppley, R. A., 1958, Earthquake history of the United States, pt. 1: Revised ed., U.S.

Coast and Geod. Survey serial 41–1, 80 p.

Karlstrom, T. N. V., 1964, Quaternary geology of the Kenai Lowland and glacial history of the Cook Inlet region, Alaska : U.S. Geol. Survey Prof. Paper 443, 69 p.

King, C. A. M., 1959, Beaches and coast : London, E. Arnold, 403 p.

LaRocque, G. A., Jr., 1941, Fluctuation of water level in wells in the Los Angeles Basin, California, during five strong earthquakes, 1933–1940 : Am. Geophys. Union Trans., v. 22, p. 374–386.

Leggette, R. M., and Taylor, G. H., 1935, Earthquakes instrumentally recorded in artesian wells : Seismol. Soc. America Bull., v. 25, no. 2, p. 169–175.

Piper, A. M., 1933, Fluctuations of water surface in observation wells and at stream-gaging stations in the Mokelumne area, California, during the earthquake of December 20, 1932 : Am. Geophys. Union Trans., 14th Ann. Mtg., p. 471–475.

Piper, A. M., Gale, H. S., Thomas, H. E., and Robinson, T. W., 1939, Geology and ground-water hydrology of the Mokelumne area, California : U.S.

Geol. Survey Water-Supply Paper 780, 230 p.

Plafker, George, 1965, Tectonic deformation associated with the 1964 Alaska earthquake : Science, v. 148, no. 3678, p. 1675–1687.

Stanley, K. W., 1965, Effects of post-earthquake conditions on the Homer Spit, Alaska, in Science in Alaska, 1964 : Alaskan Sci. Conf., 15th, College, Alaska, 1964, Proc., p. 89–90.

Stanley, K. W., and Grey, H. J., 1963, Beach erosion study of the Homer Spit and adjoining shoreline, Alaska : Alaska Dept. Natural Resources Prelim. Rept., 12 p.

Swenson, F. A., 1964, Ground-water phenomena associated with the Hebgen Lake earthquake : U.S. Geol. Survey Prof. Paper 435–N, p. 159–165.

Terzaghi, Karl, 1956, Varieties of submarine slope failures : Texas Conf. Soil Mechanics and Found. Eng., 8th, September 1956, Proc., 41 p.

Thomas, H. E., 1940, Fluctuation of ground-water levels during the earthquakes of November 10, 1938, and January 24, 1939 : Seismol. Soc. America Bull., v. 30, no. 2, p. 93–97.

Tsuya, Hiromichi, ed., 1950, The Fukui earthquake of June 28, 1948 ; report of the special committee for the study of the Fukui earthquake : Tokyo, Japan, 197 p.

U.S. Coast and Geodetic Survey, 1964a, Prince William Sound, Alaskan earthquakes, March–April 1964 : U.S. Coast and Geod. Survey, Seismology Div., Prelim. Rept., 83 p.

—— 1964b, Tidal datum plane changes Prince William Sound, Alaskan earthquakes March–April 1964 : U.S. Coast and Geod. Survey, Office of Oceanography, Prelim. Rept., 4 p.

Waller, R. M., 1963, Data on wells in the Homer area, Alaska : Alaska Dept. Health and Welfare Hydrol. Data, no. 23, 24 p.

—— 1966, Effects of the March 1964 Alaska earthquake on the hydrology of south-central Alaska : U.S. Geol. Survey Prof. Paper 544–A (in press).

Waller, R. M., Thomas, H. E., and Vorhis, R. C., 1965, Effects of the Good Friday earthquake on water supplies : Am. Water Works Assoc. Jour., v. 57, no. 2, p. 123–131.

CLARIFICATION

Geology Vol. Page	USGS Page	Column	Line	Remarks
470	D 10	3	13	Plate 1 is Plate O in Part B, the accompanying map case

GEORGE PLAFKER
U.S. GEOLOGICAL SURVEY

REUBEN KACHADOORIAN
U.S. GEOLOGICAL SURVEY

EDWIN B. ECKEL*
U.S. GEOLOGICAL SURVEY

LAWRENCE R. MAYO
U.S. GEOLOGICAL SURVEY

Reprinted with minor changes from
U.S. Geological Survey Professional Paper 542-G,
"Effects of the Earthquake of March 27, 1964,
on Various Communities"

Effects on Various Communities

ABSTRACT

The 1964 earthquake caused widespread damage to inhabited places throughout more than 50,000 square miles of south-central Alaska. This report describes damage to all communities in the area except Anchorage, Whittier, Homer, Valdez, Seward, the communities of the Kodiak group of islands, and communities in the Copper River Basin; these were discussed in previous chapters of the Geological Survey's series of reports on the earthquake. At the communities discussed herein, damage resulted primarily from sea waves of diverse origins, displacements of the land relative to sea level, and seismic shaking. Waves took all of the 31 lives lost at those communities; physical damage was primarily from the waves and vertical displacements of the land relative to sea level.

Destructive waves of local origin struck during or immediately after the earthquake throughout much of Prince William Sound, the southern Kenai Peninsula, and the shores of Kenai Lake. In Prince William Sound, waves demolished all but one home at the native village of Chenega, destroyed homesites at Point Nowell and Anderson Bay, and caused varying amounts of damage to waterfront facilities at Sawmill Bay, Latouche, Port Oceanic, Port Nellie Juan, Perry Island, and western Port Valdez. The local waves, which ran up as high as 70 feet above tide level at Chenega and more than 170 feet in several uninhabited parts of the Sound, took nearly all of the lives lost by drowning at these communities. Destructive local waves that devastated shores of Anderson Bay and adjacent parts of western Port Valdez probably were generated primarily by massive submarine slides of glacial and fluvioglacial deposits; the origin of the waves that caused damage at most of the other communities and at extensive uninhabited segments of shoreline is not known. At these places the most probable generative mechanisms are: unidentified submarine slides of unconsolidated deposits, and (or) the horizontal tectonic displacements, of 20 to more than 60 feet, that occurred in the Prince William Sound region during the earthquake.

A train of long-period seismic sea waves that began about 20 minutes after the start of the earthquake inundated shores along the Gulf of Alaska coast to a maximum height of 35 feet above tide level. At the communities described, they virtually destroyed two logging camps at Whidbey Bay and Puget Bay on the south coast of the Kenai Peninsula, caused moderate damage to boat harbors and docks at Seldovia and Cordova, floated away some beach cabins in the Cordova area, and drowned two people, one at Point Whitshed near Cordova and one at the Cape Saint Elias Light Station. The seismic sea waves were generated by regional tectonic uplift of the sea floor on the Continental Shelf.

Vertical tectonic displacements of the land relative to sea level that accompanied the earthquake affected virtually all the coastal communities. Tectonic subsidence of 5 to 6 feet, augmented locally by surficial subsidence of unconsolidated deposits, required either the relocation or raising of structures at Portage, Girdwood, and Hope on Turnagain Arm. Shoreline submergence resulting from about 3½ feet of tectonic subsidence at Seldovia necessitated raising all waterfront facilities and the airstrip above the level of high tides. On the other hand, tectonic uplift of the land in the Prince William Sound region required deepening of the small-boat harbors at Cordova and Tatitlek, dredging of the waterways in the Cordova area, and lengthening of some docks or piers at Cordova, the Cape Hinchinbrook Light Station, and in Sawmill Bay.

Significant structural damage from direct seismic shaking was largely confined to fluid containers and a pier facility near Kenai. Indirect damage from fissuring and differential settling of foundation materials in the vicinity of the Cordova airfield caused damage to a building, underground utilities, an airfield fill, and the highway. Minor amounts of direct and indirect damage from seismic vibrations were sustained by most of the communities situated on unconsolidated deposits as far east as Yakutat, north to Fairbanks, and west to King Salmon. Except for a few cracked or toppled chimneys, all the damage from shaking was confined to areas of thick, unconsolidated deposits. Foundation damage was almost entirely restricted to water-saturated unconsolidated deposits which, when liquefied by seismic shaking, could spread laterally toward free faces and (or) settle differentially through compaction.

---

*Now with The Geological Society of America.

[489]

INTRODUCTION

The great earthquake of March 27, 1964, took 114 lives and did more than $300 million damage to private and public property. Although a significant part of the damage was to interurban transportation and communications systems (Grantz, Plafker, and Kachadoorian, 1964; Eckel, 1967), by far the greater part of life and property losses occurred in cities, towns, and villages. Nearly all the inhabited places that were affected are in south central Alaska, in a relatively small part of the State but some (not discussed here) are as far away as northern California. All the larger cities that were extensively damaged, and some of the smaller communities, are covered in other reports in this series (table 1).

This report completes the U.S. Geological Survey series of descriptions of earthquake effects on communities. Damage at all previously undescribed Alaskan communities where there was loss of life or physical damage beyond such minor effects as cracked plaster, disloged building contents, or muddied wells is described herein. The communities and the nature of their damage are listed in table 2; their locations are shown on plates 1 and 2. The scores of additional inhabited places in Alaska and Canada where the earthquake was reportedly felt but where it did no damage are shown in plate 1, but they are not described here.

This report is based primarily on personal observations of Kachadoorian, Plafker, and Mayo, one or all of whom visited each of the communities as a part of their general studies of geologic effects of the earthquake throughout south-central Alaska during the field seasons of 1964 and 1965. Their information, supplemented by that from other sources, was largely assembled by Eckel while the first two authors were busy on other assignments. All four authors share responsibility for the facts presented and for their interpretation.

TABLE 1.—*Alaskan communities damaged by the earthquake of March 27, 1964, treated in other U.S. Geological Survey reports*

[Place names and locations are as given by Orth (1967); some spellings differ from that in referenced descriptions. Except as noted, populations are as of 1960 census. Deaths from Alaska Dept. Health and Welfare (1964). Numbers in descriptions column refer to U.S. Geological Survey series of Professional Papers on the Alaska Earthquake of March 27, 1964 (see "References cited"): 541, Hansen and others (1966); 542–A, Hansen (1965); 542–B, Kachadoorian (1965); 542–C, Coulter and Migliaccio (1966); 542–D, Waller (1966a); 542–E, Lemke (1967); 542–F, Kachadoorian and Plafker (1967); 543–A, McCulloch (1966); 543–D, Plafker and Kachadoorian (1966); 543–E, Ferrians (1966); 544–A, Waller (1966b); 544–B, Waller (1966c); 545–A, Logan (1967); 545–B, Eckel (1967); 545–D, McCulloch and Bonilla (1968)]

Place	Location[1]		Popula-tion 1960	Deaths	Principal causes of damage (1, primary; 2, secondary; 3, much damage also from waterfront fires)						Descriptions
	Latitude, N.	Longitude, W.			Sub-sidence	Fire	Landslides		Vibra-tion	Waves	
							Land	Sub-marine			
Afognak	58°00′30″	152°46′00″	190	0	2					1	541, s. 96, 542–F, p. 28–32; 543–D, p. 30–39.
Anchorage	61°13′05″	149°53′30″	[1] 44,237	9			1		1		541, p. 73, 83–85, 100–103; 542–A, p. 1–68; 544–B, p. 1–18; 545–B, p. 3–4, 8–9, 19–24.
Chugiak	61°23′50″	149°28′40″	51	0					1		544–A, p. 19.
Eagle River	61°19′20″	149°34′00″	130	0					1		541, p. 19.
Eklutna powerplant	61°28′	149°22′	50	0					1		545–I, p. 1–24.
Glannallen	62°07′	149°33′	169	0					1		543–E, p. 25.
Gulkana	62°16′	145°23′	59	0					1		543–E, p. 25.
Homer	59°38′40′	151°33′00″	1,247	0	1			2	2		541, p. 80, 88, 91; 542–D, p. 1–28; 544–A, p. 21; 545–B, p. 12.
Kadiak Fisheries Cannery			2	0	2				1	1	543–D, p. 13, 15–19, 43.
Kaguyak	56°51′40″	153°46′00″	36	3						1	542–F, p. 37–38; 543–D, p. 30–39.
Kodiak	57°47′20″	152°47′10″	[2] 2,628	[3] 9	2					1	541, p. 92–94; 542–F, p. 1–28; 543–D, p. 30–39; 545–B, p. 5, 14, 24.
Larsen Bay	57°32′20″	153°58′45″	72	0	1						542–F, p. 40; 543–D, p. 30–39.
Lawing	60°24′15″	149°21′50″	[4] 8	0						1	543–A, p. 12–18.
Lee's Guide Service			[4] 4	0					1		543–E, p. 25.
McCord	57°08′30″	153°11′45″	8	0	2				2		541, p. 19.
Old Harbor	57°12′15″	153°18′00″	193	0	2					1	542–F, p. 34–37; 543–D, p. 30–39.
Ouzinkie	57°55′30″	152°29′50″	214	6	2					1	542–F, p. 33–34; 543–D, p. 30–39.
Moose Pass	60°29′20″	149°22′00″	136	0					1		545–D, (in press).
Seward	60°06′30″	149°26′30″	1,891	13		3		1	2	1	541, p. 73–79, 85, 90; 542–E, p. 1–43; 544–A, p. 24–26; 545–B, p. 6, 12, 25.
Sheep Mountain Inn	61°50′	147°31′	[4] 5	0					1		543–E, p. 25.
Tazlina Glacier Lodge	62°04′	146°27′	[4] 4	0					1		543–E, p. 25.
Tonsina Lodge	61°39′20″	145°10′30″	[4] 4	0				1			543–E, p. 25.
Tsina Lodge	61°11′45″	145°33′30″	[4] 4	0				1			543–E, p. 25.
Valdez	61°07′	146°16′	1,000	31	2	3		1		1	541, p. 79, 85–87, 98–99; 542–C, p. 1–36; 544–A, p. 26; 545–B, p. 15–17, 25.
Whittier	60°46′30″	148°41′00″	[4] 70	13	1	3		2	2	1	541, p. 80, 99; 542–B, p. 1–21; 545–B, p. 6, 26.

[1] 82,833 including military personnel.
[2] 4,788 including personnel at Kodiak Naval Station.
[3] Includes 7 persons who were on highways, on boats, or in isolated places in the Kodiak Islands.
[4] Estimated by authors as of March 27, 1964.

TABLE 2.—*Alaskan communities damaged by the earthquake of March 27, 1964, treated in this report*

[Place names and locations are as given by Orth (1967); some spellings differ from that used in other U.S. Geological Survey reports on the earthquake. Locations of places marked with asterisk are shown on plate 1; all others are on plate 2. Except as noted, populations are as of 1960 census. Deaths from Alaska Dept. Health and Welfare (1964). Physical damage relative to size and importance of community]

Place	Location — Latitude N.	Location — Longitude W.	Population	Damages — Deaths	Physical damage — Major	Physical damage — Minor	subsidence	Uplift	Landslides — Land	Landslides — Submarine	Vibration	Waves
Anderson Bay and vicinity, Port Valdez	61°05'	146°33'	1	1	×							1
Cape Hinchinbrook Light Station	60°14'15"	146°38'40"	(¹) 6	0		×		2	2		2	
*Cape Saint Elias	59°47'30"	144°36'15"	4	1		×		2	2		2	1
Chenega	60°16'45"	148°04'30"	75	23	×			2		2		1
*Chisik Island (see Tyonek)	60°08'	152°35'	¹ 20									
Cooper Landing	60°29'25"	149°50'00"	100	0		×					1	
Cordova and vicinity	60°33'	145°45'	1,128	1	×			1			2	2
Crab Bay (see Sawmill Bay)	60°03'45"	148°00'00"										
Ellamar	60°53'45"	146°42'30"	1	0		×		1				
*English Bay	59°21'30"	151°55'20"	78	0		×	1				2	
*Fairbanks	64°50'45"	147°43'15"	13,311	0		×					1	
Girdwood	60°56'30"	149°10'00"	63	0	×		1					
Hope	60°55'15"	149°38'30"	54	0		×	1				2	
*Kenai and vicinity	60°33'	151°16'	778	0		×					1	
*King Salmon and vicinity	58°41'30"	156°39'30"	618	0		×					1	
Latouche	60°03'05"	147°54'	0	0	×				2			1
*Middleton Island	59°26'	146°20'	¹ 12	0		×		1				
*Naknek (see King Salmon)	58°43'40"	157°00'45"	249									
*Nikiski (see Kenai)	60°41'	151°24'										
*Palmer and vicinity	61°36'00"	149°06'30"	1,181	0		×					1	
Perry Island	60°43'	147°55'	2	0		×					2	2
Point Nowell	60°26'27"	147°56'23"	1	1	×							1
Point Whitshed (see Cordova)			¹ 10									
Portage	60°50'15"	148°58'45"	71	0	×		1				2	
Port Ashton (see Sawmill Bay)	60°03'30"	148°03'00"										
*Port Graham	59°21'10"	150°49'30"	139	0		×	1					
Port Nellie Juan	60°33'00"	148°09'45"	3	3	×							1
Port Oceanic	60°12'45"	147°49'00"	2	0		×				2		1
Puget Bay	59°56'	148°31'	¹ 2	0	×				2	2	2	1
Rocky Bay	59°14'15"	151°25'00"	¹ 4	0		×	2					1
San Juan Cannery (see Sawmill Bay)	60°03'	148°04'										
Sawmill Bay and vicinity	60°03'30"	148°00'30"	¹ 15	1	×					2	2	1
*Seldovia	59°26'15"	151°42'30"	460	0	×		1					
*South Naknek (see King Salmon)	58°41'	157°00'	142									
Sutton	61°42'40"	148°53'30"	162	0		×					1	
Tatitlek	60°52'45"	146°41'00"	96	0		×			1		2	
*Tyonek and southwest shore Cook Inlet	61°04'00"	151°08'20"	187	0		×					1	
Whidbey Bay	59°56'	158°56'	¹ 4	0	×						2	1
*Yakataga	60°04'05"	142°25'45"	48	0								
*Yakutat	59°33'	139°44'	230	0		×					1	

¹ Estimated by authors, as of March 27, 1964.

ACKNOWLEDGMENTS

We are greatly indebted to numerous individuals who provided us with eyewitness accounts of their experiences during and immediately after the earthquake. Some of these people are mentioned by name in the descriptions of the effect of the earthquake at specific communities; there were literally hundreds of others who gave useful information but whose contributions could not be specifically acknowledged here.

EARTHQUAKE QUESTIONNAIRE

As part of the Geological Survey's effort to gather as much information as possible on the geological effects of the earthquake, Earl Brabb prepared and distributed a questionnaire designed to elicit such information from as many eyewitnesses as could be reached. Copies were mailed to every postmaster in Alaska, and many other copies were delivered personally by field geologists in the course of their investigations; these men also found the questionnaires useful for jotting notes during their interviews with local people.

Response to the questionnaire was gratifying. About 75 percent of the more than 350 copies distributed were returned. Of these, virtually all contained useful information, and many provided leads to further information that was gathered by correspondence or by followup interviews. These responses increased the amount of information available far beyond what could have been collected by individual field investigators.

In order to show the kind of information that was sought and to aid future earthquake investigators, the questionnaire is reproduced here. It may seem formidable at first glance, but the response to it shows that most people found it easy to answer; indeed, many were sufficiently interested to append long notes or letters that provided a wealth of additional details. The text of the questionnaire follows.

U.S. GEOLOGICAL SURVEY
Alaskan Geology Branch
345 Middlefield Road
Menlo Park, California

EARTHQUAKE QUESTIONNAIRE FOR SUPPLEMENTARY GEOLOGIC DATA

Section A—Did you or anyone in your area feel the earthquake? __

1. Nature of ground motion:
   a. Fast __ or slow? __ Don't know __
   b. Rolling __ or jarring? __ Don't know __
   c. For how long? _____
   d. If there were different types of motion during the earthquake, estimate the duration and order of each type _____
   e. Did you see waves in the ground? __ If so, how many and how far apart? __
   f. What was the main direction of ground movement? (circle) N–S, NE–SW, E–W, SE–NW Don't know __
   g. Motion felt by several in community __, most __, all __, observer __.

2. Location of observer during earthquake:
   a. Indoors __ outdoors __
   b. If indoors, were you lying down __, sitting __ or active? __
   c. If indoors, does the house or building rest on bedrock __, filled in ground __, muskeg __, soil __, don't know __

3. Effect of earthquake on objects:
   a. Rattled windows __, doors __, dishes __
   b. Creaked walls __
   c. Swayed doors __, lamp __
   d. Shook trees and bushes slightly __, moderately __, violently __
   e. Shifted small objects __
   f. Overturned small objects __, lamps __
   g. Shifted large, heavy objects __
   h. Overturned large, heavy objects __
   i. Cracked plaster __, windows__, walls __, chimneys __
   j. Caused to fall: knicknacks __, books __, pictures __, plaster __, walls __, chimney __
   k. Broke dishes __, furniture __
   l. Caused damage to house or building: slight__, considerable __, great __, total __; house or building is log construction __, brick__, wood frame __, masonry __, concrete __
   m. Offset road __, fence __, house __ as much as __ feet.

4. Effect of earthquake on natural features:
   a. Did any cracks form in ground? __ If yes, how many? __ How long after the initial shock of the main earthquake did they form? __ seconds, __ minutes, __ hours, other __, don't know __ Average length __, average width __, average depth __; dimensions of largest crack __ long, __ wide, __ deep; approximate orientation of most cracks ____. How far apart were most of the cracks? __ Were the cracks in ice __, snow __, mud __, sand __, rock __, other __?
   b. Did any low mounds ("mole tracks") or pressure ridges form? __ If yes, how many? __ How long after the initial shock of the main earthquake did they form? __ seconds, __ minutes, __ hours, other __, don't know __. Average length __, average width __; dimensions of largest ridge __ long, __ wide; approximate orientation of most ridges __. How far apart? __ Were the ridges in ice __, snow __, mud__, sand __, rock __, other __? Were the pressure ridges along the banks of a lake __, bay __, river __, stream __, pond __, other __?
   c. Did any landslides develop? __ If so, how long after the initial shock did they develop? __ seconds, __ minutes, __ hours, other __, don't know __. How long did the movement last __? Did the ground move as a unit __ or did it break up in large blocks __ or small blocks __? Was the material in the landslide mostly rock __, mostly soil __, don't know __? Was the material mainly wet __, dry __, frozen __, don't know __. How large an area was affected by the largest landslide __ feet by __ feet? Location of this landslide:

   _____

   Were any houses __, roads __, or other structures __ damaged by the landslide? Did the slide material fall into a lake __, bay __, river __, other __? If so, was a wave created? __ If so, how high? __ Any damage from the wave? __ Did the landslide dam any rivers? __

   d. Did any ground subside (sink) __? If yes, how large an area was affected __? How much did it sink? __ Is the material in the area of subsidence mostly rock __, mostly soil __, don't know __?
   e. Did you see any water spouts __? If yes, how long after the initial shock did they occur __? Was the spout mostly water __, a mixture of mud and water __, or mostly mud __? How high was the highest one __? How long did it last __? Did it form a crater __? If so, how large was the crater __? If you did not see any water spouts, did you see any craters that could have been caused by water spouts? __ Where are the craters located?

   _____

   How large is the largest? __ Are they isolated mounds or do they occur in a line? _____
   f. Were any healthy trees broken by the force of the earthquake? __ If so, about how many? __ How large __ inches in diameter? Did they fall mainly in one directions __ If yes, which way do most of the crowns point? __

Section B—Water effects

1. Was your area affected by a tidal wave or by unusually high tides ____? If yes, what time did the first wave or tide arrive ____? How long was this after the initial shock ____? How high was the first wave or tide ____ feet? Were there more than one wave or tide ____? If so, how many ____? At what times ____? How high ____? Did the highest water level rise come during high tide ____, low tide ____, half way in between ____? From which direction did the highest water come ____? How far inland did the water come ____? How high above ocean level did the water come ____? How much damage was done?

   _____

   What is the main orientation of the shoreline affected by the wave or tide

   _____?

2. Were any of the wells in your area affected ____? Did the water get muddy ____? Change in taste ____? Did the water level rise ____, fall ____, stay

the same ____, don't know ____?
Any other changes

_____?

How long after the earthquake
was the well affected? ____?

3. Did any springs change flow
____? Increase flow ____? De-
crease flow ____? Any new
springs ____?

4. Did any streams increase flow
____? Decrease flow ____? How
long after the earthquake ____?
How long before the flow returned to normal ____?

5. Did the water level in any lakes
drop ____? Rise ____? How

many feet ____? How long after
the initial shock of the earthquake ____? Did the water level
return to normal ____? When
____?

6. Did tide level change in your
area ____? If yes, is tide lower
____ or higher ____? by how
many feet ____? When was the
change first noticed ____?
Has the time of high and low
tide changed ____? Are they
later ____ or earlier ____? By
how much ____? Was this effect
temporary ____ or is it still in
effect ____? Are measurements
on bedrock ____?

Section C—Miscellaneous Effects

1. Are there any volcanoes in your
area ____? If yes, has there been
any increase ____, or decrease
____ in their activity ____? If
so, when did this occur _____
_____?

2. Are there any glaciers in your
area ____? If yes, has there been
any increase ____ or decrease
____ in their movement? If so,
when did this occur

Remarks (anything not covered above or
any comments you wish to make)
Name of person filling out form _____

_____
Address_____
Can you be reached by telephone? __
If so, please give number _____

CATEGORIES OF EARTHQUAKE-RELATED DAMAGE

Property damage to communities described in this report resulted from a variety of causes
which, for convenience, are
grouped into the following three
broad categories: (1) seismic vibrations, (2) vertical tectonic displacements, and (3) water waves.
Seismic vibrations include both
the direct effects of shaking on
structures and their indirect effects from foundation failures
caused by ground fissuring, sliding, or differential settlement of
the materials on which the structures are built. Vertical tectonic
displacements include regional uplift and subsidence of the land relative to sea level which, in some
localities, was augmented by subsidence of surficial unconsolidated
deposits. Destructive waves include (1) local waves that were
generated during or immediately
after the earthquake by subaqueous slides, horizontal tectonic displacements, or other, unknown
causes, and (2) the train of long-
period sea waves generated by tectonic uplift of the sea floor in the
Gulf of Alaska.

Lateral or vertical displacements of the surface along earthquake-related faults can cause
enormous damage to buildings,
dams, pipelines, or other structures whose foundations they
cross. This kind of damage, indeed, is one of the most feared effects of future earthquakes in
heavily populated places on or
near active faults such as the famous San Andreas fault in California. Fortunately, the only surface fault breaks that developed
as a result of the Alaska earthquake of March 27, 1964, were on
uninhabited Montague Island and
on the sea floor southwest of the
island (Plafker, 1967). Had Montague Island been inhabited, or
had fault displacements occurred
within any of the larger towns,
the toll of death and destruction
would almost certainly have been
even greater than it was.

Of the 31 lives lost at communities discussed herein, all were by
drowning—29 in locally generated
waves and 2 in seismic sea waves.
Most of the physical damage was
caused by the waves and by verti-

cal displacements of the shore relative to sea level. Except at Kenai,
structural damage from direct
seismic vibrations was minor. The
distribution of casualties by community, as well as the nature and
extent of damage are summarized
on table 2. In this section, the general categories and distribution of
earthquake damage are discussed
briefly to provide background for
the descriptions of damage to individual communities that follow.

SEISMIC VIBRATIONS

Vibrations set up by the earthquake, which had a Richter magnitude variously estimated as 8.3
(revised U.S. Coast and Geodetic
Survey) or 8.4 (Pasadena Seismograph Station) were recorded instrumentally throughout the
world, but the places and areas
where they were felt and reported
by humans are limited to Alaska
and nearby parts of Canada (pl.
1). We have no data from the
Chukotsk Peninsula, on the Russian side of Bering Strait, but
seismic shaking quite possibly may
have been detectable there also.

As shown on plate 1, shaking was felt over a land area of more than a million square miles. Among the more distant points where movement was noted are (1) Gambell, on Gambell Island, 800 miles northwest of the epicenter; (2) Wainwright, on the arctic coast, 750 miles north; (3) Watson Lake, Yukon Territory, 650 miles east; (4) in the general vicinity of Prince Rupert, British Columbia, more than 800 miles southeast; and (5) the U.S. Weather Station on Adak Island, about 1,300 miles southwest of the epicenter.

Throughout Alaska and Canada the predominant reported direction of seismic shaking was between north-south and northwest-southeast. Some stations reported changes in direction during the earthquake, and a few reported predominant motions in east-west and northeast-southwest directions.

The duration of shaking as measured or estimated by hundreds of individuals, ranged from 15 seconds to about 8 minutes. Where it was timed at localities close to the epicentral region, it most commonly was between 3½ and 4½ minutes. Anomalously short durations of between 15 seconds and 1½ minutes were reported from Perl Island, Rocky Bay, and Seldovia at the southwestern tip of the Kenai Peninsula. In general, observers on or near bedrock reported notably shorter durations and less violent motion than those on thick deposits of unconsolidated sediments.

Reports of sensory perception of vibration varied from descriptions of rolling motions to sharp jolts; most observers on unconsolidated sedimentary materials reported rolling motions. In some outlying stations, as the one at Nome, observers reported that they felt nauseated before they realized that they were feeling an earthquake. Motion sickness was characteristic of nearly all Alaskan station reports that were more than 300 to 350 miles from the epicenter.

DIRECT VIBRATORY DAMAGE

Even though the earthquake's vibrations were felt by people over nearly all of Alaska and adjacent parts of Canada, seismic motion strong enough to damage structures was confined to a relatively small area. Such damage occurred at many places within an area of about 50,000 square miles (pl. 1), in an elongate belt that extends from Glennallen on the northeast to the southwestern part of Kodiak Island. Outside this belt, there was slight vibratory damage at Yakutat, 300 miles east of the epicenter, and in the King Salmon-Naknek area 375 miles west of the epicenter.

The most severe shaking and nearly all of the related damage to communities and major transportation routes occurred in areas of thick, saturated unconsolidated deposits; some of the larger areas of such deposits are delineated on plate 1. In these areas, structural damage resulted primarily from failure of the ground beneath buildings—failure such as ground cracking, landslides, and differential settlement of the natural unconsolidated deposits or of artificial fills. To a far lesser extent, the strong ground motion alone caused direct damage to structures in such areas. In contrast, no vibratory damage, other than a few broken chimneys and slightly cracked walls, was sustained by structures built on indurated rock anywhere in the region.

FISSURED GROUND

Fissured or cracked ground caused directly by seismic shaking or indirectly by vibration-induced movement of unconsolidated materials was widespread. Ground fissures were observed over an area of about 100,000 square miles; they were seen as far north as Fort Yukon, 400 miles north of the epicenter, at Juneau, some 500 miles to the southeast, and at Quinhagak, more than 500 miles to the west.

Except for minor fissuring in rock at the heads of some large landslides and in the immediate vicinity of the earthquake faults on Montague Island, virtually all of the fissures that were observed developed in unconsolidated sediments and soils, particularly where the materials were saturated or where the water table was close to the surface. Some fissures on deltas, outwash trains, and beach-ridge complexes were extensive; on the Copper River Delta and the coastal plain east of the delta, for example, many fissures as much as 6 feet wide and a quarter of a mile long were formed.

Ejections of fine sand and water characterized many fissures, particularly in the Copper River and Portage areas, on the Kenai Lowland, and elsewhere. Such ejections occurred mainly on the lower parts of deltas, on alluvial flood plains, along the shore of shallow bays, on sand dunes, and on elevated beach ridges.

Ground fissures and associated sand-water spouts resulted in widespread, but relatively minor, damage to roads and underground utilities in several communities discussed herein and in some of the larger communities, most notably Anchorage, Seward, and Valdez. In a few places the fissures also extended beneath buildings and cracked and dislocated foundations or walls. On the whole, however, ground fissures did far more damage to the highway and railroad systems throughout south-central Alaska than they did to the communities (Grantz, Plafker, and Kachadoorian, 1964; Kachadoorian, 1968; McCulloch and Bonilla, 1968).

CRACKED ICE

All, or nearly all, of the lakes and rivers in Alaska were ice-covered at the time of the earthquake; parts of the sea's surface, particularly in the north and along the shores of relatively calm inlets and bays, were also frozen. Within an area of 500,000 square miles, inland ice and also much sea ice was extensively cracked by the seismic vibrations (pl. 1). From the epicentral region, cracked ice was observed as far north as Wainwright on the Arctic coast, at Point Hope (775 miles distant), 400 miles east to Crillon Lake near Lituya Bay, and 430 miles west to the vicinity of Ugashik on the Alaska Peninsula. Ice on larger lakes and rivers tended to be more readily broken than that on smaller ponds and streams. Locally, pressure ridges were formed and blocks of ice piled one on another as a result of seiche waves in waters beneath the ice. Neither ice cracking nor ice shove caused any noteworthy damage to the communities of south-central Alaska.

LANDSLIDES AND AVALANCHES

Seismic vibrations triggered innumerable subaerial landslides and avalanches and subaqueous slides throughout an area of some 100,000 square miles of south-central Alaska (pl. 1). The landslides included a wide variety of falls, slides, and flows involving bedrock, unconsolidated deposits, and snow or ice in varying proportions. (The classification and nomenclature for landslides used herein correspond to those of Varnes, 1958.) The greatest concentration of landslides was in the rugged mountains that encircle the earthquake's epicenter—particularly in the Kenai Mountains, the Chugach Mountains north of Turnagain Arm and near Katalla, and the Talkeetna Mountains. Most of the slides involved hard sedimentary and metamorphic rocks of early Tertiary or pre-Tertiary age and, in a few instances, granitic intrusive rocks. Near Katalla the landslides were chiefly in younger Tertiary rocks, which are less indurated than the older ones but nevertheless are complexly folded and intensely faulted. Large subaqueous slides along the fiorded coast of Prince William Sound and the Kenai Peninsula and at Kenai Lake caused direct damage to Seward, Valdez, Whittier, Homer, and a segment of The Alaska Railroad along the shore of Kenai Lake. Such slides, however, caused no direct damage to the communities described herein, although local waves generated by them were indirect causes of damage.

Subaerial landslides and, to a lesser extent, avalanches did much damage to transportation and communication lines throughout south-central Alaska. Avalanches were particularly widespread along the Seward-Anchorage Highway, on the Richardson Highway near Thompson Pass, and in the more rugged parts of the Talkeetna and Chugach Mountains (Post 1967; Kachadoorian, 1968). However, because most of them took place in remote and uninhabited areas, their effects were of far greater geologic and geomorphic than economic interest. Only at Anchorage did subaerial landslides do more than minor damage to a community. There, great translatory slides in the residential area of Turnagain Heights and in the business heart of the city wrought even more havoc than did the seismic vibrations (Hansen, 1965). It should be emphasized that the slides at Anchorage were unique, requiring a special set of geologic conditions that are not, so far as we know, duplicated at any other community in the earthquake-affected part of Alaska.

VERTICAL TECTONIC DISPLACEMENTS

Vertical tectonic movements, both upward and downward, occurred over an area of more than 110,000 square miles in south-central Alaska (Plafker, 1969). The deformed region, which is about 600 miles long and as much as 250 miles wide, lies along the continental margin between long 142° and long 155°. It consists of a major seaward zone of uplift bordered on the northwest and north by a major zone of subsidence. These two zones are separated by a line of zero land-level change that trends northeastward to intersect the mainland between Seward and Prince William Sound. The line then curves eastward through Port Nellie Juan to the vicinity of Valdez and crosses the Copper River valley about 50 miles above the mouth of the river.

The zone of subsidence includes most of the Kodiak group of islands, Cook Inlet, the Kenai Mountains, and the Chugach Mountains. The axis of maximum subsidence within this zone trends roughly northeastward along the crest of the Kodiak and Kenai Mountains and then bends eastward in the Chugach Mountains. Maximum recorded downwarping is about 7½ feet on the south coast of the Kenai Peninsula.

In the southeastern part of the deformed area, uplift averages about 6 feet over a wide zone including most of the Prince William Sound region, the mainland east of the sound, and offshore islands as far southwest as Middleton Island at the edge of the Continental Shelf. Maximum recorded uplift on land, through combined warping and surface faulting, was 38 feet at the southwestern end of Montague Island.

Regional vertical tectonic movements seriously affected many navigable waterways and harbors, as well as land transportation routes and installations at virtually all coastal communities. Throughout the zone of uplift, docks and piers were raised above water level at most stages of tide and required lengthening in order to reach deep water. Boat harbors and channels had to be dredged in some localities to restore their pre-earthquake water depths. Many homes along the shore in uplifted areas were rendered inaccessible by boat except at the highest tides. Even more seriously affected were some shoreline installations in areas of tectonic subsidence. Many roads, railroads, canneries, and homes in such areas had to be raised to protect them from inundation during high tides. Extensive stretches of beach that had been used for cattle grazing, storage of sawn logs, or other purposes, were also partially or entirely obliterated by drowning of the shore lines.

WAVES AND RELATED SUBAQUEOUS SLIDES

Sudden violent local waves, that struck during or immediately after the earthquake, were the major cause of property damage and casualties. (As used in this report, "local wave" refers to water waves, generated either along the coast or in lakes during the earthquake, that affected areas of limited extent. The waves were originated at or close to the shoreline in part by subaqueous slides, but probably

also by other mechanisms such as tectonic movements, seiches, or subaerial landslides. The term "local wave" is used to distinguish these waves from the train of long-period seismic sea waves that first struck the coast of the Gulf of Alaska 19 to 20 minutes after the earthquake began.) These local waves were later followed by seismic sea waves that damaged property and took additional lives all along the Gulf of Alaska and as far south as northern California. Extensive damage to uninhabited coasts, in the form of scoured shorelines, smashed trees, and displaced driftwood and shoreline deposits, clearly indicates that damage would have been far more severe had the coast been more heavily populated or had the earthquake occurred at a high, rather than low, stage of tide.

Seismic sea waves were also noted at remote localities east of Prince William Sound on Middleton Island, at the Cape Saint Elias Light Station on Kayak Island, and by the fishing boat *Roald* that was anchored on the east side of Wingham Island. The *Roald* was buffeted by swift and erratic currents and rapid fluctuations in water level that began approximately half an hour after the earthquake. The current at Wingham Island was described by the captain, Joe Clark, as strong enough to move boulders along the shore.

LOCAL WAVES AND SUBAQUEOUS SLIDES

The intense and prolonged ground shaking during the earthquake triggered many subaqueous slides along the seacoast (submarine "landslides") and lake shores (sublacustrine "landslides") of south-central Alaska. A substantial part of the property damage resulting from the earthquake is attributable directly to subaqueous

slides which carried away the port facilities of Seward (Lemke, 1967) and Valdez (Coulter, and Migliaccio, 1966), the small-boat harbor at Homer (Waller, 1966a), shoreline facilities along Kenai Lake (McCulloch, 1966), and segments of the railroad and fuel docks at Whittier (Kachadoorian, 1965). Numerous other slides are known to have occurred in the sparsely inhabited epicentral area of Prince William Sound and the adjacent Kenai Peninsula; undoubtedly, many others that occurred entirely underwater have gone unrecognized. The distribution of the larger known and inferred subaqueous slides is shown on plate 2.

Violent local waves generated by subaqueous slides caused major damage to adjacent shorelines and loss of life in the cities of Seaward, Valdez, and Whittier. However, localized waves of unknown origin, though not specifically identifiable with submarine slides, were responsible for most of the shoreline damage in these same general areas, including many of the Prince William Sound communities described herein. The local waves, and combinations of local waves and subaqueous slides, caused most of the earthquake-related fatalities in Alaska (tables 1 and 2).

PHYSIOGRAPHIC SETTING OF THE AFFECTED REGION

Prince William Sound and the Kenai Peninsula to the west are regions of high rugged mountains which are indented by long, narrow glacier-scoured fiords that make good natural harbors. The rocky shores of many of these fiords drop off precipitously to depths of 600 to 2,000 feet. Subaerial and subaqueous bedrock slopes commonly exceed 35° and locally may be nearly vertical. Similar glacier-scoured valleys and basins on the mainland are occupied by deep lakes, among the largest of which is Kenai Lake.

At places, especially at the heads of the fiords, streams have built prisms of poorly consolidated alluvial and glacial deposits, which provide almost the only large level sites for buildings, dock facilities, and railroad yards. Elsewhere, glacial deposits of intercalated till and outwash form low crescentic bars or shoals across the fiords that mark the end positions of former glaciers. Lateral moraines and kame terraces that were deposited along the sides of the valley glaciers occur along the fiords of eastern Prince William Sound. Although apparently absent at the surface along the coast in much of northern and western Prince William Sound and eastern Kenai Peninsula, such deposits are quite possibly present under water in some places, because depressed cirque levels and submerged ancient forests in these areas indicate that the shorelines of the northern part of Prince William Sound and much of the Kenai Peninsula have been drowned since the last major glaciation (Grant and Higgins, 1910, p. 17–18; 1913, p. 57; Plafker, 1968, figs. 38–39).

DISTRIBUTION AND NATURE OF LOCAL WAVE DAMAGE

Most of the known localized waves and subaqueous slides were concentrated along the shores of fiords and bays in northern and western Prince William Sound, at Resurrection and Aialik Bays on the south coast of the Kenai Peninsula, and along the shore of Kenai Lake (pl. 2). Coastal damage generally occurred along the shores of steep-walled fiords and islands, but at least some of it was in shallow embayments that are virtually closed off from the sea. Shorelines damaged by the waves

show no preferred orientation, although much of the most extensive damage tends to occur at the heads of embayments on east-west or northeast-southwest shores. One of the most striking characteristics of the damage is its highly localized and seemingly erratic distribution along the shorelines. An excellent example of this localization was along the north shore of sheltered Jack Bay near the entrance to Port Valdez in northeastern Prince William Sound (pl. 2). At that locality a 600-foot-long section of shoreline was stripped bare of timber to a maximum elevation of 39 feet by a violent surge of water; yet this small area and a nearby cove are the only segments along the north shore of Jack Bay that show evidence of wave damage.

The extent of wave damage to shorelines ranged from the splashing of mud and seashells above high-water line to the stripping of vegetation and soil. The affected region is one of moderate climate and high rainfall, so a dense forest of conifers crowds the shoreline except in recently deglaciated areas or places where cliffs are too precipitous for the trees to gain a foothold. As a consequence, wave damage to shorelines was best recorded by scarred, broken, or uprooted trees and brush. Locally, muskeg and soil were stripped from the bedrock, and seashells, driftwood, and beach deposits as large as boulders were thrown up above the level of the highest tides. At a few places all trees, including some 2 feet in diameter, were uprooted or broken to heights 110 feet above tide level, barnacle-covered boulders 6 feet across were carried more than 100 feet above the shoreline, and material from marine deposits was splashed more than 170 feet above tide level. Relative intensities of the damage,

rated on a scale of increasing damage from 1 to 5, and described and shown on plate 2 and are shown in more detail on figures 1, 7, 12, 17, and 19.

In the absence of eyewitnesses, the direction of motion for the larger waves as shown on plate 2 could generally be inferred from the orientation of the damaged shorelines and from the directions in which limbs and trunks of trees and brush were scarred, bent, or broken. On shores bare of vegetation, only the orientation of the affected shoreline and the distribution of displaced driftwood and beach deposits could be used as directional indicators.

The earthquake occurred almost at a zero tide (mean lower low water). Consequently, effects of the localized waves along the coast were visible only where they were high enough to reach above the extreme high-tide line, which is approximately 15 to 20 feet above lower low water along the coasts of Prince William Sound and the Kenai Peninsula.

TIME AND SEQUENCE OF THE WAVES

An important characteristic of the damaging local waves, where observed by eyewitnesses at 10 widely scattered localities in Prince William Sound, Resurrection Bay, and Kenai Lake, is that single large waves struck during the earthquake or within minutes after it ended. Much smaller waves immediately preceded or followed the large wave, but runup from these waves rarely rose above extreme high-tide level. Nondestructive sudden water disturbances were noted by numerous other observers elsewhere in these same areas as well as in the Kodiak group of islands, on the southern Kenai Peninsula, and on the mainland coast and offshore islands east of Prince William Sound. By the time the initial crest of the train of seismic sea waves reached the outer coast of the Kenai Peninsula, 19 to 20 minutes after the earthquake began, the strong water disturbances generated by the local waves had largely subsided.

SEISMIC SEA WAVES

Most major earthquakes that involve vertical tectonic displacements beneath the sea are followed by seismic sea waves (tsunamis or "tidal" waves); the earthquake of March 27, 1964, generated one of the larger seismic sea-wave trains of modern times. These waves took 20 lives and caused destruction all along the Alaskan coast between the southern tip of Kodiak Island and Kayak Island. They were especially destructive in areas such as the Kodiak group of islands and the Kenai Peninsula, which during the earthquake were lowered relative to sea level by tectonic subsidence or by tectonic subsidence and compaction of unconsolidated deposits. Two casualties were caused by these waves at communities described in this report. In addition, the sea waves, which were recorded on tide gages throughout the Pacific Ocean, caused 15 deaths and major damage in British Columbia, Oregon, and California. The inferred source area of the seismic sea waves, reported arrival times of the initial wave at shore stations in the near-source area, and maximum runup heights are given by Van Dorn (1964) and Plafker (1969, fig. 15, table 2).

The first of a train of at least seven large-amplitude seismic sea waves with periods of 55 to 90 minutes was reported at Cape Chiniak on Kodiak Island at 6:10 p.m.—34 minutes after the earthquake. It was not preceded by a warning withdrawal of water as so commonly occurs before seismic sea waves. The wave was described as a cresting breaker at Narrow Cape on the exposed southeastern coast of Kodiak Island and as a fast-rising tide in the Kodiak area. At Narrow Cape the first wave reached farthest inland, whereas at the city of Kodiak the fourth wave (between 11:16 p.m. and 11:20 p.m.), which almost coincided with high tide, was highest, cresting at about 23 feet above high-tide level (Plafker and Kachadoorian, 1966; Kachadoorian and Plafker, 1967). In the Kodiak group of islands, the city of Kodiak, the Kodiak Naval Base, and several small communities in low-lying areas were severely damaged by the waves. The entire waterfront area of the city of Kodiak was destroyed and many fishing boats—the mainstay of the local economy—were lost or damaged.

Along the shores of Shelikof Strait and Cook Inlet the seismic sea waves, which were less than 5 feet high, caused rapid tide changes that were accompanied by swift erratic currents. However, the waves barely reached above the level of highest tides, which in this area of large tidal range exceeds 18 feet as a rule, and they caused no property damage.

Seismic sea waves that struck the south shore of the Kenai Peninsula caused heavy property losses to Seward at the head of Resurrection Bay and to three isolated logging camps along this otherwise uninhabited stretch of coast. Except for the head of Resurrection Bay, all these areas experienced a train of waves which came in as large swells but did not break. The first waves reached the logging camps at Whidbey Bay and Puget Bay on the southeast coast of the Kenai Peninsula (pl. 2) between 19 and 20 minutes after the earthquake began. The highest wave at Whidbey Bay was the second one, which followed 10 to 12 minutes after the first wave and ran up to an estimated elevation of 35 to 40 feet above the normal predicted tide stage. Within approximately 30 minutes after the start of the tremors, the first waves arrived at the logging camp at Rocky Bay near the southwest tip of the Kenai Peninsula (pl. 1) and were breaking near Seward. In contrast to the initial water motion at most nearby localities, the first wave at Rocky Bay reportedly was preceded by a withdrawal of about 18 feet. The highest wave, which came in on the high tide after midnight, left swash marks 11 feet above extreme high-tide level.

In Resurrection Bay the seismic sea waves inundated low-lying areas of Seward, the flats at the head of the Bay, and nearby Lowell Point to an estimated height of 25 to 35 feet above lower low water. The initial wave destroyed such docks as had not already been wrecked by the subaqueous slide and swept many houses and boats from the vicinity of the small-boat harbor into the lagoon north of Seward and onto the flats at the head of Resurrection Bay. Estimates of the height of the highest wave, which crested at about 11:00 p.m. near high tide, and the amount of withdrawal that preceded it, indicated that it may have had an amplitude of as much as 70 feet near Seward (Grantz, Plafker, and Kathadoorian, 1964; Lemke, 1967).

The seismic sea waves within Prince William Sound were described by all observers as fast-rising tides with associated strong currents. The first wave, which reached Boswell Bay on Hinchinbrook Island at about 6:00 p.m., was about 12 feet high. Throughout the sound the highest waves were recorded close to high tide between midnight and 1:00 a.m. They inundated shorelines in the eastern and northern parts of Prince William Sound to a maximum of about 17 feet above the existing tide level and caused some damage and one casualty at Cordova. Elsewhere in Prince William Sound, the seismic sea waves did not result in loss of life, although waves 6 to 10 feet above normal tide levels repeatedly inundated low-lying areas of Valdez that had settled differentially during the earthquake and also shorelines in those parts of northwestern Prince William Sound that had been significantly lowered by tectonic subsidence.

Seismic sea waves were experienced at remote localities east of Prince William Sound on Middleton Island, at the Cape Saint Elias Light Station on Kayak Island, and at Yakataga and Yakutat. One coastguardsman at Cape Saint Elias was drowned in the initial waves, but no wave damage was sustained at the light station or at any of the other remote localities where waves were reported.

EFFECTS ON COMMUNITIES

The following section outlines the earthquake effects on communities at which loss of life or noteworthy physical damage occurred and which are not described in other chapters of this Professional Paper. These communities are listed and the effects of the earthquake at each place are summarized in table 2. The communities are grouped into five broad geographical areas as follows: (1) communities of Prince William Sound; (2) communities of the coastal belt east of Prince William Sound and offshore islands of the Continental Shelf; (3) Kenai Peninsula communities (other than those along the shore of Prince William Sound); (4) communities of western Cook Inlet and the Alaska Peninsula; and (5) inland communities, generally along the highway and railroad net north of the coastal mountains belt.

PRINCE WILLIAM SOUND COMMUNITIES

Compared to their size, a disproportionately large amount of damage from a variety of causes was sustained by the few small fishing communities along the coast of Prince William Sound in the earthquake's epicentral region. Despite proximity to the epicenter, structural damage from shaking was relatively minor partly because of the prevailing wood-frame construction and partly because virtually all communities along the rugged fiorded coast are founded on bedrock or bedrock overlain by a relatively thin veneer of unconsolidated deposits.

Much of the property damage and all loss of life at Valdez and Whittier were related to massive vibration-induced submarine landslides and the violent waves they generated. At other localities, notably at Chenega, local waves of unknown origin that appeared suddenly during or immediately after the earthquake caused heavy damage and casualties. In contrast to the destructive effects of the sudden waves of local origin, the effect of the long-period seismic sea waves that entered the sound was to cause large quiet fluctuations in tide level. Superimposition of the waves on high tide, roughly 6 hours after the earthquake, resulted in flooding of some shorelines and moderate damage in the Cordova area.

Vertical tectonic displacements that accompanied the earthquake in Prince William Sound caused a regional northward tilting about a zero line that extends roughly from Port Nellie Juan in the western part of the sound northeastward almost through the earthquake epicenter in Unakwik Inlet and then eastward through Port Valdez. Shores north of the line were submerged as much as 7 feet, whereas those south of the line emerged as much as 38 feet (Plafker, 1969). Regional warping caused extensive long-term damage through its adverse effects on coastal installations, navigable waterways, and harbors. Docks and piers throughout the area of uplift were raised above water level at most stages of tide, and reduced water depths limited the usefulness of certain waterways and harbors. On the other hand, few communities in the area of subsidence were seriously affected by widespread inundation of waterfront areas.

In addition to the vertical movements, horizontal displacements in a relative southeasterly direction occurred. They range from about 20 to 64 feet and increase in general from north to south. These displacements resulted in no known direct damage. However,

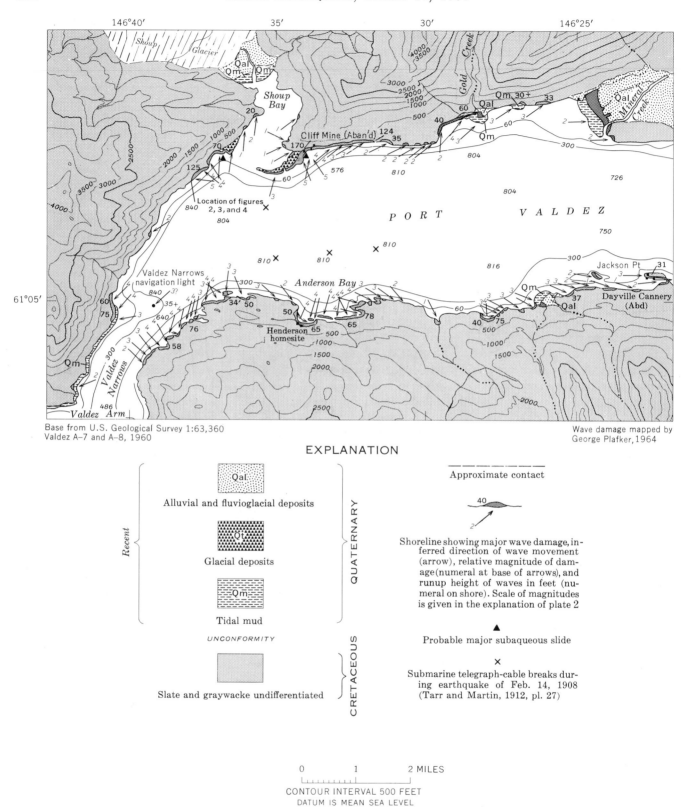

Base from U.S. Geological Survey 1:63,360
Valdez A-7 and A-8, 1960

Wave damage mapped by
George Plafker, 1964

EXPLANATION

Qal	Alluvial and fluvioglacial deposits
Qt	Glacial deposits
Qm	Tidal mud

Recent — QUATERNARY

UNCONFORMITY

Slate and graywacke undifferentiated — CRETACEOUS

— — — — — — — — —
Approximate contact

Shoreline showing major wave damage, inferred direction of wave movement
(arrow), relative magnitude of dam-
age(numeral at base of arrows), and
runup height of waves in feet (numeral on shore). Scale of magnitudes
is given in the explanation of plate 2

▲
Probable major subaqueous slide

✕
Submarine telegraph-cable breaks dur-
ing earthquake of Feb. 14, 1908
(Tarr and Martin, 1912, pl. 27)

0   1   2 MILES

CONTOUR INTERVAL 500 FEET
DATUM IS MEAN SEA LEVEL
BATHYMETRIC CONTOURS AND SPOT DEPTHS IN FEET AS SHOWN

1.—Map showing distribution and intensity of wave damage in the western part of Port Valdez.

horizontal movement of steep-sided basins and fiords relative to their contained water bodies, if it occurred fast enough, may have caused many of the unexplained water disturbances that accompanied the earthquake in Prince William Sound and elsewhere (Plafker, 1969).

The following section summarizes earthquake-related damage in all the communities along the shore of Prince William Sound with the exception of Whittier and Valdez, which have been described separately by Kachadoorian (1965) and by Coulter and Migliaccio (1966). The locations of all communities referred to, as well as shorelines damaged by wave inundation, are shown on plate 2.

ANDERSON BAY AND VICINITY

Anderson Bay, along the south shore of Port Valdez, was the site of a small fishing camp (fig. 1). Its sole inhabitant, Harry Henderson, is missing and presumably was drowned in violent local waves that struck the shore during or shortly after the earthquake. The waves, which ran up to as much as 78 feet above lower water in the bay, swept away Henderson's cabin and appurtenant structures at the camp, leaving only the driven piling foundations to mark its former location.

All structures at a large abandoned mine, the Cliff mine, located directly across Port Valdez from Anderson Bay, were also obliterated by waves that deposited driftwood 170 feet above lower low water and splashed silt and sand up to an elevation of 220 feet. The abandoned Dayville cannery at Jackson Point, 5 miles east of Anderson Bay, was extensively damaged by waves as much as 31 feet high. Elsewhere along the shore violent waves broke 24-inch-

2.—Spur west of Shoup Bay in Port Valdez that was overtopped by a local wave traveling from right to left. Trees and branches are broken to an elevation of more than 100 feet above lower low water. Location shown in figure 1.

diameter spruce trees at elevations as high as 101 feet and deposited barnacle-covered boulders estimated to weigh 1,700 pounds 88 feet above the shoreline (figs. 2, 3, and 4). The waves that moved westward out of Port Valdez overtopped and destroyed the Valdez Narrows navigation light situated on top of a reinforced concrete pedestal 35 feet above lower low water (fig. 1).

Brief examinations of the wave effects at two localities in Port Valdez, shortly after the earthquake, led Plafker to infer that the shoreline damage was caused by a wave that entered the port from the west (Grantz, Plafker, and Kachadoorian, 1964, p. 12). Detailed examination of the damage distribution during the fol-

lowup studies (Plafker and Mayo, 1965, fig. 16) clearly indicates that the highest waves in western Port Valdez probably originated mainly at the sites of large submarine slides of segments of the Shoup Glacier end moraine that blocks the mouth of the bay (fig. 1). The moraine is a crescentic deposit of coarse unconsolidated glacial debris perched at the lip of a hanging valley whose floor is more than 500 feet above the bottom of Port Valdez. The damage distribution, submarine soundings, and changes in shoreline configuration indicate that the largest slides probably originated near the Cliff mine and at the west side of Shoup Bay near the points indicated by triangles on figure 1. Downslope movement of such masses triggered by the

high wave generated by submarine sliding at the head of the fiord 10 miles east of Shoup Bay is difficult to reconcile with the directions and relative heights of waves in western Port Valdez as indicated by the pattern of wave damage along the shoreline (fig. 1).

Two eyewitnesses to the event (Delbert and "Red" Ferrier) were in a small boat outside Valdez Narrows. They saw waves coming from the direction of Shoup Bay approximately 5 minutes after the earthquake began and watched the first wave overtop and destroy the Valdez Narrows navigation light. Although the wave dissipated rapidly outside Valdez Narrows, the boat barely rode it out without swamping. On their way to Valdez, at 8 p.m., 2½ hours after the

3 (left).—Living spruce trees 2 feet in diameter that were snapped off by a local wave at elevations between 88 and 101 feet above lower low water at the locality near Shoup Bay shown in figure 1.

earthquake must have forced a sudden withdrawal of water from the area which they had occupied. Water moving into the surface depressions created high-velocity surge waves that first struck the shores immediately adjacent and then spread radially outward with gradually diminishing runup heights (fig. 1). Smaller earthquake-triggered slides elsewhere along the fiord may have contributed to the observed wave damage.

An alternative suggestion made by Coulter and Migliaccio (1966, p. C14) that wave damage in the western part of Valdez Arm was somehow caused primarily by a "component" of the 20- to 30-foot-

4 (right).—Boulder estimated to weigh 1,700 pounds thrown up 88 feet above the shoreline by a local wave at the place near Shoup Bay shown in figure 1.

5.—Aerial view of the Chenega village site at the head of Chenega Cove. Lower limits of snow, as shown by arrows, indicate the approximate limits of wave runup; the schoolhouse is circled. Photograph taken March 29, 1964.

earthquake, these men saw large numbers of dead red snappers of exceptional size floating in the water near Valdez Narrows. The red snappers, which normally inhabit deep water and are extremely sensitive to rapid pressure changes, probably were killed when they were forced up off the bottom by turbulence related to the inferred submarine slides.

A past history of repeated submarine slides in Port Valdez is suggested by breaks of submarine telegraph cables and fish kills during at least five earthquakes in 70 years (Coulter and Migliaccio, 1966, p. C9). Breakage of two submarine cables during one of these earthquakes (in 1908) between Shoup Bay and Anderson Bay, at localities shown on figure 1, is

strongly suggestive of previous submarine sliding in the same general area.

CHENEGA

Chenega was a native fishing village on the southern end of Chenega Island, on Knight Island Passage in western Prince William Sound. All its buildings except one house and the school were destroyed by sea waves, and 23 of its 75 inhabitants were lost. The village site was abandoned immediately after the earthquake and the survivors were resettled at Tatitlek after several months of care in Cordova.

Chenega was built on bedrock or thin alluvium over bedrock around the head of Chenega Cove. There are no large subaerial

masses of unconsolidated deposits along the shore anywhere at or near Chenega. Most of the 8 or 10 frame houses, the store, and the church were built on dug piling foundations on the slopes around the cove. A wood seawall protected part of the shore from erosion by normal tides. The reinforced concrete school was on slightly higher ground at an elevation of about 70 feet above post-earthquake mean lower low water (figs. 5, 6). A narrow rocky beach was below the seawall and served as a playground for the children.

The earthquake shaking, which began gently but became much stronger within 1 minute, lasted an estimated 4½ to 5 minutes. Understandably, there are no reports of vibration damage. Mike Ele-

6.—Main part of the Chenega village site. Piling in ground marks the former locations of homes that were swept away by waves. Schoolhouse on high ground was undamaged.

shansky and Joe Komkoff estimated that between 60 and 90 seconds after shaking began the first wave rose quietly but rapidly about half way up the beach. It receded rapidly almost at once, exposing the floor of the entire cove to an estimated depth of 20 or more fathoms and for a distance of about 300 yards offshore. A second and much higher wave arrived within 4 minutes of the earthquake's onset and before shaking had ceased. This wave, which was about 35 feet high, ran up to the schoolhouse foundation, a height of 70 feet. All the buildings except one house and the school were either smashed into the trees or swept out to sea with the backwash. The inundated shoreline, maximum wave runup heights,

and general direction of wave movement as inferred from damage distribution are shown on figure 7. People who were on the beach or had not had time to join the exodus to higher ground were carried away. In addition to all its other belongings, the village lost all but three of its boats. Only one of the surviving craft was in port at the time; the other two were out with hunting parties. They were welcome additions to the rescue effort the next day. The surviving villagers spent the night huddled in the snowy woods high above the school, for fear of later and even higher waves. These did not materialize and the school, with its nearby powerplant, was unharmed except for some water in the basement. As shown on fig-

ure 7, waves comparable in size to those at Chenega struck elsewhere along the coast of the island, particularly in the cove just east of Chenega. There, most of the muskeg and all of the trees were stripped from the surface; blocks of bedrock were even torn from a 20-foot seacliff.

The cause of the waves at and near Chenega is uncertain although their sudden appearance during the earthquake clearly indicates a local origin. The timing and sequence of waves suggest the possibility that they were caused by a sizable submarine slide in Knight Island Passage. Moreover, as at Anderson Bay, great numbers of large red snappers appeared at the surface of Knight Island Passage within a few hours

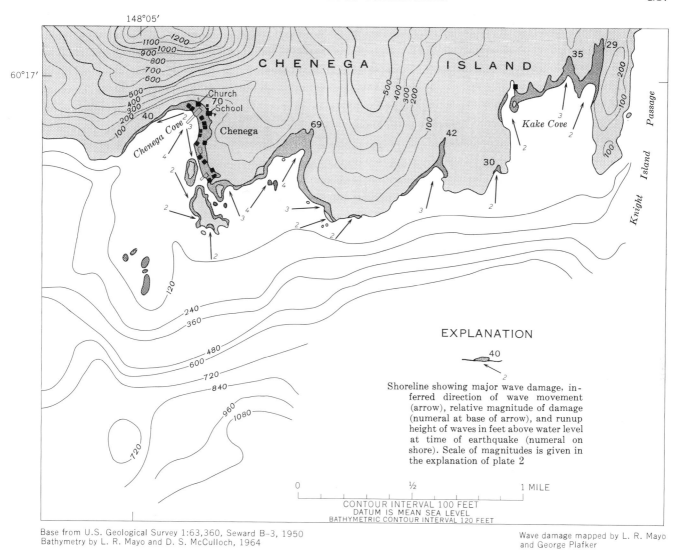

EXPLANATION

Shoreline showing major wave damage, inferred direction of wave movement
(arrow), relative magnitude of damage
(numeral at base of arrow), and runup
height of waves in feet above water level
at time of earthquake (numeral on
shore). Scale of magnitudes is given in
the explanation of plate 2

Base from U.S. Geological Survey 1:63,360, Seward B–3, 1950
Bathymetry by L. R. Mayo and D. S. McCulloch, 1964

Wave damage mapped by L. R. Mayo
and George Plafker

7.—Distribution and intensity of wave damage at Chenega and vicinity, Chenega Island.

of the earthquake. These fish may have been killed by rapid vertical movements related to landslide-generated turbidity currents. Detailed fathometer profiles of the area offshore from Chenega made by Mayo and McCulloch in 1964 (L. R. Mayo, written comm., 1965) show no significant bottom changes when compared to pre-earthquake soundings to indicate that a major submarine slide had occurred at a depth of less than 100 fathoms. On the contrary, their soundings indicate that at least the upper part of the steep submarine slope into Knight Island Passage is probably mainly bedrock without any large potential slide masses in the form of unconsolidated deposits. A possible alternative explanation is that these waves were generated by the horizontal tectonic displacement of Chenega Island southward relative to the water body in Knight Island Passage. This displacement, which amounted to roughly 55 feet (Plafker, 1969, fig. 16), could have generated the observed waves if it occurred fast enough. The fish kill in the Knight Island Passage area, however, probably resulted from submarine slides whose relationship to the destructive Chenega waves is unknown.

CORDOVA AND VICINITY

Cordova is now a fishing, canning, and distribution center for much of the Prince William Sound region; earlier in its history it was the rail-ocean transshipment point for copper ore from the rich Kennecott mining district farther inland. Of all the communities affected by the earthquake, it stands out as the one where tectonic uplift did far more damage than seismic vibration and waves combined. The city is accessible only by air or water, but

completion of the Copper River Highway, which was itself severely damaged by the earthquake (Kachadoorian, 1968), will eventually tie it to the road net of interior Alaska.

Cordova is on the mainland along the south side of Orca Inlet, opposite Hawkins Island (pl. 1). Most of the city is built on argillite and graywacke bedrock. A number of dwellings in "old town" on the south side of the city are founded on unconsolidated fluvioglacial deposits that fill a low divide between the waters of Orca Inlet and Eyak Lake, a large body of fresh water east of Cordova (fig. 8). The small-plane airport for the city is along the shore of Eyak Lake; a larger airport and Federal Aviation Agency facilities, employing about 40 people, are about 13 miles east of the city, on the edge of a great prism of unconsolidated sediments that make up the Copper River Delta (pl. 1). A few fishermen's cabins are along the shores of Orca Inlet. An FAA (Federal Aviation Agency) navigation facility, a satellite tracking station, and several homes are at the east end of Hinchinbrook Island at and near Boswell Bay.

Everyone in Cordova and at the airport felt the violent shaking of the earthquake. Estimates of its duration range from 3 to 5 minutes. Most observers agree that the initial movement was in an east-west direction, but a few individuals stated that it was more nearly north-south. It was described as a rolling motion with occasional sharp jars. The intensity of the motion apparently was considerably higher at the FAA facility on the Copper River Delta than in the city proper. Observers in town report relatively little difficulty in standing or moving about during the earthquake and negligible

shifting or toppling of items in homes and stores. In contrast, violent ground motion at the FAA facility made it difficult or impossible to stand or walk about in some homes, and large and small objects were shifted or thrown down in all homes and other buildings. Several people at the airport and along the highway saw surface ground waves, with crests, estimated at 20 to 30 feet apart, "exactly like waves on water." Ice was cracked on Eyak Lake and one pressure ridge developed there. Innumerable ground fissures occurred throughout the Copper River Delta, but none in the city itself. One observer at the FAA station reported that fissures outside the control building opened and slapped closed intermittently during the earthquake.

Despite the heavy shaking, there was no structural damage in the city. Damage at the airport was caused entirely by fissures that intersected the foundation of the FAA control building (fig. 9), taxiways, and underground utilities (Eckel, 1967). All bridges on the segment of the Copper River Highway between the city and the airport that cross unconsolidated deposits of the delta were destroyed or badly damaged, and the roadway itself settled differentially and was cut by fissures (Kachadoorian, 1968). The bridge spanning Eyak River which has foundations on bedrock was not damaged.

Reports differ as to the number and timing of the sea waves that struck Cordova. The first wave observed near Boswell Bay was a strong surge at about 6 p.m. (S. I. Starbuck, oral commun., July 1964). Many rapid but gentle rises and withdrawals, presumably due to passage of seismic sea waves, at Cordova and vicinity in the hours immediately after the cessa-

8.—Cordova, as it appeared in September 1966, with port facilities rebuilt to compensate for the 6-foot tectonic uplift of the shore-line. Looking south, with end of Eyak Lake and Copper River Highway in left center, and Cordova sawmill, destroyed by seismic sea waves, toward upper right. The white angular patch, lower right, is new land made from material dredged from the deepened and enlarged small-boat basin. Photograph by U.S. Army.

[507]

tion of shaking caused no damage. The highest wave, which almost coincided with the predicted high tide of 13 feet, struck the waterfront area at about 12:30 a.m. on the 28th. This wave, about 20 feet high, flooded the shore to a height of about 34 feet above postearthquake mean lower low water, or about 5 feet above the extreme high-water level. All waves were calm, without breakers, but high water and swift currents during these and possibly even later waves did considerable damage to the port facilities and to moored boats. The deck of the city dock was lifted off its pilings and displaced; one cannery was damaged when a boat smashed against its piling. The waves also struck the low area

---

9.—One of numerous ground fissures in fluvioglacial outwash deposits at the Cordova FAA airport station. Fissures such as this one displaced the concrete foundation of the station building in the background and broke underground utility lines throughout the facility area.

---

toward Eyak Lake, where several small structures were washed away and a sawmill was destroyed (fig. 10). The city's radio tower, on the tidal flats, swayed violently with the shock waves, but remained intact until much later when it was struck and toppled by a floating structure. The waves also damaged the roadway and washed out a bridge at Hartney Bay on the road between Cordova and Point Whitshed (pl. 1).

At Point Whitshed, a small fishing camp located 8½ miles southwest of Cordova at the mouth of Orca Inlet, 10 cabins were washed away by waves and one man was drowned. As reported by Alec Col-

---

10.—Seismic sea wave damage at the Cordova sawmill along Orca Inlet.

---

ner, the first wave to arrive was calm and like a very high tide. This wave was followed within several minutes by much higher and stronger waves that struck from opposite sides of the point on which the camp is situated, joined, and rushed up the slope behind the camp. Withdrawal of the combined wave floated the cabins away (Cordova Times, April 2, 1964).

Tectonic uplift raised the land surface in the vicinity of Cordova about 6 feet (Plafker, 1969, pl. 2). This uplift was far more disastrous to all port facilities than were the earthquake vibrations or the seismic sea waves. One cannery at Crystal Falls, on the edge of the Copper River Delta about 5 miles south of Cordova, was abandoned because boats could no longer reach it. At Cordova, all dock facilities were raised so high that they could be reached by boats only at highest tides. Several nearby canneries had to extend their docks more than 100 feet to permit access. The area in the vicinity of the city dock and the small-boat basin was above water at most tides; an extensive and difficult dredging project, together with new breakwaters and dock repairs, was necessary to make the facilities usable. In the course of this work, which was done by the Corps of Engineers, the boat basin was much enlarged, and about 20 acres of new land, eventually usable for industrial purposes, was made from material dredged from the boat basin (fig. 8).

Damage to the port facilities was not the only adverse result of tectonic uplift. The Cordova fishing fleet normally uses Orca Inlet in its travel between town and the shallow fishing grounds off the Copper River Delta. Because uplift made the inlet waters too shallow for even small boats, laden vessels had to wait for extremely

high tides or take the much longer and more hazardous route through Hinchinbrook Entrance and through Orca Bay. Because neither solution was economically practicable, it was necessary for the Corps of Engineers to dredge a new channel through almost the entire length of Orca Inlet. The total cost of dredging, port facilities, and repairs to the town's uplifted sewer outfall was about $3 million, but part of this cost was offset by enlargement of the small-boat basin over its preearthquake capacity and by development of new industrial land.

HINCHINBROOK LIGHT STATION

The Hinchinbrook Light Station, with a crew of six men, is on the southwest tip of Hinchinbrook Island in Prince William Sound. It was undamaged by the earthquake, but there were fears, later shown to be groundless, that reactivated old landslides would endanger the station.

The earthquake, which lasted about 5 minutes, was severe enough to snap some live trees, to cause the main station building to oscillate, and to displace small objects from shelves. Large movable objects were not shifted, however, and there was no structural damage to any buildings. At least 10 strong aftershocks, which occurred within the first week after the earthquake, contributed substantially to apprehensions of the crew members.

The topography and geology in the immediate vicinity of the station are shown in figure 11. The main building is on a gently undulating bench about 150 feet north of a near-vertical seacliff that is 180 to 190 feet high near the station but somewhat lower toward the west. Structures are built on well-indurated medium-grained blocky graywacke sand-

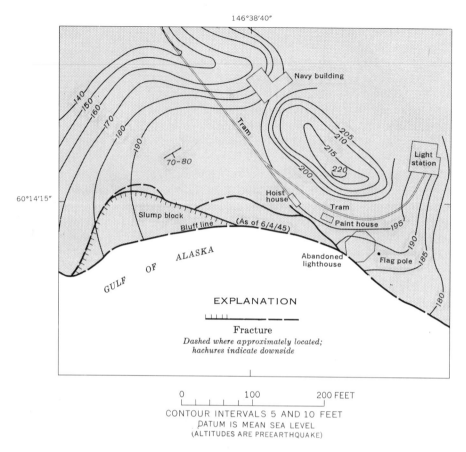

11.—Map of Cape Hinchinbrook Light Station. Present bluff is substantially north of that shown, because of erosion since 1945 when the base map was made. Bedrock is graywacke.

stone. The beds range from a few inches to at least 100 feet in thickness; some thin beds of black argillite are interlayered with the sandstone. Bedding strikes about N. 60° E. and dips 70°–80° SE.

Two fracture-bounded incipient landslide blocks are along the seacliff. The larger one, 40 feet wide, extends 200 feet westward along the cliff from the foundation of the old abandoned lighthouse. A concentric tension fracture, locally 2 feet wide and at least 15 feet deep, marks the inner edge of the block. A second incipient landslide, 75 feet long and less than 15 feet wide, is farther west of the old lighthouse site. It overlooks an old slump block, and it too is bounded by an open tension fracture. Aside from one small tension crack near

the southwest side of the hoist house, no other fractures were found in the station area.

There is abundant evidence that erosion and slumping had been causing rapid recession of the seacliff since at least 1907. Available maps show that at the abandoned lighthouse the cliff receded 20 feet from 1907 to 1931 and an additional 20 feet from 1931 to 1964. About 120 feet east of the old lighthouse the cliff receded about 40 feet from 1907 to 1931 and an unknown amount after that date. Cliff erosion also occurred west of the abandoned lighthouse—certainly 5 feet from 1945 to 1964—and an unknown amount in earlier years.

New tension cracks and incipient slides that developed during

the 1964 earthquake are but the latest episodes in a long history of cliff recession. The 8 feet of tectonic uplift that accompanied the earthquake has brought the base of the seacliff above the reach of all but extremely high storm waves; hence the former rapid erosion of the cliff has been arrested, at least for many years to come. An adverse effect of the uplift, however, was the raising of the station dock above the level of most tides; this raising required extension of the dock at a cost of nearly $100,000.

LATOUCHE AND VICINITY

Latouche is a large abandoned mining camp situated along a cove on the rocky northwest shore of Latouche Island (fig. 12). Bedrock consists of firm argillite and sandstone of early Tertiary age. There are no large masses of unconsolidated deposits along the shore at Latouche or anywhere on land in the immediate vicinity.

Because the island was uninhabited at the time of the earthquake, the effects of shaking on existing structures, most of which were in a poor state of repair, are not known. Northern Latouche Island was raised between 10 and 11 feet, by tectonic uplift, presumably during the earthquake.

Local waves of unknown origin

destroyed all the docks and piers along the shore at Latouche and either demolished or extensively damaged many of the waterfront buildings (fig. 13). Extensive wave damage with runup as high as 58 feet was also apparent elsewhere along the shore of Latouche Passage and in Sleepy Bay at the northern tip of Latouche Island. At Port Crawford, 1.3 miles northwest of Latouche, an abandoned sawmill building was displaced and damaged by the waves, and several smaller structures nearby were destroyed.

PERRY ISLAND

Perry Island is in the northwest part of Prince William Sound, between Perry Passage and Lone Passage and about 24 miles southeast of Whittier (pl. 1). A small camp consisting of a twostory house, a large storage house, and a boathouse, is at the head of South Bay near the southern tip of the island. The camp, occupied by "Chick" and "Red" Comstock, is built on a bay-head gravel bar overlying bedrock. There are no large masses of unconsolidated deposits anywhere along the shore.

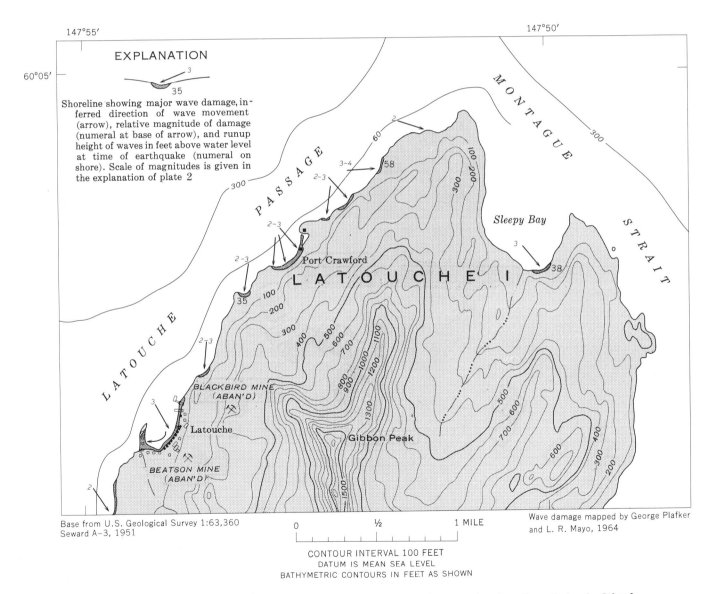

12.—Distribution and intensity of wave damage at Latouche and adjacent parts of northern Latouche Island.

13.—Remains of buildings partially damaged by waves along part of Latouche waterfront. Docks, piers, and some buildings in this area were swept away. Approximately 11 feet of tectonic uplift has raised this former port above the reach of most tides.

Shaking, in a northeast-southwest direction and gradually decreasing in intensity, lasted about 4 minutes. One chimney fell, the bay water was ruffled, and trees swayed, but there were no other effects from the shaking.

Immediately after the earthquake, and with no prior withdrawal, an 8- to 10-foot wave of unknown origin moved in with great force. The wave receded within 2 minutes and exposed the bay floor for an estimated 200 yards offshore. No sooner had the bay gone dry than another wave was seen approaching from near the lighthouse at the mouth of South Bay. This second wave moved in quietly, but flooded over the beach bar to a height of about 21 feet above lower low water. The Comstocks, who were standing out-

side the house, were washed into the slough behind the beach bar and narrowly escaped drowning. The boathouse was floated away, but the two other buildings, which were protected by snow embankments, were undamaged. No other waves reached above the normal high-water line at Perry Island.

POINT NOWELL

Point Nowell is the site of a fishing camp on a small low peninsula that juts southward from the mainland near the northern entrance to Knight Island Passage. The peninsula is underlain by bedrock; there are no large masses of unconsolidated deposits along the shore anywhere near the point.

A destructive wave entered the inlet behind the peninsula and flooded the area to a depth of at

least 37 feet above mean lower low water. Several frame buildings were displaced and some smashed into trees. Many trees 12 to 18 inches in diameter were broken by wave-propelled debris. The damage distribution indicates that the wave entered the inlet from the south. Disappearance of the one inhabitant, presumably by drowning, strongly suggests a wave that struck without warning at the time of the earthquake—a wave, similar to those observed at nearby Chenega and Perry Island.

PORT NELLIE JUAN

Port Nellie Juan was the site of an inoperative cannery on the northeast shore of McClure Bay, a small arm of the much larger body of water also called Port Nellie Juan. The cannery was

14.—Wave-damaged structures at Port Nellie Juan cannery. A wave, which ran up to the snow trimline along the shore, damaged these structures, washed away the dock, and presumably drowned the three resident caretakers of the cannery. Photograph taken April 4, 1964.

built on tightly folded argillite and graywacke of probable early Tertiary age.

All three of the resident cannery caretakers are missing and presumed to have drowned when the cannery dock was washed away in a wave that must have struck suddenly and probably at the time of the earthquake (fig. 14). Local waves with runup heights of as much as 110 feet also caused extensive damage to vegetation at numerous other localities along the uninhabited shores of Port Nellie Juan and its westward extension, Kings Bay (fig. 15). One large barge that was tied up at the mouth of a small creek on the north side of Port Nellie Juan was lifted by violent waves, overturned, and deposited 200 feet inland among the trees (fig. 16).

The cause of the destructive waves in Port Nellie Juan is unknown. Comparison of pre- and postearthquake soundings by Mayo and McCulloch (L. R. Mayo, written commun., 1965) indicates that the highest waves in Kings Bay were at least in part generated by massive submarine landslides of deltaic deposits at the head of the bay and at two localities along its north shore. There are no comparable large unconsolidated deposits exposed at the surface in Port Nellie Juan, although it is conceivable that such deposits are present but are entirely submerged.

PORT OCEANIC

Port Oceanic, the site of an inoperative cannery, is on Thumb Bay, an arm of Mummy Bay,

near the southern tip of Knight Island, in western Prince William Sound (fig. 17). The cannery is built mainly on graywacke and slate bedrock, but the bunkhouse is in part on filled land. Thumb Bay is a sheltered, shallow body of water surrounded by fairly steep forested slopes.

According to George Flemming, one of the two cannery caretakers, the quake tremors lasted 3 to 4 minutes. Motion came from the southeast or south-southeast; the ground rolled and twisted with 1- to 2-foot amplitudes and 1- to 2-second periods. Rumbling noises preceded short, sharp aftershocks at intervals during the night and for the next several days. Vibration displaced small objects and moved a stove a few inches but caused no other damage except for

15.—Shore near the head of Kings Bay swept bare of timber to an altitude of 110 feet by slide-generated local waves. Bare areas of rock on the spur in the right middle distance were scoured clean of the soil and muskeg cover.

16.—Barge, which is 60 feet long and 25 feet wide, that was broken loose from its mooring by a violent local wave in Port Nellie Juan, turned upside down, and deposited among the trees 200 feet from the shoreline at about 30 feet above mean lower low water.

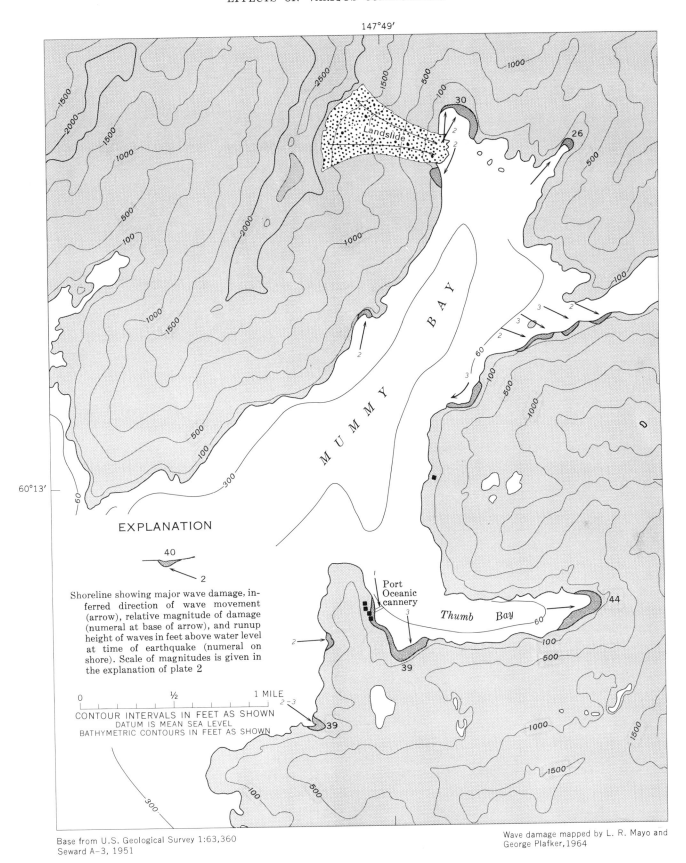

EXPLANATION

40

2

Shoreline showing major wave damage, inferred direction of wave movement
(arrow), relative magnitude of damage
(numeral at base of arrow), and runup
height of waves in feet above water level
at time of earthquake (numeral on
shore). Scale of magnitudes is given in
the explanation of plate 2

0   ½   1 MILE

CONTOUR INTERVALS IN FEET AS SHOWN
DATUM IS MEAN SEA LEVEL
BATHYMETRIC CONTOURS IN FEET AS SHOWN

Base from U.S. Geological Survey 1:63,360
Seward A–3, 1951

Wave damage mapped by L. R. Mayo and
George Plafker, 1964

17.—Distribution and intensity of wave damage in the vicinity of Port Oceanic cannery at Thumb Bay, Knight Island.

18.—Buildings at the Port Oceanic cannery damaged by a wave that struck within 2 to 3 minutes of the initial shock and had a crest height about even with the cannery floor level. Photograph taken April 4, 1964.

slight settling of one end of a bunkhouse which was built on filled land.

The area was uplifted about 6 feet during the earthquake. One wave, doubtless of local origin, arrived within 2 to 3 minutes of the initial shock. It rose about 3 feet above the tectonically elevated highest tide line at the cannery site, with a runup of at least 22 feet above that level (44 feet above mean lower low water) at the head of the bay. This wave destroyed the dock, several boats, and washed some piling supports out from under the cannery (fig. 18). No later waves were observed in Thumb Cove.

The cause of the local waves in Thumb Cove is uncertain. The cove, is less than 125 feet deep, hence probably too shallow to have had large submarine slides, but the remote possibility that slide-generated waves moved into it from Mummy Bay cannot be discounted from the available evidence. A landslide that fell into shallow water near the head of Mummy Bay (fig. 17) could not have displaced a large enough volume of water to cause damaging waves except, perhaps, in its immediate vicinity.

SAWMILL BAY AND VICINITY

Sawmill Bay, in the southwestern part of Prince William Sound, is an indentation on Evans Island off the junction of Latouche and Elrington Passages (fig. 19). Along its shores are several homes, a fuel depot, and three canneries, one of them inoperative. All these structures are on bedrock or bedrock with a thin veneer of sediments; there are no large masses of unconsolidated deposits along the shores. As at nearby Chenega, local waves did far more damage than any other earthquake-related cause.

According to estimates of several eyewitnesses, the earthquake lasted 4 to 5 minutes in the Sawmill Bay area; it was preceded and accompanied by sounds like booming thunder. Shaking began with a northwest-southeast swaying motion that soon became fast and jarring, but much of the later movement seemed to be almost vertical. Pilings of the Crab Bay cannery dock were lifted upward clear of the water, but the caps and dock deck were not displaced. Three poorly constructed chimneys were cracked or toppled and

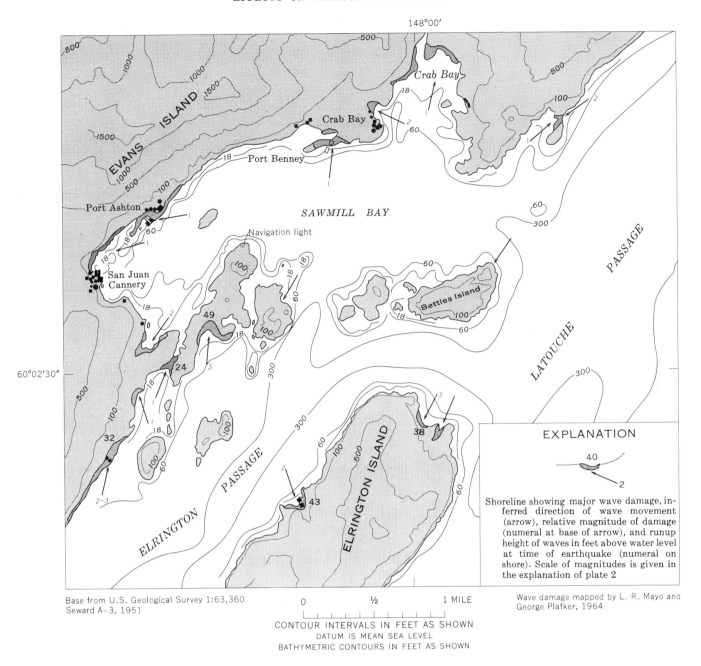

EXPLANATION

40

2

Shoreline showing major wave damage, inferred direction of wave movement
(arrow), relative magnitude of damage
(numeral at base of arrow), and runup
height of waves in feet above water level
at time of earthquake (numeral on
shore). Scale of magnitudes is given in
the explanation of plate 2

Base from U.S. Geological Survey 1:63,360
Seward A-3, 1951

0 ½ 1 MILE

CONTOUR INTERVALS IN FEET AS SHOWN
DATUM IS MEAN SEA LEVEL
BATHYMETRIC CONTOURS IN FEET AS SHOWN

Wave damage mapped by L. R. Mayo and
George Plafker, 1964

19.—Distribution and intensity of wave damage in Sawmill Bay and vicinity, Evans Island.

some movable objects in homes and canneries fell or moved about. The ice was cracked on a small artificial water-supply lake back of Port Ashton. Moreover, small leaks, not large enough to require repairs, developed beneath the lake's concrete dam. These leaks, which suggest that vibration caused some cracking of the concrete, are one of the very few examples of earthquake damage to dams throughout the stricken area. The San Juan cannery dock at the head of Sawmill Bay was not affected nor was there any other damage from the shaking.

Sawmill Bay is a short distance west of Montague Island, where the greatest recorded tectonic uplift took place. Uplift in the vicinity of the bay was about 10 feet; it required modification of the dock facilities and lengthening of grid skidways in order to float stored fishing boats before the canneries could resume operations.

Local waves of unknown origin that caused most of the damage in the vicinity of Sawmill Bay began 2 minutes after onset of the earthquake, according to Carl Blindheim. The water first rose smoothly and slowly for an estimated 1 minute, then rushed out to at least the minus 20-foot level in a few seconds; all the bottom of Crab Bay and large expanses of Sawmill Bay were exposed. Within a few moments the sea rushed back with tremendous roar and turbulence to as high as 10 feet above the extreme high-tide level along segments of the uplifted shore (fig. 19). All this happened before cessation of seismic shaking. There were no other large waves, but smaller surges continued to come in at intervals for about 5 hours on a rising tide. The highest of these, at about 1:00 a.m., reached close to the tectonically elevated

extreme high-tide level but caused no damage.

The waves damaged piling beneath some structures and demolished one dock. Vessels and skiffs near San Juan Cannery and Port Ashton were beached or carried away; two 20- by 70-foot scows were swept up into the trees and deposited one on the other. Two residents at Port Ashton who were swept into the water barely escaped drowning, but one man at Crab Bay was drowned in the first high wave while trying to secure a skiff.

Numerous local waves caused shoreline damage at various uninhabited localities along Elrington and Latouche Passages (pl. 2). Many were higher and more violent than those in Sawmill Bay. One unoccupied house on Elrington Passage, just southwest of Sawmill Bay (fig. 19), was destroyed.

The origin of the destructive waves in various parts of Sawmill Bay and vicinity is unknown. Surges observed at Sawmill Bay later during the night of March 27 and morning of March 28 undoubtedly were due to passage of the long-period seismic sea waves that entered the sound from the Gulf of Alaska.

TATITLEK AND VICINITY

Tatitlek is a fishing village on Tatitlek Narrows, between Valdez Arm and Port Fidalgo, near the northeast corner of Prince William Sound. Its population was increased to about 150 when the survivors of the Chenega tragedy (about 50) were resettled at the village. The inactive mining camp of Ellamar is nearby. Both localities are underlain by argillite-graywacke-greenstone bedrock or bedrock with a thin veneer of glacial drift. All buildings are wood, most with dug piling foundations. Damage was slight and was caused

by tectonic uplift rather than by vibration or waves.

According to Karol Kompkoff and Ivan D. Anten of Tatitlek, rumbling sounds were heard about 10 seconds before the onset of the earthquake vibrations, which lasted from 3½ to 5 minutes. The church bell rang, small objects fell from shelves, and standing was difficult to impossible, but there was no structural damage. The small village reservoir became completely empty but filled again after 2 weeks. Effects were much the same at Ellamar, though one chimney fell and some windows were broken, according to the caretaker, Carl Aranson.

The sea at Tatitlek withdrew "immediately" during the earthquake and came back up to 17 or 18 feet above normal mean lower low water, but did not reach above the extreme high-tide line, which had been tectonically elevated about 4 to 5 feet. High and erratic tides were noted for several hours after the earthquake, but none caused any damage.

Tatitlek's port facilities were actually improved somewhat as a result of the earthquake. The port, which is close to the village, depends on a natural anchorage in Tatitlek Narrows that is partly protected by rocky reefs. The normal water depth of 6 feet below mean lower low water was partially lost when the land was raised 4 to 5 feet, but the Corps of Engineers compensated for the uplift by dredging the anchorage 6 feet deeper. Because the reefs were also upraised, the basin now has more protection from storms than it did originally.

There is no obvious cause for the single wave observed at Tatitlek during the earthquake. The timing and characteristics of the high tides that followed suggest passage of seismic sea waves.

20.—Typical extensively fissured sand dune on the Copper River Delta.

COMMUNITIES OF THE COASTAL BELT EAST OF PRINCE WILLIAM SOUND

The coastal belt east of Prince William Sound and the offshore islands are sparsely inhabited, and were relatively undamaged by the earthquake. The only permanently inhabited localities include a small Coast Guard light station at Cape Saint Elias on Kayak Island, an FAA facility on Middleton Island, a small settlement at Yakataga, and a fishing village with several Government installations at Yakutat (pl. 1). There are no other communities between Yakutat and the panhandle of southeastern Alaska, a distance of about 150 miles.

The earthquake was strongly felt throughout most of the coastal belt. Seismic shaking caused widespread ground fissuring in unconsolidated fluvioglacial, alluvial, eolian, and marine deposits along the coastal belt as far east as Russell Fiord in the Yakutat area, some 300 miles east of the epicenter. Ground fissures developed in large areas of the Copper River Delta (Reimnitz and Marshall, 1965), along the margins of Controller Bay, and throughout much of the coastal lowlands extending from Cape Suckling eastward to Yakutat Bay (figs. 20–22). Many of these fissures were accompanied by extrusion of sand, gravel, and silt on sand dunes, elevated beach ridges, alluvial flood plains, and tidal flats.

Numerous landslides and avalanches, many of enormous size, were triggered in the foothills and mountains north of the coastal lowland at least as far eastward as the Yakataga area, 200 miles from the epicenter, and ice was cracked on lakes as far as Crillon Lake, about 400 miles east of the epicenter.

Tectonic uplift affected the entire coastal belt and adjacent offshore islands to the east of Prince William Sound. It was between 6 and 10 feet at the Copper River Delta and possibly as much as 14 feet at Cape Suckling; it decreased progressively eastward and died out near Yakataga (Plafker, 1969, pl. 1.)

Unlike most of the other coastal regions in the earthquake-affected area, there are no known places in the coastal belt east of Prince William Sound where local waves or seismic sea waves reached above the elevated extreme high-water levels.

[519]

CAPE SAINT ELIAS

Cape Saint Elias is the site of a Coast Guard light station on the southwestern tip of Kayak Island, just off the Bering Glacier on the north-central coast of Prince William Sound. Pinnacle Rock, a rugged rock promontory, off the tip of Kayak Island, was accessible from the light station at low tides

---

21 (upper left).—Linear fissures and extensive areas of ejected mud (dark) in the tidal flats along the shore of Controller Bay.

22 (lower left).—Fissured and slumped fluvioglacial deposits bordering a kettle lake at the eastern margin of Bering Glacier.

prior to the earthquake (see fig. 23). The promontory at the base of which the station is located and Pinnacle Rock consist of a massive porphyritic intrusive rock of middle Tertiary age.

According to William B. O'Neal, one of the station crew of four men, the fast jarring motion of the earthquake lasted about 5 minutes. There was no damage to the station except for displacement of a few small articles. Tectonic uplift at Cape Saint Elias was about 6 to 8 feet.

Within seconds after the initial shock, however, a massive rockfall was triggered at Pinnacle Rock (fig. 23). One of the crew members who was photographing sea

lions at the pinnacle had a leg broken by the falling rock. Later, as he was being carried back to the station by the other three crew members, a series of seismic sea waves that flooded over the low-lying gravel bar drowned the injured man and nearly drowned his companions. These waves reportedly struck at about 6:15 p.m., almost an hour after the start of the earthquake. The first wave, which reportedly came from the southeast, overtopped the tectonically elevated gravel bar to a depth of about 4 feet; it was immediately followed by a second and higher wave from the northwest that swept the men into the sea.

23.—Aerial view of Cape Saint Elias (left) and Pinnacle Rock (right) at the southwestern tip of Kayak Island. A portion of the earthquake-triggered rock fall from Pinnacle Rock is in the lower right corner (arrow); the Cape Saint Elias Coast Guard station is circled.

MIDDLETON ISLAND

Middleton Island, 80 miles southwest of Cordova in the Gulf of Alaska, is the site of an FAA navigation facility and emergency airfield. The island is underlain by poorly indurated sedimentary rocks of late Cenozoic age.

Earthquake tremors on the island, described as moderately strong, caused a few small items to be moved about in buildings. The only noteworthy damage was that to oil lines from the fuel storage tanks; these broke and nearly all of the oil was lost.

Tectonic uplift associated with the earthquake was roughly 11 feet, but the movement caused no damage because there are no dock or harbor facilities. According to Dwight Meeks, a seismic sea wave which struck the island from the west an estimated 20 minutes after the start of the earthquake, did not reach to the tectonically elevated high-tide level, and consequently caused no damage.

YAKATAGA

Yakataga is a small community on Cape Yakataga along the Gulf of Alaska coast, about 200 miles east of the earthquake epicenter and 100 miles west of Yakutat. It consists mainly of an FAA station, a communications facility, and dwellings of a few trappers and prospectors. The FAA facility and airstrip are built on fluvioglacial outwash deposits, whereas the communications facility and other homes are on the late Tertiary sedimentary rocks that form Cape Yakataga. Earthquake damage in the area was confined to fissuring of roads that extend from Yakataga across the coastal lowland to the west.

Ground motion in an east-west direction was strongly felt in the Yakataga area for durations estimated to be from 4 to 8 minutes

long. Small objects in some buildings reportedly were thrown off shelves or tables, water sloshed out of an emergency water tank 14 feet in diameter, and some fissures formed in the gravel airstrip. There was no structural damage. Two trappers, Clarence Tarbelt and Steve Smas, said the ground motion on the broad foreland west of Yakataga was so violent they were thrown to the ground. Within 1½ minutes after the earthquake began, they observed fissures forming in the frozen ground and a sound "like an awful rush of water". According to these 2 observers, individual fissures laced the area and some zones of fissures could be traced for a mile or more. Collapse pits along some of the fissures were as much as 9 feet in diameter and 14 feet deep. Water with mud or fine silt was ejected from some ground fissures intermittently, for a few seconds at a time, to an estimated height of 8 to 10 feet. Streams in the vicinity that were dry at the start of the shaking "were running in torrents" within a few minutes because of the vast amount of water poured out of the ground fissures, and, perhaps, because of cracking of ice-dammed lakes upstream. The high water lasted for 11 days. In spite of the strong shaking, Tarbelt reports, damage in his cabin consisted of only one spice can shaken from the shelves.

The main damage in the area consisted of extensive fissuring of abandoned oil-exploration access roads (fig. 24) and buckling of some bridges due to lateral movement of the banks inward toward the channels. Horizontal displacement across some fissures was as much as 10 feet, and pressure ridges formed from ½ to 8 feet high. Tarbelt observed that a ⅝-inch steel cable which had frozen into the ground surface was

24.—Intensely fissured road at the crest of an elevated beach ridge west of Yakataga.

cleanly parted in five places where it was crossed by fissures. The casing of a nearby abandoned oil well sheared off near the surface with a "pop like a rifle shot" a few seconds after the shaking stopped, presumably because of horizontal movement of the frozen ground.

Shortly after the earthquake ended, seismic sea waves in the form of erratic tides and swift currents were observed along the shore of Cape Yakataga. Charles Bilderback, a long-time resident of the cape, noted that the sea was calm at the time and almost at zero tide stage. The first water movement was a withdrawal that reached a low of about −6 feet at 6:25 p.m., almost 1 hour after the start of the earthquake. By using rocks on the reef as a reference for estimating tide levels, he recorded the following sequence of wave heights (relative to mean lower low water) during the evening after the earthquake:

Alaska standard time (p.m.)	High water (feet)	Low water (feet)
6:25		−6.0 to −8.0(?)
6:35	10	
6:45		0
6:55	12	
7:05		0
7:18		−1 (surge)
7:30		−6.0
7:45	8	
7:50		0
7:55	10	
7:58		0
8:07	13 (followed by 6-ft surge)	
8:16	12	
8:40		0 (followed by surge)
8:50		−4
9:20	10 (followed by surge)	
10:50	14	

The waves were followed by surges of 1 to 3 feet every few hours for about 5 days after the earthquake. No damage was caused by the waves, the highest of which reached approximately to the normal extreme high-tide level of about 15 feet.

YAKUTAT

Yakutat is the site of a native fishing village and cannery near the mouth of Yakutat Bay about half way between Juneau and Cordova, and almost 300 miles west of the earthquake epicenter. A large airfield and FAA facility are just east of the village, and a Coast Guard loran station and a microwave relay facility are along the coast nearby. Inhabited areas are on a low-lying coastal plain, the Yakutat Foreland, which is bounded on the northwest by rugged foothills of the Saint Elias

Mountains. The village is on a late Holocene end moraine, the airfield is on an extensive thick deposit of fluvioglacial outwash, and the facilities along the coast are on moraine or marine beach deposits.

The earthquake was strongly felt throughout the Yakutat Foreland as an east-west rolling or swaying motion that built up to a peak in about 30 seconds and lasted a total of 6 minutes (timed), according to A. T. Gorman of the U.S. Weather Bureau. Some individuals reported a feeling of motion sickness during the earthquake. Small items were thrown from shelves in stores and in some homes, but there was no structural damage. Ice on many lakes was broken and some lakes drained. The ground movement caused trucks parked on the airfield ramp to roll back and forth as much as 10 feet, and caused roller-mounted doors of the large FAA hangar, which are oriented northwest-southeast, to alternately open and slam closed. Rumbling noises were heard during the earthquake and a series of loud noises described as similar to "cannon shots" were heard for about 20 minutes afterward. The noises reportedly came from the vicinity of Khantaak Island, a few miles northwest of the village.

Slight damage to the concrete runway and parking ramp at the airfield resulted from vertical movement of concrete slabs and cracking of some of the slabs. According to Mr. Gorman, damage to the runway and parking ramp was somewhat greater than that which occurred during the July 10, 1958, earthquake that centered about 100 miles southeast of Yakutat (Davis and Sanders, 1960, p. 237–238).

Although ground motion was strongly felt throughout the Yakutat Foreland, two seal hunters (Jack Williams and Sam Dick)

who were camping on a bedrock site near the head of Yakutat Bay were completely unaware that an earthquake had occurred until they returned to Yakutat later in the evening. A significant difference in ground response to the passage of seismic waves in the bedrock as compared to the thick unconsolidated deposits of the foreland is thus reflected.

A single wave was observed along the shore at the village during the earthquake. The roiled and muddy water reported in the vicinity the next day suggests the possibility that a submarine slide occurred in the Khantaak Island area, the site of a disastrous slide that killed three people at the time of the 1958 earthquake (Davis and Sanders, 1960, p. 242–246). Erratic tides were observed after the earthquake and were presumably associated with passage of seismic sea waves. None of them reached above extreme high-water level or caused damage in the vicinity of the village. However, the two seal hunters at the head of Yakutat Bay reported that tide level there reached approximately 6 feet above normal highest water at about 11:00 p.m.; apprehension caused by the abnormal tides prompted them to leave their camp hurriedly and return to Yakutat by boat that evening.

KENAI PENINSULA COMMUNITIES

This section discusses only the smaller communities on the Kenai Peninsula that were damaged by the earthquake; it does not include the following towns which have already been described in the Geological Survey's Professional Paper series on the earthquake: Whittier (Kachadoorian, 1965), Seward (Lemke, 1967), Homer (Waller, 1966a), Lawing and Moose Pass (McCulloch, 1966).

Port Nellie Juan, along the shore of Prince William Sound, was discussed on page G24.

People in all the communities on the peninsula felt the earthquake of March 27, 1964. Major damage by seismic shaking occurred at Portage, at the docking facility of Nikiski, and at the military installation of Wildwood Station. Seismic sea waves inundated the waterfront of Seldovia and logging camps at Puget Bay and Whidbey Bay. The chief cause of damage to the coastal communities by the earthquake was tectonic and local surficial subsidence. English Bay, Port Graham, Girdwood, Hope, Kenai, Portage, Rocky Bay and Seldovia all subsided. Three of these—Girdwood, Hope, and Portage—were partially or completely inundated by extreme high tides after the earthquake.

COOPER LANDING

Cooper Landing is at the west end of Kenai Lake, whose outlet forms the head of Kenai River. As described by McCulloch (1966), seismic vibration was severe in this vicinity, ground fissures were very numerous, and the land surface was warped by vertical tectonic displacements.

Despite the relatively heavy shaking, damage to structures, other than the highway bridge (Kachadoorian, 1968), was relatively light. Several concrete porch slabs and foundations were cracked where fissures intersected them, cinder-block chimneys fell, and plumbing fixtures were broken. Dishes and glassware, of course, were smashed, and several small fuel-oil and propane-gas tanks broke open when their supports collapsed. Some buildings continued to settle and to develop new cracks for several days after the earthquake.

The nearby Cooper Lake hydroelectric plant was undamaged,

partly because it shut down automatically when troubled plants in Anchorage tripped overload switches on the entire power system (Eckel, 1967, p. B20).

ENGLISH BAY

English Bay, formerly called Alexandrovsk, is a fishing village on English Bay about 10 miles southwest of Seldovia. As at Seldovia and Port Graham, the only damage done by the earthquake was by tectonic subsidence of about 5 feet. A few houses that were partly flooded at high tides were torn down and replacements were built on higher ground by the Red Cross.

GIRDWOOD

The small town of Girdwood, about 55 miles west-southwest of the epicenter of the earthquake, is on a gently sloping alluvial fan where Glacier Creek flows into Turnagain Arm. The town is bordered on the east, west, and north by mountains, and on the south by Turnagain Arm.

Girdwood is underlain by silt, sand, and gravel deposits which become coarser grained from the toe toward the apex of the alluvial fan. The water table varies in depth; it is near the surface at the coastline of Turnagain Arm and becomes progressively deeper inland toward the apex of the fan.

Seismic motion at Girdwood was northwest-southeast and lasted for about 4 to 5 minutes. One person who was driving a car on the Seward-Anchorage Highway at Girdwood reported that the motion was so violent that he could not control the vehicle. When one of his passengers got out of the car she was thrown to the ground.

Many fissures developed on the lower lying areas underlain by the finer grained deposits. Water and mud were ejected from some of

the fissures. Reports on homes and other structures in Girdwood are scarce, but those obtained indicate that seismic shaking did not directly damage any structure. However, seismic shaking did generate numerous fissures throughout the town. Locally, some slight displacement downslope occurred in the water-soaked fine-grained unconsolidated sediments. Damage was widespread on the railroad grade and highway roadbed.

Five feet of regional subsidence and an additional 3 feet of local subsidence occurred at Girdwood. This total 8-foot subsidence was enough to put much of the lower lying areas of the town under water during high tides. During the high tides of April 14, 1964, all of the highway, much of the railroad west of the railroad depot, and all of the town between the railroad and highway were inundated. Water was as much as 3 feet deep in some of the buildings, and subsequently the buildings were moved to higher ground or placed on stilts.

HOPE

Hope is a small mining and fishing community on the south shore of Turnagain Arm at the mouth of Resurrection Creek. Surrounded on three sides by the rugged Kenai Mountains, the town itself is on the gently sloping surface of the creek's delta. It is underlain by relatively coarse gravel and sand, probably less than 150 feet thick. Before the earthquake the water table was less than 15 feet below the surface.

Residents of Hope reported that seismic motion started suddenly, was east-west, and lasted about 4½ minutes. They thought that the earthquake was a minor one and did not realize its severity until later. Calvin Drier, a resident of Hope since 1921, stated that the

1964 Alaska earthquake was much less intense than the one that occurred in 1936.

Most of the relatively minor earthquake damage was caused by subsidence rather than by vibration. Seismic shaking toppled one concrete-block chimney and knocked off some shelf goods. Mr. Drier's home, a log cabin resting on fine gravel, sand, and silt, settled about a foot into the ground. Seismic shaking also formed many ground fissures, the largest about ½ mile long with a maximum width of 6 inches. Water spouts, one of which was reportedly 8 feet high and lasted for 4 minutes, occurred during the earthquake.

The primary cause of damage at Hope was not seismic shaking but the effects of regional and local subsidence. Tectonic subsidence of about 5 feet and local surficial subsidence of as much as 1 foot was sufficient to flood some houses during high tides. In others, basements only were flooded. The encroaching saline water of Turnagain Arm raised the water level in many wells and made the water somewhat salty.

KENAI AND VICINITY

Kenai is on the west coast of the Kenai Peninsula, at the mouth of the Kenai River. The city is a fishing and farming center as well as a supply point for much of the Kenai Lowland. Wildwood Station, 5 miles to the north, is an Air Force base, and Nikiski, 10 miles to the north, is a shipping terminal for petroleum products from the nearby Swanson River oil field. The Kenai area is underlain by glacial till and outwash on an extremely thick sequence of poorly consolidated continental sediments of late Tertiary age. Nearly all of the relatively minor damage in the Kenai area was caused by strong seismic shaking, though a small amount of tectonic

subsidence caused accelerated erosion of natural bluffs and of a manmade embankment along the Cook Inlet side of the town.

Ceiling tiles and some light fixtures fell in the newly built Kenai Central High School, and a wall in one room parted from the floor slab but there was no other structural damage. Minor cracks formed in numerous other public and commercial buildings, but the greatest damage occurred to their contents, displaced by the shaking.

Wildwood Station, with an estimated complement of 700 men, experienced relatively severe damage from seismic vibrations. Greatest damage was to an elevated steel water tower which collapsed. The rush of released water struck the Officer's Club about 200 feet west of the tower, broke several windows, and injured one man. All power and other utilities were disrupted temporarily, but an emergency source of power supplied some electricity and steam and pumped water while main lines and facilities were under repair.

The water tower was an all steel structure supported by six posts, with an elevated tank which was full to within 5,000 gallons of its 150,000-gallon capacity. During the earthquake the tank began to sway. About halfway through the earthquake, the manhole cover at the top blew off and water spouted out of the manhole. Then the tower split in two pieces and failed; one half fell against the petroleum-oil-lubricants building southwest of the tower center and the second half fell northwest of the tower center. Figures 25 and 26 are photographs showing the destroyed water tower. Note that the tank broke across the welds rather than along them.

The pipeline that transports petroleum southward from the Swanson River oil field to loading and refinery facilities at Ni-

kiski was not damaged, nor were any of the producing wells. The catwalk over the pipeline between the shore and the offshore loading terminal collapsed during the shaking, but the pipelines themselves remained intact (fig. 27). A tanker that was loading fuel oil at the time of the earthquake pulled away from the terminal until the tremors subsided, then was able to resume loading (Cheechako News, Kenai, April 3, 1964).

At the Nikiski tank farm a small water tank collapsed, a fuel storage tank was buckled at its base, and several floating roofs on storage tanks were damaged by earthquake-generated seiche waves in the containers (Rinne, 1967). Some fire bricks were also knocked out of the refinery burner wall.

PORT GRAHAM

Port Graham is a fishing village on the south side of English Bay. It is on metamorphosed bedded rocks of Mesozoic age. As at Seldovia, 7.5 miles to the northeast, virtually all of the damage done by the earthquake was caused by tectonic subsidence of about 3 feet. According to Mrs. Vern Rimling and Mickey Moonan, a gentle swaying motion, mostly in an east-west direction, lasted from 3 to 4 minutes; a few articles fell from shelves, boats on ways swayed moderately, and trees rustled, but there was no property damage from the earthquake vibrations. Minor ground cracks appeared in unconsolidated deposits, and numerous rockfalls and rockslides were triggered in the surrounding mountains. One relatively low wave came in about 9 minutes after the earthquake but it reached only to about half-tide level and did no damage. During the night after the earthquake, erratic tides reached to the approximate ex-

25.—View westward showing southwest half of collapsed water tower at Wildwood Station. Officers' club in background. Photograph by U.S. Air Force.

26.—Northeast half of collapsed water tower at Wildwood Station. Photograph by U.S. Air Force.

27.—Collapsed catwalk at Nikiski refining facility.

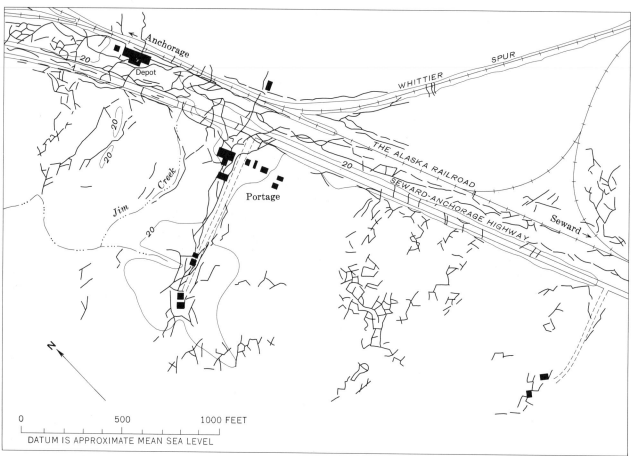

Base map by Walker & Whiteford, Inc., Seattle, Wash.
from photographs taken June 4, 1964 for
Alaska Department of Highways

Datum: Horizontal, U.S. Geological Survey;
vertical, U.S. Coast and Geodetic Survey
(as of April 17, 1964)

Fractures mapped by D. S. McCulloch

28.—Major earthquake-induced fissures in Portage area. The entire area shown was inundated by high tides on April 14, 1964.

treme high-tide level. Tectonic subsidence of about 3 feet caused flooding of the cannery by high tides, and some waterfront structures were partly damaged by high tides during the winter of 1964–65. By the spring of 1965 a new and higher beach berm had been built by natural processes and has since protected the waterfront area from flooding.

PORTAGE

The small town of Portage, about 40 miles southwest of the epicenter, is on the Seward-Anchorage Highway at the head of Turnagain Arm. The town is on a flat surface underlain by fine-grained silt, sand, and gravel. Locally, the water table is within a foot and generally not more than 3 feet from the surface.

Seismic motion at Portage was northwest-southeast and lasted for 5½ to 6 minutes. As in other localities, the motion started gently, but at Portage it became violent within a few seconds after it started. Vibration caused structural damage to several buildings in Portage and generated numerous cracks or fissures in the ground. George Larson, of Portage, reported that during seismic shaking the chimney at a gasoline station was destroyed; one-half of it fell into the building and the

other half fell outside. Most of the buildings in town were damaged to some degree by the seismic motion. In addition, further damage was caused by ground fissures that formed beneath the buildings during the earthquake. The largest of the fissures was 4 feet wide; their average width was only 2 feet.

Figure 28 shows the major patterns of fissures that developed in the ground at Portage. Some buildings are astride fissures that disturbed foundations and in some instances damaged the buildings. None of the buildings, however, were damaged beyond repair.

Numerous water spouts, some 25 to 30 feet high, occurred in the town during the earthquake. Mr. Larson reported that the water spouts continued for about 2 minutes after the earthquake. The ejected water contained a large amount of silt and sand which mantled the highway and other surfaces after the water had drained away.

Although seismic shaking and resultant ground fissures damaged buildings, the highway, and The Alaska Railroad grade, the subsidence had the most damaging effect. The Portage area had a regional subsidence of slightly more than 5 feet and, in addition, local subsidence of 1½ to 2 feet. Local subsidence was greatest in areas underlain by thick fill, such as the highway roadbed which, in places, subsided more than 3½ feet.

All the area on the map (fig. 28), which prior to the earthquake was above high-tide level, was inundated by the post earthquake high tides. Figure 29, a photograph taken on April 14, 1964, shows the extent of the flooding. Once it became evident to local residents that the town would be flooded continually during extreme high tides, they moved many of the buildings to higher ground—some were moved to Indian, about 20 miles northwest of Portage, on the Seward-Anchorage Highway.

PUGET BAY

A small logging camp at the head of Puget Bay on the rugged south coast of the Kenai Peninsula was severely damaged by destructive seismic sea waves that followed the earthquake. The earthquake caused no damage to the cabins at the camp although it broke off the tops of many dead trees, opened numerous fissures across an airstrip built on the outwash train at the bay head, and produced mud spouts, estimated to

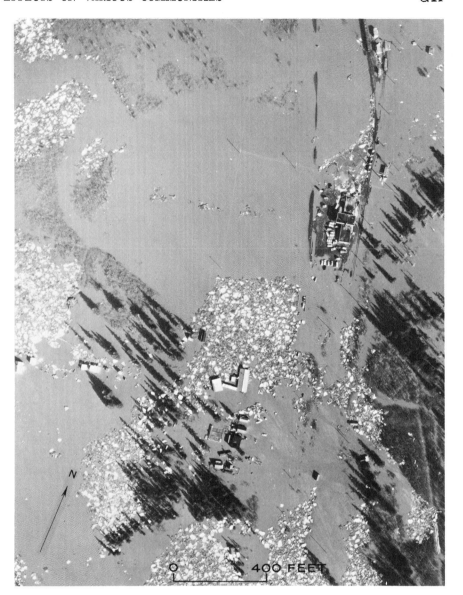

29.—Vertical aerial photograph of Portage area showing extent of inundation by high tides of April 14, 1964. Photograph by Air Photo Tech., Anchorage, Alaska.

be 20 to 30 feet high, all along the beach flats near the camp. Numerous landslides and avalanches were triggered on the nearby mountain slopes. One gigantic slide which traveled about 1¼ miles from a 3,931-foot-high peak just west of the camp to sea level with a "deafening roar," partially filled the northwest end of the bay. Sam Hatfield described the shaking as being so violent that he could not walk inside his house trailer, and could only walk with difficulty outside. Streams in the area went dry for about 3 days. Tectonic uplift during the earthquake elevated the land about 5 feet relative to sea level.

According to Mr. Hatfield, a series of waves struck the head of the bay about 20 minutes after the earthquake began. The first wave reached 18 feet above preearthquake mean lower low water on the tectonically raised shoreline; the second one, 10 to 15 minutes later, was a "little smaller"; the third and highest wave, which caused all the damage, came in about 2½ hours after the earthquake. The highest wave reached to an estimated 28 feet above mean lower low water, flooded the entire camp area, and washed away or destroyed about $8,000 worth of logs and machinery.

ROCKY BAY

Rocky Bay is a shallow irregular embayment near the southwestern tip of the Kenai Peninsula. A small logging camp, located on the west side of the bay, is underlain at shallow depth by crystalline rocks, of probable early Mesozoic age.

Strong shaking at Rocky Bay lasted only $1\frac{1}{2}$ minutes and is described as a slow north-south rolling motion with a definite dropping or sinking sensation toward the end of the shake, "as when a plane hits an air pocket" (Guy Branson, oral commun., 1964). The shaking triggered a few avalanches in the surrounding hills but did not even shift the contents of cabins. It "didn't amount to very much," according to Mr. Branson, and was considerably less severe than shaking during an earthquake that was felt for about 1 minute in July 1963. At a cattle ranch on Perl Island, about 12 miles southwest of Rocky Bay, Harley Hess also reported relatively mild tremors with an estimated duration of only 15 seconds.

The earthquake was accompanied by tectonic subsidence of 5 feet at Rocky Bay. The lowered land level adversely affected the logging operations by changing the beach configuration and removing almost all of the beach storage area for logs.

A series of seismic sea waves, described as "fast and quiet tidal surges," without breakers, washed the tectonically lowered shores of the bay. The first wave was about 9 feet high and was preceded by a withdrawal estimated to be about

18 feet. Mr. Branson believes that the first wave crested about half an hour after the earthquake began, although he was not paying much attention to the time of these tidal fluctuations. The highest wave, which came after midnight at about high tide, reached $19\frac{1}{2}$ feet above postearthquake mean lower low water, or about 5 feet above extreme high-tide level. About 70,000 board feet of logs stored on the beach were washed away by the first wave. On nearby Perl Island, the waves inundated low-lying parts of a ranch, drowned nine head of cattle, and washed out some range fencing.

SELDOVIA

Seldovia is an important fishing and cannery center on Seldovia Bay, one of the few ice-free harbors along Cook Inlet, 16 miles southwest of Homer. A small airstrip is east of the city, along a tidal slough that connects Seldovia Lagoon with the bay. The city is built on metamorphosed lower Mesozoic bedrock, and most of the business buildings and docks were strung out along a mile-long boardwalk that skirts the harbor area (see fig. 30).

Virtually all the damage to Seldovia was caused by tectonic subsidence of about 3.5 feet. In contrast to that at many communities on the Kenai Lowland, the shaking at Seldovia was felt for only about 3 minutes and was described by local residents as "mild" or "moderate"; it toppled a few small objects in stores and homes but caused no structural damage.

The sea began to recede and fill erratically during the shaking, but seismic sea waves were not noticed until after 8:00 p.m., $2\frac{1}{2}$ hours after the earthquake. There were several more waves during the

night, with the highest, one of 26 feet, coming between 4:00 and 5:00 a.m. on March 28. One of the early waves carried away the floats of the small-boat harbor, and the highest wave inundated part of the boardwalk and damaged stock in a few store buildings.

Long-term damage caused by subsidence was far greater than that caused by seismic sea waves. The boardwalk and all buildings along it became subject to flooding at high tides, as did one end of the airport runway. Breakwaters had to be raised 4 feet to protect the small-boat basin, the damaged floats had to be repaired, and the airport runway raised (Eckel, 1967). Sandbags were used temporarily to protect the boardwalk, and the city dock was raised. Direct costs of compensating for the effect of subsidence amounted to slightly more than $1 million. Later, an urban renewal plan was adopted to restore the entire waterfront by building an extensive dike and filling the land behind it to levels above the postearthquake high tides.

WHIDBEY BAY

A small logging camp is located on a bay-head gravel bar at the head of Whidbey Bay on the south coast of the Kenai Peninsula. Damage there was entirely due to the train of seismic sea waves that followed the earthquake.

Bill Sweeney reported that he timed the duration of strong shaking as $8\frac{1}{2}$ minutes. Seconds before he felt the earthquake, Mr. Sweeney heard the tanker *Alaska Standard*, then at Seward, radio that a violent "tidal" wave had struck the vessel. This report suggests that the submarine slide which generated destructive local waves at Seward was triggered almost instantaneously at the

30.—Seldovia as it appeared in March 1965, with restored inner harbor facilities and breakwaters, piers, and docks raised to compensate for the 3½-foot tectonic subsidence. Photograph by U.S. Army.

onset of the earthquake and that the vibrations were appreciably slower in reaching Whidbey Bay, even though the bay and Seward are about equidistant from the epicenter. The shaking opened fissures in the frozen ground around the camp with sounds described as "like rifle shots." Lateral movement of the beach bar caused a shallow graben 6 feet wide to open near the camp. The valley train at the head of the bay was extensively fissured and mud was ejected over large areas. Creeks reportedly went dry for about 10 days in the upper part of the valley train at the bay head and on the slopes. Numerous landslides and avalanches were triggered on the surrounding rugged mountains with "a noise like thunder." Tectonic uplift during the earthquake elevated the area between 1½ and 2 feet.

Immediately after feeling the earthquake, Sweeney and his family rode their tractor to the safety of nearby high ground in anticipation of seismic sea waves. From this vantage point they observed the first wave move rapidly into the bay and wash the shore to an estimated height of 35 feet above mean lower low water; Sweeney clocked its arrival at 19½ minutes after the initial shock was felt. Water then withdrew for 10 to 12 minutes; the bay bottom was exposed for an estimated mile from shore or about 50 feet below mean lower low water. A second, slightly higher wave then came in "like a big swell" with a loud rumble but no breakers. It washed over portions of the beach bar at the bay head, destroying the camp and everything in it. Smaller waves that came in on the rising tide throughout the night of March 27 and early morning of March 28 did not reach above the extreme high-tide line.

COMMUNITIES OF WESTERN COOK INLET AND THE ALASKA PENINSULA

Most of the communities on the remote Alaska Peninsula and in the northern Aleutian Range are small, widely spaced coastal fishing villages. The earthquake, which was strongly felt throughout the region, caused widespread ground breakage and cracking of ice on the coastal lowlands and in the larger river valleys as far southwest as Ugashik, on the Alaska Peninsula 430 miles southwest of the epicenter (pl. 1). A few small landslides, rockfalls, and avalanches occurred along the mountainous backbone of the Alaska and Aleutian Ranges, and at least one submarine slump was noted in a boat channel at Tuxedni Bay. Damage to structures, most of which are small single-story wood-frame buildings, was negligible. The only property damage reported was at Tyonek and King Salmon.

Vertical tectonic movements in the region, which amounted to less than 1½ feet along the Cook Inlet-Shelikof Strait coast and to no more than a few tenths of a foot on the Bristol Bay coast, caused no noteworthy shoreline changes or property damage. There were no destructive local waves along these coasts, and the seismic sea waves resulted only in erratic tides that nowhere reached above the level of extreme high water.

KING SALMON AND SOUTH NAKNEK

King Salmon, on the west coast of the Alaska Peninsula and nearly 400 miles west of the earthquake's epicenter, was the most distant community that sustained vibration damage. The community, with a population of about 220, is near the mouth of the Nak-

nek River on Kvichak Bay, itself an arm of Bristol Bay. It is primarily a fishing village but is also the center for field stations of the Air Force, Fish and Wildlife Service, and the Federal Aviation Agency. It is chiefly underlain by several hundred feet of morainal and outwash deposits, some of which appear to be fine grained.

According to Wilkie Meleau of the King Salmon Inn, who timed a rolling motion of ground and buildings at 7 minutes, light fixtures swayed, one window and a sewerline were cracked, and a pinball machine registered "tilt," but the ground motion was not strong enough to displace anything from shelves. There reportedly was a temporary power failure at the King Salmon Air Force Base. In nearby South Naknek, pipes laid on the surface were buckled slightly and seiches splashed some diesel fuel from tanks. Little or no effect was noted at any water wells. The earthquake was also felt at numerous villages and canneries around the head of Bristol Bay where ice reportedly was cracked in many places and some ground fissures developed locally.

Residents in Naknek agreed that tides ran a few minutes earlier after the earthquake than before, but their estimates of change in height of tides vary enough to suggest that if there was any tectonic change in land level it amounted at most to a few inches.

TYONEK AND THE WEST COAST OF COOK INLET

Along the western shores of Shelikof Strait and the southern part of Cook Inlet, the mountains of the Aleutian Range and southern end of the Alaska Range rise steeply from the sea. From Tuxedni Bay northward, however, the west coast of Cook Inlet is similar to that of the Kenai Lowland on its east coast, with comparatively low bluffs cut along the edges of a low, nearly flat, fluvioglacial terrane. Seismic sea waves similar to those that wrought much havoc along the eastern shores of the Kodiak group of islands (Plafker and Kachadoorian, 1966) struck these westerly shores. The waves caused rapid tide changes and erratic currents but no damage.

The earthquake was felt at several villages along the coast, with timed durations of from 3 to 5 minutes, but there was little property damage. At Tyonek, Albert S. Kalea, Jr., chief of the village council, reported that the church bell rang upon passage of visible ground waves and that some people heard low rumbling sounds. Ice on a shallow lake oscillated, first in an east-west direction, then north to south. One waterline, buried 8 feet deep, was broken by ground fissures where it crossed swamp deposits near the lake. Unattached articles in homes were shaken, but there was no structural damage, no chimneys fell, and a large water tank on the hill above the village was unaffected. Tyonek is founded on a series of unconsolidated sedimentary deposits, mostly sand and gravel, but containing some clay and silt. The fact that the water table is unusually deep, 58 feet below the surface in the village well, probably accounts for the light damage from seismic vibrations.

In the vicinity of Tuxedni Bay, south of Tyonek, most structures are built on rock or on shallow alluvium over bedrock. At the large Chisik Island cannery and nearby homes, a few objects toppled from shelves but there was no other property damage. According to Joe Fribrock, cannery manager, part of the tidal flat slid into the deep channel, leaving steep scarps. Just south of Tuxedni Bay, the collapse of the roof of a small

sawmill put the sawmill machinery out of operation. This property was the most seriously damaged of any along the west coast of Cook Inlet and Shelikof Strait. Mr. and Mrs. George Munger reported that about 40 percent of the beavers near Tuxedni Bay were lost when cracked pond ice pushed their food supply into the mud or actually crushed the animals. The short gravel road between Iliamna Lake and Iliamna Bay was temporarily blocked by a number of small earthquake-triggered landslides.

INLAND COMMUNITIES

The writers visited many of the inland communities after the earthquake, but only Fairbanks, Palmer and Matanuska Valley, and Sutton are discussed here. The other inland towns in which some damage occurred are in the Copper River Basin. Earthquake effects at these towns were summarized by Ferrians (1966).

FAIRBANKS

Fairbanks, the second largest city in Alaska, is in the interior of the State on a broad, flat surface along the Chena River. It is 275 miles north of the earthquake epicenter and predictably experienced only minimal damage.

Most of the Fairbanks area rests upon silt, sand, and gravel with local accumulations of loess and organic debris. Except along the Chena River and local small areas, the sediments are perennially frozen. The thickness of the sediments is unknown, but it may be as much as 300 feet locally. The water table lies close to the surface, and many of the shallow gravel pits contain water. Most small residential wells are no more than 25 feet deep.

Seismic motion at Fairbanks lasted from 4 to 5 minutes; more people reported the lesser figure

than the greater one. Motion was of a rolling nature and was chiefly northeast-southwest. The intensity of seismic motion increased gradually and once at its maximum intensity did not vary much. The motion subsided abruptly.

Top Copeland reported seeing ground waves, 4 to 6 inches high, traveling about 10 miles an hour in a northeast direction. He also reported that a parked automobile rolled back and forth 1 to 1½ feet in the same direction.

Relatively little damage was reported at Fairbanks. Shelf goods were shaken, but not toppled. There were some fissures in the ground. At the Alaska Motel, fissures 2 inches wide and 40 feet long developed during the earthquake. One edge of the structure sank about 4 inches, and some slumping occurred in the excavation beneath the motel. Some damage to utilities and to a few concete structures at Fort Wainwright was reported. The water in one 23-foot-deep well in Fairbanks was muddy for about 2 days after the earthquake.

The very light damage experienced at Fairbanks is accounted for by the distance from the earthquake epicenter and by the fact that most of the city is underlain by permafrost, which responds to seismic vibrations much as does solid rock.

PALMER AND THE MATANUSKA VALLEY

Palmer is the principal supply point for the Matanuska Valley agricultural community. It is on the Glenn Highway and The Alaska Railroad, about 48 miles northeast of Anchorage and 75 miles northwest of the epicenter. Although Palmer and other towns in the valley, such as Wasilla, Matanuska, and Sutton, are about the same distance from the earthquake epicenter as is Anchorage, they were virtually undamaged as compared with Anchorage.

Nearly all of the valley is underlain by outwash sand and gravel laid down by the Matanuska River and its ancestral streams. Bedrock crops out in places, and there are some bedrock knobs within the town of Palmer itself; ground moraine forms the surface in places, especially along the sides of the valley. All the outwash material contains much sand and some of it becomes "quick" during well-drilling operations. Most of the gravel particles are pebble sized, with but few cobble-sized stones. The water table is everywhere 10 to several scores of feet beneath the surface of the highly permeable sand and gravel beds (Trainer, 1960).

Eyewitnesses report the earthquake motion in the valley as rolling, principally in northwest-southwest directions. They also report that the motion increased gradually but ceased rather abruptly. Seismic vibration, variously estimated in different towns to have lasted from 3 to 5 minutes, cracked ice on streams and ponds and caused some ground fractures in places. Damage to buildings

was minimal. Electric power from the Eklutna hydroelectric plant was interrupted for a period of 18 hours immediately after the earthquake, but this interruption was caused by trouble at the generating plant and by an avalanche that cut the transmission line rather than by damage to the local distribution system (Logan, 1967). No airstrips were damaged. Effects on water wells, most of them minor, are described by Waller (1966b). All the relatively minor damage to manmade structures in Palmer and nearby farms and communities was caused by seismic vibration. The facts that all structures are on coarse gravelly sediments or on bedrock and that ground water is everywhere 10 or more feet beneath the surface probably explains the lack of more serious damage throughout the area.

SUTTON

Sutton, 65 miles northwest of the earthquake epicenter, sustained only slight damage from vibration. The town is about 50 miles northeast of Palmer, on the Glenn Highway and The Alaska Railroad, and is close to the Mata-

nuska River. Its chief importance is as a shipping point for coal from the mines just north of the town.

Like Palmer, Sutton rests on an unknown thickness of outwash deposits consisting of sandy gravel with minor amounts of silt. The coal seams are in a series of conglomerate, sandstone, and shale of early Tertiary age.

The rolling northwest-southeast motion of the earthquake was felt for about 5 minutes; intensity increased with time, but even at its maximum, the vibration was less severe than that at Anchorage. River ice was cracked during the shaking, and some ground fissures formed. As at Palmer, vibration damage to buildings was slight because most of the materials beneath the town are coarse gravelly sediments and because ground water is 10 or more feet below the surface. Several people reported that water in their wells became muddy, and one man reported that the water level in his well fell an unknown amount. The nearby coal mines were virtually unaffected by the earthquake, probably because the coal beds are enclosed by well-indurated rocks.

SUMMARY AND CONCLUSIONS

All of the damage and casualties related to the 1964 Alaska earthquake resulted either directly from earth tremors and tectonic displacements or indirectly from water waves generated by them. Ground motion during passage of seismic waves caused damage to structures primarily through (1) triggering of numerous subaerial and subaqueous landslides, (2) widespread fissuring of underlying unconsolidated deposits caused by differential horizontal or vertical movements, and (3) shaking of

some structures. Violent water waves that accompanied most subaqueous slides were a major indirect effect of the earth tremors. Regional vertical tectonic displacements, both upward and downward caused long-term damage to coastal communities and shoreline installations within south-central Alaska directly through changes in their positions relative to the sea and indirectly from the seismic sea waves they generated. In addition, large-scale horizontal tectonic movements may also have

generated destructive local waves along the shores of many enclosed or semienclosed water bodies within the deformed region.

GEOLOGIC CONTROL OF VIBRATORY DAMAGE DISTRIBUTION

The intensity of seismic shock and attendant damage to structures varied markedly from place to place, and appeared to be more closely controlled by the local geologic environment than by proximity to the epicenter. In general, it was greatest in areas of thick, water-saturated unconsolidated deposits, least on well-indurated bedrock, and intermediate on Quaternary unconsolidated deposits with relatively low water table or on moderately indurated sedimentary rocks of late Tertiary age. As a consequence, meaningful isoseismal lines based on the Modified Mercalli Intensity scale cannot be drawn within the region of greatest earthquake-induced damage. The generalization that both the intensity and duration of earthquake vibrations are enhanced in unconsolidated ground, particularly in areas of high water table (Gutenberg, 1957), is strikingly borne out by the distribution of the vibration-induced damage.

Significantly, nowhere in the earthquake-affected r e g i o n was there noteworthy damage to the numerous structures founded on indurated rock or bedrock veneered with thin unconsolidated deposits. At the communities described in this report, damage to structures founded on bedrock was very minor. It consisted of toppling or cracking of unreinforced brick chimneys at Sawmill Bay and El-lamar, a slight settling of one end of the bunkhouse into filled ground at Port Oceanic, and toppling of a stovepipe at Perry Island. Structural damage from seismic shock at Cordova was confined to areas east of the city on the Copper River Delta. No other damage, other than some slight breakage caused by moving about of the contents of buildings occurred at communities on bedrock sites anywhere else in the Prince William Sound epicentral region.

The habitation closest to the epicenter was the home and small hand cannery of Joe Clark at a bedrock site on Fairmont Island just 12 miles from the instrumental center of the earthquake. Yet the only effect of the vibrations there was the breaking of a few dishes that toppled from shelves and of glass ashtrays that were knocked off tables. At the home of Mr. and Mrs. Jerry Clock on Peak Island, only about 25 miles southwest of the epicenter, shaking merely threw three books from the overloaded top shelf of a ceiling-high bookcase and tipped one casserole off a tilted stove top.

Elsewhere in bedrock areas of the Chugach and Kenai Mountains and of the Kodiak group of islands, the effect of the tremors was comparable, even on large buildings of ferroconcrete. At the port of Whittier, 40 miles from the epicenter, there was no structural damage to the very large Buckner Building nor to a large modern steamplant, both of which are founded on bedrock (Kachadoorian, 1965). At other communities on bedrock sites in the southern Kenai Peninsula and the Kodiak group of islands, including the cities of Seldovia and Kodiak, direct vibration damage to structures was negligible. In all these bedrock areas the estimated Mercalli intensities, as based on effects to people and inanimate objects, probably did not exceed VI to VII.

In the Kenai Lowland, on the west shore of Cook Inlet, and in the Matanuska Valley, local structural damage was sustained from direct seismic vibrations at various communities located on late Tertiary sedimentary deposits having relatively low water tables. Thus, shaking in the vicinity of Kenai was strong enough to topple a water tank, to destroy part of the pier and to damage storage tanks at Nikishki, to crack concrete block structures, to topple some chimneys, and to knock items from shelves in almost all stores and homes. Similar minor damage was sustained at Portage, Lawing, Moose Pass, and Homer on the Kenai Peninsula. Most other communities in and around Cook Inlet on comparable foundations, such as Ninilchik, Kasilof, Soldotna, and Tyonek, were undamaged. Structures in Palmer, Wasilla, Sutton, and Matanuska in the Matanuska Valley were also undamaged. Mercalli intensities in such areas, although highly variable, were probably no more than VII, but may have reached VIII in the Kenai area.

The most severe direct vibratory damage to communities described in this report was sustained in areas of water-saturated alluvial deposits, such as the Copper River Delta area east of Cordova and at Girdwood, Hope, and Portage near the head of Turnagain Arm. At these communities, and in previously described communities in comparable geologic settings, damage resulted more from foundation failure than from vibration of structures. At the Cordova FAA station, Girdwood, and Portage, vibratory loading of noncohesive granular deposits during the earthquake resulted in local ground fissuring and foundation damage. Causes of the fissuring are probably diverse and are related to the physical properties of the materials composing each deposit, as well as to its configuration. Fissuring of natural materials and uncompacted fills under vibratory loading in these localities is most probably caused by (1) differential compaction or volume reduction due to closer packing of the constituent grains and (or) (2) varying degrees of liquefaction of saturated incoherent materials with resultant lateral spreading towards free faces. In Girdwood, Hope, Portage, and other coastal communities, additional damage resulted from inundation due to surficial subsidence that accompanied compaction and lateral spreading. The upper limit of Mercalli intensities due to seismic shaking effects on people and structures in areas of saturated unconsolidated deposits ranged between XIII and X.

Translatory block slides, such as the ones at Anchorage (Hansen, 1965) or subaqueous slides of the type that damaged the Homer Spit (Waller, 1966a), Whittier (Kachadoorian, 1965), Valdez (Coulter and Migliaccio, 1966), Lawing (McCulloch, 1966), and Seward (Lemke, 1967), did not cause direct damage at any of the communities discussed here. Waves generated by subaqueous slides, however, probably were the cause of damage and loss of at least one life at Anderson Bay in western Valdez Arm and may have caused some of the wave damage elsewhere in Prince William Sound.

VERTICAL TECTONIC DISPLACEMENTS AND SEISMIC SEA WAVES

Vertical displacements of the land relative to sea level during the earthquake caused extensive long-term damage at several coastal communities described in this report as well as in the Kodiak group of islands (Kachadoorian and Plafker, 1967), Whittier (Kachadoorian, 1965), Homer (Waller, 1966a), and Seward (Lemke, 1967). Tectonic subsidence of 5 to 6 feet, augmented by surficial subsidence of unconsolidated deposits, led to relocation or rebuilding of parts of Hope, Girdwood, and Portage and the transportation routes near these communities. At Seldovia, 3 feet of tectonic subsidence necessitated a costly compensating program of raising waterfront installations. Considerable damage from varying amounts of subsidence was also

sustained at smaller coastal communities elsewhere along the coast of the Kenai Peninsula and on the Kodiak group of islands.

Tectonic uplift of the land, most notably in the eastern and southern parts of Prince William Sound and offshore islands of the Continental Shelf, necessitated dredging of harbors and waterways at Cordova and Tatitlek and lengthening of the pier at Cape Hinchinbrook Light Station. Uplift also reduced the usefulness of docks and piers at most smaller communities throughout the affected areas.

The most important and disastrous indirect effect of the vertical tectonic displacements was the generation of a train of destructive seismic sea waves. Of the communities described here, Seldovia, Whidbey Bay, Puget Bay, the Cordova area, and Cape Saint Elias sustained light to moderate property losses and two casualties from these waves. Most of the damage from seismic sea waves in Alaska, however, was to the various communities along the seaward coast of the Kodiak group of islands (Kachadoorian and Plafker, 1967) and at Seward (Lemke, 1967).

LOCAL WAVES AND SUBAQUEOUS SLIDES

Major damage and casualties to coastal communities resulted from violent local waves that struck during or immediately after the earthquake at numerous localities in Prince William Sound, Resurrection Bay, and Aialik Bay. Of the communities described here, local waves were the main cause of destruction at Anderson Bay, Chenega, Port Oceanic, Port Nellie Juan, Nowell Point, Perry Island, Sawmill Bay, and Latouche. Comparable waves, some of them

clearly generated by subaqueous slides of unconsolidated deposits, also caused most of the damage at the ports of Valdez (Coulter and Migliaccio, 1966), Whittier (Kachadoorian, 1965), and Seward (Lemke, 1967), and at places along the shore of Kenai Lake (McCulloch, 1966).

Subaqueous slides and related destructive local waves are known or inferred to have occurred at localities along the shores of Prince William Sound, the southern Kenai Peninsula, and Kenai Lake (pl. 2). Another slide destroyed the boat harbor at Homer Spit in Kachemak Bay, but it was accompanied by only relatively minor water disturbances (Waller, 1966a). At Seward, Whittier, Valdez, and along the shore of Kenai Lake, subaqueous slides carried away segments of the waterfronts, and waves generated by the moving slide masses compounded the damage. The sequence of events reported by eyewitnesses at Seward and Thumb Cove in Resurrection Bay, at Lawing on Kenai Lake, and at Valdez clearly demonstrates (1) the instability of saturated unconsolidated deposits on steep slopes under seismic shock and (2) the ability of such slides to generate destructive waves.

Shoreline damage that occurred along uninhabited segments of the shore of Kenai Lake, Aialik Bay, Kings Bay, Blackstone Bay, and western Valdez Arm (pl. 2) is comparable in all major respects to that which accompanied known subaqueous slides. At these localities, subaqueous sliding is suggested by one or more of the following lines of evidence: (1) a pattern of wave damage that radiates outward from the vicinity of deltaic or morainal deposits, (2) subaerial scarps or oversteepened nearshore slopes on the unconsolidated deposits, and (3) differences between pre- and post-earthquake bathymetry indicative of removal of material from the upper portion of deltas or moraines and of deposition of slide debris in deeper water. Only the wave damage at Anderson Bay and adjacent shorelines in western Valdez Arm, of the communities discussed in this report, can be confidently attributed primarily to subaqueous slides on the basis of the criteria outlined above.

At all other communities where local waves were the major cause of damage, no subaqueous or subaerial slide source for the waves was identifiable. Conceivably, widespread damage along the shores of steepsided deep fiords such as at Chenega, Point Nowell, Port Nellie Juan, and Latouche could have been generated by sliding of submarine moraine-outwash

complexes that may have been perched along fiord walls. However, wave damage at some of these communities, such as Sawmill Bay and Port Oceanic, which are situated in shallow embayments or semienclosed basins, are difficult to attribute to such an origin. Furthermore, although regional tilt, submarine faulting, or seismic vibrations may have contributed to the water disturbances, none of these phenomena either alone or in combination could have caused waves as large as those observed.

A possible alternative mechanism for at least some of the water disturbances is that they were generated by inertial effects of the water bodies as the landmass was tectonically displaced horizontally beneath them in a relative southward to southeastward direction (Plafker, 1969). The magnitude of such displacements in the

Prince William Sound region, as indicated by retriangulation data, increases progressively from about 20 feet near Whittier in the northern part of the sound to more than 60 feet near Sawmill Bay and Latouche in the southern part. It is suggested that the horizontal movements, if they occurred fast enough, may have been either the primary or a contributing cause to local waves of unknown origin that devastated smaller communities and uninhabited shores around Prince William Sound and elsewhere in the earthquake-affected region. This suggested origin for the waves is consistent with (1) their sudden onset during or immediately after the earthquake, (2) the favorable orientation and configuration of affected shorelines, and (3) their occurrence in an area of large horizontal displacements.

REFERENCES CITED

Alaska Department of Health and and Welfare, 1964, Preliminary report of earthquake damage to environmental health facilities and services in Alaska: Juneau, Alaska Dept. Health and Welfare, Environmental Health Branch, 46 p.

Coulter, H. W., and Migliaccio, R.R., 1966, Effects of the earthquake of March 27, 1964, at Valdez, Alaska: U.S. Geol. Survey Prof. Paper 542–C, p. C1–C36.

Davis, T. N., and Sanders, N. K., 1960, Alaska earthquake of July 10, 1958—Intensity distribution and field investigation of northern epicentral region: Seismol. Soc. America Bull., v. 50, no. 2, p. 221–252.

Eckel, E. B., 1967, Effects of the earthquake of March 27, 1964, on air and water transport, communications, and utilities systems in south-central Alaska: U.S. Geol. Survey Prof. Paper 545–B, p. B1–B27.

Ferrians, O. J., Jr., 1966, Effects of the earthquake of March 27, 1964, in the Copper River Basin area, Alaska:

U.S. Geol. Survey Prof. Paper 543–E, p. E1–E28.

Grant, U. S., and Higgins, D. F., 1910, Reconnaissance of the geology and mineral resources of Prince William Sound, Alaska: U.S. Geol. Survey Bull. 443, 89 p.

———1913, Coastal glaciers of Prince William Sound and Kenai Peninsula, Alaska: U.S. Geol. Survey Bull. 526, 75 p.

Grantz, Arthur, Kachadoorian, Reuben, and Plafker, George, 1964, Alaska's Good Friday earthquake, March 27, 1964—a preliminary geologic evaluation: U.S. Geol. Survey Circ. 491, 35 p.

Gutenberg, Beno, 1957, Effects of ground on earthquake motion: Seismol. Soc. America Bull., v. 47, no. 3, p. 221–250.

Hansen, W. R., 1965, Effects of the earthquake of March 27, 1964, at Anchorage, Alaska: U.S. Geol. Survey Prof. Paper 542–A, p. A1–A68.

Hansen, W. R., and others, 1966, The Alaska earthquake March 27, 1964:

Field investigations and reconstruction effort: U.S. Geol. Survey Prof. Paper 541, 111 p.

Kachadoorian, Reuben, 1965, Effects of the earthquake of March 27, 1964, at Whittier, Alaska: U.S. Geol. Survey Prof. Paper 542–B, p. B1–B21.

———1968, Effects of the Alaska earthquake, March 27, 1964, on the Alaska highway system: U.S. Geol. Survey Prof. Paper 545–C, p. C1–C66.

Kachadoorian, Reuben, and Plafker, George, 1967, Effects of the earthquake of March 27, 1964, on the communities of Kodiak and nearby islands: U.S. Geol. Survey Prof. Paper 542–F, p. F1–F41.

Lemke, R. W., 1967, Effects of the earthquake of March 27, 1964, at Seward, Alaska: U.S. Geol. Survey Prof. Paper 542–E, p. E1–E43.

Logan, M. H., 1967, Effects of the earthquake of March 27, 1964, on the Eklutna hydroelectric project, Anchorage, Alaska, *with a section on* Television examination of earthquake damage to underground communication and electrical systems in Anchorage, by Lynn H. Burton: U.S. Geol. Survey Prof. Paper 545–A, p. A1–A30.

McCulloch, D. S., 1966, Slide-induced waves, seiching, and ground fracturing caused by the earthquake of March 27, 1964, at Kenai Lake, Alaska: U.S. Geol. Survey Prof. Paper 543–A, p. A1–A41.

McCulloch, D. S., and Bonilla, M. G., 1968, Effects of the Alaskan earthquake, March 27, 1964, on The Alaska Railroad: U.S. Geol. Survey Prof. Paper 545–D. (In press.)

Orth, D. J., 1967, Dictionary of Alaska place names: U.S. Geol. Survey Prof. Paper 567, 1084 p.

Plafker, George, 1967, Surface faults on Montague Island associated with the 1964 Alaska earthquake: U.S. Geol. Survey Prof. Paper 543–G, p. G1–G42.

——— 1969, Tectonics of the 1964 Alaska earthquake: U.S. Geol. Survey Prof. Paper 543–I, p. II–174.

Plafker, George, and Kachadoorian, Reuben, 1966, Geologic effects of the March 1964 earthquake and associated seismic sea waves on Kodiak and nearby islands, Alaska: U.S. Geol.

Survey Prof. Paper 543–D, p. D1–D46.

Plafker, George, and Mayo, L. R., 1965, Tectonic deformation, subaqueous slides, and destructive waves associated with the Alaskan March 27, 1964, earthquake—an interim geologic evaluation: U.S. Geol. Survey open-file report, 21 p.

Post, Austin, 1967, Effects of the March 1964 Alaska earthquake on glaciers: U.S. Geol. Survey Prof. Paper 544–D, p. D1–D42.

Reimnitz, Erk, and Marshall, N. F., 1965, Effects of the Alaska earthquake and tsunami, on recent deltaic sediments: Jour. Geophys. Research, v. 70, no. 10, p. 2363–2376.

Rinne, J. E., 1967, Oil storage tanks, in Wood, F. J., ed., Research studies: Seismology and marine geology, pt. A., Engineering seismology, v. 2 of The Prince William Sound, Alaska, earthquake of 1964 and aftershocks: U.S. Coast and Geod. Survey Pub. 10–3, p. 245–252.

Tarr, R. S., and Martin, Lawrence, 1912, The earthquake at Yakutat Bay, Alaska, in September 1899, with a preface by G. K. Gilbert: U.S. Geol. Survey Prof. Paper 69, 135 p.

Trainer, F. W., 1960, Geology and ground-water resources of the Matanuska Valley agricultural area, Alaska: U.S. Geol. Survey Water-Supply Paper 1494, 116 p.

Van Dorn, W. G., 1964, Source mechansim of the tsunami of March 28, 1964, in Alaska: Coastal Eng. Conf., 9th, Lisbon, 1964, Proc., p. 166–190.

Varnes, D. J., 1958, Landslide types and processes, in Eckel, E. B., ed., Landslides and engineering: Natl. Acad. Sci.-Natl. Research Council Pub. 544, Highway Research Board Spec. Rept. 29, p. 20–47.

Waller, R. M., 1966a, Effects of the earthquake of March 27, 1964, in the Homer area, Alaska, with a section on Beach changes on Homer Spit, by K. W. Stanley: U.S. Geol. Survey Prof. Paper 542–D, p. D1–D28.

——— 1966b, Effects of the March 1964 Alaska earthquake on the hydrology of south-central Alaska: U.S. Geol. Survey Prof. Paper 544–A, p. A1–A28.

——— 1966c, Effects of the March 1964 Alaska earthquake on the hydrology of the Anchorage area, Alaska: U.S. Geol. Survey Prof. Paper 544–B, p. B1–B18,

CLARIFICATIONS

Geology Vol. Page	USGS Page	Column	Line	Remarks
490	G 2	1	3	Elsewhere reported as 115 lives lost in Alaska
490	G 2	2	18	Plates 1 and 2 are Plates P and Q, respectively, in Part B, the accompanying map case

REUBEN KACHADOORIAN
U.S. GEOLOGICAL SURVEY

GEORGE PLAFKER
U.S. GEOLOGICAL SURVEY

Abstract reprinted with minor changes from
U.S. Geological Survey Professional Paper 542-F,
"Effects of the Earthquake of March 27, 1964, on the
Communities of Kodiak and Nearby Islands"

Effects on the Communities of Kodiak and Nearby Islands

*ABSTRACT**

The great earthquake (Richter magnitude of 8.4–8.5) that struck south central Alaska at 5:36 p.m., Alaska standard time, on March 27, 1964 (03:36, March 28, Greenwich mean time), was felt in every community on Kodiak Island and on the nearby islands. It was the most severe earthquake to strike this part of Alaska in modern time, and caused the death by drowning of 18 persons in the area, including two in Kodiak and three at Kaguyak. Property damage and loss of income to the communities is estimated at more than $45 million.

The largest community, Kodiak, had the greatest loss from the earthquake. Damage was caused chiefly by 5.6 feet of tectonic subsidence and a train of 10 tsunamis, or seismic sea waves, that inundated the low-lying areas of the town. The seismic sea waves destroyed all but one of the docking facilities and more than 215 structures; many other structures were severely damaged. The waves struck the town during the evening hours of March 27 and early morning hours of March 28. They moved from the southwest and northeast and reached their maximum height of 29–30 feet above mean lower low water at Shahafka

Cove between 11:00 and 11:45 p.m., March 27. The violently destructive seismic sea waves not only severely damaged homes, shops, and naval station structures but also temporarily crippled the fishing industry in Kodiak by destroying the processing plants and most of the fishing vessels. The waves scoured out 10 feet of sediments in the channel between Kodiak Island and Near Island and exposed bedrock. This bedrock presented a major postearthquake construction problem because no sediments remained into which piles could be driven for foundations of waterfront facilities.

Because of tectonic subsidence, high tides now flood Mission and Potatopatch lakes which, before the earthquake, had not been subject to tidal action. The subsidence also accelerated erosion of the unconsolidated sediments along the shoreline in the city of Kodiak.

Seismic shaking lasted 4½–5½ minutes at Kodiak and had a rolling motion. Inasmuch as most of Kodiak is underlain by bedrock or by only a thin veneer of unconsolidated sediments, very little damage, if any, occurred from ground motion or seismic shaking. The ground motion, however,

did cause a massive short circuit and power failure at Kodiak.

The Kodiak Naval Station, 5 miles southwest of Kodiak, was also severely damaged by the earthquake. The station was inundated by at least 10 seismic sea waves that reached a maximum height of 25 feet above postearthquake mean lower low water between 11:16 and 11:34 p.m. on March 27, 1964. The first seismic sea wave that inundated the station did not do severe damage because it behaved much like a rapid rise of tide, but the subsequent and more violent waves destroyed most of the docking facilities and several other shoreline structures. The waves struck the station from the southwest and from the east.

The shoreline structures that were not destroyed required rehabilitation because the 5.6 feet of tectonic subsidence put them under water during the highest tides. Furthermore, the subsidence accelerated erosion during high tide of the soft unconsolidated sediments and fill in the low-lying areas of the station.

Seismic shaking did little damage to the station housing facility, but it was responsible for compaction of sediments, lateral displacement of a

---

*USGS Professional Paper 542-F is on file at the NAS–NAE Library, 2101 Constitution Avenue, Washington, D.C. 20418; the 41-page original version, published in 1967, is also for sale by the Superintendent of Documents, U.S. Government Printing Office, Washington, D.C. 20402.

seawall, and the development of fissures in the aircraft parking area. The ground motion was south-southeast—north-northwest to north-south in direction.

An unusual case of radioactive contamination was reported at the naval station. The inundating seismic sea waves entered a building in which radionuclides were stored. The contamination was restricted to the building only, however, and did not spread throughout the station.

Afognak was abandoned because of the extensive damage incurred from tectonic subsidence and seismic sea waves. The seismic effects, estimated Mercalli intensity VI–VII, did not directly cause any significant property damage at Afognak. Serious long-term damage, however, resulted from tectonic subsidence estimated to be from 3½ to 5½ feet. The subsidence has resulted in rapid erosion of the coast, landward shift and building up of beach berms to the new higher sea levels, and flooding of extensive low-lying areas behind the barrier beaches. Innundation of low-lying parts of the village by a train of seismic sea waves with maximum heights of 10.8 feet above postearthquake tide level (14.5 ft above postearthquake mean lower low water) caused losses of about half a million dollars to homes, vehicles, bridges, and personal posessions.

Uzinki was damaged by tectonic subsidence and seismic sea waves. No significant damage resulted from the ground motion during the earthquake; the Mercalli intensity was about VI. However, tectonic subsidence, estimated to be 5 feet, caused inundation of a narrow zone along the waterfront. Structures and vessels were damaged as a result of the seismic sea waves that repeatedly flooded the waterfront area after the earthquake.

Old Harbor was damaged by seismic shock, subsidence, and seismic sea waves. The tremors, which had a Mercalli intensity estimated at VII–VIII, toppled two concrete-block chimneys, cracked interior walls, and caused minor breakage of personal property in the homes. Regional tectonic subsidence and superficial subsidence of the unconsolidated deposits on which the village is situated apparently caused incursion of salt water into the school well. A quarter of a million yards of fill was required to raise the waterfront areas to their preearthquake elevations relative to sea level. Seismic sea waves with a maximum runup of about 12 feet above tide level (16 ft above postearthquake mean lower low water) destroyed 34 of the 35 residences in the village and presumably drowned one man who lived immediately across the strait from Old Harbor.

At Kaguyak, seismic sea waves with a maximum runup of about 25 feet above mean lower low water carried away all 10 buildings in the village, took three lives, and damaged an unknown number of fishing vessels. The village site has been abandoned.

The communities of Akhiok, Karluk, and Larsen Bay were virtually undamaged by the earthquake tremors, which had estimated Mercalli intensities of VI–VII, but tectonic subsidence of about 2–2½ feet at Larsen Bay made it necessary to raise the cannery dock level at an estimated cost of $80,000.

III
EFFECTS ON TRANSPORTATION AND UTILITIES

DAVID S. McCULLOCH
U.S. GEOLOGICAL SURVEY

MANUEL G. BONILLA
U.S. GEOLOGICAL SURVEY

Reprinted in part* from
U.S. Geological Survey Professional Paper 545-D,
"Effects of the Earthquake of March 27, 1964, on the Alaska Railroad"

Effects on the Alaska Railroad

ABSTRACT

In the 1964 Alaska earthquake, the federally owned Alaska Railroad sustained damage of more than $35 million: 54 percent of the cost for port facilities; 25 percent, roadbed and track; 9 percent, buildings and utilities; 7 percent, bridges and culverts; and 5 percent, landslide removal. Principal causes of damage were: (1) landslides, landslide-generated waves, and seismic sea waves that destroyed costly port facilities built on deltas; (2) regional tectonic subsidence that necessitated raising and armoring 22 miles of roadbed made susceptible to marine erosion; and (3), of greatest importance in terms of potential damage in seismically active areas, a general loss of strength experienced by wet waterlaid unconsolidated granular sediments (silt to coarse gravel) that allowed embankments to settle and enabled sediments to undergo flowlike displacement toward topographic depressions, even in flat-lying areas. The term "landspreading" is proposed for the lateral displacement and distension of mobilized sediments; landspreading appears to have resulted largely from liquefaction. Because mobilization is time dependent and its effects cumulative, the long duration of strong ground motion (timed as 3 to 4 minutes) along the southern 150 miles of the rail line made landspreading an important cause of damage.

Sediments moved toward natural and manmade topographic depressions (stream valleys, gullies, drainage ditches, borrow pits, and lakes). Stream widths decreased, often about 20 inches but at some places by as much as 6.5 feet, and sediments moved upward beneath stream channels. Landspreading toward streams and even small drainage ditches crushed concrete and metal culverts. Bridge superstructures were compressed and failed by lateral buckling, or more commonly were driven into, through, or over bulkheads. Piles and piers were torn free of superstructures by moving sediments, crowded toward stream channels, and lifted in the center. The lifted piles arched the superstructures. Vertical pile displacement was independent of the depth of the pile penetration in the sediment and thus was due to vertical movement of the sediments, rather than to differential compaction. The fact that bridge piles were carried laterally without notable tilting suggests that mobilization exceeded pile depths, which averaged about 20 feet. Field observations, largely duplicated by vibrated sandbox models of stream channels, suggest that movement was distributed throughout the sediments, rather than restricted to finite failure surfaces.

Landspreading generated stress that produced cracks in the ground surface adjacent to depressions. The distribution of this stress controlled the crack patterns: tension cracks parallel to straight or concave streambanks, shear cracks intersecting at 45° to 70° on convex banks where there was some component of radial spreading, and orthogonal cracks on the insides of tight meander bends or islands where spreading was omnidirectional.

Ground cracks of these kinds commonly extended 500 feet, and occasionally about 1,000 feet, back from streams, which indicates that landspreading occurred over large areas. In areas of landspreading, highway and railroad embankments, pavements, and rails were pulled apart endways and were displaced laterally if they lay at an angle to the direction of sediment displacement. Sediment movement commonly skewed bridges that crossed streams obliquely. The maximum horizontal skew was 10 feet.

Embankment settlement, nearly universal in areas of landspreading, also occurred in areas where there was no evidence for widespread loss of strength in the unconsolidated sediments. In the latter areas embankments themselves clearly caused the loss of bearing strength in the underlying sediment. In both areas, settlement was accompanied by the formation of ground cracks approximately parallel to the embankment in the adjacent sediments. Sediment-laden ground water was discharged from the cracks, and extreme local settlements (as much as 6 ft) were associated with large discharges.

Landspreading was accompanied by transient horizontal displacement of the ground that pounded bridge ends with slight or considerable force. The deck of a 105-foot bridge was repeatedly arched up off its piles by transient compression. Bridges may also have developed high horizontal accelerations. One bridge deck, driven through its bulkhead, appears to have had an acceleration of at least 1.1 to 1.7 g; however, most evidence for high accelerations is ambiguous.

Limited standard penetration data show that landspreading damage was

*Only pages D1–D95 and the original References of the 161-page PP 545-D are reproduced here; users wishing access to the section on Distribution of Damage and its Relation to Surficial Geology and Physiography or to pages D96–D159 and Figures 78–141, which are in some instances referred to in these pages, should consult the original 1970 paper sold by the Superintendent of Documents, U.S. Government Printing Office, Washington, D.C. 20402. Also, two copies are on file at the NAS–NAE Library, 2101 Constitution Avenue, Washington, D.C. 20418.

not restricted to soft sediments. Some bridges were severely damaged by displacement of piles driven in sediments classified as compact and dense.

Total thickness of unconsolidated sediments strongly controlled the degree of damage. In areas underlain by wet water-laid sediments the degree of damage to uniformly designed and built wooden railroad bridges shows a closer correlation with total sediment thickness at the bridge site than with the grain size of the material in which the piles were driven.

Local geology and physiography largely controlled the kind, distribution, and severity of damage to the railroad. This relationship is so clear that maps of surficial geology and physiography of damaged areas of the rail belt show

that only a few geologic–physiographic units serve to identify these areas:

1. Bedrock and glacial till on bedrock. No foundation displacements, but ground vibration increased toward the area of maximum strain-energy release.
2. Glacial outwash terraces. Landspreading and damage ranged from none where the water table was low and the terrace undissected to severe where the water table was near the surface and the terrace dissected by streams.
3. Inactive flood plains. Landspreading, ground cracking, flooding by ejected ground water, and damage were generally slight but increased to severe toward lower, wetter active flood plains or river channels.

4. Active flood plains. Landspreading, ground cracking, and flooding were nearly universal and were greater than on adjacent inactive flood plains.
5. Fan deltas. Radial downhill spreading and ground cracking were considerable near the lower edges of the fan deltas and were accompanied by ground-water discharge. Landslides were common from edges of deltas.

Damage, landspreading, ground cracking, vibration, and flooding by ground water generally increased with (1) increasing thickness of unconsolidated sediments, (2) decreasing depth to the water table, (3) proximity to topographic depressions, and (4) proximity to the area of maximum strain–energy release.

INTRODUCTION

Within 2 hours after the first tremor of the Alaska earthquake of March 27, 1964, the federally owned Alaska Railroad had sustained more than $35 million worth of damage. The destructive agents took many forms. Seismic sea waves, landslides, and waves generated by slides from the edges of deltas largely destroyed or severely damaged complex and costly port facilities at Seward and Whittier — ports through which passed most of Alaska's waterborne freight. The damage was compounded by seismic shaking, ground cracking, and burning fuel carried inland by the waves (Grantz and others, 1964; Kachadoorian, 1965; Lemke, 1967). More than 100 miles of roadbed settled or was displaced and broken by ground cracks in areas underlain by unconsolidated sediments. In the same areas, 125 bridges and more than 110 culverts were damaged or destroyed. Landslides overran or carried away several miles of roadbed and destroyed

or severely damaged buildings and utilities. Other railroad structures were destroyed or damaged by seismic shaking. Tectonic subsidence lowered the land as much as 5.5 feet along the railline and made about 35 miles along the shore susceptible to flooding at high tide and to accelerated marine erosion.

The type and severity of the damage to the rail belt were largely controlled by the geology, the physiography, and the proximity to the area of strain release. Damage was concentrated in areas underlain by wet water-laid noncohesive young sediments in which grain size ranged from silt to gravel. Similar structures on older drier sediments, or on till or bedrock, were nearly undamaged. The seismic shaking mobilized the sediments, which then spread laterally toward topographic depressions carrying along the overlying embankments. At stream crossings the bridge superstructures were compressed, and their supports

crowded together as the sediments moved toward the stream channels (McCulloch and Bonilla, 1967). In addition to being damaged by these permanent displacements of the foundation materials, bridges were subjected to transient horizontal displacements, some of which had considerable force.

Spreading of unconsolidated granular sediments commonly occurred on fans and deltas, but was more widespread and highly damaging to structures on the extensive flat or nearly flat areas. The term "landspreading" is proposed for this type of ground movement, first to describe the distension that occurs within the sediments, and second to bring attention to the fact that it occurs on flat or nearly flat ground as opposed to landsliding which has the connotation of downslope movement. The phenomena described as landspreading can probably be largely attributed to liquefaction. However, because landspreading may have been due in part to other causes, it is preferable to avoid a term that specifies a single mechanism.

This report has two parts. The first describes damage to structures as an indication of the behavior of foundation materials during the earthquake. These observations are then used to explain the formation, location, and pattern of some of the ground cracking that occurred over very large areas. Other topical subjects are included in this first part. In an effort to be of use to designers building structures in similar areas, the damage is described in some detail and some estimates are made of the forces that were exerted on the structures.

The second part of this report is a mile-by-mile description of the surficial geology and the damage to the railroad and some of the adjacent areas. This part documents the close relation of the geology to the distribution, severity, and type of damage; it serves as a record which should prove useful in the future development of these and similar areas; and it provides an opportunity to record details of damage to particular structures not included in the preceding topical discussions.

As a preface to the discussion of railroad damage, the following descriptions, by I. P. Cook (written commun. 1969), chief engineer, and from the Railbelt Reporter (1964, p. 4–5), of the events following the earthquake are given so that the reader may appreciate the tremendous job that faced the small staff of The Alaska Railroad, and their immediate and energetic response.

I. P. Cook wrote that, on Friday, immediately following the earthquake:

First to arrive at the dispatching headquarters of the Railroad's Terminal Building was John Manley, the General Manager. True to Railroad tradition, other Railroaders appeared on the scene and each began to check out his particular responsibility.

Communication with line points of the Railroad was virtually wiped out, and the only assessment that could be made before darkness set in by headquarters staff people was that in the immediate area of the Anchorage Terminal.

With the first rays of dawn on Saturday, various officials met with the General Manager and a plan was outlined for assessing damages and corrective action. Helicopters and fixed-wing airplanes were brought into service from commercial companies to gain access for inspection and determination of damage. On this first morning after the earthquake, General Manager John Manley, together with Cliff Fuglestad, Engineer of Track, made a helicopter flight as far as the Hunter Flats and also over to Tunnel Door 2 on the Whittier Branch. Simultaneously, Engineer of Structures, Bruce Cannon, together with Roadmaster Paul Watts, started north over the Railroad as far as Willow, determining damage. A fixed-wing airplane was dispatched to Seward with Assistant Chief Engineer Charles Griffith. He was met at Seward by Chief Engineer Irvin Cook, who had made his way in from the Kenai Lake area.

Assistant General Manager, Dick Bruce, and General Roadmaster, Jack Church, traveling by car and on foot were able to survey the damage between Anchorage and Suntrana, source of the coal used to generate much of the heat and power consumed in Anchorage.

As these various flights and reports arrived back in Anchorage and a summation was made of the damage, initial loss could readily be placed at $20 million dollars. Some 200 miles of railroad were totally immobilized. The flights revealed that in excess of 110 bridges were rendered unserviceable. Miles of track were warped out of line and rails twisted. Landslides accounted for over 2½ miles of lost grade. Numerous avalanches which had been triggered by the shock covered the tracks as much as 20 to 30 feet and had carried away communication lines. The port of Seward facilities were virtually wiped out by a combination of seismic action, tidal waves, and fire. Our secondary Port of Whittier fared somewhat better, but was far from operable. The vital car barge slip was gone.

Several major shops and industrial structures were either 100 percent destroyed or required extensive repair at our Anchorage headquarters and other line points; 225 pieces of rolling stock were either lost, or badly damaged.

Emergency communication lines were quickly restored to allow Railroad personnel at various points along the Railroad to gain communication and to receive instructions as to restoration procedures.

On Saturday, the Railbelt Reporter said that:

Communications employees were back on the job and they managed to get the microwave system south going as far as Mile 92 by running all repeater stations on emergency power. Men started north to clean up the open wire circuits.

In the office, employees were trying to bring order out of the jumble. File cabinets had toppled over, light fixtures had fallen, spraying desks, chairs and floors with glass; cabinets had opened, spilling contents.

March 29, 1964 — By Sunday night, our Communications people had the microwave system in operation to Portage, despite the fact that both the 150-foot tower and the wooden tower at Portage had been severely damaged.

From March 30, 1964 on — After a harrowing weekend, punctuated by over 40 aftershocks, Alaska Railroaders in full force rolled up their sleeves and started putting their railroad back together again.

Communications had a 'whoop and holler' circuit into Seward by March 30 and by March 31, they had five channels of communication into that stricken city.

Train and enginemen offered their services wherever they were needed, and helped with the gigantic clean-up job.

Anchorage Freight Depot employees, their regular jobs temporarily eliminated by the quake, were recruited for other jobs. All through that first week they worked, righting file cabinets, pounding drawers back into shape, cleaning up broken glass and furniture, filling Preco heaters, carrying water for rest rooms, moving furniture. There was no heat in the General Office Building and no water. Employees brought jugs of water for drinking and making coffee. Of necessity, slacks, warm sweaters, jackets, and fur-lined boots became the accepted attire of women employees.

* * * * *

During the next few days, Harriet LaZelle and her girls in the Employment Bureau, hired between 200 and 300 temporary employees to assist in the big job ahead. Long lines of men extended into the passenger depot, as they waited to be fingerprinted by the special agents before being transported to damaged areas.

Mechanical employees busied themselves tearing down the Wheel Shop, two walls of which had collapsed during the quake. They set up offices for the chief mechanical officer and his staff in the Diesel Building as fast as furniture and equipment could be retrieved from the condemned Wheel Shop.

*   *   *   *   *

Secretary to the Chief Engineer, Fran Moore, had this to say about Engineering:

"On Monday morning, following the quake, the department moved ahead en masse and despite much adversity (lack of communication, transportation, etc.), things began happening. Contractors moved in along the line, and with their huge machines began at once the clearing and dozing operations needed in the rebuilding of Uncle Sam's farthest north railroad.

"Within days, on April 6, the first freight train moved north from Anchorage to Fairbanks; the Palmer branch was opened, and work along the southern portion of the line was progressing rapidly.

"Fills were made, bridges repaired, and rail was laid. Divers were sent to Whittier to probe under the water for possible salvage. 'Whirly-birds' airlifted personnel up and down the line, surveying the wreckage, and brought them back to report what they had seen and what was needed for repairs. Work-weary, red-eyed roadmasters and supervisors reported in, received their new instructions, and went back to the job and their equally tired men. Sleep was all but forgotten, but The Alaska Railroad is being rebuilt."

The story was the same, from devastated Whittier and Seward to the south, to Fairbanks in the north, Alaska Railroaders rallied to do their bit in this great catastrophe.

ACKNOWLEDGMENTS

The authors are grateful to many employees of the railroad who took some of their valuable time during the busy days of reconstruction to be of assistance, especially the following: J. E. Manley, general manager; I. P. Cook, chief engineer; C. L. Griffith, assistant chief engineer; B. E. Cannon, engineer of structures; Clifford Fugelstad, engineer of track; Jack Church, trackmaster; James Morrison and Arnie Hesness, engineers; Carl Nelson, electrical supervisor; and Francis Weeks, accountant. In addition, subsurface and other information along the highway was obtained from Bruce Campbell and Frank Buskie of the Alaska Department of Highways. C. A. Hill, D. K. Conger, and C. H. Harned of the consulting engineering firm of Clair A. Hill and Associates of Redding, Calif., provided reports on changes in railroad grade, information on the Potter Hill landslide and borings in the Portage area. Aerial photographs of the railroad were made available by the U.S. Army in Anchorage. Professor A. M. Johnson of the geology department of Stanford University derived the equations used in the analysis of compressive forces that were exerted on a bridge; A. Kennedy of the U.S. Forest Service, Anchorage, supplied several of the photographs; Webb Hayes, of the engineering firm of Earl and Wright, of San Francisco, which acted as a consultant to the railroad during reconstruction, reviewed the description of damage to railroad buildings in Anchorage; and Frank McClure, of McClure and Messinger, consulting structural engineers, Oakland, Calif., reviewed the sections titled "Summary and Conclusions" and "Construction in Areas of Potential Landspreading."

LOCATION AND PHYSIOGRAPHIC SETTING

The southern terminus of The Alaska Railroad is the deepwater all-weather port of Seward, built on a fan delta in Resurrection Bay fiord on the Gulf of Alaska (fig. 1). North from Seward (mile 0) the rail line runs about 64 miles across the steep and rugged glaciated terrain of Kenai Peninsula to Portage, where it is joined by a 12-mile spur line to a second deepwater all-weather port at Whittier, on Prince William Sound. From Portage to Anchorage the rail line is built along the north shore of

1.—Location of The Alaska Railroad.

Turnagain Arm at the foot of steep mountains; at Potter it swings inland over gently rolling plains of glacial deposits to the main rail yards in Anchorage, mile 114, on the shore of Cook Inlet. Leaving Anchorage, the line continues across the glacial plain along the southeast side of Knik Arm to the wide flood plain of the Knik and Matanuska Rivers that empty into the head of the arm at about mile 146. At Matanuska, on the northern edge of the flood plain, the line is joined by a 22-mile spur that follows the northwest side of the Matanuska River to Palmer, Sutton, Jonesville, and Eska. The main line turns west at Matanuska, then swings north in a long curve along the valley of the Susitna River which it follows through the mountainous terrain near Mount McKinley National Park. Crossing the drainage divide of the Alaska Range at Summit (mile 312.5) the rail line continues north in the Nenana River valley to the town of Nenana at mile 411.7. From here it swings to the northeast and reaches Fairbanks at mile 470.3.

The mountainous topography between Seward, Whittier, and Potter, and in the Mount McKinley Park area has restricted possible railroad location. Across the Kenai Peninsula the rail line is built on the floors of steep-walled elongate glaciated valleys, and, except where crowded to the side of the valley by lakes or rivers, it is built far enough from the walls to avoid snow avalanches and landslides. Because of these restrictions, the rail line had to be built on marshes, active flood plains, and in the Nenana River valley on known landslides (Wahrhaftig and Black, 1958). Thus much of the damage to the rail line that resulted from displacements or loss of bearing strength of the soft sediments could not have been avoided.

THE EARTHQUAKE

The great Alaska earthquake occurred at 5:36 p.m., Alaska standard time, on March 27, 1964. The epicenter has been located approximately 80 miles east-southeast of Anchorage, on the shore of Unakwik Inlet (fig. 2). The hypocentral depth is not known, but is thought to have been between 12.5 and 31 miles (20 to 50 km). The epicenter lies between elongate southwest-trending belts in which the surface of the earth was uplifted and subsided. The amount and distribution of the land-level changes have been mapped by Plafker (1965, 1968), and he proposed the following low-angle thrust model to explain the regional uplift and subsidence: Prior to the earthquake, strains were generated within the continental crust as it was underridden by the oceanic crust and mantle. At some critical strain, rupture occurred along a major zone of weakness, or megathrust, that may coincide with the base of the continental crust along the continental margin. Wilson and Tørum (1967) have suggested that the rupture was triggered by the coincidence of large-amplitude earth tides which increased the stress with low-water tides (Berg, 1966) which reduced the resistance to thrusting by unloading the surface above the thrust. At the time of rupture, that part of the strain which had been stored elastically in the continental rocks above the rupture was released, and the rocks were driven to the southeast over the rupture surface. From the surface deformation pattern and seismic data, Plafker infers that the rupture surface may have intersected the Aleutian Trench, and then dipped gently to the northwest for a distance of about 300 km, to a depth of about 40 km. Thus, with the release of elastic strain a zone of surface uplift was produced when continental rocks were driven up the dip of the rupture surface; while to the northwest, the land surface was lowered by elastic horizontal extension and vertical attenuation of the crust behind the thrust block. A thrust is also favored by Stauder and Bollinger (1966) who have demonstrated that there was a uniformity of motion in one preshock, the main shock and the aftershock sequence. They believe the combined P-wave first motion and S-wave polarization in the aftershocks favor movement on a low-angle thrust plane, not on a steeply dipping plane as suggested by Press and Jackson (1965).

Large horizontal displacements were measured by the U.S. Coast and Geodetic Survey during their 1964–1965 retriangulation of the preearthquake triangulation net (Parkin, 1966). Accepting Parkin's assumption that a station about 35 miles northeast of Anchorage was not displaced hori-

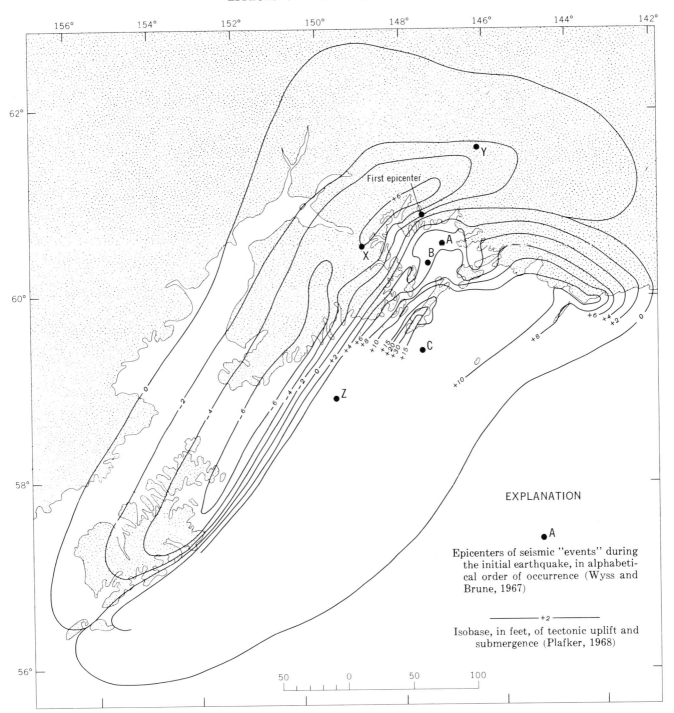

2.—Location of the epicenters of recognizable seismic events that occurred during the earthquake (Wyss and Brune, 1967) and areas of tectonic uplift and subsidence in south-central Alaska (Plafker, 1968).

zontally, the resurvey indicates a general and increasing horizontal displacement to the southeast in the subsided and landward part of the uplifted areas (fig. 3). The horizontal displacements have been interpreted as indicating a widening of about 5 feet across Matanuska Valley and a right-lateral displacement of about 5 feet along the net between Sunrise and Seward (Wood, 1966, p. 121). There is as yet no independent evidence for lateral displacement along this latter part of the net; however, from Moose Pass to Seward the net follows a conspicuous topographic trough which probably owes its origin to faulting. The possibility of displacement along the line from Moose

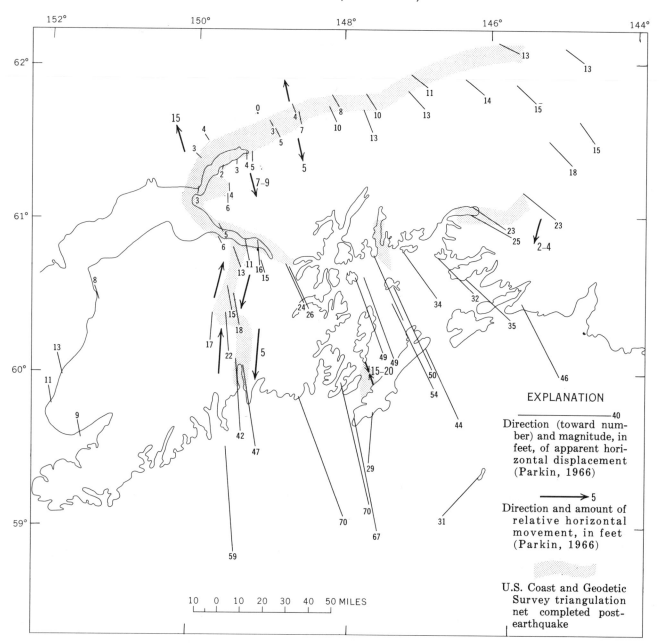

3.—Horizontal displacement that accompanied the earthquake.

Pass to Seward may be important in assessing the damage to the railroad, which lies in this trough.

Because much of the damage to the railroad resulted from changes in foundation materials that are time-dependent and cumulative, the duration of seismic vibration was of extreme importance in determining the kinds and degree of damage. Wyss and Brune (1967) have shown in an analysis of *P*-phases on worldwide seismo-

grams that there were three distinct and an additional three probable events during the main shock (fig. 2). These events occurred at increasing distances from the epicenter at 9, 19, 28, 29, 44, and 72 seconds after the initial origin time. The Richter magnitude of the first *P*-pulse was 6.6; successive phases had larger amplitudes. The largest *P*-wave amplitudes had a magnitude of 7.8, and occurred about 60 seconds after the

first arrival of the *P*-wave train. The distribution of the epicenters and the time of origin of the events indicate that the railroad was subjected to a long period of severe shaking from seismic waves that were generated over a wide area.

Estimates of the duration of strong ground motion along the rail line range from 3 to 4 minutes, and estimates of the total duration of perceptible ground motion vary even more. In Anchorage, shaking timed by watch indicates that on unconsolidated sediments strong motion lasted 3 to 4 minutes and perceptible shaking had a total duration of about 7 minutes (Shannon and Wilson, Inc., 1964a). At Portage, which is underlain by several hundred feet of water-saturated fine-grained sediments, perceptible ground motion may have lasted as much as

15 minutes (Kachadoorian, 1965). To the south, at the west end of Kenai Lake in an area also underlain by at least 200 feet of unconsolidated sediment, John Ingraham reported that after a period of about 8 minutes, the large trees were still swaying as if in a high wind. John Kehdon made the same observation in the same area (Railbelt Reporter, 1964). In Sew-

ard, at the southern end of the rail line, also on unconsolidated sediments, strong motion lasted 3 to 4 minutes (Lemke, 1967).

The earthquake was followed by a series of strong aftershocks with magnitudes reported to be as high as 6.7 (Wood, 1966, p. 68). Despite the size of these aftershocks, there is no evidence that any caused additional damage to the railroad.

EARTHQUAKE EFFECTS

BRIDGE DAMAGE CAUSED BY DISPLACEMENT OF FOUNDATION MATERIALS

Damaged railroad bridges have been described in many studies of earthquakes (Hobbs, 1908; Hollis, 1958; Japan Soc. Civil Engineers, 1960; Duke, 1960). It is difficult, however, to compare these descriptions and to understand the damage-causing mechanisms because (1) the bridges were damaged by different seismic events, (2) the bridges vary greatly, from those built of bamboo to those built of heavy masonry, and (3) the kinds measurements taken by the various observers are not consistent. In contrast, for the Alaska earthquake it was possible to make comparable measurements of damage to many bridges of the same design and construction.

Most of the bridges within the area affected by the earthquake are the type shown in Figure 4. They are open wood trestles, supported on wood piling, with wood bulkheads. Piles are driven to a calculated bearing capacity of 15 tons. In larger and more complex bridges on steel piles, the piles are driven to a calculated bearing capacity of 35 to 50 tons. Some few

bridges have concrete or multiple piers and steel decks.

Bridge damage resulted from (1) permanent horizontal and vertical displacements of foundation materials, (2) transient horizontal displacement of the ground, and (3) high accelerations generated within bridge structures by the amplification of ground motion. Because damage usually resulted from some combination of these elements, it is necessary to discuss some details of the damage to evaluate each of these elements. In a few cases, observations provide approximations of the forces that were exerted, which may be useful in the design of similar structures in other seismically active areas. But of equal importance is the conclusion that the observations provide evidence that the gross behavior of a wide range of noncohesive materials can be generally predicted without detailed site information.

HORIZONTAL DISPLACEMENT

In nearly every damaged bridge, bents were shifted both horizontally and vertically, as shown diagrammatically in figure 5. Shifting occurred without vertical rotation; thus bents remained nearly vertical. Most horizontal displace-

ment took place in the line of the bridge. In addition, where the bridge deck buckled laterally there were up- or downstream movements of the bents, but these piles appear to have been dragged by the deflecting superstructure (see p. D116).

Most displaced bents were torn free of the superstructure. Some pile caps remained attached to the piles and were pulled from the bolts that secured them to the stringers (fig. 5). Other pile caps remained secured to the stringers, but the piles pulled free of the drift pins that attach them to the pile cap and the sway braces were often split and detached from the caps. In other bridges, the pile caps were partially pulled from the stringers and the piles and were rotated between the shifting piles and the deck. Displacements of the bents probably very nearly reflect the movement of the foundation materials, because the connections between the piling and the superstructure appear to have offered little resistance to the horizontal displacement of the piles. If the connections at the tops of the bents had held, their bases would have rotated streamward, as were the bases of some of the piers

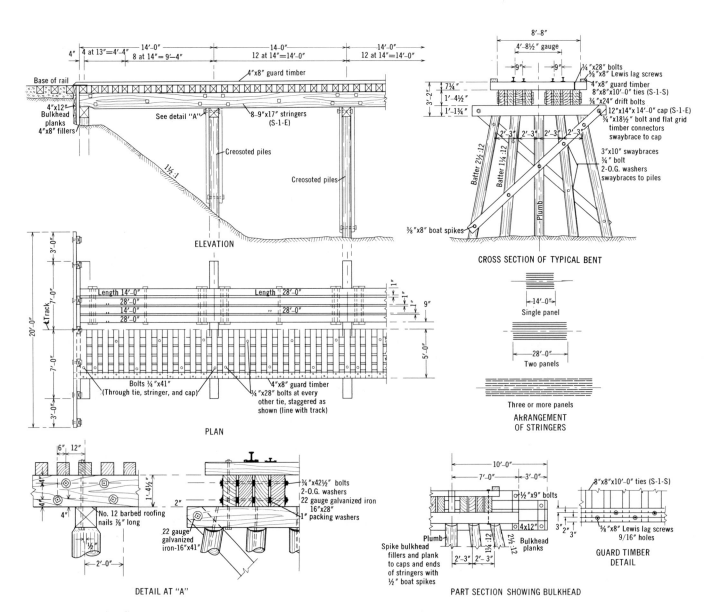

4.—Construction plans for a standard open-deck wood-pile trestle. Drawings by The Alaska Railroad.

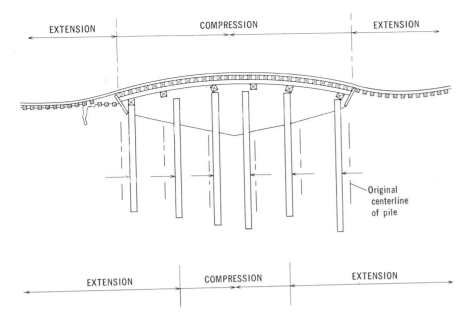

5.—Typical displacement of bridge piles. Most piles were crowded toward the center of the stream. The distance between piles increased at the bridge ends and decreased toward the bridge center. Piles in the center usually stood higher than at the ends.

under the highway bridges whose tops were held apart by steel decks (fig. 6).

Relative horizontal displacements between bents, as determined by measuring offsets between the pre- and postearthquake position of the bents on the stringers, are plotted as bar graphs on figures 7 and 8. Distances between bents increased, remained unchanged, or decreased. The displacements are shown on the graphs in terms of the interpreted behavior of the foundation material as extension, no change, or compression.

In figure 9 the movements between bents are summarized for the short (12- to 45-ft), intermediate (60- to 98-ft), and long (105- to 150-ft) bridges shown in figures 7 and 8. In order to compare bent movement in bridges of various lengths, the amount of movement between adjacent bents is given as the percentage of the bridge length.

Most bents were shifted toward the streams. The fact that distances between bents generally were increased near the bridge ends and were decreased toward the centers of the streams indicates that there were zones of extension at the margins and compression at the centers. This is most clearly shown in the short bridges. In intermediate and long bridges the bent movements were more complex. There was usually extension at the margins but there were often several zones of compression and extension on the valley floor. Some, but not all, zones of compression were located at distinct channels.

In all but six bridges, the net compression shown by interbent measurements exceeded the net extension (fig. 10). Net compression was generally 20 inches or less, regardless of bridge length, but in two bridges compression was as large as 64 and 81.5 inches.

In addition to having their supporting bents torn free, most stringers were put into compression by converging streambanks. Distances between streambanks

were decreased by as much as 6.5 feet (table 1). As a result, the stringers acted as struts, and either jammed into the fillers on the bulkheads (fig. 11) or, where compression was greater, drove through the bulkhead planks (fig. 44). In some bridges most of the compression was released at one end, and the stringers were thrust up over the top of the bulkhead onto one of the approach fills.

Compressive forces not released by failures at the bulkheads produced lateral deflections in the decks of several bridges (those at mile 37.0, 37.3, 63.0). Stringers were either thrown into long horizontal bends, or were broken at sharp kinks, with as much as 8 feet of lateral deflection at the apex of the bends (figs. 12, 18). At mile 34.5 the distance between bulkheads of a 105-foot wood bridge was decreased by 2.0 feet. The resulting compression jackknifed the deck up off its pilings (fig. 13). The apex of the bend in the deck occurred where four of the eight stringers were butt-jointed; the remaining four stringers were broken. This is the only bridge in which it is clear that compression contributed to arching. In other arched bridges the decks lay in contact with most of the piling, and arching resulted primarily from vertical displacement of piling (see p. D114), on which the deck lay passively.

VERTICAL DISPLACEMENT

Displaced foundation materials often had a vertical component of movement; at many bridges the tops of piles were higher at midstream than near the banks. Less commonly, there was no vertical displacement, and pile tops were level. There were no bridges in which piling was lower in stream centers. As a result, many bridges were arched upward and others

6.—The pier of a highway bridge at Resurrection River that was rotated as its base was carried toward the channel while its top was restrained by the deep central steel deck beam. A crack that formed in the pier is visible just above the water.

compression by streamward movement of the banks. It is improbable that the arching of the deck pulled the piling upward because the skin friction of the outward battered piles would have greatly exceeded the strength of the connections between the stringers and the piles. This is not to say that compressional arching could not have contributed to uplifting of the piles to the point at which these connections failed, for in one bridge (34.5), as previously described, compression alone produced arching in stringers torn free of their supporting piling. However, both in this bridge and in most others, upward pile movement occurred despite the fact that these connections had been severed by horizontal displacements of the bents. Furthermore, piles were also higher under the centers of bridges in which the stringers were not compressed—where arching decreased the distance between the ends of the stringers sufficiently to avoid compression between converging bulkheads. Thus, vertical pile displacements, whether slightly assisted by the arching or opposed by the weight and stiffness of the stringers, indicate an increasing vertical component of movement of the foundation materials toward the stream centers.

The independence of vertical pile displacement from deformation of the bridge superstructure is shown clearly by an observation of Lawson and others (1908, p. 218) after the great 1906 California earthquake:

* * * At the bridge over Coyote Creek, on the Alviso-Milpitas road, the concrete abutments were thrust inward toward each other about 3 feet. A pile driven in the middle of the stream, which had been cut off below the water-level, was lifted about 2 feet and now rises above the water.

remained relatively flat. In only one bridge (63.5) was there a downward arch in a superstructure. However, even in this bridge the piling was higher in the stream center. The downward arch was formed when the stringers were thrust upward over the top of the

bulkhead and onto the approach fill which left the superstructure unsupported to the place where the sagging stringers again found bearing on the piling (fig. 14).

Vertically displaced piles were common in arched bridges in which the stringers were put into

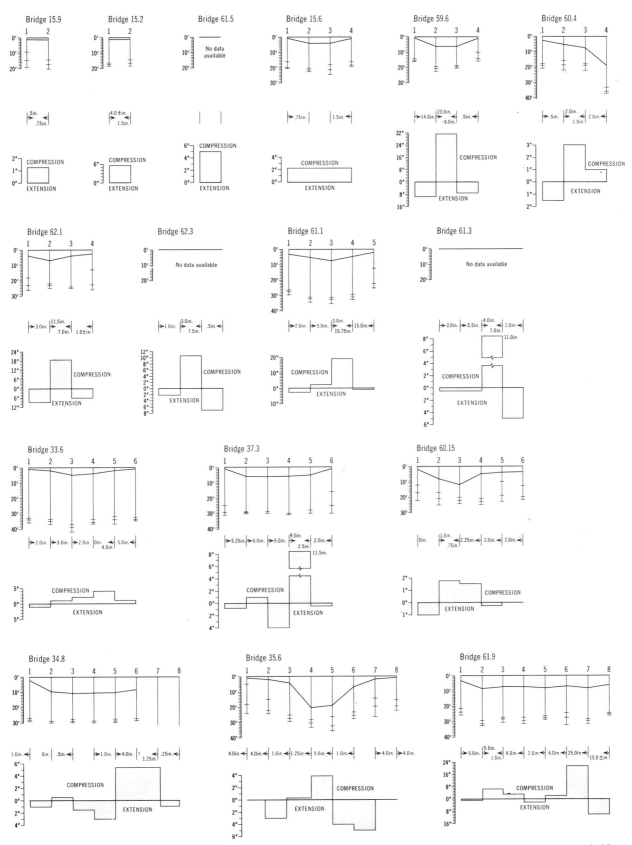

7.—Pile penetration length and relative horizontal displacement of bents of one- to seven-span open wood trestle bridges. The horizontal displacements are shown in terms of interpreted behavior of the foundation material: Extension, distance between bents increased; no change; and compression, distance between bents decreased. The shallowest, average, and greatest depths of penetration in each bent are indicated by horizontal lines.

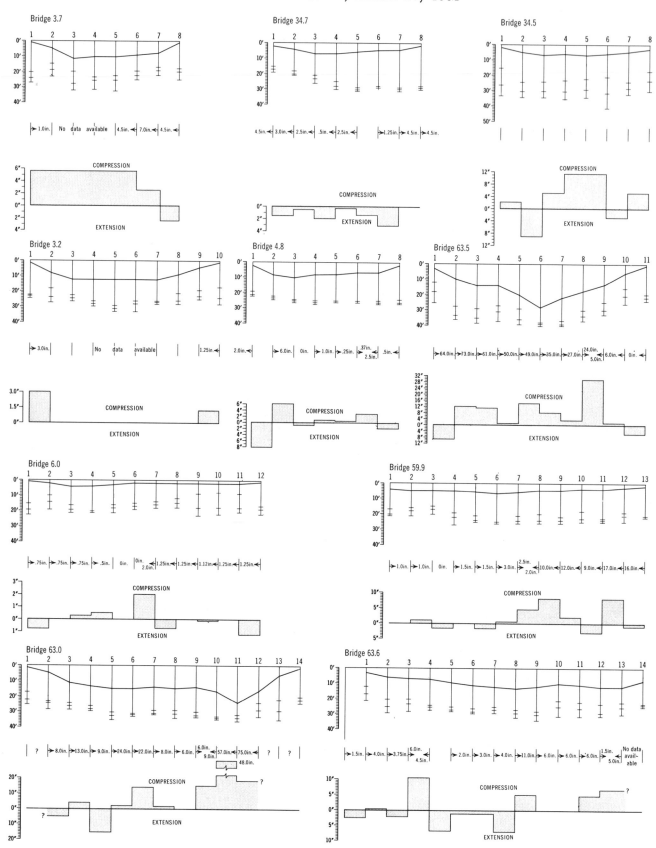

8.—Pile penetration length and relative horizontal displacement of bents of seven- to 14-span open wood trestle bridges. The horizontal displacements are shown in terms of interpreted behavior of the foundation material: Extension, distance between bents increased: no change; and compression, distance between bents decreased. The shallowest, average, and greatest depths of penetration in each bent are indicated by horizontal lines.

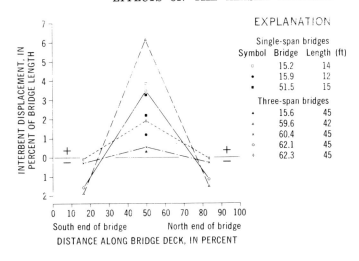

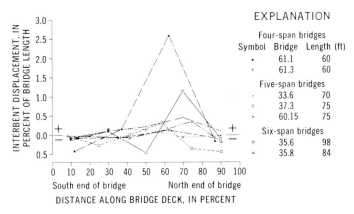

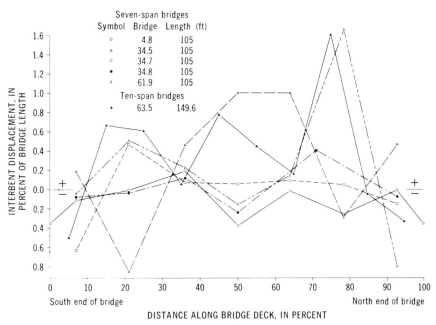

9.—Relative horizontal displacements between bents of open wood trestle bridges plotted as the percentage of the bridge length. Horizontal compression of foundation materials indicated by +, horizontal extension by —.

TABLE 1.—*Damage to*

Bridge	Length (feet)	Type	Vertical distortion	Horizontal distortion	Compressed (C) or extended (E)	Measured streambank convergence (C) or divergence (D) (measured stringer length minus measured distance between bulkheads at level of top of bents)	Net compression or extension of streambed sediments determined by relative horizontal movement of bents	
							Compression	Extension
Mile 3.0	187	Two 80-ft through steel girder spans with one 13.5-ft open wood trestle on each end.	None	Central pier 8 in. west and outer piers 2± in. west of approaches.	C			
3.2	135	Open wood trestle; nine 15± ft spans.	3-in. arch	Middle of bridge 10 in. west of approaches.	C		9.5 in	
3.3	136	One 80-ft through steel girder span with two 14± ft open wood trestles on each end.	None	Middle span 30 in. west of south bulkhead and 6 in. west of north bulkhead.	C			
3.7	105	Open wood trestle; seven 15± ft spans.	6-in. arch with 4th and 5th bent high.	North approach 1 ft west of south approach.	C		5.5 in	0
4.3	42	Open wood trestle; three 14± ft spans.	Arched 1 in		C			
4.8	105	Open wood trestle; seven 15± ft spans.	Arched about 8 in	5-in. horizontal displacement between approaches.	E		0	3.5 in
6.0	165	Open wood trestle; eleven 15± ft spans.	½-in. arch at 5th bent	5th through 12th bent moved 2 in. to west of bents 1 through 4.	C		1.88 in	0
6.6	135	Ballast deck, wood; nine 15± ft spans.	None	None	Neither		0	0
14.5 15.2	14	Open wood trestle; one 14± ft span.	None	South end bridge 18 in. east of north end.	C		6.5 in	0
15.6	45	Open wood trestle; three 15± ft spans.	2-in. arch	South approach offset 20 in. east relative to north approach.	C		1.75 in	0
15.9	12	Open wood trestle; one 12± ft span.	None	None	C		1.75 in	0
16.1 16.6	60	Open wood trestle; four 15± ft spans.	None	None	Neither			
20.0	252	Open wood trestle; eighteen 14± ft spans.	8-in. arch at 6th bent	None	E			
21.4	30	Open wood trestle; two 15± ft spans.	Slight		E			
23.5	105	Open wood trestle; seven 15± ft spans.	None	None	Neither			
25.5	120	Open wood trestle; eight 15± ft spans.	None	None	Neither			
29.5	285	Open wood trestle; nineteen 15± ft spans.	None	None	C			
33.0 33.6	70	Open wood trestle; five 14± ft spans.	6-in. arch with maximum at 4th bent.	North approach offset to west relative to south approach.	C		7 in	0
34.5	105.3	Open wood trestle; seven 15± ft spans.	Jacknifed at 4th bent breaking stringers. At peak deck approximately 4½-ft high.	North approach offset 1.2 ft west relative to south approach.	C	2.0 ft C	2.2 ft	0
34.7	105.0	Open wood trestle; seven 15± ft spans.	2-ft arch over whole bridge with maximum at 5th bent.		E	1.1 ft D	0	18 in
34.8	105	Open wood trestle; seven 15± ft spans.	2-ft arch over whole bridge with maximum at 4th bent.	North approach offset 2 ft east relative to south approach.	E		0	¾ in
35.6	98	Open wood trestle; seven 14± ft spans.	1.5-ft arch over whole bridge with maximum at 4th and 5th bents.	North approach offset 2 ft west relative to south approach.	E		0	8 in
35.8	84	Open wood trestle; six 14± ft spans.	10-in. arech over whole bridge with maximum at 4th bent.		C		1.55 in	0
36.7	28	Open wood trestle; two 14± ft spans.						
37.0	435	Open wood trestle; twenty-nine 15± ft spans.	Slight lowering of end bents and ends of bridge.	North approach offset 2 ft east relative to south. Sharp kink with 6-ft displacement between bents 24 and 28.	C			
37.3	75	Open wood trestle; five 15± ft spans.	6-in. arch primarily by lowering of embankment on north side of bridge.	North approach offset 2 ft west relative to south. Sharp kink with 4-ft displacement between bents 1 and 4.	C		7.25 in	
41.6	70	Open wood trestle; five 14± ft spans.	3-in. arch due to lowering of fill on north approach.	North approach offset 0.5 ft west relative to south approach.	C			
46.8	75	Ballasted deck truss on concrete piers on bedrock.						
47.2	60	One 60-ft deck girder on bedrock.						
47.55	21	One 21-ft beam span ballasted deck on piles built of concrete capped rails.						
51.8	161	One 133-ft deck truss with one 14-ft beam span on each approach.						
52.0	85	One 85-ft deck truss						
52.45	29	One 29-ft beam span						

railroad bridges

Compression (C) or extension (E) measured at level of stringers and (or) steel spans (inches)	Evidence of repetitive compressive blows at bridge ends		Bridge higher than approach fills at bulkheads		Bulkheads								Remarks
					Rammed		Rotated		Raised above (+) or lowered below (−) bridge (inches)		Horizontal skew (inches)		
	South	North	South end	North end	South	North	South	North	South	North	South	North	
16.5 C	0	2	5.5 in	0	Yes	Yes	Yes	Yes	0	−0.75			
9.5 C	0	0	8 in	5 in	Yes	Yes	Yes	Yes	0	−3	E7		
21 C	0	4	8 in	8±in	Yes	Yes	Yes	Yes	−.5			W5.5	
5.5 C	0	0	6 in	4±in	Yes	Yes	Yes	Yes	−2.5	−1⅛			
	0	0	Slightly	Slightly	Yes	Yes	Yes	Yes		−½		W1¹⁄₁₆	
1.5 E	0	2	¾–4½ in	1½ in	No	Yes	No	Yes	−2⅝	−¾	No	E½	
2 C	0	0	0	0	Yes	Yes	Yes	Yes			No	No	
0	0	0	4	0	No	No	No	No	0	0	No	No	
6.5 C	0	0	0	8 in	Yes	Yes	Yes	Yes					
1.75 C	1	0	Slightly	Slightly	Yes	Yes	Yes	Yes					
1.75 C	0	2	Slightly	2 in	Yes		Yes	Yes	0	−1⅞			
	0	0	0	0	Yes	No	No	Yes	−1	−1½			
12 E	0	0	0	0	No	No	No	No	0	0	0	0	
7½ E	0	5			Yes	Yes	Yes	Yes					
	0	1	0	½ in	No	Yes	No	No	0	0	0	0	
	2+	2+	½ in	0	Yes	Yes							
	0	0	0	0	Yes	Yes	Yes	Yes	0	0	0	0	
7 C	0	0	0	½ in	Yes	Yes	Yes	Yes					
	4	4	0	0	Yes	Yes	Yes	Yes					
	2	0	0	0	Yes	Yes	Yes	Yes					
¾ E	0	0	0	0	No	Yes	No	Yes	−3½	−½	W1½	0	
8 E	2	1			Yes	Yes	Yes	Yes	0	−3	0	E1	
					Yes	Yes			−2	0			
21½ C				10 in	Yes	Yes		Yes		−3		W2½	
		Several			Yes	Yes	Yes			−3			
			0	1.5 ft	Yes	Yes							
													No damage to bridge. Bridge on bedrock. Report by B. E. Cannon; not see by authors. Do.
													Slight spalling on abutments; anchor bolts and expansion joints not damaged. Report by B. E. Cannon; not seen by authors. No damage to bridge. Built on bedrock. Report by B. E. Cannon; not seen by authors. Do. Do.

TABLE 1.—*Damage to*

Bridge	Length (feet)	Type	Vertical distortion	Horizontal distortion	Compressed (C) or extended (E)	Measured streambank convergence (C) or divergence (D) (measured stringer length minus measured distance between bulkheads at level of top of bents)	Net compression or extension of streambed sediments determined by relative horizontal movement of bents	
							Compression	Extension
54.1	256	One 200-ft through girder with one 28-ft wood span in each approach.	--------	--				
58.7	180	Open wood trestle; twelve 15± ft spans.	Slight lowering of bridge ends with lowering of approach fills.	North approach offset approximately 2.5 ft relative to south approach.	C			
59.6	44.95	Open wood trestle; three 14± ft spans.	3-in. arch over whole bridge.	North approach offset approximately 8 in. east relative to south approach.	C	1.45 ft C	14.5 in	
59.9	180	Open wood trestle; twelve 15± ft spans.	None	North approach offset approximately 3 ft east relative to south approach.	C		17 in	
60.15	75	Open wood trestle; five 15± ft spans.	10-in. arch over whole bridge with maximum at 3d bent.	None	C		1 in	
60.4	45	Open wood trestle; three 15± ft spans.	4-in. arch over whole bridge with maximum at 2d bent.	North approach offset approximately 2 to 4 in. east relative to south approach.	C		2.5 in	
61.1	60	Open wood trestle; four 15± ft spans.	5-in. arch by lowering of north bulkhead bent.	North approach offset approximately 8 in to west relative to south approach.	C		16.75 in	
61.3	60	Open wood trestle; four 15±ft spans.	6-in. arch over whole bridge.	North approach offset 4 to 5 in. east relative to north end.	C		5 in	
61.5	13.8	Open wood trestle; one span.	1-in. arch over whole bridge.	North approach offset approximately 18 in. east relative to south approach.	C	4 in. C	4 to 6 in	
61.9	103.8	Open wood trestle; seven 15±ft spans.	1-ft arch over whole bridge with maximum at 4th and 5th bents.	North approach offset 2 ft west relative to south approach.	C	1.8 ft C	20 in	
62.1	43	Open wood trestle; three 15±ft spans.	10 in. arch over whole bridge.	North approach offset unmeasured distance to east relative to south approach.	C	.6 ft C	4 in	
62.3	45	Open wood trestle; three 15±ft spans.	6 in	North approach is old bridge covered with embankment. Now 1±ft. east relative to south approach	C		8 in	
63.0	194.8	Open wood trestle with planked walkways outside rails; thirteen 15±ft spans.	1.6 ft	Sharp bend of 8 ft maximum displacement in 45 ft. North approach. approximately 14 in. west of south approach	C	4.4 ft C	83 in	
63.5	149.6	Open wood trestle; ten 15±ft spans.	North half of bridge arched up 1 ft at bent 7; south half of bridge arched down 1 ft at bent 3.	North approach offset 10 ft west relative to south approach.	C		64 in	
63.6	208.95	Open wood trestle; fifteen 15±ft spans.	2.5-ft arch over whole bridge.	North approach offset 7 ft west relative to south approach.	C			
75.2	75	Open wood trestle; five 14±ft spans.			C		4 in	
83.0	75	Open wood trestle; five 14± ft spans.	4-in. arch over whole bridge with maximum at 4th bent.	Center of bridge displaced 2¾ in. west.	C			
83.5	75	Open wood trestle; five 14-± ft. spans.	6-in. arch over whole bridge with maximum between 3d and 4th bents.	None	C			
93.46	60	One 60-ft steel deck truss on concrete abutments.	None		C			
112.8	192	One 80-ft steel deck girder with four 14-± ft open wood trestle spans on each approach pile pier at end of steel span.	None	None	C			
114.3	193	One 123-ft through steel truss with one 35-ft steel beam span on each approach.	None		C			
127.5	308	Five steel deck girders. From south to north they are 74 ft, 40 ft, 80 ft, 40 ft, 74 ft. Concrete piers and abutments.	4 to 5-in. arch		Neither			
136.4	86	One 60-ft steel through girder with one 13-ft open wood trestle on each approach.			Probably neither.			
140.8	80	One 80-ft steel through girder on concrete piers.			C			

railroad bridges—Continued

Compression (C) or extension (E) measured at level of stringers and (or) steel spans (inches)	Evidence of repetitive compressive blows at bridge ends		Bridge higher than approach fills at bulkheads		Bulkheads								Remarks
					Rammed		Rotated		Raised above (+) or lowered below (−) bridge (inches)		Horizontal skew (inches)		
	South	North	South end	North end	South	North	South	North	South	North	South	North	
--------	--------	--------	--------	--------	--------	--------	--------	--------	--------	--------	--------	--------	No damage to bridge. Report by B. E. Cannon; not seen by authors.
--------	--------	--------			Yes	Yes	--------	--------	--------	--------	--------	--------	
14.5 C	0	0	1.5 ft	5 in	Yes	Yes	Yes	Yes	0	0	0	0	
17 C	0	0	21 in	31 in	Yes	Yes	Yes	Yes					
	0	0	0	3 in	No	Yes	No	Yes					Buried bulkhead three ties north of bridge. Embankment dropped 2.5 ft on north side of this buried bulkhead.
	0	0	0	0	Yes	Yes		Yes					
	0	0	1 ft	1.5 ft	Yes	Yes	Yes	Yes					
C	0	0	4–8 in	6 in	Yes	Yes	Yes	Yes					
	0	0	6–10 in	1.5 ft	Yes	Yes	Yes	Yes			W1.5	E	
	0	0		2.5 ft	Yes	Yes	Yes	Yes					
	0	0		4 in	Yes	Yes	Yes	Yes		−3¾	E3		
					Yes	Yes	Yes	Yes					
	0	0	8 in	2 ft	Yes	Yes	Yes	Yes			E3		
	0	2	0	1.7 ft	Yes	Yes	Yes	Yes					
	0	5	0	1.5 ft	Yes	Yes	Yes	Yes					
			Yes	Yes	Yes				−4	−6½			
			0	0		Yes		Yes	0	0			
1–4½ C													Concrete abutment on north end has rotated toward stream at its base.
2½ C			10 in	Slightly	Yes	No	Yes						Pile pier at south end of span moved estimated 2 to 4 in. streamward.
15½ C													No evidence of movement.
				Slightly?									No evidence of movement of steel on concrete piers. No data on wooden spans.
1¾ C			1–2 in	1–2 in									Concrete abutments crowded together. Steel jammed tight. B. E. Cannon.

TABLE 1.—*Damage to*

Bridge	Length (feet)	Type	Vertical distortion	Horizontal distortion	Compressed (C) or extended (E)	Measured stream-bank convergence (C) or divergence (D) (measured stringer length minus measured distance between bulkheads at level of top of bents)	Net compression or extension of streambed sediments determined by relative horizontal movement of bents	
							Compression	Extension
142.9	112	Open wood trestle; eight 14±ft spans.	8½-in. arch over whole bridge with maximum at 5th bent.	---------				
146.4	856	Ten 80-ft steel through girders and four 14±ft open wood trestle spans on north approach.	---------					
147.1	--------	Three 123-ft steel through trusses with one 25-ft 7-in. steel beam span on each approach.	---------					
147.4	--------	One 123-ft steel through truss with one 25-ft 7-in. steel beam span on each approach.	---------					
148.3	--------		---------					
152.1	--------	Open wood trestle; five 14± ft spans.	---------					
152.3	--------	Open wood trestle, two 14± ft spans.	---------					
154.86	--------	Ballast deck, wood; seven 13-ft 6-in. spans.	---------					
264.1	--------		---------					
266.7	--------							
284.2	--------		---------					

WHITTIER

F 1.2	126	Open wood trestle; nine 14 ± ft spans.	---------					
F 2.1	211	Open wood trestle; fifteen 14 ± ft spans.	---------					
F 5.7	196	Open wood trestle; fourteen 14 ± ft spans.	---------	None visible on aerial photographs.	Probably C.	---------		
F 9.4	56	Open wood trestle; four 14 ± ft spans.	Slight arch over whole bridge seen on oblique aerial photographs.	East end of bridge moved 1 to 2 ft north of west end as seen on aerial photographs.	Probably C.	---------		
F 10.7	98	Open wood trestle; seven 14 ± ft spans.	Arch over whole bridge with maximum at northwest end seen on oblique aerial photographs.	Aerial photographs show northwest end of bridge moved southwest relative to southeast end of bridge.	Probably C.	---------		

SUTTON

A 0.3	112	Open wood trestle; eight 14 ± ft spans.	---------	---------	Probably C.	---------	0 to 7 in.	---------
A 12.0	56	Open wood trestle; four 14 ± ft spans.	---------	---------				
A 12.6	302	Two 14 ± ft open wood trestles; one 60-ft steel through girder; six 14-ft open wood trestles; one 60-ft steel through girder; five 14 ± ft open wood trestles.	---------					
A 17.0	70	Open wood trestle; five 14 ± ft spans.	---------		Probably C.			
A 18.0	98	Open wood trestle; seven 14 ± ft spans.	---------					

railroad bridges—Continued

Compression (C) or extension (E) measured at level of stringers and (or) steel spans (inches)	Evidence of repetitive compressive blows at bridge ends		Bridge higher than approach fills at bulkheads		Bulkheads							Remarks
					Rammed		Rotated		Raised above (+) or lowered below (−) bridge (inches)		Horizontal skew (inches)	
	South	North	South end	North end	South	North	South	North	South	North	South North	
					Yes	No						
												"Erratic pier movement, but not serious. Trestle damaged." B. E. Cannon.
												Broken concrete pier (No. 3) Base of pier shifted south 12 in. Expansion normal in trusses. Tail spans jammed; anchor bolts spalled out of concrete. B. E. Cannon.
												North pier and abutment shifted west about 12 in. Pier 3 moved south about 12 in. off one roller of two roller bearings. Tail spans jammed. B. E. Cannon.
												Seventy-foot span sheared anchor bolts and jammed. Lurch crack humped bridge but did not break piles. Pile bents 48 to 59 demolished. B. E. Cannon.
												Piling moved out from caps about 2 or 3 in. B. E. Cannon.
												No damage; on good ground. B. E. Cannon.
												Rocked on rocker joints. Movement about 3 in. Had to reset expansion joints. B. E. Cannon.
												Steel spans jammed together.
												Two deck truss spans jammed against central arch span. B. E. Cannon.

BRANCH

												Tidal wave damage: broke some piles. B. E. Cannon.
												Undamaged. B. E. Cannon.
												Out of shape. Three bents at south and two at north end crowded toward center. B. E. Cannon.
												Had to add fillers over some pile caps. B. E. Cannon. (That is, bridge was arched.)
												Two bents at southeast end of bridge moved northeast; two bents at northwest end of bridge moved southwest. Three bents have been removed but bridge is still 4 ft out of line. B. E. Cannon.

BRANCH

												Bents crowded toward center and end bents shoved in. B. E. Cannon.
												No damage. B. E. Cannon.
												Do.
												Bents crowded toward center. B. E. Cannon.
												Thirty-inch offset in approaches. Piles moved more than 24 in. in bent 2 and tipped. Heavy movement in bents 1, 6, 7, and 8. B. E. Cannon.

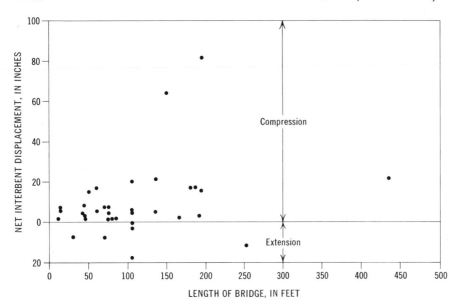

10.—Net horizontal compression or extension of bents, compared with the lengths of bridges.

It should be emphasized that the vertical displacements given above are in relative terms only, and that without some reference one could also say that there was downward displacement of the end bents. The true sense of movement is difficult to establish because of the lack of postearthquake control, and the fact that damaged bridges were in areas in which there is reason to believe that there was general, but unmeasured, consolidation and settlement.

There is, however, some evidence from the Portage area that there was actual upward movement of the piles in the stream centers. In table 2 the preearthquake elevations of bridges are compared with the postearthquake elevations as determined by a level survey made by Bonilla and William Webb of The Alaska Railroad. The effects of regional subsidence are eliminated by referring both pre- and postearthquake elevations to nearby bedrock (U.S. Coast and Geod. Survey bench mark Q12). The survey was run in a closed loop from mile 64.21 to bridge 63.0 and in an open-ended line from mile 63.0 south to bridge 61.9. Closure error on the loop of 0.42 foot appears from reoccupied stations to have been cumulative, and is thus redistributed proportionally over the loop.

The differences in the pre- and postearthquake altitudes indicate that the tops of the arched bridges varied from 1.46 feet below to 0.93 foot above their preearthquake positions. However, these differences ignore consolidation. Consolidation of 1.33 feet was measured where the ground surface settled around the 600-foot-deep casing of the Union Oil Co. well (fig. 111). Undoubtedly consolidation varied over the area, and may have been less or greater than 1.33 feet. If 1.33 feet is taken as representative, at all but one bridge (62.1) there was upward movement of foundation materials relative to the land surface — movement that ranged from 0.26 to 2.26 feet.

It might be argued that differential consolidation of the foundation materials played some role in the vertical movements of the piling. If differential consolidation were important, shallow piling within surface materials, which presumably would have undergone the most consolidation, would be moved farther downward than more deeply driven piling, which penetrated more compact layers. However, the available pile-penetration data for arched bridges (fig. 15) suggest that penetration depth and vertical displacement are relatively independent. Arching always occurred in the stream centers — regardless of the length of pile penetration.

Vertical displacements of sediments in stream and channel centers have been noted in many earthquakes, and it appears that the phenomenon is general. For example, H. H. Hayden (in Oldham, 1899, p. 285) showed a photograph of a bamboo bridge over a canal, about which he says:

The canal being, as already stated, a line of weakness, it is not surprising to find that the banks on each side are

TABLE 2.—*Adjusted relative postearthquake elevations, in feet, of bridges in the Portage area*

Bridge (mile post)	Preearthquake elevation	Postearthquake elevation [1]	Closure correction [2]	Elevation change	Elevation change corrected for 1.33 ft consolidation [3]
61.9	33.48	32.8	----------	−0.68	+0.65
62.1	32.99	31.53	----------	−1.46	− .13
62.3	32.67	31.6	----------	−1.07	+ .26
63.0	32.14	31.3	+0.21	− .63	+ .70
63.5	31.86	31.7	+ .14	− .02	+1.31
63.6	31.69	32.5	+ .115	+ .93	+2.26

[1] Preearthquake elevations corrected for regional subsidence.
[2] Distributed proportionally to horizontal distance on survey loop.
[3] Consolidation measured at Union Oil well, Portage.

cut up by fissures, while its bed has risen, in some cases through several feet, the central portion now being above the water: this is well shown by the bamboo bridges which have shot up in the center. The same effect is seen in numerous places between Rangpur and Kuch Bihar, where bridges of small span cross canals, small water channels or swamps. If the bridge has a central pier, then this pier has been thrust up and the bridge broken.

Similarly, Steinbrugge and Moran (1956, p. 25) state that in irrigated areas with a high water table that were affected by the Fallon-Stillwater earthquake of 1954 there were

* * * spectacular cracks due to ground movement of canal banks and adjoining land, lurching toward canals or streams were noted. * * * These cracks tended to parallel the canals or streams. A corollary to this type of ground movement was the rising of the bottoms of canals, which often rose above the former water surface.

They show a photograph of the central part of a canal bottom protruding from the water and they cite an unpublished U.S. Bureau of Reclamation study that states (p. 31):

In the Lone Tree and Stillwater areas, canal banks settled from 1 to 3 feet, at the same time the bottoms of canals were raised from 1 to 2 feet, and in an extreme case the bottom of a drain ditch was forced up approximately 5 to 6 feet, by the heaving action of the earthquake.

The great 1906 San Francisco earthquake produced a similar observation by Adams and others (1907, p. 341) who state that

* * * on marsh land near the Bay Shore, one mile west of Alvarado * * *. During the quake the channel of the creek [probably Alameda Creek] disappeared, its bottom being raised to the general level of the adjoining land.

This earthquake produced a somewhat similar observation by Jordan (1906, p. 298) in marshy ground at the south end of Tomales Bay:

11.—Stringers jammed into the bulkhead planking as the result of a decrease in distance of 14½ inches between streambanks at bridge 59.6.

The two banks of the stream [Paper Mill Creek] were forced toward each other so that the length of the bridge was shortened by about six feet and the bridge was correspondingly humped at its north end, an arch about six feet high being forced up.

FOUNDATION MATERIAL FAILURES INDICATED BY BRIDGE DAMAGE

The patterns of damage to bridges, and, in particular, the horizontal and vertical displacements of piles, piers, and abutments make it possible to infer the movement of the foundation materials at bridges and their mechanism of failure. Because connections between piles and superstructures were so easily broken, it can be assumed that piles were carried nearly passively and that their displacements generally reflect those of the foundation materials. A cross section of a typical compressed bridge (fig. 16) shows that piles were shifted streamward and upward, and that the founda-

12.—Laterally buckled and broken stringers of bridge 37.3, resulting from 7¼ inches of streambank closure.

companied by an upward displacement on the floors of the streams, indicate that the foundation materials underwent a kind of flowage in which there was rearrangement of the materials at the intergranular level. Sand ejected from cracks on stream floors (figs. 13, 17) indicates that excess water pressures developed within the sediments. These observations suggest that the foundation materials may have undergone liquefaction. Liquefaction is known to occur during earthquakes (Seed, 1967) and results when ground motion compacts saturated granular sediments. If the water in the sediments cannot escape, or escapes only slowly, the grains of the sediment become reordered in such a way as to increase the load on the interstitial water. As the pressure of the confined water increases, the sediment starts to liquefy and lose strength; when the water pressure is equal to the load of the overlying materials, the sediment will have become completely liquefied and will have no strength.

Field observations show that as the foundation materials became liquefied, they were subjected to increasing hydrostatic forces fixed in large part by the amount of relief and shape of the stream valley. The sediments responded with flowlike displacement that produced a general lowering of the streambanks accompanied the upward movement of the sediments under the stream floors. If sediments moved upward only under the floors of valleys in which there was net horizontal compression, the upward movement might be attributed to compression of the sediments under the centers of the stream floors resulting from the extension of the adjacent sedi-

tion materials were extended at the the stream edges and compressed in the middle of the valleys. Because the piles were shifted with little or no tilting, movement of the foundation materials was probably as deep or deeper than the pile tips. Pile penetration in open wood trestles ranged from about 10 to 30 feet, but in longer bridges it was as much as 125 feet. Bending of the piles cannot be ruled out, and undoubtedly some occurred in the

very long piles; however, there is no independent evidence to show that any piles were bent. If bending did occur it was well below the surface, and there probably were no large differences in the amount of horizontal displacement of the foundation materials within the depths of the average wood pile.

The absence of tilting in the piling, or any other evidence of rotational failures, and the attenuation and compression of the moving foundation materials ac-

13.—Bridge 34.5 jackknifed upward by compression at the bulkheads. Note the mounds of fine-grained sediments ejected with ground water through cracks in the stream floor.

ments; however, bridges in which all interbent distances were increased, yet which were arched (for example, 34.7, 34.8, 35.6), make it clear that even though all the sediments are undergoing extension, they still react to hydrostatic forces, and move upward in an effort to fill the depression.

The fact that all bridges were either flat or arched upward suggests that the foundation materials maintained some strength and did not become completely liquefied. If liquefaction had been complete, piling would have been driven downward by the weight of the decks. The static load per pile of an open wood trestle with piles 30 feet long would be approximately 2,820 pounds. The buoyancy of the piles would reduce the effective downward force on each pile; however, the buoyancy of a 10-inch-diameter pile embedded 20 feet in sediment having a density of 2 would be only 1,360 pounds. This leaves a downward force of 1,460 pounds per

pile. It also seems unlikely that the sediments became completely liquefied in a zone at some depth below the surface, while the surface materials retained enough strength to support the piles, because the piles shifted without tilting and the surface sediments

underwent attenuation and compression. It seems, rather, that movement must have been distributed throughout the sediments for most of the depth of the piles. Borings indicate the sediments are generally layered, inhomogenous, and lenticular, and the varying resistance to penetration indicates that they are of differing density. If such an inhomogenous soil system is subjected to seismic vibrations, one would expect that some parts of the soil column would become liquefied more easily than others, because of the differences in density and the ease or difficulty with which water might move into or out of a given soil layer. It is also probable that, in addition to the varying capacities of the materials to liquefy, the water in the soil was subjected to repeated transient reversals in hydrostatic pressure resulting from compression and dilation of the sediments during seismic vibrations. It has been demonstrated that such changes in pressure occur during

14.—Streambank closure of 64 inches drove the deck of bridge 63.5 through the south bulkhead up onto the top of the embankment. The tops of the piles beneath the deck describe an upward arch, and the deck sagged at the right until it encountered the piles. Photograph by The Alaska Railroad.

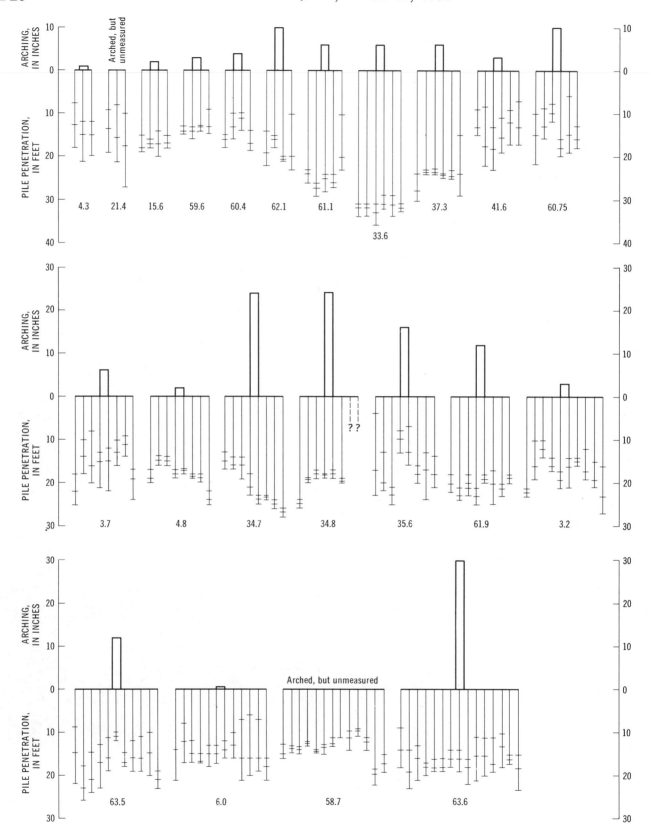

15.—Arching of decks and pile penetration in open wood trestles. The shallowest, average, and greatest depth of penetration in each bent are indicated by horizontal lines. Arching always occurred in the stream centers, regardless of the distribution of the pile penetration.

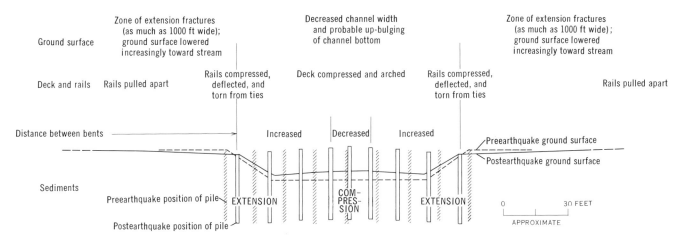

16.—Generalized diagram of a typical compressed open wood trestle. Piles were displaced toward the stream and upward in the stream center. The fact that interbent distances increased at the ends of the bridge and decreased under the middle shows that the sediments were extended at the edges and compressed at the center of the stream channel. Extension, continuing back from the streambanks, formed fractures in the ground and embankments and pulled rails apart.

earthquakes if the water is confined (Leggette and Taylor, 1935) as it must be if liquefaction is to occur. It has also been pointed out by Eaton and Takasaki (1959) that all four major types of earthquake waves produce changes in pressure; P and Rayleigh waves, being dilatational and compressional, cause pressure changes directly, while S and Love waves, being shear waves, may produce pressure changes by originating additional P and Rayleigh waves. Fluctuations in hydrostatic pressure resulting from seismic waves cannot be calculated without considerable knowledge of the geometry of each confining body (Cooper and others, 1965). However, it is possible that the hydrostatic pressures generated by seismic waves make a small but critical contribution to pore-water pressures which allow some layers to liquefy, while with succeeding dilation the reduction in pore-water pressure allows the layer to develop some strength. Because the Alaska earthquake was accompanied by a long period of P-wave generation (see p. D8), changes in

pore-water pressure due to the passage of seismic waves may have been an important factor in the degree of mobility reached by the sediments.

In addition to undergoing fluctuations in pore-water pressure, the vertical component of ground motion of the sediments would alternately increase and decrease

the weight of the overburden on any given layer. Because of their generally inelastic behavior, soft wet sediments respond more to low- than to high-frequency vibrations (Gutenberg, 1957). If such sediments are relatively deep, and lie within a bowl, there is some evidence that the sediments may resonate (Newmark, 1965).

17.—Mounds of sand ejected with ground water from cracks in the floor of the stream at bridge 34.7 on Hunter Flats.

Mobile seismic arrays of the U.S. Geological Survey have recorded resonancelike oscillations on tide lands adjacent to San Francisco Bay (R. Borcherdt, oral commun., 1968). If resonance occurs, it would increase the magnitude and velocity of the surface displacements by generating nearly periodic loops of ground motion, with successive positive and negative peaks which in turn would maximize the change in the overburden load on any given layer. Because the degree of liquefaction (partial or complete) depends upon how closely the pore-water pressure approaches the overburden load, periodic changes in the overburden load might produce changes in the degree of liquefaction. Thus the soil mass might be characterized as containing many discrete areas in which varying degrees of liquefaction occur during a succession of pulses. The soil mass would thus be able to flow intermittently while maintaining enough strength to support the bridges.

In addition, the discharge of ground water to the surface that occurred throughout the shaking must have lowered pore-water pressure, and is likely to have resulted in partial rather than complete liquefaction of the sediments.

Movement of the sediments toward the stream valleys extended for some distance back from the streambanks. Embankments were broken by tension fractures and the rails pulled apart (fig. 18) as the underlying sediments moved toward the stream valleys. Tension fractures in embankments as much as 600 feet from a stream valley (fig. 19) suggest that the sediments became mobilized long distances away from the streams.

18.—View to the south of bridge 63.0. Compression, which deflected the deck 8 feet to the east in a sharp kink, broke the stringers. A wide tension fracture in the foreground broke the embankment; it shifted to the right at the fracture and skewed the bridge.

MODEL STUDY OF FOUNDATION FAILURES

An approximation of both the horizontal and vertical movements at some depth within the sediments can be made by comparing pre– and postearthquake positions of piles, if one makes the following assumptions: that the piles were not bent below the ground surface, that the movement of a pile is representative of the displacement of the sediments along its entire length, and that the vertical displacements are upward. Figure 20 shows the inferred sediment movement for a three– and a seven-span bridge. At each bridge the inferred direction of particle movement as represented

by flow lines is directed toward, and steepens in, the center of the valley. However, the number of assumptions makes this interpretation suspect.

To get some feel for the distribution of particle movement with depth, several sandbox experiments were performed. The box containing the model (fig. 21) was 24 inches square by 8 inches deep, and had a removable side. Rounded quartz-sand of the grain-size distribution shown on figure 22 was spread in horizontal layers alternating with either one or four layers of 100-mesh carborundum. The carborundum was sifted in a thin layer onto the sand surface. The position of each dark layer

and the top of the sand were transferred to a record on the top of
the box with a sliding wire gage
mounted on a rider.

The sand was then saturated by
slowly admitting water through a
perforated plastic tube at the base
of the side walls. When the sand
was thoroughly wet, each side of
the box was raised an inch or so
off the table and then quickly
lowered to strike the table top to
consolidate the sand. During consolidation, water rose above the
surface of the sand. The water was
then very slowly withdrawn with
a pipette from the plastic filler
tube until it was just below the
level to which a channel was then
cut by making successive passes
with a trough-shaped metal scoop.
The position of the surface was remeasured, and the shape of the
channel recorded. Water was added slowly until there was about
one-sixteenth of an inch standing
on the channel bottom; the model
was again repeatedly raised and
quickly lowered to the table top
until the channel edges were seen
to have converged. The box was
then drained, and the sand cut
away to expose a face in the middle of the box where the surface
measurements had been taken.

In a one- and a four-layer model (figs. 21, 23, 24), the surface
outside the channel was generally
lowered. The amount of lowering
increased toward the channel
edges. The channel edges also
moved together, and the slope of
their sides decreased. The channel
bottoms were raised above their
original positions.

Beneath the channels, the dark
layers were arched upward. If one
assumes that the lowering of the
surface well back from the channel
was due only to consolidation and
that consolidation decreased proportionately with depth, then the
central arched portions of the

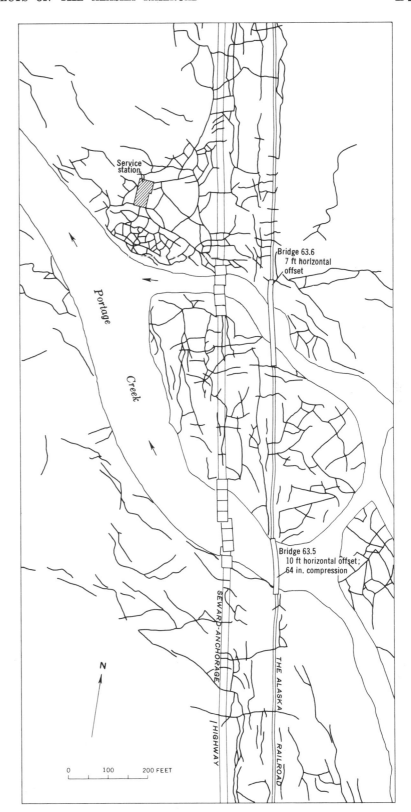

19.—Ground cracks at Portage Creek, as mapped from aerial photographs.
Note the open network of fractures south of the service station, on the island,
and on the point of land southeast of the island; note also that the
tension fractures are generally perpendicular to the highway and railroad
embankments.

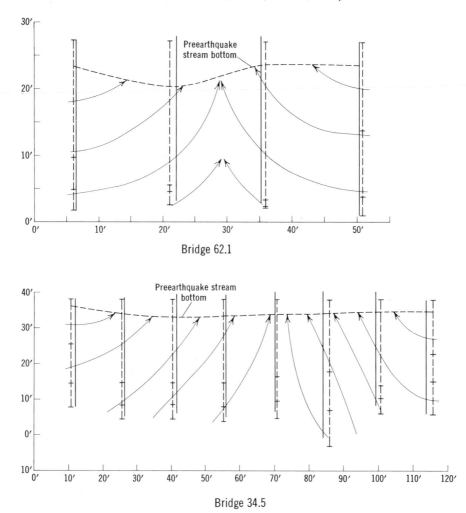

Bridge 62.1

Bridge 34.5

20.—Sediment movement suggested by displacement of bents in two arched bridges, based on the assumptions given in the text. The preearthquake bent positions are indicated by dashed lines, on which the shallowest, average, and deepest pile penetration lengths are indicated by horizontal lines.

black layers also were raised above their original positions.

The rising of the channel bottoms to above the preshake position clearly indicates that some material moved upward, and therefore also laterally. However, having only horizontal layers in the model, lateral movement could only be measured by relative thinning or thickening between dark layers — because consolidation occurred during the final shaking, changes in thickness of these beds might also be attributed in part to differential compaction.

To measure lateral movement more directly, a four-layer model was built into which a vertical grid of carborundum was injected through a cannula (fig. 25). The pre- and postshake grids are compared in figure 26A. The preshake positions of the horizontal layers have been lowered, as described for previous models, to allow for consolidation.

The distribution of particle movement throughout the model is shown by vectors that originate at the preshake positions of the grid intersections, and pass through the postshake positions (fig. 26B); the length of each vector is doubled in the figure to make small movements visible.

The vectors make it possible to draw particle flow lines — lines drawn in the direction of particle movement — as indicated by the displacement of the grid intersections. The flow lines show that, to the sides of the channel, material rose obliquely toward the channel to about the height of the channel bottom, where it converged with material moving somewhat downward and more directly toward the channel. Under the channel, flow lines become progressively steeper and become vertical in an area of convergence to the left of the channel center. Eight additional vectors were drawn between

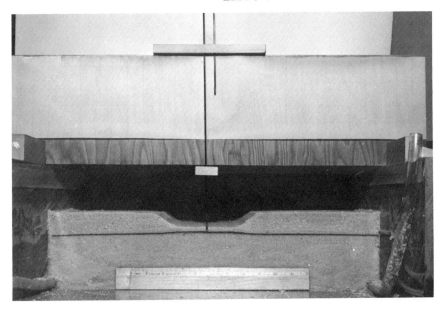

21.—Sandbox with one side removed. The box measures 24 inches square and 8 inches high. Water was injected through a perforated plastic pipe at the base of the side walls. Measurements were transferred with a sliding wire gage from the model to a record above. The point of the wire gage is at the top of an arched carborundum layer under the center of the channel.

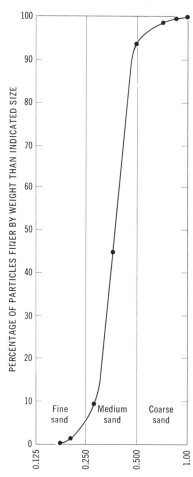

22.—Grain size distribution of well-rounded quartz sand used in the sandbox model.

the upper dark layer and the surface by connecting the midpoints of four of the pre- and postshake vertical lines on either side of the channel. The asymmetry of the flow lines and the development of diverging flow lines at the lower outside edges of the model are probably the result of unequal application of the distorting force, sidewall effects, and some consolidation around the plastic filler pipe at the base of the sidewalls.

The particle displacement can also be treated quantitatively, and in figure 26B contours are drawn in which each contour interval is one-ninth of the length of the largest vector, and the value at any vector is taken to be located at the postshake position of the grid intersection. The large displacements at the channel sideslopes suggest that they are local failures not related directly to particle movement in other parts of the model. Distortion of the vertical lines at the sideslopes (fig.

25) indicates that these local failures occurred by movement distributed throughout the sideslope material, rather than on a single failure surface. Counterparts of these local failures in the model did not occur in the field.

These models show the following movements of material that are similar to those observed on the surface at stream crossings, or are inferred from pile displace-

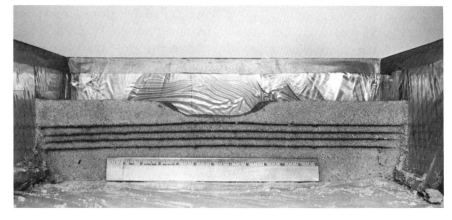

23.—A four-layer model showing upward arching of the carborundum layers beneath the channel. Note that the amplitude decreases in successively lower layers.

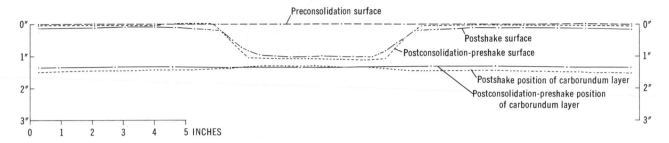

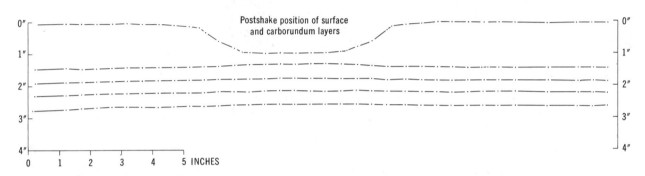

24.—*Upper:* A single-layer model showing the location of the carborundum layer and model surface before consolidation, the location of the surface and the channel cut after consolidation, and the final postshake position of the surface, channel, and carborundum layer. Note that the surface of the model was progressively lowered toward the channel. The edges of the channel were displaced toward the channel; the bottom of the channel rose to above its postconsolidation position, and the carborundum layer was arched above its original position. *Lower:* A four-layer model showing lowering of the surface toward the channel and arching of the carborundum layers beneath the channel.

ments to have taken place beneath the surface.

1. Areas of lateral extension on the surface adjacent to the channel (the areas of extension fracturing in embankments and ground surface).

2. Progressive lowering of the surface toward the edges of the channels.

3. Closure of the channel edges.

4. A pattern of flow lines similar to those inferred from displaced piling (fig. 20).

5. Rising of the channel bottoms (as shown by bridge arching).

6. Horizontal extension of material to some depth to the side and under the edges of the chan-

nels and compression under the central part of the channel.

Zones of horizontal compression and extension in the model are shown in figure 26C. If a properly scaled imaginary bridge (pile penetration of 20 ft and maximum unsupported pile length of 10 ft) were built across the model channel, it would be a five-bent bridge, with bents located as shown in figure 26C. Horizontal displacements of the sediments would have produced compression between central bents and extension, or no compression, between the outside bents. Assuming that the vertical displacement of each bent was the mean of the vertical displacements of the material at the bent, the

deck would have developed an upward arch of about 4 inches, with the crest of the arch at the central bent. Thus the horizontal and vertical displacements of the imaginary bents would have been quite similar to those observed in real bridges.

Although these models appear to produce effects similar to those observed at stream crossings, in the absence of a dimensional analysis, we hesitate to draw direct conclusions about the real case from the model. It should be pointed out, however, that in real cases the displacements of sediments are similar through a wide range of physical parameters and probable energy inputs. Thus the parameters to be used in a dimensional analysis vary greatly. For example, the size of the materials varies by several orders of magnitude, from silt to coarse cobble gravel; stream valley widths vary by at least one order of magnitude, from less than 15 feet to more than 400 feet; and the bridges, which lie in diverse orientations and different physiographic situations, 45 to 90 miles from the epicenter, undoubtedly were subjected to seismic energy that differed in frequency distribution, amplitude, direction, and duration.

The foregoing model of displacement distributed throughout the soil differs from previously proposed explanations for similar surface observations in other great earthquakes. Decreases in stream channel widths have usually been attributed to block gliding of a soil mass on a horizontal incompetent layer that is exposed in the side or at the bottom of a stream channel (for example, Oldham, 1882, p. 52-54; 1899, p. 87; Fuller, 1912, p. 48). It has been suggested that if the force of the horizontal component of ground motion exceeds the tensile strength of the soil mass, a block of soil will be detached and move on the incompetent layer toward the free or unconfined face at the stream channel. Large block-glide slides did occur in Alaska (Hansen, 1965); however, no evidence for block gliding was found at the edges of stream channels (see p. D56–D57). This mechanism is restrictive, for it necessitates the presence of an incompetent layer at the proper depth in all places where stream channel widths are decreased. The large areas over which stream narrowing occurred makes the presence of such a layer unlikely.

The upward movement of the bottoms of stream channels has

25.—Postshake view of a four-layer model with a vertical carborundum grid shown in figure 26.

also been widely observed in great earthquakes. A good example is given by R. D. Oldham (1899, p. 105–106; also see p. D22–D23, this paper):

This filling up of river channels took place over a large area, but probably nowhere so conspicuously as in the tract of lowland which lies between the foot of the Garo Hills and the Brahmaputra. This tract is intersected by numerous channels, which carry a limited drainage in dry weather, but, when the Brahmaputra is in flood, help to carry off the surplus waters that would otherwise submerge the country they drain. Before the earthquake these channels were from 15 to 20 feet deep, and in the dry weather the country was intersected by steep-sided depressions of this depth, at the bottom of which flowed a shallow stream. During the earthquake the bottoms of all these channels were forced up till level with the banks on either side, and during the ensuing dry weather the drainage of this tract, instead of flowing in deeply sunken channels flowed nearly level with the general surface of the land in shallow sandy channels.

Oldham (p. 105) suggested that at some depth beneath the alluvium into which the stream channels are cut, there is a bed of loose sand in which (hydrostatic?) pressure is built up during the earthquake. The stream channels, being the thinnest part of the alluvium over this layer, are forced upward in response to the pressure within the sand bed.

This mechanism has the distinct disadvantage of no substantiation for the existence of a sand bed. Further, it requires the special circumstances of such a sand layer over very large areas — not only in India but also in Alaska.

In addition to the objections given above, these explanations for narrowing and uplifting of stream channels do not account for the simultaneous occurrence of both narrowing and uplift. The model of movement distributed throughout the sediment, as inferred from the pile displacements and the sandbox model, appears to have the advantage of predicting that both should occur. This model also seems more realistic because

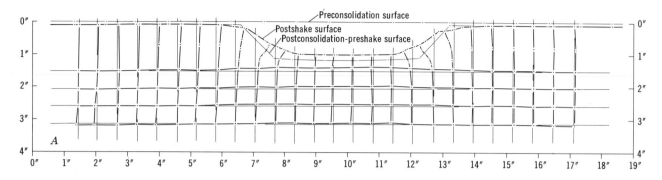

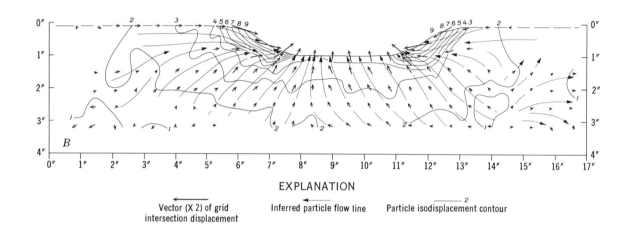

EXPLANATION

⟶ Vector (X 2) of grid intersection displacement   ⟵ Inferred particle flow line   ⟶² Particle isodisplacement contour

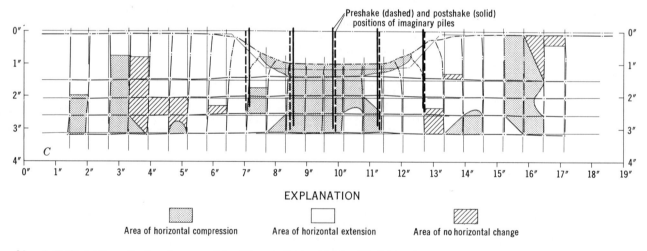

EXPLANATION

Area of horizontal compression   Area of horizontal extension   Area of no horizontal change

26.—A, Deformation of a four-layer model with a vertical grid (fig. 25). Light lines indicate the pre- and postconsolidation positions of the surface and the vertical grid, and the positions of the horizontal layers in which the preshake consolidation has been distributed proportionately with depth. Dark lines indicate postshake positions of the surface and vertical and horizontal grid. B, Particle flow lines indicated by vectors drawn from the pre- to the postshake positions of the grid intersections shown in A. The length of each vector has been doubled to make small displacements visible. Contours of equal particle displacement are drawn as ninths of the length of the longest vector. C, Areas of horizontal compression in the model shown in B, and the preshake and postshake positions of bents of an imaginary bridge. Light and dark grid lines same as in A.

it does not require a special geologic situation.

FOUNDATION DISPLACEMENT DAMAGE TO LARGE BRIDGES

Many large bridges of complex structure were damaged by movements of the foundation materials. Being generally more deeply driven than in small bridges, the displaced piles of the large bridges may present evidence of still deeper movements in the foundation materials. In the following sections of this report, three bridges just north of Seward are first discussed as a unit to show the generally similar pattern of damage to somewhat dissimilar bridges in the same physiographic and geologic environment. This discussion is followed by brief descriptions of damage to five large bridges, the northernmost of which is at mile 146.4 on Knik River. Damage to other large bridges is recorded in table 1 and in the mile-by-mile description of the railroad.

RESURRECTION RIVER–MINERAL CREEK BRIDGES

Three railroad and three adjacent highway bridges that cross the flood plain shared by Resurrection River and Mineral Creek just north of Seward were severely damaged. All three railroad bridges had to be replaced with entirely new structures. The low-relief flood-plain surface was severely fractured. Fracturing (figs. 27, 28) was accompanied by the ejection of a considerable amount of water.

All the railroad bridges were damaged by compression at the deck level, and their supporting piles were shifted streamward. In addition, the railroad embankment shifted to the southeast, parallel to the contours, and carried the ends of the bridges along with it.

The damage to each of the three bridges is described below.

Bridge 3.0 crosses the southern branch of Resurrection River and is 187 feet long (fig. 29). Its two 13.5-foot open wood-trestle end spans bear on a seven-pile bent at the bulkheads and a cribbing on pile-supported piers that carry two 80-foot through steel girders. The central pier rests on four rows of nine piles, and the outer piers have three rows of nine piles. Compression at the deck level totaled 13½ inches. The steel deck beams were driven 4 and 5½ inches into the ends of the wood stringers, and the wood stringers were driven 1.5 and 2.5 inches into the bulkheads. Compression was accompanied by endways pounding (shown by pebble dents between the last tie and fillers on the north bulkhead).

Piles at the bulkheads and piers were shifted streamward. All moved with no detected vertical rotation. The horizontal displacements ranged from 1½ to 11 inches; there was extension of the valley bottom sediments at the stream edges and compression in the center (fig. 29). The centers of the piers, originally under the bridge shoes, were displaced as shown by vertical chalk lines drawn up from the centerline of the central row of piles (fig. 29). As the piers shifted, rockers on the bridge shoes were driven to their extreme positions, and with continued movement of the piers, the cribbing was rotated, which placed more weight on the outside row of piles in each pier. The redistribution of the weight may have caused the vertical movements that occurred in piles under the piers. The tops of the piles in each row stood successively higher toward the streams. Despite the greater heights streamward, the cribbing was cantilevered off most

of the streamward row of piles. In the south pier, only three of the nine piles in the row were bearing; the rest ranged from three quarters of an inch to 6 inches below the cribbing. In the north pier all the streamward piles stood an inch or so below the cribbing. The transfer of the load to the outside piling and the decrease in skin friction which must have occurred during the movement of the sediments probably caused the outer row of piles to be driven downward into the sediments. Because these piers are closely spaced and depend primarily on skin friction for most of their bearing capacity, it also seems likely that downward movement of the overloaded piles may have produced a negative skin friction which pulled the unloaded streamward row of piles downward.

In addition to moving streamward, the outer piers shifted 8 inches downstream of the central pier, and the bulkheads and approach fills were carried 4 to 5 inches more; the central pier was thus left 12 to 13 inches upstream of the approaches. As shown in figure 29, the downstream edges of the steel girders were jammed together, and the metal shoes were rocked inward, their bases lifting ¾ and 1¾ inches off the cribbing. On the upstream side of the same pier the girders were pulled 3-3/16 inches apart. The compression of the steel spans at the downstream edge of this central pier may have exerted some downward force, for the top of the pier was tilted about 2 inches in the downstream direction.

For comparison, the adjacent highway bridge is shown in figure 30. Deck level compression drove the steel into the abutment, breaking the back wall. The abutment and pier were shifted streamward. The top of the pier was prevented

27.—Ground cracking on the flood plains of Resurrection River and Mineral Creek. Numbers indicate borings, the logs of which are given on figures 29, 31, and 32. Cracks were mapped from aerial photographs taken by Air Photo Tech, Anchorage.

28.—Aerial photograph of area mapped on figure 27 of Resurrection River and Mineral Creek flood plains. Photograph by Air Photo Tech, Anchorage.

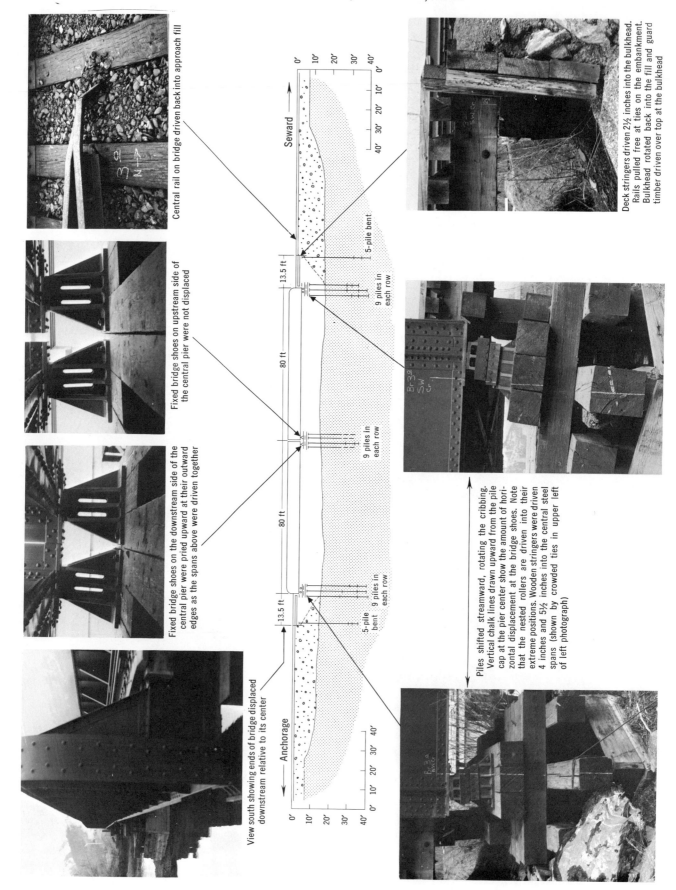

Central rail on bridge driven back into approach fill

Deck stringers driven 2½ inches into the bulkhead. Rails pulled free at ties on the embankment. Bulkhead rotated back into the fill and guard timber driven over top at the bulkhead

Fixed bridge shoes on upstream side of the central pier were not displaced

Fixed bridge shoes on the downstream side of the central pier were pried upward at their outward edges as the spans above were driven together

View south showing ends of bridge displaced downstream relative to its center

Piles shifted streamward, rotating the cribbing. Vertical chalk lines drawn upward from the pile cap at the pier center show the amount of horizontal displacement at the bridge shoes. Note that the nested rollers are driven into their extreme positions. Wooden stringers were driven 4 inches and 5½ inches into the central steel spans (shown by crowded ties in upper left of left photograph)

Seward

5-pile bent

9 piles in each row

13.5 ft   80 ft   80 ft   13.5 ft

9 piles in each row

5-pile bent 9 piles in each row

Anchorage

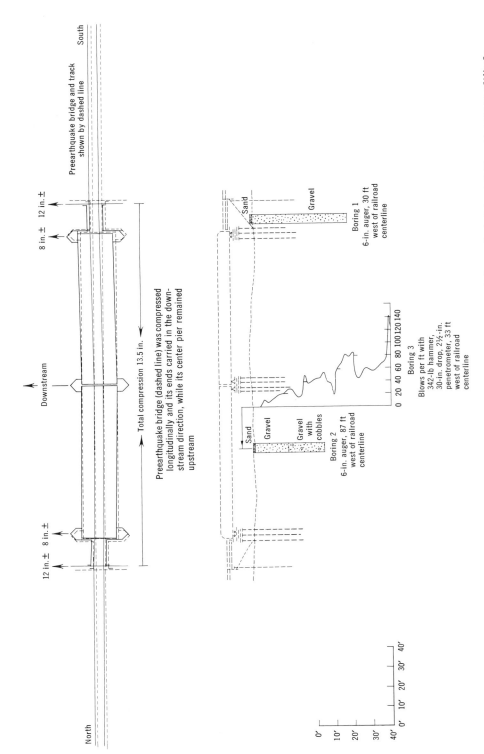

29.—Bridge 3.0; construction, damage, and subsurface information. Subsurface data projected to rail line at proper altitude.

30.—Looking southeast toward highway bridge (No. 596) at Resurrection River. Streamward movement of the foundation materials compressed the deck, breaking the abutment backwall, and carried the abutments and bases of the piers toward the channel. Being restrained at the top, the pier was broken at the ground line. Similar damage occurred at the other end of the bridge.

from moving laterally by the deep central steel span, but its base was carried streamward, rotating the pier and cracking it at the waterline. Damage to this bridge was typical of the adjacent highway bridges—in all of which the abutments were rammed by the steel, and the piers were broken and shifted streamward at their bases.

Bridge 3.2, a nine-span 135-foot open wood trestle (fig. 31), crosses the northern branch of Resurrection River. Pile data for this bridge are shown in figure 8. Deck-level compression drove the stringers 1¼ inches into the north bulkhead, crushed the fillers, and drove the top of the bulkhead back into the fill. At the south bulkhead the stringers were driven 8 inches past the piles into the bulkhead, and here, too, the top of the bulkhead was shoved back into the fill.

There was no appreciable settlement of the south approach fill, but the north fill settled about 5 inches relative to the bulkhead, and the bulkhead was pulled down about 3 inches below the deck by the fill. Settlement of about this same amount continued to the next bridge (fig. 31).

As shown in figure 31, the downstream shifting of the bents increased away from the center of the stream, the ends of the bridge and the approach fills being carried about 10 inches downstream from the center of the bridge. There was also some crowding of the piles toward the stream, but the displacements were not measured.

Mineral Creek bridge, at mile 3.3, has a total length of 136 feet and is built with an 80-foot central steel through girder and two 14-foot pile-supported open wood trestles at each end (fig. 32). The damage to this bridge was very much like the damage to the similar bridge at mile 3.0. Compression, totaling about 19 inches developed at the deck level, driving stringers into bulkheads and into the central steel spans. At the north bulkhead the stringers were

shoved at least an inch past the piles, forcing the top of the bulkhead bents into the fill. Multiple pebble dents between the last tie and the filler show that compression was accompanied by at least four compressive blows.

At the south bulkhead the stringers drove about a foot past the piles. The pile cap was torn nearly free of the piles, and the stringers shoved the bulkhead planks back into the fill, tearing the planks free of one of the fillers. The stringers were driven at least 2 inches into the north end of the steel girder and 4 inches into the south end, crushing the intervening ties.

Piles in the bents and piers shifted streamward, horizontal displacements ranging from 1 to 20 inches. The valley bottom sediments were extended at the valley margins and compressed in the center (fig. 32). There was no detected vertical rotation of the piles, with the exception of the piles between the southern wood trestle, whose tops were tilted 4° toward the stream.

As the pier piles shifted streamward, the nested rollers in the south bridge bearings were driven to their extreme positions, and the northern fixed bearings were rotated, their streamward edges lifting up off the cribbing about ¾ of an inch. Rotation of the cribbing streamward at its base increased the weight on the outer row of piles. As at bridge 3.0, the outer row of piles were all bearing on the cribbing, most of the central piles were bearing, and the cribbing was cantilevered an inch or more above the inner rows of piles.

Settlement of the grade of about half a foot both north and south of the bridge left the bridge standing high, and tore the track from the ties on the approach fills. The set-

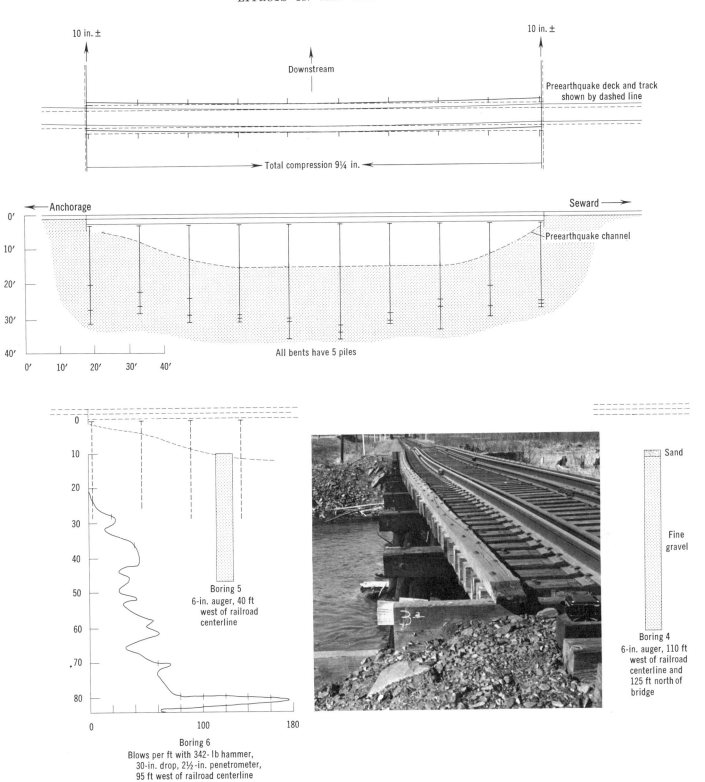

31.—Bridge 3.2; construction, damage, and subsurface information. Subsurface data projected to rail line at proper altitude.

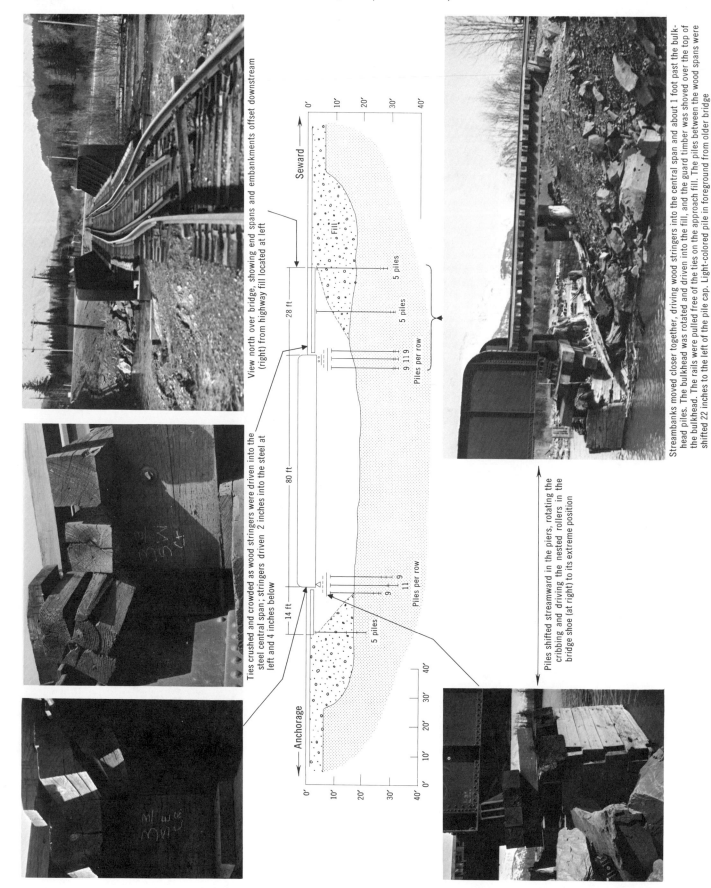

View north over bridge, showing end spans and embankments offset downstream (right) from highway fill located at left

Ties crushed and crowded as wood stringers were driven into the steel central span; stringers driven 2 inches into the steel at left and 4 inches below

Piles shifted streamward in the piers, rotating the cribbing and driving the nested rollers in the bridge shoe (at right) to its extreme position

Streambanks moved closer together, driving wood stringers into the central span and about 1 foot past the bulkhead piles. The bulkhead was rotated and driven into the fill, and the guard timber was shoved over the top of the bulkhead. The rails were pulled free of the ties on the approach fill. The piles between the wood spans were shifted 22 inches to the left of the pile cap. Light-colored pile in foreground from older bridge

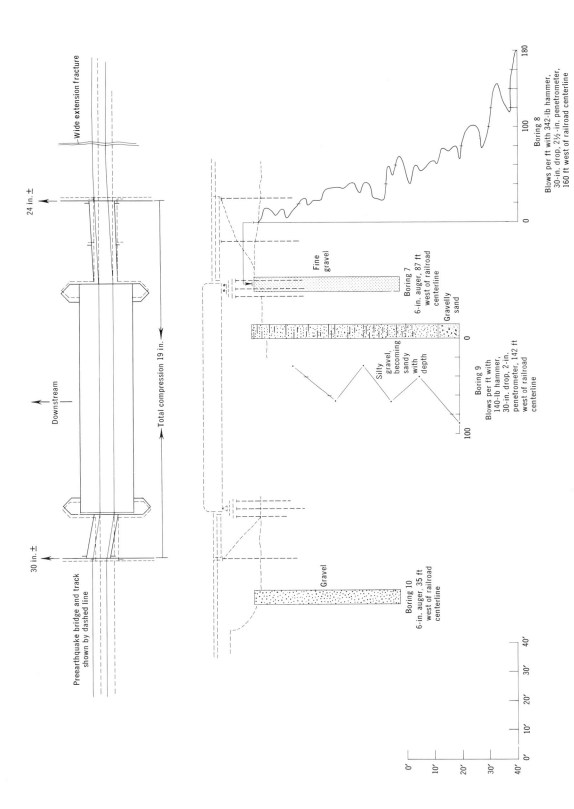

32.—Bridge 3.3; construction, damage, and subsurface information. Subsurface data projected to rail line at proper altitude.

tling of the fill and possibly the lowering of the sediments under the fill pulled some of the bulkhead piles downward and left them about an inch below the caps. The bulkheads were also pulled down. The lower plank and eastern filler of the northern bulkhead were pulled 2 inches downward and 2 inches eastward with the shifting fill, while the upper planks and bulkhead cap were held by the stringers to which they were bolted.

As at the adjacent bridges, the grade was shifted to the southeast, parallel to the stream which skewed the approach spans and left the central span about 30 inches upstream. The bulkhead bents were carried with the grade; the bents under the wood trestle spans between the bulkheads and piers were carried a somewhat lesser distance.

The foundation materials involved in the displacements that damaged the three bridges just described are known from borings made in 1964 along the highway just west of the rail line. The locations of the borings are shown in figure 27 and the subsurface data are projected at their proper altitudes in relation to the rail line in figures 29, 31, and 32. All the sediments are noncohesive; field identifications range from sandy and silty gravel to fine gravel to gravel. With the exception of hole 2, at bridge 3.0, in which cobbles were found below 20 feet, the gravel averaged less than three-fourths of an inch in diameter, with a maximum of about 3 inches. All the sediments were saturated, the ground-water table lying at, or within 2 feet of, the surface. Penetration resistance generally increased downward, although there were some inversions. Within the depth of the sediments penetrated by the piling, the materials were compact to dense. Penetra-

tion resistance on a standard penetrometer (140-lb hammer, 30-in. drop, 2-in. sample spoon) was 30 to 40 blows per foot, and a second penetrometer (342-lb hammer, 30-in. drop, 2½-in. penetrometer) encountered resistance of 20 to 25 blows per foot. In summary, the materials were noncohesive, saturated, and compact to dense.

SNOW RIVER BRIDGE

Construction and displacements of the sub- and superstructure of the Snow River bridge (14.5) are shown in figure 33. The concrete piers and abutments rest on steel piling composed of three 70-lb-per-yd railroad rails welded at the crowns. In piers 4–7 and the northern abutment, these piles gain their bearing by friction, while at the south end of the bridge the abutment and piles of the first three piers probably bear on bedrock. These latter piers and abutments did not move. The remain-

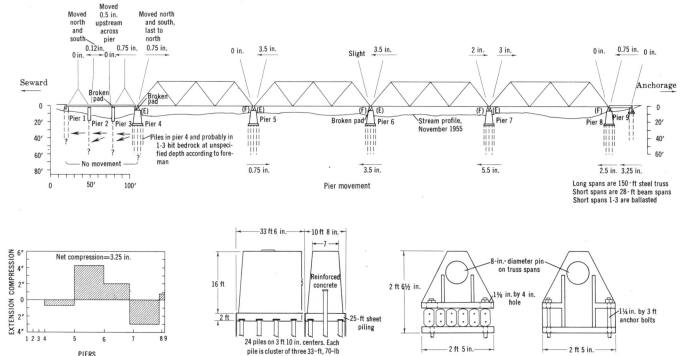

33.—Construction and damage to Snow River bridge (14.5).

34.—Fixed end bearing lifted from pier at north end of sixth span of bridge 14.5. Anchor bolt pulled free of concrete. In adjacent expansion bearing, nested rollers were driven to the extreme position.

der move generally toward the river. Maximum displacement was 5.5 inches. Piers shifted without tipping, and, if the piling was not bent, sediments to depths in excess of 45 to 55 feet must have been involved in the displacement. There was neither upward movement nor settling of the piers, and no noticeable upstream or downstream displacement. Rollers on expansion bearings of piers 5 and 6 were driven to their extreme positions. Fixed bearings were shifted, and on the north end of the sixth span, where compression was maximum, the edge of the bearing was rocked upward off the pier (fig. 34). Anchor bolts were bent and stretched but none were sheared. No boring data are available for this bridge.

TWENTYMILE RIVER BRIDGE

The long heavy Twentymile River bridge (64.7) is built of seven 70-foot 1-inch steel deck trusses supported on concrete piers and abutments (figs. 35, 36). Re-

pairs were made before the authors had the opportunity to record differential movements of all spans on all piers; thus real displacements cannot be determined. Displacements shown on the figure are only the larger movements of two piers relative to the bearings of the overlying spans. Movement of the piers must have been more general, because compression at the deck level jammed all the trusses together, and drove the end trusses into the abutments and broke away the backwalls (fig. 37). Anchor bolts were sheared on three piers and the abutments. The positions of the rebuilt abutment backwalls and the base of the pre-earthquake abutments indicate that total compression was about 5 feet 2 inches. The piers and abutments were carried on 11 to 14 piles composed of three 65- to 70-lb-per-yd railroad rails welded at the crowns. Penetration ranged from about 32 to 49 feet, and, as noted on p. D132, the sediments into which the piles were driven consisted of 2 to 20 feet of sandy

fine gravel underlain by sand, often containing small amounts of fine gravel (holes 8–13, fig. 112).

No rotation of the piers was observed, but there was some downward displacement. Postearthquake releveling by The Alaska Railroad shows that the northern abutment was displaced downward 0.88 foot relative to U.S. Coast and Geodetic Survey bench mark Q12 located on bedrock 1.8 miles to the north. Because there were no differential vertical displacements in the substructure, similar downward displacements probably occurred in all substructure elements, and may have resulted from compaction of sediments, rather than downward movement of the piers through the sediment.

SHIP CREEK BRIDGE

Ship Creek bridge (114.3) has two 35-foot steel-beam span approaches and a central 123-foot through truss carried on pile-supported concrete abutments and piers (fig. 38). Abutments and piers shifted streamward, the deck was put in compression, and each end span jammed against the central span and into the abutment backwalls. Total compression at the deck was about 13 inches. Movement of the piers was so great that the expansion bearings were reset 9½ inches from their former positions and the fixed bearings were displaced 5½ inches. Although reported to be undamaged (Fisher and Merkle, 1965, p. 255–256), the bridge was closed to traffic until new bearing surfaces were constructed on the pier tops.

Piers are carried on 45 wood piles 30 to 35 feet in length. Piles in the abutments are three 70-lb-per-yd railroad rails welded at the crowns; their lengths range from 66 to 128 feet, and the outside rows are battered outward at about 13°.

35.—Railroad bridge (64.7) and highway bridge at Twentymile River, Portage. All concrete deck sections of the highway bridge except one were knocked from their piles, and some piles were driven through the concrete. The railroad bridge was compressed and some of its piers shifted (see fig. 36). Note the severe cracking in the embankments, flood-plain, and tidal sediments (see pl. 3). Photograph by Arthur Kennedy, U.S. Forest Service, Anchorage.

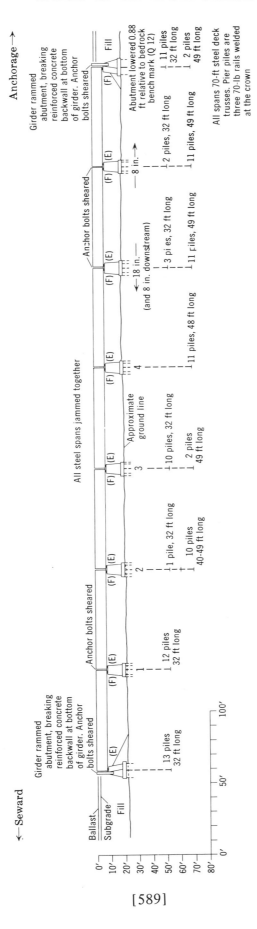

36.—Construction of and damage to Twentymile River bridge (64.7).

37.—Damage to Twentymile River bridge. Left: Concrete abutment broken away after earthquake to relieve pressure on spans. Note tilted bearing shoe and missing sheared-off anchor bolt. Right: North abutment backwall broken by thrust of steel deck.

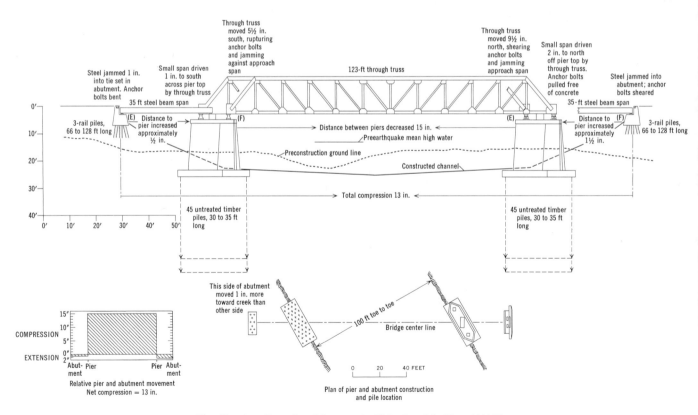

38.—Construction of and damage to Ship Creek bridge (114.3).

The surface sediments at the bridge site are estuarine, probably predominantly in the silt-clay size range (fig. 126). No subsurface data are available at this location; however, it is likely that the deeper piling in the abutments may enter the gravels that form low terraces a short distance upstream.

KNIK RIVER BRIDGE

The Knik River bridge (146.4) crosses the southernmost channel of Knik River (pl. 1). Its ten 80-foot through steel girders are supported on piers of two types — most are wood cribbing on wood piles, but those near the channels, where scour is greatest (piers 1, 8, 9), were replaced prior to the earthquake by concrete piers on welded-rail piling (fig. 39). The southern span rests on a concrete abutment built on bedrock. The northern steel span is joined to four 15-foot open wood trestles. Displacements of the piers and decks show a maximum of 9.12 inches for a pier and 6.37 inches for a deck. No measurements were made of the displacements of the wood trestles on their pile bents.

The next four large bridges to the north (147.1, 147.4, 147.5, 148.3; pl. 1) were damaged by similar displacements of piling and decks. This damage is described on page D156 and is summarized in table 1. The properties of the underlying sediments are described in the section on the relationship of damage to grain size, thickness, and density of foundation materials (p. D66–D67).

SUMMARY

1. Damage to the long complex bridges followed the same pattern as that of the small wood trestles. Decks were compressed with considerable force (concrete abutments broken, anchor bolts sheared, bridge bearings torn free of piers, and stringers crushed), as the piers and abutments were generally crowded toward the rivers. With the exception of Knik River, where sediment displacement was complex, sediments were extended at river margins and compressed in the middles, in the pattern typical of smaller creeks.

2. Vertical arching so common in wood trestles was absent or very small in long bridges. The absence or near absence of arching in long bridges may be due in part to downward movement of the heavily loaded piles through the mobilized sediments (as suggested by differential vertical pile displacement at Resurrection River and Mineral Creek bridges, and by releveling to piers and abutments on Twentymile River bridge). It may also reflect the fact that sediments everywhere achieved nearly the same general degree of mobility, so that in a given duration of shaking only a certain amount of movement could occur toward topographic depressions. This suggested relation of shaking duration and degree of mobility would explain why, for a wide range of channel widths, compression usually amounted to about 20 inches or less (fig. 10). The bridges that had larger total compressions were in the Portage area, where eyewitnesses described considerably longer ground motion.

3. Long piles did not prevent damaging streamward displacement of piers and abutments.

4. Where piles were on, or close to, bedrock (Snow River and Knik River bridges), there was no permanent lateral displacement of the substructure but there was some minor displacement of the overlying deck.

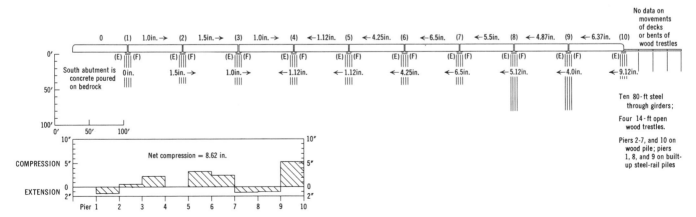

39.—Construction of and damage to Knik River bridge (146.4).

TRANSIENT HORIZONTAL DISPLACEMENT OF GROUND, AND RELATED BRIDGE DAMAGE

Endways pounding damaged both railroad and highway bridges. The steel girders of highway bridges were slammed repeatedly into their concrete abutments, and wooden stringers of railroad bridges rammed and damaged the wood bulkheads.

The force of the repetitive horizontal blows is difficult to estimate, because their effects are combined with those produced by compression resulting from streamward shifting of bulkheads and abutments. However, Charles P. Smith (1965, p. 25), chief bridge engineer for the Alaska Department of Highways, concluded from a study of damaged highway bridges that "most of these structures were subjected to large horizontal acceleration which resulted in almost every case in failure of the superstructure to substructure connections." From the strength of sheared anchor bolts and the deadweight of the superstructures, he concluded (p. 23) "a horizontal force approaching 2 g was necessary to shear such bolts. Actual forces may have been greater."

Among our observations on railroad and adjacent highway bridges, there were none which showed that the shearing of anchor bolts could clearly be attributed solely to large horizontal accelerations. Anchor bolts were sheared where there was streamward shifting of the abutments, and, because these compressive forces were great enough to break concrete abutments and piers and tear pilings from decks, there is little doubt that they were sufficiently great to shear anchor bolts as well.

The series of dents made by pebbles that were caught between bulkhead fillers and end ties of bridge decks provide one source of evidence for transient horizontal displacement. During compression the pebbles were driven into the wood, and during relaxation the pebbles fell, only to be caught again by the succeeding compression. Repetitive pebble dents were common (table 1) despite the special circumstance of requiring that pebbles be in the proper place during the earthquake. Thus, transient horizontal displacement must have been the rule, rather than the exception.

Not only were pebble dents common, but they occurred in all types of displacement—in bridges highly compressed by streamward movement of sediments, and in bridges pulled apart endways on fans and deltas by radial downhill spreading of the sediments. At the bridges that pulled apart, the dents provide evidence that considerable force was associated with the transient horizontal displacement. For example, the following three bridges were ultimately pulled apart, yet all were damaged by transient horizontal displacement: (1) At bridge 34.8 the stringers hit the north bulkhead with sufficient force to crush and split the fillers; (2) the stringers of adjacent bridge 34.7 drove the top of the south bulkhead back into the fill; (3) and at bridge 21.4 pebble dents record at least four blows, and the stringers rammed the bulkhead planks, tore them from the fillers, and forced them back into the fill.

The pounding rate can be approximated at one bridge by interpreting a series of pebble dents. The pebble dents shown in figure 40 range from about 1 to 1½ inches apart. Assuming that the pebble was in free fall between dents, the time that elapsed between dents can be calculated by $t = \sqrt{\dfrac{2s}{g}}$, where t is the time of fall in seconds, s the distance in centimeters, and g the force of gravity. Times required for the free fall of 1 to 1½ inches are 0.07 to 0.09 second.

40.—Multiple dents on the end tie of a bridge deck made by a pebble that was caught as it fell between the filler (foreground) and tie during endways compression.

Using 0.07 to 0.09 seconds for the free-fall times making the assumption that the pounding was harmonic, a pounding rate can be estimated. If one assumes a wide range for the part of the compression-relaxation cycle during which the pebble was in free fall, the real rate should lie between the extremes. Assuming that the free-fall time was from 1/5 to 1/2 the cycle, the pounding rate should lie between 2.22 to 7.14 cycles per second. Clearly the assumptions make these figures questionable; furthermore they represent data from only one bridge. However, their magnitude suggests that this transient horizontal displacement is produced by considerably higher frequency ground displacements than those of observed surface waves, where periods are in the range of several seconds. (See, for example, Coulter and Migliaccio, 1966, p. C10.)

Although pebble dents provide a means of estimating the pounding rate, they do not distinguish horizontal motion of the ground from horizontal motion of the bridge. Further, they do not give an indication of the forces involved. However, both the sense of horizontal ground motion and a minimum estimate of the forces involved in the transient horizontal displacement can be determined from the damage to a 105-foot-long open wood trestle at mile 34.5 on Hunter Flats (see p. D114). The deck of this bridge was alternately arched upward off the piles by compression, and dropped down onto the piles during relaxation. Impact holes in the pile tops, made by the drift pins that normally connect the pile caps to the piles, record from two to four compressive episodes, and there may have been more (fig. 41).

Although it is clear that transient horizontal displacement re-

41.—Two impact holes made by a drift pin in the pile cap as the deck of the bridge was alternately raised and lowered onto the piles (see also figs. 13, 95). Stream channel is to the right.

sulted in compression of the bridge deck, it is difficult to assess the forces involved. For example, had the deck been flat and firmly secured to the piles, the force needed to arch the structure would have been extremely large. On the other hand, if the connections between the deck and piles had already been severed, or if the deck had been initially arched by vertical pile movements, the requisite force would have been less. Some connections to piles may have been severed, because there is evidence of streamward movement of piling during the transient compression. This movement is indicated by the shift in position of the impact holes from the drift pins; they lie toward the streambank side (left) of the original position of the pin (fig. 41). The bridge was also probably slightly arched by the vertical pile displacements that accompanied streamward shifting (fig. 42).

Assuming that connections to the piles were severed and that

there was some initial arching due to vertical pile displacement, the minimum force required to arch the deck a small but finite amount up from the supporting piles can be calculated as follows (Professor Arvid Johnson, Geology Dept., Stanford Univ., written commun., 1968):

$$1 = P\left[\frac{1}{P-1} - \frac{3/8wL^4}{EI\pi^2h}\right],$$

where

$w =$ weight per linear inch of deck per stringer (6 lb),
$L =$ length of deck (1,260 in.),
$E =$ Young's modulus for the stringer (1.4×10^6),
$I =$ [moment of inertia = stringer width (9 in.) $\times$ stringer depth (17 in.) $\times \frac{\pi}{L}] \div 12$,
$h =$ height of initial arch in bridge deck,

and

$$P = \frac{p}{Fs},$$

where

$$p = EI\left(\frac{\pi^2}{L}\right),$$

$Fs =$ horizontal compressive force exerted on each

stringer. Thus, the total compressive force needed to lift the deck from the piles is $Fs \times 8$ (number of stringers).

The force necessary to arch the deck off the piles is calculated for initial arches of 1 to 40 inches (fig. 43). The initial arch in the deck, resulting from vertical pile displacement, is unknown, but it was probably less than the 24 inches described by the pile tops after the earthquake (fig. 42). (The force that would have been exerted by the embankment on the bulkhead to develop the compression on the deck is also shown in figure 43).

It should be emphasized that these are minimum forces, because the arching is treated as static, rather than dynamic; the additional resistance to arching that must have resulted from both the inertia of the deck and the increased resistance to rapid bending of the stringers is ignored. If the compression was as rapid as

was suggested by the pounding rate indicated by the pebble dents, the actual forces would have been considerably greater.

As noted earlier, the evidence for high horizontal accelerations in bridges is made ambiguous by the effects of compression that resulted from streamward displacement of foundation materials. However, the ambiguity does not mean that the possibility of high accelerations can be safely ignored. Accordingly, an estimate of horizontal accelerations is warranted.

At mile 61.9, the stringers of a 105-foot open wood trestle were driven through the planking of one bulkhead. The fact that the ends of the stringers were not broomed or battered (fig. 44) suggests that penetration occurred either as the result of slow continuous compression, which seems unlikely in light of the widespread evidence for horizontal pounding, or as the result of rapid horizontal acceleration.

An estimate can be made of the

force needed to penetrate the planks. Static resistance to penetration of washers as much as 2½ inches in diameter on bolts pulled across the grain of Douglas-fir reaches a maximum of 1,000 pounds per perimeter inch of washer (Scholten, 1966). If the force is dynamic rather than static, the wood offers considerably more resistance; William Bohannon (U.S. Forest Products Laboratory, Madison, Wisc., oral commun., 1968) suggests that the dynamic resistance would be increased to between 2,000 to 3,000 pounds per perimeter inch.

If one considers the stringers in bridge 61.9 to be a single penetrating body, and disregards breakage parallel to the length of the bulkhead planks along the top and bottom of the packet of stringers, penetration can very conservatively be said to have occurred only along the two 17-inch vertical edges of the penetrating body. Thus, penetration occurred for a length of 34 inches. If penetration resistance varied from 2,000 to 3,000 pounds per inch, the force exerted on the bulkhead must have exceeded some value between 68,000 and 102,000 pounds.

It must now be asked if the embankment fill would have been able to withstand such force without failing. By assuming that the embankment was not frozen and that it would fail as a wedge, as shown in figure 45, the force needed to produce failure can be calculated by Coulomb theory (Taylor, 1948, p. 499):

$$P = \frac{1}{2}\gamma H^2 Kp,$$

where P is force per horizontal foot of bulkhead, γ the unit weight (assumed to be 100 lbs per ft ^{3}), H the height along the bulkhead, and Kp the passive pressure coefficient. Assuming the angle of internal friction for the granular

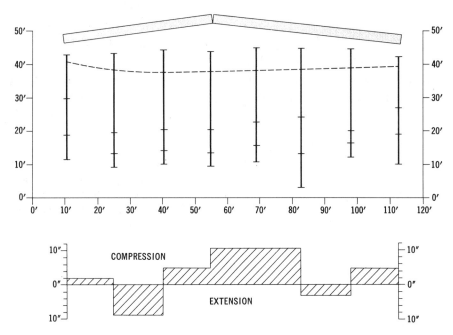

42.—Postearthquake positions on bents and deck of bridge 34.5. Relative interbent movements shown in graph.

noncohesive fill to be 30° and the force directed normal to the bulkhead, $Kp=3$ (Taylor, 1948, p. 500). By this equation, $P=630$ pounds. Treating the fill as if its vertical transverse cross section were rectangular and its width equal to the longest bulkhead plank (20 ft) rather than tapering upward (to a width of 14 ft), a somewhat liberal estimate of the force required to produce failure would be $20P$ or 12,000 pounds. Thus, the force needed to produce passive failure is only about one-third that needed to produce static penetration of the bulkhead by the stringers and between one-fifth and one-fourth that needed to produce dynamic penetration. If the embankment fill did not have sufficient seasonal frost to significantly change its shear strength, resistance to penetration would have been developed by the inertia of the fill rather than by its resistance to failure along a plane, and thus penetration may have been due to the rapid application of force.

If penetration resulted solely from horizontal acceleration of the bridge deck, the acceleration, as calculated by the dead weight of the entire superstructure (16,932 lbs) and the penetration resistance of the bulkhead planks would range from 1.12 to 1.68 g. Even the lowest of these values must exceed ground-surface accelerations that occurred in this area; thus, the high accelerations may have been produced by amplification (whipping) within the bridge structure. As shown by Parmelee and others (1964) in a theoretical study for the design of a pile-supported bridge for Elkhorn Slough, Calif., high accelerations, which greatly exceed ground-surface acceleration, can be developed within this type of structure. In the bridge which they studied, they conclud-ed that, given ground-surface acceleration of 0.28 g, an acceleration of 1.2 g would be developed at the bridge deck.

GROUND CRACKING

Ground cracks formed during the earthquake over an extremely large area—an area approximately the size of the state of California. The ground cracking occurred in a coastal belt that extended from the southwest end of Kodiak Island to the northeast. The area includes the Kenai Peninsula, extends about 150 miles north of Valdez along the northern edge of the Copper River Basin, and then swings to the southeast to the vicinity of Yakutat. Much of this ground cracking has been described in the U.S. Geological Survey Professional Paper series on the Alaska earthquake, as well as in other papers such as those by Reimnitz and Marshall (1965) and McCulloch and Bonilla (1967).

Most ground cracks, exclusive of those associated with landsliding, occurred in granular water-laid deposits on fans, deltas, flood

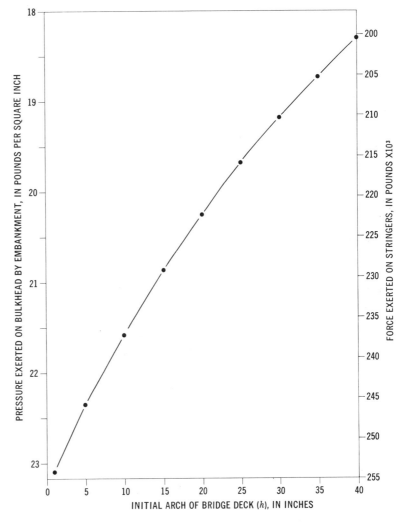

43.—Compressive force on the stringers of a 105-foot open wood trestle necessary to lift the superstructure just free of the piles, given some initial arch in the deck. The force exerted on the bulkhead by the embankment is also given.

44.—Unbattered stringers of bridge 61.9 driven through the south bulkhead planks.

plains, and tidal flats. The few exceptions were (1) cracks in glacial till that have been attributed to movement along a possible deeply buried fault on the northwest side of Kenai Peninsula (Foster and Karlstrom, 1967) and (2) a few cracks in till, observed by the authors at Portage Lake, which may have propagated upward from the underlying glacial outwash. Cracks were also observed in sandy till on steep slopes adjacent to lakes in the Copper River Basin (Oscar Ferrians, oral commun., 1968). The position of the water table had an important influence on the presence or absence of ground cracking and on the horizontal displacement of foundation materials. For example, the most severe ground cracking occurred in low-lying active flood-plain terraces that were nearly at the water table. Inactive flood-plain terraces in these same areas, the tops of which stand somewhat higher above the water table, were considerably less fractured. The exact depth to the water table is not known in most places, but in the areas of severe cracking it probably was less than 10 feet below the surface. Similarly, on most alluvial fans and deltas, cracking was limited to a fringe at the distal edge, where the water table approaches the surface; water was commonly ejected from cracks at the lower edge of this fringe of cracking.

The following types of ground cracks were most important in their effects on the railroad structures: (1) cracks resulting from landspreading—permanent lateral displacement and spreading of unconsolidated sediments, and (2) cracks formed by embankments.

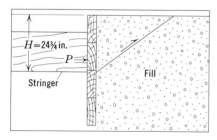

45.—Location of a possible Coulomb failure surface in an embankment due to force exerted on the embankment by bridge stringers.

CRACKS CAUSED BY PERMANENT LATERAL DISPLACEMENT OF FOUNDATION MATERIALS

One of the most common kinds of ground cracking was that which occurred along the margins of streams, gullies, and other topographic depressions (pls. 1–3; figs. 19, 27, 100, 136). The location and pattern of much of this cracking appear to be related to stress formed in the ground surface in response to the relatively deep permanent lateral displacement and spreading of the underlying sediments toward topographic depressions (McCulloch and Bonilla, 1967). It is clear from the horizontal offsetting and tension fracturing in embankments and from the pull-aparts in the rails, which commonly occurred as much as 500, or a maximum of about 1,000, feet back from the edges of streams, that wide areas underwent lateral displacement toward depressions. It is also evident from the horizontal displacements of embankments at stream crossings that sediments moved more or less directly toward the adjacent depressions.

The probable relationship between the surface stress distribution and cracking adjacent to stream valleys is shown in figure 46, in which the inferred stress directions are shown by arrows. In areas affected by this kind of ground cracking that were bounded by straight or concave streambanks (A, fig. 46), the movement of the underlying sediment was somewhat convergent or unidirectional. Cracks that formed were generally parallel to the stream and normal to the stress, suggesting that they are tensional failures. Adjacent to convex streambanks (B, fig. 46), where the cracking resulting from streamward movement did not extend far back from the stream edge, the spreading of the underlying sediments formed two perpendicular principal directions of stress, the major stress perpendicular and the minor stress parallel to the streambank. The resulting cracks formed at an intermediate position between the strain axes, and intersected at about 45° to 70°, suggesting that they were shear fractures. Cracks of this type were the most common kind on the distal edges of fans and deltas where the distortions of embankments and powerlines and the extension of bridges indicate that radial downhill spreading of the sediments occurred at some depth beneath the surface (see Sections 5, 6, 9, 10). In areas where the sediments spread in many directions, such as on the insides of meander bends and on small islands (*C*, fig. 46), the dominant crack pattern was an open network of curved or linear fractures that commonly intersected at right angles. The pattern of these cracks is similar in several respects to orthogonal thermal contraction cracks in frozen ground (Lachenbruch, 1962) that result from progressive tension failures. Where the stress in the surface layer is isotropic, orthogonal contraction cracks are curvilinear, intersecting at about 90°, and the crack-bounded blocks are randomly distributed. Where there is some preferred stress, the crack pattern can become highly rectilinear. In the formation of thermal contraction cracks, the preferred stress may result from a local heat source, such as a stream, whereas the rectilinear orthogonal fractures produced during the earthquake appear to have been due to the concentration of stress in the axes of abandoned channels that form small, elongate, generally parallel depressions in the surface.

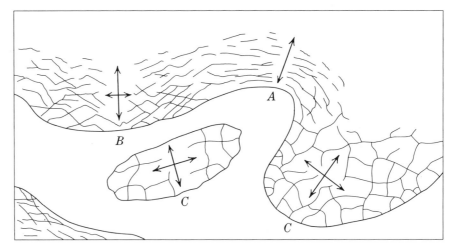

46.—Relationship between probable stress and ground cracking produced by landspreading toward a topographic depression. Arrows indicate directions of principal stress. Tension cracks form at right angles to the stress on straight and concave banks (*A*); shear fractures form on convex banks where the largest principal stress is perpendicular to the bank (*B*); cracks are orthogonal where stress is omnidirectional, as on islands or highly convex areas (*C*).

It was commonly observed that the distances between adjacent fracture-bounded surface blocks increased toward the streams and depressions. This observation is consistent with the model of surface failure, in which lateral displacement of the underlying sediments is initiated at the depression, and then progresses outward to the adjacent area.

On the cracked parts of fans, deltas, and flood plains, ground cracks commonly formed at the external corners of buildings. One such building, the U.S. Forest Service crew house on the flood plain in Portage valley, is shown in figure 47. The ground cracks went through the foundation, and the building had to be moved to a new foundation (Arthur Kennedy, U.S. Forest Service, Anchorage, written commun., 1967). Similar cracking on fans, deltas, and flood plains is shown in figure 48, in which the general direction of the lateral displacement of the sediments beneath the surface was to the right. Three of the houses shown in this figure are from a map by R. W. Lemke and R. D.

Miller (in Lemke, 1967, fig. 15) of the cracking on Jap Creek fan just north of Seward (see p. D98). On this map, 14 houses are shown to have been intersected by 46 cracks, 36 of which extend diagonally from the corners of the buildings. Lemke noted that such cracks were common but gave no explanation of their occurrence.

If, as suggested above, the surface materials were put in tension by lateral displacement of the underlying sediments, any sharp external angle in a hole through the frozen plate of surface sediments would concentrate the strain, and should be the site of a fracture. Once a fracture has been formed, the amount of force necessary to propagate the crack is reduced, because the sides of the fracture act as lever arms and increase the stress at the point of rupture; Inglis (1913) has shown that the stress at the apex of a crack in a plate is proportional to the square root of the length of the crack and inversely proportional to the radius of curvature of the angle at the apex of the crack. Because these cracks are initiated at weak

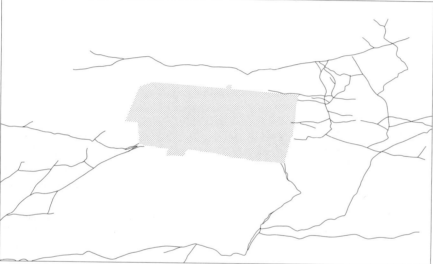

47.—Photograph and sketch of ground cracks localized at the corners of the U.S. Forest Service crew house on Portage Creek flood plain. Cracks broke the foundation and the building was moved to a new foundation. Photograph by Arthur Kennedy, U.S. Forest Service, Anchorage.

points in the surface and because the force needed to produce continued fracturing decreases as the fracture develops, such fractures should form early in the development of surface stress and the cracks should be relatively long.

Similar cracks, located at the corners of houses, were common behind the scarps of the big block-glide slides in the Anchorage area (see, for example, Shannon and Wilson, Inc., 1964a, pl. 8.2). This stress in the surface appears to

have extended back from the slide scarps.

LANDSLIDING AND LURCHING

Ground cracks that form beside streams and rivers during earthquakes have commonly been ascribed to landsliding and lurching. The sliding is often described as being of the block-glide type, in which surface blocks move on some weak nearly horizontal stratum, such as a clay or liquefied

sand layer, Oldham, 1899; Fuller, 1912) at or above the level of the river bottom. The lack of tilting in the displaced bridge piles suggests that landsliding of the rotational type did not occur along the streams. Lurch cracks, as defined by Steinbrugge and Bush (1960), are "* * * surface cracks due to horizontal vibration forces (as opposed to gravity forces associated with landslides)." Although these mechanisms clearly produce ground cracks, there is little evidence that they were important in the stream-margin cracking in the areas studied along the railroad.

The evidence against the importance of landsliding and lurching is as follows: If shallow block-gliding or lurching were important, the horizontal displacement of the surface material should exceed that of the underlying material. However, the net horizontal displacement of sediments beneath the surface as measured by displacements of bridge piles closely approximated that of the surface sediments as measured at the deck level (table 1). In three of the bridges, in which interbent measurements indicated net extension of the underlying sediments and in which measurements were also made at the deck level, there was exact agreement in two and a discrepancy of only 2 inches in the third (table 1). Thus, even where the bridges exerted no compressive force on the adjacent surface materials, there was no evidence of lurching or landsliding.

Lurching and shallow landsliding are also argued against by the fact that in most areas the ground was frozen, and it is unlikely that either the horizontal vibrations or shallow slides, in which the strength of the surface material would have been important, could have developed sufficient force to break frozen ground (the strength of the frozen ground is discussed on p. D58). In addition, lurching and shallow block-gliding would not produce the commonly observed upward movement of adjacent midstream sediments. Finally, the fact that cracking was omnipresent and omnidirectional would necessitate either omnidirectional vibrational forces of sufficient strength to produce such fractures or the presence everywhere of materials at the proper depths to provide glide surfaces along which sliding occurred. Neither of these possibilities seems likely.

In summary: All the evidence— (1) the patterns of many ground cracks, (2) their location beside topographic depressions and on fans and deltas, where displaced embankments and bridge pilings indicate deep lateral displacement of underlying materials, (3) the concentrations of cracks at corners of buildings, (4) the increasing distances between fracture-bounded blocks toward topographic depressions, and (5) the evidence that lurching and landsliding were not important in producing these cracks — is consistent with the proposition that many ground cracks result from stress generated in the surface materials by lateral displacement and spreading of the underlying sediments. Although these cracks were important in causing damage to railroad and highway embankments, bridges, and buildings, possibly of even greater importance is the fact that they clearly indicate that even on relatively flat areas, where the only topographic relief is provided by a local depression, the depression may cause permanent lateral displacement of both the surface and underlying material for a distance of as much as sev-

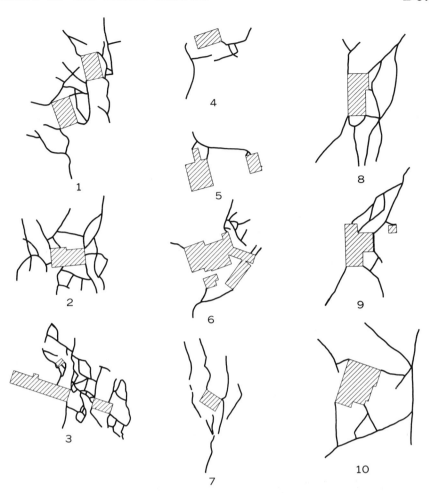

48.—Ground cracks localized at the corners of houses on flood plains (1, 2, 4–6), on deltas (3, 7), and on alluvial fans (8–10). All houses oriented with the principal direction of landspreading to the right. Houses 1 and 2 on Portage Creek flood plain; 3, Lowell Creek delta; 4–6, Resurrection River flood plain; 7, Rocky Creek delta; 8–10 on Jap Creek fan (after Lemke, 1967, fig. 15).

eral hundreds of feet in the adjacent sediments.

The term "landspreading" is proposed for this type of ground movement; first, to describe the spreading within the sediments, and second, to bring attention to the fact that it occurs on flat or nearly flat ground, as opposed to "landsliding," which has the connotation of downslope movement. Probably many of the phenomena ascribed to landspreading resulted primarily from liquefaction within the sediments. However, other mechanisms may have been operating; therefore the term "land-

spreading" is used, for it includes the effects of liquefaction and all other means by which similar displacements might occur.

CRACKS PRODUCED BY EMBANKMENTS

Embankments produced anastomosing cracks that were subparallel to the embankments, some within the embankment toes, some in the side drainage ditches, and others in a zone about 25 to 30 feet wide in the adjacent sediments. The embankments superimposed this crack pattern across areas of ground cracks on deltas, fans, and flat-lying ground in which other cracks were due to lateral displacement of the underlying sediments (pl. 3; figs. 19, 49). The embankments also produced these cracks where there were no other ground cracks.

Similar cracks have been observed in other great earthquakes. Oldham (1899, p. 89) described such cracks in the 1897 Indian earthquake: "A very noteworthy point about the fissures, formed away from and independent of, the river courses, is the manner in which they usually run parallel to, and along either side of, any road or embankment."

It is not clear how these cracks formed. Grossly similar cracks in surface sediments adjacent to an embankment are ascribed to block gliding by Newmark (1965). He believes that the embankment became detached on a buried horizontal glide surface and, in sliding back and forth, produced tension fractures in the sediments at some distance from the embankment. The likelihood that liquefaction occurred beneath the embankments in Alaska and allowed them to oscillate sidewise, as if on a glide surface, makes this mechanism attractive (see p. D75). However, because the surface sediments were frozen, they would have had considerable tensile strength, and seemingly not enough force was available to produce fracturing by this process. For example, in figure 50, the inertial force per linear foot of 3-, 4-, and 5-foot-high embankments are plotted against horizontal gravitational accelerations. The inertias are calculated on the assumption that the embankment underwent horizontal displacement without internal deformation. Seed and Martin (1966) have suggested that this approach may be valid for low, stiff embankments. Also on figure 50, inertias are calculated on the assumption that there was an equal mass of consolidated sediment beneath the embankment that did not liquefy (fig. 54) and whose mass was added to that of the embankment. Even the lower set of these inertial forces probably err by being too large. Furthermore, the peak ground accelerations were probably below 0.3 g; for example, Cloud (1967, p. 320) suggests, with reservations, that maximum accelerations in Anchorage may have been 0.14 g, and Newmark (1965, p. 142) cites estimates of 0.15 and 0.18 g.

A minimum value for the force needed to produce tension fractures in the frozen sediments can be estimated by using a low value (30 psi) for static (rather than dynamic) tensile strength of a granular soil (U.S. Army Corps of Engineers, 1952). Such a frozen layer, with a thickness of 4 feet, would have a tensile strength of 17,280 pounds per linear foot of embankment. This strength far exceeds the probable inertial force developed by the embankment. Thus, even a maximum inertial force and a minimum tensile strength appear insufficient to produce tension failures in the frozen sediments.

In addition, the fact that there were usually several fractures on each side of the embankment also argues that they were not produced by tension generated by block gliding of the embankment, for unless all fractures are formed simultaneously, a single fracture would preclude additional tension fracturing.

A possible explanation for the formation of these ground cracks may be that, as the embankment sank into the underlying sediments, it depressed the immediately adjacent frozen surface,

49.—Ground cracks generated by an embankment in Portage. Note dark areas flooded by ground water. Photograph by U.S. Army.

while at some distance the surface was bulged upward slightly by the displaced, possibly liquefied, sediments. The formation of a trough and bulge would have produced a zone of increased stress in the frozen surface sediments approximately parallel to the embankment. Then perhaps with the passage of surface ground waves, and in some areas the development of additional stress due to landspreading, the localized stress may have produced the cracks beside the embankment.

EMBANKMENT AND TRACK DAMAGE

Nearly all damage to embankments and their overlying tracks and ties occurred in areas underlain by water-laid unconsolidated sediments. The only damaged embankment on till or bedrock was along Turnagain Arm, where regional subsidence exposed the embankment to marine erosion. Embankment damage can be divided into three categories:

1. Fill failures, in which failure was restricted to the fill.

2. Active failures, in which the embankment played an active part in producing changes in the foundation materials that resulted in damage to the embankment.

3. Passive failures, in which displacement or cracking in the foundation materials produced damage to the embankment which acted passively. It should be noted that the terms "active" and "passive" are used here in the general rather than the specific sense of soil mechanics nomenclature.

Because the types of damage are generally related to the behavior of the foundation materials and these in turn are largely governed by the physiography, it is possible

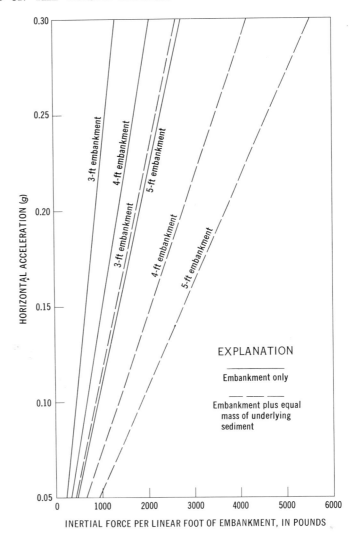

50.—Inertial force per linear foot of 3-, 4-, and 5-foot-high embankments (with and without a comparable mass of consolidated sediment beneath the embankment) at horizontal accelerations of 0.05 to 0.3 *g*.

to predict the damage to embankments subjected to a similar seismic condition.

A typical design cross section of the railroad embankment is shown in figure 51. Most of the embankment was constructed as follows (Cliff Fuglestad, engineer of track, oral commun., 1967): The line was cleared by hand, and the organic layer was left. The subgrade fill was usually side borrow, and it included organic material. Subgrade fill was placed by hand with a Fresno scraper. Berms on

the subgrade were fixed by eye, and the side slopes determined by the angle of repose of the subgrade fill. The subgrades were a maximum of 20 feet wide; in the Portage area, they were closer to 18 feet. The ballast was enddumped and raised, and from Seward to Indian (fig. 1) it is composed of crushed gravel. Most of the embankment was placed prior to 1914; in addition to yearly maintenance since that time, the Seward to Portage line had a major rehabilitation in 1955–56.

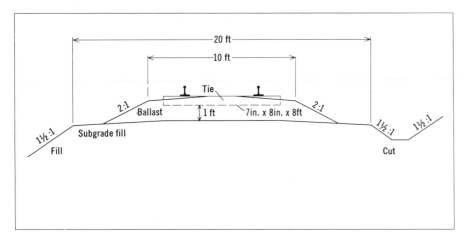

51.—Design cross section of a typical railroad embankment.

FILL FAILURES

Failures solely within the embankment (not related to shifting of, or interaction with, the foundation materials) were difficult to recognize, for several reasons. There was a virtual absence of easily identifiable discrete surface failures, either rotational or on inclined flat surfaces, that were restricted to the fill. The only rotational failures that affected the embankment, other than the large slides from deltas, occurred at mile 4.6 (see p. D99), where borrow had been removed at the embankment toe, and there the failure surface probably passed into the foundation materials. Other failures on discrete surfaces, although more common than rotational failures, appeared to involve the underlying sediments.

There is some evidence for failure by shear distributed throughout the fill, as shown by spreading of embankments at bridge bulkheads. Commonly, bulkhead fillers, rammed and compressed for the full stringer depth in the early part of the shaking when the bulkhead was vertical, were later rotated, their bases being pushed streamward by the spreading fill during the continued shaking (fig. 52). At several bridges the spread-

ing fill covered the bulkhead piles —which also suggests that movement was distributed throughout the fill.

Spreading may have been more general, but if so it was small, and the lack of strict adherence to design cross sections and the absence of as-built cross sections would have made it very difficult to detect. Where undeniable spreading occurred, it was associated with the displacement of sediments beneath the fill.

According to C. L. Griffith, as-

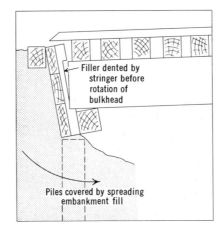

52.—A bulkhead filler that was rammed and dented by the stringer while it was still vertical. With continued shaking the base of the embankment fill spread over the bulkhead piles and the bulkhead was rotated.

sistant chief engineer, the seasonal frost within the embankments from Portage to Seward probably extended to a depth of 4 or 5 feet. The lack of failures restricted to the fill, either on discrete surfaces or as distributed shear, may have been due to the increase in shear strength afforded by the interstitial ice.

ACTIVE FAILURES

Damage to the embankment from changes in the foundation materials, resulting from the load of the embankment fill, was widespread and severe in areas underlain by wet noncohesive sediments. These failures took several forms. The most damaging was the general and irregular settling of the embankment fill, which lowered long sections of the embankment as much as 6 feet. Cross sections of the embankment in the Portage area made at local dips in the generally settled embankment are shown in figure 53. Each postearthquake profile is compared with design profiles at the preearthquake position and at the height of the postearthquake embankment. The comparisons of the design and postquake profiles show that the embankment fill settled largely en masse. At places there was almost no lateral spreading, and even where spreading was greatest, it does not appear to have been great enough to account for the total lowering.

Settlement was almost universal in areas underlain by wet unconsolidated noncohesive sediments and was greatest in areas of widespread ground cracking, such as active flood plains and the highly fractured margins of fans and deltas. Generally less severe, but locally as large, settlements occurred where the only ground fracturing was produced by the embankment. These latter settlements were in the otherwise unfractured parts of deltas, fans, and inactive flood plains. Settlement was usually accompanied by the expulsion of sediment-laden water from the adjacent ground cracks. A close relationship between the ejection of sediment-laden ground water and settlement was seen in some areas where local extreme settlements occurred where large volumes of sediments, as coarse as cobble gravel, were brought to the surface beside the embankment. (See, for example, mile 16–16.2 p. D103.)

The fact that the embankments were lowered more than can be accounted for by spreading, and that they appear to have settled where ground water was expelled (even where the only ground cracks present were produced by the embankment), suggests that the foundation material became liquefied.

It is of note that in many places where there was no other evidence of liquefaction in adjacent areas, the embankment still settled and produced high pore-water pressures in the underlying sediments. Thus the embankment appears to have been the cause of liquefaction of the underlying sediments. A somewhat similar observation was made by Shiraishi (1968) who reports that during the 7.8 magnitude Tokachioki earthquake in Japan on May 16, 1968 "* * * liquefaction took place only under and around objects such as parked freight cars in a railroad marshalling yard, and not in open areas."

Figure 54 is a hypothetical sketch of liquefaction beneath an embankment. Although the field observations do not determine where liquefaction started, they strongly suggest that the embankments produced the liquefaction, and that sediments beneath the embankments became liquefied.

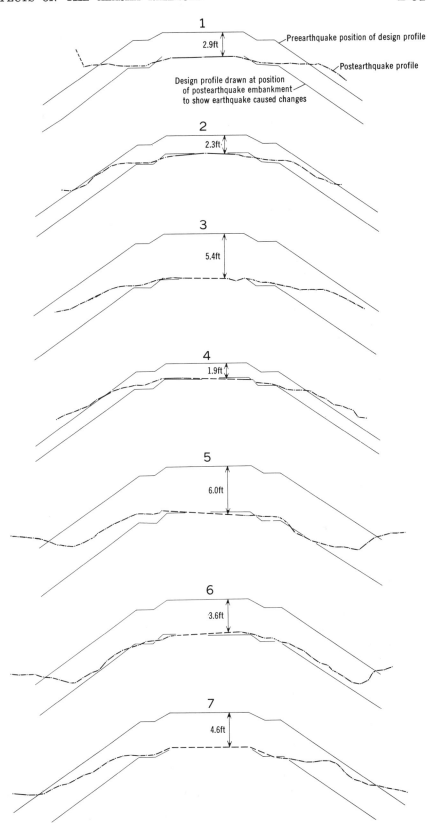

53.—Transverse profiles of settled railroad embankments in the Portage area measured by M. G. Bonilla and R. Kachadoorian. Each profile is compared with the design profile at the original and postearthquake height of the embankment. Profiles are located on figure 114.

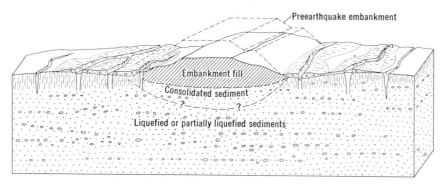

54.—Hypothetical sketch through an embankment underlain by liquefied sediments into which the embankment settled. Cracks formed by the embankment tapped the zone of high pore-water pressure, and sediments were carried to the surface by the escaping water.

Heavy traffic over the roadbed undoubtedly had densified the subfill materials and made them less susceptible to the increased densification needed to produce liquefaction than the adjacent materials. It is possible that inertial differences between an embankment and the adjacent sediments increase the stress locally during shaking and initiate liquefaction adjacent to the fill, in much the same way that differential movements of piles and their enclosing sediments might produce liquefaction locally surrounding the piles (Seed and Idress, 1967). Once high pore-water pressure had been developed in the soil adjacent to the fill, it could propagate downward and laterally, possibly extending under the embankment. With the formation of cracks in the frozen surface sediments adjacent to the fill, some of the high water pressure would be relieved. The close relationship observed between surface discharge and local sags suggests that in some cases liquefaction had occurred beneath the fill at the time of discharge. If it had not, the sinking fill would not have been able to displace the underlying material.

PASSIVE FAILURES

Discussions of embankments subjected to seismic loading commonly consider the distorting forces within the embankment and failures in foundation materials produced by the embankment. Passive failures in embankments that traverse areas in which there was ground cracking or permanent displacement of the ground are generally not considered. However, the widespread cracking and ground displacements that accompanied the Alaska earthquake made passive failures an important cause of damage. Because passive embankment failures depend upon the response of the underlying ground to seismic loading, it is possible to describe these failures in geologic and physiographic terms.

Passive failures are described in detail in Sections 1 to 19 (p. D95–D157), and will only be summarized here, examples being referred to generally by section or specifically by mile.

Passive failures have caused damage in other large earthquakes. For example, Wallace, Phillips, Drake, and Boggs (1907, p. 349) state that in the 1906 San Francisco earthquake "[Railroad] embankments across marshes, or with soft strata underlying them, settled more or less. In some cases the settlement was vertical; in other cases there was consider-

able horizontal with the vertical movement."

STREAM CROSSINGS

The most damaging passive failures of the embankments were at stream crossings, where landspreading was greatest. Because displacement was generally toward the stream valleys, embankments that approached valleys obliquely were offset horizontally in opposite directions on opposite sides of the streams (fig. 55) and the bridges were skewed horizontally. Horizontal offsets between embankment centerlines on opposite sides of stream channels measured at 27 bridges ranged from several inches to 10 feet (table 1). Twenty-one of these bridges are shown in figure 56; the offsetting of each bridge is described in pages D98–D157. As can be seen in figure 56, offsetting generally occurred as the result of movement toward the stream channels, but it also was produced by movement toward depressions

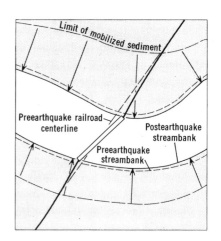

55.—Bridge skewed by streamward movement of sediments. Landspreading toward stream moved the banks closer together, and railroad grades that crossed streams at acute angles were carried sidewise in opposite directions on opposite sides of the stream, skewing the bridges.

(often wet) beside the embankments (bridges 33.6, 34.8, 37.0, 61.5). In one bridge (62.3), displacement was in the opposite sense, possibly because of local displacement of the high, narrow embankments of this bridge on the low active flood plain. In three large bridges (3.0, 3.2, and 3.3), the bridge ends and adjacent embankments were displaced laterally in the same directions parallel to the contours, offsetting them from the centers of the spans (figs. 29, 31, 32).

The absence of tilting in the displaced bridge piles driven largely through fill (bridges 3.0, 3.3) or the underlying sediments (bridges 3.0, 3.2) demonstrates that lateral shifting was not restricted to the fill, but that the fill was carried passively as the underlying material shifted. The minimal lateral displacement of the bridge centers suggests that movement parallel to the contours resulted from some force on the interstream areas. On the interstream areas the railroad lies adjacent to a large highway fill (fig. 27). Both the highway and railroad fills settled, and as shown by the extensive ground fracturing, expulsion of ground water, and streamward displacement of the foundation materials, the sediments were extensively mobilized by the shaking. The sinking of the large highway fill probably produced an outward flow of foundation materials that carried the adjacent railroad fill sidewise (fig. 57). This outward flow is also suggested by the fact that where the highway swings away from the railroad just north of bridge 3.3, the railroad fill was not displaced laterally (fig. 58). In the middle ground of this same figure, a lateral kink can be seen where the rails crossed a small road (Nash

Road, fig. 27). This road fill, lying at right angles to the railroad fill, appears to have resisted the lateral displacement, possibly because of its resistance to longitudinal compression.

In addition to being displaced laterally, bridge approach embankments were broken by fractures in areas where the underlying materials spread toward the stream valleys (pls. 2, 3; figs. 18, 19). The resulting fractures varied considerably in detail, but most were tension fractures that crossed the embankment at nearly right angles. The fractures were nearly vertical, and the block on the streamward side was often downdropped. At many places where the underlying materials were displaced laterally, there was also some horizontal displacement along the fractures. This fracturing is shown diagrammatically in figure 59.

Despite the fact that most of the bridge approaches were put in tension, the ends of the embankments abutting the bulkheads were deformed by compression resulting from the thrust of the compressed bridge decks. Bulkheads, driven back into the fills, bulldozed up the fills, some as much as a foot or more. As a result, the rails were torn from the embankment and either the ties were pulled upward out of the ballast, or, if the ballast was frozen, the rails were torn free of the fish plates that secured them to the ties (figs. 104, 106, 109).

Embankments built over filled-in channels or filled-over bridges behaved somewhat like those at stream crossings. For example, at miles 34.3 and 34.4 embankments were moved toward filled-in creeks and were bulged upward over the old stream channel. The accompanying compression deflected the

rails laterally at the bulges and pulled the ties sidewise through the ballast. The embankment settled around filled-over bridges at miles 60.2 and 62.1; at 62.1 the north end of the embankment was offset abruptly 3 feet and the rails were also deflected by compression (fig. 60).

FLOOD PLAINS

Principal passive damage to the embankment on flood plains was caused by permanent horizontal displacements of the underlying flood-plain sediments that carried some embankment sections more than 1,000 feet long out of horizontal alinement. These displacements were as great as several feet and were the rule rather than the exception on active flood-plain sediments. Displacements occurred toward bodies of water, nearby stream channels, borrow pits, areas of low ground, or other topographic depressions. Generally, where the flood-plain sediments were fractured, the embankment was also fractured. Commonly, fractures that approached the embankment obliquely swung normal to the rail line as they cut across the embankment (see, for example, fig. 19).

Rails were occasionally thrown into compressive kinks, even at long distances from bridges (fig. 27). It is possible that the embankment was compressed longitudinally. However, the kinks may have been formed as the result of a transient compression developed during the passage of surface ground waves. That surface ground waves do form compression at the surface is suggested by many eyewitness reports from large earthquakes in which ground cracks open on the crest of a wave and close, often with the ejection of water, as the trough passes.

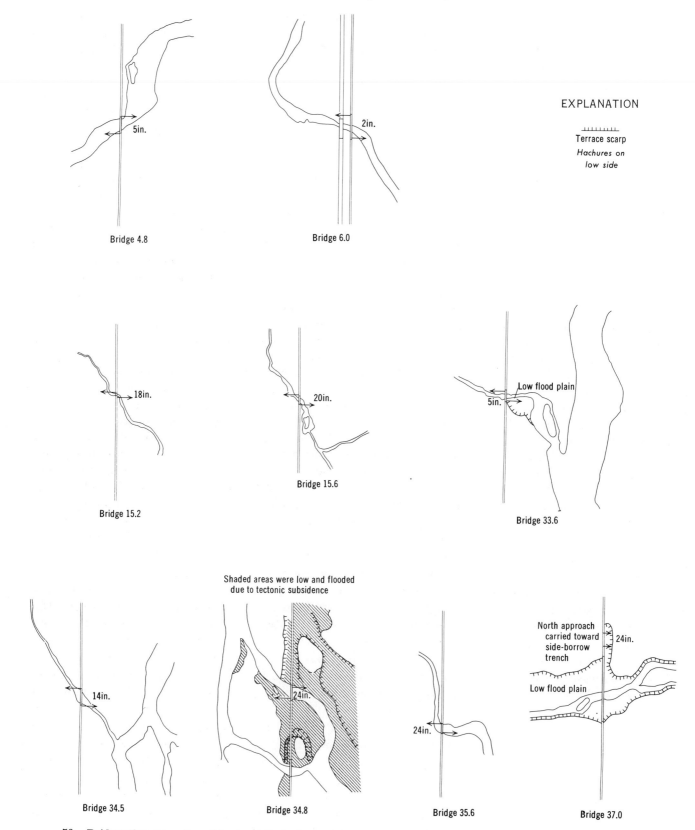

56.—Bridges that were skewed horizontally by landspreading toward stream channels or topographically low areas. All figures oriented with increasing mileage from bottom to top.

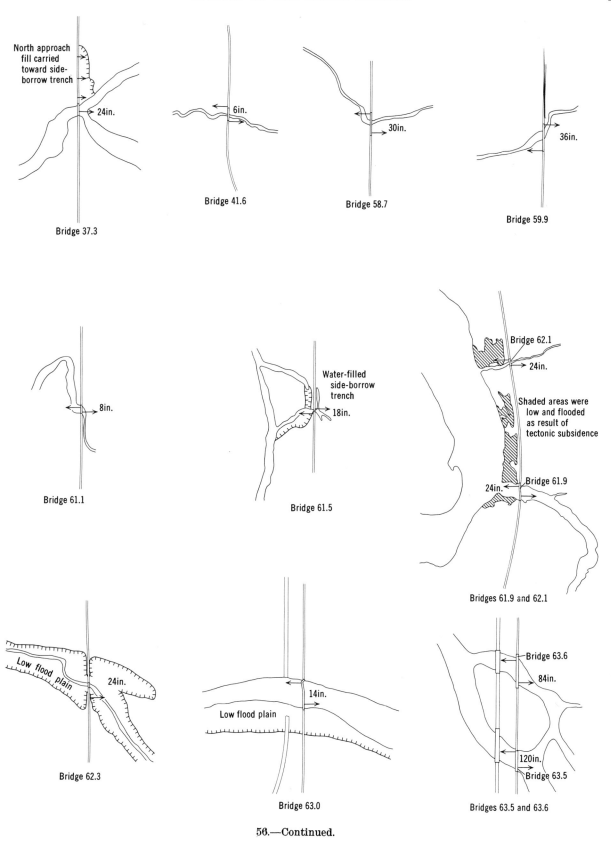

Bridge 37.3

Bridge 41.6

Bridge 58.7

Bridge 59.9

Bridge 61.1

Bridge 61.5

Bridges 61.9 and 62.1

Bridge 62.3

Bridge 63.0

Bridges 63.5 and 63.6

56.—Continued.

DELTAS AND FANS

The unconsolidated materials of deltas and fans spread radially downhill. The overlying embankments were carried laterally as much as 4 feet, and, having little tensile strength, were broken by tension fractures running normal to the embankment. Tension fractures in the embankments were particularly well developed on the margins of deltas and fans, where radial spreading was pronounced. In some places, tensional fractures occurred at about 30- to 50-foot intervals for as much as 1,000 feet. Some of the tension fractures were 1 foot wide. Tension skidded the rails over the ties, opened expansion joints to their extreme positions, and at several places sheared bolts in the angle bars that connect the rails and pulled them as much as 17 inches apart. Bridges on fans and deltas (bridges 20.0 and 21.4) were also pulled apart. Because the distances between the bents was increased, stringers were pulled partly off end bearings and ties and guard rails were split.

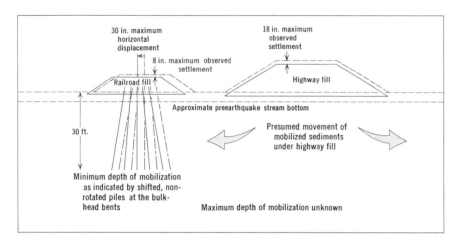

57.—Cross section of the railroad and highway fills at Resurrection River (fig. 27). Sediments displaced laterally beneath the sinking highway fill displaced the railroad fill and ends of bridges a maximum of 30 inches laterally, parallel to the contours. The lack of tilting in the bridge piling indicates that the depth of lateral displacement probably exceeded the pile depths. Dashed lines indicate preearthquake positions of embankments and piles.

58.—Sinking of large highway fill (at left) displaced adjacent sediments that carried the railroad embankment to the right and kinked the rails at smaller road fill (Nash Road, mile 3.4 figs. 27, 28) that was unaffected by the displacement, possibly because of its resistance to longitudinal compression. Lateral displacement decreased where the highway turns away from the railroad.

BRIDGE DAMAGE RELATED TO GRAIN SIZE, THICKNESS, AND DENSITY OF FOUNDATION MATERIALS

Almost all damage to bridges resulted from transient and permanent displacements of the foundation materials into which the pilings were driven. Thus, the degree of damage is largely governed by the level of mobility attained by the foundation material and by the length of time during which it moved; these factors in turn are determined by the ease with which a given foundation material becomes mobilized and by the duration and the intensity of the ground motion. In the following discussion, the severity of bridge damage is compared with these variables, by using (1) the dominant grain size of the foundation material into which the piles are driven as a measure of the propensity for mobilization and (2) the total thickness of the unconsolidated sediments at the bridge site as a measure of the duration and intensity of ground motion. These variables are compared in tables 3 and 4.

In these tables the dominant grain size of the foundation material at some bridges is known from adjacent borings (for example, Resurrection River, Portage area, Knik and Matanuska crossings). At others, the grain size of the sediment is based on field examination, the landform in question, and inferences from the surficial geology. Some of the total or minimum sediment thicknesses are also known from borings; others are estimated from a combination of the adjacent bedrock relief, seismic refraction data (near Seward), the areal extent of the unconsolidated sediment, and the geologic history of any given area as outlined in the mile-by-mile description of the damage.

The degree of damage to any bridge is assigned on the basis of the necessary repairs as follows:

Severe—replacements required:

Entire bridge (or culvert substituted).

All or some new piling, pile caps, and sway braces.

All or some new stringers.

All or some new deck, walkways, and guard rails.

New abutment backwalls and bulkheads.

New bearings built on concrete piers and abutments.

Moderate—repairs required:

Some new piles, pile caps, and sway braces.

Some to deck and bulkheads.

Installation of wide caps to carry shifted stringers.

Steel spans reset on piers and abutments that shifted.

New anchor bolts for steel spans.

Slight—repairs required:

Minor repairs to bulkheads and decks.

Blocking shims added to bents to compensate for vertical pile displacements.

Minor horizontal readjustments.

Repositioning steel spans to relieve endways shifting.

In terms of damage to the structures, these divisions represent gradations in the amount of (1) horizontal and vertical displacement of piles, piers, bulkheads, and abutments, (2) ramming of bulkheads and abutments, (3) lateral buckling or rupturing of stringers by compression, (4) lateral skewing of the bridge, and

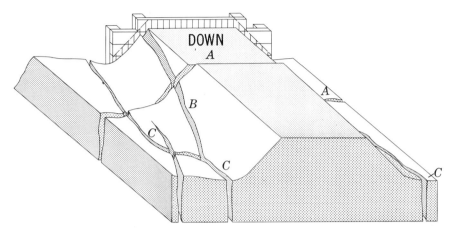

59.—Typical fractures at a bridge approach. A block of fill was lowered at the bulkhead and along a fracture (A) running perpendicular to the embankment. Fractures (B) formed on both sides of the embankment and ran diagonally back from the upper edge of the fill and joined fractures (C) that were approximately parallel to the fill in the adjacent ground.

60.—Lateral offsetting and compression at the end of filled-over bridge (looking north toward bridge 62.3). Note the ends of pile caps exposed to left of the ties.

(5) endways shifting of steel decks. Where the repairs were not known, the bridge was assigned to one of the divisions in which the observed damage to the structure was comparable.

The comparison of damage to foundation materials in table 3 shows:

1. All bridges damaged by displaced foundation materials (this excludes three bridges on till or bedrock damaged by lateral displacement of decks, not displacement of piers) were built on foundation materials that have the following common characteristics:

    a. All are water-laid sediments.

    b. All are noncohesive (no railroad bridges were built on clay).

    c. All are either modern sediments or are very young geologically.

    d. All have a high water content, the water table lying at or within a few feet of the surface.

The relation of the distribution of ground cracks to permanent lateral displacement of foundation materials and the distribution of damage to embankments show that little displacement occurred in sediments that are older and (or) drier.

2. The table shows that the severity of bridge damage increases as the grain size of the foundation material decreases. However, the grain size of water-laid sediments commonly decreases away from margins of sediment-filled basins. Thus, sand is more common than gravel where the sediment thickness is great.

The obvious tie between sediment thickness and damage immediately raises the question as to whether the grain size of the material (its propensity for mobilization) or the total thickness (the intensity and duration of the ground motion) is more important in determining the severity of damage to a bridge or embankment (and other structures affected by displacement of foundation materials). By replotting the damage against the sediment thickness (table 4) it appears that there is a stronger correlation between total sediment depth and the severity of the damage. All severely damaged bridges were underlain by more than 100 feet of sediments, and of all the bridges underlain by more than 100 feet of sediment, 88 percent were severely damaged.

The relative dependence of severe damage on the thickness and grain size can be demonstrated as follows: By considering only the grain size of the foundation materials, one would predict that 71 percent (17 of 24) of all bridges on sand and 47 percent (18 of 38) of all bridges on sand and gravel would be severely damaged. How-

TABLE 3.—*Damage to bridges, related to material in which piles were embedded*

Materials in which piles were embedded	Damage to bridges			
	None	Slight	Moderate	Severe
Silt		S M M	M	D
Sand		M D [M] [D]	M D D	D D D D D D D D D D D D D D D [D] [D]
Sand and gravel	M	S S S M M M	S S S S M M M M M D [D] [D] [D]	D D D D D D D D D D D D D D D [D] [D] [D]
Gravel	S (S) (S) (S)	[S] [S] [M] [D]	M M	
Till and (or) bedrock	□ □ □ □ □ □	□ □ ○		

Depth of unconsolidated sediment (to bedrock on glacial drift)

S 0–50'

M 50'–100'

D >100'

Type of bridge

S   Open wood trestle

[S] Wood and steel deck or steel on wood and (or) concrete piers

(S) Ballasted wood trestle

ever, if one used sediment thickness greater than 100 feet as related directly to severe damage, one could predict that 81 percent (17 of 21) of those on sand and 82 percent (18 of 22) of those on sand and gravel would be severely damaged. The same dependence of damage on sediment thickness is shown in the case of slight versus moderate damage on sand and gravel (table 4). The data available for damage on silt are scant, but they suggest a similar dependence of damage on sediment thickness. Four of the bridges built on silt are along the north shore of Turnagain Arm, where the silt is probably thin and rests on glacial drift that veneers the adjacent bedrock. The one bridge built on silt overlying a thick section of unconsolidated sediments (bridge 63.0) was severely damaged.

The relative dependence of damage on the grain size of the foundation material and the thickness of the underlying sediments can be compared in figure 61. In these graphs open wood trestles on wood piles are distinguished from other bridges. Open wood trestles are built uniformly to a standard design. Thus, one of the major variables—the differences in individual structures—which makes it difficult to evaluate the relation between structural damage and seismic ground response, is largely eliminated. Again, these graphs make it quite clear that the thickness of the sediments is a far more reliable indicator of potential damage than the grain size of the foundation material.

The discussion presented above ignores the density (compaction) of the sediments involved in foundation displacements. Is one justified in doing so? The strong relation of total sediment thickness to damage suggests that whatever

the range of the densities of the foundation materials at the sites of the 76 bridges built on waterlaid sediments, it had no great effect on the severity of the damage. However, for design purposes, it is useful to know the range in densities. Densities are sometimes estimated from standard penetrometer resistance values (N values: blows per ft of a 140-lb hammer falling 30 in. on a 2-in.-diameter penetrometer); however, there is some question as to the validity of this approach (Peck, 1967). To avoid the problem of translating N values to densities, only the N values are shown for the two areas in which they are available.

N values determined in six borings in the Portage area are plotted against depth in figure 62, and

an estimated average N curve is drawn. As shown by a generalized geologic section, the average N value which is low (15–20) in the upper 10 feet of gravel, increases to a maximum (50) in the underlying sand, and decreases as the section becomes silty near the base.

N values are also plotted from borings along the highway that was under construction across Knik-Matanuska River flood plain at the time of the earthquake (fig. 63). The generalized geologic section (based on 24 borings) shows sand and gravel to a depth of about 40 feet. The base of the sand and gravel is interbedded with silt and fine sand that continue, in beds several feet thick, to some unknown depth below the bottom of the deepest hole (−152

TABLE 4.—*Damage to bridges, related to total sediment thickness at bridge site*

Estimated total sediment thickness at the bridge site (feet)	Damage to bridges			
	None	Slight	Moderate	Severe
0–50'	4 ④ ④ [4]	1 3 3 3 [4] [4]	3 3 3 3	
50'–100'	3	1 1 2 [2] 3 3 3 [4]	1 2 3 3 3 3 3 4 4	
>100'		2 [2] 4	2 2 3 [3] [3] [3]	1 2 2 2 2 2 2 2 2 2 2 2 2 2 2 2 [2] [2] 3 3 3 3 3 3 3 3 3 3 3 3 3 3 3 [3] [3] [3]

Material in which piles were embedded
1 Silt
2 Sand
3 Sand and gravel
4 Gravel

Type of bridge
1 Open wood trestle
[1] Wood and steel or steel deck on wood and concrete or concrete
(1) Ballasted wood trestle

ft). The estimated average penetration resistance increases with depth.

Also shown in figure 63 are the depths of the tips of steel and wood piles in five large railroad bridges. The construction and damage to these bridges are described in table 1, in the discussion of damage to large bridges (p. D49), or on pages D155–D156, and can be summarized as follows:

All steel and wood pile-supported abutments and piers beneath steel spans were displaced streamward. Anchor bolts on steel spans were commonly sheared, and steel spans jammed together, damaging span bearings. Streamward displacement of wood pile bents occurred in those with open wood trestle approach spans (146.4, 148.3). Three of the bridges were severely damaged (147.1, 147.5, 148.3) and the remaining two were moderately damaged. The N values at the tips of the piles of these damaged bridges are compared with those of four severely damaged open wood trestles in the Portage area in figure 64. (Damage to the Portage bridges is described in section 12b p. D128, and pile displacements are shown on figs. 7, 8). Each bridge is indicated by a horizontal line that crosses

EXPLANATION

Damage
1—None
2—Slight
3—Moderate
4—Severe

☐ Open wood trestles on wood piles

☐ Steel and steel-wood spans on wood and steel piles and concrete abutments and piers—also, ballasted trestles

61.—The degree of damage to bridges compared with the grain size of the material in which the piles were embedded and the total thickness of all unconsolidated sediments at the bridge sites. As shown in table 3 and 4, the severity of the damage appears to be related most directly to the total sediment thickness.

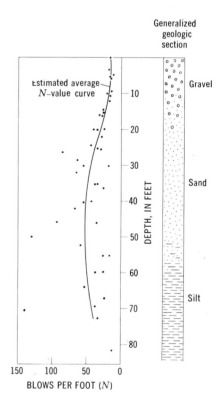

62.—Standard penetrometer values (N, blows per ft) and an estimated average N curve for six borings in the Portage area. Borings are located in figure 111, and logs are given on figure 112.

its respective average N curve at the average depth of the piles in the bridge. The ends of the horizontal lines indicate the N values at the tips of the deepest and shallowest pile in each bridge.

The considerable range in the density of the sediments associated with displaced foundations of these damaged bridges is shown in figure 64; those at Portage lie within the compact to dense range, and those at Knik-Matanuska crossings within the slightly compact to compact range. The more severe damage to bridges in denser sediments at Portage probably is due to the fact that Portage is considerably closer to the area of high strain release (fig. 2). Thus, in these two areas in which the sediments are relatively thick, the large difference in density of the foundation material appears to have had less effect on the degree of damage than the severity of the ground motion.

An informative comparison can be made between these two areas and damage associated with the 1964 Niigata earthquake in Japan. The Niigata earthquake was smaller (magnitude 7.3) and closer to Niigata (35 miles) than either the Portage or Knik-Matanuska area was to any of the large Alaska events. The shaded area in figure 64 is the range of penetration resistance values at the tips of piles under heavily damaged structures in Niigata (Seed and Idress, 1967; Koizumi in Seed and Idress, 1967), and damaged Knik-Matanuska bridges lie within this zone. However, the Knik-Matanuska area is nearly twice as far from the epicenter (65 miles) as Niigata and four times as far from the largest event (event C, magnitude 7.8, fig. 2). The Portage area bridges lie closer to the source of the seismic energy, yet were built in considerably denser

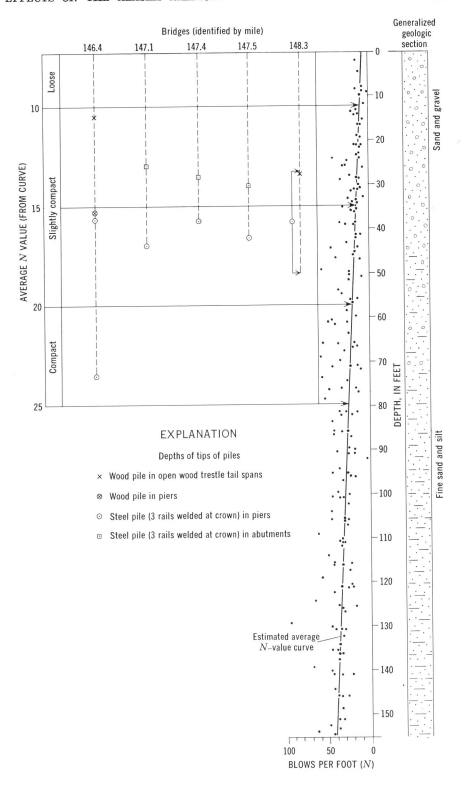

EXPLANATION

Depths of tips of piles

× Wood pile in open wood trestle tail spans

⊗ Wood pile in piers

⊙ Steel pile (3 rails welded at crown) in piers

▢ Steel pile (3 rails welded at crown) in abutments

63.—Standard penetrometer values (N, blows per ft), an estimated average N-value curve for 22 borings across Knik and Matanuska River floodplains, and a generalized geologic section based on 24 borings. The average penetrometer values are compared with the tips of piles in five bridges located on plate 1. Six of the deeper borings are located on plate 1 and their logs are shown in figure 137. Data supplied by the Alaska Department of Highways.

sediments than those that were severely damaged at Niigata. These comparisons show that the choice of the magnitude, location, and duration of the "design earthquake" are extremely important when considering the possible behavior of foundation materials.

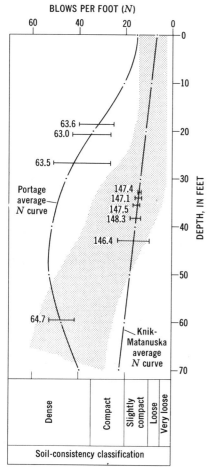

BLOWS PER FOOT (N)

63.6
63.0
63.5

Portage average N curve

147.4
147.1
147.5
148.3

146.4

64.7

Knik-Matanuska average N curve

DEPTH, IN FEET

Dense | Compact | Slightly compact | Loose | Very loose

Soil-consistency classification

64.—Range of N-values (horizontal line) at tips of shallowest and deepest piles in damaged bridges in Portage and Knik-Matanuska areas, plotted on their respective average penetration resistance curves. Bridges in less dense sediments, far from the area of strain release at Knik-Matanuska area, were less severely damaged than those in denser sediments, nearer the area of greater strain release at Portage. The shaded area is the range of penetrometer values in sediments under severely damaged pile-supported structures in the 1964 Niigata earthquake in Japan (Seed and Idress, 1967).

In summary:

1. Foundation materials in which damaging displacements occurred were young noncohesive water-laid wet sediments. Bridges on bedrock, till, or older drier water-laid sediments were undamaged by foundation displacements.

2. Severity of the damage increased with the thickness of the sediments, and all severely damaged bridges were on sediments more than 100 feet thick.

3. Severity of the damage appeared to be less influenced by grain size of the wet water-laid foundation materials than by the total sediment thickness.

4. Displacements occurred in foundation materials with penetration resistance values even above 50 blows per foot (dense soil).

5. Of the two areas in which there is data, the proximity to the area of strain release appears to have been more important in determining the severity of the damage than the penetration resistance of the foundation materials.

These observations can be further summarized in the following useful generalization: In an area subjected to a large long-duration earthquake, structures on thick water-laid noncohesive wet young sediments that range from silt to gravel and have a wide range in penetration resistance values should be expected to sustain severe damage, either from displacements of the foundation materials or from severe ground motion.

LANDSLIDES

Subaqueous landslides were responsible for a considerable part of the total cost of repairing the railroad. Slides at Seward, Whittier, and Kenai Lake have been described by Grantz, Plafker, and Kachadoorian (1964), Lemke (1967), Kachadoorian (1965), and McCulloch (1966). Subaerial landslides also caused damage at Potter Hill (mile 103-104), in and adjacent to the railroad yards in Anchorage, at mile 138.4 on the main line, and at mile 16.5 on the Sutton Branch.

POTTER HILL SLIDES

Landsliding occurred for about 4,200 feet between mile 103 and 104. The railroad was built in cuts and fills across the face of a bluff at Potter Hill, about 2.5 miles north of Potter (fig. 1). Two sections of embankment and track, totaling 1,550 feet, were carried away by the slides (fig. 65). The following paragraphs summarize the report of an investigation of the slides prepared by the authors for The Alaska Railroad. A longer summary of this report is given in Hansen (1965, p. A31-A33).

At the north end of the slide area the bluff is composed of glacial till resting on glacial outwash, which in turn rests on silt and fine sand. To the south, the till is lower in the bluff, and is overlain by glacial outwash. A water well (well 571, Cedarstrom and others, 1964), 900 feet east of the railroad, penetrated a 20-foot bed of "blue mud," from 2 feet above to 18 feet below mean lower low water, resting on alternating thick beds of sand and blue clay to a depth of 375 feet below mean lower low water. This "mud," sand, and clay may be the Bootlegger Cove Clay, in which the slides occurred in the city of Anchorage.

The scarp along which the railroad gradually ascends is an abandoned wave-cut cliff that was cut when sea level was higher with respect to the land. As the subsequent relative lowering of sea level occurred, the shoreline shifted toward Turnagain Arm and left a wide tidal flat exposed. Coniferous trees growing on this surface show that it is above the highest tides (fig. 65). This flat tidal plain is composed of a sheet of sediments that rest on an erosion surface cut across unconsolidated sediments. The erosion surface slopes gently from the toe of the bluff toward Turnagain Arm. The tidal-plain sediments are probably largely of silt size, as are most of the sediments in modern Turnagain Arm.

Sliding was caused by flowage of material near the base of the bluff. Flowage may have been initiated in either, or both, the fine sand and silt that underlie the base of the bluff, or the adjacent fine tidal-flat sediments which must have underlain some of the embankment fill. The resulting slumping and flowage carried disintegrating blocks of earth, track, and ties down and away from the bluff; some ties and rails were carried as much as 140 feet horizontally. Where flowage occurred, the material was probably saturated, because depressions in the slide debris were rapidly filled with water, and sand craters and mounds were found where water under pressure was driven to the surface of the debris. Because the ground surface was frozen, this water was undoubtedly ground

65.—View of Potter Hill slides. Note the overthrusts in the low-lying tidal flat in the foreground, and dark strata of water-saturated sediments in the slide scarps. Photograph by The Alaska Railroad.

water. Water wells inland from the bluff encounter water from 240 to 30 feet above sea level, and the dark bands of saturated sediments visible in figure 65 show that ground water is discharged along the base and at several levels throughout the height of the bluff. The dark tone of the soil in figure 68 also shows that water was plentiful at the scarp of the slump that cut deepest into the bluff.

Pressure ridges formed within the slide debris and at their margins. In the ridge at the outer margin of the slide, lateral force transmitted through the frozen surface sediments drove the tree-covered frozen sediments up over adjacent trees (fig. 66). Some upper blocks were completely detached at their edges, which suggests that the overthrusting may have been relatively rapid. Lateral thrust in the frozen sediments continued beyond the outer edge of the slides and formed overthrust ridges well out in the adjacent tidal flats (pl. 4; fig. 65).

Comparisons of pre- and post-slide cross sections (pl. 4) indicate that the volume of slide material that accumulated at the base of the slope and adjacent tidal flats was less than the material removed from the slope by sliding. The apparent loss in volume may be due to lateral flowage of the fine-grained tidal flat sediments away from the bluff. The lateral flowage probably occurred beneath and contributed to the thrusting of the frozen surface layer that extended as much as one-third mile beyond the edge of the slides. Marginal cracks formed on adjacent parts of the bluff face, where slumps did not develop. These cracks were approximately parallel to the bluff in natural bank material and in the fill up to the level of the tracks, in the roadbed, and in the drainage ditch between the tracks and the bluff. Near Rabbit Creek, cracks occurred to the top of the bluff face. Cracks from which sand-bearing water was ejected were also observed by James A. Morrison of the Engineering Department of The Alaska Railroad on the surface of the bluff, about 400 feet back from the scarp.

After this study was made, Clair A. Hill and Associates of Redding, Calif., investigated the slide area preparatory to designing a new alinement and associated drainage structures ("Potter Hill Slide investigations for The Alaska Railroad," Aug. 1964, 20 p.). Borings were made in the slide debris and undisturbed bank material. Logs of the borings and a topographic map prepared from aerial photographs from this report are shown on plate 4. The aerial photographs were taken after the rail line had been relocated in a cut across the slide area; thus the slide scarp that was mapped earlier appears to lie on a slope.

Borings B 8 and B 6 straddle the northern slide. In the interval of suspected failure (from somewhere below the embankment at an altitude of 82 ft, to somewhere below the bluff base at an altitude of 20 ft), both borings penetrated predominantly sand-size material containing varying amounts of silt and fine gravel. Between altitudes of 10 and 20 feet, both borings penetrated water-bearing strata. The inversion of penetration resistance values in hole B 8 that shows low values between 0 and 35 feet—the interval encompassing the water-bearing strata—suggests that failure might have occurred within this zone. However, blow counts in B 6 give no indication of a comparable zone. It is possible that more closely spaced measurements of penetration resistance in B 6 might have isolated a weak zone.

Borings B 1 and B 2 are located just upslope, and B 3 just north, of the other major slide area. Of these three borings only B 3 was deep enough to have penetrated the zone of suspected failure. The

66.—Entirely detached block of frozen soil and uprooted trees that was thrust up over the adjacent tree-covered ground in a pressure ridge at the toe of Potter Hill slide.

partial cementation and very dense consistency of the sediments suggest that no failure occurred in these materials; possibly most or all of the sliding at this location was in fill. No detailed records showing the distribution of cuts and fills are available for this area; however, in the recollection of Mr. Cliff Fugelstad, engineer of track, this was an area of fill. Some unknown amount of fill might also have been involved in the slide to the north, but our field observations showed that natural materials were exposed along the northern part of the slide scarp.

The type and extent of failures in fill placed on the estuarine sediments at the toe of the bluff during reconstruction add some credence to the inference that part of the landsliding involved failures within these sediments where they were overlain by embankment fill. The failures produced pressure ridges separated by water-filled troughs resembling those formed by the landslides. The following account of the failure during reconstruction is from a letter written to The Alaska Railroad on April 24, 1965, by Dan K. Conger, resident engineer for Clair A. Hill and Associates. The letter de-

scribes failure associated with a 5- to 12-foot-thick 400- by 5,000-foot spoil area built on the tidal flat adjacent to the toe of the slides.

"A general subsidence is experienced in most areas as evidenced by a 3 to 5 foot depression formed at the forward toe of the earth fill and heaving of the tundra surface beyond [fig. 67A].

Water usually appears in the depression, and sizable streams issue from beneath the fill. Cracks form in the fill surface indicating settlement as well as forward movement. Shock waves are felt at considerable distances, and weaving of the surface beneath wheels is common.

Instantaneous slipouts have occurred which were triggered by the earthmoving

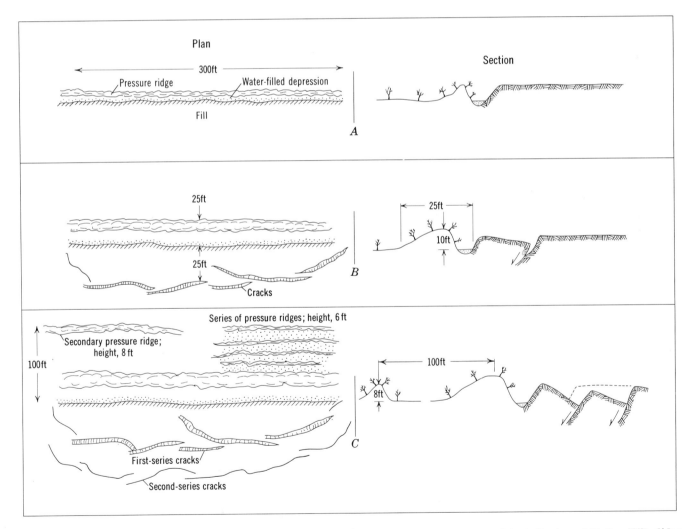

67.—Field sketches of successive failures that occurred in a spoil area and adjacent tidal flat at the toe of Potter Hill slides during reconstruction. Sketches redrawn from Dan K. Conger, Clair A. Hill and Associates.

equipment, and required considerable effort to extricate the machine. Of particular note was an occurrence on Monday, April 20, 1965, which will be further described with related reactions of the tundra.

Opposite Railroad Survey Stations 2886 to 2889, a section of the fill approximately 25 ft. by 300 feet, dropped suddenly and started moving out. A short time later cracks appeared about 25 feet further back and a new section was seen to be subsiding and moving toward the tundra [fig. 67B].

A characteristic rotation of the blocks of earth was noted, having minor subsidence of the forward edge, with the rear edges continuing to subside during the periods of forward motion. The surface of the first section dipped 45° from horizontal, reaching a maximum settlement of 10 feet. The second section attained a dip of about 30° and experienced somewhat less settlement.

Late in the day a semblance of stability was reached, where the materials rested in a state of uncertain equilibrium, and movements were not readily discernible. Several thousand cubic yards of fill added to the sunken area had not restored the original grade.

Transformations of the tundra occur as a result of the subsiding fills and is evidenced by the formation of pressure ridges, which rise to heights of 6 to 10 feet, a distance of 25 feet in advance of fill [fig. 67C]. In the instance cited, a secondary pressure ridge appeared about 100 feet beyond the first, reaching a height of 8 feet, indicating that pressure was being transmitted through the underlying muds to considerable distance. At the northerly end of the section a series of pressure ridges developed, reaching about 5 feet in height, and extending about 100 feet beyond. The intervening troughs filled with water.

Of particular interest was the manner in which the crest of pressure ridges appears to flow beneath the turf. Matted vegetation is first raised, then as the crest moves forward is draped over the back side of the ridge, presenting much the same appearance on both sides. Forward motion of the ridges is not rapid, but is apparent from occasional miscellaneous movements, which continue until some degree of equilibrium is re-established.

This is the third time the section between miles 103 and 104 has been damaged by slides within

about a 35-year period. In the late 1920's and early 1930's heavy rains caused sliding; the largest slide removed about 1,000 feet of track (Bert Wennerstrom, chief accountant, The Alaska Railroad, oral commun., 1964). On October 3, 1954, landsliding resulting from an earthquake again destroyed some of the rail line. A report on slides, between mile posts 103 and 104, after the earthquake is on file at The Alaska Railroad Office (James A. Morrison, unpub. data). Since the 1964 earthquake the rail line has been rebuilt close to the pre-1964 alinement in a slightly deeper cut across the face of the bluff.

ROCKY CREEK DELTA

The delta of Rocky Creek (21.4; also called Boulder Creek) on the east shore of Kenai Lake was extensively fractured, and a series of small slumps into the lake trimmed back the edge of the delta as much as 150 feet (McCulloch, 1966, fig. 29). One slump carried away 261 feet of the railroad embankment. The following description of the slumping and fracturing in the deltas is taken in part from a 1964 unpublished report prepared by the authors for The Alaska Railroad ("Report on a landslide at mile 21.4, Kenai Lake, resulting from the earthquake on March 27, 1964").

Fractures in the delta occurred in the pattern typical of fans and deltas—two sets of fractures that intersected at about 60°, to form parallelogram-shaped blocks having long axes parallel to the contours. Single blocks at the edge of the delta were lowered and rotated downward along the fractures; farther up the delta the blocks appeared to have moved downslope without rotation.

Soundings made down the axis of the scarp of the slide that car-

ried away the rail line showed that the water was 9 feet deep where before the track had been 12 feet above the water. The slide scarp sloped at about 32° to a depth of about 100 feet, and then continued to a depth of approximately 375 feet at a slope of 27°.

The 1964 report recommended that the rail line be relocated farther up the slope of the delta, not only because of the difficulty of placing and maintaining a fill in the steep slide scarps, but also to avoid the zone of deep fractures at the edge of the delta that might slump in a subsequent earthquake. It was also suggested that heavy traffic, which might trigger a slide, be avoided until relocation was complete. Since the earthquake, 1,500 feet of roadbed has been relocated a maximum of 75 feet upslope of the preearthquake alinement, and the small open wood trestle (mile 21.4) that was pulled apart by the spreading delta sediments was replaced by an 8-foot-diameter steel culvert.

ANCHORAGE

Landslides that occurred along the edges of the high bluffs beside Knik Arm and the valley of Ship Creek (fig. 68) have been described in detail by Shannon and Wilson, Inc. (1964a) and by Hansen (1965). The L Street slide, the Fourth Avenue slide, the Government Hill slide, and some of the slides along Railroad Bluff damaged tracks, buildings, buried utilities, and rolling stock of the railroad (see Section 15, p. D143). Ship Creek valley probably has a long history of landsliding. A 1914 topographic map made by the Alaska Engineering Commission (fig. 69) shows landforms that are clearly landslides along the bluffs surrounding the railyards. Although Miller and Dobrovolny (1959) recognized old landslides along the bluffs in the Anchorage area, these slides are not shown on their map. The 1914 map shows two distinct slides on the northwest side of Government Hill. The northernmost, with a nearly circular toe, appears to have been little modified by erosion and may have occurred not long before 1914. An oil-tank farm has since been built on this landslide. On the south side of Government Hill, just northeast of the present railyard, hummocky side-slope topography and a terracelike form with

a linear depression at its back edge that resembles the grabens formed behind many of the 1964 Anchorage slides suggest that there had been sliding in the area in which the 1964 Government Hill slide occurred.

On the south side of Ship Creek there is hummocky side-slope topography along most of the bluff east of the location of the modern railroad depot. Of special interest is the reentrant in the bluff at the position of the 1964 Fourth Avenue slide, in which there is a low

hummocky area with a lobate tongue that protrudes out into the adjacent flood plain. As Hansen states (1965, p. A66), several people have concluded that the Fourth Avenue slide occurred in an old slide area:

The alcove-like area centered at the city parking lot * * * probably also is the scar of an old landslide (Shannon and Wilson, Inc., 1964, p. 39; R. M. Waller, written commun., 1965). The area coincides almost exactly with the Fourth Avenue slide of March 27, except that the Fourth Avenue slide retrogressed farther into the bluff.

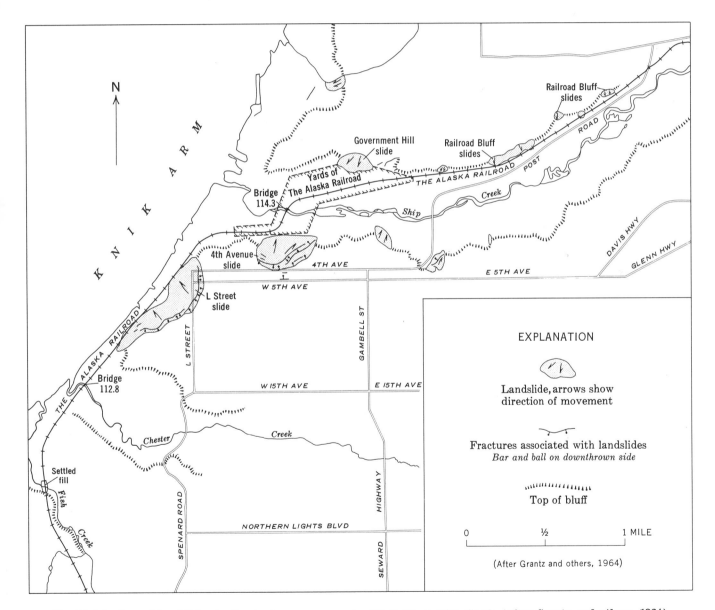

68.—Distribution of landslides in the Anchorage area and settled fill on Fish Creek (after Grantz and others, 1964).

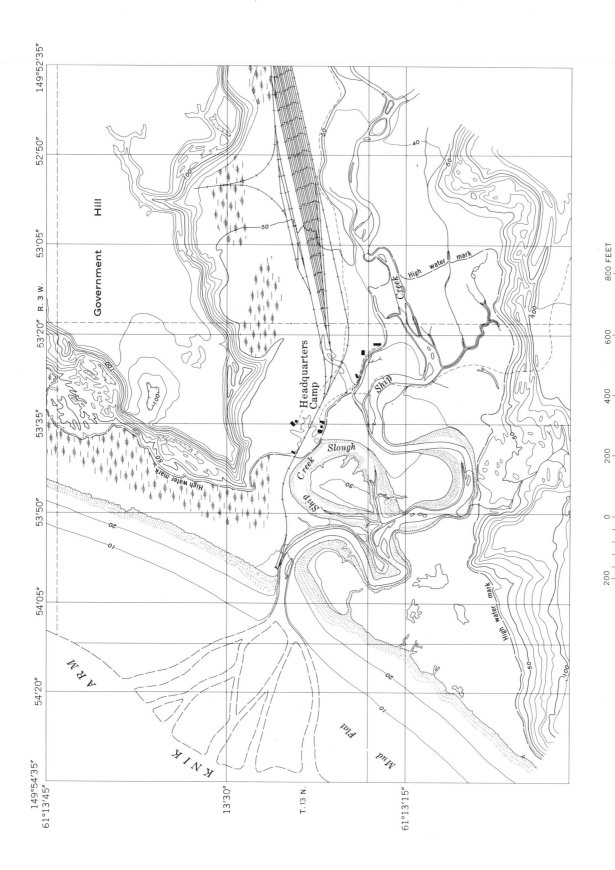

69.—Alaska Engineering Commission 1914 topographic map of Ship Creek valley, Anchorage. The landforms indicate two distinct slides backed by elongate grabens. These slides are on the west side of Government Hill, on either side of a topographic depression interpreted as being an ice-kettle hole. Two slides are also discernible on the south side of Government Hill, the easternmost in the position of the 1964 slide. On the south side of the creek, jumbled side-slope topography suggests extensive sliding from the area of the 1964 Fourth Avenue slide eastward for a distance of approximately 2,600 feet.

The topography shown on the 1914 map clearly confirms this conclusion. It also indicates that there was a flowing stream with several tributaries in the slide area. Although the topographer indicated small gullies up the face of the bluff, the fact that this is the only stream that he drew suggests that it was of some consequence. As drawn, the tributary pattern shows that the stream was largely fed from springs located in the slide mass and in the scarp at its head.

Groundwater discharge into this slide area seems to have persisted after 1914, for as Shannon and Wilson, Inc., state (1964a, p. 40),

At some fairly recent date, the area now occupied by a parking lot between Fourth Avenue and Third Avenue was filled with gravel. Prior to filling, this area was wet and swampy. Early records show a 12-inch drain pipe was installed prior to filling, and that this drain still discharges water just above First Avenue

The persistently high groundwater discharge probably contributed to both the 1914 and 1964 slides.

Landslide damage to the railroad in, and adjacent to, the Anchorage railroad yard (p. D146–D150) can be summarized as follows: The L Street slide carried the embankment and tracks possibly several feet laterally toward Knik Arm. The Fourth Avenue slide (1) broke foundations of unused dormitory buildings on the slide; the buildings have been razed; (2) displaced laterally and heaved up on pressure ridges the buried concrete utilidor along First Avenue and B Street; the utility lines have been rebuilt above ground; (3) contributed to the damage to the office annex building; it has subsequently been razed; (4) displaced foundation piles under a long freight depot north of First Avenue; and (5) may have dis-

placed the depot-office building slightly to the north. The Government Hill slide overran a prefabricated metal Butler building used for on-track equipment storage, destroyed the building, covered adjacent trackage, and damaged some rolling stock. Slides from Railroad Bluff covered the tracks, but did no important damage.

SUTTON BRANCH SLIDE

At mile 16.5 on the Sutton branch line, about 2 miles south of Sutton (fig. 1), a small landslide was dislodged from the bluff along the north bank of the Matanuska River — a bluff that rises steeply above the flood plain on which the rail line is built. The slide overrode about 300 feet of track, but at the time the following observations were made the tracks had been cleared and repaired, and most of the toe of the slide had been removed.

Sliding occurred on the very steep 40° to 45° face of a 150-foot-high bluff cut in outwash sand and gravel. The area affected by the slide was about 700 feet wide and extended to about 100 feet above the bluff base; thus, about 21,000 cubic yards of material were involved. As far as could be determined, the only material in the slide was an approximately 6-foot-thick layer of silty sand that had been blown from the adjacent valley floor onto the face of the bluff. The eolian material was tied together by the root mat of conifers, some deciduous trees, and low shrubs; it may have been frozen at the time of the earthquake. Several large pieces of this root mat tore free and skidded downslope. The movement occurred at the contact with the underlying outwash sand and gravel, and at no place was the sand and gravel seen to be involved in the slide (fig. 70). It is not known if water played any role in the sliding. Some water was seen in the jumbled slide debris at the base of the slope, but none was found above where the outwash was laid bare on the skid surface. Similar slides in which windblown sand was dis-

70.—Root mat development in windblown silty sand that became detached and skidded downslope along its contact with glacial outwash sand and gravel at mile 16.5 on the Sutton branch line.

lodged from a bluff face were studied by the present authors along several miles of bluff between Point Campbell and Campbell Creek southwest of Anchorage (Hansen and others, 1966, p. 56), and are described by Hansen (1965, p. A30–A31).

SLIDE AT MILE 138.4

At mile 138.4 the rail line crosses a small creek, which drains Mirror Lake (fig. 136). The creek has cut a wide reentrant into the edge of the adjacent bluff that rises to about 125 feet just southeast of the rail line. Ground cracks formed in the bluff along the edge of the reentrant as well as on the floor of the reentrant, where water was ponded behind pressure ridges. From about 35 to 525 feet north of the culvert through which the creek discharges, the turf on the northwest side of the rail line was buckled upward in an arcuate pressure ridge. The pressure ridge was hollow. Its walls were made of frozen turf

that had been jackknifed upward 3 to 8 feet, and it was possible to walk in the hollow under the center of the pressure ridge, beneath the roof of frozen turf (fig. 71). Adjacent to the pressure ridge, 450 feet of embankment was displaced laterally and lowered irregularly as much as 5 feet. The sliding appeared to have been shallow, and was probably produced largely by flowage of material beneath the surface, because there was neither a scarp at the head of the slide nor an upthrust, or upbulged toe, which might suggest rotational failure. The upward buckling of the frozen turf probably was produced by the resistance of the frozen surface to lateral transport of the flowing sediments below, in much the same way as the overthrusts in the frozen sediments beyond the edges of the slide at Potter Hill.

This area appears to have a history of sliding, for there are old pressure ridges and hummocky slide topography on the

floor of the reentrant southeast of the tracks, which clearly predate the 1964 movement. Although no pre-1964 slides are recorded, this section of track has required considerable maintenance to keep the line at grade level. It is also notorious for "glaciering," that is, the growth of ice out over the tracks which suggests that ground water is discharged through the shallow slide debris. The excess ground water undoubtedly contributed to the instability of the slide by increasing whatever propensity the sediments had for sliding.

DISTRIBUTION OF REGIONAL TECTONIC SUBSIDENCE AND ITS RELATED DAMAGE

Turnagain Arm and Portage lie in the area of regional subsidence (fig. 2). The lowering of bench marks on bedrock relative to their 1923 altitudes is shown in figure 72. Elevations measured in two surveys in May to October of 1964 (Wood, 1966, table 11, p. 124) indicate that the maximum subsidence occurred between Girdwood and Portage and may have been as much as 5.72 feet.

In the Portage area, the shoreline of the first period of high tides in late April after the earthquake was as much as 2 miles inland from the preearthquake mean high water shoreline (fig. 73). The town of Portage was inundated and covered with a blanket of silt. Both the railroad depot, which had been severely damaged by ground cracking and seismic shaking, and a microwave building, just across the track from the depot, were flooded. At high water, parts of the embankment and most of the marshaling yards on the Whittier branch were submerged. Much of the highway, which was at a lower altitude than the railroad, was covered by water,

71.—Frozen turf arched upward in a hollow pressure ridge at the toe of the slide at mile 138.4. The hollow center can be seen where the ridge is broken by an extension fracture. The slide lies behind the viewer.

and all transportation between Seward, Whittier, and Anchorage was halted. Large blocks of ice carried ashore by the wind and incoming tides were left stranded on the highway and townsite as the tides retreated (fig. 74) and the outgoing water, which was channeled beneath the bridges, eroded the approach fills and gullied the highway fill between the broken blocks of pavement.

Throughout the Portage area, and to the west along Turnagain Arm, local settling of the embankment into unconsolidated sediments, which themselves also underwent some unknown and variable amount of compaction, combined with the regional tectonic subsidence to lower the railroad grade (fig. 75). Adding the 5.49 feet of regional subsidence to local lowering due to compaction and settling in the Portage area generally lowered the grade about 8.5 to 9.5 feet; local dips were as much as 11.5 feet. The amount and distribution of lowering northwest of Portage, where repairs were made before the line was surveyed, are not so well known. The pre-and postearthquake top-of-rail profiles are compared in figure 75, and the total lowering of the grade is compared with the regional subsidence shown by lowering of bench marks on bedrock. Where apparent lowering was less than regional subsidence, the line had been regraded prior to the surveying; lowering in excess of regional subsidence was due to local settling and compaction. There may be errors in the survey, for at mile 80.77, where the grade and bench mark are both on bedrock, lowering exceeded regional subsidence.

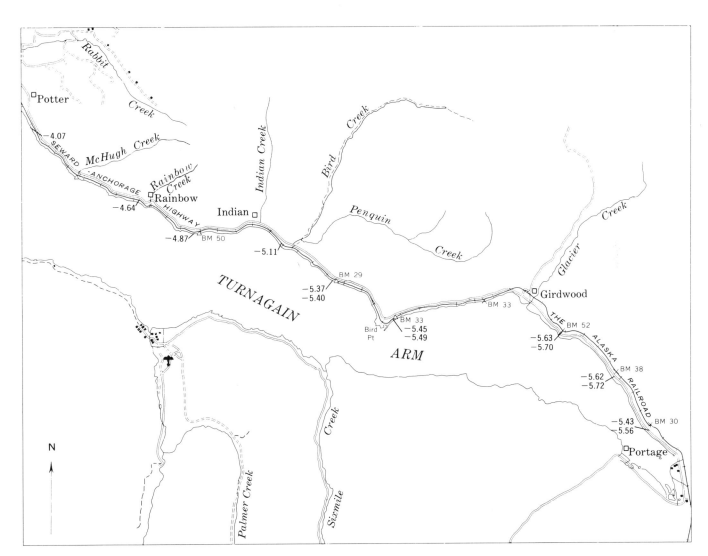

72.—The amount of lowering of bench marks on bedrock due to tectonic subsidence along Turnagain Arm, as determined by two U.S. Coast and Geodetic Survey level lines (Wood, 1966, p. 124). Single and top elevations were measured on a survey along the highway; bottom elevations east of Bird Creek were measured on a survey along the railroad.

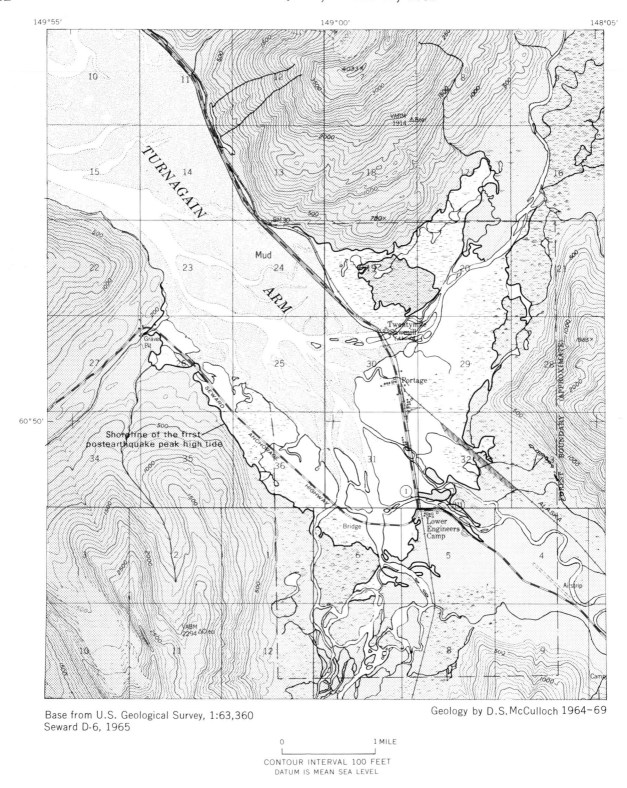

Base from U.S. Geological Survey, 1:63,360
Seward D-6, 1965

Geology by D.S.McCulloch 1964–69

0   1 MILE

CONTOUR INTERVAL 100 FEET
DATUM IS MEAN SEA LEVEL

73.—Shorelines of the preearthquake mean high water and the first postearthquake peak high tides in the Portage area. The postearthquake high-tide limit is drawn from photographs by Air Photo Tech, Inc., Anchorage.

When lowered, long sections of the embankment were submerged and subjected to erosion by swift tidal currents (fig. 76). These currents accompany the large diurnal tide range of as much as 33 feet (measured at Sunrise, U.S. Coast and Geod. Survey, 1964.) Grass-covered tide flats at the waters edge that had protected parts of the embankment were rapidly eaten away by the currents. Waves driven by the notoriously high winds that blow from the northwest up the arm also attacked the rail line west of mile 78, where it was not protected by the highway embankment. Winds of 80 to 100 miles per hour have been recorded here for periods of 3 hours or more, and winds of

74.—View south over Portage after the postearthquake high tide had left ice blocks strewn over the townsite and a small house stranded on the railroad embankment (at left).

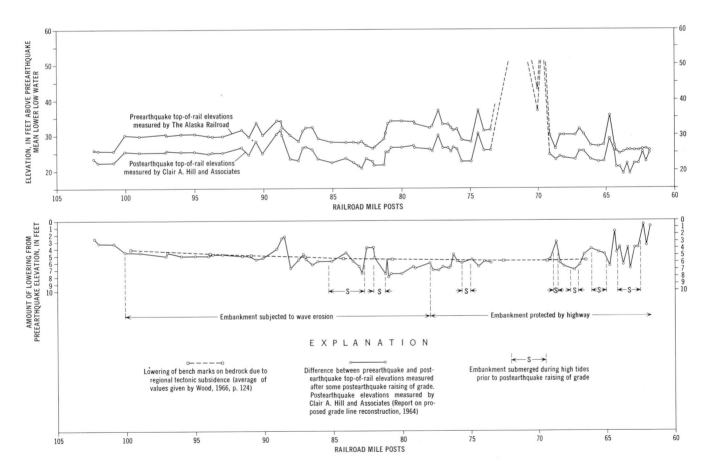

75.—A comparison of the as-built top-of-rail profile and the postearthquake top-of-rail profile from mile 62 to mile 102.5 along Turnagain Arm, and a comparison of the lowering of the rail line and bench marks on bedrock.

76.—Waves eroding the railroad embankment lowered by tectonic subsidence along Turnagain Arm. Photograph by The Alaska Railroad.

150 miles per hour have been observed for shorter periods (Clair A. Hill and Associates, "Report on proposed gradeline reconstruction" for The Alaska Railroad, Dec. 1964, 92 p.).

All along Turnagain Arm, railroad personnel waged a day-and-night battle to save the embankments from the late April high tides. They were fighting to keep the line open to Whittier from which material and provisions were brought for the repair and rebuilding in Anchorage. In all, 1,086,000 cubic yards of common fill were placed on this part of the line — some 200,000 cubic yards worked by off-track equipment, and 886,000 cubic yards hauled by train. The pressing need for fill necessitated using materials that would not have been used under normal circumstances. Just east of Bird Creek, bluffs of glacial till and outwash were mined with on-track equipment; outwash gravel west of Girdwood and talus aprons behind a small lagoon 1½ to 2 miles east of Bird Point were worked by off-track equipment. A new bedrock quarry was opened on Bird Point; it provided 865,000 cubic yards of rock to armor the embankment.

Plafker and Rubin (1967) have shown that there is clear and widespread evidence that tectonic subsidence occurred in zones that had previously been uplifted and depressed—that is, long before the 1964 earthquake. At Girdwood in Turnagain Arm (fig. 72), Karlstrom (1964, pl. 7) collected wood 2½ feet below the Girdwood datum (1953 high tide) that has a radiocarbon age of 700 ±250 years (W–175) and wood from a buried peat 15 below the Girdwood datum that has a radiocarbon age of 2,800 ±180 years (W–299). These dates suggest that this part of Turnagain Arm has been subsiding. There is, however, some evidence that sea level may have been somewhat higher with respect to the land in this area at a fairly recent time.

Linear elongate traces approximately parallel to the shoreline visible on preearthquake aerial photographs of the Portage area may be old shorelines cut during a period when sea level was relatively higher (fig. 103, p. D137). The postearthquake shoreline (fig. 73) lies along a section of this possible old shoreline at the south end of the arm, and lies inland but parallel to it east of the town of Portage. To the north, along the shore near and north of Potter Hill, old tide flats adjacent to steep wave-cut bluffs may have been elevated above high-tide level prior to the earthquake. Small stands of spruce and shrubs had established themselves on the flats (fig. 65) and water no longer reached the base of the wave-cut cliffs.

Alternatively, prograding may have caused the seaward displacement of the shorelines in both these areas. However, until the evidence is evaluated the possibility remains that sea level was recently relatively higher along this coast.

COST DISTRIBUTION OF DAMAGE

Damage to the railroad can be divided into five major categories, and the distribution of this damage, expressed as the geographic distribution of the cost, reflects the geologic control of the earthquake damage. In table 5, the cost per major category is shown for 10 geographic areas. The total cost of $22,300,880 given in table 5 is less than the full cost of the damage, which was approximately $26,-784,000. The difference includes the cost of new purchases, upgrading of equipment, and temporary repairs to docks, buildings, roadbed, and track. Not considered in this total cost is the loss of property, which in Seward alone is estimated to have been approximately 8.5 million dollars, the loss of income during the rehabilitation, and the loss of future freight haulage resulting from the development of Anchorage as an all-weather shipping port (Eckel, 1967).

TABLE 5.—Cost of damage to the railroad, by geographic distribution and category

[Cost figures from I. P. Cook, chief engineer, memorandum of Feb. 4, 1966. Progress report of earthquake repairs to Feb. 1, 1966; and F. Weeks, accountant. Disaster recovery projects expenditures, Dec. 31, 1966]

Area	Bridges and culverts (steel and wood)	Roadbed and track (fill, armor, new rail, realinement)	Slides (removal, regrading, land purchase)	Buildings and utilities	Port facilities (piers, yards, buildings)	Cost	
						Per area	Percent of total
Seward					10,900,053	10,900,053	48.88
Seward to Portage	941,158	763,961	59,096			1,764,215	7.91
Whittier		18,755			1,202,172	1,220,927	5.47
Whittier to Portage	21,626	302,946				324,572	1.45
Portage				71,515		71,515	0.32
Portage to Anchorage	247,416	4,121,976	977,599			5,346,991	23.98
Anchorage				1,927,796		1,927,796	8.64
Anchorage to Matanuska	142,645	277,342	99,893			519,880	2.33
Matanuska to Sutton	16,166		95,400			111,566	0.5
Matanuska to Fairbanks	89,183	24,132				113,315	0.5
Total	1,458,194	5,509,1.2	1,231,988	1,999,3.1	12,102,225	22,300,830	
Percent of total	6.54	24.70	5.52	8.96	54.27		

Damage in each of the major categories can be summarized as follows:

1. Bridges and culverts:
   (a) Steel bridges (work done on 52 bridges) _____ $497,892
       Reset 72 sets of span and bearings.
       Install new concrete piers and abutments.
       Reestablish two girder-span bridges.
       Repair 52 damaged piers and abutments on 15 bridges.
       Replace one concrete pier shaft.
       Encase broken concrete pier.
       Raise and install new concrete foundations on two bridges
           (elevate deck to clear tide water and ice).
       Install three new steel-span bridges on concrete piers and
           abutments to replace wood trestles.
   (b) Wood trestles (work done on 73 bridges—617 spans, or 9,255
           lineal ft) _____ $808,610
       Redrive or make major repairs to 648 wood pile bents.
       Replace stringers and decks on 273 spans (4,095 lineal ft).
       Fill in or replace with culverts 108 spans (1,620 lineal ft).
   (c) Culverts _____ $151,692
       Install 110 culverts to replace damaged culverts or filled-
           in bridges, or to accommodate drainage changes associated
           with land-level changes.
       An additional 65 culverts still to be repaired or replaced
           as of February 1966 (40 from Portage to Anchorage, 25
           from Anchorage to Matanuska).
           　　　　Total, bridges and culverts_____ $1,458,194

2. Roadbed and track:
   (a) Load, haul dump, and place the following fill:
       1,356,000 cu yd common material to restore approximately
           70 miles of track to original grade line south of Anchorage,
           and to raise grade above tidal reach along Turnagain
           Arm _____
       865,000 cu yd rock riprap to armor subgrade from marine
           erosion along Turnagain Arm_____
       58,000 cu yd common materials and rock to restore ap-
           proximately 8 miles of track to original grade line north of
           Anchorage and to protect grade from mile 146.5–148.5
           against tidal erosion_____
   (b) Place 130,000 cu yd crushed gravel ballast_____
   (c) Replace bent rail and shift rail to adjust expansion joints_____

           　　　　Total, roadbed and track_____ $5,509,112

3. Landslides:
   Damage includes debris removal, engineering studies, land purchase
       where necessary, temporary repairs, and final repairs. In Anchor-
       age, debris from several slides was removed. The slides crossed
       the tracks and damaged buildings and rolling stock.
           Rocky Creek delta, Kenai Lake_____ $59,096
           Potter Hill, mile 102–104_____ $977,599
           Mile 138–9_____ $99,893
           Sutton branch slides_____ $95,400

           　　　　Total, landslides_____ $1,231,988

4. Buildings and Utilities:
   (a) Anchorage (damage to these structures and utilities described
           in section 15, p. D143
           Replace office annex building_____ $300,433
           Replace wheel shop and mechanical offices building__ $381,724
           Replace east bay of car and coach shop_____ $621,624
           Repair heavy equipment-diesel repair shop and general
               repair shop_____ $206,775
           Repairs to various small buildings_____ $138,240

(b) Portage, section house and dormitory_____ $71, 515
(c) Utilities, repair and replace steam, water, sewer, and com-
    munications system_____ $279, 000

        Total, buildings and utilities_____ $1, 999, 311

5. Port facilities (includes docks, piers, associated buildings, and rail
    yards):
    (a) Seward
        Land acquisition and survey_____ $114, 499
        Dredge and build new pier_____ $8, 000, 000
        New transit shed_____ $260, 000
        New engine house_____ $304, 000
        Clear fill and construct new marshaling yards_____ $970, 000
        Underground utilities_____
        Total, Seward port facilities_____ $10, 900, 053

    (b) Whittier:
        Replace car barge slip_____ $545, 699
        Repair marginal wharf and transit shed_____ $399, 000
        Repair depot building _____
        Repair composite shop building_____
        Repair deck and approach of De Long pier_____
        Repair Hodge building (Kachadorian, 1965)_____

        Total, Whittier port facilities_____ $1, 202, 172

        Total, port facillities_____ $12, 102, 225

By far the most damage to the railroad was done on the fan deltas of Seward and Whittier, where slides, slide-generated and seismic seawaves, burning petroleum, ground cracking, and lateral displacement largely destroyed or damaged concentrated and expensive structures, rolling stock, and trackage. Although of great importance to the railroad, this damage is probably of less interest generally than the more widespread damage to bridges and culverts and to the roadbed and track, on flat or nearly flat areas, because the former is a specialized physiographic situation while the latter has applications to many areas.

In figure 77, the distribution of some of the damage is shown diagrammatically to emphasize the geologic control. Bridge and culvert damage (the uppermost graph) increased dramatically to the south, 83 percent of all such damage lying south of Anchorage. As shown in a preceding discussion and in the detailed descriptions of damage and geology later, this distribution is largely due to a combination of two circumstances: (1) South of Anchorage the rail line is built on several bedrock basins filled with young wet unconsolidated sediments, and (2) the seismic energy increased to the south.

Regional subsidence played the greatest role in controlling the cost of roadbed and track damage —75 percent of all such damage occurred in the section along Turnagain Arm. Again, nearly all such damage (95 percent) lay south of Anchorage, and, where not caused by regional subsidence, it was due to the mobilization of foundation materials and their attendant loss of bearing strength, surface cracking, and horizontal displacements. The lowermost graph (fig. 77) is an attempt to show the distribution of roadbed and track damage due solely to mobilization of foundation materials by eliminating that part of the cost resulting from regional subsidence of the roadbed along Turnagain Arm. In this graph the cost of armoring the grade with rock riprap and three-quarters of the cost of raising this 35-mile section of roadbed between 3 and 5 feet (total $3,700,000) have been removed. One-quarter of the cost of raising the grade has been maintained to allow for local settling. With this estimated adjustment, the distribution of roadbed and track damage resembles that of bridges and culverts, and reflects the geologic control and the distribution of the seismic energy.

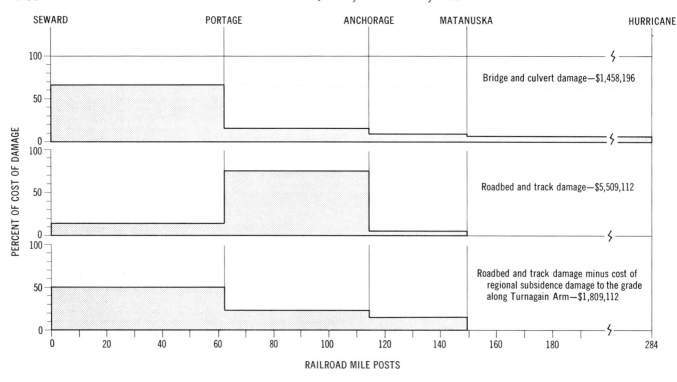

77.—Geographic distribution of the cost of the damage to bridges and culverts (top graph) and to roadbed and track (middle graph), Bridge and culvert damage increased to the south, toward the area of maximum strain release, but the cost of roadbed and track damage was greatest in the area of subsidence along Turnagain Arm. Eliminating costs due to regional subsidence (lower graph) shows that the roadbed and track damage also increased to the south, toward the area of maximum strain release.

SUMMARY AND CONCLUSIONS

THE EARTHQUAKE

The great 1964 Alaska earthquake consisted of a series of large discrete bursts of seismic energy released over a period of about 70 seconds. These were produced when a large part of the earth's crust beneath Prince William Sound and the adjacent land tore loose from the underlying mantle and was thrust southward up a gently dipping rupture surface. Epicenters of the discrete seismic events lie in a linear zone approximately 150 miles long that runs southwest from the first epicenter 80 miles east of Anchorage to about 40 miles southeast of Seward. This zone is subparallel to the rail line for about 150 miles. As a result, this portion of The

Alaska Railroad was subjected to a long period of severe ground motion. Timed strong ground motion lasted 3 to 4 minutes from Anchorage to Seward. This long duration of strong motion is three to four times that reported in other large earthquakes and was responsible for much of the damage that resulted from changes in natural foundation materials — changes that are time dependent and cumulative.

DAMAGE COST

The total cost of the damage to The Alaska Railroad including the loss of preearthquake facilities was in excess of $30,000,000. The total cost of rebuilding and repair, and some minor upgrading of

equipment, was $26,784,000. The cost was distributed among five major categories as follows: rebuilding port facilities at Seward and Whittier (54 percent), roadbed and track damage (25 percent), rebuilding and repair of buildings and utilities (9 percent), repair and replacement of bridges and culverts (7 percent), and landslide removal and repair (5 percent).

KINDS OF DAMAGE

The destructive agents that caused this damage took many forms. Landslides were dislodged from the edges of deltas on which the deepwater ports of Seward and Whittier are built. Portions of the railroad port facilities were carried away by the slides and most of the remaining facilities were overrun by extremely destructive seismic sea waves and waves generated by the slides. Landsliding also carried away a short section of track on Kenai Lake, and landslides overran and destroyed several miles of roadbed or damaged buildings and rolling stock at seven other localities. Regional tectonic subsidence of as much as 5½ feet made it necessary to raise and armor approximately 22 miles of roadbed that was made susceptible to marine erosion along Turnagain Arm. Most of the remaining damage — the damage to which this study is addressed — resulted from a general loss of strength in wet water-laid noncohesive granular sediments that allowed embankments to settle and enable the sediments to undergo flowlike displacements in a downslope direction, or more commonly toward topographic depressions, even on relatively flat surfaces. The term "landspreading" is proposed for these lateral displacements. Landspreading may have been due largely to liquefaction of the sediments. Failures produced by landspreading were extensive, sometimes affecting areas of several tens of square miles.

LANDSPREADING AND BRIDGE DAMAGE

The amount and direction of sediment displacement that occurred as a result of landspreading are clearly shown by the pattern of damage to the rail line, track, embankment, and bridges; by the damage to highway embankments, bridges, and utility pole lines; and by the patterns of associated ground cracks. Mobilization of the sediments appears to have been initiated at the edges of streams and other topographic depressions. As shaking continued, the width of the mobilized area increased; in some places it extended several hundreds, or as much as a thousand, feet away from the streambanks. The mobilized sediments moved streamward and produced zones of surface extension beside the streambanks in which railroad rails at right angles to the streams were pulled apart, railroad and highway embankments were broken by tension fractures on which there was horizontal separation, and telephone lines and powerlines were pulled taut. Bridge piles were carried toward the centers of the stream channels; although all piles were displaced streamward, the fact that distances between those near the bridge ends were usually increased suggests that the extension flow observed adjacent to the streambanks continued beneath the edges of the stream channels. In stream centers, the distances between piles were generally decreased, showing that the sediments had undergone compression. Piles and piers of railroad bridges were displaced with little or no vertical rotation — which indicates that flowage occurred to depths in excess of the pile depths. Displaced piles averaged less than 35 feet deep, but sediment displacements affected some piles driven as deeply as 125 feet. Streamward movement of the sediments was usually accompanied by some upward component of movement of the sediments under the stream channels that carried the central piles upward relative to piles near the ends. As a result, many bridges were arched upward in the center. The vertical displacements were independent of the length of pile penetration, which indicates that arching was due to flowage of the sediments rather than to differential compaction.

Bridge superstructures were subjected to compressive forces when streamward flow of the sediments decreased stream widths — by as much as 6½ feet. Compression was released as stringers drove into bulkheads and bulldozed up approach fills, or in more extreme cases, drove either entirely through or over the bulkheads into, or onto, the approach fills. Some deck stringers were buckled laterally and broken. Compression probably made little or no contribution to the upward displacement of piles or arching of the superstructure at stream centers because: (1) the connections between the superstructures and piles were commonly broken by lateral displacement of the piles, (2) even if the connections were not broken they were considerably weaker than the upward pull needed to overcome the skin friction of the outward-battered piles, and (3) arching due solely to pile displacement occurred in bridges in which there was no evidence for compression of the superstructure.

Movement of the unconsolidated sediments in flat-lying areas was directly toward the adjacent stream channel or topographic depression, as shown by the horizontal displacement of railroad and highway embankments and utility pole lines. As a result, bridges that crossed streams or even small gullies at an oblique angle were skewed horizontally as embankments on opposite sides of the stream were offset. The largest measured horizontal offset across a stream was 10 feet.

MODEL OF SEDIMENT DISPLACEMENTS

Sandbox models of a stream channel were made to examine the pattern of sediment displacement that occurs beneath stream channels during shaking. The sand used was rounded, well-sorted quartz of medium grain size (average diameter approximately 0.35 mm). Single and multiple horizontal layers and a vertical grid of 100-mesh carborundum powder were placed in the sand. The sand was saturated and compacted. Then water was withdrawn to the depth to which a flat-bottomed channel was cut. Water was again added until it covered the channel bottom, and the edges of the model were raised a few inches and dropped onto a table until visible surface deformation occurred. The model was drained and sectioned vertically, perpendicular to the channel, and the pre- and postshake positions of the horizontal layers and vertical grid were compared. During shaking the channel banks were lowered, and bank-to-bank distances decreased. Sediments moved toward the channel centers and produced zones of extension beside and under the edges of the channel, and sediments in the channel centers were compressed. Sediments also moved upward from considerable depth beneath the channels and raised channel floors to above the preshake positions. The displacements of sediments observed in the models are similar to those observed or inferred from field observations.

GROUND CRACKS CAUSED BY LANDSPREADING AND EMBANKMENTS

The large size of areas affected by landspreading was indicated by the ground cracks that occurred in patterns consistent with the orientation of probable stress fields that would be formed in the ground surface by movement of the underlying sediments toward streams or other topographic depressions. Cracks approximately parallel to streambanks resulted from nearly unidirectional stress on straight or concave streambanks. Cracks intersecting at 45° to 70°, and probably representing failure by shear, formed on convex banks where principal stress directions were parallel and perpendicular to the streambank. Cracks on small islands or on the insides of meander bends, where spreading was nearly radial and stress nearly omnidirectional, became orthogonal (rectilinear or curvilinear cracks with right-angle intersections). Ground cracks with these three patterns commonly occurred for widths of as much as several hundred feet, and in some places as much as 1,000 feet back from the edges of rivers and streams.

In areas of ground cracking attributed to landspreading on deltas, fans, and flood plains, ground cracks commonly radiated outward from the external corners of houses. These cracks also suggest that tension was generated in the ground surface, for stresses should be concentrated at the external corners of holes in sediments that are subjected to tension.

Lurching and shallow blockglide landsliding at or above stream bottoms, both commonly described in earthquakes, do not appear to have been important contributors to movement of sediment or to production of cracks at stream margins. If lurching or block-gliding had been important, the surface materials would have moved farther toward streams than the underlying materials. The generally close agreement between the amount of longitudinal compression of the bridge superstructures and the net horizontal compression of the underlying piles shows that the surface sediments were carried passively toward the streams, rather than undergoing independent movement.

A second principal type of ground cracking that affected the railroad was that generated where embankments settled into the underlying sediments. The cracks formed within embankment toes and in an adjacent zone several tens of feet wide on flood plains, tidal flats, deltas, and alluvial fans. Sediment-laden ground water was commonly ejected from the cracks. The cause of this cracking is not clear. It probably was not caused by horizontal block-gliding of the embankments, for the inertial force developed by embankments during horizontal acceleration is considerably smaller than the static, and far less than the dynamic tensile strength of the adjacent frozen sediments. It is suggested that the cracks formed as the result of stresses generated as the sinking embankments depressed the immediately adjacent frozen surface, while at some distance the surface was bulged upward by sediments displaced from beneath the embankments.

TRANSIENT HORIZONTAL COMPRESSION OF BRIDGES

Many bridges over a wide area were subjected to transient horizontal compression that pounded superstructures repeatedly against bulkheads and abutments. The transient compression appears to have started early in the shaking and to have persisted throughout the period of lateral displacement of the foundation materials. The force of the transient horizontal compression varied considerably, from bridges in which there was evidence of only minor pounding to a 105-foot wooden bridge, the deck of which was repeatedly arched from, and dropped back onto, its piles. The repetitive arching was recorded by multiple drift-pin holes punched into the pile tops. A minimum estimate of the compressive force on this bridge (treating the deformation as static, rather than dynamic) ranges from about 255,000 to 200,000 pounds for initial arches of 1 to 40 inches; the force delivered to the bulkhead by the embankment ranges from about 23 to 18 pounds per square inch for this same range of initial arching. The rate at which pounding occurred probably varied considerably. At one bridge a series of dents made by a falling pebble that was repeatedly caught between pounding bridge members indicates that the transient compression had a rate of between 2 and 7 cycles per second.

HORIZONTAL BRIDGE ACCELERATIONS

Evidence for high horizontal accelerations in bridges is made ambiguous by similar damage that resulted from compression produced by streamward movement of foundation materials. However, at one wooden bridge where the stringers appear to have been driven rapidly through the bulkhead timbers, the force needed to overcome the static resistance to penetration of the bulkhead timbers is approximately an order of

magnitude larger than the force needed to produce Coulomb failure of the fill behind the bulkhead. It is suggested, therefore, that penetration may have been rapid and that resistance was offered principally by the inertia, rather than by the shearing strength, of the fill. The minimum horizontal acceleration of the bridge deck needed to produce rapid penetration (using the dynamic strength of the bulkhead timbers and the superstructure deadweight) would have been between about 1.1 to 1.7 g. It is suggested that the high acceleration is the result of amplification of ground motion by the bridge structure.

EMBANKMENT DAMAGE

Embankments suffered four general types of damage. Approximately half the cost of all embankment damage resulted from the necessity of raising and armoring about 22 miles of embankment along Turnagain Arm where regional tectonic subsidence of about 4 to 5½ feet, consolidation of tidal sediments beneath the rail line, and sinking of the embankment into the underlying sediments exposed the embankment to erosion by waves and swift tidal currents.

Second most important kind of embankment damage were those failures (called active failures) in which the weight of the embankment and the shaking produced a loss of bearing strength, flowage, and high pore-water pressures within the underlying and adjacent sediments into which the embankment fills sank nearly en masse. Sinking of several feet was common and at many places was accompanied by the expulsion of sediment-laden water from embankment-generated ground cracks. Local extreme settlement

occurred where ejected sediment volumes were large. Settlements (and the associated embankment-generated ground cracks) were largest and most extensive in areas where there was evidence of landspreading. However, the fact that settlement and the associated cracking also occurred in areas where there was no such evidence suggests that the fill produced the mobilization of the underlying materials. Settlement was nearly universal in areas underlain by wet unconsolidated young waterlaid noncohesive sediments on flood plains, deltas, tide flats, and alluvial fans.

Landspreading was the third greatest cause of damage. This damage (called passive failure) included lateral and longitudinal displacement and cracking of the embankment as the underlying sediments moved toward lakes, gullies, abandoned river channels, borrow pits, streams, and marine shorelines. Sections of embankments more than 1,000 feet long were displaced as much as several feet horizontally, and, as noted previously, embankments that crossed streams obliquely were offset on opposite sides of the streams. Radial downhill spreading on deltas and alluvial fans produced passive failures that carried the rail line downslope several feet and subjected it to tension which broke the embankment and pulled rails apart endways.

Of least importance were failures entirely within the embankment fills (called fill failures). The infrequency of this type of failure may have been largely due to the presence of interstitial ice in the frozen embankments that afforded additional shear strength to the fill materials.

BRIDGE DAMAGE AS RELATED TO GRAIN SIZE AND THICKNESS OF SEDIMENTS

The severity of damage to many similar bridges was compared with the grain size of the material in which the piles were embedded and the total thickness of the unconsolidated sediments at each bridge site. Foundations of bridges on till or bedrock were not displaced. Bridges on young unconsolidated wet water-laid noncohesive sediments suffered increasing damage as the grain size of the embankment material decreased. However, a stronger correlation was found between the severity of the damage and the total thickness of the underlying unconsolidated sediments. It is suggested that the difference in the propensity for mobilization, probably controlled by the grain size of the pile-embedment material, was less important in controlling the amount of damage than the severity and duration of ground motion which are related to the total sediment thickness.

Limited standard penetrometer data for two areas show that away from the area of maximum seismic strain energy release (that is, the belt generally defined by the epicenters of the multiple seismic events that occurred during the earthquake) foundation displacements occurred in sediments classified as slightly compact to compact, whereas closer to the area of maximum strain release more severe displacements occurred even in denser sediments classified as compact to dense.

GEOLOGIC CONTROLS OF DAMAGE

The geographic distribution of the severity of the ground response and the degree of mobilization that occurred in geologic materials beneath many miles of the railroad line are grossly reflected by the geographic distribution of the cost of repairs to the roadbed and track and the bridges and culverts. If expenditures arising from regional tectonic subsidence are omitted (raising and armoring the grade along Turnagain Arm), the costs of both of these types of damage increase dramatically to the south, that is, toward the area of maximum strain release.

When the distribution of these and other kinds of damage (especially those caused by landspreading) is considered in more detail (as it is on p. D98–D158), it is apparent that the local geology and physiography strongly controlled the kind, the distribution, and the severity of the damage. This point merits considerable emphasis, for it provides a basis for predicting the kinds and severity of damage and ground response that should be expected in these and similar areas in large earthquakes. Surficial geologic-physiographic maps made for most of the rail belt along which there was damage show that only a few easily distinguishable geologic-physiographic units need be mapped to isolate areas of damage. These units and the related damage sustained are as follows:

1. Bedrock and glacial till on bedrock.— Embankments and open wooden trestle bridges on wood piles were undamaged. Steel superstructures on bridges were either unmoved or slightly shifted (often with a rocking motion) on piers and abutments. There were no permanent displacements of piers, piles, or abutments, no ground cracking, and no evidence of landspreading. Limited observations of damage to buildings and the shifting of steel bridge superstructures suggest that ground motion was relatively strong, especially toward the area of maximum strain release.

2. Glacial outwash terraces. — There was little or no damage to the railroad on glacial outwash terraces which were undissected, were well drained, and had a water table well below the surface, or which consisted of relatively thin deposits lying on till or bedrock. Embankment settlement, ground cracking, and landspreading — especially along terrace margins that abut lower modern flood plains—increased as the height of the outwash terrace surface decreased to that of the flood plain and as the water table approached the surface. These relationships are clearly shown by the fact that there was less severe damage on glacial outwash terraces close to the area of maximum strain release than on glacial outwash terraces considerably farther away (Knik and Matanuska River valleys, 40 miles northeast of Anchorage), where there was a relatively thick section of unconsolidated sediments (probably well in excess of 200 ft), a shallow water table (about a 10-ft maximum depth), and considerable dissection by stream channels.

3. Inactive flood plains.—Landspreading and its associated ground cracking, and lateral displacement, settlement, and embankment-generated ground cracks were severe on inactive flood plains that lay adjacent to

lower active flood plains or other topographically lower areas. Farther from topographically low areas landspreading largely disappeared, but almost universally there was settlement of embankments accompanied by embankment-generated ground cracks and the expulsion of ground water. Landspreading also decreased as the depth to underlying bedrock or till decreased.

4. Active flood plains.—As the rail line passed from areas underlain by till or bedrock onto adjacent valley floors, the active flood-plain sediments, being closest to the modern stream channels and generally lying at or within a few feet of the ground-water table, were the first to show evidence of a general loss of strength and flowage by landspreading. Thus all the associated damage caused by ground cracking, lateral displacement, settlement, and the ejection of ground water was most extreme in these areas. Even within these most unstable sediments, there is an obvious increase in the damage with increasing depth to till or bedrock.

5. Fan deltas.—Damage on alluvial fans was similar to that on deltas in many respects, the major difference being that landslides commonly occurred at delta margins. These two units are mapped together because tidewater or lakes commonly lie close to mountains along the rail belt, and the distal parts of many alluvial fans are deltaic where deposited in water. Mobilized sediments spread radially downslope on fans and deltas. Railroad embankments were carried as much as 4 feet down-

slope and were broken by tension fractures; rails were pulled apart endways and the wires on utility poles were pulled taut. Spreading extended to some depth and increased distances between piling driven as deeply as 30 feet under railroad bridges that were pulled apart longitudinally. Radial downhill spreading also produced a fringe of ground cracks at fan and delta margins. Cracks were orthogonal (common on low-slope deltas where spreading was omnidirectional) or shear fractures intersecting at about 45° to 70° (on fans and steeper deltas where principal stresses were oriented downslope and parallel to the fan or delta margin). Cracking of the fringe of fans and deltas appears to be related to the depth to the ground-water table. For example, ground water was commonly ejected only from cracks at the downslope edge of the cracked fringe. The fact that cracking extended only a short distance upslope from the cracks that expelled ground water suggests that when the water table exceeds some critical depth below the surface, the sediments do not undergo sufficient mobilization and landspreading to generate cracking surface stress. However, upslope of the cracked fringe, railroad embankments did produce mobilization, usually underwent settlement, and usually generated cracks from which additional sediment-laden water was ejected. Additional ground cracks that expelled ground water were formed on flood plains, just beyond the toes of the fans. These cracks were irregular but generally were parallel to radii of the fan.

PRINCIPAL GEOLOGIC CONTROLS OF DAMAGE

The foregoing observations can be generalized by defining six principal geologic controls on the damage produced primarily by the mobilization of natural materials. Arranged in decreasing order of apparent importance these are:

1. The difference in foundation materials.— In areas of exposed till and bedrock, there was no damage, and in areas of young unconsolidated water-laid noncohesive sediments, all mobilization damage occurred.

2. The total thickness of the sediments.— Other things being equal, damage increased dramatically with sediment thickness. For example, damage to railroad bridges was slight on sediments less than 50 feet thick, moderate on sediments 50 to 100 feet thick, and severe where sediments were more than 100 feet thick.

3. The depth of the ground-water table beneath the surface.— In the most severely damaged areas the water table probably was about 10 feet or less beneath the surface.

4. The distance to a topographically lower area.— The amount of lateral spreading increased toward stream channels, gullies, borrow pits, or adjacent lower terraces.

5. The slope of the ground surface. — Steeper slopes, such as those on deltas and fans have a greater propensity for spreading.

6. The proximity to the area of maximum strain release.— The closer to the source of the seismic energy, the stronger was the ground motion.

CONSTRUCTION IN AREAS OF POTENTIAL LANDSPREADING

There was a general pattern to the deformation of a wide textural range of granular sediments during the earthquake. Thus some general recommendations may be made concerning construction in areas underlain by granular sediments where safety demands, and economics permit, the building of structures that are to survive a large earthquake with minimal damage. It would be ideal to avoid problem sites for schools and hospitals, for pumping, generating, fire, and radio stations, and for all other structures that involve public safety or public investment. Unfortunately this option is not always available, and thus the following recommendations are offered to reduce damage in these areas:

1. Structures that cannot withstand distention or cracking of their foundations (or foundation materials) should be built where landspreading is least likely to occur — well away from topographically low areas, where the water table is well below the surface and where the unconsolidated sediments are thinnest, or where depth to bedrock is least.

2. Landspreading may be reduced by the elimination of surface depressions; however, this may not eliminate landspreading because some occurred toward filled channels. Conversely, artificial waterways or other artificial depressions may increase landspreading.

3. The practice of side-borrowing to build embankments promoted lateral displacement and should be avoided.

4. Narrow linear fills (railroad and highway), although well compacted, should be expected to settle and form ground cracks for a width of several tens of feet on either side of the embankment, both within and outside of the area of landspreading.

5. Narrow railroad fills settled largely en masse. In wider highway fills, the outward flow of sediments was greater from under the edges than the center, with the result that the edges of the highway fills were lowered in relation to the middle, and tension failures occurred down the embankment centerlines. Thus, in a given area subjected to a given earthquake, there is some finite width of embankment or fill from under which the underlying materials have time to flow. Accordingly structures that are placed on wider fills and kept well back from the edges of the fills, will stand less chance of being damaged by this sort of failure. However, even wider fills will be subject to ground cracking in areas of landspreading and to lowering by the compaction of the underlying materials.

6. The width of the zone of embankment-generated ground cracks (commonly several tens of feet wide on either side of the embankments) is more than doubled beside adjacent parallel fills. Thus, if such fills were combined into a single fill, the width of the cracked zone (and the width of sediments mobilized by the fills) probably would be substantially reduced.

7. Utilities buried within or adjacent to linear fills will probably be subjected to tension and compression resulting from differential settlement of the fills or to shear in the zone of embankment-generated ground cracking. In such areas, damage may be substantially reduced by decoupling utilities from the ground.

8. Because ground cracks commonly radiate away from the corners of buildings in areas where there is landspreading, damage to buried utilities, paved walks, and driveways may be reduced if they are not placed close to building corners.

9. Given the option, the toes of alluvial fans and deltas, which were severely fractured, and on which radial downhill spreading was marked, might be avoided. If such areas must be crossed, the older, higher, better drained upper segments of fans and deltas will probably be more stable.

10. Adjacent to topographic lows and the lower parts of fans and deltas where landspreading might occur, damage to pipelines and similar structures might be minimized if the structures are built on the surface and if some provision such as the use of expansion loops is made to accommodate longitudinal tension.

11. Similar provisions in structures at the edges of stream channels (or other topographically low areas) would accommodate both the compression that develops as streambanks moved closer together and the horizontal skewing that usually accompanies compression.

12. Culverts beneath embankment fills were subjected to crushing loads where landspreading displaced foundation materials toward streams and even shallow drainage ditches. Such loads might be anticipated in culvert design.

13. Bridge construction. Although the following recommendations are based on observations of damage to Alaskan bridges, some of these construction details have already been incorporated in the design of existing bridges in Japan and the United States (Eng. News-Record, 1945; Japan Soc. Civil Engineers, 1960, p. 95-104).

(a) Single spans supported only on the ends would avoid arching due to the differential vertical displacement of foundation materials that drives piling upward under the centers of bridges.

(b) Longitudinal compression (commonly 20 inches but as much as 6½ feet) of superstructures could be accommodated by wide abutment-bearing surfaces that support telescoping end sections and by bridge bearings that will allow considerable end travel.

(c) If several spans are used and the spans are simply butted at the piers or bents and have no through-going structural member, spans could be kept from falling by safety connections that join the spans together. The Alaska Railroad has installed such safety links on some of its bridges since the earthquake.

(d) Many highway bridges built with multiple concrete deck sections that butted on wood pile bents were destroyed when deck sections lost their end bearings and fell, sometimes becoming impaled on piles driven through the concrete decks. By contrast, almost every adjacent wooden railroad bridge, all of which have continuous superstructures and more closely spaced piles to carry heavier transient loads, could, and in some places did, carry auto traffic after the earthquake—despite the fact that the piling in these bridges had undergone considerable longitudinal displacement. The addition of through-going structural members to the superstructure, and an increased number of more heavily braced bents that would maintain their integrity and therefore their support of the superstructure, would probably have permitted use of many highway bridges after the earthquake.

(e) Provision for longitudinal movement of the tops of piers and piles beneath superstructures should prevent their being tilted as their bases are displaced by streamward movement of the foundation materials. Concrete piers held stationary at their tops were commonly rotated inward at the base and broken at the ground line; many wood pile bents were torn loose from their pile caps and thus escaped rotation and breaking.

(f) Lateral skewing of bridges, which was common and as large as 10 feet, could be avoided or reduced by crossing water courses or other topographically low areas parallel to the direction in which streambank sediments are likely to move. This direction is generally at right angles to the stream course.

(g) Concrete piers were broken along joints between successive pours. Careful attention should be given to such joints during construction.

REFERENCES CITED

Adams, A. L., Marx, C.D., Wing, C. B., Moore, C. E., Hyde, C. G., Gilman, C. E., Dillman, G. L., Riffle, F., and Harroun, P. E., 1907, Report of committee on the effect of the earthquake on water-works structures: Am. Soc. Civil Engineers Proc., v. 33, no. 3, p. 336–346.

Barnes, F. F., 1943, Geology of the Portage Pass area, Alaska: U.S. Geol. Survey Bull. 926–D, p. 211–235.

Berg, Edward, 1966, Fundamental and applied research in seismology in Alaska: Alaska Univ. Geophy. Inst., [rept.] ser. UAG R–179, 44 p.

Berg, G. V., and Stratta, J. L., 1964, Anchorage and the Alaska earthquake of March 27, 1964: New York, Am. Iron and Steel Inst., 83 p.

Cedarstrom, D. J., Trainer, F. W., and Waller, R. M., 1964, Geology and ground-water resources of the Anchorage area, Alaska: U.S. Geol. Survey Water-Supply Paper 1773, 108 p.

Chance, Genie, 1966. Chronology of physical events of the Alaskan earthquake: Prepared under a National Science Foundation Grant to the University of Alaska. Copyright by Genie Chance, 1966. 173 p.

Cloud, W. K., 1967, Strong-motion and building-period measurements, in Wood, F. J., ed., 1967, Research studies—seismology and marine geology, engineering seismology, v. 2, pt. 4, of The Prince William Sound, Alaska, earthquake of 1964 and aftershocks: U.S. Coast and Geod. Survey Pub. 10–3, p. 319–331.

Cooper, H. H., Jr., Bredehoeft, J. D., Papadopulos, I. S., and Bennett, R. R., 1965. The response of well aquifer systems to seismic waves; Jour Geophys. Research, v. 70, no. 16, p. 3915–3926.

Coulter, H. W., and Migliaccio. R. R., 1966, Effects of the earthquake of March 27, 1964, at Valdez, Alaska: U.S. Geol. Survey Prof. Paper 542–C, p. Cl–C36.

Duke, C. M., 1960, Foundations and earth structures in earthquakes: World Conf. Earthquake Eng., 2d, Toyko and Kyoto, Japan, 1960, Proc., v. 1, p. 435–455.

Eaton, J. P., and Takasaki, K. J., 1959, Seismological interpretation of earthquake-induced water-level fluctuations in wells [Hawaii]: Seismol. Soc. America Bull., v. 49, no. 3, p. 227–245.

Eckel, E. B., 1967, Effects of the earthquake of March 27, 1964, on air and water transport, communications, and utilities systems in south-central Alaska: U.S. Geol. Survey Prof. Paper 545–B, p. B1–B27.

Engineering News-Record, 1945, Deck-girder railroad bridge has earthquake-resistant features: Eng. News-Record, v. 134, no. 4, p. 120–121.

Fisher, W. E., and Merkle, W. E., 1965, The Great Alaska earthquake: U.S. Air Force Weapons Lab. Tech. Rept. AFWL–TR–65–92, v. 2, 312 p.

Foster, H. L., and Karlstrom, T. N. V., 1967, Ground breakage and associated effects in the Cook Inlet area, Alaska, resulting from the March 27, 1964, earthquake: U.S. Geol. Survey Prof. Paper 543–F, p. F1–F28.

Fuller, M. L., 1912, The New Madrid earthquake: U.S. Geol. Survey Bull. 494, 119 p.

Grantz, Arthur, Plafker, George, and Kachadoorian, Reuben, 1964, Alaska's Good Friday earthquake, March 27, 1964, a preliminary geologic evaluation: U.S. Geol. Survey Circ. 491, 35 p.

Gutenberg, Beno, 1957, Effects of ground on earthquake motion: Seismol. Soc. America Bull., v. 47, no. 3, p. 221–250.

Hansen, W. R., 1965, Effects of the earthquake of March 27, 1964, at Anchorage, Alaska: U.S. Geol. Survey Prof. Paper 542–A, p. A1–A68.

Hansen, W. R., and other, 1966, The Alaska earthquake, March 27, 1964—Field investigations and reconstruction effort: U.S. Geol. Survey Prof. Paper 541, 111 p.

Hobbs, W. H., 1908, A study of the damage to bridges during earthquakes: Jour. Geology, v. 16, p. 636–653.

Hollis, E. P., 1958, Bibliography of engineering seismology, 2d ed.: San Francisco, Calif., Earthquake Eng. Research Inst., 144 p.

Inglis, C. E., 1913, Stresses in a plate due to the presence of cracks and sharp corners: Royal Inst. Naval Architecture Trans., v. 55, p. 219–241.

Japan Society of Civil Engineers, 1960, Bridge on earthquake engineering, in Earthquake resistant design for civil engineering structures, earth structures and foundations in Japan: Japan Soc. Civil Engineers, Bridge and Structural Comm., p. 73–106.

Jordan, D. S., 1906, The earthquake rift of 1906: Popular Sci. Monthly, v. 69, no. 19, p. 289–309.

Kachadoorian, Reuben, 1965, Effects of the earthquake of March 27, 1964, at Whittier, Alaska: U.S. —Geol. Survey Prof. Paper 542–B, p. B1–B21.

——— 1968, Effects of the Alaskan earthquake, March 27, 1964, on the Alaskan highway system: U.S. Geol. Survey Prof. Paper 543–C, p. C1–C66.

Karlstrom, T. N. V., 1964, Quarternary geology of the Kenai Lowland and glacial history of the Cook Inlet region, Alaska: U.S. Geol. Survey Prof. Paper 443, 69 p.

Lachenbruch, A. H., 1962, Mechanics of thermal contraction cracks and ice-wedge polygons in permafrost: U.S. Geol. Soc. America Spec. Paper 70, 69 p.

Lawson, A. C., and others, 1908, The California earthquake of April 18, 1906—Report of the State Earthquake Investigation Commission: Carnegie Inst. Washington Pub. 87, v. 1, pt. 2, p. 255–451.

Leggette, R. M., and Taylor, G. H., 1935, Earthquake instrumentally recorded in artesian wells: Seismol. Soc. America Bull., v. 25, no. 2. p. 169–175.

Lemke, R. W., 1967, Effects of the earthquake of March 27, 1964, at Seward, Alaska: U.S. Geol. Survey Prof. Paper 542–E, p. E1–E43.

Logan, M. H., 1967, Effect of the earthquake of March 27, 1964, on the Eklutna Hydroelectric Project, Anchorage, Alaska, *with a section on* Television examination of earthquake damage to underground communication and electrical systems in Anchorage, by Lynn R. Burton: U.S. Geol. Survey Prof. Paper 545–A, p. A1–A30.

McCulloch, D. S., 1966, Slide-induced waves, seiching, and ground fracturing caused by the earthquake of March 27, 1964, at Kenai Lake, Alaska: U.S. Geol. Survey Prof. Paper 543–A, p. A1–A41.

McCulloch, D. S., and Bonilla, M. G., 1967. Railroad damage in the Alaska earthquake: Am. Soc. Civil Engineers Proc. Paper 5423, Jour. Soil Mechanics Found. Div., v. 93, pt. 1, no. SM5, p. 89–100.

Mellor, Malcolm, 1968, Avalanches: U.S. Army Cold Regions Research and Engineering Laboratory, Hanover, N.H., CRSE III–A3d, DA Project 1V025001A130, 215 p.

Miller, R. D., and Dobrovolny, Ernest, 1959, Surficial geology of Anchorage and vicinity, Alaska: U.S. Geol. Survey Bull. 1093, 128 p.

Newmark, N.M., 1965, Effects of earthquakes on dams and embankments: Géotechnique, v. 15, no. 2, p. 139–160.

Oldham, R. D., 1899, Report on the great earthquake of 12th June 1897: India Geol. Survey Mem. 29, p. 1–379.

Oldham, Thomas, 1882, The Cachar earthquake of 10th January, 1869, edited by R. D. Oldham: India Geol. Survey Mem., v. 19, 89 p.

Parkin, E. J., 1966, Horizontal displacements, pt. 2 *of* Alaskan surveys to determine crustal movement: U.S. Coast and Geodetic Survey, 11 p.

Parmelee. R. A.. Penzien, J., Scheffey, C. F., Seed, H. B., and Thiers, G. R., 1964, Seismic effects on structures supported on piles extending through deep sensitive clays: California Univ. (Berkeley) Inst. Eng.

Research, Dept. Civil Eng. Rept. SESM 64–2 to California Div. Highways, 81 p., app. A–D.

Peck, R. B., 1967, Analysis of soil liquefaction—Niigata earthquake, a discussion [of paper by H. B. Seed and I. M. Idress] Am. Soc. Civil Engineers Proc., Jour. Soil Mechanics Found. Div., v. 93, no. SM5, p. 365–366.

Plafker, George, 1965, Tectonic deformation associated with the 1964 Alaskan earthquake: Science, v. 148, no. 3678, p. 1675–1687.

——— 1968, Tectonics of the 1964 Alaska earthquake: U.S. Geol. Survey Prof. Paper 543–I. (In press.)

Plafker, George, and Rubin, Meyer, 1967, Vertical tectonic displacements in south-central Alaska during and prior to the great 1964 earthquake: Osaka City Univ. Jour. Geosciences, v. 10, art. 1–7, p. 1–14.

Press, Frank, and Jackson, David, 1965, Alaskan earthquake, 27 March 1964—Vertical extent of faulting and elastic strain energy release: Science, v. 147, no. 3660, p. 867–868.

Railbelt Reporter, 1964, [The Alaska Railroad, Anchorage, Alaska], v. 12, no. 3, p. 3–7.

Reimnitz, Erk, and Marshall, N. F., 1965, Effects of the Alaskan earthquake and tsunami on recent deltaic sediments: Jour. Geophys. Reserach, v. 70, no. 10, p. 2363–2376.

Scholten, J. A., 1966, Resistance of wood and plywood to embedment of fastener heads: Madison, Wisc., Forest Products Lab. (in coop. with Naval Ship Systems Command), U.S. Forest Service Research Paper, 7 p.

Seed, H. B., 1967, Slope stability during earthquakes: Am. Soc. Civil Engineers Proc. (Paper 5319), Jour. Soil Mechanics Found. Div., v. 93, no. SM4, p. 299–323.

Seed, H. B., and Idress, I. M., 1967, Analysis of soil liquefaction—Niigata earthquake: Am. Soc. Civil Engineers Proc. (Paper 5233), Jour. Soil Mechanics Found. Div., v. 93, no. SM3, p. 83–108.

Seed, H. B., and Martin, G. R., 1966, The seismic coefficient in earth dam design: Am. Soc. Civil Engineers Proc. (Paper 4284), Jour. Soil Mechanics Found. Div., v. 92, no. SM3, p. 25–58.

Shannon and Wilson, Inc., 1964a, Report on Anchorage area soil studies, Alaska, to U.S. Army Engineer,

Anchorage District, Alaska: Seattle, Wash., 109 p., app. A–K, 104 p.

Shannon and Wilson, Inc., 1964b, Report on subsurface investigation for city of Seward, Alaska, and vicinity, to U.S. Army Engineer District, Anchorage, Alaska; Seattle, Wash., 38 p.

Shiraishi, Shunta, 1968, Effects of Japan's Tokachioki earthquake of May 1968: Civil Eng., v. 38, no. 8, p. 101.

Smith, C. P., 1965, Highway destruction in Alaska: Am. Highways, v. 43 (Jan. 1965), p. 23–29.

Stauder, William, and Bollinger, G. A., 1966, The focal mechanism of the Alaskan earthquake of March 28, 1964, and its aftershock sequence: Jour. Geophys. Research, v. 71, no. 22, p. 5283–5296.

Steinbrugge, K. V., and Bush. V. R., 1960, Earthquake experience in North America, 1950–1959: World Conf. Earthquake Eng., 2d, Tokyo and Kyoto, Japan, 1960, Proc., v. 1, p. 381–396.

Steinbrugge, K. V., and Moran, D. F., 1956, Damage caused by the earthquakes of July 6 and August 23, 1954: Seismol. Soc. America Bull., v. 46, no. 1, p. 15–33.

Taylor, D. W., 1948, Fundamentals of soil mechanics: New York, John Wiley and Sons, Inc., 700 p.

Trainer, F. W., 1953, Preliminary report on the geology and ground-water resources of the Matanuska Valley agricultural area, Alaska: U.S. Geol. Survey Circ. 268, 43 p.

——— 1960, Geology and ground-water resources of the Matanuska Valley agricultural area, Alaska: U.S. Geol. Survey Water-Supply Paper 1494, 116 p.

——— 1961, Eolian deposits of the Matanuska agricultural area. Alaska: U.S. Geol. Survey Bull. 1121–C, p. C1–C35.

U.S. Army Corps of Engineers, Frost Effects Laboratory, 1952, Investigation of description, classification, and strength properties of frozen soils: U.S. Army Snow Ice and Permafrost Research Establishment, SIPRE Rept. 8, v. 1, 88 p.

U.S. Coast and Geodetic Survey, 1964, Tide tables—High and low water predictions, 1964, West Coast, North and South America including Hawaiian Islands: U.S. Coast and Geod. Survey, 224 p.

Wahrhaftig, Clyde, and Black, R. F., 1958, Engineering geology along part of The Alaska Railroad: U.S. Geol. Survey Prof. Paper 293–B, p. 69–118.

Wallace, J. H., Phillips, H. C., Drake, R. M., and Boggs, E. M., 1907, Report of the committee on the effect of the earthquake on railway structures: Am. Soc. Civil Engineers Proc., v. 33, no. 3, p. 349–353.

Waller, R. M., 1966, Effects of the March 1964 Alaska earthquake on the hydrology of south-central Alaska: U.S. Geol. Survey Prof. Paper 544–A, 28 p.

Wilson, B. W., and Tørum, Alf, 1967, Engineering damage from the tsunami of the Alaskan earthquake of March 27, 1964: U.S. Army Corps Engineers, Report prepared for Coastal Eng. Research Center. 422 p.

Wood, F. J., ed.-in-chief, 1966, The Prince William Sound, Alaska, earthquake of 1964 and aftershocks, v. 1: U.S. Coast and Geod. Survey.c. Pub. 10–3, 263 p.

Wyss, Max and Brune, J. N., 1967, The Alaska earthquake of 28 March 1964—A complex multiple rupture: Seismol. Soc. America Bull., v. 57, no. 5, p. 1017–1023.

CLARIFICATIONS

Geology Vol. Page	USGS Page	Column	Line	Remarks
591	D 49	1	13	Plate 1 is Plate R in Part B, the accompanying map case
596	D 54	3	8	Plates 2 and 3 are Plates S and T, respectively, in Part B, the accompanying map case
616	D 74	1	29	Plate 4 is Plate U in Part B, the accompanying map case

REUBEN KACHADOORIAN
U.S. GEOLOGICAL SURVEY

Reprinted with minor changes fron
U.S. Geological Survey Professional Paper 545-C,
"Effects of the Earthquake of March 27, 1964, on the Alaska Highway System"

Effects on the Alaska Highway System

ABSTRACT

The great earthquake that struck Alaska about 5:36 p.m., Alaska standard time, Friday, March 27, 1964 (03:36:13.0, Greenwich mean time, March 28, 1964), severely crippled the highway system in the south-central part of the State. All the major highways and most secondary roads were impaired. Damage totaled more than $46 million, well over $25 million to bridges and nearly $21 million to roadways. Of the 204 bridges in south-central Alaska, 141 were damaged; 92 were severely damaged or destroyed. The earthquake damaged 186 of the 830 miles of roadway in south-central Alaska, 83 miles so severely that replacement or relocation was required.

Earthquake damage to the roadways and bridges was chiefly by (1) seismic shaking, (2) compaction of fills as well as the underlying sediments, (3) lateral displacement of the roadway and bridges, (4) fractures, (5) landslides, (6) avalanches, (7) inundation by seismic sea waves, (8) scouring by seismic sea waves, (9) regional tectonic subsidence, causing inundation and erosion by high tides in subsided areas.

The intensity of damage was controlled primarily by the geologic environment (including the depth of the water table) upon which the highway structures rested, and secondarily by the engineering characteristics of the structures. Structures on bedrock were only slightly damaged if at all, whereas those on unconsolidated sediments were slightly to severely damaged, or were completely destroyed by seismic shaking. The low-lying areas underlain by saturated sediments, such as the Snow River Crossing and Turnagain Arm sections of the Seward-Anchorage Highway, were the most severely damaged stretches of the highway system in south-central Alaska. At Snow River and Turnagain Arm, the sediments underlying the roadway are fine grained and the water table is shallow. These factors were responsible for the intense damage along this stretch of the highway.

All the bridges on the Copper River Highway except for one on bedrock were damaged by seismic shaking. Lateral displacement of sediments toward a free face, which placed the bridges in compression, was the chief cause for the damage. This type of failure was extensive and widespread throughout the highway system.

The chief engineering characteristics responsible for the type and intensity of damage include (1) thickness of roadway fills, (2) type of pile bents and masonry piers, (3) the weight ratio between the substructure and superstructure, and (4) the tie between the substructure and superstructure.

The thicker the roadway fills, the more severe the damage. Wood piles did not break as extensively as piles constructed of three railroad rails welded together. Bridges that had relatively heavy superstructures, for example those with concrete decks on wood piles, were more severely damaged than those with all-wood or concrete decks on concrete piers. Failure first occurred at the tie between the superstructure and the substructure; the poorer this tie, the sooner the failure.

Seismic sea waves destroyed 12 bridges on the Chiniak Highway on Kodiak Island, one bridge on Point Whitshed road near Cordova, and about 14 miles of roadway.

The combination of regional tectonic subsidence and local subsidence and compaction of sediments caused inundation of many miles of highway by high tides, especially around Turnagain Arm. Total subsidence in some places amounted to more than 13 feet.

INTRODUCTION

The great earthquake that struck Alaska at about 5:36 p.m., Alaska standard time, Friday, March 27, 1964 (03:36:13.0 Greenwich mean time, March 28, 1964) severely crippled the highway system in the south-central part of the State. This part of Alaska has approximately 60 percent of the total population and produces more than 55 percent of the State's gross product and revenue. Thus, the disastrous effects of the earthquake upon the highway system materially affected the economy of the whole State. After the seismic shaking and attendant seismic sea waves had stopped, much of the

C1

highway system lay in ruins. Roadways were fractured or were blocked by avalanches; locally they had sunk out of sight or had been washed away. Most of the bridges were damaged and many were completely destroyed. Some of the destroyed bridges lay in the creeks and rivers they once spanned; others had been washed away. This destruction isolated communities on the Kenai Peninsula from Anchorage and the rest of the State. On Kodiak Island, Chiniak was isolated from the town of Kodiak.

In south-central Alaska there were, at the time of the earthquake, 830 miles of primary and secondary roads with 204 bridges. Approximately 186 miles of roadway and 141 bridges were damaged; 88 of the 186 miles was severely damaged. Ninety-two bridges required replacement. Total damage amounted to about $46,798,292 (Bruce A. Campbell, written commun., 1965).

The Alaska Department of Highways responded quickly to the emergency, and by early summer of 1964 all damaged routes were passable. The only section of road not reopened by the fall of 1966 was the Copper River Highway between the Copper River (mile 27.1) and the Million Dollar Bridge (mile 49.0).

FIELDWORK

During the summer of 1964, the author examined all bridges and roadways of the Richardson Highway between Valdez and Glennallen, Sterling Highway, Hope Road, Glenn Highway between Anchorage and the Richardson Highway, Copper River Highway, and Seward-Anchorage Highway (fig. 1), and, in addition, most of the roadways on Kodiak Island.

The author was assisted during the study by the following members of the Geological Survey: George Plafker on the Copper River and part of the Richardson Highways, M. G. Bonilla on parts of the Glenn and Seward-Anchorage Highways, and Roger Waller on parts of the Sterling and Seward-Anchorage Highways. Thor Karlstrom and Helen Foster furnished some data on the Seward-Anchorage and Sterling Highways. Richard Lemke collected and furnished the data on the Snow River Crossing on the Seward-Anchorage Highway.

ACKNOWLEDGMENTS

This report could not have been completed without the cooperation of, and the data supplied by, Bruce Campbell and Ralph Migliaccio of the Alaska Department of Highways, the U.S. Army, the U.S. Navy, and the numerous residents of Alaska who provided the eyewitness accounts.

EFFECTS OF THE EARTHQUAKE

GEOLOGIC SETTING

The terrain over which the highway system in south-central Alaska passes is varied, and this variation played an important role in the type and extent of damage to roadways and bridges. The terrain, in turn, is controlled by the geologic environment.

In general, the highways are underlain by bedrock consisting primarily of argillite and graywacke or by unconsolidated material composed of glacial debris, swamp deposits, stream deposits, colluvium, and tidal deposits. With few exceptions, the low-lying areas that the highways cross are underlain by unconsolidated deposits, and most of the damage to the highway system was in these low-lying areas. The water table is close to the surface where the highway skirts a body of water or where it crosses tidal or deltaic deposits, especially on the Seward-Anchorage Highway at the head of Turnagain Arm and where the highway crosses the Snow River delta at the south end of Kenai Lake.

SUMMARY OF DAMAGE

The earthquake that shook south-central Alaska on March 27, 1964, had a magnitude of 8.4. Its epicenter was at lat 61.06° N. and long 147.44° W., and its depth was about 21 kilometers (U.S. Coast and Geodetic Survey, 1966). Although there have been earthquakes of equal or greater magnitude, the damage created by the Alaska earthquake was particularly devastating because the shaking lasted 4 to 5 minutes. The effects of this earthquake upon the highway system in south-central Alaska were staggering. All the major highways and most of the secondary roads were damaged; these include the Sterling, Seward-Anchorage, Glenn, Edgerton, Richardson, Chiniak, Copper River Highways, and Point Whitshed Road.

1.—Index map showing earthquake epicenter and location of highways in south-central Alaska.

The total cost of repairing the highway system in south-central Alaska, including Kodiak Island, was estimated at $46,798,292 (table 1), $20,898,816 for roadways, and $25,899,476 for bridges. About 186 of the 830 miles of primary and secondary roads and 141 of the 204 bridges in the area were damaged (table 2); 88 of the 186 miles was severely damaged.

The roadways and bridges were damaged by (1) seismic shaking, (2) fracturing, (3) compaction of sediments, (4) lateral extension or displacement of sediments, (5) compression of bridges, (6) landslides, (7) avalanches, (8) seismic sea waves, (9) regional subsidence, (10) erosion, and (11) postearthquake scouring and erosion by the inundating seas in the low-lying coastal areas.

This report will not discuss in complete detail the extensive damage to the highways, but, instead, will attempt to correlate the damage with the geologic environment, and, for bridges, also with the engineering characteristics of the structures.

DAMAGE TO ROADWAYS

About 88 miles of roadway in south-central Alaska required replacement or relocation, but approximately 186 miles of roadway were affected in one manner or another by the earthquake. This total consists of 45 miles on the Copper River Highway, 35 miles on the Seward-Anchorage Highway, 40 miles on the Richardson Highway, approximately 16 miles on the Glenn Highway, 18 miles on the Kodiak Island road system, 11 miles on the Sterling Highway (including Homer Split), and 7 miles on the Portage Glacier Road. The remaining 10 miles of damaged roadway were on secondary roads.

The 88 miles of roadway that required replacement or relocation is considered severe damage in this report. Of the 88 miles, 30 were on the Copper River Highway, 25 on the Seward-Anchorage Highway, 5 on the Sterling Highway, 5 on the Richardson Highway, 2 on the Glenn Highway, 2 on Point Whitshed Road, 1 on Portage Glacier Road, and 18 miles on the Kodiak Island road system.

Figures 2–7 show the type and location of the damage on the major highways in south-central Alaska. A correlation between foundation material of the Seward-Anchorage, Sterling, Glenn, and Richardson Highways and damage sustained is shown on tables 3–6 (p. C53, C54).

TABLE 1. *Estimated cost of repairs or replacement of highway structures damaged by the Alaska earthquake* [1]

Highway	Roadway	Bridges	Total
Copper River	$4,253,089	$19,175,596	$23,428,685
Glenn	682,812	41,957	724,769
Hope Road	152,194	----------	152,194
Portage Glacier Road	590,888	318,375	909,263
Point Whitshed Road	50,793	32,165	82,958
Richardson	1,261,034	277,176	1,538,210
Seward-Anchorage	9,606,405	5,264,762	14,871,167
Sterling	2,947,657	602,116	3,549,773
Kodiak Island (Chiniak Highway, Anton Larsen Bay Road, Pasagshak Bay Road, Chiniak Highway to Spruce Cape via Kodiak)	1,116,108	183,175	1,299,283
Secondary roads	237,836	4,154	241,990
Total	20,898,816	25,899,476	46,798,292

[1] This estimate differs from that given by Eckel and Schaem (1966, p. 49). The estimate given above is based on a 1965 revision and does not include Federal aid for secondary roads in towns.

TABLE 2.—*Effects of the Alaska earthquake upon roads and bridges in south-central Alaska*

Highway or road [1]	Roadway Total (miles)	Roadway Damage (miles) Total	Roadway Damage (miles) Severe	Bridges Total	Bridges Number damaged
Copper River Highway	59	45	30	53	52
Edgerton Highway	40	0	0	4	1
Glenn Highway	188	16	2	21	11
Hope Road	16	0	0	2	0
Kenai-Nikishka Road	30	0	0	1	0
Portage Glacier Road	7	7	1	3	3
Point Whitshed Road	9	2	2	5	1
Richardson Highway	115	40	5	20	8
Seward-Anchorage Highway	130	35	25	54	39
Sterling Highway	145	11	5	13	5
Kodiak Island:					
Chiniak Highway	42	6	6	20	15
Anton Larsen Bay Road	10	5	4½	4	2
Saltery Cove Road	14	3	3	0	0
Pasagshak Bay Road	15	5	4½	3	3
Chiniak Highway to Spruce Cape via Kodiak	10	1	0	1	1
Secondary roads	------	10	0	------	------
Total	830	186	88	204	141

[1] Only primary and secondary highways listed. Streets and bridges in communities not included.

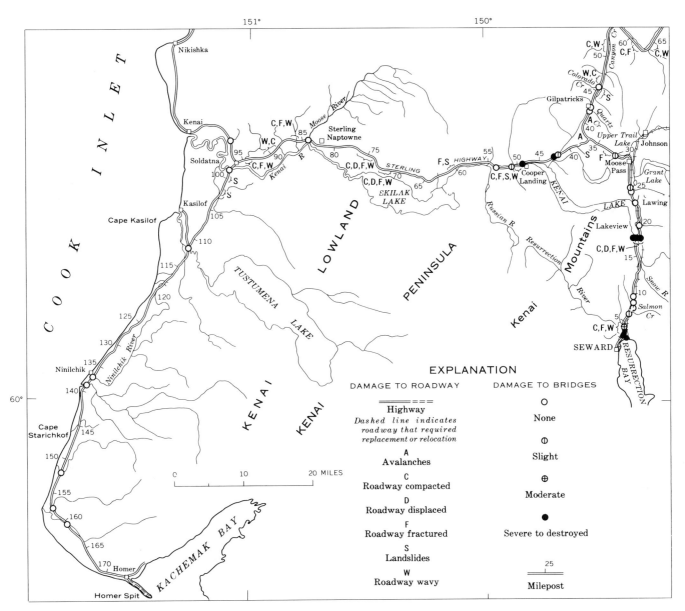

EXPLANATION

DAMAGE TO ROADWAY

Highway
Dashed line indicates
roadway that required
replacement or relocation

A
Avalanches

C
Roadway compacted

D
Roadway displaced

F
Roadway fractured

S
Landslides

W
Roadway wavy

DAMAGE TO BRIDGES

○
None

⊕
Slight

⊕
Moderate

●
Severe to destroyed

25
Milepost

2.—Routes of Sterling Highway and part of Seward-Anchorage Highway, and effects of the earthquake upon the highways.

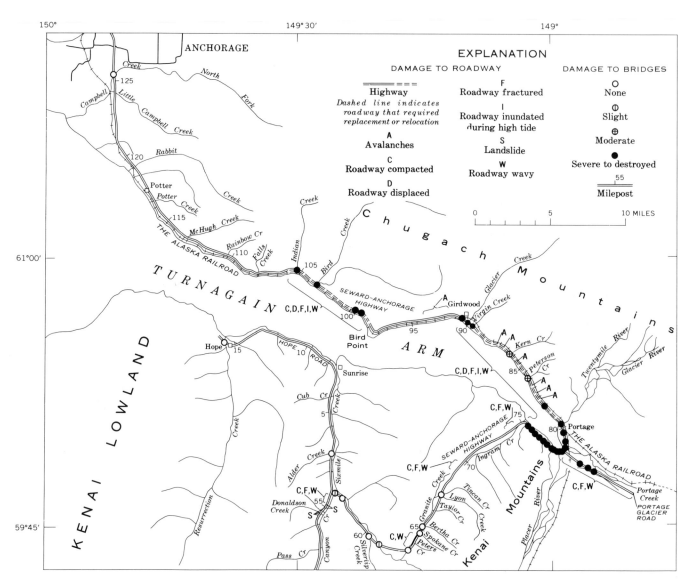

3.—Routes of part of Seward-Anchorage Highway, the Hope Road, the Portage Glacier Road, and effects of the earthquake upon the highways.

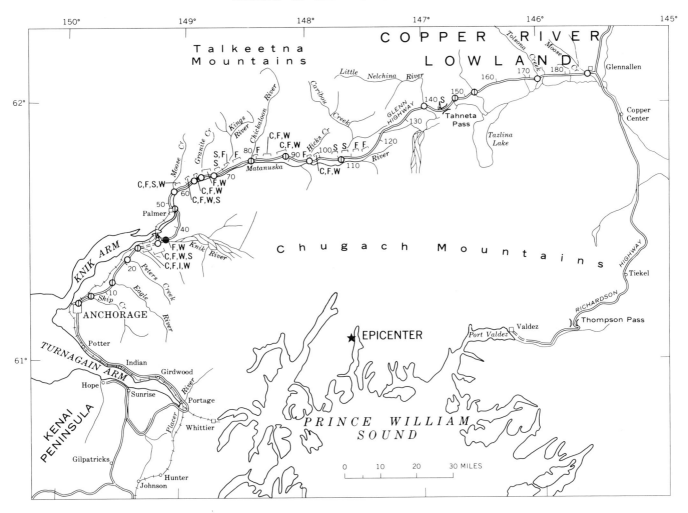

4.—Route of Glenn Highway and effects of the earthquake upon the highway.

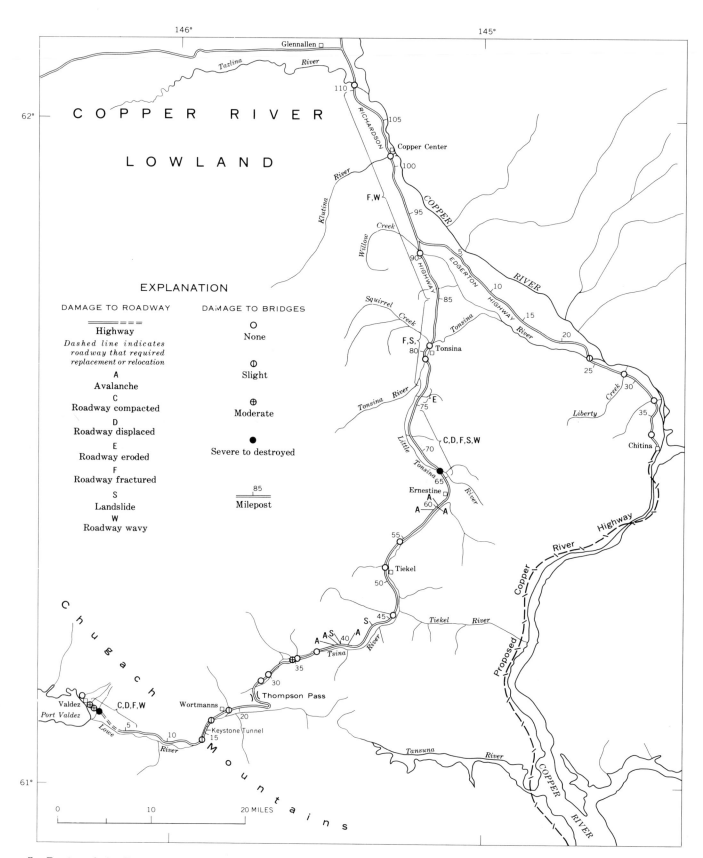

5.—Routes of the Edgerton Highway and part of the Richardson Highway, and effects of the earthquake on the highways.

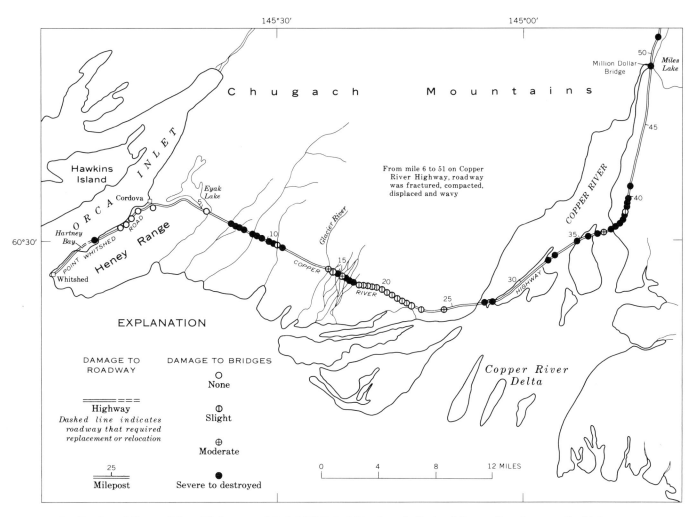

6.—Routes of Copper River Highway and Point Whitshed Road, and effects of the earthquake upon the highways.

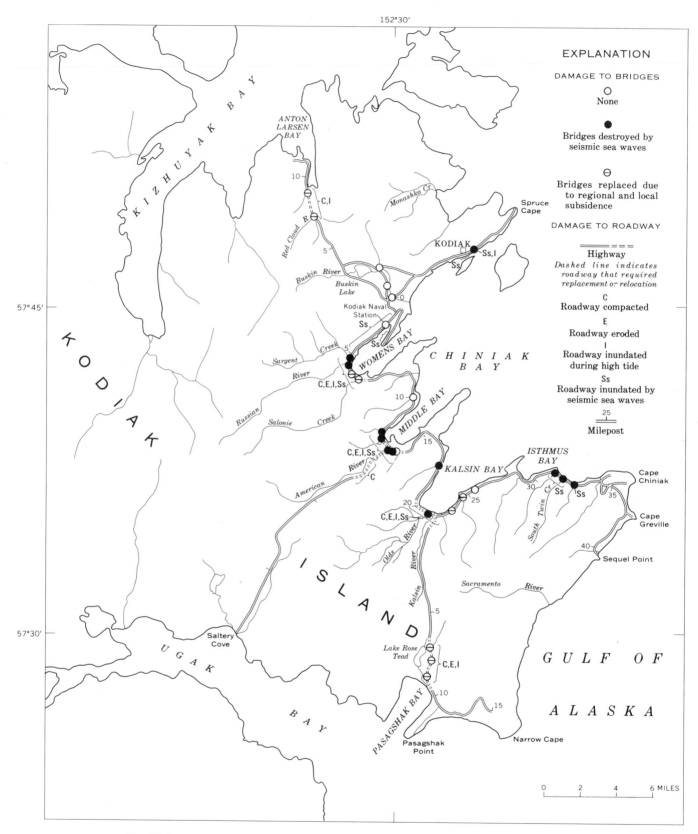

7.—Highway routes on Kodiak Island and effects of the earthquake upon the highways.

The earthquake damaged the roadways chiefly by (1) seismic shaking, (2) compaction of the roadway fill as well as the underlying sediments, (3) lateral displacement of the roadway and underlying sediments, (4) fractures in the roadway, especially on the paved surfaces, (5) landslides onto the roadway and of the roadway itself, (6) avalanches upon the roadway, (7) inundation and erosion of the roadway by seismic sea waves, (8) inundation by the sea of the roadway along low-lying coastal areas because of regional subsidence and differential compaction of the highway, and (9) differential compaction of roadway which caused a wavy effect. Much of this damage can be directly correlated with the geologic environment of the roadway. The damage by seismic sea waves was due, of course, not to the geologic conditions but to the proximity to the open sea.

The most severe damage to roadways occurred at Snow River Crossing (fig. 2) and from mile 75.1 to about mile 90 (fig. 3) on the Seward-Anchorage Highway, on the Copper River Highway (fig. 6), and from mile 1 to mile 5 on the Richardson Highway (fig. 5). The Snow River Crossing is underlain by nonplastic silt and sand (fig. 8; table 7, p. C55). Here the groundwater table is generally within 1 foot of the surface. The Turnagain Arm section of the Seward - Anchorage Highway (mile 75.1 to mile 90) is primarily underlain by silt and sand with minor amounts of gravel (fig. 9). The sediments are nonplastic (tables 8, 9, p. C55, C56). Although not indicated on the graphic logs of the test holes, the water table lies generally within 3 feet of the surface; in the vicinity of the town of Portage the

water table is within 2 feet of the surface.

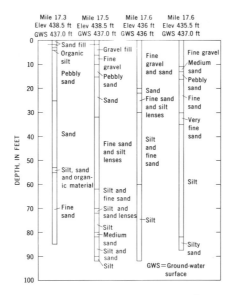

8.—Graphic logs of test holes at Snow River Crossing on Seward-Anchorage Highway. Logged by Alaska Department of Highways.

The Copper River Highway is also underlain by nonplastic sediments consisting primarily of silt, sand, and sandy gravel (fig. 10; table 10, p. C56). The water table lies within 6 feet of the surface between mile 5 and mile 18 and locally is within 1 foot of the surface. Within a few feet of the surface, much of the underlying sediments contain organic material. This material leaves much to be desired as road foundation because it will compact when fill is placed upon it or will subside or compact differentially when subjected to seismic shaking.

The Richardson Highway roadway was most severely damaged on nonplastic glacial outwash sediments consisting of sandy gravel and minor amounts of silt (fig. 11; table 11, p. C56). The water table lies within 10 feet of the ground upon which the road fill was first placed. At mile 2.1 the water table is within 1 foot of the surface, at mile 2.56 within 3 feet of the surface.

FRACTURES

The seismic shock of the earthquake fractured the roadways of all the major highways in the south-central part of the Alaska mainland, but no fractures were observed on the Kodiak Island system except for those noted on paved streets on the Kodiak Naval Station about 6 miles south of Kodiak. This does not necessarily mean that the seismic shaking did not develop any fractures, but rather that they were not visible during our study in the summer of 1964. Nor were any fractures visible in the low-lying coastal areas where they may have developed either they did not exist or they were not visible at the time of this study; repeated postearthquake inundation and scouring by the sea may well have destroyed the fractures or eroded the roadway away completely. At the time of the Alaska earthquake, the Glenn Highway was unpaved from about mile 55 to Glennallen. Roadwork was underway in most of this stretch of the highway during the summer of 1964; this roadwork obviously destroyed any fractures in the roadway. The most reliable indications of earthquake-generated fractures were on paved roads, and some of the fractures there had to be examined carefully to determine whether they were pre- or postearthquake.

Not including fractures due to landslides, the Alaska earthquake generated at least five major fracture patterns on the Alaska roadways (fig. 12). Fractures formed (1) normal to the roadway, (2) along the center of the roadway, (3) on the shoulders parallel to the roadway, (4) as oblique fractures on original ground, then refracted normal to the roadway, and, once across the roadway, again oblique to it, and (5) oblique

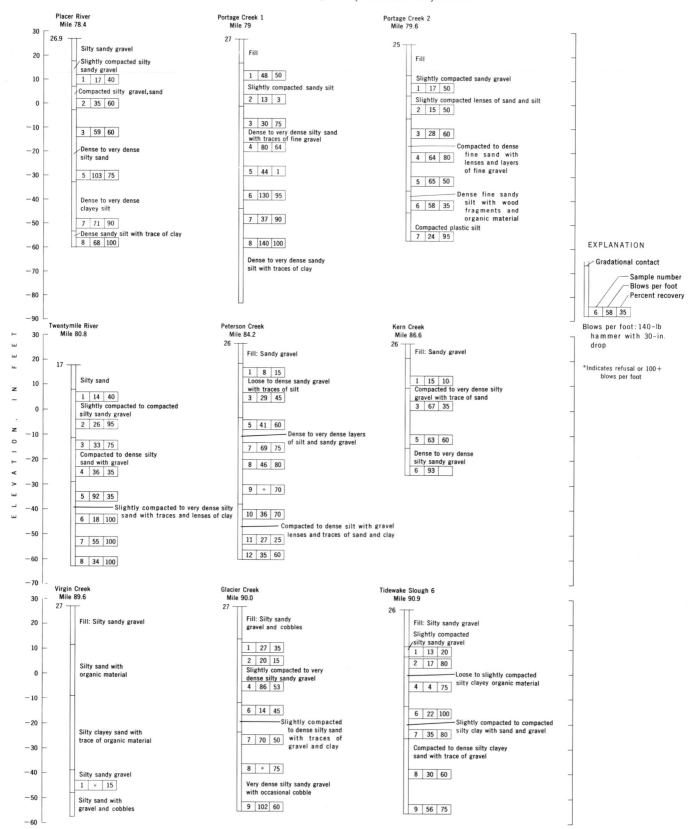

9.—Graphic logs of test holes at miles 78.4, 79.0, 79.6, 80.8, 84.2, 86.6, 89.6, 90.0, and 90.9, Seward-Anchorage Highway.

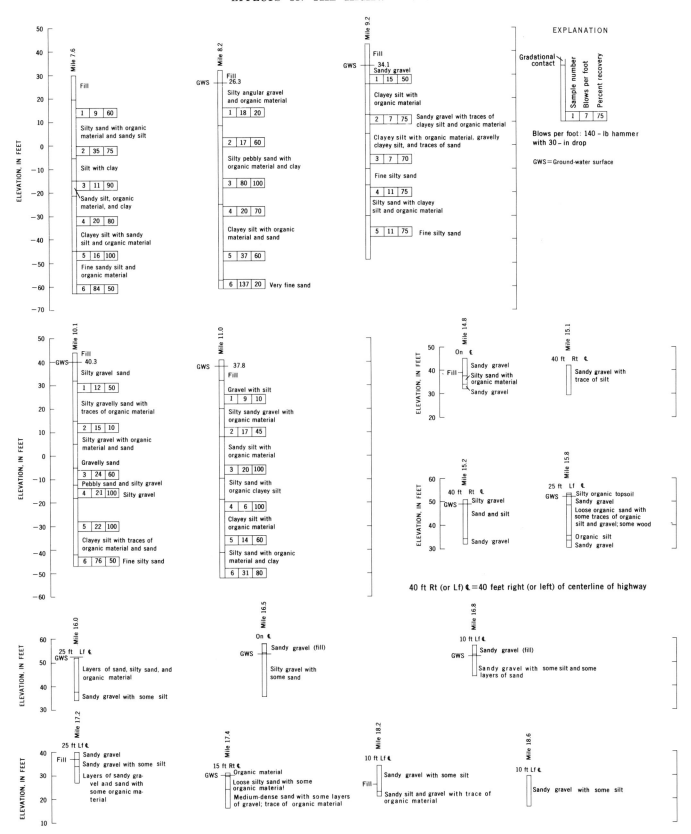

10.—Graphic logs of test holes at miles 7.6, 8.2, 9.2, 10.1, 11.0, 14.8, 15.1, 15.2, 15.8, 16.0, 16.5, 16.8, 17.2, 17.4, 18.2, and 18.6, Copper River Highway.

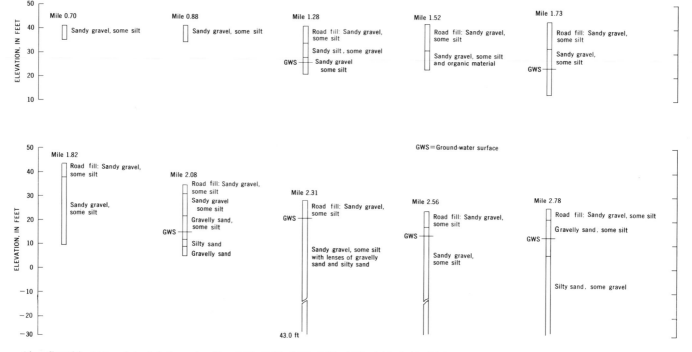

11.—Graphic logs of test holes at miles 0.70, 0.82, 1.28, 1.52, 1.73, 1.82, 2.08, 2.56, and 2.73, Richardson Highway. Analysis by Alaska Department of Highways.

to the roadway. Some stretches of roadway had more than one fracture pattern.

Much of the highway system was fractured by seismic shaking (figs. 2–7). The most spectacular fractures occurred on the Seward-Anchorage Highway from mile 75.1 to mile 90, but extensive fracturing also occurred on the Richardson Highway between miles 0 and 5, between miles 64 and 80, and on the Copper River Highway. The extent and nature of the fractures depended upon the type and thickness of the sediments and the depth to the water table. Fractures were conspicuous in swamp deposits and in thick accumulations of silt and sand, especially if the water table was within 6 feet of the ground surface. In general, the closer the water table was to the ground surface, the more extensive and varied the fracture patterns were. For example, at the southeast end of Turnagain Arm near Portage the Seward-Anchor-

age Highway passes over silt and sand, and the water table is within 2 feet of the ground surface. The fractures here were very extensive. The fractures on the highway were more pronounced than those on the roadbed of the railroad, but the railroad was displaced horizontally for about the same distance as the highway.

There are several reasons why the fracture pattern is more pronounced on the highway than on the railroad. The highway roadway is generally constructed of well-graded (poorly sorted) compacted fill and is paved. In contrast, the railroad roadbed was originally constructed by using about 1 foot of ballast that consisted chiefly of coarse gravel. Over a period of years the railroad roadbed was raised to grade by adding coarse gravel, and thus the thickness of coarse poorly graded gravel is much greater than it was originally. When the earthquake struck the Portage area and the

sediments were displaced, the denser highway roadway was easily fractured, whereas the coarse gravel of the railroad roadbed, although displaced, was not extensively fractured.

As stated earlier, the most extensive fracturing occurred on the Seward-Anchorage Highway at the head of Turnagain Arm. Table 12 (p. C57) shows the correlation of foundation material and fractures from mile 75.1 (Ingram Creek) to mile 95.0.

FRACTURES NORMAL TO THE HIGHWAY

The most conspicuous fractures observed were those normal to the axis of the roadway (figs. 12E, 13); they were extensive along the Seward-Anchorage Highway and on the Richardson, Sterling, and Glenn Highways, particularly in paved sections. These fractures, plus the oblique type shown on figure 12F(2), represent about 90

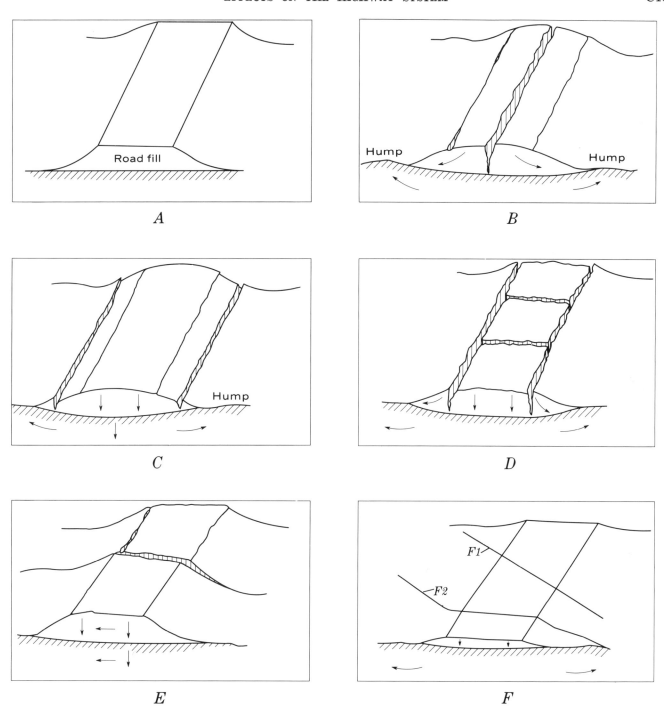

12.—Schematic drawing of types of fracture generated by earthquake in roadways. A, Preearthquake. B, Underlying sediments compact and displace laterally. Roadway settles differentially and is moved laterally by underlying sediments; roadway fractures along centerline and is wavy; hump is formed off roadway. C, Underlying sediments compact and move laterally; roadway settles and longitudinal fractures develop along edges; roadway also wavy. D, Longitudinal fractures form as in C; as underlying sediments continue to compact and displace laterally, roadway settles differentially and transverse fractures develop. E, Fracture forms owing to horizontal displacement of roadway and underlying sediments; fracture generally originates off roadway. F, Fracture forms in original ground oblique to roadway; as it strikes roadway, it either continues at oblique angle (F1) or is refracted normal to roadway and, when past roadway, becomes oblique again (F2); these fractures occur chiefly in small roadway fills.

13.—View northwest showing conspicuous centerline fracture and more typical perpendicular fractures on Seward-Anchorage Highway between Portage and Twentymile River. Photograph by D. S. McCulloch.

14.—Centerline fracture on unpaved Copper River Highway at south approach of Clear Creek bridge 329 at mile 41.0. Photograph by George Plafker.

percent of those observed on the Richardson, Glenn, and Sterling Highways and about 75 percent of those on the Seward-Anchorage Highway.

From mile 75.1 to mile 91 and from mile 99 to mile 105 on the Seward-Anchorage Highway, the fractures normal to the axis of the highway were spaced 75 to 200 feet apart. Horizontal displacement of as much as 5 feet and vertical displacement of 1 foot were noted. Where the highway passed over fine-grained sediments and swamp debris, such as the Sterling Highway near mile 71 and again near mile 75, the roadway was skewed and displaced as much as 4 feet horizontally and 8 to 10 inches vertically, and the spacing of the fractures was as close as 10 feet.

FRACTURES ALONG HIGHWAY CENTERLINE

Fractures along the centerline of the highway (fig. 12B) formed near Portage on the Seward-Anchorage Highway (fig. 13) and on the unpaved Copper River Highway, especially from mile 40 to the Million Dollar bridge (fig. 14). This type of fracture occurred (1) where a relatively thick roadway fill was underlain by fine-grained saturated sediments in swamp deposits, and (2) where the roadway was underlain by fine-grained silty sand and gravel and the water table was within 2 feet of the surface. Most of the axes of the fractures on the centerline of the highway were normal or nearly normal to the direction of seismic

motion. The centerline fractures along the Portage and Copper River Highways are perpendicular to the slope of terrain.

The largest centerline fracture occurred between Portage and Twentymile River on the Seward-Anchorage Highway (fig. 13). The fracture was about 500 feet long, as much as 10 feet wide, and 6 to 8 feet deep.

FRACTURES ALONG HIGHWAY EDGE

Fractures formed locally along the edges of all the highways. This type of fracture (fig. 12C) was responsible for considerable damage, especially on the Copper River Highway and the Seward-Anchorage Highway near mile

75.0. Because of the differential settling of the roadway associated with this fracture pattern, the roadway is wavy.

FRACTURES NORMAL TO AND ALONG HIGHWAY EDGE

On the Copper River Highway severe fracturing occurred along the edges of the roadway (fig. 15) as well as normal to the roadway, primarily in the roadway fill (fig. 12D). The fractures shown on figure 15 were in a fill 8 to 10 feet thick which subsided about 3 feet into the underlying fine sand and silt desposited by the Copper River. The waviness of the road- way shown on figure 15 indicates differential compaction and lat- eral displacement of the under- lying sediments.

OBLIQUE FRACTURES

Oblique fractures, an interesting but not commonly destructive fracture system, occurred during the earthquake (fig. 12F). These fractures originate on the ground off the highway fill and intersect the shoulders of the fill at oblique angles. Some continue through the fill at the same angle and into the ground again (fig. 12F(1)). More commonly, however, where the fracture strikes the roadway it is refracted normal to the roadway axis. Once through the roadway, the fractures once again become oblique and attain their original heading (fig. 12F(2)). This re- fracted fracture is especially com- mon where the roadway is paved. Such fractures occurred on the road at the north end of Hood Lake in Anchorage, on parts of the Richardson Highway, on the Copper River flats, and on the Seward-Anchorage Highway a few miles south of Anchorage.

Displacement, both vertical and horizontal, is very slight and thus is not very destructive.

15.—Fractures normal to and along highway edge, Copper River Highway. Looking east from Copper River bridge 2, mile 27.1. Approach subsided 3 feet and fractured.

COMPLEX FRACTURES

Where the highway passed over saturated fine sand and silt with a free face close by, a very distinct and destructive fracture system developed (fig. 16). The fractures of this system have horizontal dis- placements of as much as 2 feet and vertical displacements of 18 inches. Figure 16 shows that lat- eral displacements and slumping toward a free face occurred with movement to the right. Fractures normal to the roadway near the Allen River indicate that the sedi- ments also moved toward the river, although this movement is not clear on the illustration. In addition, the underlying support- ing sediments failed.

ORIGIN OF FRACTURES

At the time of the earthquake, much of the roadway and ground beneath it was frozen to depths of 4 to 5 feet. A frozen roadway is more brittle than a thawed road- way, but the frozen ground prob- ably did not play a major role in the origin of a fracture; however, once the fracture developed in a frozen roadway, it maintained its integrity.

NORMAL TO HIGHWAY

Fractures normal to the road- way are due to shear and tension (fig. 12E). The fractures due to shear first form in the ground be- cause of mass displacement of the underlying sediments toward a free face. The lateral displacement is general, and the roadway does not show the total horizontal displacement in one fracture but in a series of them; thus, the roadway when viewed in plan is askew. At the same time, differential compaction and lateral displacement of the underlying sediments parallel to the axis of the roadway cause tension and vertical as well as horizontal displacements.

ALONG HIGHWAY CENTERLINE

Failures along the centerline of the highway fill are due to tension (fig. 12B). As the roadway and underlying sediments are subjected to seismic shaking, the denser roadway subsides into the underlying less-dense sediments. The sediments then flow outward and the overlying fill fails. The underlying sediments are not necessarily liquefied; failure can occur prior to liquefaction. There is generally a hump or fracture on the original ground where the compacted and laterally displaced underlying sediments flow toward the surface. Intense seismic shaking of relatively long duration is necessary to produce centerline fractures. Eyewitness accounts indicate that such shaking did indeed occur in the Portage and Copper River areas.

NORMAL TO AND ALONG HIGHWAY EDGE

Fractures along the edges and parallel to the roadway (fig. 12C, D) are caused by compaction of the underlying sediments and lateral spreading of the ground. As seen in figure 12C the roadway, although wavy from differential compaction, has maintained its integrity. As the roadway is subsiding differentially, it is also being displaced along the axis owing to displacement of the underlying sediment. Thus, normal and longitudinal fractures are due to tension and are confined to the road fill.

SUBSIDENCE OF ROADWAY

Throughout south-central Alaska the highway system experienced much local subsidence because of compaction and lateral displacement of the underlying

16.—Complex fractures with relatively large lateral and vertical displacements, produced by movement of saturated fine sand and silt toward free faces. View north near mile 58.5, Copper River Highway. The Allen River, which drains Allen Glacier, is in the background.

sediments. Although not as spectacular as the damage from fractures, this damage was the most widespread. The only places that escaped were those where the roadway was on bedrock. The local differential subsidence made the roadways undulating and wavy and dropped the approaches to most of the bridges.

The most spectacular local subsidence occurred (1) on the Richardson Highway between mile 0.0 and mile 5.0, (2) on the Copper River Highway near mile 28.0, and (3) on the Seward-Anchorage Highway at Snow River Crossing and from mile 75.1 to mile 91.0. Figure 17 shows pre- and postearthquake profiles from mile 0.7 to mile 2.5 of the Richardson Highway; figure 18, pre- and postearthquake profiles from mile 5.9 to mile 11.0 of the Copper River Highway; figure 19, pre- and postearthquake profiles from mile 75.1 to mile 85.0 of the Seward-Anchorage Highway; and figure 20, pre- and postearthquake profiles and pier elevations at the Snow River Crossing of the Seward-Anchorage Highway.

None of the postearthquake profiles indicate tectonic subsidence or uplift; they represent only subsidence of the roadway due to compaction and lateral displacement of the underlying sediments. A few profiles indicate uplift due to bulldozing of sediments against bridge abutments or to ground waves. Bulldozing occurs when the laterally displaced sediments of the bridge approaches strike the resisting bridge abutments and form a mound of sediments at the contact between the two.

Another type of subsidence was noted at Snow River. At the time of the earthquake, the Alaska Department of Highways was constructing a second crossing there.

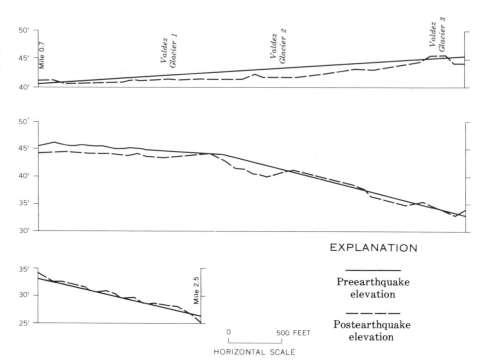

17.—Pre- and postearthquake profiles from mile 0.7 to mile 2.5, Richardson Highway. Data from Alaska Department of Highways.

The piers shown on figures 20 and 21, which are part of the new crossing and which subsided as much as 4 feet, rest on 18-inch tubular piles driven to depths of as much as 160 feet. The subsidence of these piers indicates that the underlying sediments either compacted to great depths or that seismic shaking in fine silt liquefied the sediments and allowed the piles to sink. In addition, when the piles at abutment 1 (fig. 20) were pulled, they were found to be distorted and bent by the earthquake below the ground surface.

The roadway fill at the Snow River Crossing prior to the earthquake was from 4 to 7 feet thick. After the earthquake the 4-foot part of the fill had subsided as much as 2 feet beneath the ground surface. The profile in figure 20 indicates that the ground surface subsided about 5 feet. Thus, in places the roadway must have subsided as much as 11 feet, that is, the 4-foot fill subsided 6 feet and

the sediments subsided 5 feet. This is the maximum recorded local subsidence due to compaction and displacement of the underlying sediment. Figure 22 shows the western bridge at the crossing; the road fill here had to be almost completely replaced.

The Snow River Crossing is underlain by fine sand and silt, covered with a thin veneer of fine gravel (fig. 8). The water table is in many cases at or within a foot of the surface. The fine-grained saturated sediments had very little strength, and, when the seismic shaking struck the area, the sediments failed primarily by liquefaction and lateral spreading or displacement.

A large amount of local subsidence of the roadway occurred in the Portage area on the Seward-Anchorage Highway. Here a maximum subsidence of 54 inches was measured by the Alaska Department of Highways at mile 79.3 between Portage Creek 1 and

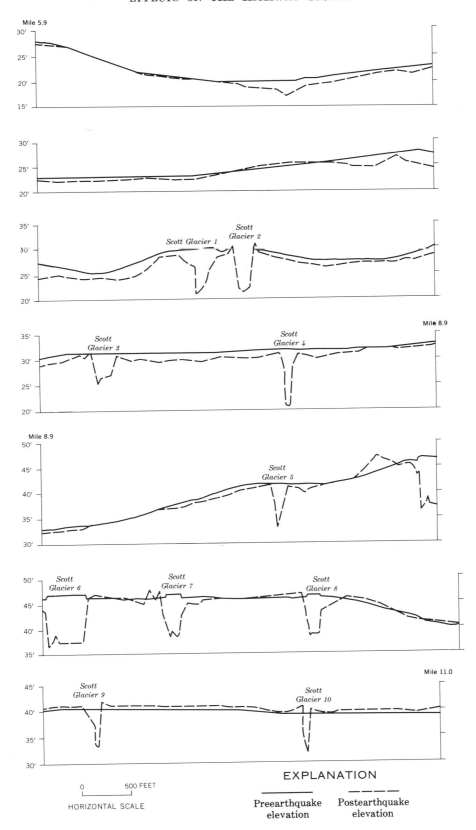

18.—Pre- and postearthquake profiles from mile 5.9 to mile 11.0, Copper River Highway. Data from Alaska Department of Highways.

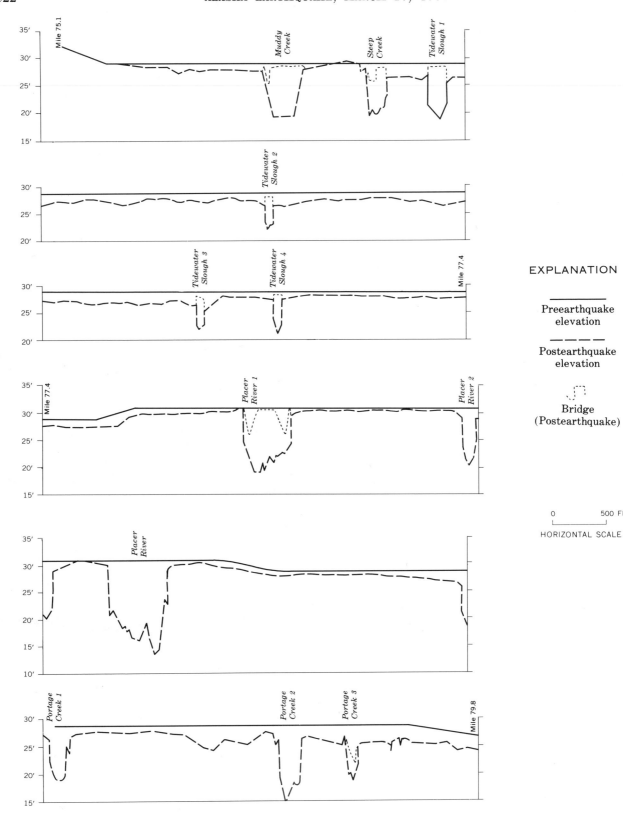

EXPLANATION

Preearthquake
elevation

Postearthquake
elevation

Bridge
(Postearthquake)

0   500 FEET

HORIZONTAL SCALE

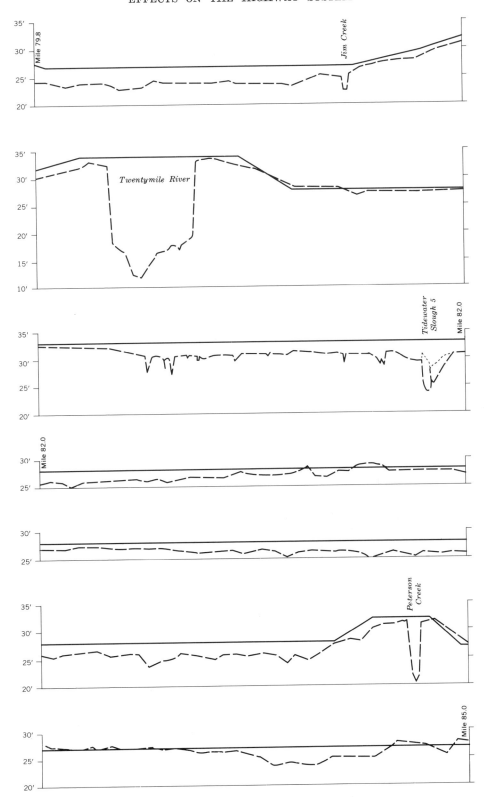

19. (Above and left)—Pre- and postearthquake profiles from mile 75.1 to mile 85.0, Seward-Anchorage Highway. Data from Alaska Department of Highways.

ELEVATION OF TOP OF PIER, IN FEET	PIER 3	PIER 5	PIER 6	PIER 7
	This pier is canted ⅜ in per ft S.¹⁵⁄₁₆, in per ft E	This pier is canted ¹⁵⁄₁₆ in per ft S. ⅜ in per ft W	This pier is canted 1 in per ft S, ¼ in per ft W	This pier is canted ⅜⁄₂ in per ft W.¹⁵⁄₁₆ in per ft S
	N □ S	N □ S	N □ S	N □ S
Before earthquake	446.13	446.13	446.13	446.13
After earthquake North side	444.43	442.77	443.95	444.01
South side	444.18	442.17	443.33	443.43

The original elevation on these columns was plus or minus 0.05 feet

A

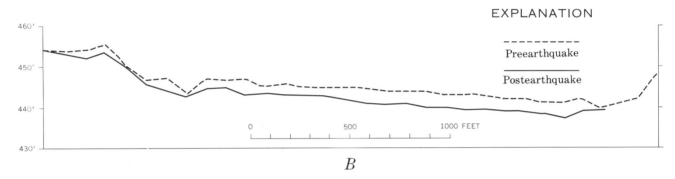

EXPLANATION

- - - - - - - Preearthquake

———— Postearthquake

B

20.—Pre- and postearthquake pier elevations (*A*) and profiles (*B*) near mile 17.3 at Snow River Crossing, Seward-Anchorage Highway. Profiles are at east side of Snow River Crossing. Data supplied by Alaska Department of Highways.

21.—Bridge pier for new crossing at Snow River displaced by compaction of underlying sediments or by liquefaction of fine silts. Photograph by D. S. McCulloch.

22.—View, looking west, of arched bridge at Snow River Crossing. Note that new fill in foreground was added to compensate for subsidence of approach fills and arching of bridge. Some of the original road fill had to be completely replaced. Photograph by D. S. McCulloch.

Portage Creek 2 and at mile 82.1, 0.1 mile north of Tidewater Slough 5 bridge (fig. 19). Much subsidence also occurred in the finer grained sediments around Turnagain Arm. At mile 79.3 the roadway is underlain chiefly by silty sand deposited by Portage Creek, and at mile 82.1 the roadway is underlain predominantly by silt and sand.

Local subsidence of the roadway fill caused uptilting of culverts in places on the Portage Glacier Road, the Seward-Anchorage Highway, and the Richardson Highway.

In the Portage area on the Seward-Anchorage Highway there is a definite correlation between local subsidence of roadway, type of sediments, and thickness of the roadway fill (compare fig. 9 with fig. 19). The coarser the underlying sediments, the less the roadway subsided; the thicker the roadway fill, the more the roadway subsided. Another very important factor is the location of the water table; the closer the water table was to the surface, the more the roadway subsided and the more the underlying sediments moved laterally from beneath the roadway fill.

The Richardson Highway between mile 0.7 and mile 2.5 is underlain chiefly by sandy gravel, and the maximum local subsidence of the roadway was 25 inches (compare fig. 11 with fig. 17). The water table generally is more than 6 feet below the ground surface.

Pre- and postearthquake profiles for the Copper River Highway are only available from mile 5.9 to mile 13. In this stretch of the highway a maximum local subsidence of 48 inches occurred at about mile 7.6. Here the roadway is underlain by clay, silt, sand, and organic debris (fig. 10). At mile 10.1, where the roadway is underlain by silty gravelly sand and silty gravel, it did not subside. There was about 18 inches of subsidence at mile 11.0 where the highway is underlain chiefly by silty sandy gravel, sandy silt, and silty sand (all containing organic material; fig. 10); the water table there is about 2 feet from the surface.

The Chiniak Highway on Kodiak Island also failed because of compaction and lateral displacement of the underlying unconsolidated deposits. Maximum local subsidence occurred at the heads of Womens Bay, Middle Bay, and Kalsin Bay. The amount of subsidence was not measured but is estimated to be from 3 to 4 feet at Womens Bay and Middle Bay and 3 feet at Kalsin Bay.

Wherever a highway passes from fill to bedrock, there was settlement of the fill because of seismic shaking. Commonly, the subsidence is very pronounced and may even be expressed as a fracture at or near the bedrock-sediment contact. Roadway-fill approaches to the bedrock outcrop at Bird Point on the Seward-Anchorage Highway settled 2½ to 3 feet. The pavement on both sides of the bedrock outcrop is fractured, but the vertical displacement on each individual fracture is less than 2 inches. In contrast, on the Seward-Anchorage Highway near Ingram Creek (fig. 23), a single fracture was noted between bedrock and sediments along which 22 inches of vertical displacement took place.

LATERAL DISPLACEMENT OF ROADWAY

Severe seismic shaking caused downslope lateral displacement of some sediments and the roadway resting on them. The maximum horizontal displacement measured on roadways was 13½ feet at Snow River Crossing on the Seward-Anchorage Highway. The horizontal displacement at Snow River as well as elsewhere was differential.

The maximum measured horizontal displacement on the Richardson Highway was 5.3 feet at about mile 1.6.

The amount of horizontal displacement in the Portage area of the Seward-Anchorage Highway is unknown, but the railroad in this area was displaced about 10 feet (David McCulloch, oral commun., 1966), so it is not unreasonable to assume that the highway was displaced a similar distance.

LANDSLIDES

The earthquake triggered numerous small roadway landslides; the locations of slides are shown on figures 2–5. Most were small and only affected part of the roadway; on the Seward-Anchorage Highway near mile 44.5, for instance, about 100 feet of the road-

23.—Vertical displacement of roadway southeast of Ingram Creek on the Seward-Anchorage Highway. Pavement in foregound is underlain by sediments; in background, by bedrock. Trench shovel handle is 19 inches long. Photographs by Helen Foster.

way was displaced toward Summit Lake (fig. 24). There were also several small landslides between mile 54 and mile 56 on the Seward-Anchorage Highway.

The only relatively destructive landslides on the Sterling Highway were near Cooper Landing and at mile 60.5. On the Glenn Highway there were 10 slides; these occurred near mile 30, at Moose River, mile 61, mile 69, mile

70, at both approaches to Caribou Creek at mile 106.9, mile 139, and mile 140. The most destructive of these slides were at Caribou Creek.

The slides that caused the most damage were on the Richardson Highway at mile 65 and at the bridge crossing the Little Tonsina River. The landslide compressed the bridge and left a 3- to 4-foot hump where the asphalt paving meets the bulkhead.

A much larger landslide was generated in glacial debris at mile 72.5 on the Richardson Highway where about 300 feet of the roadway was displaced about 7 inches downslope.

AVALANCHES

The numerous avalanches generated by the earthquake caused only minor damage to the highway system in south-central Alaska. Most of the avalanches that caused highway damage occurred on the Seward-Anchorage Highway between mile 83 and mile 95; here the largest covered the roadway with at least 20 feet of snow.

Large avalanches occurred at miles 38, 39, and 42 in the rugged terrain of the Chugach Mountains through which the Richardson Highway passes. At mile 44, a rock slide developed. Although not on the roadway, a large avalanche near mile 50 dammed the Tiekel River and had to be removed by explosives because the rising waters were endangering the highway. A 200-foot landslide on the Edgerton Highway at Lower Tonsina Hill, a short distance north of Lower Tonsina, was noted by Ferrians (1966).

SAND EJECTA BLANKETS

Formation of sand ejecta blankets, an interesting but nondestructive phenomenon, was noted along the highway system in south-central Alaska. These blankets, most common on the Richardson and Copper River Highways, were formed by the ejection of generally very fine sand, through fissures in the ground where the depth to the water table was usually less than 10 feet. The largest ejecta blanket was on the Copper River Highway about 30 miles from Cordova; it covered an area of at least an acre to a depth of as much as 3 feet.

SEISMIC SEA WAVES

Seismic sea waves that struck Kodiak Island destroyed 13 miles of the highway net (Plafker and Kachadoorian, 1966). The waves were particularly damaging to the low-lying roadway and bridges at Womens Bay, Middle Bay, and Kalsin Bay (figs. 7, 25).

The waves ran inland as much as 1½ miles in Women's Bay, 2½ miles in Middle Bay, and about 3 miles in Kalsin Bay. The in- and outgoing water was especially violent in Kalsin and Middle Bays (Plafker and Kachadoorian, 1966, pl. 3) and in Womens Bay (Plafker and Kachadoorian, 1966, p. D42). Three miles of road was destroyed at Womens Bay, 3 miles at Middle Bay, 1 mile at Mayflower Creek, 4 miles at Kalsin Bay, and about 3 miles at Twin Creeks east of Isthmus Bay. The roadways in these areas had to be realined because compaction of the underlying sediments and regional subsidence left them under water during high tides.

Most of the 4-mile stretch of the Chiniak Highway from the Kodiak Naval Station to Womens Bay was inundated by the seismic sea waves, but the roadway was only slightly damaged because the asphalt pavement prevented extensive erosion.

The Point Whitshed Road, between Cordova and Point Whitshed, crosses Hartney Bay on an artificial fill about 12 feet thick, 28 feet wide, and about 1 mile long. At the time of the earthquake the roadway was unpaved. Eighteen feet of the original 28 feet still remains; about 10 feet of the inland side of the roadway was cut off as if by one stroke of a huge cleaver (fig. 26). This remarkably straight-line failure could not have been along a construction joint because the fill was placed as a unit. During the earthquake, severe seismic shaking probably generated a longitudinal fracture along the axis of the fill about 18 feet from the Orca Inlet side or 10 feet from the inland side of the fill. This fracture was due to compaction and lateral displacement of the underlying saturated silt and

24.—Small landslide on Seward-Anchorage Highway near mile 44.5, along shore of Summit Lake.

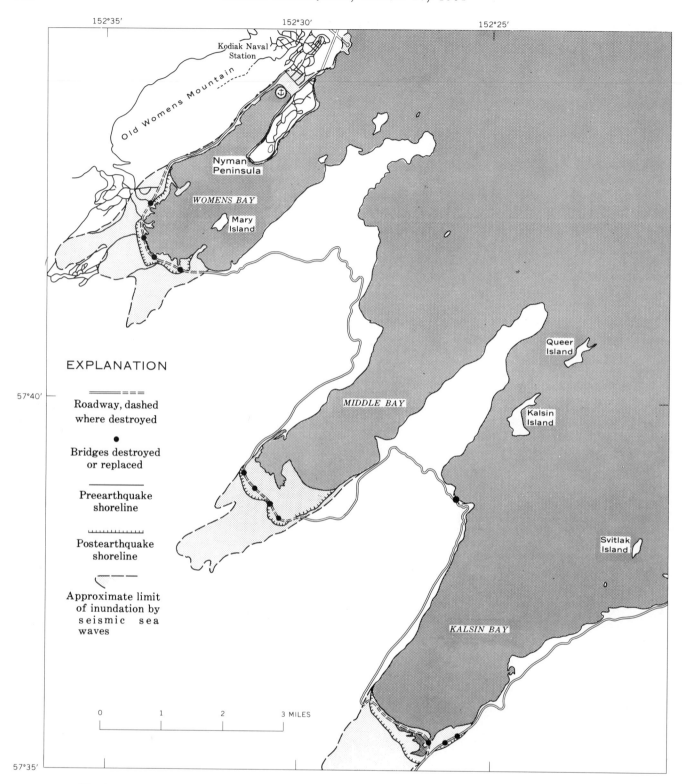

25.—Pre- and postearthquake shorelines and area of inundation by seismic sea waves on Kodiak Island.

gravel. When the incoming (from left to right in fig. 26) seismic sea waves topped the roadway, they must have had sufficient force to topple the inward 10-foot part of the roadway. As the seismic sea waves receded, they scoured away part of the toppled roadway.

TECTONIC SUBSIDENCE

The Alaska earthquake caused vertical land changes throughout much of south-central Alaska (Grantz, Plafker, and Kachadoorian, 1964; Plafker, 1965). Where the highways were underlain by areas that were uplifted, no long-range damage was done. Definite problems did arise, however, where the highway passed over low-lying areas that were affected by regional tectonic subsidence. Widespread effects of subsidence were not felt until the spring tides in April 1964. These and subsequent high tides submerged much of the Seward-Anchorage Highway around Turnagain Arm from mile 75.1 to mile 91.0 (fig. 27). The town of Portage as well as the highway were inundated by the high tide.

Tectonic subsidence in the Turnagain Arm area was about 5.2 feet with additional local subsidence of as much as 4.5 feet; thus, parts of the Seward-Anchorage Highway subsided 9.7 feet. Figure 28 shows the preearthquake shoreline which is mean high water and the area inundated by the 33-foot tide of April 14, 1964.

The low-lying areas at the head of Womens Bay, Middle Bay, Kalsin Bay, and the small bay east of Isthmus Bay on Kodiak Island became subject to flooding during high tides. During a 4½-foot tide the Chiniak Highway at the head of Womens Bay was mostly under water. The area had a regional tectonic subsidence of 5.6 feet plus 3 to 4 feet of subsidence due to compaction and lateral displacement of sediments; thus, total subsidence here was 8½ to 9½ feet.

On Kodiak Island, regional tectonic subsidence plus local differential subsidence required replacing 5 miles of roadway in addition to the 13 miles destroyed by seismic sea waves. This total of 18 miles includes about 2½ miles of roadway at Pasagshak Bay and 2½ miles at Anton Larsen Bay (fig. 7).

About half a mile of the Glenn Highway near mile 27 was inundated during high tides. Tectonic subsidence was about 2 feet, but there must have been another 6 feet of subsidence due to compaction and lateral displacement of underlying sediments—otherwise the roadway would not have been flooded during high tides.

Regional tectonic subsidence and local differential subsidence have caused a definite long-range hazard to the highway system on the Seward-Anchorage Highway around Turnagain Arm. Because space and economic factors do not permit a major change of alinement, the roadway must be brought to grade by the addition of fill. The fill will have to be riprapped because it will be subjected to tidal action and erosion during high tides.

DAMAGE TO BRIDGE APPROACHES AND BRIDGES

The Alaska earthquake and attendant seismic sea waves raised havoc with the highway bridges in south-central Alaska. When the seismic shaking stopped, 119 bridges had been damaged. An additional 13 bridges were destroyed by seismic sea waves, and 9 more had to be replaced because regional tectonic subsidence or local subsidence of the sediments placed them under water during high tides.

On March 27, 1964, in the 586,400 square miles of Alaska, there were 480 bridges having an aggregate length of about 77,300 feet. Of these, 204 bridges with a total length of 36,311 were in south-central Alaska (tables 13, 14, p. C58). One hundred forty-one bridges or about 30 percent of the 480 bridges were damaged; 92 bridges or 19 percent were severely damaged or destroyed; and 23,267 feet or 30 percent of the total bridge footage in Alaska required replacement.

If we consider only the bridges in south-central Alaska, the statistics become even more staggering. Only 63 bridges or 31 percent were not damaged; 39 bridges or 19 percent received slight damage; 10 bridges or 5 percent sustained moderate damage; and 92 bridges or 45 percent were severely damaged or destroyed. Of the total bridge footage in south-central Alaska, 64 percent was damaged severely enough to require replacement (tables 13, 14, p. C58). The cost of repairing or replacing the structures amounted to $25,899,476. This is a tremendous loss to any State's highway system and economy.

The bridges on the Copper River Highway that were farthest from the epicenter (fig. 1) suffered the greatest damage. Of the 53 bridges on the highway, 52 were damaged and 32 were severely damaged or destroyed (tables 13, 14, p. C58). The only bridge that was not damaged rested on bedrock and spanned the Eyak River at mile 5.9. Table 14 gives the intensity of bridge damage on the other highways or roads in south-central Alaska.

Seismic shaking and its effects upon the foundations of the bridges were responsible for damage to 120 bridges. These effects include compaction of the

26.—Right side of Point Whitshed Road destroyed by seismic sea waves. Waves advanced over roadway from the left and cut sharp edge on right side of roadway. View northeast; Hartney Bay is to the right.

27.—View of Portage on Seward-Anchorage Highway during 28-foot tide, after regional subsidence caused by the earthquake. Highway is under water, just below railroad grade in far background. Photograph taken August 10, 1964.

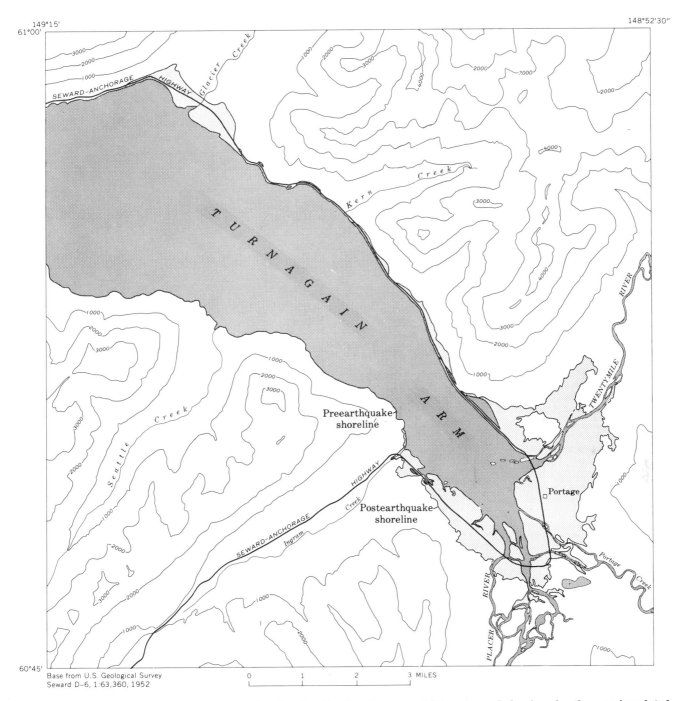

28.—Map of Turnagain Arm showing pre-earthquake shoreline based on mean high water and showing also the area inundated by the 33-foot tide of April 14, 1964. Tide height datum is mean lower low water.

sediments upon which the bridges rested and lateral displacement of the sediments toward free faces. Only five bridges on bedrock were damaged, and those only slightly. The remaining 114 bridges were underlain by unconsolidated sediments.

The damage to roadway fill approaches to a highway bridge can easily be explained, but an analysis of bridge damage is not so simple. There is a definite correlation between the damage to bridges on bedrock and to those on sediments, but analyses of damage to the bridges on sediments is more complex. Damage intensity is not only a function of the type of sediment but also the type of structure.

Tables 15–19, p. C59–C66 list the bridges on the Copper River, Seward-Anchorage, Glenn, Richardson, and Sterling Highways, respectively, and show the location, length, type, foundation material, and earthquake damage. The descriptions of damage, particularly of severe damage or total destruction, are brief and do not include all failures. The terms used in the tables are shown in figure 29, which indicates the various structural elements that make up a typical bridge.

SEISMIC SHAKING

The approaches to nearly all the bridges in south-central Alaska subsided in relation to the bridge decks (fig. 30). Even where fill approaches were placed on bedrock, some subsidence or compaction took place.

The maximum compaction and settlement recorded for any bridge approach was 7½ to 8 feet at the north approach to Tidewater Slough 5 bridge on the Seward-Anchorage Highway at mile 82.0 (table 16, p. C63). There, the roadway is underlain chiefly by sand

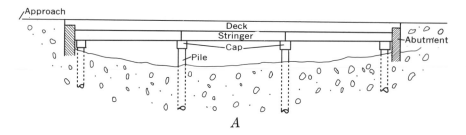

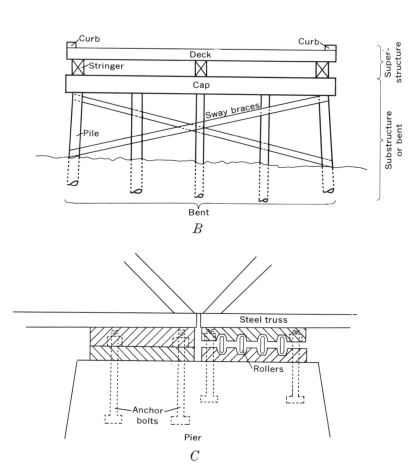

29.—Schematic drawing showing various elements of a bridge. *A*, view parallel to stream; *B*, view perpendicular to stream; *C*, view parallel to stream.

and silt. On the Seward-Anchorage Highway all the bridge approaches subsided because of compaction except the structures spanning Quartz Creek, Summit Creek, Colorado Creek, Spokane Creek, Bertha Creek, and Lyon and Tincan Creek. Quartz Summit and Colorado Creek bridges are short 22-foot spans anchored in bedrock with a thin veneer of coarse gravel for approaches. Lyon and Tincan,

Bertha, and Spokane Creek bridges are on a thin layer of coarse gravel overlying bedrock and do not have thick approach fills.

The factors chiefly responsible for large subsidence of approaches on the Turnagain Arm section of the Seward-Anchorage Highway were (1) the highway is underlain by fine-grained silt and sand and silty gravel, (2) the water table is close to the surface, generally within 2 feet, and (3) most of the roadway and approach fills are thick. In places between Twenty-mile River and the town of Portage there was as much as 12 feet of fill. All these factors combined to cause failure of the underlying confining sediments by lateral displacement toward the creek and displacement normal to the roadway fill and approach.

All the bridge approaches on the Copper River Highway underwent compaction and subsidence by seismic shaking with the exception of those at the Eyak River bridge at mile 5.9. Maximum compaction of 3 feet occurred at the east approach of Copper River 2 bridge at mile 27.1. Figure 31 shows the vertical displacement of the approach. This approach fill

30.—Subsidence of bridge approach fill at Tidewater Slough 2 bridge, mile 76.4, Seward-Anchorage Highway. View is west. Photograph by Helen Foster.

31.—View looking west, Copper River bridge 2, mile 27.1, Copper River Highway. Approach subsided 3 feet as a result of seismic shaking.

32.—Mound formed by bulldozing of approach fill against bridge deck (foreground), at north end of Copper River 12 bridge, mile 36.9, Copper River Highway.

is about 10 feet thick and is underlain chiefly by silt and sand.

Displacement of the north approach of Copper River 12 bridge, mile 36.9 on the Copper River Highway (fig. 32), was unique. Here, instead of subsiding, the approach fill formed a mound 18 inches high against the north abutment of the bridge. The silty gravel fill was moved laterally against the resisting abutment and, because the bulkhead did not fail, the mound was formed. A similar mound was formed at the Little Tonsina River bridge on the Richardson Highway by a landslide.

Although the seismic shaking caused some compaction and subsidence on all the Copper River Highway bridge approaches, there were no large vertical displacements chiefly because (1) the fine-grained sediments that underlie much of the highway are coarser than those that underlie the Turnagain Arm section of the Seward-Anchorage Highway where approach subsidence was so extensive, (2) the water table on the Copper River Highway is deeper than that a Turnagain Arm, and (3) the roadway fills are generally only a thin veneer on the original ground.

The bridge approaches on the Glenn and Sterling Highways sustained only minor damage. However, even in fill approaches placed on bedrock some subsidence or compaction took place. The Chickaloon River bridge (mile 78.2) and the Puritan Creek bridge (mile 89.3) on the Glenn Highway rest on bedrock, but the approaches are constructed of sandy gravel fill. At Puritan Creek the east approach has 10 feet of fill that subsided 3 inches; the west approach has a 6-foot fill over bedrock and subsided 1 inch. The Chickaloon River bridge approaches have 4 to 5 feet of sandy gravel fill; both approaches compacted or subsided at least 1 inch. Maximum subsidence of approaches was 3 inches recorded at Puritan Creek and at the west approach of the Little Nelchina River, mile 137.5.

On the Sterling Highway both the approaches to the Kenai River bridge, mile 48.9, subsided 8 inches (table 19, p. C66). Subsidence was not expressed as single displacements between the abutments and the approaches, but instead of spread over an area of several feet.

Maximum vertical displacement of bridge approaches on the Richardson Highway was about 6 inches (table 18, p. C65). The displacement at nearly all localities was in glacial sediments, although the Stuart Creek bridge, mile 45.6, the approaches are thick fills overlying bedrock. The main reason for the lack of large vertical displacements of approaches and roadway is the fact that the depth to the water table generally is more than 6 feet and commonly more than 10 feet.

Many types of bridges were in use in south-central Alaska at the time of the earthquake (see tables 15–19, p. C59–C66). If these bridges had rested on the same kind of sediments, the damage could have been analyzed with relative ease, but because the structures rested on different kinds of sediments, analysis was more difficult. The structural damage at first appeared to be random, but further studies indicated a pattern of failure.

The bridges failed in various ways as a result of seismic shaking. Some bridges collapsed completely; in others, anchor bolts sheared off, pilings were displaced, abutments were crowded, structures were compressed, and structural elements were displaced horizontally or vertically. Failure of the bridges on the Turnagain Arm stretch of the Seward-Anchorage Highway, was particularly spectacular. These bridges, simple T-beam spans on timber bent substructures, were underlain chiefly by silt, sand, and silty gravel, so most of the wooden piles were bottomed in this material.

33.—Wreckage of Portage Creek bridges 2 and 3, Seward-Anchorage Highway. The Alaska Railroad grade and bridges are in foreground of highway. Photograph by U.S. Army.

Damage to these bridges occurred because of (1) failure of the wood bents, (2) lateral displacement of the sediments toward the creek which forced the abutments closer together and literally crowded the deck and compressed the bridge (fig. 33), and (3) failure at the tie between the substructure and superstructure. The seismic shaking and lateral displacement of the sediments pulled the wood ties off the caps, and the superstructure became independent of the substructure. The deck or superstructure had a vertical as well as a horizontal component of movement during the earthquake. Eventually the wood bents failed beneath the superstructure and the bridge collapsed. In many bridges the wood piles were driven through the reinforced concrete deck (fig. 34). Eyewitness reports show that the decks had an up-and-down motion period of about 1 second. That is, a wave apparently passed through the deck, and, as it passed through, the

superstructure moved up and down in about a 1-second cycle. It is hard to believe that a wood pile could be driven through a reinforced concrete deck by this motion, and that at many places the saw marks could then still be seen at the end of the piles. Apparently at the same time the deck was coming down, a ground wave was displacing the piles upward. These statements should not be construed to mean that the piles actually had a higher altitude after the earthquake than they had before: Nowhere along the highways in south-central Alaska had piles been pulled out of the ground or displaced vertically upwards. On the contrary, all the piles were at lower altitudes after the earthquake, partly because of the pounding of the deck upon the piles but primarily because of the lack of strength of the sediments supporting the piles. Seismic shaking partially or completely liquefied the sediments around the piles.

The overhead at the east end of Snow River Crossing was destroyed by seismic shaking. It rested on wood piles and collapsed upon the tracks of The Alaska Railroad (fig. 35).

Among the severely damaged bridges along the Copper River Highway was the Million Dollar Bridge at mile 49.0. This bridge, constructed in 1910 by the Copper River and Northwestern Railway, made it possible to carry copper ore from Chitina to Cordova. The railroad was abandoned before World War II, and most of its larger bridges and roadbed from Cordova to mile 51 were reoccupied by the Copper River Highway. The rails were salvaged and used as piles on 22 of the highway bridges. Three rails (about 50-pound rails that is, rails that weigh 50 pounds a linear yard) were welded heads together and driven, but there was a history of failure even while they were being driven.

[675]

34.—Collapsed bridge across Twentymile River. Railroad bridge in upper right photograph did not collapse.

35.—Overhead at east side of Snow River Crossing. Structure collapsed upon tracks of The Alaska Railroad. Photograph by U.S. Army.

The Million Dollar Bridge, which spans the Copper River as it leaves Miles Lake at the mouth of Copper River canyon, is a historic structure in Alaska. The completion of this bridge is indeed a tribute to the engineers and construction men who built it. Rex Beach, in his book "The Iron Trail," published in 1913, did much to bring these men to the attention of the world.

The bridge consists of four steel truss spans 400, 300, 450, and 400 feet long. Migliaccio (1966) stated that caissons for piers 1, 2, and 3 were landed at 36, 36, and 50 feet below the stream bed. The foundations for all the piers except pier 3 are sand and gravel and boulders from 1 to 10 cubic feet in volume. Migliaccio reported that the foundation supporting pier 3 is sand, gravel, and boulders smaller than those underlying the

36.—Million Dollar Bridge, Copper River Highway; No. 4 span off No. 4 pier. View is southwest.

other piers. Maximum foundation pressures were less than 4 tons per square foot.

Although the bridge was very severely damaged (figs. 36, 37), the Alaska Department of Highways will no doubt make all efforts to save it because of its historic value. In view of the magnitude of this venture a more complete description of damage is presented here than is possible in table 15. The following damage report was made by Harry Golub of the

Alaska Department of Highways:

Abutment 1 relatively undamaged—no sign of movement of abutment itself. Span 1 is displaced 1½ inch south and 1 foot upstream. The top of the backwall and wings are cracked and chipped from pounding of deck. Backwall is pockmarked from rivets at end of truss. New stringer seats have small sections of concrete broken away by contact with end of truss. Anchor bolts are sheared. Truss apparently undamaged. At pier 2 both spans have moved enough to turn their rollers over flat and bend their anchor bolts. In their final position bolts are about in the middle of

expansion slots. Span 1 moved south and span 2 moved north. The spans are jammed tight on upstream side, separated by about 2 inches downstream, jamming together pulverized sliding beams between spans as well as the ends of the concrete deck and bent the finger joint and its connections. The bottom chords of the trusses show some crimping from passage over the rollers, but actual damage is difficult to assess without raising trusses. Only a short length of chord and some of its connecting angles are affected.

At pier 3 the following displacements were measured.

37.—Collapsed No. 4 span and horizontal fracture in No. 4 pier of Million Dollar Bridge, Copper River Highway. View is northeast.

Upstream bearings:
    Span 2
        19 inches upstream
        10 inches north
    Span 3
        18 inches upstream
        3 inches north
There is about 3½ inches between ends of trusses.
Downstream bearings:
    Span 2
        19 inches upstream
        13 inches north
    Span 3
        19 inches upstream
        4 inches north
Ends of trusses jammed together—all anchor bolts sheared. Sliding beams between spans have been pulverized—those on railroad stringer lines have damaged the end floor beam webs. Joint angles and ends of concrete slab badly damaged. Piers 2 and 3 seem to have suffered no structural damage. Pier 4 is virtually destroyed. The upper por-

tion has split into three parts, with each of the end pieces separated from the middle by a crack up to 2 feet wide. The middle portion has a vertical crack running completely through it. The upper half of the pier has also sheared horizontally and has moved about 2 feet south in respect to the lower half. The entire pier has a list toward the south. There is no evidence of reinforcement in the upper pier and failures seem to be along construction joints. The bearings of span 3 are displaced 9 feet 9 inches from their former position on pier 4 in a northward direction and approximately 6 feet transversely. Bottom lateral bracing is mutilated from contact with the pier and the bottom chords have been dragged over the concrete, popping rivets and doing an indeterminable amount of damage to the bottom chord and its connections.

Span 4 has dropped off pier 4 and is in the river, probably resting on the bottom since the river is quite shallow

north of pier 4. The truss and concrete deck appear undamaged from L_0' to L_2, where the deck is broken and the chords apparently bent or broken by the fall. Verticals $L_1 U_1$ are bent completely out of shape in compression. End posts show no damage above water. The span is collecting some drift, but the shallowness of the river protects it from fast water or large pieces of floating ice. The span may stay where it is for some time.

Abutment 5 does not show signs of any major damage. There is, of course, some spalling and breaking of concrete at the bridge seats caused by the fall of span 4 and all anchor bolts are either broken or bent, but the abutment itself seems structurally sound.

Mr. Golub's description of damage to the Million Dollar Bridge indicates that some crowding of the superstructure relative to the abutments and compression of the spans against one another has occurred. The abutments moved an unknown amount toward the center of the Copper River because of lateral displacement of sediments to an unknown depth. At pier 3 the relative displacement of the pier was upstream. Either the superstructure moved downstream or, more probably, the pier moved upstream because of lateral displacement of the underlying sediments. The largest free face is upstream, toward Miles Lake. There was probably some slumping or spreading of sediments upstream into the deep lake, which would account for the apparent movement of the piers upstream rather than downstream.

During the earthquake all the bridges supported by piles made of the old rails were severely damaged or destroyed (table 15, p. C59) because the brittle rail piles were unable to withstand the severe seismic shaking generated by the earthquake (fig. 38). Figure 39 is a photograph of a collapsed bent on Copper River 5 bridge, mile 35.0, and figure 40 is a view showing how the bent was constructed. The concrete between the rails provides protection to the bent against winter ice. This bent either broke because of partial or total liquefaction of the supporting fine-grained sand and silt sediments. The bridge deck collapsed because of differential movement of the deck and bent, lateral displacement of the bent, or a combination of the two.

The Copper River 2 bridge consisted of a reoccupied steel truss bridge of the Copper River and Northwestern Railway and a concrete deck supported by welded rail bents. The truss moved eastward relative to the concrete section of the bridge (fig. 41). The

38.—Broken rail piles on Scott Glacier 6 bridge, mile 5.9, Copper River Highway.

39.—Collapsed bent and deck of Copper River 5 bridge, mile 35.0, Copper River Highway.

bridge elements were compressed or crowded against each other by the movement caused by the seismic shaking.

Lateral displacement of sediments toward a free face caused movement of the abutments toward the middle of the stream and

made the superstructure too long for the abutments; the structure was thus compressed or crowded. Most if not all of this horizontal displacement was taken up at only one end of the structure (compare figs. 42, 43). Figure 42 shows the west abutment of Scott Glacier 5

40.—Collapsed deck on Copper River 5 bridge, mile 35.0, Copper River Highway.
Concrete between rail piles is to protect rails against ice.

41.—Contact between steel truss and concrete deck on pier 26, Copper River 2 bridge, mile 27.1, Copper River Highway.

42.—West abutment of Scott Glacier 5 bridge, mile 9.2, Copper River Highway. Concrete cap displaced 2 inches to the left off the pile bent. Compare with figure 43.

bridge, mile 9.2, on the Copper River Highway; here the concrete cap was displaced westward off the pile bent. Figure 43 shows the east abutment of the bridge; at this end of the structure, the superstructure rammed through the wood abutment and was displaced about 2 feet to the east relative to the abutment. Maximum horizontal displacement of superstructure relative to substructure or compression of a bridge on the Copper River Highway was 6 feet. This displacement occurred at the north abutment of the Clear Creek bridge at mile 41.0 (fig. 44) and also at the south abutment of the Copper River 16 bridge at mile 38.1.

The sediments that underlie the Copper River Highway become progressively coarser eastward toward mile 22.3; they become progressively thinner from about mile 16.6 to mile 22.3, where bedrock is exposed. Thirteen slightly damaged bridges are in this stretch of the highway, but, they are all wooden structures and should not be compared with other types of structures. Rather they should be compared with similar bridges at miles 14.8, 15.3, 15.8, 15.9, 16.1, and 16.5. The bridges at miles 14.8 and 15.8 were moderately damaged; those at miles 15.3, 15.9, 16.1, and 16.5 were severely damaged or destroyed. This pattern of damage to

similar bridges affords an opportunity to evaluate the effects of geologic environment on the amount of damage. Those bridges which received moderate to severe damage or were destroyed were underlain by a thicker prism of sediments than those that were only slightly damaged. The thinner the underlying sediment the less the damage, and the coarser the grain size of the underlying sediments the less the damage from seismic shaking.

Seismic damage to the bridges on the Sterling Highway was light compared to that to bridges on the Seward-Anchorage and Copper River Highways (compare figs. 2, 3, 6; tables 15, 16, 19, p. C59, C62, C66). The Quartz Creek bridge at mile 41.7 is underlain by a fine-grained thin veneer of silt and sand overlying stream gravel. The damage to this bridge was more than might have been expected because the structure was resting on concrete abutments and concrete piers. Damage was chiefly due to lateral displacement of the abut-

43.—East abutment of Scott Glacier Creek 5 bridge at mile 9.2, Copper River Highway. Superstructure is displaced about 2 feet to the right, relative to the abutment. Compare with figure 42.

44.—North abutment of Clear Creek bridge 329, mile 41.0, Copper River Highway. Superstructure is displaced to the right relative to the abutment.

ments toward the center of the creek, which placed the structure in compression. The bridge at mile 48.9 crossed the Kenai River at the outlet of Kenai Lake. The bridge, which rested on silt, sand, and gravel deposited by the river, collapsed during the earthquake. The wood piles, on some of which the saw marks were still visible when the bridge was inspected by survey personnel, were driven through the reinforced concrete deck (p. C43; fig. 45).

The three concrete bridges that span Portage Creek Overflows 1, 2, and 3, at miles 3.3, 3.8, and 4.3, respectively, on Portage Glacier Road were severely dam-aged. These bridges which rest on silt, sand, and gravel, were se-verely compressed after the earth-quake and had to be replaced.

SEISMIC SEA WAVES

The train of 10 seismic sea waves associated with the Alaska earthquake destroyed 13 bridges in south-central Alaska, 12 on Kodiak Island, and 1 on the Point Whitshed Road at Hartney Bay. Of the 12 bridges destroyed on Kodiak Island, 11 were on the Chiniak Highway and 1 at Mis-sion Bay in the town of Kodiak.

The 11 bridges on the Chiniak Highway that were destroyed by waves spanned Sargent Creek at mile 5.0, Russian Creek at mile 5.2, the American River at mile 13.3, Mayflower Creek at mile 17.2, the Kalsin River at mile 22.8, West and East Forks of the Twin River at miles 32.7 and 32.9, respectively, and four small unnamed creeks at miles 12.0, 12.3, 13.6, and 33.7.

Eyewitness reports indicate that the first seismic sea wave was like a rapid rise of sea level and that the following waves were ac-tually breaking. The damage to the bridges was due to the rapid retreat of the initial wave and to subsequent breaking waves. The first outgoing seismic sea wave was in part responsible for destruction of some of the bridges, but the subsequent incoming waves played the major role.

The waves destroyed the structures either by moving the superstructure off the substructure or by destroying the bents supporting the deck of the bridge. Most of the decks that were moved off their piles were carried upstream. Some ruins, however, were not found and no doubt had been carried out to sea by the outgoing waves.

REGIONAL SUBSIDENCE AND LOCAL SUBSIDENCE

Several otherwise undamaged bridges had to be replaced on the Chiniak Highway and between mile 75.1 and mile 105 on the Seward-Anchorage Highway because of flooding caused by regional tectonic subsidence and local differential subsidence. This postearthquake flooding by high tides affected the sites of 44 bridges in south-central Alaska and in itself would have required replacement of the bridges; 35 of the 44, however, had already been damaged by either seismic shaking or seismic sea wave. The nine undamaged bridges that had to be

45.—Collapsed bridge across Kenai River at Kenai Lake, mile 48.9, Sterling Highway. Wood piles are driven through the collapsed reinforced concrete deck. Photograph by Helen Foster.

replaced because of flooding are on Kodiak Island and include (1) three bridges at Pasagshak Bay, (2) the Red Cloud River bridge (mile 7.7) and an unnamed creek bridge at mile 9.0 at Anton Larsen

Bay, and (3) the bridges on the Chiniak Highway spanning Lost Creek at mile 5.8, Salonie Creek at mile 6.4, Frank Creek at mile 23.6, and an unnamed small creek at mile 24.9.

GEOLOGIC FACTORS INFLUENCING DAMAGE INTENSITY

GRAIN SIZE OF SEDIMENTS

The type of sediments upon which the highway rested played a major role in the amount and type of damage the structures experienced. For example, highway roadways underlain by coarsegrained sand and gravel were fractured substantially less than were roadways underlain by finer

grained sand and silt. Roadways, fills, and approaches constructed of coarser grained sediments also were not fractured as much as those constructed of finer material. For example, in the Portage area, the Seward-Anchorage Highway and The Alaska Railroad are adjacent to one another. The highway roadway is constructed of well-graded (poorly sorted) compacted silt, sand, and gravel

whereas the railroad roadbed is constructed primarily of poorly compacted sand and gravel. The finer grained highway fill was substantially more fractured than the railroad fill.

Structures on fine-grained sediments subsided more than those on coarse-grained sediments. For example, maximum subsidence of a highway roadway of as much as 11 feet occurred at Snow River

Crossing on the Seward-Anchorage Highway. The roadway subsided 7½ to 8 feet at mile 82.0, Seward-Anchorage Highway, on the north approach of Tidewater Slough 5 bridge. Both of these areas are underlain by sand and silt. The subsidence was due to the lateral displacement and compaction of the underlying sediments.

THICKNESS OF SEDIMENTS

The thickness of sediments also influenced the extent of damage. The prism of sediments that underlie the Copper River Highway from mile 5.9 to mile 22.3 thins from mile 16.6 to mile 22.3 where bedrock is exposed. The sediments also became progressively coarser eastward, toward mile 22.3. In this section of the highway there were 13 slightly damaged all-wood bridges whereas all-wood bridges west of mile 16.6 received severe damage or were destroyed. The two geologic factors that controlled the extent of damage to the all-wood bridges were: the thinning of the prism of sediments underlying the roadway, and the progressive coarsening of the sediments eastward.

DEPTH OF WATER TABLE

Other than foundation material, the most important geologic factor controlling damage is the depth of the water table. In any given geologic condition, the closer the water table to the surface, the more damage to the highway system. For example, at Snow River Crossing where the maximum compaction of 11 feet occurred, the water table is within 1 foot of the surface. At Tidewater Slough 5 bridge, the water table is within 4 feet of the surface. In the Turnagain Arm area on the

Seward-Anchorage Highway, the roadway from miles 75.1 to 81.0 is underlain by silt, sand, and fine gravel. The most extensive fracture damage along the highway occurred between miles 78.4 and 81.0 where the water table is generally within 2 to 3 feet of the surface. Between miles 75.1 and 78.4, where the damage was less severe, the water table is generally 1 foot deeper.

AMOUNT OF COMPACTION

During the earthquake both the sediments underlying the roadway and the roadway fill itself compacted. The exact amount of compaction of each is difficult to determine; however, most of the subsidence was in the underlying sediments. The sediments were not only compacted but were laterally displaced from beneath the roadway fill.

The roadway subsided as much as 11 feet, but the surrounding ground did not subside as much. Data obtained from water wells indicates that maximum measured compaction of the undisturbed sediments did not occur at Snow River Crossing or in the Portage area, but a Homer Spit near the town of Homer.

Homer Spit is underlain by the following unconsolidated deposits (Grantz, Plafker, and Kachadoorian, 1964):

	Feet
Silt, sand, and gravel	0–200
Sand	200–289
Marine sand and clay	289–321
Soft clay, locally mushy	321–462
Hard clay	462–468
Kenai(?) formation	468–477+

Here the sediments compacted at least 2.5 feet. Compaction no doubt

occurred in the upper part of the silt, sand, and gravel layer.

The log of the water well at the Union Oil Station at Portage shows that the station is underlain (Grantz, Plafker, Kachadoorian, 1964) by:

	Feet
Sand and gravel	0–20
Clay	20–425
Sand	425–426
Clay	426–600

The floor of the station subsided 16 inches around the casing of the well. Comparison of the data from Homer Spit and the Union Oil well at Portage may seem invalid, in as much as the well at Homer Spit had no structure around it, whereas the one at Portage did. However, the author feels that comparison is valid, because maximum compaction in a given area occurred where a structure was placed on original ground. Therefore, the 16 inches at the Union Oil Station is a maximum figure for compaction of original ground at Portage.

The chief factors responsible for the amount of compaction are the coarseness and the thickness of the sediments subjected to seismic shaking. The coarser the sediments the more they are compacted, and the thicker the sediments the more they are compacted. For example, there is 200 feet of silt, sand, and gravel at Homer Spit and 20 feet of sand and gravel at the Union Oil Station at Portage. According to the well logs the Homer Spit sediments are finer, but the author examined both sites and found that the Homer Spit sediments are actually coarser. The apparent discrepancy is due to the fact that the wells were logged by two different laymen.

The depth to which compaction by seismic shaking extends in the undisturbed ground is unknown.

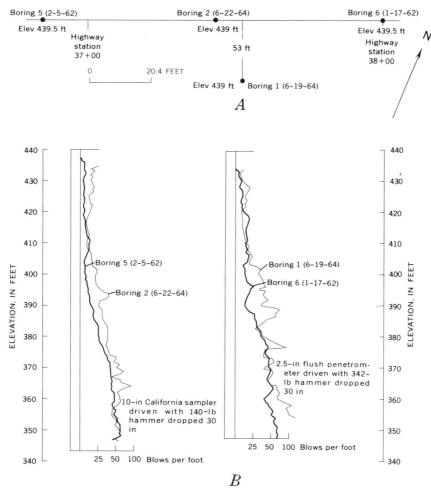

46.—Sketch of boring locations (*A*) and pre- and postearthquake penetrometer tests (*B*) at Snow River bridge 605, mile 17.7, Seward-Anchorage Highway. Data after George E. Utermole, Jr., Alaska Department of Highways.

The only data available about depth of compaction are from the highway and railroad roadbeds, but these are engineered or semi-engineered fills placed upon the sediments. Furthermore, during seismic shaking, some of the vertical displacement of the highway roadway or railroad roadbed is due to lateral displacement of the underlying sediments. The railroad's Twentymile bridge rests upon piles about 60 feet deep. The right-of-way to the bridge approaches subsided 1 to 1½ feet more than the bridge (Grantz, Plafker, Kachadoorian, 1964). Thus, the top 50 to 60 feet of the unconsolidated material must have compacted relatively more than the material below the piers.

The Alaska Department of Highways conducted some postearthquake penetrometer tests at Snow River Crossing Bridge 605, mile 17.7, on the Seward-Anchorage Highway and compared the results with preearthquake data. George E. Utermole, Jr., foundation geologist, Alaska Department of Highways, suggests that the postearthquake density of the sediments underlying Snow River Crossing Bridge 605 is greater than the preearthquake; however, he points out that "how much of this increase in density is due to the earthquake cannot be estab-

lished" (Alaska Dept. Highways, unpub. data). Figure 46 shows the location of the borings and the results of the tests.

LIQUEFACTION OF SEDIMENTS

Failure because of liquefaction of saturated soils was extensive in south-central Alaska, especially at the Snow River Crossing and Turnagain Arm sections of the Seward-Anchorage Highway. Failure developed locally at partial liquefaction before complete liquefaction of the saturated soils. However, at Snow River Crossing, Turnagain Arm, and on the Richardson Highway from mile 0.0 to 5.0, most of the soil was completely liquefied.

Liquefaction was responsible for both vertical and horizontal displacement of sediments. The sediments underlying the roadway where liquefaction occurred actually flowed out and downslope from underneath the roadway fill. Where this flow occurred, the roadway (1) subsided into the sediments and at some places, as at the Snow River Crossing, was completely submerged into the sediments, (2) was displaced laterally, and (3) was fractured. Statement by eyewitnesses that water spouts continued for several minutes after the seismic vibration stopped at Portage indicate that failure of the sediments underlying the roadway in the area must also have continued after the earthquake had stopped.

Field tests by the author and M. G. Bonilla at Portage also indicated that liquefaction continued after the vibrating force was removed. A small plot underlain by silt was selected for the test. Prior to any vibration the silt looked dry and one could walk upon it without difficulty. The silt was vibrated by foot for about one-half minute at which time moisture began to collect at the surface. When moisture appeared, the vibration was stopped. The depth of liquefied silt was 1½ inches. The water continued to seep out, and in 2 minutes it started to flow out as fountains in the center of the vibrated mass. Four minutes after the force was applied, water began to flow out of the liquefied jelly-like mass of silt. After 7 minutes the water began to clear up, although it was still flowing. The depth to firm ground had migrated down to 4 inches within 8 minutes after vibration was

stopped. The test was abandoned after 8 minutes. The area that was liquefied was about 18 inches square and the softest spot was in the center where the initial force was applied.

The sediments that underlie the Snow River Crossing were especially prone to liquefaction. During testing in 1962, many of the samples collapsed in sampling tubes when vibrated or when a shock was applied. In addition, some of the silt contained gases (derived from the decomposition of organic debris in the silt) under pressure and was thixotropic.

Mrs. Hadley Roberts of Lawing, Alaska, described what occurred at Snow River to a friend. Part of the letter is quoted here:

* * * Don and Ed Estes had been caught in the mile stretch crossing Snow River and the flats. They said the whole highway across there was waving up and down like someone was shaking a blanket. As it would heave up the pavement would crack and it would come together again as it settled down. Finally the mud started oozing through the cracks and they no longer would come together, and the pavement then started settling into the mud. They finally had to abandon the car about 50 yards from the other side as the cracks were too big. They ran for bedrock with the mud licking at their heels. This was quite a run for them as it was all uphill now and lots of cracks to jump over. Their car was pulled out of the mud a few days later. * * *

This description brings out three important facts: (1) fractures developed before liquefaction of the sediments and were caused by seismic ground waves, (2) liquefaction did not occur immediately, and (3) the roadway, although cracked, settled into the underlying sediments a f t e r liquefaction developed. The first point appears to conflict with the statement made earlier on this page that when

liquefaction occurred the underlying sediments flowed out and downslope from beneath the roadway, and that this outflow caused fracturing of the roadway. The fractures at Snow River Crossing were first caused by shear and tension failure, because the roadway was differentially displaced laterally; additional later fractures may have been caused by liquefaction.

LATERAL DISPLACEMENT

Seismic shock was the chief cause for lateral displacement of sediments. As seismic ground waves passed through the ground, they imparted a motion to the sediments similar to that which a vibrating table does to debris upon it. The sediments were displaced laterally downslope or toward a free face. This type of failure was extensive in the Copper River Highway and was responsible for moving bridge abutments toward the centers of creeks. When this movement occurred, a bridge was either compressed or, more commonly, the superstructure became substantially too long for the span between the abutments and one end of the deck was displaced as much as 6 feet over an abutment. Lateral displacement due to seismic shock not only moved the abutments, piers, and bents toward the center of the creek, but it also moved them upstream or downstream.

As the sediments were displaced laterally, the roadway failed in tension and fractures formed. Some of these fractures formed during the passing of the seismic ground wave before the actual displacement of the sediments.

Lateral displacement and subsidence occurred in bridge approach fills overlying bedrock owing to seismic shaking; it was noted even in completely dry fills less than 10 feet thick.

ENGINEERING FACTORS INFLUENCING DAMAGE INTENSITY

Although geologic factors played the major role in controlling intensity of damage to the roadways and bridges, they were by no means solely responsible. The engineering characteristics of the roadways and bridges also influenced the damage intensity.

In low-lying saturated areas, especially those at Portage and at Snow River, the roadway fill had a higher density than the supporting underlying sediments. In short, the fill was floating upon the sediments. The thicker the fill, the heavier the load on the underlying sediments. When the earthquake struck, the sediments were unable to support the roadway and failed. At Snow River, the roadway locally sank out of sight into the sediments. Failure, no doubt, first occurred at sites where fills were thickest. The maximum thickness of fill in the Turnagain Arm section of the Seward-Anchorage Highway was at about mile 80.5 near the Twentymile River and was about 12 feet. The geologic conditions from mile 78.4 to mile 81.0 are similar, yet the roadway at mile 80.5 was the most severely damaged by the earthquake. Therefore, it is proposed that under given geologic conditions, especially in saturated soils, the thicker and heavier the fill, the greater the damage to the roadway.

An analysis of the damage to bridges on the Seward-Anchorage and Copper River Highways indicates that there is a correlation between damage and the type of bridge. Figure 47 is a chart show-

Superstructure	Substructure	Foundation	DAMAGE			
			None	Slight	Moderate	Severe or destroyed
Concrete	Concrete abutments	Bedrock	381-1137-1138-1139			
Concrete	Concrete abutments	Sediments	741			603-604 605-606
Steel	Concrete abutments	Sediments	617	600	330-599	333
Concrete	Concrete piers	Sediments		615		
Concrete	Wood	Sediments	608-609-611	601-610		603-605-606-621-622-623-624-625-626-627-628-629-630-631-632-633-634-635-638-640-641-642
Wood	Wood	Bedrock		395		
Wood	Wood	Sediments	602	368-369-370-371-372-373-374-375-376-377-378-379-395	361-364	363-365-366-367
Steel	Concrete piers	Sediments				331-332-206-596-597-598-620-644
Steel	Wood piles	Sediments	619		636	348-349-350-351-352-639-643
Steel	Railroad rails	Sediments		410-343	337	406-407-408-409-411-354-334-335-336-338-339-340-341-342-344-345-346-329-331
Steel	Wood	Bedrock	607			
Steel	Steel	Bedrock	613	612		
Steel	Concrete piers	Bedrock	614	616	637	

47.—Chart showing type of bridge, foundation material, and intensity of damage to bridges on Seward-Anchorage and Copper River Highways. Numbers are bridge designations (see tables 15, 16). The 200, 300, and 400 series structures are on the Copper River Highway; the others are on the Seward-Anchorage Highway. Length of bar is proportional to number of bridges damaged.

ing type of bridge, foundation material, and intensity of damage to bridges on the Seward-Anchorage and Copper River Highways.

The most significant engineering fact that the chart shows is the relation between the superstructure and substructure. During the construction of 22 of the bridges on the Copper River Highway, Copper River and Northwest Railway rails were used as piles. Three of these rails, believed to be 50-pound rails were welded with their heads together. They were then driven, and when a bent was completed the rails were cut off and a concrete cap placed upon them. At some places, steel sway braces were welded on the rails. Where icing of the creek would present a problem, concrete curtains were placed between the rails (fig. 40). These rails are brittle, and one of the techniques track-layers used to cut off a rail was to first mark it with a chisel and then strike the rail sharply with a hammer. The rail would break at the chisel mark. During the driving, the welded rail piles were occasionally broken. When the earthquake struck, all except two (Scott Glacier 10, mile 10.8, and Copper River 14, mile 37.5) of the bridges whose bents consisted of rail piles were moderately or severely damaged or were destroyed. The rail piles were broken above the waterline in most of the structures that did not have a concrete curtain. In those that had concrete curtains, failure of the piles generally occurred below the waterline. Figure 39 shows results of such a failure.

A significant comparison between all-wood bridges and bridges with concrete superstructure and wood substructure can also be made. For example, a remarkable difference in damage intensity can be seen if we compare the all-wood structures on the

48.—North abutment of Copper River 9 bridge, 338, mile 36.1, Copper River Highway, showing displacement of deck laterally to the left relative to substructure. Photograph by George Plafker.

Copper River Highway with the concrete and wood bridges on the Seward-Anchorage Highway, neglecting for a moment the geologic conditions. Most of the all-wood bridges were only slightly damaged whereas most of the concrete and wood bridges were severely damaged or destroyed (fig. 47). If we now take into account the geologic factors, the comparison becomes more complex. The Turnagain Arm bridges were definitely in a more geologically unfavorable environment. The extent to which this unfavorable environment would have affected all-wood highway structures is unknown. However, on the basis of the types of damage to concrete and wood bridges, all-concrete bridges (on Portage Glacier Road), and all-wood bridges caused by the earthquake, it is proposed that if the superstructure was relatively heavier than the substructure, the

bridge was more severely damaged. If the deck is heavier than the substructure, the tie between them is more easily broken because of differential movement of the two units by seismic shaking. When this movement occurs, the substructure and superstructure, in effect, become independent of one another and, instead of reinforcing one another they actually compound the effects of seismic shaking. Figure 48 is a photograph looking south at Copper River 9 bridge, 338, mile 36.1, on the Copper River Highway. The deck of the structure apparently had a seismically induced motion independent of the substructure and actually destroyed the top of much of the north abutment. Note that the final position of the superstructure indicates that the deck was displaced to the east relative to the abutment and the remainder of the substructure.

SUMMARY

The earthquake of March 27, 1964, caused $46,798,292 worth of damage to the highway system in south-central Alaska. Damage was caused by seismic shaking, seismic sea waves, and regional tectonic subsidence. The table summarizes the effects associated with these three major causes of damage. Seismic shaking and the effects associated with it apparently caused the most damage. The effects of the Alaska earthquake upon the highway system once again demonstrated the significant fact that structures on bedrock were not damaged as much as those on sediments.

Effects on highway system caused by seismic shaking, seismic sea waves, and regional tectonic subsidence by the Alaska earthquake

Seismic shaking

Lateral displacement of sediments:
 Subsidence of roadway and bridge approaches

Lateral displacement of sediments—Continued
 Displacement of roadway parallel to highway axis
 Displacement of roadway normal to highway axis
 Displacement of bridge abutments, bents, and piers toward center of creek
 Displacement of bridge piers and bents upstream and downstream
 Placement of bridges in compression
 Formation of fractures:
  Along roadway centerline
  Along roadway edges or shoulders
  Normal to axis of roadway
  Oblique fractures:
   Refracted normal to roadway
   Continued through roadway at oblique angles
Compactions of sediments:
 Fractures in roadway normal to axis
 Fractures along edge of roadway
 Subsidence of roadway and bridge approaches
 Inundation during high tides
 Wavy roadway due to differential compaction
Landslides:
 Slides onto roadway
 Slides in roadway:
  Fracture of roadway normal to axis
  Fracture of roadway parallel to axis
  Displacement of roadway normal to axis

Landslides—Continued
 Slides in roadway—Continued
  Displacement of roadway parallel to axis
  Destruction of bridge
Seismic shock:
 Damage to bridges:
  Differential movement of structural elements
  Broken tie between superstructure and substructure
  Bridge in compression
 Seismic wave in bridges:
  Vertical movement of bridge during shaking
  Horizontal movement of bridge during shaking:
   Displacement of deck upstream or downstream
   Displacement of deck along axis of bridge
  Bridge in compression
 Ground waves in roadway
Avalanches: Upon roadway
Sand and mud ejecta: In roadway

Seismic sea waves

Destruction of bridges:
 Sweeping away of superstructure
 Destruction of substructure
Damage to roadway: Scouring of fill

Regional tectonic subsidence (coupled with compaction of sediments)

Inundation of roadway during high tides
Inundation of bridge sites
Erosion of roadway by high tides

REFERENCES CITED

Eckel, E. B., and Schaem, W. E., 1966, in Hansen, W. R., and others, The Alaska earthquake, March 27, 1964: Field investigations and reconstruction effort: U.S. Geological Survey Professional Paper 541, p. 46–69.

Ferrians, O. J., Jr., 1966, Effects of the earthquake of March 27, 1964, in the Copper River Basin area, Alaska: U.S. Geol. Survey Prof. Paper 543–E, p. E1–E28.

Golub, Harvey, 1964, Bridge damage report—mile 13 to mile 59, Copper River Highway—FAS 851: Alaska Dept. Highways Document.

Grantz, Arthur, Plafker, George, and Kachadoorian, Reuben, 1964, Alaska's Good Friday earthquake, March 27, 1964, a preliminary geologic evaluation: U.S. Geol. Survey Circ. 491, 35 p.

Kachadoorian, Reuben, 1965, Effects of the earthquake of March 27, 1964, at Whittier, Alaska: U.S. Geol. Survey Prof. Paper 542–B, p. B1–B21.

Migliaccio, R. R., 1966, Earthquake damage to highways in the Valdez district, Alaska: Natl. Research Council, Highway Research Board, Highway Research Rec. 91, p. 64–72.

Plafker, George, 1965, Tectonic deformation associated with the 1964 Alaskan earthquake: Science, v. 148, no. 3678, p. 1675–1687.

Plafker, George, and Kachadoorian, Reuben, 1966, Geologic effects of the March 1964 earthquake and associated seismic sea waves on Kodiak and nearby islands, Alaska: U.S. Geol. Survey Prof. Paper 543–D, p. D1–D46.

U.S. Coast and Geodetic Survey, 1966, The Prince William Sound, Alaska, earthquake of 1964 and aftershocks: Washington, U.S. Govt. Printing Office, v. 1, 263 p.

TABLE 3.—*Foundation material and major effects of Alaska earthquake on the roadway of Seward-Anchorage Highway*

Mile	Foundation material	Effects of earthquake
1 to 3	Stream sediment	Roadway fractured, wavy; differential compaction.
17	Silt and sand	Two-foot slump where road goes onto Snow River delta.
17 to 20	----do	Roadway down as much as 11 feet, horizontally displaced 13½ ft.
33.0 to 33.0	Stream sand and gravel.	Roadway fractured.
35	Bedrock	Avalanche from east side of road.
40.0 to 40.5	Swamp sediments on stream sediments.	Roadway wavy; differential compaction of sediments.
40.4	----do	Culvert up 1½ ft; compacted sediments.
41.7	----do	Avalanche from east side of road.
44.8 to 45.6	Till	Roadway slumped into Summit Lake.
46.3 to 46.7	Swamp deposits over stream deposits.	Roadway wavy; mile 46.6 culvert bent.
51.1 to 51.8	Fine till	Roadway wavy; maximum subsidence is 6 in.
54.5, 54.9, 55.0, 56.0.	Till	Small slides onto road.
56.0 to 56.4	----do	Roadway fractured, compacted, and wavy.
61.8 to 62.0	Stream sediments	Roadway fractured; local subsidence.
63.2 to 64.9	Fine till	Roadway wavy; subsidence as much as 6 in.
66.8 to 67.2	----do	Roadway fractured; local subsidence.
73.2 to 73.6	Fill over swamp deposits.	Roadway fractured, wavy; subsided 6 in.
75.0 to 90.5	Tidal sediments	Roadway fractured, displaced vertically and horizontally; maximum compaction of 4.4 ft plus regional subsidence of 5.6 ft, total subsidence of 11 feet; six large avalanches between mile 82.5 and mile 87.5.
92.0 to 93.5	Bedrock	Eight large avalanches.
98.5 to 105.5	Tidal silt, sand, and gravel.	Roadway compacted, fractured, wavy; inundated during high tides.

TABLE 4.—*Foundation material and major effects of Alaska earthquake on roadway of Sterling Highway*

Mile	Foundation material	Effects of earthquake
39.5	Coarse sediments	Slide across roadway.
44.9	----do	Landslide across roadway.
44.9 to 51	Stream gravel	Roadway fractured, compacted, and wavy.
60.0 to 60.2	Till over bedrock	Roadway fractured; slide across road.
70.5 to 71.5	Swamp deposits over till.	Roadway compacted 2–3 ft; displaced south 4 ft; severely fractured, wavy.
74.9 to 76.5	----do	Roadway compacted, fractured, wavy, and displaced.
85.8	Swamp deposits over glacial outwash.	Roadway fractured, compacted, and wavy.
90.0	----do	Roadway compacted and wavy.
94.8	----do	Roadway fractured, compacted, and wavy.
100	Lake sediments	Slumps on road.
102	Lake silts and sands	Do.
Homer Spit	Gravel	Compacted, subsided; eroded by the sea.

TABLE 5.—*Foundation material and major effects of Alaska earthquake on roadway of Glenn Highway*

Mile	Foundation material	Effects of earthquake
27 to 35____	Swamp deposits_____	Roadway compacted, fractured, wavy; locally displaced and inundated during high tides.
37_____	Bedrock_____	Slide across roadway.
38_____	____do_____	Large avalanche across roadway.
39 to 40____	Outwash gravel_____	Roadway slightly fractured and wavy.
58 to 59____	Ground moraine_____	Roadway fractured, compacted, wavy; small slide at mile 59.
60.5 to 60.7__	____do_____	Roadway compacted, fractured, and wavy; small slide at mile 60.6.
61.0 to 61.2__	Ground moraine and stream sediments.	Roadway compacted, fractured, wavy.
63.5 to 65.5__	Terrace gravels_____	Roadway fractured and wavy.
69_____	____do_____	Small slide on roadway edge.
71_____	___do_____	Do.
74_____	Ground moraine_____	Roadway slightly fractured.
78.5_____	____do_____	Do.
82.0 to 82.5__	Outwash gravel_____	Roadway compacted, slightly fractured, and wavy.
88.5 to 89.5__	____do_____	Roadway slightly compacted, fractured, and wavy.
97.7 to 98.3__	Ground moraine_____	Roadway fractured.
99.0 to 100__	____do_____	Roadway compacted, fractured, and wavy.
106, 107.2___	____do_____	Roadway slid downslope.
111_____	____do_____	Roadway fractured.
114_____	____do_____	Do.
138_____	____do_____	Roadway slid two places.
140_____	____do_____	Do.

TABLE 6.—*Foundation material and major effects of the Alaska earthquake on the roadway of the Richardson Highway*

Mile	Foundation material	Effects of earthquake
0 to 6_____	Glacial outwash_____	Roadway compacted, displaced, fractured, and wavy.
38_____	Bedrock_____	Avalanche.
39_____	____do_____	Do.
40_____	Stream sediments_____	Landslide.
42_____	Bedrock_____	Avalanche.
44_____	____do_____	Rockslide.
59 to 61_____	Gravel_____	Three avalanches.
64 to 75_____	Glacio-lacustrine sediments.	Roadway compacted, displaced, fractured; landslide at Tonsina Bridge (mile 66.0) and Tonsina Hill (mile 73).
75 to 85_____	Stream deposits, silt and clay.	Roadway fractured; at mile 80, four landslides; at mile 76, water eroding roadway.
85 to 110____	Sand and gravel_____	Local fractures in roadway and small stretches of wavy road.

TABLE 7.—*Analyses of sediments at Snow River Crossing, Seward-Anchorage Highway*

[Analyses by Alaska Dept. Highways. NV, no value; NP, nonplastic]

Material	Mile	Depth (feet)	3/4 in.	1/2 in.	3/8 in.	No. 4	No. 10	No. 40	No. 200	0.02 mm	0.005 mm	Liquid limit	Plastic index	Natural moisture content (percent)
Pebbly sand	17.3	13–15			100	95	71	18	4			NV	NP	15
Do	17.3	23–25	100	91	78	45	9	0	0			NV	NP	4
Sand	17.3	43–45		100	98	94	85	73	15	3	1	NV	NP	16
Sand-silt	17.3	53–55		100	98	93	88	59	16	6	2	NV	NP	23
Fine sand	17.3	63–65				100			35	8	4	NV	NP	28
Do	17.3	73–75				100		90	20	5	3	NV	NP	24
Do	17.3	83–85					100	98	29	7	4	NV	NP	27
Sand	17.5	20–22	100	99	98	96	92	61	11	5	4	NV	NP	20
Silty sand	17.5	50–52						100	72	27	9	24	NP	30
Silt and sand	17.5	60–62					100	94	54	17	9	25	NP	30
Silt	17.5	70–72						100	88	35	12	27	NP	32
Sand and silt lenses	17.5	90–92					100	76	64	37	12	27	NP	27
Pebbly sand	17.6	20–22	100	93	84	81	80	78	21	6	3	NV	NP	18
Silt and fine sand	17.6	30–32						100	60	14	6	26	NP	32
Do	17.6	40–42						100	68	21	4	25	NP	34
Silt	17.6	60–62						100	98	49	16	29	NP	33
Do	17.6	70–72						100	99	64	20	31	NP	33
Do	17.6	90–92							100	66	14	31	NP	40
Medium sand	17.6	10–12		100	99	88	97	66	4	3	1	NV	NP	20.7
Fine sand	17.6	20–22					100	98	18	5	2	NV	NP	26.5
Do	17.6	25–27					100	96	52	19	5	NV	NP	26
Very fine sand	17.6	30–32						100	50	13	5	NV	NP	24.7
Silt	17.6	40–42						100	92	50	17	NV	NP	26.1
Do	17.6	45–47						100	88	43	13	NV	NP	28.4
Do	17.6	50–52							100	64	23	NV	NP	24.5
Do	17.6	55–57						100	98	63	22	NV	NP	29.5
Do	17.6	60–62						100	98	61	19	NV	NP	32.1
Do	17.6	65–67							100	68	24	NV	NP	25.1
Do	17.6	70–72							100	70	25	NV	NP	27.6
Do	17.6	75–77							100	76	31	NV	NP	25.3
Do	17.6	80–82				100	98	98	98	78	33	NV	NP	25.9
Silty sand	17.6	85–87			100	99	99	95	93	81	41	NV	NP	35.8

TABLE 8.—*Analyses of sediments at miles 78.4, 79, and 80.8 on Seward-Anchorage Highway*

[Analyses by Alaska Dept. Highways. NV, no value; NP, nonplastic]

Material	Mile	Depth (feet)	1 in.	3/4 in.	1/2 in.	3/8 in.	No. 4	No. 10	No. 40	No. 200	0.02 mm	0.005 mm	Liquid limit	Plastic index
Silty sandy gravel	78.4	15–17						47	24	4				
Silty gravel sand	78.4	25–27						66	25	5				
Dense silty sand	78.4	35–37						83	49	13				
Do	78.4	55–57						98	83	22				
Dense clayey silt	78.4	75–76.5						100	97	94				
Dense sandy silt	78.4	85–86.5								100				
Compact sandy silt	79	15–17								100				
Dense silty sand	79	25–27						94	72	66				
Do	79	35–37						65	27	4				
Do	79	45–47						69	21	4				
Do	79	55–57						3	1	0				
Do	79	65–66.5						35	24	10				
Dense sandy silt	79	75–77						99	92	87				
Do	79	85–86.5						89	83	74				
Compact sandy gravel	79.6	15–17	100	93	83	78	55	29	8	3			NV	NP
Sand and silt lenses	79.6	25–27					100	98	93	66	53		21	NP
Compact fine sand	79.6	35–37		100	98	94	85	75	42	5			NV	NP
Do	79.6	45–47					100	94	76	26	5		NV	NP
Do	79.6	55–57					100	98	96	84	31		NV	NP
Dense sandy silt	79.6	65–67						100	99	97	53	12	22	NP
Compact plastic silt	79.6	80–82							100	99	84		43	NP
Silty sandy gravel	80.8	10–12		100	88	79	61	44	16	4			NV	NP
Do	80.8	20–22		100	99	96	83	56	18	4			NV	NP
Silty sand	80.8	30–32					100	96	82	32	6		NV	NP
Do	80.8	40–42					100	99	98	81	20		NV	NP
Compact silty sand	80.8	50–52						100	97	47	16		NV	NP
Do	80.8	60–62							100	81	31		22	NP
Do	80.8	70–72							100	68	34		NV	NP
Do	80.8	78–80							100	80	42		22	NP

TABLE 9.—*Analyses of sediments at miles 84.2, 86.6, 89.6, 90.0, and 90.4 on Seward-Anchorage Highway*

[Analyses by Alaska Dept. Highways. NV, no value; NP, nonplastic]

Material	Mile	Depth (feet)	Grading analysis: percent passing—										Atterberg limits	
			1 in.	¾ in.	½ in.	⅜ in.	No. 4	No. 10	No. 40	No. 200	0.02 mm	0.005 mm	Liquid limit	Plastic index
Dense sandy gravel	84.2	10–12	100	87	69	50	32	15	3	1			NV	NP
Do	84.2	20–22	87	82	70	64	50	32	13	6			NV	NP
Layers silt and sandy gravel	84.2	30–32	100	90	86	77	60	39	17	11			NV	NP
Do	84.2	40–42	100	99	89	83	69	57	45	37	4		24	NP
Do	84.2	45–47			100	95	87	81	78	63	5		24	NP
Do	84.2	55–57	100	94	85	76	56	38	23	9			NV	NP
Silt, gravel clay	84.2	65–67						100	99	80	10		22	NP
Do	84.2	75–77	100	95	85	78	61	35	17	8			NV	NP
Do	84.2	85–87	100	97	94	92	82	72	10	46	8		24	NP
Sandy (fill) gravel	86.6	15–17											NV	NP
Silty gravel	86.6	25–27	89	80	62	57	45	29	12	7			NV	NP
Do	86.6	40–42	82	69	65	58	41	23	9	5			NV	NP
Do	86.6	50–52	93	83	73	67	52	30	14	7			NV	NP
Silty sandy gravel	89.6	70–71	100	74	65	55	35	16	3	1			NV	NP
Do	90.0	15–17	92	89	74	65	44	25	6	2			NV	NP
Do	90.0	20–22	84	84	82	73	41	15	1	0			NV	NP
Do	90.0	30–32	100	93	76	67	48	31	17	5			NV	NP
Silty sand with gravel and clay	90.0	40–42		100	97	94	83	61	20	8			NV	NP
Do	90.0	50–52	93	88	72	65	47	31	12	5			NV	NP
Silty sandy gravel	90.0	65–67	86	71	61	58	40	22	6	2			NV	NP
Do	90.0	80–82	100	84	72	61	44	27	11	5			NV	NP
Do	90.4	15–17	100	100	84	75	55	34	17	8			24	NP
Silty clay	90.4	20–22								100	26		50	11
Do	90.4	30–32								100	83		27	NP
Silty clay with sand	90.4	40–42						100	99	94	46		28	NP
Do	90.4	50–52							100	87	13		23	NP
Silty clayey sand	90.4	65–67							100	67	12		NV	NP
Do	90.4	80–82	100	96	89	86	72	53	20	4			NV	NP

TABLE 10.—*Analyses of sediments underlying Copper River Highway*

[Analyses by Alaska Dept. Highways. NV, no value; NP, nonplastic]

Mile	Boring and sample No.	Depth (feet)	Grading analysis: percent passing—						Atterberg limits		Moisture content (percent)	Specific gravity
			3 in.	No. 10	No. 40	No. 200	0.02 mm	0.005 mm	Liquid limit	Plastic index		
14.8	TH 3	5–7	100	35	20	8.0	4.4	2.1	NV	NP	4.2	2.75
14.8	TH 3	9–10	100	72	54	19.9	8.1	3.6	NV	NP	14.3	2.73
15.1	TH 5	10–13	100	44	23	4.1	2.2	1.1	NV	NP	6.8	2.74
15.8	TH 15	3½–4½	100	8	3	.4	.3	.2	NV	NP	1.3	2.71
15.8	TH 15	8–9½	100	78	68	35.6	11.2	2.9	NV	NP	23.5	2.70
15.8	TH 15	13–14½	100	97	90	47.3	14.9	3.8	NV	NP	34.1	2.69
15.8	TH 15	18–19	100	97	95	85.3	48.9	20.7	27	NP	48.4	2.65
16.0	TH 19	3–4½	100	100	89	33.6	10.3	2.4	NV	NP	29.7	2.73
16.5	TH 24	5–7	100	42	26	15.2	9.3	5.1	23	NP	13.2	2.73
16.7	TH 34	4–5	100	37	21	14.1	10.3	6.0	22	6	5.1	2.74
17.4	TH 38	3–4½	100	89	77	29.0	11.1	3.5	NV	NP	26.2	2.73
17.4	TH 38	8–9½	100	70	49	24.2	13.4	5.4	NV	NP	36.1	2.74
17.4	TH 38	13–14½	100	70	56	9.8	3.3	1.2	NV	NP	17.1	2.73
18.2	TH 46	1–3	100	39	20	8.1	5.2	2.8	NV	NP	3.3	2.71
18.2	TH 46	11–12	100	67	56	35.5	19.0	7.6	17	NP	15.1	2.70
18.6	TH 50	2–4	100	43	23	11.4	7.9	4.2	NV	NP	3.2	2.74
18.6	TH 50	11–13	100	48	23	5.7	3.4	1.8	NV	NP	8.5	2.73

TABLE 11.—*Analyses of sediments on Richardson Highway from mile 1.00 to mile 2.78*

[Analyses by Alaska Dept. Highways. NV, no value; NP, nonplastic]

Mile	Boring and sample No.	Depth (feet)	Grading analysis: percent passing—						Atterberg limits		Moisture content (percent)
			3 in.	No. 10	No. 40	No. 200	0.02 mm	0.005 mm	Liquid limit	Plastic index	
1.03	TH 1	8	100	84	72	42.4	24.6	10.2	NV	NP	18.0
1.03	TH 1	18	100	63	40	16.0	9.0	5.0	NV	NP	12.5
1.28	TH 2	7	100	36	20	8.7	6.6	3.4	NV	NP	2.8
1.28	TH 2	13	100	56	31	15.7	11.0	5.6	NV	NP	13.2
1.28	TH 2	19	100	54	40	22.1	13.5	6.1	NV	NP	13.4
1.52	TH 3	15	100	47	28	15.9	10.4	5.7	16	NP	3.8
1.52	TH 3	29	100	48	27	14.1	10.0	5.8	NV	NP	5.6
1.73	TH 5	15	100	46	24	8.6	6.0	3.9	NV	NP	3.6
1.73	TH 5	25	100	52	18	5.3	3.8	2.7	NV	NP	9.8
1.82	TH 6	12	100	83	66	34.5	18.5	7.4	NV	NP	25.3
1.82	TH 6	25	100	95.4	86	52.7	23.6	8.8	NV	NP	26.2
1.82	TH 6	33	100	90.3	77	38.6	19.0	8.0	NV	NP	24.0
2.08	TH 8	5	100	21.4	10	5.3	3.5	2.0	NV	NP	1.6
2.08	TH 8	18	100	64.3	37	6.6	4.7	3.0	NV	NP	12.1
2.08	TH 8	25	100	92	80	39.2	23.6	11.1	NV	NP	29.7
2.08	TH 8	28	100	67	30	10.2	7.4	3.7	NV	NP	15.0
2.31	TH 10	28	100	63	31	9.3	6.2	3.4	NV	NP	12.8
2.56	TH 12	15	100	50	30	15.6	8.5	4.4	NV	NP	9.5
2.56	TH 12	32	100	58	28	9.4	5.7	2.7	NV	NP	13.7
2.78	TH 14	15	100	81	52	16.8	10.1	5.8	NV	NP	8.2
2.78	TH 14	22	100	73	64	31.7	14.4	6.6	NV	NP	14.0

TABLE 12.—*Correlation of foundation material of roadway and fractures of Seward-Anchorage Highway from mile 75.1 (Ingram Creek) to mile 95.0*

Mile	Foundation material	Extent and nature of fractures
75.1 to 77.1__	Silt, sand, and fine gravel; water table generally within 3 ft of surface.	Fractures normal to and along edge of roadway; normal fractures, spaced about 75 ft apart, have vertical displacement of as much as 6 in.; fractures along edge are as much as ¼ mile long, 6 in. wide, with north or downslope side down as much as 6 inches. From mile 76.4 to mile 76.9, fractures about 100–125 ft apart.
77.1 to 78.4__	____do_____	Fractures normal and along edge of roadway, but larger than those from mile 75.1 to mile 77.1; fractures refracted normal to roadway, cross roadway, and then continue on original heading. Have vertical displacements as much as 6 inches, horizontal to 1 ft.
78.4 to 81.0__	Silt, sand, and fine gravel; water table generally within 2–3 ft of surface.	Heavily fractured; fractures normal to roadway, along edges, and in center of roadway; largest fracture occurred in this section of roadway (figs. 12, 13). Fractures normal or perpendicular to roadway may have 4 feet horizontal displacement and 1 foot vertical; spaced 100 to 150 feet apart. Maximum width of fracture in center of roadway 10 ft, length 500 ft depth 6–8 ft.
81.0 to 82.6__	Silt, sand, and sandy gravel; water table within 4 ft of surface.	Series of fractures normal or perpendicular to highway spaced 200–250 ft apart with horizontal displacement to 6 in. and vertical displacement to 4 in.; fractures along edge of roadway, although not as extensive as those from mile 77.1 to mile 78.4.
82.6_____	Bedrock for 150 ft_____	No fractures; fill at each end fractured at contact.
82.7 to 84.9__	Coarse sand and sandy gravel; water table more than 6 ft from surface.	Fractures, normal to roadway, occur as series locally spaced 75–100 ft apart; series are at miles 82.8–82.9, 83.2, 84.1–84.2; at mile 84.2–84.9, single fractures normal to highway spaced 400–500 ft apart; very little displacement on fractures in this section of roadway.
84.9 to 84.95_	Bedrock_____	No fractures; fill at each end fractured and compacted; displaced vertically 3–3½ ft.
84.95 to 86.6_	Coarse sand and sandy gravel.	Series of small fractures normal to roadway; no displacement; bedrock from mile 85.6 to mile 85.7.
86.6 to 87.8__	Talus over bedrock___	No fractures.
87.8 to 87.9__	Swamp deposits over bedrock.	Closely spaced fractures normal to roadway; displacement slight because swamp deposits shallow.
87.9 to 88.9__	Bedrock_____	No fractures.
88.9 to 91.0__	Tidal silt and sand; water table close to surface locally, especially at Girdwood.	Small fractures normal to roadway and locally along edge of roadway. Only slight horizontal displacement in normal fractures.
91.0 to 95.0__	Veneer of glacial outwash less than 10 ft thick overlying bedrock.	No fractures.

TABLE 13.—*Bridges in south-central Alaska severely damaged or destroyed by the Alaska earthquake*

[Only primary and secondary highways listed; streets and bridges in communities not included]

Highway or road	Number of bridges	Length (feet)	Severely damaged or destroyed			
			Number of bridges	Length (feet)	Bridges (percent)	Length (percent)
Copper River Highway_____	53	14, 208	32	12, 015	60	85
Edgerton Highway_____	4	642	0	0	0	0
Glenn Highway_____	21	5, 000	1	2, 006	5	40
Hope Road_____	2	200	0	0	0	0
Kenai-Nikiska Road_____	1	75	0	0	0	0
Portage Glacier Road_____	3	279	3	279	100	100
Point Whitshed Road_____	5	374	1	100	20	27
Richardson Highway_____	20	2, 739	2	231	10	8
Seward-Anchorage Highway_____	54	9, 318	30	6, 370	55	68
Sterling Highway_____	13	1, 220	2	553	15	45
Chiniak Highway_____	20	1, 700	15	1, 330	75	78
Anton Larsen Bay Road____	4	256	2	83	50	32
Saltery Cove Road_____	0	0	0	0	0	0
Pasagshak Bay Road_____	3	250	3	250	100	100
Chiniak Highway-Spruce Cape Road_____	1	50	1	50	100	100
Total_____	204	36, 311	92	23, 267	45	64

TABLE 14.—*Intensity of damage to bridges on primary and secondary roads in south-central Alaska*

[Only primary and secondary highways and roads listed; streets and bridges in communities not included]

Highway or road	Number of bridges	Damage intensity								Damage total	
		None		Slight		Moderate		Severe or destroyed		Number	Percent
		Number	Percent	Number	Percent	Number	Percent	Number	Percent		
Copper River Highway_____	53	1	2	16	30	4	8	32	61	52	98
Edgerton Highway_____	4	3	75	1	25	0	0	0	0	1	25
Glenn Highway_____	21	10	47. 5	10	47. 5	0	0	1	5	11	52. 5
Hope Road_____	2	2	100	0	0	0	0	0	0	0	0
Kenai-Nikiska Road_____	1	1	100	0	0	0	0	0	0	0	0
Portage Glacier Road_____	3	0	0	0	0	0	0	3	100	3	100
Point Whitshed Road_____	5	4	80	0	0	0	0	1	20	1	20
Richardson Highway_____	20	12	60	3	15	3	15	2	10	8	40
Seward-Anchorage Highway__	54	15	28	6	11	3	6	30	55	39	72
Sterling Highway_____	13	8	62	3	23	0	0	2	15	5	38
Chiniak Highway_____	20	5	25	0	0	0	0	15	75	15	75
Anton Larsen Bay Road_____	4	2	50	0	0	0	0	2	50	2	50
Saltery Cove Road_____	0	0	0	0	0	0	0	0	0	0	0
Pasagshak Bay Road_____	3	0	0	0	0	0	0	3	100	3	100
Chiniak Highway-Spruce Cape_____	1	0	0	0	0	0	0	1	100	1	100
Total_____	204	63	31	39	19	10	5	92	45	141	69

TABLE 15.—*Damage to bridge approaches and bridges (except Allen River bridge) along the Copper River Highway*

[Designations west and east are used to indicate direction from Cordova (mile 0) to Bridge 332, Copper River 3 (mile 27.9) respectively. South and north designation is used from mile 33.0 to Million Dollar Bridge (mile 49.0); south and east is toward Cordova, north and west toward Chitina. Numbering of spans and bents runs west to east from mile 0 to mile 27.9 and south to north from mile 33.0 to Million Dollar Bridge. All displacement of spans is measured in relation to movement from original position of bearings on substructure units. Abbreviations used for structure and deck types are (structure type first, deck type second): PCG, prestressed concrete girder; PCS, prestressed concrete slab; SA, steel arch; SS, steel stringer; STT, steel through truss; TTS, treated timber stringer; TS, timber stringer; LT, laminated timber; TP, timber plank; RC, reinforced concrete; prefix T, preservative-treated material; suffix R, running plank. Bridge number and name and route mileage from Alaska Dept. Highways, Bridge Inventory Rating Report, 1964. Length and superstructure data primarily from Alaska Dept. Highways, Bridge Inventory Rating Report, 1964, supplemented by U.S. Geol. Survey data. Bridge damage data from U.S. Geol. Survey and Alaska Dept. Highways]

Bridge		Route mile-age	Length		Type		Foundation material	Damage	
No.	Name		Ft	In.	Super-structure	Substructure		Approaches	Bridges
381	Eyak River	5.9	225	0	PCS	Concrete abutments.	Bedrock	None	None.
348	Scott Glacier 1	7.6	150	0	SS, RC	Wood piles	Fine-grained silty sandy gravel.	East approach subsided 3 in.; west approach subsided slightly.	Destroyed. East abutment subsided about 3 in. Bent 1: north pile down 3 in., west 8 in. Bent 2: north pile down 2½ in., west 8 in. Bent 3: north pile down 1 in., west 2 in. Bent 4: north pile down 4 in., west 5 in. Bent 5: north pile went east 8 in. Concrete deck raised about 5 in. off stringer. Deck moved about 3 in. west and broke concrete bulkhead between stringers. Some piles were split due to pounding.
349	Scott Glacier 2	7.7	200	0	SS, RC	...do...	...do...	Approaches subsided unknown amount.	Severe. East abutment piles driven down as much as 2 in.; center pile moved 4 in. west. Bent 1: north pile down 3 in., two piles split. Bent 2: north pile down 4 in., west 4 in.; No. 5 pile split. Bent 4: north pile down 3 in., east 3 in. Bent 6: north pile down 3 in., east 3 in. Bent 7: north pile down 3 in., east 3 in.
350	Scott Glacier 3	8.2	150	0	SS, RC	...do...	...do...	Unknown	Destroyed. Bridge collapsed over bent 5; stringers not resting on piles in several places.
351	Scott Glacier 4	8.6	75	0	SS, RC	...do...	...do...	West approach subsided about 10 in.; east approach subsided about 3 in.	Destroyed. East end: concrete cap moved 2 in. east, deck jammed into bulkhead. Piles apparently moved beneath the bridge toward center of creek; west end of deck collapsed.
352	Scott Glacier 5	9.2	75	0	SS, RC	...do...	...do...	Unknown	Severe. Concrete bulkhead between steel stringers and tied to concrete cap moved east about 2 ft. Bent 1: stringers moved off piles eastward. West end: stringers off piles; fell behind piles and down about 2 ft.
406	Scott Glacier 6	9.5	375	0	SS, RC	Railroad rails welded together.	...do...	East approach subsided and fractured; west approach subsided unknown amount.	Destroyed. Bridge collapsed over broken piles in bents 3, 6-9, 12, and 13.
407	Scott Glacier 7	9.8	175	0	SS, RC	...do...	...do...	West approach subsided 3 in.; east approach unknown.	Destroyed. Bridge collapsed at bents 3 and 4. Many broken piles.
408	Scott Glacier 8	10.1	151	2	SS, RC	...do...	...do...	West approach fractured; east approach subsided unknown amount.	Severe. East end: compression cracks in bulkheads. Bent 2 cap cracked above north pile. Rails cracked in bents 1, 2, 4, and 5.
409	Scott Glacier 9	10.4	75	8	SS, RC	...do...	...do...	East approach subsided about 3 in.; west approach subsided unknown amount.	Severe. Slight break in east abutment. Deck 6 in. over abutment bulkhead at west end. Bulkhead cracked.
410	Scott Glacier 10	10.8	75	8	SS, RC	...do...	...do...	Both approaches subsided about 1 ft.	Slight. East abutment cracked; west abutment slightly cracked.
411	Scott Glacier 11	11.0	352	6	SS, RC	...do...	...do...	...do...	Severe. Rail bents broken. East and west abutments broken due to movement of bridge deck. Caps on four rail pilings and several piles broken, especially in center of bridge. Every bent has some rail pilings cracked. Bridge wavy. East end steel stringer broken loose and abutment bulkhead cracked.
361	Sheridan Glacier 2.	14.8	151	8	TTS, TLT	Wood piles	...do...	East approach subsided 1 ft. West approach subsided about 10 in.	Moderate. Pile bracing split on bent 3. Upstream pile of bent 4 shifted from under cap. Timber cap split on bent 5. Backing plank on abutment 6 pushed away from piles. Span 5 stringers split.
230	Sheridan Glacier 3.	14.9	201	4	PCG, RC	Steel casing piles	...do...	Both approaches subsided about 8 in.	Slight. Backwall of abutment 1 is broken above the bridge seat; slight spalling of upstream stringer at abutment 1.
363	Sheridan Glacier	15.3	201	8	TTS, TLT	Wood piles	...do...	West approach subsided 5 in. East approach subsided about 6 in.	Severe. Pile cap at pier 2 split; spans dropped on top of piles. Abutment 1 crowded, causing buckling of laminated deck.
364	...do...	15.8	26	8	TTS, TLT	...do...	...do...	Both approaches subsided about 6 in.	Moderate. West abutment moved east 2 in.; east abutment west 4 in.; bridge in compression.
365	...do...	15.9	39	8	TTS, TLT	...do...	...do...	Both approaches subsided more than 6 in.	Severe. Abutment 1 cap is tipped and not bearing on piles; backing plank is tipped back.
366	...do...	16.1	27	8	TTS, TLT	...do...	...do...	Both approaches subsided slightly.	Severe. Abutment 2 cap has moved off center of piles; two piles are split.
367	...do...	16.5	50	0	TTS, TLT	...do...	...do...	Both approaches subsided about 1 ft.	Destroyed. Span 4 severely damaged; in bent 2 the cap is split and downstream pile is split.

TABLE 15.—*Damage to bridge approaches and bridges (except Allen River bridge) along the Copper River Highway*—Continued

No.	Name	Route mile-age	Ft	In.	Super-structure	Substructure	Foundation material	Approaches	Bridges
368	Sheridan Glacier__	16.6	51	8	TTS, TLT	Wood piles_____	Fine-grained silty sandy gravel.	Approaches subsided unknown amount.	Slight. Change in drainage putting more water under bridge than it can safely carry. Bridge in compression; deck moved west 4 in.; down 1 in.
369	_____do_____	16.9	101	8	TTS, TLT	_____do_____	_____do_____	West approach subsided 4 in.; east approach subsided very little.	Slight. Change in drainage pattern of area directs more water under bridge and aggravates scour at abutment 5.
370	_____do_____	17.4	26	8	TTS, TLT	_____do_____	_____do_____	Both approaches subsided slightly.	Slight. Deck moved west about 2 in.; bridge in compression.
371	_____do_____	17.9	39	8	TTS, TLT	_____do_____	_____do_____	West approach subsided 6 in.; east approach subsided very little.	Slight. Bridge in compression; west end deck moved west 4 in.
372	_____do_____	18.2	51	8	TTS, TLT	_____do_____	_____do_____	Approaches subsided about 4 in.	Slight. Cap and backing plank on abutment 1 have both moved in relation to piles; bridge in compression about 8 in.
373	_____do_____	18.3	101	8	TTS, TLT	_____do_____	_____do_____	Both approaches subsided about 5 in.	Slight. Bridge in compression about 8 in.; west abutment moved east 5 in.; east abutment moved west 3 in.
374	_____do_____	18.9	101	8	TTS, TLT	_____do_____	_____do_____	Unknown.	Slight. Deck moved east about 10 in.; bridge in compression.
375	Alaganik Slough__	19.3	51	8	TTS, TLT	_____do_____	Silt and sand____	Both approaches subsided slightly.	Slight. Bridge in slight compression.
376	_____do_____	19.8	101	8	TTS, TLT	_____do_____	_____do_____	West approach subsided and has large fracture 15 ft from deck; east approach subsided slightly.	Slight. Bridge in compression; one pile broken.
377	_____do_____	20.2	151	8	TTS, TLT	_____do_____	_____do_____	Both approaches subsided slightly.	Slight. Bridge in compression; deck moved 2 in. to the east.
378	_____do_____	20.8	58	8	TTS, TLT	_____do_____	_____do_____	Unknown.	Slight. Bridge in slight compression.
379	_____do_____	21.9	151	8	TTS, TLT	_____do_____	West end, bedrock; east end, sediments.	No damage to west approach; east approach subsided 4 in.	Slight. Bridge compressed and curved upstream; damage at east end; deck moved 2 in. east off of caps.
395	_____do_____	22.3	176	8	TTS, TLT	_____do_____	Silt and sand____	East approach subsided 4 in.	Slight. Damage on east end of bridge; railing clamps broken; bridge in slight compression.
330	_____do_____	24.0	42	0	SS, RC	Concrete abutments.	_____do_____	Both approaches subsided slightly.	Moderate. Curbs at east end are broken where tied to abutments. All abutment backwalls have been spalled and cracked by movement of curbs. Curb reinforced steel extends into backwalls. Diaphragm concrete has moved away from backwalls.
331	Copper River 2___	27.1	2,437	0	STT, TLT, SS, RC.	Concrete piers and welded rails.	Fine-grained silt_	East approach subsided 3 ft; west approach subsided about 3 in.	Severe. Span 1, a 300-ft through truss, has been displaced approximately 22 in. east and 8 in. downstream. Abutment 1 anchor bolts sheared off or bent out of shape. Rollers in roller nests lying flat on their sides. Span 2 displaced 19 in. eastward and 5 in. downstream. Span 3 displaced 25 in. eastward and 1½ in. downstream. Piers show sheared or bent anchor bolts and some spalling. Spans 3 and 4 jammed together at pier 4. Several broken piles; webwalls cracked on almost all bents. Truss spans 22–25 moved westward. Abutment 36 tipped back and badly cracked.
332	Copper River 3___	27.9	About 800	0	STT, TLT	Concrete piers____	_____do_____	Approaches subsided as much as 2½ ft.	Destroyed. Middle pier has disappeared; span 1 still hanging from west abutment with other end in river; span 2 in river.
354	Long Island Overflow.	33.0	124	4	SS, RC	Railroad rails welded together.	_____do_____	Approaches subsided 1 ft; side of roadway subsided 2 ft; downstream shoulders subsided the most.	Severe. Abutment 1 backwall cracked and spalled from tied-in curb ends, and anchor bolts bent. Pier 2 concrete curb spalled over pier, pier tipped northward; downstream end is low, pier cap cracked. Span 2 slab has separated from beams near pier 2. Abutment 3 backwall has been destroyed by movement of superstructure.
333	Copper River 4___	33.9	766	7	STT, TLT	Concrete piers____	_____do_____	Approaches subsided 10 to 12 in.	Severe. Pier 2 concrete bolster columns cracked; end of deck and curbs of span 2 broken up by movement. Span 1 downstream bearing rollers lying flat, displaced 5 in. northward, bolts sheared. Spans 2–4 and piers 3–5 appear to be tipped upstream. At pier 6 concrete bolster columns cracked. Curb ends and top of backwall of span 5 broken by movement. Span 6 rollers at full travel with bolts bent, 5 in. southward movement. Span 7 anchor bolts sheared, displaced 8 in. southward.
334	Copper River 5___	35.0	1,576	0	SS, RC	Railroad rails in concrete.	_____do_____	Approaches subsided 4 in.	Destroyed. Spans 2–5 and piers 3–5 completely destroyed; span 15 fallen off pier 16.
335	Copper River 6___	35.6	122	0	SS, RC____	_____do_____	_____do_____	Approaches subsided slightly.	Severe. Abutment 1 shows backwall and curb end cracking. Spans 2, 3, and 4 show 1 in. northward displacement, shearing bolts on span 2 at pier 3, span 3 at pier 4, and breaking sole plate welds on span 4 at pier 4. The backwall of abutment 5 has been destroyed by the northern movement of the steel.

TABLE 15.—*Damage to bridge approaches and bridges (except Allen River bridge) along the Copper River Highway*—Continued

Bridge		Route mile-age	Length		Type		Foundation material	Damage	
No.	Name		Ft	In.	Super-structure	Substructure		Approaches	Bridges
336	Copper River 7___	35.8	282	0	SS, RC	Railroad rails in concrete.	Fine-grained silt_	Approaches subsided about 3 in.	Severe. Abutment 1 settled ±1 ft. Back wall cracked and spalled at curb ends. Slab and curb cracked over pier 2 owing to abutment settlement. Pier 3 tipped northward, shows severe cracking of webwall at downstream pile. Concrete cap cracked. Sole plate welds on span 2 are broken; no residual displacement. Pier 4 tipped northward. Webwall failed at downstream pile, concrete cap cracked over pile. Span 4 twisted; expansion joint closed at downstream curb and open about 3 in. at upstream curb. Pier 5 tipped northward. Spans 4 and 5 are 18 in. off their bearings to the north. Piers 6 and 7 settled and tipped downstream. Abutment 8 demolished; superstructure was driven through it.
337	Copper River 8___	36.0	182	0	SS, RC	_____do_____	____do_____	North approach subsided 3 in.; south approach subsided 2 in.	Moderate. Abutments cracked by curb ends; settled 6± in. Expansion joints opened to fullest travel; joint filler material fallen out.
338	Copper River 9___	36.1	182	0	SS, RC	_____do_____	____do_____	Both approaches generally subsided about 6 in.; at north approach 1-ft mound at abutment.	Severe. Abutment 1 curb cracked and spalled. Pier 3 webwall broken at upstream pile and tipped northward, a pile broken, a cap broken. At pier 4, span 3 displaced 4 in. north. At pier 5, spans 4 and 5 displaced 6 in. north. At pier 6, span 5 displaced 6 in. north and expansion joint jammed shut, crushing the deck concrete. Span 6 driven through abutment 7, demolishing it. Abutment 7 settled about 6 in.
339	Copper River 10__	36.4	422	0	SS, RC	_____do_____	____do_____	North approach subsided about 2 ft; south approach subsided about 6 in.	Severe. Abutment 1 demolished by southward movement of superstructure; appears to have settled about 1 ft. Entire superstructure displaced southward 18 in. with respect to piers; shows a definite undulation. Abutment 8 moved forward with the superstructure and settled about 1 ft.
340	Copper River 11__	36.7	242	0	SS, RC	_____do_____	____do_____	North approach subsided, but 18 in. mound bulldozed at abutment; south approach subsided 4 in.	Severe. Fill settled away under abutment 1. Abutment backwall badly cracked at curbs. At pier 2, spans 1 and 2 displaced 7 in. north. At pier 3, spans 2 and 3 displaced 4 in. south. Piers 3 and 4 tipped north. Abutment 5 demolished by northbound superstructure.
341	Copper River 12__	36.9	142	0	SS, RC	_____do_____	____do_____	North approach subsided 2 in.; south approach subsided 4 in.	Severe. Both abutments have settled about 1 ft and show backwall cracking and spalling at curbs. At pier 3 the step in the concrete cap is cracked at the downstream bearing. Expansion joints are jammed shut by a northward movement.
342	Copper River 13__	37.2	282	0	SS, RC	_____do_____	____do_____	Both approaches subsided about 6–8 in.	Severe. Cap of pier 3 is cracked. Pier 4 failed completely, dropping spans 3 and 4 into the river. Pier 5 tipped southward. Spans 5 and 6 show crimping of their bottom flanges due to compression. Abutment 7 has a cracked backwall.
343	Copper River 14__	37.5	122	0	SS, RC	_____do_____	____do_____	Both approaches subsided about 3 in.	Slight. Abutment 1 shows usual cracking at curbs; appears to have settled about 6 in. Piers 2 and 3 show slab and curb cracking over supports. At pier 4 the expansion joint is open about 3 in.; joint filler has fallen out and bolts are at limit of travel in their slotted holes.
344	Copper River 15__	37.8	272	0	SS, RC	_____do_____	____do_____	North approach subsided 4–5 in.; south approach subsided about 1 ft.	Severe. Abutment 1 shows backwall damage at curbs. Pier 2 has severe webwall cracking. At pier 4 both spans are displaced about 2 in. north, and anchor bolts are sheared. There has been a definite vertical displacement in this bridge; pier 4 has probably been uplifted.
345	Copper River 16__	38.1	362	0	SS, RC	_____do_____	____do_____	South approach subsided 1½ ft; north approach subsided 3 in.	Severe. Abutment 1 tipped northward and superstructure driven through backwall with resultant displacement of ±6 ft. Pier 2 tipped south 4 to 6 in. At pier 3, span 2 is 1 in. north of masonry plate. Sole plate welds failed. At pier 4, spans 3 and 4 are 4 in. north of bearings and 8 in. downstream. Anchor bolts sheared. Pier 4 tipped southward. Pier 5 cap cracked at upstream bearing. At pier 6 both spans displaced 4 in. north and 2 in. upstream. Diaphragm bolts are gone.
346	Clear Creek_____	38.9	182	0	SS, RC	_____do_____	Outwash gravel_	South approach subsided about 3 in.; north approach subsided about 1 ft.	Severe. Abutment 1 demolished by bridge going south; also appears to have settled. Pier 2 tipped about 2 ft south. At pier 3, span 2 is displaced 4 in. south. Pier has settled. Span 3 is 6 in. south of bearing. Abutment 4 shows usual curb cracking and appears to have settled.

TABLE 15.—*Damage to bridge approaches and bridges (except Allen River bridge) along the Copper River Highway*—Continued

No.	Name	Route mile-age	Length Ft	In.	Super-structure	Substructure	Foundation material	Approaches	Bridges
329	Clear Creek	41.0	182	0	SS, RC	Railroad rails in concrete.	Outwash gravel	South approach cracked in middle of road for 500 ft. Fractures 2 ft wide; road subsided 2½–3 ft. North approach fractured about 500 ft and subsided 1½ ft.	Severe. South abutment demolished by southward movement of superstructure about 3 feet. Pier 2 tipped northward. Spans 1 and 2 are displaced 4 in. southward at pier 2. At pier 3 both spans displaced 1 ft northward. At pier 4 both spans are displaced 18 in. northward; at pier 5 both spans displaced 32 in. northward and 6 in. upstream. At pier 6, which tipped south, the spans are displaced 55 in. north and 1 ft upstream. Abutment 7 demolished by superstructure. Piers 5 and 6 moved laterally.
206	Million Dollar Bridge.	49.0	1,400	0	STT, RC	Concrete piers	....do	Both approaches subsided 6–8 in.	Destroyed. Span 4 dropped off pier 4 and is in the river. Pier 4 is virtually destroyed. Rest of bridge has been damaged and shows displacements.

TABLE 16.—*Damage to bridge approaches and bridges along the Seward-Anchorage Highway*

[Abbreviations used for structure and deck types are (structure type first, deck type second): CG, concrete girder; PCG, prestressed concrete girder; SS, steel stringer; TTS, treated timber stringer; RFC, rigid frame concrete; SPG, steel plate girder; TS, timber stringer; suffix C, cantilever or continuous bridge; A, asphalt; LTA, laminated timber and asphalt; RC, reinforced concrete; TP, timber plank. Bridge number and name and route mileage from Alaska Department of Highways, Bridge Inventory Rating Report, 1964. Length and superstructure data primarily from Alaska Dept. Highways, Bridge Inventory Rating Report, 1964, supplemented by U.S. Geol. Survey data. Damage data collected by U.S. Army and U.S. Geol. Survey]

No.	Name	Route mile-age	Length Ft	In.	Super-structure	Substructure	Foundation material	Approaches	Bridges
596	Resurrection River 1.	2.9	198	0	SS, RC	Concrete piers	Stream sediment.	Subsided unknown amount.	Severe. Abutments cracked; anchor bolts sheared; pier cracked; spans down; piers subsided; span moved south and north. Maximum movement on south span as much as 7 in. north and 2 in. west.
597	Resurrection River 2.	2.9	135	6	SS, RC	....do	....do	North approach subsided 16 in. South approach estimated subsidence 12 in.	Severe. Abutments cracked; bridge in compression; span moved as much as 8 in.
598	Resurrection River 3.	3.0	185	6	SS, RC	....do	....do	Both subsided several inches.	Severe. Abutments cracked; north pier cracked at base, moved north and out of plumb; bridge in compression; span moved north 4 in., east 2 in.; center span down ½ in.; anchor bolts sheared.
599	Clear Creek	3.5	75	0	SS, LTA	Concrete abutments.	Sediments	Unknown	Moderate. Bridge in compression.
600	Salmon Creek	6.5	125	6	SS, RC	Concrete piers	Sandy gravel	Slight subsidence, up to 3 in. in both approaches.	Slight. Decks moved south about 1 in.; slight crack in south abutment; north abutment moved north about 1 in.; bridge in compression.
601	Bear Creek	7.0	51	8	CG, RC	Wood piles	....do	North approach subsided about ½ in.	Slight. North abutment subsided about ½ in.
602	Grouse Creek 1	8.0	39	8	TTS, RC	....do	Stream sediments.	Fill compacted 3–4 in.	None.
741	Grouse Creek 2	9.4	23	8	RFC, A	Concrete abutments.	....do	Subsided 3–4 in.	Do.
603 [1]	Snow River 1	17.3			TS, TPA	Wood piles	Fine-grained silt and sand.	Subsided about 4–6 ft	Severe. Bridge in compression; deck wavy; deck, in places, is off cap.
604 [1]	Snow River 2	17.6	95	0	TS, TPA	....do	....do	Approaches subsided about 6 ft. Surrounding sediments settled about 12 ft.	Severe. Roadway bowed up in middle; bridge in compression; deck wavy; deck in places, is off cap.
605 [1]	Snow River 3	17.7	209	0	TS, TPA	....do	....do	Approaches subsided about 6 ft. Surrounding sediments settled about 12 ft.	Destroyed. Third bent from north end did not settle. All others settled as much as 12 ft; 3 spans nearest south end slightly twisted and rolled.
606 [1]	Snow River Overhead (4)	18.2	1,471	0	TS, TPA	....do	....do	West approach subsided unknown amount; east approach subsided about 18 in.	Destroyed. South end of bridge pulled 6 in. away from abutment; bridge slightly canted and wavy. Piles on west side settled 6 in. to 2 ft lower than east side in first 1,120 ft (from south end). For next 100 ft, timber bents all canted south and offset. Last 225–250 ft (north end) completely destroyed; it fell or twisted to ground about 75 ft below, destroying roadway and bents.
603A	Snow River, west channel.	17.1	188	6	PCG, RC	....do	....do	Under construction	Bridge under construction. No decks; piers moved downstream as much as 5 ft and canted.
605	Snow River, center channel.	17.7	648	6	PCG, RC	....do	....do	....do	Do.
606	Snow River Overhead.	18.2	289	2	PCG, RC	....do	....do	....do	Do.
607	Victory Creek	20.0	197	3	SSC, RC	....do	Fill on bedrock	Fill subsided 2–3 in.	None.
608	Ptarmigan Creek	23.5	151	8	CG, RC	....do	Outwash gravel and stream gravel.	Fill subsided 4–5 in.	Do.
609	Falls Creek	25.0	126	9	CG, RC	....do	Sediments	....do	Do.
610	Trail River	25.5	351	8	CG, RC	....do	....do	Fill subsided 3–4 in.	Slight. Bridge in compression.

TABLE 16.—*Damage to bridge approaches and bridges along the Seward-Anchorage Highway*—Continued

No.	Name	Route mile-age	Ft	In.	Super-structure	Substructure	Foundation material	Approaches	Bridges
611	Moose Creek_____	32.0	76	8	CG, RC	Wood piles_____	Sediments_____	Both approaches subsided 2–3 in.	Slight, Bridge in compression.
1137	Quartz Creek_____	42.0	22	1	RFC	Concrete abutments.	Bedrock_____	None_____	None.
1138	Summit Creek____	42.6	22	1	RFC	____do_____	___do_____	____do_____	Do.
1139	Colorado Creek___	45.8	22	1	RFC	____do_____	___do_____	____do_____	Do.
612	Canyon Creek____	56.8	302	0	SS, RC	Steel towers_____	___do_____	Fill subsided_____	Slight.
613	Dry Gulch Creek_	57.1	120	0	SSC, RC	____do_____	Thin veneer of sediments over bedrock.	___do_____	None.
614	Silvertip Creek___	60.7	86	6	SS, RC	Concrete piers____	Bedrock_____	____do_____	Do.
615	East Fork Six Mile Creek.	61.6	265	9	SPGC, RC	____do_____	Stream deposits___	North approach subsided 6 in. in about 10 ft fill over stream deposits. South approach subsided about 2 in.	Slight.
616	Granite Creek____	63.2	206	3	SS, RC	____do_____	Bedrock_____	Fill subsided 2 in_____	None.
617	Spokane Creek____	64.9	86	0	SS, RC	Concrete abutments.	Coarse gravel____	None_____	Do.
618	Bertha Creek_____	65.6	145	0	SS, RC	Unknown_____	___do_____	____do_____	Do.
619	Lyon and Tin Can Creek.	67.8	146	0	SS, RC	Wood piles_____	___do_____	____do_____	Do.
620	Ingram Creek_____	75.1	206	0	SS, RC	Concrete piers___	Sand and gravel__	Unknown amount_____	Severe. Bridge in compression; abutments moved toward center of creek.
621	Muddy Creek____	75.8	375	0	CG, RC	Wood piles_____	Silty sand and gravel.	East approach subsided 14 in., west approach subsided 17 in.	Destroyed. From east end: 2 piles under first 12 spans are split. All bracings split. All piles on east side are canted west. Pilings under last 3 spans are crushed and spans are collapsed. Bridge bowed north; not straight across.
622	Steep Creek_____	75.8	200	0	CG, RC	____do_____	____do_____	East approach subsided 30 in.; west approach fractured and subsided 12 in.	Destroyed. Western half of bridge, 4 span buckled and canted over split, crushed, or canted piles.
623	Tidewater Slough 1.	75.9	176	0	CG, RC	____do_____	____do_____	Fill. East approach subsided 38 in.; west approach subsided 21–36 in.	Severe. Two piles settled with road and are not supporting bridge. Separations of 4 in. and 2 in. between spans in 2 places; replaced.
624	Tidewater Slough 2.	76.4	76	0	CG, RC___	Wood piles_____	Silt, sand and silty gravel.	Fill. East approach subsided 30 in.; west approach subsided 24 in.	Structure received only slight damage from seismic shock, but bridge was flooded during high tide and had to be replaced. Effects of earthquake therefore are considered severe.
625	Tidewater Slough 3.	77.0	76	0	CG, RC	____do_____	____do_____	Fill. East approach subsided 40 in.; west approach subsided 28 in.	Do.
626	Tidewater Slough 4.	77.1	76	0	CG, RC	____do_____	____do_____	Fill. East approach subsided 15 in.; west approach subsided 17 in.	Do.
627	Placer River 1_____	77.9	450	0	CG, RC	____do_____	____do_____	West abutment up about 2 in. West approach subsided about 8 in.; east approach subsided 16 in.	Destroyed. Westernmost spans collapsed over first bent (pilings crushed); easternmost 6 spans collapsed over crushed piles.
628	Placer River 2_____	78.2	125	0	CG, RC	____do_____	____do_____	West approach subsided 22 in.; east approach subsided 24 in.	Destroyed. East abutment damaged; pilings in center bent crushed and spans collapsed over them.
629	Placer River Main Crossing.	78.4	600	0	CG, RC	____do_____	____do_____	West approach subsided 7 in.; east approach subsided 22 in.	Destroyed. Both abutments destroyed; all pilings destroyed; many punched through concrete roadway; all spans collapsed.
630	Portage Creek 1___	79.0	175	0	CG, RC	____do_____	Silty sand_____	South approach subsided 27 in.; north approach subsided 42 in.	Destroyed. Pilings destroyed; some driven up through concrete deck; all spans collapsed.
631	Portage Creek 2___	79.6	225	0	CG, RC	____do_____	Sand, silt, and sandy gravel.	South approach subsided 18 in.; north approach subsided 24 in.	Destroyed. Both abutments destroyed; all pilings destroyed, spans twisted and collapsed, some under water.
632	Portage Creek 3___	79.6	125	0	CG, RC	____do_____	____do_____	South approach subsided 23–42 in.; north approach subsided 46 in.	Destroyed. Abutments slightly damaged. Center piles crushed and deck collapsed over them.
633	Jim's Creek_____	80.3	50	0	CG, RC	____do_____	Silt, sand, and silty gravel.	South approach subsided 24 in.; north approach subsided 22 in.	Severe. Abutments slightly damaged; deck settled over center bent; replaced.
634	Twentymile River.	80.8	820	0	CG, RC	____do_____	Silty sand and sandy gravel.	South approach subsided 21 in.; north approach subsided 5 in.	Destroyed. North abutment destroyed by fissures. All pilings destroyed, and in many places are driven through the concrete deck. All spans collapsed and under water.
635	Tidewater Slough 5.	82.0	140	0	CG, RC	____do_____	Silt and sand____	South approach subsided 45 in.; north approach subsided 90–96 in.	Severe. Deck raised on either end and bowed down in center.

[1] Numbers 603, 605, and 606 have been reassigned to bridges under construction at the time of the earthquake. 604 no longer exists.

TABLE 16.—*Damage to bridge approaches and bridges along the Seward-Anchorage Highway*—Continued

| Bridge | | Route mileage | Length | | Type | | Foundation material | Damage | |
No.	Name		Ft	In.	Super-structure	Substructure		Approaches	Bridges
636	Peterson Creek	84.2	126	6	CG, RC	Wood piles	Sandy gravel	South approach subsided 9 in.; north approach subsided 9 in.	Moderate. Replaced.
637	Kern Creek	86.6	155	6	SS, RC	Concrete piers	North, bedrock; south, stream gravel.	South approach down 4 in.; north approach down 1 in.	Do.
638	Virgin Creek	89.6	100	0	CG, RC	Wood piles	Silty sand	South approach subsided about 3 in.; north approach subsided 6 in.	Destroyed. Both abutments damaged; bridge collapsed over northernmost bent; pilings shifted and slightly crushed under all spans.
639	Glacier Creek	90.0	155	6	SS, RC	----do	Silty sandy gravel.	South approach subsided 6 in.; north approach subsided 4 in.	Severe. Both abutments damaged.
640	Tidewater Slough 6.	90.9	120	0	CG, RC	----do	----do	South approach subsided 12 in.; north approach subsided 20 in.	Destroyed. North abutment slightly crushed; south abutment entirely crushed; bridge collapsed over center bent; piles driven through reinforced concrete.
641	Tidewater Slough 7.	98.3	76	0	CG, RC	----do	----do	----do	Awash at high tide. Replaced; damage considered severe.
642	Tidewater Slough 8.	98.9	76	6	CG, RC	----do	----do	South approach subsided 18 in.; north approach subsided 12 in.	Severe. Awash at high tide.
643	Bird Creek	103.8	205	4	SS, RC	----do	Sand and gravel	South approach subsided 12 in.; north approach subsided 12 in.	Severe.
644	Indian Creek	105.3	165	6	SS, RC	Concrete piers(?)	----do	Unknown	Severe. Bridge in compression.
645	Campbell Creek	125.3	22	0	SS, RC	------	----do	Approach subsided about 2 in.	None.

TABLE 17.—*Damage to bridge approaches and bridges along Glenn Highway from Anchorage to Richardson Highway*

[Abbreviations used for structure and deck types are (structure type first, deck type second): SA, steel arch; SPG, steel plate girder; SPT, steel pony truss; SS, steel stringer; TTS, treated timber stringer; TS, timber stringer; STT, steel through truss; suffix C, cantilever or continuous bridge; TPA, timber plank with asphalt-wearing surface; LTA, laminated timber with asphalt-wearing surface; RC, reinforced concrete. Bridge number and name, route mileage, and superstructure data from Alaska Dept. Highways, Bridge Inventory Rating Report, 1964. Substructure and damage data by U.S. Geol. Survey]

| Bridge | | Route mileage | Length | | Type | | Foundation material | Damage | |
No.	Name		Ft	In.	Super-structure	Substructure		Approaches	Bridges
417	Ship Creek	0.4	163	0	TTS, TPA	Wood piles	Stream sediments	------	Slight. Bridge in compression.
534	----do	3.2	73	6	TS, LTA	----do	----do	------	Do.
535	Eagle River	13.5	243	5	SS, RC	Concrete piers	Glacial gravel	Both approaches subsided 1½ in.	Slight. Bridge has 5 stringers; all bolts on stringers 1, 2, 4 and 5 are sheared; downstream shoe bolt on stringer 3 sheared. Opened up about 1 in. above first pier from south.
536	Peters Creek	21.6	103	8	SPT, RC	----do	Bedrock	Ten ft of fill; no subsidence.	None.
537	Eklutna River	26.0	257	0	SA, RC	----do	----do	None	Slight. North abutment moved about 2 in. North end shows 1-in. tension crack between abutment and bridge.
538	Goat Creek	36.0	77	0	TS, LTA	Unknown	Sediments(?)	----do	None.
539	Knik River	38.7	2,006	6	STT, LTA	Concrete piers	Stream sediments	Both approaches subsided unknown amount.	Severe. Concrete pier cracked and canted; piers slightly displaced toward center of creek.
540	Matanuska River	46.8	353	8	STT, RC	----do	East abutment, bedrock; west abutment, gravel.	None	Slight. Bridge in compression; crack on pier at waterline; west abutment moved east about 1 in.
541	Moose Creek	54.9	183	2	SSC, RC	----do	Coarse gravel	----do	None.
542	Eska Creek	61.0	31	7	SS, RC	Steel piles	Glacial gravel	Subsided about ½ in.	Do.
543	Granite Creek	62.6	183	2	SSC, RC	Concrete piers	Coarse gravel	----do	Do.
544	Kings River	66.8	243	7	SS, RC	----do	----do	Subsided ½ in.	Do.
545	Chickaloon River	78.2	253	10	SSC, RC	----do	Fill over bedrock	Fill subsided about 1 in.	Slight. On east abutment, downstream sliding shoe broke at weld with stringer.
546	Puritan Creek	89.3	21	7	SS, RC	Steel piles	----do	East approach: 10 ft fill subsided 3 in.; west approach: 6 ft fill over bedrock subsided 1 in.	Slight. Anchor bolts on shoe plates sheared; shoe moved 2 in. west; deck moved 2-2½ in. (west abutment).
547	Hicks Creek	96.7	133	3	SSC, RC	Concrete piers	Bedrock	None	None.
548	Caribou Creek	106.9	233	2	SS, RC	----do	----do	East approach subsided slightly.	Slight. West abutment separated from span about 1½ in.; all cracks on abutment between middle stringers.
549	Little Nelchina River.	137.5	183	2	SS, RC	Steel H-piles	Silt, sand, gravel	West approach subsided 3 in.; east approach subsided 2 in.	None.
550	Cache Creek	147.2	22	3	SS, RC	----do	----do	Both subsided 2 in.; approaches on about 15 ft of fill.	Slight. Bridge in compression; bottom of both bulkheads moved toward middle of stream.
551	Mendeltna Creek	152.7	61	5	SS, RC	----do	----do	Subsided unknown amount, probably not more than 3 in.	Slight. East concrete abutment has small cracks; concrete deck cracked at east abutment.
552	Tolsona Creek	172.6	81	5	SS, RC	------	----do	Subsided unknown amount, probably not more than 2-3 in.	None.
553	Moose Creek	186.2	41	6	SS, RC	Concrete abutment(?).	----do	Subsided unknown amount.	Do.

TABLE 18.—*Damage to bridge approaches and bridges along the Richardson Highway from Valdez to Glenn Highway*

[Abbreviations used for structure and deck types are (structure type first, deck type second): SPG, steel plate girder; SS, steel stringer; SDT, steel deck truss; STT, steel through truss; TS, timber stringer; TTS, treated timber stringer; suffix C denotes cantilever or continuous bridge; LT, laminated timber; TP, timber plank; RC, reinforced concrete; prefix T, preservative-treated material; suffix A, asphalt-wearing surface; suffix R, running plank. Bridge number and name and route mileage from Alaska Dept. Highways, Bridge Inventory Rating Report, 1964. Superstructure data primarily from Alaska Department of Highways, Bridge Inventory Rating Report, 1964, supplemented by U.S. Geological Survey data. Substructure, foundation materials, and damage data collected by U.S. Geological Survey]

Bridge		Route mileage	Length		Type		Foundation materials	Damage	
No.	Name		Ft	In.	Superstructure	Substructure		Approaches	Bridges
554	Valdez Glacier Stream 1.	0.9	134	0	TTS, TTPR.	Wood piles	Glacial sediments.	Approaches subsided 2–5 in.; roadway wavy.	Moderate. West abutment jammed about 1 ft to west; bridge in severe compression; deck wavy.
555	Valdez Glacier Stream 2.	1.1	216	0	TTS, TTPR.	----do	----do	Approaches subsided 2–6 in.; roadway wavy.	Moderate. Seventy-five ft from east end, bridge has moved downstream about 1 ft to 18 in. Fourth bent from east end, downstream pile moved about 4 in. Second bent from west end, downstream 3 in. Fifth bent, 2 center piles moved to east about 3 in. Downstream pile cracked through about 3 in. from surface. Sixth bent, downstream pile split; middle 2 piles moved east about 3 in.
556	Valdez Glacier Stream 3.	1.4	196	5	SS, RC	Concrete piers	----do	Approaches subsided 3–6 in.	Severe. West abutment cracked; displaced west about 18 in., bulkhead down about 1 ft in tension. East abutment sidewall cracked.
557	Lowe River Lower Crossing.	14.7	254	7	STT, TLTA.	Concrete piers(?)	Bedrock	None.	Slight. South abutment has pushed against span, and bridge is in compression.
701	Keystone Tunnel	15.8	636	0	Tunnel		----do	----do	None.
558	Lowe River Upper Crossing.	16.6	193	0	SS, RC	Steel piles	----do	----do	Slight. Bridge compressed and low at each end.
559	Sheep Creek	19.0	193	0	SPG, RC	Concrete piers	Glacial outwash	----do	Slight. Anchor bolts, north pier, bent north. Anchor bolts bent, north abutment. Bridge may have moved 2 in.
560	Worthington Glacier 1.	29.2	41	0	TTS, LTA.	Wood piles	----do	Approaches subsided 4–5 in.	None.
561	Worthington River.	30.1	61	6	TTS, TLTA.	----do	----do	Approaches subsided 4–6 in.	Do.
562	Cascade Creek	35.1	58	0	TS, TPR.	----do	Silt, sand, gravel	North approach subsided slightly.	Moderate. Piles canted. Some moved downstream about 2–3 in., especially on south abutment.
563	Small Creek	35.9	23	0	TS, LTA.	Wood abutments	----do	Approaches subsided slightly.	None.
564	Tsina River	37.8	163	8	SDT, RC.	Concrete abutments.	Bedrock	----do	Do.
565	Stuart Creek	45.6	81	8	SS, RC	Steel H-piles	----do	South approach subsided about 2 in.; north approach subsided about 6 in.	Do.
566	Boulder Creek	51.5	26	8	TTS, TLTA.	Wood abutments	Silt, sand, gravel	None.	Do.
567	Squaw Creek	54.8	41	5	SS, RC	----do	----do	Approaches subsided slightly.	Do.
568	Little Tonsina River.	66.0	35	0	TS, TP	----do	----do	Mound about 2½ ft high; roadway fractured at both approaches.	Severe. North end moved south about 17–20 in. Stringer 6 in. by 14 in. split. Other stringers are broken or split at north end. Bridge replaced.
569	Tonsina River	79.1	255	10	SSC, RC.	Concrete piers(?)	----do	Approaches subsided 2–3 in.	None.
570	Squirrel Creek	80.4	22	6	TTS, LTA.	Wood abutments	----do	None.	Do.
571	Willow Creek	90.7	27	0	TTS, TLTA.	----do	----do	----do	Do.
572	Klutina River	101.0	242	9	SPGC, RC.	Concrete piers(?)	----do	----do	Do.
573	Tazlina River	110.4	463	2	STT, LTA.	Concrete piers and steel H-piles.	----do	----do	Do.

TABLE 19.—*Damage to bridge approaches and bridges along Sterling Highway*

[Abbreviations used for structure and deck types are (structure type first, deck type second): CG, concrete girder; SS, steel stringer; STT, steel through truss; CMP, corrugated metal pipe-multiplate and arch; TS, timber stringer; RFC, rigid frame concrete; suffix C indicates cantilever or continuous bridge; RC, reinforced concrete; LTR, laminated timber with running plank; TLTA, preservative-treated laminated timber with asphalt-wearing surface. Bridge number and name, route mileage, length and superstructure data from Alaska Dept. Highways, Bridge Inventory Rating Report, 1964. Substructure, foundation materials, and damage data collected by U.S. Geological Survey]

Bridge		Route mileage	Length		Type		Foundation materials	Damage	
No.	Name		Ft	In.	Super-structure	Substructure		Approaches	Bridges
680	Daves Creek	41.3	21	0	RFC	Concrete abutments.	Bedrock	None	Slight. Bridge in compression.
676	Quartz Creek	41.7	152	1	CG, RC	Concrete piers	Thin veneer of fine-grained sediments.	Fill differentially subsided about 1½–2 in. on each side of bridge.	Severe. East end moved south relative to middle section and west end moved north about 3–4 in. Expansion cracks in deck widened about 2 in.
675	Kenai River	48.9	400	1	CG, RC	Wood piles	Sediments	Approaches subsided as much as 8 in.	Destroyed. Wood piles driven through 6-in. reinforced concrete. Bridge collapsed.
674	Cooper Creek	52.6	67	6	SS, RC	Concrete abutments.	Deltaic sediments	Both approaches had 2 in. slumps.	Slight. Anchor bolts slipped ½ inch. Abutment cracked. Flashing between bridge and abutment squeezed out.
673	Kenai River	54.1	282	0	SS, RC	Steel piles	Sediments-terrace gravels.	None	Under construction.
672	Moose River	84.0	159	0	SSC, RC	Concrete piers	Sediments	Both approaches wavy	Slight. West abutment and bridge deck opened 1½ in.
671	Kenai River	97.8	379	9	STT, TLTA	Steel piles	----do----	None	None.
670	Kasilof River	111.6	273	6	STT, TLTA	----do----	----do----	----do----	Do.
669	Ninilchik River	137.0	159	2	SSC, RC	Unknown	----do----	----do----	Do.
668	Deep Creek	139.0	135	3	SS, RC	----do----	----do----	----do----	Do.
667	Stariski Creek	152.0	76	6	TS, LTR	----do----	----do----	----do----	Do.
796	North Fork Anchor River.	161.7	32	0	CMP	----do----	----do----	----do----	Do.
666	South Fork Anchor River.	196.7	80	9	SS, RC	----do----	----do----	----do----	Do.

1.—South central Alaska, showing main power (short-dashed) and gas-transmission (solid) lines and principal communities whose ports, airports, or utility systems were damaged by the earthquake. Land to left of zero land level change line was generally lowered; land to right of line was raised.

EDWIN B. ECKEL*
U.S. GEOLOGICAL SURVEY

Reprinted with minor changes from
U.S. Geological Survey Professional Paper 545-B,
"Effects of the Earthquake of March 27, 1964, on Air and Water Transport,
Communications, and Utilities Systems"

Effects on Air and Water Transport, Communications, and Utilities Systems

ABSTRACT

The earthquake of March 27, 1964, wrecked or severely hampered all forms of transportation, all utilities, and all communications systems over a very large part of south-central Alaska. Effects on air transportation were minor as compared to those on the water, highway, and railroad transport systems. A few planes were damaged or wrecked by seismic vibration or by flooding. Numerous airport facilities were damaged by vibration or by secondary effects of the earthquake, notably seismic sea and landslide-generated waves, tectonic subsidence, and compaction. Nearly all air facilities were partly or wholly operational within a few hours after the earthquake.

The earthquake inflicted enormous damage on the shipping industry, which is indispensable to a State that imports fully 90 percent of its requirements—mostly by water—and whose largest single industry is fishing. Except for those of Anchorage, all port facilities in the earthquake-affected area were destroyed or made inoperable by submarine slides, waves, tectonic uplift, and fire. No large vessels were lost, but more than 200 smaller ones (mostly crab or salmon boats) were lost or severely damaged. Navigation aids were destroyed, and hitherto well-known waterways were greatly altered by uplift or subsidence. All these effects wrought far-reaching changes in the shipping economy of Alaska, many of them to it betterment.

Virtually all utilities and communications in south-central Alaska were damaged or wrecked by the earthquake, but temporary repairs were effected in remarkably short times. Communications systems were silenced almost everywhere by loss of power or by downed lines; their place was quickly taken by a patchwork of self-powered radio transmitters. A complex power-generating system that served much of the stricken area from steam, diesel, and hydro-generating plants was disrupted in many places by vibration damage to equipment and by broken transmission lines. Landslides in Anchorage broke gas-distribution lines in many places, but the main transmission line from the Kenai Peninsula was virtually undamaged. Petroleum supplies were disrupted, principally by breakage or loss of storage tanks caused by seismic vibration, slides, waves, and fire. Water-supply and sewer lines were also broken in many towns.

INTRODUCTION

The earthquake of March 27, 1964, wrecked or severely hampered all forms of transportation, all utilities, and all communications systems over a very large part of south-central Alaska.

The relationship of geology to the earthquake's effects on the highway and railroad systems was studied in detail by Reuben Kachadoorian and by D. S. McCulloch and M. G. Bonilla, respectively, and their findings will be reported separately in this series. Similarly, effects on water supplies, from both surface and underground sources, are described in detail by Waller (1966a, b). The earthquake damage to one of the chief sources of electric power in the Anchorage area—the U.S. Bureau of Reclamation's Eklutna Hydroelectric Project—is described by Logan (1967), and a novel method of tracing breaks in underground utility lines by means of a portable television camera is described by Burton (in Logan, 1967).

In order to complete the picture of the earthquake's effects on the works of man, its effects on air and water transport and on utilities are briefly summarized here. The principal places affected are shown on figure 1. The report is necessarily a synthesis of information collected and reported by others in the course of investigating various regional or topical phases of the earthquake story; most of these sources are listed in the bibliography. In addition, several of the writer's colleagues, particularly Reuben Kachadoorian and George Plafker, have contributed many pieces of information; this compilation would have been far less complete without their help.

*Now with The Geological Society of America.

AIR TRANSPORT

The earthquake's effects on air transportation were minor as compared to those on the water, highway, and railroad transport systems. This minor damage was doubly fortunate, for the earthquake catastrophe itself made immediate massive airlifts essential. Moreover, air transport of people and goods is much more important in Alaska than elsewhere in the United States. In addition to the great military and commercial air capability, Alaska has one aircraft for each 156 people; one person in every 55 is a licensed pilot.

The few planes that were airborne at the moment the earthquake struck were of course not damaged, though some had communications difficulties and some were diverted to other airports. Planes on the ground or in hangars were damaged by being battered against each other or against fixed objects; at least one plane was badly damaged by water immersion on a ramp at the Kodiak Naval Station, one was destroyed at Kodiak, and several small planes were wrecked by waves at Seward.

Damages to airport facilities were caused in part by earthquake vibrations, in part by secondary effects, notably waves, and in part by tectonic subsidence and compaction. Numerous buildings

2.—Control tower at Anchorage International Airport, collapsed by earthquake shaking. Photograph by Federal Aviation Agency.

were damaged and their utilities disrupted by seismic shaking. The wrecked control tower at Anchorage International Airport was one of the greatest single losses, caused by vibration, that directly affected the aviation system (figs. 2, 3). Some subsidiary buildings, however, such as the military hospital at Elmendorf Air Base, sustained greater damages in terms of total repair costs. Many runways, aprons, and taxiways were cracked and made uneven by shaking and the resultant differential consolidation of alluvial materials or artifical fill. Hangars, seaplane ramps, and parts of the runways at Kodiak Naval Station were flooded by a series of seismic sea waves, and a few smaller airstrips were either destroyed by waves or were subjected to partial flooding by high tides due to regional subsidence. Despite all these difficulties, total damage to Alaska's air facilities amounted to only a few million dollars, as compared with more than $100 million worth of damages to the water, rail, and highway systems. More significant than the relatively small dollar losses, perhaps, is the fact that nearly all air facilities were partly or wholly operational within a few hours after the earthquake. This made possible the enormous air transport of people, food, and supplies that were required at once.

ANCHORAGE

All three major airfields at Anchorage—Elmendorf Air Force Base. Anchorage International Airport, and Merrill Field—escaped the huge landslides that wrought so much havoc in parts of Anchorage (Hansen, 1965), but all sustained some degree of damage by earthquake vibration. Merrill Field, heavily used by the

3.—New control tower for Anchorage International Airport, built by Federal Aviation Agency at a cost of $850,000. One of the first of the new O-type towers in the nation, it was operational by February, 1965. Photograph by Federal Aviation Agency.

Civil Air Patrol and by private planes, was back in full operation within an hour of the quake, and served as a control center for all air traffic in the Anchorage area while control facilities at Elmendorf and Anchorage International were being repaired.

The two chief military installations at Anchorage—Fort Richardson and Elmendorf Air Force Base—are on a broad plain north of the city. They are founded on thick outwash gravels of the El-

mendorf moraine (Miller and Dobrovolny, 1959). Except for a few minor slipouts along the north bluff of Ship Creek, there were no landslides of the kind that devastated nearby Government Hill and other parts of Anchorage (Hansen, 1965), and there were but few ground cracks. Many large and small buildings on both military reservations, however, sustained structural damage from shaking by the earthquake. Those directly connected with air transportation were two of the hangars at Elmendorf and the control tower at that base. Disrupted power and communications facilities, of course, added to the difficulties of maintaining the military air capability. Despite these difficulties, the Elmendorf airfield remained operational; even during the initial shaking, and despite violent swaying, the control tower maintained radio contacts. Soon after the shaking subsided, however, air-traffic control was transferred to facilities installed in a parked aircraft, and 2 days after the earthquake the aircraft was replaced by a mobile control tower that was used until the damaged tower was rebuilt.

Anchorage International Airport is southwest of the city. It is built on a thin layer of silt that overlies older glacial deposits. These, in turn, probably overlie the Bootlegger Cove Clay, whose weakness under earthquake stresses led to the disastrous landslides at Turnagain Heights 2 miles north of the airfield. Anchorage Airport is too far inland to have had similar landslides, but it sustained significant damage from the earthquake shocks. The runways and taxiways cracked in a few places, but were easily resurfaced. The greatest single loss was the new 50-foot reinforced-concrete control tower, which toppled to the ground, carrying one operator to his death. The tower was later replaced (figs. 2, 3). After the disaster, traffic controllers first used a parked small plane to talk with Merrill Field, which was still operational. Later, the tower of the nearby Lake Hood seaplane facility was used by Anchorage air control. A hangar and part of the 3-story steel-frame terminal building also collapsed during the earthquake.

Among other facilities, the Weather Bureau station in the terminal building was demolished.

CORDOVA

At Cordova airport the main 150-foot-wide surfaced runway was virtually unaffected by the earthquake, but the bordering runway aprons, which are each 150 feet wide, and the nearby F.A.A. (Federal Aviation Agency) facilities sustained moderate damage from ground cracking; the violent ground motion caused powerlines to snap. The airport and appurtenant facilities are on thick alluvial deposits of the flat poorly drained Copper River delta 13 miles east of Cordova. Drainage ditches 10–12 feet deep and about 75 feet wide parallel the airstrip on either side. Seismic shaking caused the aprons to spread laterally toward the bordering ditches with resultant cracking of the apron surfaces. Most of the cracks thus formed were extension cracks, as much as 8 inches wide, that were parallel to the edge of the airstrip.

A single ground crack split the reinforced-concrete slab floor of the F.A.A. office building and control tower at the airport, but did not interrupt operation of the facility. The fact that the crack was parallel to, and about 20–50 feet from, a small creek suggests that it resulted from lateral movement of the surficial deposits toward the creek channel. Underground water and steam lines at the F.A.A. facility were broken in so many places by ground cracking that most of the system had to be replaced.

KODIAK NAVAL STATION

Air facilities at Kodiak Naval Station, which serves both military and scheduled civilian traf-

fic, were moderately damaged by flooding, tectonic subsidence, and vibration. Damage to the naval port facilities is described on page B15.

The earthquake vibrations cracked water mains and caused other minor damage. A series of seismic sea waves that began about 45 minutes after the earthquake inundated many buildings, including the three main hangars and the central power station. The inundating waters damaged runway lights, the Operations Control generator, the Tactical Air Command and Navigation generator, and the Rawin Aerological Building. These structures are essential in controlling the smooth flow of air traffic in and out of the naval station. Debris and ice were dumped on aprons in the hangar area. The seaplane ramps on Womens Bay were partly submerged at high tides, owing to the tectonic subsidence of more than 5 feet. The main runways were only damaged near the seaward ends, but asphalt taxiways were cracked, either by the vibration itself or as a result of consolidation of underlying materials (Tudor, 1964; Stroh, 1964; Kachadoorian and Plafker, 1967). The seaward end of the main runway was subjected to erosion by high tides as a result of regional subsidence; this erosion will be a continuing problem.

A sheet-pile bulkhead between two seaplane ramps on Womens Bay failed and moved outward at a point where the piles had been driven into soft sediments in an old channel (Stroh, 1964).

Hangars and apron slabs at the naval station were built on artifical fill approximately 17 feet thick; heavier structures were supported by piles. Differential consolidation of the fill, plus scour by receding seismic sea

4.—Tectonic subsidence required raising of airstrip at Seldovia.   U.S. Army photograph.

waves, led to settlement at one corner of a hangar. More important, settlement of aprons in front of hangar doors caused formation of "lips" from 1 to 6 inches high that made it difficult to move planes in and out of the hangars. These conditions were repaired by constructing wooden ramps and later by raising the apron slabs by injection of grout beneath them (Stroh, 1964).

The Kodiak city airstrip was undamaged. However, all installations of Kodiak Airways, which were along the waterfront in downtown Kodiak, were totally destroyed. Seaplane ramps, hangars, offices, and one aircraft were swept away by seismic sea waves. For more than a year after the earthquake, aircraft operated out of the city airport while waterfront facilities were being rebuilt.

KENAI PENINSULA

Most of the airstrips on the Kenai Peninsula were damaged by vibration, surficial settlement, and tectonic subsidence. Parts of the Seldovia airstrip had to be built up as much as 4–5 feet, at an estimated cost of $600,000, to raise the strip above tide level (fig. 4). Runways at Ninilchik, Kenai, Soldatna, and Hope sustained minor cracks. The airport at Homer was undamaged, but new construction work there was delayed, and made more costly, when the once-ample source of gravel on Homer Spit became difficult to obtain because of tectonic subsidence and consolidation of the spit materials. The only undamaged airstrip on the Kenai Peninsula was the one at Lawing.

SEWARD

Some ground cracks formed on the gravel-surfaced runway at Seward, and the runway drainage system required repair. Several planes on the field were smashed by waves. Regional subsidence, aided by compaction of deltaic sediments at the head of Resurrection Bay, led to partial submergence of the Seward airstrip by high tides. The control tower, which had been put out of commission by waves and the general power failure, was reestablished by noon of March 28, 1964, operating on batteries. It was desperately needed, for aircraft provided the only means of movement in and out of Seward for some days (Fay, 1964; Lemke, 1967).

WHITTIER

The 2,200-foot northeast-trending airstrip at Whittier was severely damaged and became unusable after the earthquake. The airstrip lies on deltaic deposits at the head of Passage Canal nearly a mile west of Whittier. The eastern 500 feet of the strip was constructed on fill that extended into Passage Canal. During the earthquake, the end of this 500-foot section slid into the canal. In addition, regional subsidence, differential compaction of the fill, and landslide-generated waves severely damaged the part of the fill section that did not slide into Passage Canal. The loss of 500 feet of airstrip was great enough to prevent use of the strip by other than small single-engine aircraft (Kachadoorian, 1965).

OTHER AIRPORTS

Small airstrips at Chitina, Portage, Palmer, and Thompson Pass and the South Campbell strip at Anchorage had minor cracks in the runways. Airstrips at Talkeetna, Gakona, Gulkana, Tazlina, and Wasilla were not damaged.

Yakutat airport, situated on a glacial-outwash plain some 280 miles east of the earthquake epicenter, sustained minor damage to the concrete runways and ramp as a result of differential movement of the slabs during the shaking. Long-period ground waves also caused minor damage to two huge sliding hangar doors weighing several tons, each of which rolled back and forth, banging against the hangar sides.

A few small cracks also were found in the gravel runway of the Yakataga airport about half way between Yakutat and Cordova.

The strip at Girdwood, on Turnagain Arm, was subjected to tidal flooding by the tectonic subsidence and compaction of the sediments (Federal Aviation Agency, 1965). Air-navigation aids at nearby Portage and at Hinchinbrook Island in Prince William Sound required restoration. At Valdez, the runway and parking areas were cracked and required grading, but remained in usable condition.

The Federal Aviation Agency's dock at Woody Island, near Kodiak, was so damaged by seismic sea waves that it had to be replaced. The airstrip at Afognak in the Kodiak Island group was inundated repeatedly by waves, and several hundred feet of it was permanently flooded as a result of tectonic subsidence and surficial compaction. A new airstrip was built at the new town of Port Lions on Kodiak Island where the former inhabitants of Afognak were relocated. Gravelled airstrips at Old Harbor and Ouzinkie were partly submerged by tectonic subsidence and local differential compaction of the sediments. They were later repaired and somewhat enlarged by filling and resurfacing.

In all, the Federal Aviation Agency inspected 64 airports throughout the stricken area. Of these, 13 had sustained runway and taxiway damage, including broken underground cables (Federal Aviation Agency, 1965).

SHIPPING

The shipping industry is indispensable to Alaska, because fully 90 percent of all civilian and military requirements must be imported, nearly all by water. Fisheries, moreover, constitute the State's largest single industry—all of it dependent on water transport, from movement of catch and supplies to canneries to final export of the product.

The earthquake inflicted enormous damage on the water-transportation industry. In all south-central Alaska, only the port at Anchorage remained operational, and even it was temporarily incapacitated and was restricted in its operations for some time.

Damage to port facilities at Anchorage, Seward, Valdez,

Homer, Kodiak, Cordova, Whittier, and Seldovia amounted to about $30 million. This figure includes private and public docking facilities only, and not such waterside facilities as canneries. Damage to these facilities was primarily due to submarine landslides and waves generated by them, seismic sea waves, compaction of sediments, and regional subsidence.

Whittier, Seward, and Valdez are the only all-weather ice-free ports in Alaska that have access to the interior of the State. Whittier and Seward are terminals for The Alaska Railroad and Valdez for the Alaska Highway. Anchorage is not an ice-free port and until the earthquake was only used during the summer months. The destruction of the Whittier, Seward and Valdez ports therefore created a serious problem in the movement of supplies, food, and material to the interior of the State. Sitka, on Baranof Island, was the only port in southeast Alaska that reported significant damage. Docks and other harbor structures there were struck by seismic sea waves, and about $1 million in damage was done.

No large vessels were destroyed though some had narrow escapes. In general, vessels at sea were undamaged, but a few experienced bumps that felt to the crews as if their ships had run aground. A few free-floating small boats were capsized and sunk. Most of the boats that were lost, however, were tied up at docks, were in small-boat harbors where they were engulfed by giant waves, or were involved in the submarine slides that destroyed several ports. When the earthquake struck, 820 vessels of more than 5 tons and 2,850 smaller boats were operating in south-central Alaska (Office of Emergency Planning, 1964). Of these, more than 200 vessels, most of them crab or salmon boats, were lost or severely damaged. Many seafood-processing plants were washed away or flooded.

EFFECT ON ECONOMIC PATTERN

One of the most far-reaching and long-lasting effects of the earthquake was the change that it wrought in the economic pattern of water and rail transport. Despite the fact that Anchorage is Alaska's largest city, its port business had always been relatively small as compared to that of several smaller cities. The municipally owned port facilities, in fact, had operated at a loss ever since they were built in 1961. The earthquake resulted in an enormous increase in Anchorage port facilities and commerce, and resultant decreases in traffic at the ports of Seward and Whitter and a parallel decrease in revenues for The Alaska Railroad. Weekly van-ship service was initiated from Seattle to Anchorage within a few months after the earthquake, and later experience showed that these larger vessels could surmount the ice problems that had previously kept Anchorage from being considered an all-weather port (Anchorage Daily Times, March 26, 1965).

Major changes in the economy of the region were also effected when petroleum-product terminals at Whittier and Seward were moved permanently to Anchorage. The Alaska Steamship line, one of the major cargo carriers between Seattle and Alaska, stopped calling at Seward and moved its operations to Whittier.

Devastated as it was by loss of boats, gear, and canneries, the seafood industry also underwent major changes that could only lead to its betterment over the long term. Immediately after the earthquake, salmon and crab catches at Kodiak and elsewhere were curtailed, not so much by loss of boats as by lack of processing capacity. Most seafood-processing plants were rebuilt promptly, however, and equipped with more modern machinery than they had had before. Floating canneries were introduced. Unlike property owners on land, few of whom had earthquake insurance, nearly all owners of vessels were covered by marine insurance; claims were paid promptly. The U.S. Bureau of Commercial Fisheries and the Small Business Administration lent money on easy terms for replacements of boats and processing plants. The Congress also authorized direct subsidies of as much as 55 percent for new fishing vessels. The net results were that the seafood industry obtained modern boats and better equipment and that debts were refunded at lower interest rates (U.S. Bureau of Land Management, 1964).

NAVIGATION AIDS

Many lights, buoys, tide gages, and other navigation aids were wrecked or displaced by waves, not only in the devastated harbors but along virtually all of the coastline of south-central Alaska. These aids were replaced quickly by the Coast Guard, the Navy, the Coast and Geodetic Survey, and other responsible agencies.

The Cape Hinchinbrook Light Station, on the southwest tip of Hinchinbrook Island in Prince William Sound, was severely shaken and two landslides were activated along the bluff on which the light is built, but the station remained in operation. The slides were but two more episodes in a long history of cliff erosion on Cape Hinchinbrook, and one of the few directly beneficial effects of the earthquake of 1964 was to raise the base of the cliff some 8 feet and thereby retard the erosion process. (Reuben Kachadoorian and George Plafker, written commun., 1965.)

The tectonic uplift that affected most of the Prince William Sound area resulted in shoaling of waters that had been navigable before the earthquake (fig. 1); during the first weeks after the quake some small craft were grounded or damaged by hidden rocks or were stranded by low tides. At least one cannery in the area of uplift—the Crystal Falls cannery at Mountain Slough, not far from Cordova—became inaccessible to fishermen and was declared a total loss (Alaska Dept. Fish and Game, 1965).

Tectonic subsidence in the westerly part of the earthquake-affected zone, especially around Kodiak Island and along Cook Inlet and the Kenai Peninsula, of course resulted in deeper water (fig. 1). This deeper water in itself would not have affected navigation adversely, but the subsidence also drowned old and familiar shorelines and at least locally, as in Turnagain Arm, led to increased sedimentation. The net result of subsidence, therefore, was a relatively large area of new and uncharted water.

Within hours after the earthquake, the U.S. Coast and Geodetic Survey began the difficult but essential job of recharting all navigable waterways in the area affected by the earthquake and replacing tide gages that had been destroyed. It also began a long-term geodetic resurvey of permanent horizontal and vertical changes that had

taken place along shorelines and on land.

The Coast and Geodetic Survey's rapid revision of nautical charts was accomplished by ship reconnaissance, tidal surveys, and aerial photogrammetry. The resulting chart revisions, showing significant changes in channels, shoal areas, shorelines, and navigation aids were issued as "chartlets," designed to be pasted over parts of existing charts. These chartlets were upgraded as new information from more precise surveys became available. The first preliminary chartlets that were issued to navigators less then a month after the earthquake showed the harbors of Crescent City, Calif., and of Valdez, Whittier, Seward, Kodiak, and Womens Bay on Kodiak Island; chartlets of Fire Island shoal in Cook Inlet and the harbors at Anchorage and Homer soon followed. By the end of 1964, revised editions of seven nautical charts had been issued and many others, covering most of the earthquake-affected area, were made available during the next 2 years (Wood, 1966).

ANCHORAGE

The Anchorage harbor is on Cook Inlet, just north of the mouth of Ship Creek. Port facilities, though incapacitated for a short time, were almost undamaged in contrast to all other ports in the earthquake-affected area. Tectonic subsidence was too small to do much damage, there were no waves or fires, and the bluffs above the port were not affected by the disastrous translatory landslides that wrecked several other parts of Anchorage (Hansen, 1965). Virtually all the damage to port structures was caused by earthquake vibrations and by related

ground fractures and consolidation and settlement of sediments.

The municipally owned Anchorage wharf is the largest port structure (fig. 5). It consists of two adjacent reinforced-concrete docks on concrete-filled tubular piles. The joint between the two docks was opened 4–12 inches; all four cranes were shaken off their tracks, and their undercarriages and counterweight arms were damaged. The steel-frame transit shed was cracked and twisted but only to a minor degree. Some steel piles broke at their caps; battered H-piles were sprung out of line when the main dock structure shifted its position (Berg and Stratta, 1964; Alaska Construction Consultant Committee, 1964).

The so-called old Army Dock (fig. 5), a timber structure that was already much deteriorated, was made unusable for offloading of private and military petroleum supplies; a temporary petroleum dock was built to replace the old Army Dock, but it was severely damaged by ice and did not last through the following winter. Petroleum pipelines and approach roads and rail lines were broken or twisted by settlement and vibration. A cement bin, 30 feet high and 30 feet in diameter, collapsed on its pedestal. The walls of several petroleum storage tanks developed bulges at ground level. Berg and Stratta (1964) suggested that the bulges may have been caused by an earthquake-induced swirling of the tank contents, which in turn induced large vertical forces acting over a small zone at the base of the cylinder.

The port was able to handle its first ship only 3 days after the earthquake. Within 2 years, both facilities and commerce were greatly increased over preearthquake times.

5.—Anchorage municipal wharf area shortly after the earthquake, at low tide.   The main dock was only slightly damaged, but the lolder Army dock (upper left), was ruined.   Vibration and ground fractures damaged some structures in the port area, including the petroleum tank (lower right).   U.S. Army photograph.

6.—Cordova harbor as it appeared in February 1965. Tectonic uplift left docks inaccessible to ships except at very high tides Reconstruction involved dredging of harbor and rebuilding of docks and small-boat basin. U. S. Army photograph.

CORDOVA

The Cordova area was raised about 6 feet by tectonic uplift, and the docks were thereby made inaccessible to ships except at very high tides. The deck of the main city dock was lifted and displaced by seismic sea waves and was battered by ships tied up to it. The ferry terminal dock was also damaged by waves, but these damages were insignificant as compared to the effect of regional uplift.

The city dock, ferry slip, and breakwater were rebuilt and the small-boat basin and other parts of the harbor were dredged 10 feet deeper by the U.S. Army Corps of Engineers (fig. 6). Under an urban renewal plan, the entire waterfront was rebuilt with material dredged from the harbor for fill. Much of this work involved enlargement and improvement of existing facilities rather than replacement of damaged facilities (Alaskan Construction Consultant Committee, 1964; Anchorage Daily Times, March 26, 1965). The Cordova canneries had to extend their docks an average of 110 feet to reach water depths equal to those which prevailed before the earthquake.

Because of the uplift, Orca Inlet, which is the most direct waterway from Cordova to the open sea and the important Copper River Delta salmon-fishing and clamming areas, is too shallow for all but the smallest vessels at most stages of tide. The alternative route via Orca Bay and Hinchinbrook Entrance is much longer and considerably more hazardous.

WHITTIER

The port of Whittier is at the head of Passage Canal, a western arm of Prince William Sound (fig. 1). The town was originally constructed as a military railroad terminal, having been built during World War II to serve as a backup for Seward as a second all-weather railroad port. Town and port are owned by The Alaska Railroad and the Department of Defense, but some land is privately leased.

Though many of Whittier's buildings, particularly those on bedrock, sustained but slight damage from seismic shock, the port facilities, which are on unconsolidated sediments, were so extensively damaged by the earthquake as to make them inoperable. In addition to seismic shock, other causes of damage were tectonic subsidence, ground fractures, differential subsidence due to compaction, landslides, great waves generated by submarine slides, and fire. Of these, the landslide-generated waves caused all loss of life and by far the greatest damage to port facilities. All docks were damaged or destroyed, a privately owned lumber mill was totally destroyed, and all the petroleum storage tanks along the waterfront were burned—but only after being severely damaged by seismic vibration and by waves (Kachadoorian, 1965).

Despite the extensive damage,

the Whittier port facilities were back in operation in a remarkably short time, ready to aid in supplying the massive reconstruction effort elsewhere. The first train reached Whittier on April 20, was loaded at the partially repaired car slip, and returned to Anchorage. Regular weekly train-ship service, characterized by a 3-day trip between Whittier and New Westminster, B.C., began in June, less than 3 months after the disaster. Not a little of the speed with which Whittier was brought back to life was due to close cooperation between The Alaska Railroad and several military entities. Thus, while the car slip was still under repair, the Army lent a floating crane, with maximum lift of 200,000 pounds, to lift cars and vans from barges. The Navy lent a 3,000-horsepower tug to move the crane from Beaver, Oreg.; it sailed April 3 and arrived in Whittier April 13. The National Guard sent a tug from Seattle to service the crane (Fitch, 1964).

SMALLER PRINCE WILLIAM SOUND COMMUNITIES

Several smaller communities and canneries in Prince William Sound sustained varying degrees of damage from tectonic uplift and from the local violent waves of unknown origin that accompanied and immediately followed the earthquake. Damage resulting from seismic shaking or from the long-period seismic sea waves that came later was negligible (Plafker and Mayo, 1965).

Sawmill Bay on Evans Island in western Prince William Sound is the site of two operative canneries, one inoperative cannery in a poor state of repair, a fuel depot, and several permanent residences.

Violent local waves that accompanied the earthquake in Sawmill Bay drowned one man, destroyed the dock of the inoperative cannery, partially damaged the fuel dock and several smaller docks, and wrecked two barges. Tectonic uplift of about 8 feet left fishing boats that had been stored on grids for the winter high above the reach of tides. The grid skidways had to be extended and some modifications to dock facilities were required before the canneries could be put back into operation.

Similar waves wiped out the entire native village of Chenega except for the school and one home and swept away 25 of its 76 inhabitants. All the minimal waterfront facilities and all but three of the boats belonging to the villagers were destroyed. The remaining population of Chenega has been relocated at Tatitlek; no repairs were made to the village site.

Other similar, but much lower, waves were experienced almost simultaneously at the inoperative canneries at Port Nellie Juan and Port Oceanic in nearby parts of the Sound. The dock of the Port Nellie Juan cannery was washed away and the cannery watchman and his family of two are missing and presumably drowned. A cannery barge 25 feet wide by 60 feet long that was tied up at the mouth of a small creek near the cannery was lifted by violent local waves, turned over end for end, moved 200 feet up the creek valley, and deposited upside down in the trees, 15 feet above high-water level. Waves at Port Oceanic destroyed the dock and washed away foundation piling from beneath the cannery; one 27-foot fishing boat that was in the bay was sunk.

At the native village of Tatitlek and the nearby inoperative Ellamar cannery, the waterfront

7.—New small-boat basin, excavated in end of Homer Spit. Former basin, on left side of the spit, was destroyed by a small offshore slide. The fact that the entire end of the spit is submerged by high tides because of tectonic subsidence and compaction necessitates dikes around new basin. U.S. Army photograph.

facilities were impaired by about 4 feet of tectonic uplift; dredging and other improvements to the harbor area at Tatitlek by the Corps of Engineers have resulted in a harbor that is at least as good, if not better, than the preearthquake one.

HOMER

At Homer, at the mouth of Kachemak Bay on Cook Inlet (fig. 1), virtually all port facilities were put out of commission by tectonic subsidence, consolidation of sediments on Homer Spit, and an offshore landslide.

The almost new small-boat basin was completely destroyed, the timber city dock was usable but had subsided 6 feet, and oil tanks and warehouses required raising to place them above water that flooded the spit at high tides. A new and larger small-boat basin (fig. 7) was constructed by the Corps of Engineers by excavation of a part of the spit (Alaskan Construction Consultant Committee, 1964; Waller, 1966c; George and Lyle, 1966).

SEWARD

Seward, at the head of Resurrection Bay on the east side of Kenai Peninsula (fig. 1), is a fisheries center, but its main importance in the economy is as the chief year-round port for The Alaska Railroad to Anchorage and Fairbanks. All Seward's port facilities were destroyed by submarine slides, giant waves, and fire. Because both highway and rail routes were disrupted between Anchorage and Seward, the port was cut off for some days from all means of communication and transportation except radio and air travel.

Extensive geologic and soil studies of the fan delta on which Seward is built led to the conclusion that the new waterfront is unstable and subject to further submarine sliding in the event of future earthquakes. The decision was therefore made to rebuild the port elsewhere and to use the original waterfront area, under an urban renewal plan, only for parks and light industrial building. A new small-boat basin was built, and the main harbor facilities, dominated by The Alaska Railroad port terminal, were constructed on deltaic deposits at the mouth of Resurrection River, just north of the main town (fig. 8). The new site for the port required much dredging, but the chances of major submarine slides and the resultant waves are minimal (Lemke, 1967; George and Lyle, 1966).

SELDOVIA

Seldovia, a small fishing port near the southern end of the Kenai Peninsula, is the only

8.—Part of new small-boat basin and nearly completed railroad dock at Seward, November 1965. All former Seward waterfront facilities (to left of picture) were destroyed by submarine slides, waves, and fire. U.S. Army photograph.

9.—Seldovia at low tide in March 1965, with raised breakwater and small-boat basin in use. Tectonic subsidence submerged boardwalk (curving structure at shore end of docks in foreground) at high tide. The boardwalk has been replaced on new fill. Urban renewal project will alter buildings and utilities to conform with higher water levels. U.S. Army photograph.

protected harbor between Seward and Anchorage that can accommodate ocean vessels (fig. 1). Tectonic subsidence lowered the area about 3.5 feet so that most harbor facilities, including the mile-long boardwalk on which the business section of the town is built, were awash at high tides. The Corps of Engineers built a new breakwater, raised docks, and restored the small-boat harbor which had undergone subsidence and piling damage (fig. 9). An urban renewal plan was finally adopted to move the main town to higher ground, some of it to be made of fill as much as 32 feet thick (Alaskan Construction Consultant Committee, 1964; Anchorage Daily Times, March 26, 1965).

KODIAK AND KODIAK NAVAL STATION

Kodiak, near the northeast tip of Kodiak Island (fig. 1), is the headquarters of one of the largest fishing fleets in Alaska. It is best known as the center of the king crab industry, but also produces large catches of salmon, halibut, shrimp, and scallop. The nearby Kodiak Naval Station is the largest U.S. Navy installation in Alaska for both surface vessels and aircraft. The naval station was moderately damaged by the earthquake and its aftereffects, but the port of Kodiak and much of the fishing fleet were devastated—almost entirely by seismic sea waves. Neither the town nor the naval station received more than minor damage from vibration.

At the naval station, several buildings that were set on piles without adequate ties were floated away. Flooding of the power station cut off power and central steam heat for the entire facility for some days. Seismic sea waves destroyed the Navy's cargo dock, already old and deteriorated, and severely damaged the fuel pier and three structures at the crash boat harbor. Waves caused moored ships to raise the bollards and to damage fendering. Sections of the decking were lifted and displaced by waves, and some piles, placed in holes augered to the rocky bottom, were uprooted. Regional subsidence added to the toll by causing tidal inundation of the dock's remains. The marginal pier, on the peninsula side of Womens Bay, sustained only minor damage from a moored barge (Stroh, 1964; Tudor, 1964).

Tectonic subsidence left the Kodiak waterfront and the small-boat basin permanently subject to flooding by high tides. A temporary small-boat basin was established in Gibson Cove, between Kodiak and the naval station. It was used until the original basin had been rebuilt by the Corps of Engineers and its two submerged breakwaters had been raised 6 feet.

Greatest damage to the naval station and to the port of Kodiak was caused by a series of gigantic seismic sea waves, some of them non-breaking, that began about 45 minutes after the earthquake and continued far into the night. These waves destroyed or incapacitated all waterfront structures at Kodiak and inundated all of the lower part of the town. Scores of vessels were smashed or overturned and many were washed inland among flooded buildings as much as half a mile from the harbor (Plafker and Kachadoorian, 1966).

The timber city dock and its warehouse subsided and sustained wave damage, but was partly usable. Privately owned petroleum storage tanks were undamaged, but their related piers and buildings were heavily damaged or destroyed (Alaska Construction Consultant Committee, 1964). The U.S. Fish and Wildlife pier and warehouse were swept away by receding waves. The decking of the pier was lifted from the piles and the approach decking floated away. Bulkheads and about 25 piles beneath the pier were destroyed. The harbormaster's building was destroyed when a large fishing vessel collided with it. Numerous small privately owned docks on Near Channel, Potatopatch Lake, Mission Lake, and Inner Anchorage were swept away by the waves.

Of the four major seafood-processing plants, two were severely damaged and two were destroyed. Canneries at Shearwater Bay, south of Kodiak, and at Ouzinkie, north of the port, were also destroyed; the Shearwater cannery carried with it 30 salmon boats that had been in storage. Most canneries were rebuilt shortly after the earthquake, and floating canneries were brought in to add to the industry's capabilities.

Docks and buildings at four other operative canneries within the zone of tectonic subsidence had to be raised above the new higher extreme high-tide level (Plafker and Kachadoorian, 1966).

Docks at two small lumber mills near Afognak and Ouzinkie were also damaged by the seismic sea waves.

A Navy seaplane tender was sent from Oak Harbor, Wash. Arriving on March 31, 1964, it immediately hooked its generators to naval station lines and supplied a part of the station's power needs for some days. The Navy also brought a dock landing ship, with a 160-foot pontoon dock from San Diego. It was lent to the city of Kodiak to help in rehabilitation of the fishing fleet (Kachadoorian and Plafker, 1967; Stroh, 1964; Tudor, 1964).

VALDEZ

Valdez is the northernmost all-weather port in Alaska. Unlike Seward and Whittier, which are also all-weather ports, it is not a railhead but is connected with Fairbanks and the interior by highway. The town is on Port Valdez, the northeasternmost extension of Prince William Sound (fig. 1).

All port facilities were destroyed by the earthquake (fig. 10). A gigantic submarine slide off the face of the delta on which Valdez is built was the single most disastrous event—it completely destroyed all docks and superstructures. Waves, ground cracks, shaking, and fire left all other port facilities and the seaward part of the town in ruins.

Shortly after the earthquake, the Corps of Engineers built a temporary dock on the newly formed waterfront, primarily for

10.—Old and new Valdez. All waterfront structures and utilities in old Valdez were destroyed (lower center). The new town-site (upper left) is protected from slides by chain of bedrock hills. U.S. Army photograph.

offloading of supplies needed in rehabilitation of the town but also to permit the small commercial and sport-fishing industries to resume work. Meanwhile, the likelihood of further submarine slides and continued settlement along the waterfront, and the danger of flooding by the Valdez glacier stream that built the delta, led geologists to advise complete abandonment of Valdez. This advice was followed by town officials who decided to build a new town at Mineral Point, about 4 miles by road west of the devastated community. The new site is far less likely than the old to be damaged by future earthquakes, and the modern docks and ferry slip that will allow Valdez to resume its place among Alaskan ports are founded on bedrock that is not susceptible to underwater slides (figs. 10, 11; Coulter and Migliaccio, 1936).

11.—Harbor facilities at new town of Valdez, winter 1966. Townsite is just to left of picture, behind protective bedrock hills. U.S. Army photograph.

COMMUNICATIONS AND UTILITIES

To an extent that is seldom realized except when they are disrupted, modern man depends on public utilities and communications. All are necessary for his comfort and survival within his own community and for ties with other communities—water, sewage disposal, power and heat, and radio, telephone, and television communication. In Alaska's subarctic climate, reliable sources of heat and power are even more important than they are elsewhere. Communications facilities, too, are more vital in Alaska than elsewhere, for much of the population is thinly scattered and in poorly accessible places and also because Alaska itself is far removed from the rest of the United States.

Virtually all utilities and communications in south-central Alaska were damaged or wrecked by the great earthquake. The total cost of damages to utility systems was initially estimated to be about $25 million (Alaska Construction Consultant Committee, 1964). This figure is small in comparison to the total cost of the earthquake, and fails to give a true picture of the emotional and physical effects wrought by disrupted utilities and communications during the recovery and rehabilitation periods. Predictably, utilities at Anchorage and its neighboring military establishments represented at least two-thirds of the total losses. This high proportion was only because Anchorage is the largest community, with consequently greater development of utilities. Several other towns lost greater proportions of their utility systems than did Anchorage.

Complete repairs and replacements required many months of effort, but essential services that sufficed to alleviate panic and suffering and to prevent disease that commonly follows on disruption of utilities were restored in a short time. This fast restoration was due to the prodigious cooperative efforts of the utility suppliers, both private and public, working in conjunction with the military and civilian authorities (U.S. Army Alaskan Command, 1964).

Because they tend to be widespread geographically, rather than confined to single towns, the communications system, the oil- and gas-distribution facilities, and the power systems are described separately. These generalizations are followed by descriptions of the effects on all utility systems in certain towns.

COMMUNICATIONS SYSTEMS

South-central Alaska has a well-developed communications system—telephone, radio and television. Because of the great land and water distances and the mountainous terrain, greater dependence is placed on radio and radiotelephone facilities than elsewhere in the United States.

Most telephone lines are above ground, though in parts of Anchorage and in some of the rugged mountains both military and civilian lines are in buried cables. Nearly all telephone communications were disrupted by loss of power soon after the onset of the earthquake. In a few places, services were restored almost immediately by use of batteries or other auxiliary power units. Elsewhere, however, cen-

tral stations were severely shaken or were wrecked by waves and other aftereffects of the earthquake shocks.

Overhead lines, both power and telephone, sustained much damage from the shaking. Tautened wires broke in tension. Utility poles were subject to the same whipping action as trees, but because they were less resilient a greater proportion of them were broken. Other poles survived the shaking itself but were brought down by avalanches or landslides. Still others, as in Turnagain Arm, were wrecked when the silt in which they were placed shifted on the sea bottom (figs. 12, 13).

Despite the widespread damages and a great variety of problems, most telephone systems were fully or partially restored to service within a few hours of the earthquake.

Nearly all commercial and military radio and television communications went off the air immediately as a result of power failures. While power was being restored, they were replaced temporarily by a fantastic patchwork of amateur radios in Alaska and the conterminous United States, mobile broadcast units, and short-wave transmitters in ships, taxis, parked planes, police cars, and many other vehicles and places. These means served well in reestablishing contacts with isolated communities and with the outside world, in getting relief and reconstruction underway, and in preventing panic.

Firefighting organizations and their equipment remained intact in all the earthquake-affected

12.—Power and telephone poles along Turnagain Arm were tipped when the silt in which they were embedded was liquefied by earthquake vibrations. Photograph by Chugach Electric Association, Inc.

13.—Some power-transmission poles on Turnagain Arm were destroyed by liquefaction of silt foundation and by floating ice. Photograph by Chugach Electric Association, Inc.

towns, but disruption of water supplies made them virtually useless in Seward, Valdez, and Whittier, where large waterfront fires developed; they would also have been helpless in Anchorage had there been fires. The readiness of all fire departments was also hampered by difficulties in communications (National Board of Fire Underwriters, 1964).

POWER SYSTEMS IN ANCHORAGE, THE MATANUSKA VALLEY, AND ON THE KENAI PENINSULA

In the general vicinity of Anchorage, electric power is provided from four sources—(1) a city-owned steam generating system, (2) military-operated steamplants that serve Fort Richardson and Elmendorf Air Base, (3) the Bureau of Reclamation's Eklutna hydroelectric project, serving Palmer, the Matanuska Valley, parts of Anchorage, and (4) the Chugach Electric Association's hydro- and steam-power generation system serving part of Anchorage and most communities on the Kenai Peninsula (fig. 1).

All these systems were damaged, some severely, by the earthquake of March 27, 1964. Though disastrous and expensive, the power-system failures were fortunate in some ways. The fact that power was shut off immediately in Anchorage, for example, is widely credited for the almost complete lack of fires there. Virtually all of the damage to transmission lines was of the kind ordinarily expected during Alaskan winters, but damage was more widely scattered geographically and far more concentrated in time than usual. These conditions made repair work much more difficult and costly than normal, even though most of the maintenance problems were familiar ones.

Earthquake damages to the Eklutna hydroelectric system, caused almost entirely by ground vibration and related cracks and subsidence, are described by Logan (1967).

The military powerplants at Fort Richardson and Elmendorf Air Base use coal-fired steam turbines. Both systems sustained much structural damage from seismic vibration. Tanks, piping, and other equipment were distorted or broken by twisting, overturning, or failure of supports. Despite the widespread damages, central heating for the military bases was maintained with almost no interruption, and power was restored to large parts of both bases within 24 hours (Powers, 1965; U.S. Army Alaskan Command, 1964; Stephenson, 1964).

Parts of Anchorage, including the heavily damaged Turnagain Heights section, and most of the Kenai Peninsula are served power by the Chugach Electric Association, a cooperative financed by the Rural Electrification Administration. Much of the rather complex integrated system was heavily damaged by the earthquake, but ties with other power sources and close cooperation of all suppliers, military and civilian, resulted in restoration of power to most of the affected areas within a very few days.

Principal units of the Chugach system are the Knik Arm coal-fired steamplant near the mouth of Ship Creek in Anchorage, the Bernice Lake gas turbine plant just north of Kenai (fig. 1), and the Cooper Lake hydroelectric plant. The Cooper Lake generating plant is actually on the south shore of Kenai Lake, but it drops water from nearby Cooper Lake through a mile long tunnel and a penstock. The Knik Arm and Bernice Lake plants produce some steam for local distribution in addition to electricity. Bernice Lake supplies power to several communities on the Kenai Peninsula, including Homer, which also has a diesel-electric generating plant. Seward is served power from Cooper Lake.

Except for vibration damage to turbine blades at Bernice Lake, neither this nor the Cooper Lake plant was seriously injured. Failure of the power system in the Anchorage area overloaded the entire transmission network and caused automatic overload switches to trip at the other generating plants. Because Anchorage was closer to the epicentral region in northern Prince William Sound, failures there occurred an estimated 15–20 seconds before the tremors were first felt at the Bernice Lake plant; this time lapse was enough to allow the plant operator to shut off the power before the potentially damaging vibrations reached the plant. The Knik Arm plant, however, was severely shaken, and coal bunkers, ash handling system, and other structural elements were either weakened or destroyed. The most serious damage was not noticed until 2 weeks after the earthquake when high tides made apparent the fact that tectonic subsidence and local compaction had lowered the mouth of Ship Creek. Sea water flooded the cooling pond and the ash aisle in the basement of the plant.

Damages to the Chugach distribution system were less severe than to the generating plants but were nevertheless substantial. About 50 poles broke and 25 transformers were dropped to the ground. Underground lines and several substations in downtown Anchorage were destroyed by landslides (Chugach Electric Assoc., 1964).

In Palmer and the surrounding Matanuska Valley, northeast of Anchorage, power outage lasted for 18 hours. The distribution system itself was undamaged, but the transmission line from the Eklutna plant was downed by an avalanche near the Knik River (Logan, 1967).

Automatic vibration controls reacted to the first earthquake shocks to shut down the Anchorage municipal gas-turbine plant. The plant itself survived in good condition, but breaks in the gasline cut off the fuel supply. Six standby diesel generators were also inoperative because water-main breaks stopped the supply of cooling water. Some intermittent power was restored to the city within 2½ hours after the earthquake, when the turbine plant was started with bottled gas and then converted to oil for fuel. Rupture of oil tanks, with consequent loss of fuel, caused further delays in delivery of firm power, but an emergency supply of oil from Elmendorf Air Base was used until the gaslines were repaired. As a result, power was restored to nearly all of Anchorage by midnight Sunday, March 29. The municipal power-distribution system, both aerial and underground, was almost undamaged except in the slide areas. Two substations were wrecked by slides and had to be relocated (Stephenson, 1964).

Most substations sustained light to moderate damage from vibration. Transmission and distribution lines were disrupted in many places. In the Turnagain section and elsewhere in Anchorage, lines were broken by the gigantic translatory landslides that were the principal geologic effects of the earthquake there (Hansen, 1965). The transmission line along the north side of Turnagain Arm, particularly between Girdwood and Portage, was very severely damaged—13 tower structures were destroyed and 60 others required extensive repairs. Most of the structures tipped or broke when the silt in in which they were embedded was liquefied by vibration, but later the tidal action and increased ice shove that resulted from tectonic subsidence of the area did further damage (figs. 12, 13). In the mountains, earthquake-triggered avalanches destroyed several towers on the line between Portage and Cooper Lake and between Cooper Lake and Seward (Chugach Electric Assoc., 1964).

PETROLEUM AND NATURAL GAS FACILITIES

Alaska depends as heavily as any other modern society on petroleum products and on natural gas for heat, power, and transportation. Most of the petroleum products used in Alaska are brought in by water from West Coast refineries or from fields in Cook Inlet and along its shores (fig. 1). Like all other water-transported goods, fuel supplies were disrupted and dislocated by destruction of most of the ports in south-central Alaska. In addition to water transport, however, three pipe lines play significant parts in transmission of petroleum and gas products; none of these was appreciably damaged.

A single leak developed in the 93-mile line that transmits natural gas from fields near Kenai to Anchorage. An 18-mile pipeline (not shown on fig. 1) transmits crude oil from wells on the Swanson River and Soldatna Creek, on the Kenai peninsula, to loading facilities at Nikishka on Cook Inlet. The line itself was unscathed but storage tanks at the terminal were slightly damaged.

A few leaks also developed in storage tanks at a small refinery near Nikishka but they were easily repaired (Office of Emergency planning, 1964).

A military multiproduct pipeline, much of it above ground, extends 686 miles from Haines in southeastern Alaska, to Fairbanks. Roughly parallel to the Alcan Highway, it handles more military petroleum products than does the port of Anchorage. Far from the area of disturbance, the pipeline was not damaged by the earthquake and service was not interrupted. Water wells at a few of the booster stations, however, were slightly damaged.

Many storage tanks, notably in Anchorage, Seward, Valdez, and Kodiak, developed leaks from earthquake vibration or were totally destroyed by waves or fire. Quick repairs to tank farms, and early resumption of water transport for fuel supplies, prevented development of critical shortages of petroleum products.

Many homes and businesses throughout the stricken area depend on individual bottled-gas units for heating. Fortunately, very few of these installations were damaged outside the areas of total destruction caused by waves, fires, and landslides. Piped natural gas is available only in Anchorage and several small towns near Kenai. The damages to this system, and the methods used to restore service, are well documented by Stump (1965), from whose paper most of the following information is abstracted.

The natural gas used by Anchorage is produced from the Kenai field near Kalifonsky Beach on Cook Inlet. It is supplied by the privately owned Anchorage Natural Gas Corp. and its sister organization, The Alaska Pipeline Co.

A 12-inch pipeline, 93 miles long, brings gas to Anchorage (fig. 1). Much of the line is in rugged country that is accessible only by tracked vehicles or by air. There are three airstrips along the right-of-way, which is itself cleared to permit use of helicopters. The 8-mile-long segment across Turnagain Arm, 30 miles south of Anchorage, has parallel pipelines that are embedded in the silt of the Arm. The earthquake caused little damage to the underwater line, but tectonic subsidence in the area necessitated raising the automatic control valves above the new high-tide levels. Only one small but potentially serious break occurred in the entire pipeline. This one, doubtless caused by ground vibration, was at milepost 55 and consisted of a circumferential crack next to a weld in the pipe. Access was difficult but, once reached, the break was easily and quickly repaired.

Damages to the 120-mile-long gas-distribution system within Anchorage amounted to nearly $1 million, a heavy blow to a company that was less than 3 years old and was just beginning to reach financial stability. Nevertheless, there was far less damage to this entirely new system whose components were all designed and constructed to modern code specifications than there would have been to old or poorly built equipment. As would be expected, most major breaks in the distribution system occurred at landslide grabens where near-surface materials moved both laterally and vertically (Hansen, 1965). Some of the more than 200 breaks in gaslines, however, were caused by ground cracks which had little or no visible displacement. Steel and copper pipes reacted similarly to the earthquake forces. Some lines failed in compression or tension; others failed by shear or by repeated flexing (fig. 14).

In Anchorage, the high-pressure gas main was broken by the landslide at Third Avenue and Post Road, near the Alaska Native Hospital (fig. 15). A second break in the main was caused by a slide near the Municipal Power and Light Plant on Ship Creek. This slide ruptured fuel tanks and flooded the area with 300,000 gallons of diesel fuel.

The making of repairs was greatly aided by the loan of experts from several natural-gas companies in the Pacific Northwest; priorities were given to the city powerplant, hospitals, restaurants, and laundries, in that order. Gas service was restored to the municipal powerplant within 30 hours after the earthquake, a remarkable accomplishment considering that temporary lines had to be laid on steep slopes and on a surface that was covered by ice and by a thick layer of diesel oil. The city's two gas-fired turbines furnished most of the electric power for Anchorage for some weeks. Gas became available in homes and businesses in Spenard and the southern part of Anchorage within 48 hours, and 90 percent of the entire system was restored within 2 weeks after the earthquake.

During the spring and summer of 1964, and after all known leaks had been repaired and service restored, the company made a novel use of geologic maps. The ground in Anchorage was frozen to depths of 6 feet or more at the time of the earthquake, and buried pipes could not move or adjust to stresses except at ground breaks. The pipes therefore

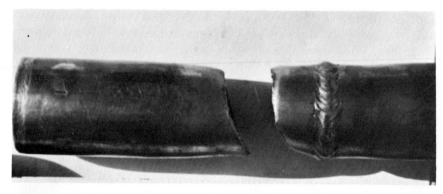

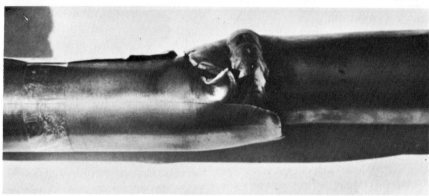

14.—Buried gaslines ruptured by earthquake forces. Above, in tension; below, in compression. Photographs by W. J. Stump.

15.—Twelve-inch gas main, supplying fuel for municipal powerplant, was ruptured by landslide at Third Avenue and Post Road, Anchorage. Photograph by W. J. Stump.

required relief from stresses imposed by the earthquake, because these stresses, plus those that would be imposed by future thawing and frost action, would undoubtedly cause additional failures in the system.

All excavations where repairs had been performed on gas, sewer, and water lines were mapped by the gas company, and the assumption was made that stresses had been relieved in these areas. Maps prepared by the Engineering Geology Evaluation Group (1964) were then used in conjunction with the company's accurate as-built maps and records of its distribution system. By studying the two sets of maps, about 50 places were identified where earthquake-caused ground fractures meant that there must be residual stresses in the gaslines. At the center of each such area the line was exposed and cut. Some pipes were under such tension that the cuts opened as much as 2 inches; elsewhere compressive forces shortened the pipes. Successive exposures and cuts in the lines were then made at 50-foot intervals away from the origins until points were reached where cuts resulted in no movement of the pipes. The same method was used for the transmission line. The entire line was examined by helicopter traverse. Wherever ground cracks were observed to cross the line, excavations were made to allow the pipe to move and thus relieve residual stresses.

ANCHORAGE

Much of the following information on Anchorage public utilities is taken from Stephenson's report (1964).

Except for radio and television, which were interrupted only because of lack of electric power,

all public-utility systems in Anchorage were affected similarly by the earthquake but in somewhat varying degrees. All utilities that depended on underground transmission or distribution—telephone, water, sewer, power, and gas—were disrupted when lines were broken by landslides and earth fissures.

Anchorage and the nearby military posts obtain water by diversions from Ship Creek and from a few deep wells. There are also some shallow private wells, mainly in the suburbs. In order to take advantage of the extra heat available in ground water, the wells are used more extensively in winter than in summer.

The earthquake caused moderate damage to the city treatment plant, and several of the wells were destroyed by ground movements. Ground-water levels dropped temporarily and water from many wells was muddy. The Ship Creek supply was cut off for a short time when an avalanche blocked the stream above the diversion points, but water was restored to the system when the temporary dam was overtopped and cut through by natural streamflow (Waller, 1966b).

By far the greatest damage to the Anchorage water system was in the distribution system, where ground fractures and landslides broke pipes in nearly 100 places. All types of pipe were affected by these ground movements. Immediately after the earthquake the delivery rate nearly quadrupled because of the numerous breaks in the lines. It was necessary to shut off the supply completely and to repair it section by section.

Service was restored to more than half of Anchorage within

the first 5 days, and most of the city had water within 2 weeks. Much of the repair work was of a temporary nature. Firehose and portable pumps and chlorinators were used first, but these were soon replaced in the Turnagain and port areas, and to a lesser extent elsewhere, by aluminum irrigation pipe laid on the surface and connected to dwellings with garden hoses. Completion of more permanent repairs to the underground systems required many months, in part because of the havoc caused by landslides in parts of the city and in part by the necessary delays for exploration of the slide areas and for planning how they should be treated. (Alaska Depart. Health and Welfare, 1964; Waller, 1966b; Stephenson, 1964).

Except for the Spenard area, which has a treatment plant, the Anchorage and nearby military sewage systems discharge untreated wastes directly to Knik Arm. Outfalls were damaged by earthquake vibration and required replacement. The underground systems, built primarily with concrete pipe, were broken by landslides, earth cracks, and vibration in a manner and in places similar to the breaks in the water-supply systems (Stephenson, 1964; Alaska Depart. Health and Welfare, 1964). A portable television camera was used effectively to find breaks in the sewer lines (Burton, in Logan, 1967).

The central telephone office in downtown Anchorage was severely shaken and fuses were blown. In the Alaska Communications System toll building on Government Hill, two 15-ton battery plants collapsed by shaking and caught fire, but the fire was quickly controlled.

The aerial wire system, which serves most of Anchorage, sustained only minor damage except where poles were broken or dislodged by landslides. In contrast to underground powerlines, however, which were only slightly damaged, almost all of the 25-mile underground telephone-cable system in downtown Anchorage was put out of commission. Tension, caused by stretching of the ground incident to ground cracks and landslides, pulled the cables away from manhole connections.

CORDOVA

Utilities in the main residential area and business district of Cordova—a town built almost entirely on indurated bedrock—were unaffected by the tremors. Slight damage was sustained by utilities in the waterfront area, mainly as a result of shifting of the docks and piers on which the utilities were located and of inundation of low-lying areas. All utilities functioned continuously throughout the earthquake. Minimal damage resulted from tectonic uplift that left sewage outfalls above high tides (Office of Emergency Planning, 1964).

Utilities at the Cordova airport which is on thick alluvial deposits 13 miles from the town, were disrupted by vibration and ground fractures. Overhead powerlines were snapped by violent motions of their poles, and underground steam, water, and sewer pipes were broken and made inoperative by innumerable ground cracks.

Cordova depends largely on diverted surface water for its water supply; but also has two deep standby wells. Earthquake damage to the distribution system and to the sewer system was minimal except for the fracturing of pipes in the waterfront area and at the airport.

KODIAK

Communications facilities at Kodiak Naval Station were hard hit. Except for Fleet Weather Central, which required less than 5 minutes to convert to standby power sources, naval station communications were without power for some hours. Not only was the central powerplant inoperative, but 2½ miles of line between the station and the radio transmitter had been washed out by waves. Generators for Operations Control and for the Tactical Air Command and Navigation centers were also damaged.

In the town of Kodiak, the central telephone office was flooded, and the line to a long-distance radio-telephone transmitter atop Pillar Mountain was downed by earthquake shocks. Long-distance communications with the mainland were reestablished the morning after the quake, but for 3 weeks the only local communications were supplied by a few portable field telephones and by short-wave radios in taxicabs and police vehicles. Within a month after the earthquake about 100 telephone circuits had been restored (Tudor, 1964; National Board of Fire Underwriters, 1964; Kachadoorian and Plafker, 1967).

The powerplant at Kodiak Naval Station was repeatedly flooded by waves and electricity and steam heat for the entire installation was cut off. Emergency generators on land and on a seaplane tender that was rushed from Whidby Sound, Wash. (Kasperick, 1964), supplied partial needs for power to the station for 2 weeks while the main plant was being repaired. A massive power failure occurred in the town of Kodiak at 5:39± p.m. This failure was during the early phase of the seismic shaking. Automatic equipment in the Kodiak Electric Association generating plant made four unsuccessful attempts in 3 seconds to reclose the circuits. Flashes were emanating from the plant, and the power failure resulted apparently from a short circuit at the generating plant rather than in the feeder or distribution line. Had the power failure not occurred before the first seismic sea wave struck the city of Kodiak, the inundating waves would undoubtedly have caused failure.

Kodiak's water and sewage lines were cracked in a few places by earthquake vibration, but they sustained very little damage except in the lower part of town that was destroyed by seismic sea waves. Kodiak is served by two water reservoirs north of town. One of these was very slightly damaged by shaking and both reservoirs were closed for a few hours after the earthquake to conserve water for fighting fires that were expected but fortunately did not materialize. Service of untreated water was restored the day after the quake, and chlorination of water was restored on March 29 (F. R. B. Norton and J. E. Haas, written commun., 1966; Alaska Depart. Health and Welfare, 1964).

The Kodiak sewage system was affected similarly to the water distribution system; that is, it sustained only minor damage except near the waterfront where it was severely damaged. Tectonic submergence of the shoreline (Kachadoorian and Plafker, 1967) lowered the sewage pumping station to such an extent that it had to be replaced.

SEWARD

Submarine slides and giant waves destroyed Seward's port facilities, including utility systems near the waterfront. In addition, vibration and ground fractures disrupted water and sewer lines in many other parts of town and in suburban Forest Acres (Lemke, 1967).

Seward is served power by the Chugach Electric Association from its Cooper Lake hydroelectric plant; transmission-line damages disrupted the service. Temporary restoration of part of the power was effected in May 1964 by the installation of small portable generators. The distribution system was repaired by November of the same year, and a new standby city powerplant (fig. 16) was completed in 1965 (Lemke, 1967; office of Emergency Planning, 1964; Chugach Electric Assoc., Inc., 1964). The Seward telephone system was completely disrupted for a few hours, and service was spasmodic for some weeks after the earthquake. Batteries were used early in the emergency period, but portable generators were installed later (National Board of Fire Underwriters, 1964).

Seward obtains most of its water by diversion from Jap and Marathon Creeks, and it also had four deep wells. Three of the wells were put out of operation by earthquake shaking, but the surface supplies survived with only minor damage. Both water and sewer lines sustained breaks in many places throughout Seward and the suburban areas, and water service was cut off for periods ranging from 12 hours to more than a week after the earthquake. These damages, however, were minor as compared to those in the port area, where all facilities, including water mains and sewage outfalls, were com-

16.—Emergency standby generators at Seward, August 1965. Seward normally receives power from Cooper Lake hydroelectric plant, but all power was cut off by the earthquake. U.S. Army photograph.

pletely destroyed by submarine slides and waves (Lemke, 1967; Alaska Dept. Health and Welfare, 1964). An emergency salt-water system that might have helped in controlling the subsequent fires was inoperable because its waterfront pump station was wrecked (National Board of Fire Underwriters, 1964).

VALDEZ

Before the earthquake, Valdez was served water from two deep wells close to the town. Neither the wells nor the elevated storage tank adjacent to them were damaged, but water and sewage lines throughout the town were broken by ground fractures in many places. Total destruction of the waterfront by a gigantic submarine slide of course wrecked waterlines and sewer outfalls completely in that area (Coulter and Migliaccio,

1966). Local telephones remained in service, except for the strip along the waterfront. The powerplant, also, was undamaged. A few distribution lines fell, but the power supply was continuous to most parts of town except the waterfront (National Board of Fire Underwriters, 1964). Because of the decision to abandon the townsite and to rebuild Valdez elsewhere, only temporary repairs were made to the systems.

Design and construction of modern underground utilities at the new townsite were based in part on knowledge of earthquake response of various materials gained by study of damages at Anchorage, old Valdez, and elsewhere. The principles of utilities design in an earthquake-prone region that is also subject to heavy snow cover and deep frost penetration are described by Poirot (1965).

WHITTIER

Most of Whittier's water is obtained by impoundment of Cove Creek, backed up by two drilled standby wells. These sources were not materially damaged by the earthquake, but the distribution system and the outfall sewer system were damaged extensively—especially in the port area—by shaking, ground fractures, and landslide-generated waves (Kachadoorian, 1965; Alaska Depart.

Health and Welfare, 1964). A deep well at the head of Passage Canal was ruined by extrusion of the casing and well head as a result of differential compaction and by flooding of the site at high tides.

The powerplant was shut down during the earthquake when two 10-inch waterlines from the Cove Creek impoundment were broken. The plant was instantly switched to standby auxiliary generators which supplied emergency power

for a period of 6 hours, until the main plant was put back into operation with water pumped through a firehose from Passage Canal. The powerplant itself, which is on a foundation of solid rock, was virtually undamaged by the earthquake. However, some of the feeder lines that were destroyed along the inundated waterfront area had to be either repaired or cut off the circuit before full power could be restored.

REFERENCES CITED

Alaska Department of Fish and Game, 1965, Post-earthquake fisheries evaluation; an interim report on the March 1964 earthquake effects of Alaska's fishery resources: Juneau, Alaska, 72 p.

Alaska Department of Health and Welfare, 1964, Preliminary report of earthquake damage to environmental health facilities and services in Alaska: Juneau, Alaska Dept. Health and Welfare Environmental Health Br., 45 p.

Alaskan Construction Consultant Committee [1964], Reconstruction and development survey of earthquake damages in Alaska: Prepared for Federal Reconstruction and Devel. Plan. Comm. for Alaska, 98 p.

Berg, G. V., and Stratta, J. L., 1964, Anchorage and the Alaska earthquake of March 27, 1964: New York, Am. Iron and Steel Inst., 83 p.

Chugach Electric Association, Inc., 1964, Survey of damage caused by the great Alaska earthquake: Anchorage, Alaska, 35 p., illus. and map.

Coulter, H. W., and Migliaccio, R. R., 1966, Effects of the earthquake of March 27, 1964, at Valdez, Alaska: U.S. Geol. Survey Prof. Paper 542–C, p. C1–C36.

Engineering Geology Evaluation Group, 1964, Geologic report—27 March 1964 earthquake in Greater Anchorage area: Prepared for Alaska State Housing Authority and the city of Anchorage, Anchorage, Alaska, 34 p., 12 figs., pls. 1–17.

Fay, G. T., 1964, The big breakup: FAA [Federal Aviation Agency] Horizons, May 1964, p. 4–7.

Federal Aviation Agency, 1965, Alaska takes on new look: FAA Horizons, March 1965, p. 14–15.

Fitch, E. M., 1964, The Alaska Railroad meets its greatest challenge: Our Public Lands, v. 14, no. 1, p. 12–15.

George, Warren, and Lyle, R. E., 1966, Reconstruction by the Corps of Engineers—methods and accomplishments, in Hansen, W. R., and others, The Alaska earthquake, March 27, 1964—Field investigations and reconstruction effort: U.S. Geol. Survey Prof. Paper 541 [1967].

Hansen, W. R., 1965, Effects of the earthquake of March 27, 1964, Anchorage, Alaska: U.S. Geol. Survey Prof. Paper 542–A, p. A1–A68.

Kachadoorian, Reuben, 1965, Effects of the earthquake of March 27, 1964, at Whittier, Alaska: U.S. Geol. Survey Prof. Paper 542–B, p. B1–B21.

Kachadoorian, Reuben, and Plafker, George, 1967, Effects of the earthquake of March 27, 1964, on the communities of Kodiak and nearby islands: U.S. Geol. Survey Prof. Paper 542–F. (In press.)

Kasperick, Dan, 1964, In the wake of Alaska's earthquake: All Hands [Bur. Naval Personnel Career Pub.], July 1964, p. 10–14.

Lemke, R. W., 1967, Effects of the earthquake of March 27, 1964, at Seward, Alaska: U.S. Geol. Survey Prof. Paper 542–E. (In press.)

Logan, M. H., 1967, Effects of the earthquake of March 27, 1964, on the Eklutna hydroelectric project, Anchorage, Alaska, with a section on Television examination of earthquake damage to underground communication and electrical systems in Anchorage, by Lynn R. Burton: U.S. Geol. Survey Prof. Paper 545–A.

Miller, R. D., and Dobrovolny, Ernest, 1959, Surficial geology of Anchorage and vicinity, Alaska: U.S. Geol. Survey Bull. 1093, 128 p.

National Board of Fire Underwriters and Pacific Fire Rating Bureau, 1964, The Alaska earthquake, March 27, 1964: San Francisco, Calif., distributed by Am. Insurance Assoc., 35 p.

Office of Emergency Planning, 1964, Impact of earthquake of March 27, 1964, upon the economy of Alaska: Prepared for Federal Reconstruction and Devel. Plan. Comm. for Alaska, 27 p.

Plafker, George, 1965, Tectonic deformation associated with the 1964 Alaska earthquake: Science, v. 148, no. 3678, p. 1675–1687.

Plafker, George, and Kachadoorian, Reuben, 1966, Geologic effects of the March 27, 1964, earthquake and associated seismic sea waves on Kodiak and nearby islands, Alaska: U.S. Geol. Survey Prof. Paper 543-D, 46 p.

Plafker, George, and Mayo, L. R., 1965, Tectonic deformation, subaqueous slides, and destructive waves associated with the Alaskan March 27, 1964, earthquake—an interim geologic evaluation: U.S. Geol. Survey open-file report, 21 p.

Poirot, J. W., 1965, Utilities for a relocated town in Alaska: Civil Eng., v. 35, no. 3, p. 50–53.

Powers, J. R., 1965, An engineering glimpse of the Alaskan earthquake: [U.S.] Air Force Civil Engineer, v. 6, February 1965, p. 2–5.

Stephenson, J. M., 1964, Earthquake damage to Anchorage area utilities—March 1964: Port Hueneme, Calif., U.S. Naval Civil Eng. Lab. Tech. Note N-607, 17 p., 41 figs.

Stroh, Alfred, Jr., 1964, Navy operations at Kodiak: Military Engineer, v. 56, no. 372, p. 254–255.

Stump, W. J., 1965, Restoration of gas service after an earthquake: Pacific Coast Gas Assoc. Proc., v. 56, p. 123–126.

Tudor, W. J., 1964, Tsunami damage at Kodiak, Alaska, and Crescent City, California, from Alaska earthquake of 27 March 1964: Port Hueneme, Calif., U.S. Naval Civil Eng. Lab. Tech. Note N-622, 124 p.

U.S. Army Alaskan Command, 1964, Operation Helping Hand—The Armed Forces react to earthquake disaster: Seattle, Wash., Alaskan Command Headquarters, 83 p.

U.S. Bureau of Land Management, 1964, Four-point program aims to rebuild fishing industry: Our Public Lands, v. 14, no. 1, p. 16–17.

Waller, R. M., 1966a, Effects of the March 1964 Alaska earthquake on the hydrology of south-central Alaska: U.S. Geol. Survey Prof. Paper 544-A, p. Al-A28.

Waller, R. M., 1966b, Effects of the March 1964 Alaska earthquake on the hydrology of the Anchorage area: U.S. Geol. Survey, Prof. Paper 544-B, p. B1–B18.

——1966c, Effects of the earthquake of March 27, 1964, in the Homer area, Alaska, *with a section on* Beach changes on Homer Spit by Kirk W. Stanley: U.S. Geol. Survey Prof. Paper 542-D, 28 p.

Wood, F. J., ed., 1966, Operational phases of the Coast and Geodetic Survey program in Alaska for the period March 27 to December 31, 1964, v. 1 *of* The Prince William Sound, Alaska, earthquake of 1964 and aftershocks: U.S. Coast and Geodetic Survey Pub. 10-3, 263 p.

MALCOLM H. LOGAN
U.S. BUREAU OF RECLAMATION

Abstract reprinted with minor changes from
U.S. Geological Survey Professional Paper 545-A,
"Effect of the Earthquake of March 27, 1964,
on the Eklutna Hydroelectric Project, Anchorage, Alaska"

Effect on the Eklutna Hydroelectric Project, Anchorage

ABSTRACT*

The March 27, 1964, Alaska earthquake and its associated aftershocks caused damage requiring several million dollars' worth of repair to the Eklutna Hydroelectric Project, 34 miles northeast of Anchorage. Electric service from the Eklutna powerplant was interrupted during the early phase of the March 27 earthquake, but was restored (intermittently) until May 9, 1964, when the plant was closed for inspection and repair.

Water for the Eklutna project is transported from Eklutna Lake to the powerplant at tidewater on Knik Arm of Cook Inlet by an underwater intake connected to a 4.46-mile tunnel penstock. The primary damage caused by the earthquake was at the intake structure in Eklutna Lake. No damage to the power tunnel was observed. The pile-supported powerplant and appurtenant structures, Anchorage and Palmer substations, and the transmission lines suffered minor damage. Most damage occurred to facilities constructed on unconsolidated sediments and overburden which densified and subsided during the earthquake. Structures built on bedrock experienced little or no damage.

Underground communication and electrical systems in Anchorage were examined with a small-diameter television camera to locate damaged areas requiring repair. Most of the damage was concentrated at or near valley slopes. Those parts of the systems within the major slide areas of the city were destroyed.

---

*USGS Professional Paper 545-A is on file at the NAS–NAE Library, 2101 Constitution Avenue, Washington, D.C. 20418; the 30-page original version, published in 1967, is also for sale by the Superintendent of Documents, U.S. Government Printing Office, Washington, D.C. 20402.

IV
SUMMARY

ERNEST DOBROVOLNY
U.S. GEOLOGICAL SURVEY

Landslide Susceptibility in and near Anchorage as Interpreted from Topographic and Geologic Maps

ABSTRACT

Topographic and geologic maps contain basic data that may be used to construct interpretive maps showing relative degree of landslide susceptibility of geologic materials in response to strong earthquakes. Where the interpretation also is based on historical records of landslides triggered by earthquakes, the interpretive map has a high degree of reliability within specified limits. The purpose of the landslide-susceptibility map is to point out areas of potential landslide problems with the intent that these areas be investigated in detail to determine the degree of hazard for the proposed use of the land before development. Where the ground in its natural state is determined to be potentially unstable for the proposed use, an engineering solution to the problem must be devised and implemented before development can proceed with safety.

INTRODUCTION

The purpose of this report is to show how topographic and geologic maps may be used to determine areas where landslides are likely to occur in the event of a strong earthquake. Catastrophic landslides were triggered in the Anchorage area by the great 1964 earthquake, and landslide hazard continues to exist in this area. Landslide hazard is a function of slope stability, frequency of triggering events, population density, and types of man-made structures in unstable areas.

Topographic and geologic maps can be used to determine areas in which landslides are most likely to occur during a strong earthquake, because slope stability during an earthquake depends mainly on steepness of the free face and on the response of the underlying geologic materials to seismic shock. Determination of this landslide potential is sharpened by the knowledge gained from the 1964 earthquake of the way in which the geologic materials of the Anchorage area do in fact respond to shock.

The existence of adequate topographic and geologic maps and of pertinent information on the geologic materials of an area will not guarantee awareness of landslide susceptibility and hazard. For that awareness, an adequate structure for communication among geologists, engineers, public officials, and the general public is needed.

Modern topographic and geologic maps of Anchorage, Alaska, and vicinity were available before the earthquake of 1964, and a geologic report (Miller and Dobrovolny, 1959, p. 103–107) mentioned the possibility of earthquake-triggered landslides; however, as the events of March 1964 clearly demonstrated, there was no general awareness on the part of the public or of responsible officials that such a landslide potential existed. The importance of establishing means of communication among planners, public officials, and physical and social scientists is one of the prime lessons that was learned from the disaster. Even though natural forces cannot be controlled, their destructive effects can be minimized by planning based on knowledge of the physical setting.

As a result of this new understanding on the part of public officials that they can profitably use geological assistance, a geologic-mapping project covering the entire Greater Anchorage Area Borough was started in 1965 by the U.S. Geological Survey at the request of the Chairman of the Borough. The project, scheduled for completion in 1972, will include a standard geologic map to be prepared on the most recent topographic base available, a landslide-susceptibility map, and other interpretive maps showing foundation and excavation conditions and sources of construction materials. Interpretive water resources maps will be prepared under a continuing project that was started before 1964 and will include maps on availability of groundwater, depth to confined and unconfined aquifers, and principal recharge areas. Only the topographic and geologic maps are discussed in this report, but the entire series is designed to serve as part of a forum through which the geologist can speak to the lay members of the community.

The landslide-susceptibility map contained in this report was prepared in large part from data that were available before 1964. However, inferences as to kinds of landslides and particularly their size and headward extension are based on observations made after the earthquake of March 27, 1964.

TOPOGRAPHIC MAPS

Topographic maps show the shape of the land—the hills and valleys, the streams and swamps—and the man-made features such as roads, railroads, and towns. These maps are familiar to the general public. They are indispensable tools in all phases of civil engineering, in traversing the land, and in many types of land planning. The scale of a map is critical in determining how much information—such as data on geology, soils, and vegetation—can be added to it by a specialist who uses the map as a base.

The topographic map accompanying this report (Figure 1) has an approximate scale of 1:125,000; it was compiled from maps of larger scale, and a few of the cultural features are included for purposes of orientation. Maps of larger scale are necessary for detailed planning.

SLOPE MAP

The generalized slope map (Figure 2) is a special kind of topographic map. "Slope" refers to the inclination of the ground surface measured from the horizontal and commonly is expressed as a percentage. Percent of slope is the unit rise in elevation for 100 units of horizontal distance. A slope of 100 percent would be the hypotenuse of a right triangle 100 ft long on the base and 100 ft high on the side. This map classifies the dominant slopes as follows: 0–15 percent, 15–45 percent, 45–100 percent, and more than 100 percent. A subcategory of slopes ranging from 0 to 5 percent is locally differentiated within the 0–15 percent category because many large areas have slopes of less than 5 percent. Only one small area along the right-angle bend of South Fork Campbell Creek has slopes exceeding 100 percent.

The category of 45–100 percent slopes was selected because in evaluating terrain for military cross-country movement, 45 percent is commonly used as the reasonable upper limit for maneuvering tracked vehicles. On slopes of more than 100 percent, problems are greatly intensified; many operations become impractical and many materials become unstable. Categories of lower slopes are included because they show a general relation to the geology and also may be useful in land-development planning. The emphasis in this report, however, is on the significance of slopes exceeding 45 percent, because these slopes identify areas where landslides are most likely to occur.

GEOLOGIC MAPS

Geologic maps and the usually accompanying cross sections show the kinds and shapes of rock bodies that form the land surface and that lie beneath it. They are prepared primarily for scientific purposes, but contain many facts about the physical environment that are critical in planning for optimum utilization of the land. Two geologic maps of Anchorage and vicinity are included in this report. One, of the surface geology (Figure 3), shows Mesozoic metamorphic rocks and the overlying Quaternary deposits; the other gives the distribution of the Bootlegger Cove Clay, largely beneath the surface (Figure 4).

Figure 3 is generalized and condensed from larger-scale geologic maps by Cederstrom, Trainer, and Waller (1964, plate 1) and by Miller and Dobrovolny (1959, plate 1). A comprehensive description of the geology of the area is given in these publications. The units shown in Figure 3 are described briefly below.

Metamorphic rocks constitute the bedrock of the area, as distinguished from the overlying poorly consolidated deposits. They consist of greenstone, graywacke, argillite, and slate and originally were of igneous and sedimentary origin.

Older moraines and associated deposits consist of till and well-to-poorly sorted sand, gravel, and silt. They were laid down beneath glacier ice, and in deltas and lakes and along stream

[736]

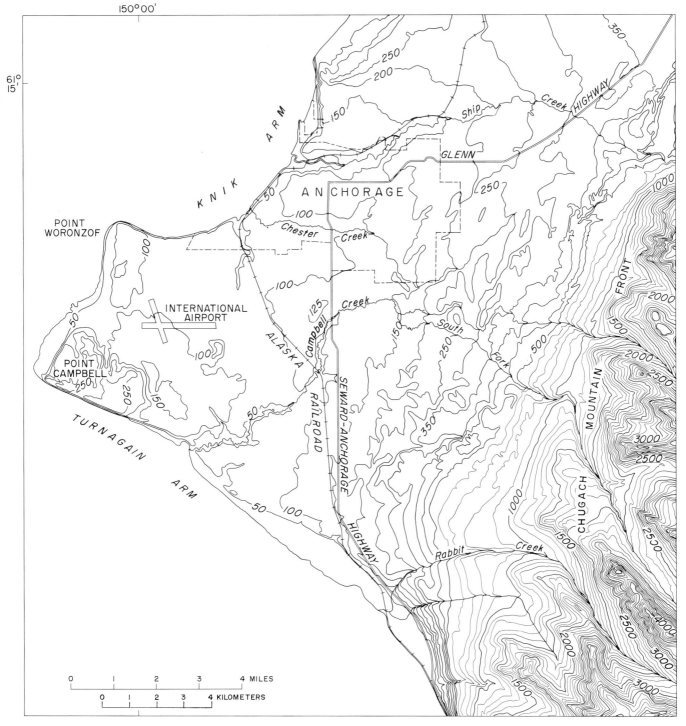

1.—Topographic map of Anchorage and vicinity. Contour interval is 50 ft from sea level to 500 ft; above 500 ft, the interval is 100 ft.

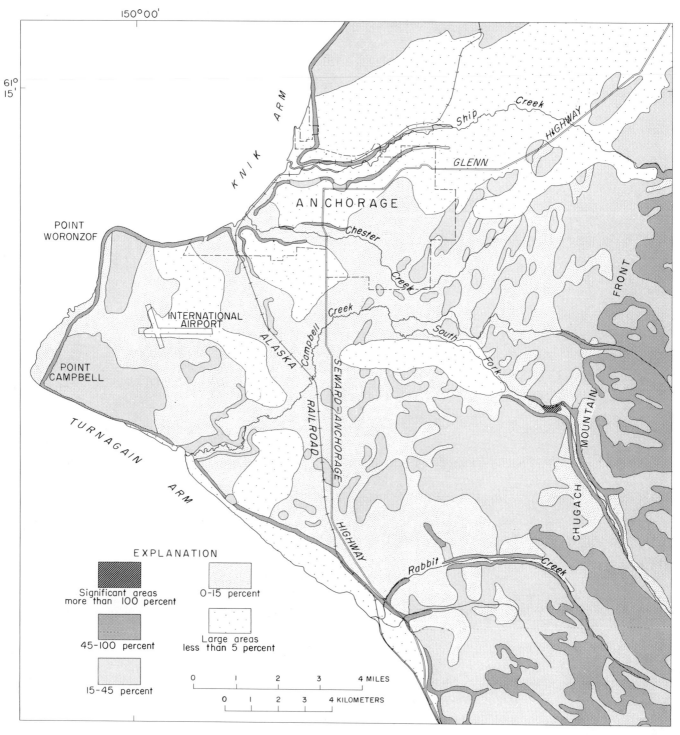

U.S. Geological Survey

2.—Map of Anchorage and vicinity, showing dominant slope in each area. Other slopes may be present locally.

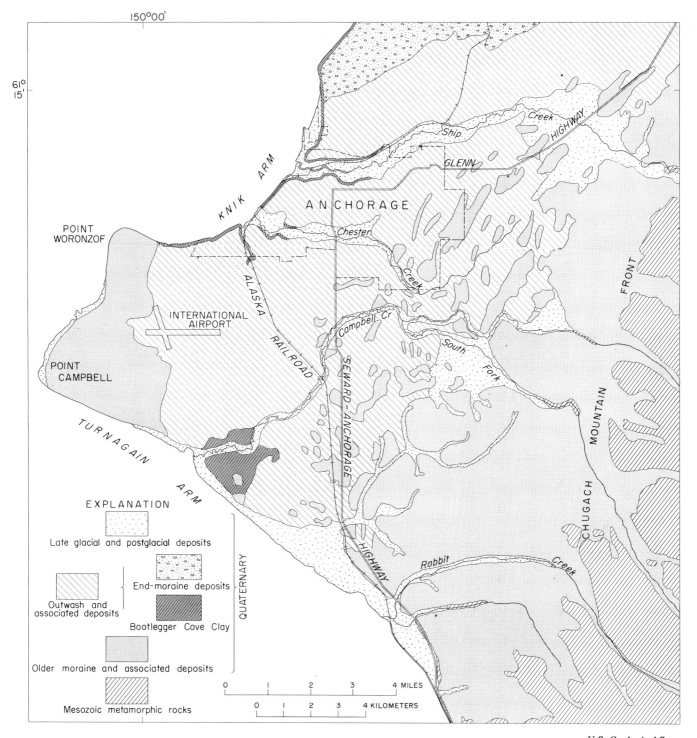

EXPLANATION

Late glacial and postglacial deposits

End-moraine deposits

Outwash and associated deposits

Bootlegger Cove Clay

QUATERNARY

Older moraine and associated deposits

Mesozoic metamorphic rocks

0   1   2   3   4 MILES

0   1   2   3   4 KILOMETERS

U.S. Geological Survey

3.—Surface geology map of Anchorage and vicinity.

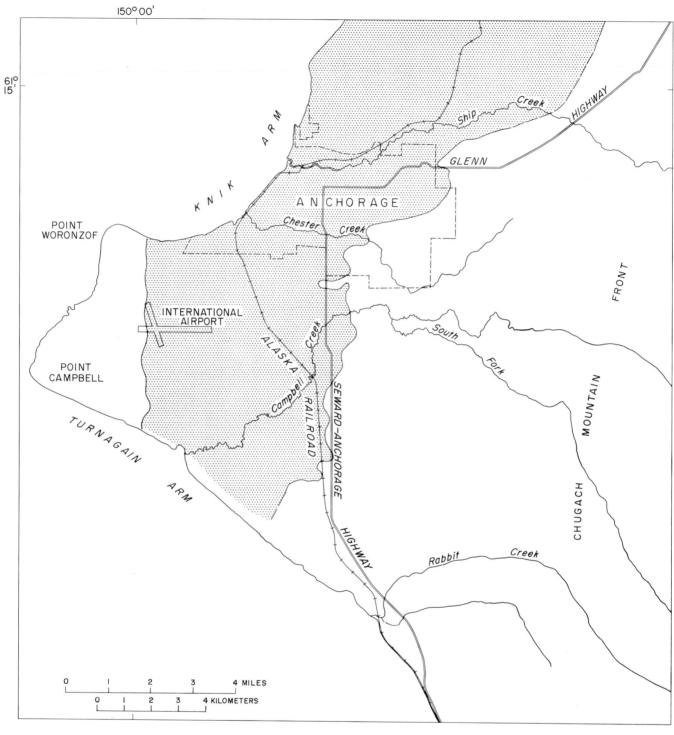

U.S. Geological Survey

4.—Distribution of the Bootlegger Cove Clay (stippled) in Anchorage and vicinity.

valleys. They include the oldest glacial deposits exposed in the area.

Bootlegger Cove Clay consists of clay, silt, and lenses of medium- to fine-grained sand. When dry, the clay is hard and compact and breaks with a conchoidal fracture; when wet, it is soft and sticky. Though the physical properties of the Bootlegger Cove Clay are far from uniform, the deposit as a whole is one of the most distinctive geologic units in the local sequence of surficial materials and, as such, is readily differentiated from other map units. Its distinctive characteristics relate significantly to landslide potential. Additional information on the physical properties of the Bootlegger Cove Clay is reported by Hansen (1965, p. A12–

A21) and Shannon & Wilson, Inc. (1964). The clay, which was deposited on an irregular surface in an estuary, is contemporaneous with some of the older glacial deposits described above.

The distribution of the Bootlegger Cove Clay is shown on Figure 4, which is a special kind of geologic map in that it shows the subsurface extent of the formation as determined from well logs. The clay ranges in thickness up to about 250 ft, and it has a highly irregular base and top (Trainer and Waller, 1965, p. D173–D174).

End-moraine deposits consist of till and well-to-poorly sorted sand, gravel, and silt in the Elmendorf moraine. The moraine was deposited at the front of the last glacier that occu-

pied the Anchorage lowland.

Outwash and associated deposits consist of sand, gravel, and silt that were deposited by outwash streams flowing into the area from the northeast when most of the meltwater drainage was confined between the Elmendorf moraine and the Chugach Mountains. Swamp deposits now overlie the outwash deposit in much of the southern part of the area where the deposit has low topographic relief and is predominantly fine-grained sand and silt.

Late glacial and postglacial deposits consist of sand and gravel along major stream valleys, alluvial fans, and estuarine silt.

GENERALIZED LANDSLIDE-SUSCEPTIBILITY MAP

The generalized landslide-susceptibility map (Figure 5) is an interpretation derived by combining the slope map with the geologic map and applying knowledge of the probable behavior of geologic materials in response to seismic shock. Landslides occur mainly on steep slopes and along such sharp topographic discontinuities as bluffs. They do not occur in areas of low relief that are far removed from breaks in topography. In this report, primary emphasis is directed toward those areas with slopes of 45 percent or greater, even though some slopes of less than 45 percent may be susceptible to landsliding.

The process of isolating areas susceptible to landslides involves the following steps:

1. Identification of steep slopes. Not all areas with the same range of slope percent have the same landslide susceptibility, because the vulnerability of steep slopes to landsliding depends on the nature of the underlying geologic materials.
2. Evaluation of the relative stability of the geologic materials in the

areas with slopes exceeding 45 percent. This evaluation is based on widely disseminated published information about the relative strength and stability of earth materials in general; on specific behavior of materials in the Anchorage area in response to the earthquake of March 27, 1964; and on past performance, which is a generally reliable key for predicting response of geologic materials to strong seismic shock.

In constructing Figure 5, geologic materials were grouped into three major units on the basis of their relative susceptibility to landsliding: (a) predominantly fine-grained, poorly consolidated deposits such as silt and clay in which landslide susceptibility is high in the event of an earthquake— this unit includes the Bootlegger Cove Clay and, locally, estuarine silt that is undifferentiated in the geologic map unit referred to as late glacial and postglacial deposits; (b) predominantly coarse-grained, poorly consolidated deposits such as gravel, sand, and till in which landslide susceptibility ranges from fairly low to fairly high—this unit

includes the geologic map units referred to as older moraines and associated deposits, end-moraine deposits, and outwash and associated deposits; (c) consolidated rocks in which landslide susceptibility is low to very low. This unit includes only the metamorphic rocks shown on the geologic map. The distribution of these three geologic units within areas of steep slopes thus indicates three categories of landslide susceptibility. A fourth classification in which the above three geologic units are undifferentiated is added to the landslide-susceptibility map for areas with slopes less than 45 percent; in these areas landslide susceptibility is very low. In the following paragraphs these four categories are described in more detail as they relate to landslide potential.

1. *The unit with high landslide susceptibility* consists of steep bluffs (slopes greater than 45 percent) that are underlain by poorly consolidated clay, silt, and some discontinuous thin beds of fine sand, mainly Bootlegger Cove Clay. Under normal conditions fine-grained deposits, such as silt and

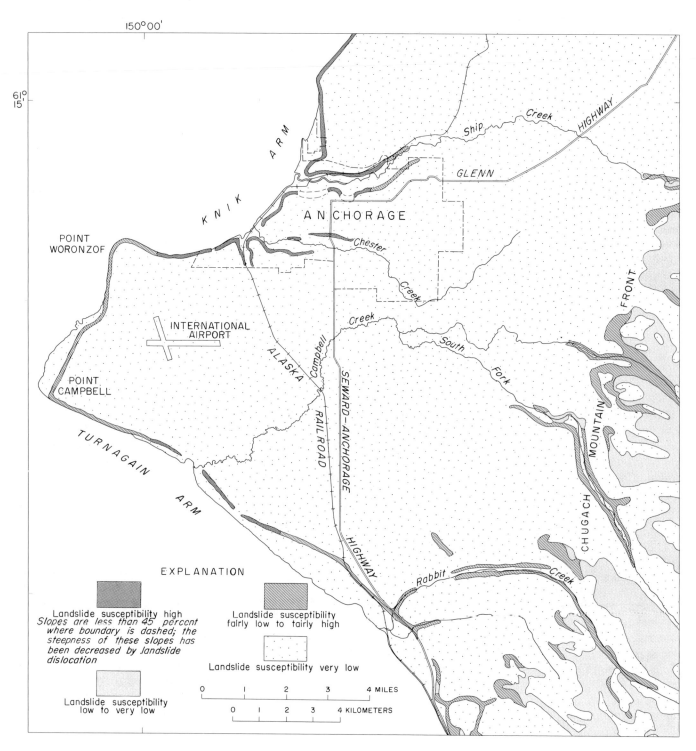

EXPLANATION

Landslide susceptibility high
*Slopes are less than 45 percent
where boundary is dashed; the
steepness of these slopes has
been decreased by landslide
dislocation*

Landslide susceptibility
low to very low

Landslide susceptibility
fairly low to fairly high

Landslide susceptibility very low

0   1   2   3   4 MILES

0   1   2   3   4 KILOMETERS

U.S. Geological Survey

5.–Generalized landslide-susceptibility map of Anchorage and vicinity.

clay, are the most unstable naturally occurring materials; under earthquake-loading conditions, loose saturated sand is even less stable than most clay. All these materials have low shear strength and, where unconfined, as along steep bluffs, they offer little resistance to landsliding. When saturated, they are particularly unstable (Seed and Lee, 1966). Where lenses of fine sand are present, liquefaction resulting from repeated earthquake vibration may produce translatory landslides. Failure in these materials is mainly by lateral spreading and rotation. Landslide scarps and ground fractures related to the landslides may extend hundreds of feet back from the bluff. Examples are the L Street and Turnagain landslides (Hansen, 1965, p. A43 and A59).

An exception to the definition of this category is the area along the south valley wall of Ship Creek where the boundary is shown in Figure 5 by dashed lines. The slopes between the dashed lines are less than 45 percent, but they are underlain by the Bootlegger Cove Clay. These slopes extend over existing landslide blocks and associated debris of the Fourth Avenue slide and an area east of the Native Hospital slide (Hansen, 1965, p. A41 and A49). At some previous stage in the local cycle of erosion these slopes may have exceeded 45 percent, but they have now been modified by landslide movement to slopes of lower percent. Expert judgment is that landslide susceptibility is still high (Shannon & Wilson, Inc., 1964, p. 42). For this reason a buttress was constructed in 1964–1967 along the lower part of the Fourth Avenue slide to provide stability for the landslide mass and to protect the area south of Fourth Avenue from severe ground dislocations in the event of a future strong earthquake.

2. *The unit with fairly low to fairly high landslide susceptibility* consists of steep bluffs that are underlain by poorly consolidated sand and gravel deposits that locally contain beds of silt and clay. Till is included with these deposits. Coarse-grained deposits such as these are generally more stable than silt and clay. The landslide potential ranges from fairly low to fairly high, depending on degree of saturation, dominant grain size of the deposit, and configuration of individual beds. Failure in these materials is mainly by debris slides and slumping. Landslide scarps and ground fractures related to the failure may extend tens of feet back from the bluff; a few fractures rarely may extend as much as 100 ft back from the bluff. Examples are the landslides at Point Woronzof and the Potter Hill slide (Hansen, 1965, p. A31–A33).

3. *The unit with low to very low landslide susceptibility* consists of steep slopes that are underlain by metamorphic rocks. These rocks are strong and their resistance to loading is considerably greater than that of unconsolidated deposits of sand and gravel. Landslides are unlikely in these rocks except along certain zones of weakness. Rockfalls may occur, however, where slopes exceed about 100 percent. Rockfalls of small size may occur along the gorge at the right-angle bend of Campbell Creek, where stream erosion has caused oversteepening. In the mountains east of the area of Figure 5, rockfalls and landslides may occur along some fault zones and on exceptionally steep bedrock slopes that have been eroded by glaciers.

4. *The unit with very low landslide susceptibility* consists of areas of moderate to low relief with slopes from 0 to 45 percent that are underlain by poorly consolidated gravel, sand, silt, and peat, or by bedrock. Landslides are restricted to very small areas of locally steep slopes or lower slopes underlain by highly saturated fine-grained material.

ACCURACY AND USE OF THE LANDSLIDE-SUSCEPTIBILITY MAP

The generalized landslide-susceptibility map differentiates the relative landslide probability for each of the units as defined. It predicts that the possibility that landslides will occur in response to a strong earthquake is greater in areas of steep slopes underlain by silt and clay than in areas of steep slopes underlain by other materials. Bluff areas of high landslide susceptibility are shown on the map in Figure 5 as narrow bands, but the scarp of landslides and fractures caused by landslides may, in places, extend farther back from the bluff line than is represented by the width of the steep slope. The low slopes extending outward from the base of the bluffs may be overridden by landslide debris, displaced locally where the slip plane of the slide lies below the surface of the flat slope, or they may be disturbed by pressure ridges. An example is the Turnagain Heights landslide where maximum headward retrogression from the preearthquake bluff was about 1,200 ft, and the relatively flat slope along the shoreline below the bluff was overridden by landslide debris (Hansen, 1965, p. A59). For the unit as a whole, the accuracy of prediction is fairly high, but on a lot-by-lot or even block-by-block basis the accuracy of the prediction is low. No firm prediction can be made from the map as to where, within the unit, individual landslides are likely to occur. Discrimination within the broadly defined units should be determined by detailed site investigations conducted by the developer of the land. The validity of the interpretive landslide-susceptibility map, based in large part on information available before 1964, is supported by the distribution of the landslides triggered by the March 27, 1964, earthquake as compiled by Hansen (1965, Figure 1, p. A3) and reproduced here as Figure 6.

The landslide-susceptibility map points out areas where potential land-

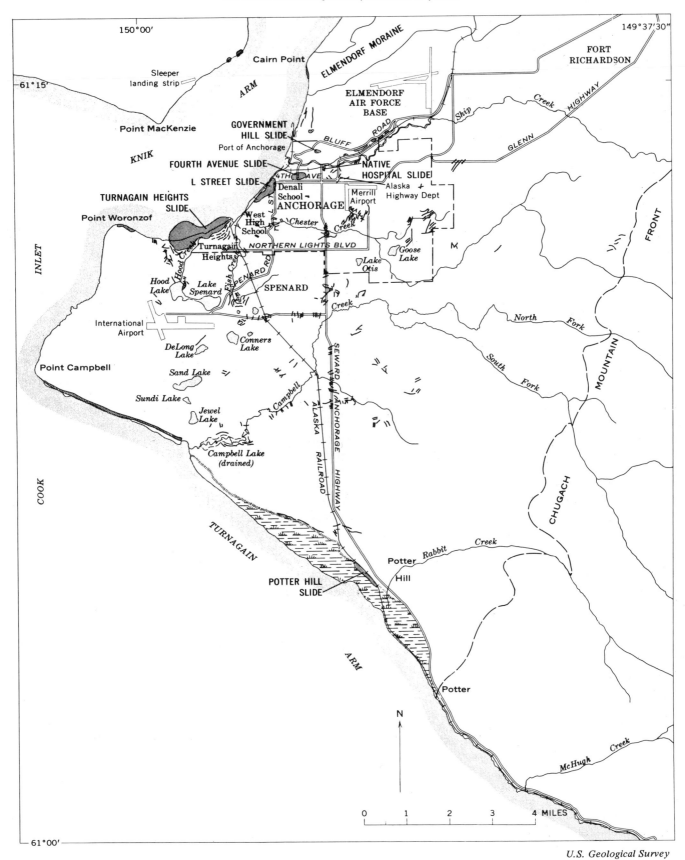

6.—Map of Anchorage and vicinity, showing locations of major landslides and ground cracks (much generalized).

U.S. Geological Survey

slide problems require more detailed investigation before land is developed; it is intended as a preliminary guide for planners and developers. A more detailed study may show that the ground conditions at the particular site are safe if certain regulations and methods of construction are followed. On the other hand, detailed investigations may show the site to be unsafe for the intended facility and may require an engineering solution, such as the buttress that was judged necessary for stabilization of the Fourth Avenue landslide (Shannon & Wilson, Inc., 1964, p. 43). The landslide-susceptibility map is an overall assessment intended to supply background information in establishing guidelines and procedures in land-development planning.

CONCLUSIONS AND RECOMMENDATIONS

Excellent topographic maps of Anchorage and vicinity were available before the earthquake of March 27, 1964. A published report had documented the geologic setting, had mentioned the possibility that landslides might be triggered by earthquakes, and had identified bluff areas that were concealed by landslides, slumps, and flows when the map was prepared. Though the data were available, they were not presented to the general public in a form useful in preparing long-range plans for land development. However basic to rational understanding of the ground conditions a general geologic map may be, it does not, by itself, convey useful information directly to a planner. Even had interpretive maps such as the one in this report been available, they probably would not have had significant use because the planners at that time were not experienced in translating the interpreted information into terms usable in community planning. Before the earthquake such maps probably would have been overlooked. Now, the need for them is apparent.

The earthquake demonstrated the potential value of geologic maps. It reaffirmed and refined earlier concepts of the probable response of different earth materials to seismic shock and thereby provided the geologist with more reliable data on which to base predictions. Above all, the experience gained from the earthquake and its effects demonstrated that physical scientists, public officials, and industrial planners must henceforth work together more closely to provide safer and more economical development of the land.

Response of earth materials to seismic shock is still imperfectly understood, but the experience in the Alaska earthquake has taught much that can be applied to other seismically active areas. Some of the information gained can be represented on maps and then by inference applied to similar topographic and geologic conditions elsewhere. Geologic mapping has proved effective in discovering ground conditions critical to land development and in providing means for their evaluation. For this reason, it is recommended that geologic maps and interpretations for special needs be prepared for all populated seismically active areas to serve as a basis for long-range development plans.

REFERENCES

Cederstrom, D. J., Frank W. Trainer, and Roger M. Waller, 1964. Geology and ground-water resources of the Anchorage area, Alaska. U.S. Geological Survey Water-Supply Paper 1773. Washington: Government Printing Office. 108 p.

Hansen, Wallace R., 1965. Effects of the earthquake of March 27, 1964, at Anchorage, Alaska. U.S. Geological Survey Professional Paper 542-A. Washington: Government Printing Office. 68 p. Also *in* The Great Alaska Earthquake of 1964:

Geology. NAS Pub. 1601. Washington: National Academy of Sciences, 1971.

Miller, Robert D., and Ernest Dobrovolny, 1959. Surficial geology of Anchorage and vicinity, Alaska. U.S. Geological Survey Bulletin 1093. Washington: Government Printing Office. 128 p.

Seed, H. Bolton, and Kenneth L. Lee, 1966. Liquefaction of saturated sands during cyclic loading. *Journal of the Soil Mechanics and Foundations Division*, 92, 105–134.

Shannon & Wilson, Inc., 1964. Report on Anchorage area soil studies, Alaska, to U.S. Army Engineer District, Alaska, August 28. Seattle: Shannon & Wilson, Inc. 300 p.

Trainer, Frank W., and Roger M. Waller, 1965. Subsurface stratigraphy of drift at Anchorage, Alaska, *in* Geological Survey Research 1965: U.S. Geological Survey Professional Paper 525-D. Washington: Government Printing Office. p. D167–D174.

EDWIN B. ECKEL*
U.S. GEOLOGICAL SURVEY

Reprinted with minor changes from
U.S. Geological Survey Professional Paper 546,
"The Alaska Earthquake, March 27, 1964: Lessons and Conclusions"

Lessons and Conclusions

ABSTRACT

One of the greatest earthquakes of all time struck south-central Alaska on March 27, 1964. Strong motion lasted longer than for most recorded earthquakes, and more land surface was dislocated, vertically and horizontally, than by any known previous temblor. Never before were so many effects on earth processes and on the works of man available for study by scientists and engineers over so great an area.

The seismic vibrations, which directly or indirectly caused most of the damage, were but surface manifestations of a great geologic event—the dislocation of a huge segment of the crust along a deeply buried fault whose nature and even exact location are still subjects for speculation. Not only was the land surface tilted by the great tectonic event beneath it, with resultant seismic sea waves that traversed the entire Pacific, but an enormous mass of land and sea floor moved several tens of feet horizontally toward the Gulf of Alaska.

Downslope mass movements of rock, earth, and snow were initiated. Subaqueous slides along lake shores and seacoasts, near-horizontal movements of mobilized soil ("landspreading"), and giant translatory slides in sensitive clay did the most damage and provided the most new knowledge as to the origin, mechanics, and possible means of control or avoidance of such movements. The slopes of most of the deltas that slid in 1964, and that produced destructive local waves, are still as steep or steeper than they were before the earthquake and hence would be unstable or metastable in the event of another great earthquake. Rockslide avalanches provided new evidence that such masses may travel on cushions of compressed air, but a widely held theory that glaciers surge after an earthquake has not been substantiated.

Innumerable ground fissures, many of them marked by copious emissions of water, caused much damage in towns and along transportation routes. Vibration also consolidated loose granular materials. In some coastal areas, local subsidence was superimposed on regional tectonic subsidence to heighten the flooding damage. Ground and surface waters were measurably affected by the earthquake, not only in Alaska but throughout the world.

Expectably, local geologic conditions largely controlled the extent of structural damage, whether caused directly by seismic vibrations or by secondary effects such as those just described. Intensity was greatest in areas underlain by thick saturated unconsolidated deposits, least on indurated bedrock or permanently frozen ground, and intermediate on coarse well-drained gravel, on morainal deposits, or on moderately indurated sedimentary rocks.

Local and even regional geology also controlled the distribution and extent of the earthquake's effects on hydrologic systems. In the conterminous United States, for example, seiches in wells and bodies of surface water were controlled by geologic structures of regional dimension.

Devastating as the earthquake was, it had many long-term beneficial effects. Many of these were socioeconomic or engineering in nature; others were of scientific value. Much new and corroborative basic geologic and hydrologic information was accumulated in the course of the earthquake studies, and many new or improved investigative techniques were developed. Chief among these, perhaps, were the recognition that lakes can be used as giant tiltmeters, the refinement of methods for measuring land-level changes by observing displacements of barnacles and other sessile organisms, and the relating of hydrology to seismology by worldwide study of hydroseisms in surface-water bodies and in wells.

The geologic and hydrologic lessons learned from studies of the Alaska earthquake also lead directly to better definition of the research needed to further our understanding of earthquakes and of how to avoid or lessen the effects of future ones. Research is needed on the origins and mechanisms of earthquakes, on crustal structure, and on the generation of tsunamis and local waves. Better earthquake-hazard maps, based on improved knowledge of regional geology, fault behavior, and earthquake mechanisms, are needed for the entire country. Their preparation will require the close collaboration of engineers, seismologists, and geologists. Geologic maps of all inhabited places in earthquake-prone parts of the country are also needed by city planners and others, because the direct relationship between local geology and potential earthquake damage is now well understood.

Improved and enlarged nets of earthquake-sensing instruments, sited in relation to known geology, are needed, as are many more geodetic and hydrographic measurements.

Every large earthquake, wherever located, should be regarded as a full-scale laboratory experiment whose study can give scientific and engineering information unobtainable from any other source. Plans must be made before the event to insure staffing, funding, and coordination of effort for the scientific and engineering study of future earthquakes. Advice of earth scientists and engineers should be used in the decision-making processes involved in reconstruction after any future disastrous earthquake, as was done after the Alaska earthquake.

---

*Now with The Geological Society of America.

"...and lo, there was a great earthquake...

and every mountain and island were moved

out of their places." Revelation VI, 12, 14

INTRODUCTION

One of the greatest earthquakes of all time struck in south-central Alaska in the late afternoon of March 27, 1964 (fig. 1). Variously called the Good Friday earthquake, the Prince William Sound earthquake, and the 1964 Alaska earthquake, it devastated the most highly developed and populous part of Alaska and took more than 130 lives there and along the coast of North America. Its effects could be seen or felt by people in most of Alaska and adjacent parts of Canada, and were measured by instruments throughout the world.

Strong motion from this earthquake lasted longer than most recorded ones; it also resulted in measurable vertical and horizontal dislocations of more land surface than any previous earthquake. Few of its effects on earth processes and on the works of man were new to science or engineering, but never before had so many effects become available for study over so great an area. A massive relief and reconstruction program began at once—

a program in which the Federal Government played a greater part than for any previous physical disaster in the United States.

The Alaska earthquake received more intensive study from scientists and engineers of all disciplines and specialties than any major earthquake in history. Much has been, and is still being, learned from these investigations. The findings apply not only to documentation of the Alaska earthquake itself, but toward better understanding of the nature and origins of earthquakes in general, of their effects, and of how man can plan or build to avoid or ameliorate those effects.

This report is primarily a summary of geologic and hydrologic findings of the U.S. Geological Survey with only incidental excursions into the findings of other organizations and disciplines. For this reason, the enormous amount of new information amassed and published by others is not stressed, though references to it appear in the selected bibliography, and all of it was used by Survey authors as it became available in reaching their conclusions.

The story of the earthquake is told in a general nontechnical way by Hansen and others (1966). More detailed descriptions of many facets of the earthquake and its effects, treated partly by topic and partly by locality, are contained in other reports in this series; the bibliographies in each report, of course, contain references to many other descriptions. No attempt is made here to repeat all these details or even to summarize them. Instead, the intent is to sort out that which was significant or different about the Alaska earthquake as compared with previous ones. Emphasis is given to the lessons learned from it, both technical and philosophic, that can be applied to the studies of future earthquakes

and to better understanding of the earthquake process.

GEOLOGICAL SURVEY REPORTS ON THE EARTHQUAKE

The Survey's first report on the earthquake, by Grantz, Plafker, and Kachadoorian (1964), was published only a few weeks after the event. It described in a remarkably accurate and thorough fashion the essential facts about the earthquake and its effects as they were learned during the initial reconnaissance investigations. This preliminary report has been followed by a series of six Professional Papers, under the overall title "The Alaska Earthquake, March 27, 1964," of which this is the concluding paper. Together, these reports constitute a comprehensive description of the earthquake's effects on geologic and hydrologic materials and processes, considerable emphasis being placed on the bearing of those effects on man and his works. They are based primarily on the Geological Survey's own investigations, but several contributions from other authors were sought out and included for more complete coverage.

Parts or all of the series are available for purchase from the Superintendent of Documents, U.S. Government Printing Office, Washington, D.C. 20401.

The Geological Survey Professional Papers on the March 27, 1964, Alaska earthquake and the short titles of their parts are listed here, with a brief statement of their contents. Those reprinted with minor changes in this volume are preceded by a bullet (•); those abstracted in this volume, by an asterisk (*); and those reprinted with minor changes in the Hydrology volume, by a dagger (†). Professional Paper 541, "Field in-

[749]

vestigations and reconstruction efforts," by W. R. Hansen and others (1966): This nontechnical introductory volume describes the time, duration, and extent of the earthquake, its physiographic-geologic setting, and its effects on the communities and transportation facilities of Alaska; it also contains a brief description of the sea-wave damages at coastal communities in British Columbia, Washington, Oregon, and California. Biologic, atmospheric, and possible magnetic effects of the quake are outlined. Separate sections note the governmental and private response to the disaster and the contribution of both sectors to the reconstruction. The following subtitles indicate the contents of the sections:

- "A Summary Description of the Alaska Earthquake—Its Setting and Effects," by W. R. Hansen and E. B. Eckel.
"Investigations by the Geological Survey," by W. R. Hansen.
"The Work of the Scientific and Engineering Task Force—Earth Science Applied To Policy Decisions in Early Relief and Reconstruction," by E. B. Eckel and W. E. Schaem.
"Activities of the Corps of Engineers—Cleanup and Early Reconstruction," by R. E. Lyle and Warren George.
"Reconstruction by the Corps of Engineers—Methods and Accomplishments," by Warren George and R. E. Lyle.
"The Year of Decision and Action," by Genie Chance.
Professional Paper 542: "Effects on Communities," in seven chapters:
- A, "Anchorage," by W. R. Hansen (1965). Seismic vibration damaged many multistory

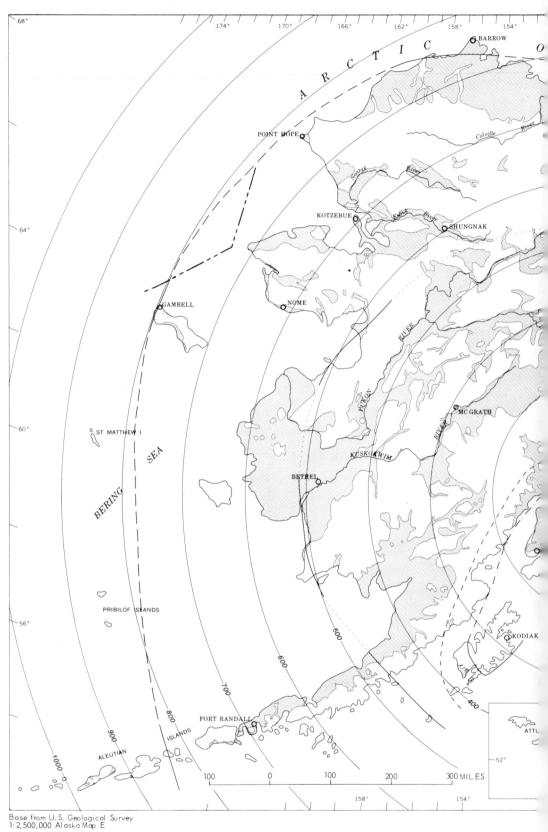

1.—Map showing extent and nature of the effects

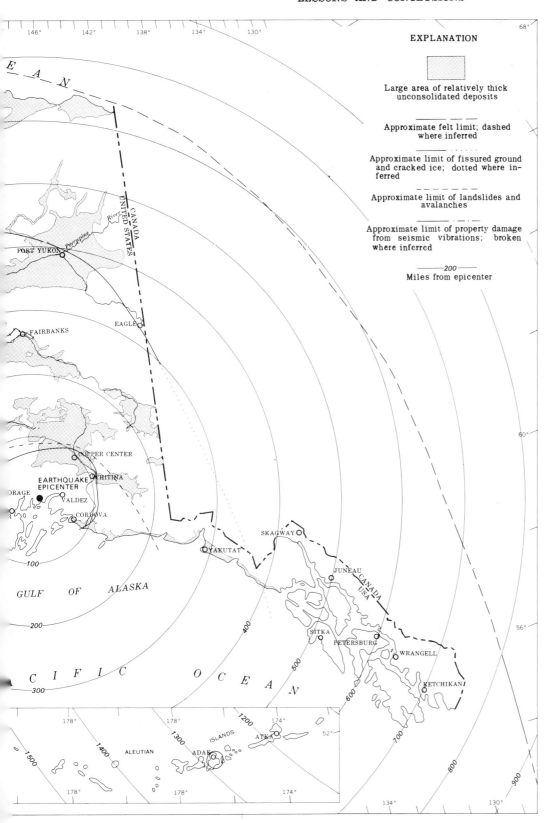

EXPLANATION

Large area of relatively thick
unconsolidated deposits

Approximate felt limit; dashed
where inferred

Approximate limit of fissured ground
and cracked ice; dotted where inferred

Approximate limit of landslides and
avalanches

Approximate limit of property damage
from seismic vibrations; broken
where inferred

————200————
Miles from epicenter

of seismic vibrations related to the earthquake.

buildings, caused extensive ground fissures, and triggered disastrous translatory landslides in some bluff areas underlain by sensitive clays. Because of its size, Anchorage had greater total property damage than all the rest of Alaska.

- B, "Whittier," by Reuben Kachadoorian (1965). Land subsidence, waves generated by submarine landslides, fire, and seismic vibration wrecked much of the waterfront area in this small port-rail terminal.

- C, "Valdez," by H. W. Coulter and R. R. Migliaccio (1966). Ground fissures, waves, and fire did much damage, and a gigantic submarine slide off the front of the delta town site carried the waterfront away and dictated relocation of the town.

- D, "Homer," by R. M. Waller (1966). Submergence caused by tectonic subsidence and by consolidation of sediments exposed much of Homer Spit, economic heart of the community, to the reach of high tides. A separate section by K. W. Stanley describes the beach changes on Homer Spit that resulted from subsidence.

- E, "Seward," by R. W. Lemke (1967). Seismic sea waves, submarine slides, and fires destroyed the town's waterfront and necessitated relocation of the Alaska Railroad terminal. Ground fissures damaged numerous buildings, particularly in suburban areas.

* F, "Kodiak Area," by Reuben Kachadoorian and George Plafker (1967). Seismic sea waves flooded Kodiak, the nearby Naval Station, and several smaller communities in the Kodiak island group. Regional tectonic subsidence caused further damage in many places.

- G, "Various Communities," by George Plafker, Reuben Kachadoorian, E. B. Eckel, and L. B. Mayo (1969). Effects on several scores of miscellaneous communities, where there was loss of life or significant physical damage, are described, as are the extensive wave damage in coastal areas and evidence of vibration throughout Alaska.

Professional Paper 543: "Regional Effects," in 10 chapters:

*† A, "Slide-Induced Waves, Seiching, and Ground Fracturing at Kenai Lake," by D. S. McCulloch (1966). The earthquake dislodged subaqueous slides from deltas in Kenai Lake that generated destructive waves. The lake basin was tilted and a seiche wave was excited in it.

* B, "Martin-Bering Rivers Areas," by S. J. Tuthill and W. M. Laird (1966). Widespread geomorphic changes took place in a large uninhabited area east of the Copper River. Ground fissures—some with associated ejections of mud or water—avalanches, and landslides were among the more important effects.

- C, "Gravity Survey and Regional Geology of the Epicentral Region," by J. E. Case, D. F. Barnes, George Plafker, and S. L. Robbins (1966). Gravity stations and reconnaissance geologic mapping in the Prince William Sound area provided background for other investigations of the earthquake. A regional gravity gradient, caused by thickening of the continental crust and local anomalies related to differences in lithology were measured.

- D, "Kodiak and Nearby Islands," by George Plafker and Reuben Kachadoorian

(1966). Seismic sea waves caused the greatest physical damage throughout the Kodiak Island area. Tectonic subsidence adversely affected much of the shoreline. Vibration, ground fissures, and landslides affected unconsolidated materials but not bedrock.

* E, "Copper River Basin Area," by O. J. Ferrians, Jr. (1966). Extensive ground fissures formed in flood plains, deltas, and the toes of alluvial fans. Terrain underlain by permafrost behaved like bedrock and did not crack. Avalanches and rockslides were released in the mountains.

* F, "Ground Breakage in the Cook Inlet Area," by H. L. Foster and T. V. N. Karlstrom (1967). Ground fissures, many of which ejected water or sediment, formed on the Kenai Lowland; most of them were on thick bodies of unconsolidated materials. Zonal concentration of ground fissures may have been concentrated along a buried fault.

- G, "Surface Faults on Montague Island," by George Plafker (1967). Two reactivated steep reverse faults in Prince William Sound are the only known surface faults caused by the earthquake. They are probably part of a fault system that extends discontinuously for more than 300 miles from Montague Island past the southeast coast of Kodiak Island.

* H, "Shoreline Erosion and Deposition on Montague Island," by M. J. Kirkby and A. V. Kirkby (1969). Modification of the shore by subaerial and marine processes began immediately after tectonic uplift. The effect and rate of each process on various materials were measured. Evidence was found of two relative sea-level changes prior to 1964.

- I, "Tectonics of the Earthquake," by George Plafker (1969). The earthquake was accompanied by crustal warping, horizontal distortion, and surface faulting over an area of more than 110,000 square miles. Focal mechanism studies, combined with the patterns of deformation and seismicity, suggest that the earthquake probably resulted from movement along a complex thrust fault that dips at a low angle beneath the continental margin. Radiocarbon dating of pre-1964 displaced shorelines provides data on long-term tectonic movements in the earthquake region and on the time interval since the last major earthquake-related movements.

- J, "Shore Processes and Beach Morphology," by K. W. Stanley (1968). All coastal features began to readjust to changed conditions immediately after the earthquake. In the subsided areas, beaches flattened and receded; in uplifted areas, they were stranded. Emergence and submergence posed problems of land use and ownership and changed wildlife habitats.

Professional Paper 544, "Effects on the Hydrologic Regimen," in five chapters:

- † A, "South-Central Alaska," by R. M. Waller (1966). Surface waters were affected by ice breakage, seiching, fissuring of streambeds, and temporary damming. Ground water was also drastically affected, mostly in unconsolidated aquifers. Many temporary and permanent changes occurred in water levels and artesian pressures.

- † B, "Anchorage Area," by R. M. Waller (1966). Immediate effects on the Anchorage hydrologic system included increased stream discharge, seiches on lakes, and fluctuations in ground-water levels; water supplies were temporarily disrupted by damming of streams.

- † C, "Outside Alaska," by R. C. Vorhis (1967). The earthquake caused measurable changes of water levels in wells and surface waters throughout nearly all of the United States and in many other countries. A separate section by E. E. Rexin and R. C. Vorhis describes hydroseismograms from a well in Wisconsin and one by R. W. Coble the effects on ground water in Iowa.

- † D, "Glaciers," by Austin Post (1967). Many rockslide avalanches extended onto the glaciers; some traveled long distances, possibly over layers of compressed air. No large snow and ice avalanches occurred on any of the hundreds of glaciers. Little evidence of earthquake-induced surges of glaciers was found.

- † E, "Seismic Seiches," by Arthur McGarr and R. C. Vorhis (1968). Hundreds of water-level instruments on streams, lakes, and reservoirs throughout the United States, Canada, and Australia recorded measurable seiches, or hydroseisms. Such recorders can thus serve as useful adjuncts of seismograph networks in earthquake studies.

Professional Paper 545, "Effects on Transportation, Communications, and Utilities," in four chapters:

- * A, "Eklutna Power Project," by M. H. Logan (1967). Vibration-induced consolidation of sediments damaged the underwater intake structure, and permitted sand, gravel, and cobbles to enter the tunnel. Lesser damage was done by vibration and ground fractures. A separate section by L. R. Burton describes the use of a portable television camera to locate breaks in underground communication systems.

- B, "Air and Water Transport, Communications, and Utilities," by E. B. Eckel (1967). All forms of transportation, utilities, and communication systems were wrecked or severely hampered by the earthquake. Numerous airports and all seaports were affected by vibration, subaqueous slides, waves, fire and tectonic uplift or subsidence. Aboveground transmission lines were extensively broken, but buried utility lines were virtually undamaged except where the ground fractured or slid.

- C, "The Highway System," by Reuben Kachadoorian (1968). Widespread damage resulted chiefly from destruction of bridges and roadways by seismic vibration and subsidence of foundations. Snowslides,

[753]

landslides, and shoreline submergence also damaged or drowned some roadways.

- D, "The Alaska Railroad," by D. S. McCulloch and M. G. Bonilla (1970). The rail system was extensively damaged; bridges and tracks were destroyed, and port facilities were lost at Seward and Whittier.

"Landspreading" (a term for sediments that were mobilized by vibration and moved toward topographic depressions) was the single most important source of trouble.

ACKNOWLEDGMENTS

Sincere thanks go to all the authors whose work is summarized here and to all my colleagues who played parts in publishing the U.S. Geological Survey's series of reports on the earthquake. Early drafts of this report were reviewed by the authors of each paper in the series and by many other friends, particularly the members of the Committee on the Alaska Earthquake of the National Academy of Sciences. All of these were very helpful in correcting factual and interpretative errors. Special thanks are due Wallace R. Hansen, George Plafker, and David S. McCulloch, who went beyond the call of duty in helping to improve this presentation. Catherine Campbell, who had primary responsibility for processing all the reports in the series; and Elna Bishop and her associates, who did the final editing and saw the reports through the press, deserve the thanks of all authors and readers. Robert A. Reilly used imagination, skill, and patience in preparing the line drawings for these pages.

TECTONICS

THE EARTHQUAKE

The earthquake struck about 5:36 p.m., Friday, March 27, 1964, Alaska standard time, or, as recorded by seismologists, at 03:36:11.9 to 12.4, Saturday, March 28, 1964, Greenwich mean time. Its Richter magnitude, computed by different observatories as from 8.3 to possibly as high as 8.75 (that of the greatest known earthquake is 8.9), has generally come to be described as 8.4–8.6. Its intensity on the Modified Mercalli scale ranged between very wide limits, depending partly on distance from the epicenter but much more on local geologic and hydrologic conditions and distribution of population; hence isointensity lines are difficult or impossible to draw.

The epicenter was instrumentally determined to be close to College Fiord at the head of Prince William Sound, on the south flank of the rugged Chugach Mountains (fig. 2). Calculations of the epicenter vary, but all place it within a 9-mile (15-km) radius of 61.1° N., 147.7° W. The focus, or point of origin, was 12–30 miles (20–50 km) below the surface. References to a single epicenter or depth of focus are misleading in that they imply that the earthquake had a point source. As interpreted by Wyss and Brune (1967), the earthquake rupture propagated in a series of events, with six widely distributed "epicenters" recorded during the first 72 seconds. Thus, energy was released by the earthquake itself over a broad area south and southwest of the epicenter; the thousands of aftershocks were dispersed throughout an area of about 100,000 square miles, mainly along the Continental Shelf between the Aleutian Trench and the mainland.

The long duration of strong ground motion intensified many of the earthquake's effects and added greatly to its scientific significance. At the time, there were no instruments in Alaska capable of recording the duration of motion, but many observers timed or estimated the period of strong shaking as from 1½ to 7 minutes. In most places the time was between 3 and 4 minutes. The majority of observers reported either continuous strong shaking throughout the earthquake or gradually diminishing motion. There is evidence, however, that in Anchorage and possibly elsewhere there were several pulses of strong shaking, separated by periods of diminished vibration.

The earthquake vibrations were felt by people throughout Alaska and parts of British Columbia (fig. 1); they were recorded by seismographs throughout the world. The vibrations themselves, or their immediate effects on bodies of water, were measured on streams and lakes and in wells throughout the United States and in many other countries. Earthquake-caused atmospheric pressure waves and subaudible sound waves were also recorded by instruments at widely separated stations in the conterminous States.

There is general agreement among seismologists and geologists that shallow earthquakes are caused by sudden release of elastic strain energy that has accumulated in the earth's crust and upper mantle. There is no unanimity of opinion, however, as to why the strains are released when and where they are nor as to the details of the earthquake-generation process or mechanism. The Alaska earthquake of 1964 gave some additional insight into these problems but did not solve them all by any means.

Much has been made by both technical and popular writers of the fortunate circumstances that brought the Alaska earthquake on the late afternoon of Good Friday, or Passover, at a time of low tides, and during the off-season for fishing, when there were few people on docks and boats and in nearshore canneries. There is no question that this combination of circumstances resulted in less loss of life than would have occurred at almost any other time.

Wilson and Tørum (1968) make the interesting suggestion that the timing of the release of strain was perhaps not fortuitous at all, but was the product of astronomic forces. They base their suggestion on the fact that the earthquake occurred near the time of the vernal equinox—the date on which the religious seasons of Easter and Passover are also based—when the earth, moon, and sun were in opposition at syzygies and ocean tides were at maximum spring range. Wilson and Tørum inferred that six other great earthquakes in recent history occurred at or near the lunar position of syzygy either in opposition or conjunction; they concluded that the maximum earth and ocean tides that result from these conditions are perhaps important triggering devices for releasing built-up strain in the earth's crust. Whether or not their hypothesis is correct, the earthquake could hardly have struck at a time more favorable to minimizing damage and loss of life.

DEFORMATION AND VIBRATION OF THE LAND SURFACE

An earthquake by definition is a shaking of the ground surface and the structures on it, but the shaking is really only symptomatic of the great geotectonic events that are affecting a part of the earth's crust. This truism was well demonstrated by the Alaska earthquake. Vibrations from few, if any, earthquakes in history have been felt by people over a wider area, or have persisted for a longer time. Much of the damage was caused by the vibrations themselves or by their direct results— ground cracks, compaction of sediments, landslides and subaqueous slides, and local waves originated by such slides. But perceptible and disastrous as they were, these effects were insignificant compared to the great geologic event that caused them, even though most other effects of that event were not even recognizable as such until long after shaking had subsided. Indeed, the nature and location of the assumed fault along which the main event occurred are still subjects for inference and speculation, despite intensive studies by many able investigators.

Some other effects were nearly or quite as destructive as were the seismic vibrations. The uplift and subsidence that disrupted ports and navigation routes throughout the affected area had far-reaching, long-term effects (fig. 2). Massive tilting of the ocean bottom undoubtedly initiated the seismic sea waves or tsunamis that wrecked Kodiak and other towns in Alaska and caused many of the deaths there and as far down the coast as Crescent City, Calif. The horizontal seaward movement of the landmass, though not measurable as such without precise geodetic studies and interpretations, may itself have initiated disastrous slides and waves along the shores of

"* * * the timing of the release of strain was perhaps not fortuitous at all, but was the product of astronomic forces."

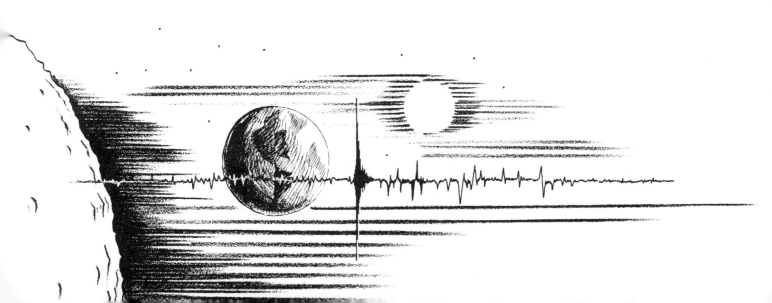

2.—Map of south-central Alaska, showing areas of tectonic land-level changes.

Prince William Sound and elsewhere.

Perhaps the most significant aspect of the Alaska earthquake was the great expanse of measurable land dislocation. Most of our knowledge of the crustal deformation that marks large earthquakes comes from analysis of the elastic waves that they generate; more direct observations are commonly limited by a lack of critical ground control. In Alaska these deformations were measurable by geodetic and other methods over much of the displacement field (Malloy, 1964, 1965; Plafker, 1965; Parkin, 1966, 1969; Small and Parkin, 1967; and Small and Wharton, 1969). The vast quantity of available facts are interpreted in tectonic terms by Plafker (1969), from whose report most of the following information is taken.

VERTICAL DEFORMATION

Over an area of more than 100,000 square miles, the earth's surface was measurably displaced by the earthquake (fig. 2). Displacements occurred in two arcuate zones parallel to the continental margin, together about 600 miles long and as much as 250 miles wide. West and north of a curving isobase line that extends around the head of Prince William Sound, thence southwestward past the southeast shores of the Kenai Peninsula and the most southeasterly fringes of Kodiak Island, the land and sea-bottom surface subsided an average of 2½ feet and a maximum of 7½ feet. Southeast, or seaward of the isobase line, the surface was uplifted an average of 6 feet and a measured maximum of 38 feet, on Montague Island, where surface faults developed along a zone of severe deformation. There is some evidence that the land west of the subsided zone, involving the Aleutian and Alaska ranges, was uplifted a maximum of 1½ feet, but less is known about this area.

Besides the tsunamis that spread across the entire Pacific Ocean, subsidence and uplift had other consequences, particularly along the seacoasts. Nearly every report in this series describes these effects as observed in some part of the earthquake-affected region. Some effects were immediately apparent to observers; others were not even recognized until hours or days later, when anomalous waves had subsided and new tide levels were affirmed. Only then did people begin to realize the magnitude of the tectonic changes.

Real measurements of the distribution and amount of land-level change required geodetic resurveys of previously established land nets and hundreds of measurements of vertically displaced intertidal sessile organisms. The fact that certain marine plants and animals have definite vertical growth limits relative to tide levels has long been known but, following the early lead of Tarr and Martin (1912), its usefulness in determining relative land-level changes resulting from earthquakes was greatly expanded by Plafker (1969) and his colleagues. The potential accuracy of the method is limited only by the number of observations that can be made with available time, energy, and funds; by the accuracy of our knowledge as to the growth habits of these sessile organisms; and by the accuracy of the observer's estimates of tide stages at the time of observation. In south-central Alaska it provided far more detailed and reliable information on the nature and size of land deformation than could have been determined from the relatively sparse geodetic, hydrographic, and tide-gage control that was available.

HORIZONTAL DEFORMATION

Large-scale horizontal deformation also accompanied the earthquake (Parkin, 1966, 1969; Plafker, 1969). Horizontal movement of the land mass was not noted by observers and could not in any case have been distinguished by human senses from the back-and-forth sensations caused by the seismic waves. Its net results, however, were measured geodetically.

Retriangulation by the U.S. Coast and Geodetic Survey over about 25,000 square miles of uplifted and subsided ground in and around the Prince William Sound region shows definitely that the landmass moved relatively seaward, or southeastward. The amount and distribution of the displacement has been determined relatively but not absolutely. Plafker's interpretation shows systematic horizontal shifts, in a south to southwestward direction, of as much as 64 feet. Parkin, using the same data, found maximum displacements of about 70 feet and in slightly different directions. Whatever the differences in detail and interpretation, there is little doubt that a large mass of land and sea floor moved several tens of feet toward the Gulf of Alaska.

The horizontal land movements produced no known direct effects on man and his structures. Malloy (1965), Wilson and Tørum (1968), Plafker (1969), Plafker and others (1969), all suggest, however, that the sudden seaward land motion may well have caused waves in certain confined and semiconfined bodies of surface water. Too, porosity changes that caused temporary water losses from surface streams and lakes, and lowering of water levels in some wells that tap

"The Alaska earthquake of 1964 produced only two known surface faults, both on uninhabited Montague Island, in Prince William Sound."

confined aquifers, may have resulted from the horizontal land movements (Waller, 1966a, b).

SURFACE FAULTS

Surface fault displacements accompany many large earthquakes and are much feared because of potential damage to buildings.

The Alaska earthquake of 1964 produced only two surface faults, both on uninhabited Montague Island, in Prince William Sound (Plafker, 1967). They are significant, however, because of their tectonic implications, their large displacements, and their reverse habits. So far as is known, reverse faults rarely accompany earthquakes. The two faults, called the Patton Bay fault and the Hanning Bay fault, were reactivated along preexisting fault traces on the southwestern part of Montague Island. These faults had been mapped by Condon and Cass (1958). New scarps, fissures, flexures, and large landslides ap-

peared in bedrock and in surficial deposits along both traces. Both strike northeast and dip steeply northwest. Vertical displacements are 20 to 23 feet on the Patton Bay fault and 16 feet on the shorter Hanning Bay fault. Both blocks of each fault are uplifted relative to sea level, but the northwestern block of each is relatively higher than the southeastern one. The Patton Bay fault is 22 miles long on land and extends seaward to the southwest at least 17 miles; indirect evidence suggests that the fault system extends southwestward on the sea floor more than 300 miles (Plafker, 1967).

The faults on Montague Island and their postulated extensions southwestward are in the zone of maximum tectonic uplift. Their geologic setting and positions relative to the zone of regional uplift and aftershocks suggest to Plafker (1969) that they are not the primary causative faults of the earthquake but are subsidiary

fractures. The hypothetical causative fault is viewed as a low-angle thrust beneath the continental margin.

Inconclusive evidence suggests that ground fissures on the Kenai Peninsula may reflect earthquake-induced movement along an undiscovered buried fault zone (Foster and Karlstrom, 1967). The cracks may, however, have been caused by refraction of seismic vibrations off subsurface bedrock irregularities. Similarly, his bathymetric surveys indicate to G. A. Rusnak of the U.S. Geological Survey (oral commun., 1968) that the earthquake may have formed fault-bounded grabens on the floor of Resurrection Bay, as well as somewhat similar displacements in Passage Canal. Evidence for these suggestions is tenuous, particularly because no direct indications of the postulated earthquake-caused structural features have been found on land, despite diligent search.

MECHANISM OF THE EARTHQUAKE

The widespread vertical and horizontal displacements of the land surface, and the surface faults on Montague Island and southwest thereof, were manifestations of a great geologic event—the sudden release of crustal strains that caused movement along a great fault deep beneath the surface. Nearly all seismologists and geologists agree that such a fault exists, but its exact position, orientation, and sense of displacement are obscure, and will probably remain so.

The elastic rebound theory for the generation of earthquakes states that shallow-focus earthquakes (at depths less than about 40 km.), such as the Alaska one, are generated by sudden fracturing or faulting following slow accumulation of deformation and strain. When the strength of the rocks is exceeded, failure occurs and the elastic strain is suddenly released in the form of heat, crushing, and seismic-wave radiation. Most investigators believe that this sequence of events took place in Alaska. Most believe further that the 1964 earthquake was but one pulse in a long history of regional deformation; this history is summarized by Plafker (1969). Geologic evidence, supported by numerous new radiocarbon datings, indicates that most of the deformed region has been undergoing gradual tectonic submergence for the past 930 to 1,360 years; Plafker tentatively interprets this submergence as direct evidence that regional strain with a downward-directed component had been accumulating in the region for about that length of time.

Intensive studies of the earthquake, and of its foreshocks and aftershocks, have led seismologists to agree that movement was initiated on a new or a reactivated old major fault or fault zone beneath Prince William Sound. Seismologists also agree that the fault is elongate, extending several hundred miles southwestward from near the epicenter to or beyond Kodiak Island and that it is 12 to 30 miles beneath the surface at the epicenter of the main shock. Focal-mechanism studies are inconclusive as to whether the postulated fault dips steeply or at low angles. Either angle fits the available data.

Plafker (1969), who considers the focal-mechanism studies by seismologists in conjunction with the regional geologic history and with regional patterns of tectonic deformation and seismicity, believes that the fault is most probably a low-angle thrust (reverse fault). According to his interpretation, the earthquake originated along a complex thrust fault that dips northwestward beneath the Aleutian Trench. Subsidiary reverse faulting on Montague Island occurred in the upper plate. In his postulated model, the observed and inferred tectonic displacements resulted primarily from (1) relative seaward displacement and uplift of the frontal end of the thrust block along the primary fault and subsidiary reverse faults, such as those on Montague Island, and (2) simultaneous elastic horizontal extension, leading to subsidence, behind the overthrust block.

The concept of a primary low-angle thrust, with the landmass moving relatively toward the Gulf of Alaska, fits most of the known geologic, geodetic, and seismologic facts. Stauder and Bollinger (1966) have shown that focal-mechanism solutions of the main shock and numerous aftershocks based on both P and S waves favor a low-angle thrust. These same writers, and Savage and Hastie (1966), show that the observed vertical displacements in the major zones of deformation are in reasonably close agreement with the theoretical displacements obtained by applying dislocation theory to a low-angle or horizontal-thrust model.

The low-angle thrust model does not fit all the data, however. For example, Press and Jackson (1965) and Harding and Algermissen (1969) present alternative interpretations of the seismologic data that favor a steeply dipping fault, rather than a thrust. Savage and Hastie (1966) have shown that the theoretical surface displacements from such a model diverge considerably from the observations, and they point out that the surface-wave fault-plane data cited by Press and Jackson in support of a steep fault would apply equally well to a low-angle fault because rupture propagation was along the null axis. However, P- and S-wave solutions of the main shock suggest to Harding and Algermissen movement on a steep plane. Von Huene and others (1967), too, present oceanographic evidence from the Gulf of Alaska and the Aleutian Trench which they interpret to preclude overthrusting of the continental margin.

There appears to be no unambiguous explanation of the mechanism of the Alaska earthquake. All major arc-related earthquakes, such as this one, are difficult to study because much of the displacement field is invariably submarine; data on earthquakes with offshore epicenters cannot be obtained as readily as for those centered on land. It can be hoped that better seismograph records of long-period motions, together with continuing precise geodetic measurements that would give evidence of the strain accumulations and deformations on land, will permit less ambiguous interpretations of the causes of future Alaska earthquakes. These data would require new techniques for determining subsea displacements and the hypocentral depths and first motions of offshore earthquakes in arc environments.

EFFECTS ON THE PHYSICAL ENVIRONMENT

The shaking and land deformations had profound and lasting effects on the geologic, hydrologic, and oceanographic environments of a large part of south-central Alaska and, to a lesser extent, of an enormously greater area (fig. 1). These effects in turn had immediate and drastic effects on man and manmade structures. The various categories of effects, which were responsible for all the deaths and destruction, are discussed in succeeding paragraphs. Many other effects, such as those on the bird, animal, fish, and shellfish populations and their habitats, are not described here, though they were of outstanding importance to science and to the economy of Alaska.

GEOLOGIC EFFECTS

DOWNSLOPE MASS MOVEMENTS

Of the many downslope mass movements during the earthquake, only four kinds provided much new knowledge about their character and origins. These were (1) the enormous rockslide avalanches on some glaciers, (2) the disastrous subaqueous slides from lakeshores and sea coasts, (3) the near-horizontal movement of vibration-mobilized soil, and (4) the giant translatory slides in sensitive clay at Anchorage.

Earthquakes have long been known to cause landslides and rock or snow avalanches, but they are generally subordinate to other more usual causes such as gravity interacting with water or ice (Varnes, 1958). It is not surprising that a great earthquake in a rugged land like south-central Alaska should bring down thousands of landslides and avalanches in the mountains and many subaqueous slides in the deep lakes and fiords.

Property damage from slides in the mountains was generally limited to roads and railroads. Rockslides contributed to only one known death. At Cape Saint Elias, a coastguardsman, seriously injured by a large rockfall, was later drowned by waves (Plafker and others, 1969).

Several writers have attributed the relatively small amount of damage done by avalanches and slides to the sparse population in the mountains. That the rockslides were unprecedented in size and number in recent centuries is demonstrated by the absence of similar deposits of debris on most glaciers before the 1964 event. Large-scale slides triggered by earthquakes doubtless do present a serious hazard in the mountainous regions of Alaska where steep, unstable slopes are present.

With a few outstanding exceptions, most of the slides and avalanches were comparatively simple well-known types and, because they caused little physical damage, they received little attention by investigators.

The landslides along the Patton Bay and Hanning Bay faults on Montague Island (Plafker, 1967) are of interest chiefly because they are related to the only known earthquake-caused surface faults. Although their study added little to general knowledge of landslide processes, Plafker (1967) has noted that, by their very nature,

"By far the greatest damage done by slides and avalanches was along the highway and rail net, south and east of Anchorage."

active thrust faults tend to conceal their traces automatically by initiating linear zones of landslides.

Debris slides and rotational slumps developed in many places in and near Anchorage (Hansen, 1965), but they did far less damage and were less important scientifically than the gigantic translatory slides discussed separately below. Slides and slumps on steep slopes near Whittier (Kachadoorian, 1965), Seward (Lemke, 1967), and Homer (Waller, 1966a) also did little damage as compared to submarine slides, waves, and subsidence.

Many landslides occurred on the Kodiak island group in a great variety of geologic settings (Plafker and Kachadoorian, 1966), but aside from temporarily blocking a few roads, they did no significant damage.

By far the greatest damage done by slides and avalanches was along the highway and rail net, south and east of Anchorage. The plotted distribution of these features (Kachadoorian, 1968; McCulloch and Bonilla, 1970) shows how widespread and numerous they were along the roads and railroads. This distribution probably represents fairly well the distribution of downslope mass movements throughout the earthquake-shaken area, with some allowance for the fact that manmade cuts and fills tend to diminish slope stability, hence to increase the number of slides.

ROCKSLIDE AVALANCHES

Glaciers and snowfields cover more than 20 percent of the land area that was shaken violently. Almost 2,000 avalanches and snow slides were seen on postearthquake aerial photographs examined by Hackman (1965). Most of these he suspected were caused by the earthquake but as Post (1967)

"* * * the avalanches initially descended very steep slopes and attained high velocities. * * * These features * * * help substantiate the hypothesis that some large rock avalanches travel on cushions of compressed air."

and several others point out, none of these snow and ice avalanches were large enough to materially affect any glacier's regime.

As compared with slides of snow and ice, rockslide avalanches were fewer but much larger. The most thoroughly studied of these is on Sherman Glacier in the Chugach Mountains, 20 miles east of Cordova. There, an enormous mass of rock and some snow and ice fell from two peaks, traveled at high speed, and spread out over half of the glacier's ablation area (Shreve, 1966; Post, 1967; Plafker, 1968). The effects of such deposits on glacier regimes have yet to be fully assessed, but reduction in ice ablation sufficient to favor positive annual mass balances has already been measured. A future modest advance of the Sherman

Glacier's terminus can be expected.

Various investigations show that the Sherman and other avalanches tend to have certain common characteristics: (a) the areas were cliffs currently undergoing glacial erosion; (b) the unstable rock available for movement was hundreds of thousands of cubic yards in volume; (c) the avalanches initially descended very steep slopes and attained high velocities; (d) the rock debris spread out over surficial features of the glacier surfaces without greatly modifying them; and (e) the gradients of the avalanches on the glacier surface were very low, yet the material traveled very long distances (Post, 1967). These features together help substantiate the hypothesis that some large rock avalanches travel on cushions of compressed air (Shreve, 1959, 1966b, 1968; Crandell and Fahnestock, 1965).

HORIZONTAL MOVEMENTS OF MOBILIZED SOIL

The movements of mobilized water-saturated soil toward topographic depressions deserve special mention. These movements took place throughout the strongly shaken part of Alaska and were among the major causes of ground fractures along river banks, deltas, and elsewhere. They were best seen and recorded along the highway and railroad systems and were major sources of damage to both (Kachadoorian, 1968; McCulloch and Bonilla, 1970). Elsewhere in thinly populated regions like the Martin and Bering River area (Tuthill and Laird, 1966), lateral spreading did less damage but was nevertheless an important geomorphic process.

In detailed studies of earthquake damage to the Alaska Railroad, McCulloch and Bonilla (1970) observed that ordinary rotational slumps were surprisingly rare and that the elastic response of unconsolidated sediment was a less important source of damage than were near-horizontal displacements or "landspreading." This phenomenon has been observed in studies of other great earthquakes. McCulloch and Bonilla describe the distension that occurs within the sediments and note that landspreading takes place on flat or nearly flat ground; thus they differentiate from landsliding, which connotes downslope movement.

Along the railroad, ground fissures, loss of bearing strength, and other effects all took their toll; but in terms of dollars lost, damage caused by landspreading was second only to the loss of terminal facilities at Whittier and Seward caused by submarine slides, waves, and fire (Kachadoorian, 1965;

Lemke, 1967). Water-laid saturated sediments responded to the earthquake's vibrations by mobilizing and moving laterally toward free topographic faces that ranged in size from small drainage ditches to wide valleys. The spreading of the mobilized sediments generated stress in their frozen surfaces and caused ground cracking that tore apart railroad tracks and highway pavements. In addition, streamward spreading of the mobilized sediments compressed or skewed numerous bridges by streamward movements of banks. Even deeply driven piles moved toward stream centers, and there was a tendency toward compression and uplift beneath some bridges.

Many of the movements took place in areas where surfaces were nearly flat. Some extended as much as a quarter of a mile back from the topographic depression and offset rail lines or other linear features. McCulloch and Bonilla conclude that the tendency toward mobilization of sediments should be considered in design of structures in earthquake-prone areas. They suggest that it might be minimized by eliminating strong surface irregularities and linear features insofar as possible; skewing of bridges might be reduced by placing crossings at right angles to streambanks.

SUBAQUEOUS SLIDES

Subaqueous slides, and gigantic local waves that were closely related to them in time and origin, caused high loss of life and property. A very few similar slides and their associated waves have been known from other earthquakes, but none had received much study.

Throughout the earthquake-shaken area, steep-fronted deltas collapsed into many of the deeper lakes. The new fronts were gen-

erally steeper and less stable than the old ones (Tuthill and Laird, 1966; Ferrians, 1966; Lemke, 1967). Except on Kenai Lake (McCulloch, 1966), none of these slides did much damage, and they were not studied intensively. The several slides along the shores of Kenai Lake yielded more information on the mechanics of sliding and the distribution of resultant debris than was available for the seacoast slides. McCulloch (1966) found that sliding removed the protruding parts of deltas—often the youngest and least consolidated parts—and steepened the delta fronts. He suggests that protruding portions should be the least stable, for they contain the most mass bounded by the shortest possible failure surface. Fathograms show that large slides spread for thousands of feet over the horizontal lake floor and that some of the debris moved so rapidly that it pushed water waves ahead of it and up on the opposite shores.

Because of the presence of coastal communities, submarine slides in the fiords of Prince William Sound and along the south coast of the Kenai Peninsula were far more destructive than those on lakes. The most disastrous ones were at Valdez (Coulter and Migliaccio, 1966), Seward (Lemke, 1967), and Whittier (Kachadoorian, 1965), but there were also slides at Homer on Cook Inlet (Waller, 1966a) and at many other inhabited places. Some of these, and their associated waves, did more damage in proportion to the size of the communities affected than did the better known ones at Seward and Valdez (Plafker and Mayo, 1965; Plafker and others, 1969). In addition to those known to be related to submarine slides, there were numerous destructive waves of unknown origin throughout much of Prince William

Sound. Some of the unexplained waves may have been related to unidentified submarine slides, but some are believed to have been generated by permanent horizontal shifts of the land relative to partly or wholly confined bodies of water (Plafker, 1969; Plafker and others, 1969). How much of the sliding was caused by direct prolonged vibration and how much by the southeasterly shift of the landmass during the earthquake is unknown. It seems probable, however, that vibration was the primary cause of most of it.

All the subaqueous slides that were studied in any detail left new slopes nearly or quite as steep as the preearthquake ones, some even steeper. This is the most significant and ominous finding from the investigations of these features, for it means that the delta fronts are still only marginally stable and hence are subject to renewed sliding, triggered by future earthquakes. The lesson is clear—any steep-faced delta of fine to moderately coarse materials in deep water presents inherent dangers of future offshore slides and destructive waves, whether or not it has slid in the past.

One somewhat unexpected result of the offshore slides, observed on Kenai Lake and at Valdez and Whittier, may well have occurred on other narrow lakes or fiords: the wide and rapid spread of slide debris on the bottom. Some of the debris at Kenai Lake crossed the lake, pushed water ahead of it, and caused wave runups on the far shores (McCulloch, 1966). This feature means that, under some conditions at least, the shore opposite a steep-faced delta may be almost as poor a place for buildings or anchorages as is the delta itself.

In summary, the 1964 earthquake showed that any deep-water delta, such as those in the fiords and many lakes of south-central Alaska, may produce subaqueous slides and associated destructive waves if shaken by a severe earthquake. Such deltas commonly contain much sand or finer grained material, are saturated with water, and have steep fronts; hence they are apt to have very low stability under dynamic conditions.

TRANSLATORY LANDSLIDES IN ANCHORAGE

All the highly destructive landslides in the built-up parts of Anchorage moved chiefly by translation rather than rotation—that is, they moved laterally on nearly horizontal slip surfaces, following drastic loss of strength in an already weak layer of sensitive clay. The translatory slides at Anchorage ranged from block glides, in which the slide mass remained more or less intact, to those that are best classed as failures by lateral spreading (Varnes, 1958).

Translatory slides, caused by earthquakes or other agencies, are uncommon, but they have long been known, and studied to some extent, in Scandinavia, Chile, and the United States (Hansen, 1965). The Anchorage slides of 1964, however, promise to become a classic reference point in the scientific and engineering literature on near-horizontal mass movement of material. They had many novel aspects, and, because facts were needed for far-reaching decisions on the reconstruction of important parts of a thriving city, the Anchorage translatory slides probably received more study by soils engineers and geologists than any comparable group of landslides in history.

Several million dollars was spent by the Corps of Engineers in intensive soils studies of all the Anchorage slides: (1) to determine where reconstruction should be permitted, (2) to build a gigantic stabilizing buttress in the midst of downtown Anchorage, and (3) to experiment

"All the highly destructive landslides in the built-up parts of Anchorage moved chiefly by translation rather than rotation—that is, they moved laterally on nearly horizontal slip surfaces, following drastic loss of strength in an already weak layer of sensitive clay."

with explosive and electro-osmotic methods of stabilizing the great slide at Turnagain Heights. The slides at Anchorage have also sparked other studies of the stability of slopes in sensitive clays, particularly under dynamic conditions.

All the Anchorage slides involved a hitherto obscure but now famous geologic formation—the Bootlegger Cove Clay of Pleistocene age (Miller and Dobrovolny, 1959). This deposit of glacial estuarine-marine origin underlies much of Anchorage; it is overlain by outwash gravel. All the destructive slides occurred where the Bootlegger Cove Clay crops out along steep bluffs. The formation is comprised largely of clay and silt, with a few thin, discontinuous lenses of sand. The middle part of the formation contains zones characterized by low shear strength, high water content, and high sensitivity; these failed under the earthquake's vibrations.

The most thorough report on the geology of the Anchorage slides, as distinct from the soils engineering aspects, is that by Hansen in which he reconstructed the highly complex Turnagain slide by maps and cross sections (Hansen, 1965, pls. 1, 2). Many other reports on the mechanics of the Anchorage slides or on theoretical and experimental work engendered by the Anchorage experience have already appeared in the civil engineering literature (Shannon and Wilson, Inc., 1964; Long and George, 1967a, b; Seed and Wilson, 1967), and more will appear in the future.

As described by Hansen (1965) earthquake vibrations reduced the shear strength of saturated sensitive zones in the clay. A prismatic block of earth moved laterally on a nearly horizontal surface toward a free face, or bluff. Tension fractures formed at the head of the slide and allowed collapse of a wedge-shaped mass, or graben. Pressure ridges were formed at the toe of the slide block. In complex slides, and with continued shaking, the process was repeated so that slice after slice moved forward toward or beyond the former bluff face.

Seed and Wilson (1967) agree in most respects with Hansen's view of the mechanics of the Anchorage slides. They are much more inclined, however, to ascribe the initial translatory motion to liquefaction of layers or lenses of sand in the clay than to weakening of the clay itself. Seed has found by experiment with modified triaxial shear devices that laboratory-reconstructed sand, similar to that in the Bootlegger Cove Clay, liquefies and loses all its shear strength with far fewer vibratory pulses than are required to liquefy the clay. He is doubtlessly correct as to the initiating mechanism, but there is no question that drastic weakening of the clay contributed to the lateral movements once they had begun. Even under static conditions prior to the earthquake, the bluffline at Turnagain Heights was being undermined at its foot in a continuous zone of clay slumps and liquefied-clay mudflows.

Large-scale field tests were made at Turnagain Heights to determine if remodeling by blasting or treatment by electro-osmosis might add to the strength of the jumbled mass of clay that slid seaward during the 1964 earthquake. Neither method produced very promising results, but when the tests were abandoned the Corps of Engineers and its consultants had determined that the landslide material along Knik Arm had naturally regained all its preearthquake strength. The Corps concluded therefore that the new slopes in the Turnagain area now form a natural buttress to the undisturbed bluff behind the slide that should withstand a future earthquake similar to that of 1964, provided the buttress toe is protected against erosion. In 1969 there were no plans for such erosion protection.

The greatest unanswered question about the Anchorage translatory slides is whether they will recur in the event of another great earthquake, and if so, what can be done to prevent them. There is abundant evidence that repeated similar slides, some in the same places, have been triggered by earlier earthquakes or by other causes (Miller and Dobrovolny, 1959: Hansen, 1965; McCulloch and Bonilla, 1970). There is also every reason to suppose that new slides will develop if and when another severe earthquake occurs. With present knowledge, the most practical means of avoiding or ameliorating future translatory slides would seem to be to reduce the slopes on bluffs, to avoid loading the upper parts of slopes or bluffs, or to construct gigantic earth buttresses like that at the Fourth Avenue slide. Other means of slide prevention may be developed in the future. Meanwhile, the U.S. Geological Survey, in cooperation with Anchorage Borough authorities, is preparing detailed maps that will show, among other things, the outcrops of the Bootlegger Cove Clay and the distribution of steep slopes (Dobrovolny and Schmoll, 1968). Such maps should be useful to borough and city officials in determining the general areas where slides are most likely to occur. Very detailed investigations will, of course, be necessary at any specific site in order to determine the soil conditions and to design corrective or preventive measures.

GROUND FISSURES

Ground fissures, also called cracks or fractures by various authors, are formed by nearly all severe earthquakes and by some smaller ones. Possibly more resulted from the 1964 earthquake than from any previously recorded earthquake. Certainly they were more noticeable and more intensely studied, especially by means of aerial photographs. The ground surface was frozen in nearly all of the earthquake-affected area; this condition not only resulted in more fissures but favored their preservation long enough to permit observation, photographing, and mapping.

General distribution of fissured ground throughout the earthquake-affected area is shown by Plafker and others (1969). Only a very few of the fissures that developed have been mapped, but good examples of their patterns, character, and geologic settings are shown in maps of the Kenai Lake area (McCulloch, 1966); along the railroad and highway nets (Kachadoorian, 1968; McCulloch and Bonilla, 1970); at Valdez (Coulter and Migliaccio, 1966); at Anchorage (Hansen, 1965; Engineering Geology Evaluation Group, 1964); at Seward (Lemke, 1967); and elsewhere. In addition, Ferrians (1966) and Tuthill and Laird (1966) made detailed studies of the fissures and associated landforms in the Copper River Basin and Martin-Bearing Rivers areas. The very extensive ground breakage on the Kenai Lowland was mapped by Foster and Karlstrom (1967).

Ground fissures, many marked by copious emissions of muddy or sandy water or by minor local collapse features, were widespread within about 100 miles of the epi-center, but they were noted as far as 450 miles away (fig. 1).

Flood plains, the tops and fronts of deltas, toes of alluvial fans, low terraces with steep fronts, and lake margins were among the geomorphic features most affected. Fissures varied greatly in length but some individual ones could be traced for thousands of feet. Some open fissures were several feet wide; many fissures opened and closed with the passage of seismic waves.

Most ground fissures were necessarily studied only at the surface. Some fissures on the Kenai Lowland, however, and on Kodiak Island and elsewhere are known to have extended at least 20 to 25 feet beneath the surface, because coal, gravel, pumice, and other materials that exist at those depths were brought to the surface by spouting water (Foster and Karlstrom, 1967; Plafker and Kachadoorian, 1966).

Great quantities of water, mixed with varying amounts of sand and silt, were ejected as fountains or sheets of water from ground fissures in many places (Waller, 1966b). Most ejections came from linear fractures, but in flat-lying homogeneous sediments some came from point sources. Among the chief consequences of the ejections were local subsidence of the land surface and further cracking by removal of water and material from below.

Geologically, most ground fissures were ephemeral features and, of themselves, left little permanent evidence of their presence. Cracked mats of peat, however, were still preserved in 1967, and clastic dikes formed by sand or mud injections may last for many years. Evidence of local subsidence caused by ejection of water and mud from fissures is somewhat more permanent also, as are a few other minor landforms that resulted from them. Several unusual geologic-geomorphic features, such as mud-vent deposits, fountain craters, subsidence craters, and snow cones, are described by Tuthill and Laird (1966) in the Martin-Bering Rivers area. Most of these are related to the pumping of water and sediments from ground fissures. Similar deposits were left by mud spouts or by melting of snow avalanches in many parts of the earthquake-affected area (Waller, 1966a, b; Lemke, 1967; McCulloch and Bonilla, 1970). All these features are of some scientific interest, but they are ephemeral and are not likely to be preserved in the geologic record unless they are soon buried by other deposits.

Widespread damage resulted from fissures, though on the whole it was minor as compared to that from other sources. Ground fissures disrupted buried utility lines and did other damage in Anchorage (Hansen, 1965; Burton, in Logan, 1967; McCulloch and Bonilla, 1970). At Seward, remaining parts of the fan-delta whose front slid into Resurrection Bay were severely cracked and left unstable. Fissures also damaged many homes and roads in Forest Acres outside of Seward (Lemke, 1967). At Valdez, 40 percent of the homes and most commercial buildings that were not wrecked by the giant submarine slide were seriously damaged by earth fissures that destroyed their structural integrity, broke pipes, and pumped immense quantities of sand and silt into their lower parts (Coulter and Migliaccio, 1966). At the Eklutna Lake powerplant, numerous cracks, some of them damaging, developed in both natural and artificially compacted sediments (Logan, 1967). At the Cordova airport, the foundation of the

FAA office building was split by a ground fissure, and underground utility lines were broken in so many places that most had to be replaced (Eckel, 1967).

All fissures were directly related to local geologic conditions. Many of them formed in thick coarse-grained unconsolidated deposits, where the water table was close to the surface and where the topmost layers were frozen, hence brittle. Many others, as on the mudflats of the Copper River Delta, Controller Bay, and near Portage, developed in fine-grained deposits. Artificial fills were very susceptible. Many cracks followed backfilled utility trenches. Many highway fills compacted and cracked marginally. Few fissures formed in well-drained surficial deposits, and hardly any in bedrock or in permafrost.

Only on the Kenai Lowland was there any suggestion of tectonic control of the fracture patterns (other, of course, than the regional tectonic factors that controlled the general distribution of all the earthquake's effects). On the lowland, and to some extent in the Chugach Mountains north of it, Foster and Karlstrom (1967) noted an alinement of ground fractures that suggested to them that the fractures might reflect earthquake-caused movement along hypothetical faults in the underlying bedrock.

Seismic vibration was the ultimate cause of virtually all the fissures. Some were formed directly by the shaking, others by differential horizontal or vertical compaction, others by local subsidence. Many formed near slopes or surface irregularities when underlying materials liquefied or, mobilized by vibration, moved toward topographic depressions. The best known examples perhaps are the ground fractures back of the

translatory slides at Anchorage (Hansen, 1965), the extensive fissures on the Resurrection River Delta near Seward (Lemke, 1967), and the thousands of fissures along the rail and road systems (Kachadoorian, 1968; McCulloch and Bonilla, 1970). Unconfined slopes were not essential to the formation of fissures, however; many formed on flat unbroken surfaces such as that of the Copper River Delta.

As a possible explanation for the origin of a certain type of ground fissure that formed in the Copper River Basin in flat-lying areas where there were no free faces toward which the materials could move, Ferrians (1966) suggests that surface waves flexing the layer of frozen surficial materials, which was in a state of tension, caused the initial cracking of the surface. The passing surface waves subjected the saturated sediments beneath the seasonal frost to repeated compression and dilation in the horizontal direction; consequently, large quantities of water and silt- and sand-sized material were ejected from the cracks, and sediment particles were rearranged. The net result of these forces was horizontal compaction, which caused the formation of numerous ground cracks that extended for great distances and formed a systematic reticulate pattern in the flood plains of some of the larger rivers.

Permanently frozen ground, because it behaves dynamically like bedrock, had few if any fissures; in some places, however, where water-bearing layers were perched between the permafrost and the seasonal frost layer at the ground surface, there was extensive cracking (Ferrians, 1966).

Except in a general way, the occurrence and distribution of ground fissures would be difficult to predict for any given earth-

"All fissures were directly related to local geologic conditions. Many of them formed in thick coarse-grained unconsolidated deposits, where the water table was close to the surface and where the topmost layers were frozen, hence brittle."

quake. The conditions under which they develop are now well known, and it is possible to identify bodies of sediments that are susceptible to fissuring during a large earthquake of long duration (McCulloch and Bonilla, 1970). Formation of individual fissures or fissure systems is so dependent on local geologic and ground-water conditions, however, that highly detailed knowledge of local surface, subsurface, and subaerial conditions would be required for precise predictions.

CONSOLIDATION SUBSIDENCE

Seismic vibration caused consolidation of loose granular materials in many places. Rearrangement of constituent particles, aided by ejection of interstitial water through waterspouts or mud spouts, caused compaction and local differential subsidence of the surface. Lateral spreading, too, caused lowering of surface levels in places. In coastal areas where local subsidence was superimposed on regional tectonic subsidence, as on Homer Spit (Grantz and others, 1964; Waller, 1966a), Kodiak Island (Plafker and Kachadoorian, 1966), and near the head of Turnagain Arm (Plafker and others, 1969), for example, the likelihood of destructive flooding was heightened.

The intake and spillway at Eklutna Lake, which feeds the Bureau of Reclamation's Eklutna hydroelectric plant, provided special instances of damage by consolidation subsidence. The concrete intake structure was cracked when the lake sediments beneath it compacted and subsided. As a direct result, about 2,000 cubic yards of sand and rock passed through the broken intake and into the main tunnel. The concrete spillway gate at Eklutna Dam was also severely cracked, but not until long after the earthquake. As described by Logan (1967), saturated alluvium below the frozen surface layer subsided as it was consolidated by the earthquake and left a void below the frozen layer. Later as thawing progressed, the frozen material collapsed into the void, breaking the gate structure.

SHORE PROCESSES

Thousands of miles of coastlines were modified by the earthquake, partly by transitory but highly destructive water waves and, more generally and much more permanently, by uplift or subsidence. All but a few reports in this series describe such damage, particularly at inhabited places along the coast. There were, however, comparatively few studies of the coastal processes themselves. The changes in beach-forming processes at Homer Spit, because of their economic importance, were investigated in detail by Stanley (in Waller, 1966a) and by Gronewald and Duncan (1966). Similarly, but for scientific reasons only, stream mouths and beach changes caused by sudden uplift on Montague Island were studied by Kirkby and Kirkby (1969), and the shallow deltaic sediments off the mouth of the Copper River were investigated by Reimnitz and Marshall (1965). The Geological Survey itself made few detailed studies of shore processes (McCulloch, 1966; Waller, 1966a, b) but, with support from the Committee on the Alaska Earthquake, National Academy of Sciences, the Survey persuaded K. W. Stanley (1968) to prepare a general report on this subject based on his own observations and on summaries of the sparse published work of others. Periodic detailed observations over many years would be needed to provide a more complete understanding of the many geologic and biologic adjustments still in progress along the coasts.

All along the coasts, the shoreline began immediately to conform to new relative sea levels. Subsided beaches moved shoreward, building new berms and slopes. Relatively higher tides attacked receding blufflines. Faster erosion

locally scoured source areas for beach nourishment, and thus provided more material to replenish losses caused by subsidence. Streams whose mouths were drowned began to aggrade their beds.

In the uplifted areas, on the other hand, beaches were stranded above tidewater and some surf-cut platforms became terraces or benches. Wave erosion of bluffs was stopped, and bluff recession was slowed to the rate set by subaerial processes. Uplift speeded streamflow, with consequent entrenchment and increased sediment load. New beaches began to form below the abandoned ones.

Within the span of a few minutes, the earthquake caused changes in coastal conditions and processes that normally require centuries. In the subsided areas it also wrought changes that are usually associated only with rare severe storms.

HYDROLOGIC EFFECTS

The hydrologic regimen other than glaciers was studied by fewer investigators than were most other phenomena. Nevertheless, these studies produced much new knowledge. Hydrologic effects possibly were more extensive than any previously observed on the North American continent; quite certainly they were the greatest ever recorded, for fluctuations of surface and ground-water level were measured not only throughout most of North America but in many other parts of the world.

GLACIERS

Glaciers cover about 20 percent of the land area that was violently shaken by the earthquake. Numerous glaciologists and geomorphologists, particularly those who had continuing interests in the life histories of specific glaciers, were eager to study the effects of the earthquake. But aside from the great rock avalanches, surprisingly few effects were observed within the first several years.

Studies added weight to the theory that some rock avalanches descend on a cushion of compressed air (Shreve, 1959, 1966b, 1968). It is also quite clear that the avalanche debris will drastically alter the regimens of the glaciers by insulating the ice surfaces on which they came to rest. Aside from these facts, most of the glacial studies had indecisive results. There were several enormous rockslide avalanches, but no large snow or ice avalanches, and relatively few small ones occurred on glaciers, despite the fact that avalanche hazard was already high at the time of the earthquake (Post, 1967). There were no significant changes in the calving of icebergs from tidewater glaciers, although some glacier fronts were shattered and glacial ice was thrown out onto ice-covered lakes that fronted them (Waller, 1966b). Few changes occurred in glacial streams or ice-dammed lakes. There was no evidence of dynamic response to earthquake shaking or to avalanche loading. The glaciers' response to tectonic uplift, subsidence, or lateral movement was too small to detect, at least during the few years that have been available for study.

By far the most significant conclusion reached by the glaciologists was a refutation of Tarr and Martin's theory (1912) that earthquakes are likely to initiate rapid advances or surges in glaciers by triggering extraordinary numbers of avalanches in the glaciers' alimentation area. Post (1967), on the basis of long-continued studies, thinks that the surges actually

bear no relation to earthquakes. Many such surges involve sudden advances of ice from the upper to the lower parts of glaciers, with little or no advances of the termini. Knowledge that surges did not immediately result from this earthquake does not remove the danger that sudden advances of glaciers from other causes may increase flood hazards to places like Valdez (Coulter and Migliaccio, 1966).

ICE BREAKAGE

In Alaska and nearby Canada, ice was broken on lakes, streams, and bays over an area of more than 100,000 square miles (fig. 1). The cracked ice afforded an easily observed measure of the geographic spread of the earthquake's effects, but otherwise it had minimal significance (Waller, 1966a, b; Plafker and others, 1969). Breakage did little physical damage except to a few beaver houses; in fact, the ice cover on many bodies of water probably diminished the intensity of destructive wave action.

Some of the cracking was caused directly by seismic vibrations, but much more resulted from long-continued seiches, as on Portage Lake (Waller, 1966b) and on Kenai Lake (McCulloch, 1966). Horizontal tectonic movements of the landmass may have been a factor in causing ice breakage in some places. Cracking of ice in lakes and fiords was doubtlessly initiated by subaqueous slides off delta fronts and by the local waves engendered by the slides. Still lacking is a firm explanation as to why the ice on a few lakes and stream segments, even near the earthquake epicenter, was unbroken. Possibly the earthquake vibrations did not coincide with the natural periods of these water bodies, so that there was no buildup of resonance.

GROUND WATER

The surging of water in wells and the temporary or long-lasting changes in water levels as a result of earthquakes have possibly been known ever since man has had wells. Within Alaska these effects from the 1964 earthquake were not much different from those observed in the past, though their magnitudes and durations may have been greater. Over most of the violently shaken area in south-central Alaska, ejection of vast quantities of sediment-laden water through ground fractures lead in places to subsidence of the water-bearing sediments. As described by Waller (1966a, b), the water in many shallow wells surged, with or without permanent changes in level, pump systems failed, and water became turbid. In some of the subsided areas, coastal salt water encroached into some wells. Most of these effects were temporary, but some were permanent or semipermanent.

Many artesian wells were also greatly affected. In several of these wells, at Anchorage for example, artesian-pressure levels dropped as much as 15 feet, either permanently or for several months. Perhaps this change was caused by porosity-increasing grain rearrangements in the aquifers, or by material displacements that permitted freer discharge of water at submarine exposures of the aquifers. Significantly, all such wells were in areas of known or inferred regional horizontal extension and vertical subsidence where porosity-increasing changes must have occurred in the aquifers (Plafker, 1969).

The observations of the earthquake's effects on ground water outside Alaska were of tremendous scientific significance. Other earthquakes have caused fluctuations or disturbances in the ground-water regime at far-distant points, but never before have such effects been noted at as many recording stations and over the entire world (Vorhis, 1967; McGarr and Vorhis, 1968). "Hydroseisms" (a word coined by Vorhis to include all seismically induced water-level fluctuations other than tsunamis) were recorded in more than 700 water wells in Europe, Asia, Africa and Australia, and in all but four of the 50 States. Most records showed only brief fluctuation of the water level, but the fact that about a fourth of them showed either a lasting rise or decline in water level suggests that the earthquake caused a redistribution of strain throughout North America. Especially sensitive well stations recorded both the surface seismic waves that traveled the long way and those that traveled the short way around the globe. Some wells as far away as Georgia were muddied.

SURFACE WATER

Research into the earthquake's effects on surface waters yielded even more significant information than studies related to ground water. Within Alaska the effects were widespread, though they taught little that was new (Waller, 1966 a, b). Seiches dewatered some lakes, fissures in streambeds and lakeshores caused water losses, regional tilting may have reduced the flow of some rivers, and landslides or avalanches blocked or diverted some streams. Recording gages on streams measured seiches like those on lakes. Perhaps the most interesting side effect of local surface-water reaction to the earthquake was the realization that some large Alaskan lakes may be useful as giant tiltmeters for future vertical strain measurements (McCulloch, 1966; Hansen and others, 1966).

The observations of the effects on surface waters outside Alaska also were scientifically illuminating. The worldwide distribution of these effects was first reported by Vorhis (1967); later the findings were elaborated by McGarr and Vorhis (1968) to answer some of the theoretical questions that arose earlier.

Seismic seiches caused by the Alaska earthquake were recorded at more than 850 gaging stations on lakes, ponds, and streams throughout North America and at four stations in Australia. The seiches are believed to be related to the amplitude distribution of short-period seismic surface waves, particularly those having periods that coincide with similar-length oscillation periods of certain bodies of water. They were concentrated in areas underlain by thick soft sediments or where sediment thickness increases abruptly. Major tectonic features exerted a strong control; the Rocky Mountains, for example, provided a wave guide along which seiches were more numerous than to either side.

Preliminary as they are, the findings of McGarr and Vorhis have far-reaching significance in the understanding of the worldwide amplitude distribution of short-period seismic surface waves. Most importantly, McGarr and Vorhis (1968) have shown that records of seiches on surface-water bodies, as measured by the network of water-level recorders that is necessarily much denser than any seismograph network can be, are powerful potential tools in future studies of seismic waves and of earthquake intensities.

Another lesson learned from the earthquake's effects on hydrology was that long-continued records from properly equipped observa-

tion wells and gaging stations are essential to proper interpretation of postearthquake observations.

OCEANOGRAPHIC EFFECTS

Violent waves of diverse kinds and origins wrought havoc along the shores of south-central and southeast Alaska and on the northern Pacific shores from British Columbia to California; they also took most of the lives that were lost. Had the coast been more heavily populated or had the earthquake struck at high tide, damage would have been even more extensive than it was.

The terminology applied to earthquake-generated water waves differs among various authorities, but in this series a general distinction is made between seismic sea waves, or tsunamis, and local waves. Local waves were generated along the coast or in lakes and affected areas of limited extent; they characteristically struck during or immediately after the earthquake. Seismic sea waves, or tsunamis, on the other hand, comprised a train of long-period waves that spread rapidly over the entire Pacific Ocean and struck the Alaskan coast, after shaking had subsided. Locally, seiches, caused by the to-and-fro sloshing of water in partly or wholly confined basins, complicated the overall wave picture.

Within Alaska, there were few instrumentally determined records of the waves, because all nearby tide gages were destroyed or incapacitated. The nature of both seismic sea waves and local waves, therefore, was deduced from the accounts of eyewitnesses, from direct observations of wave effects on shores, and from indirect underwater investigations.

The wave histories at specific communities, and descriptions of their effects, are discussed in reports on Whittier (Kachadoorian, 1965); Valdez (Coulter and Migliaccio, 1966); Homer (Waller, 1966a); Kodiak (Kachadoorian and Plafker, 1967); and Seward (Lemke, 1967).

Wave effects were also studied along most of the shores of Prince William Sound, along the south end of the Kenai Peninsula, and on the Kodiak island group (Plafker and Kachadoorian, 1966; and Plafker and others, 1969). Concurrently oceanographic studies of the effects of slides and waves were being studied in much of Prince William Sound, Resurrection Bay, and Ailiak Bay (G. A. Rusnak, unpublished data).

The history and significance of the seismic sea waves, both near the origin and throughout the Pacific, were investigated by Van Dorn (1964), among others. Though necessarily based in large part on a synthesis of facts collected by others shortly after the earthquake, the exhaustive treatment of all the kinds of waves and of their effects on coastal engineering structures by Wilson and Tørum (1968) is the most comprehensive that has appeared.

LOCAL WAVES

Knowledge of the origin and importance of earthquake-induced local waves, hitherto very sparse, was greatly augmented by studies of the Alaska earthquake. One of the most striking characteristics of the waves was their localized and seemingly erratic distribution, though actually it was the distribution of the causative slides that was erratic, rather than the waves. Furthermore, the local waves struck during the earthquake, or immediately after it, and had generally subsided long before the arrival of the train of seismic sea waves, or tsunamis.

There is much evidence of the genetic relationship of the local waves to subaqueous slides. In general, this evidence consists of (1) wave-damage patterns that radiate from the vicinity of deltaic or morainal deposits, (2) presence of subaerial scarps or oversteepened near-shore slopes, and (3) bathymetric measurements that in-

dicate removal of material from upper parts of slopes and deposition of slide debris in deeper water.

Many of the destructive local waves, however, cannot be attributed with any assurance to subaqueous slides. Some formed in shallow embayments or semi-enclosed basins, where slides are unlikely to have occurred. It seems possible that the horizontal displacement of the landmass may have been either a primary or a contributing cause (Malloy, 1965; Plafker, 1969, and Plafker and others, 1969). Other factors that may have played a part are regional tilt, submarine faulting, and seismic vibrations, but none of these should have caused waves as large as some of those observed. Plafker (1969) has suggested that the long-period high-amplitude seiche waves recorded at Kenai Lake may have been caused primarily by horizontal shift of the lake basin rather than by regional tilt as originally suggested by McCulloch (1966).

"* * * violent local waves * * * generated directly or indirectly by the earthquake at many places throughout the affected area * * * were more destructive than any similar waves ever recorded from previous earthquakes."

The origin of many of the local waves must remain in doubt, but it is known, (1) that violent local waves were generated directly or indirectly by the earthquake at many places throughout the affected area, (2) that, except for the giant waves of Lituya Bay (Miller, 1960), they were more destructive than any similar waves ever recorded from previous earthquakes, and (3) that a basis for predicting the recurrence of some of them exists.

SEISMIC SEA WAVES

The first of a train of seismic sea waves (tsunamis) struck the shores of Kodiak Island, the Kenai Peninsula, and Prince William Sound from 20 to 30 minutes after the earthquake. Succeeding waves, with periods ranging roughly from 1 to 1½ hours, followed during the night—the highest waves of the series commonly striking around midnight near the time of high tide. These waves were generally much lower in amplitude than the locally generated waves, and in some places resembled high fast-moving tides more than they did breaking waves. They flooded large areas and wrecked many vessels and shore installations, particularly where the land had already subsided because of tectonic downdrop or compaction of sediments.

Outside Alaska, the seismic sea waves were measured instrumentally at many stations around the Pacific, even as far away as Antarctica (Donn, 1964; Donn and Posmentier, 1964). The second measurement ever recorded of the passage of a seismic sea wave in the open ocean was made near Wake Island (Van Dorn, 1964). The first such measurement, also made on the gage near Wake Island, recorded the tsunami from the March 9, 1957, earthquake in the Aleutian Trench (Van Dorn, 1959).

The seismic sea waves were generated on the Continental Shelf within the Gulf of Alaska. This was shown clearly by the arrival times of initial waves, the distribution of wave damage, and the orientation of damaged shorelines. Other evidence, such as tide-gage records outside the area affected by the earthquake, demonstrates conclusively that the violent upward tilt of an enormous segment of the sea floor provided the force that initiated the seismic sea waves and oriented the wave train. The waves thus began along the linear belt of maximum tectonic uplift that extends from Montague Island to near Sitkalidak Island, southwest of Kodiak Island (Van Dorn, 1964; Spaeth and Berkman, 1965; Pararas-Carayannis, 1967; Plafker, 1969; Wilson and Tørum, 1968). Most of the shallow Continental Shelf off the coast of south-central Alaska was involved in the upward tilting of the sea floor, which forced a great quantity of water to drain rapidly from the shelf and into deeper water. Reconstruction of the source volume from available data on the area and amount of uplift suggests that the potential energy of the seismic sea waves was of the order of 2×10^{22} ergs, or roughly 0.1 to 0.5 percent of the seismic energy released by the earthquake (Plafker, 1969).

The source area of a train of seismic sea waves and their originating mechanisms were better defined for the Alaska earthquake of 1964 than for most other earthquakes that have been studied. As Van Dorn says (1964), "Never before has sufficient detailed knowledge been obtained on sea-floor motion, type of motion, and the deep-water spectrum offshore, to permit a convincing reconstruction of the generating mechanism." Furthermore, the seismic sea waves generated by the Alaska earthquake largely confirmed empirical-statistical data used by oceanographers to relate the size of the source area and tsunami heights and periods to the energy released by the initiating earthquake (Wilson and Tørum, 1968).

"The first of a train of seismic sea waves (tsunamis) struck the shores of Kodiak Island, the Kenai Peninsula, and Prince William Sound from 20 to 30 minutes after the earthquake. * * * They flooded large areas, and wrecked many vessels and shore installations, particularly where the land had already subsided because of tectonic downdrop or compaction of sediments."

MISCELLANEOUS EFFECTS

The earthquake had many other effects of great economic, sociologic, and biologic importance. These are summarized briefly by Hansen and others (1966) and are treated at length by many writers. There remain a few effects, at least partly related to geology, that are worth noting here.

AUDIBLE AND SUBAUDIBLE EARTHQUAKE SOUNDS

Audible sounds that accompany or even precede the onset of an earthquake have been reported many times in history, but such sounds have never been instrumentally recorded and seldom have they been scientifically authenticated. The Alaska earthquake of 1964 followed the pattern—numerous observers reported hearing sounds, but, so far as is known, no instrumental records were made of these sounds.

On Kodiak Island, several witnesses heard a low-pitched rumbling noise about 5 seconds before the initial tremors were felt. Many Kodiak people also heard deep rumbles just before some of the aftershocks were felt (Plafker and Kachadoorian, 1966). At Homer, too, and at Portage Lake near Turnagain Arm, some people heard rumbling sounds a few seconds before feeling the initial shock. They also heard sounds variously described as rumbling, cracking, and popping during the period of violent earth motion (Waller, 1966 a, b), as well as the windlike noise of rapidly swaying tree branches. Crackling sounds in the ground were heard at South Naknek, 350 miles southwest of the epicenter (Plafker and others, 1969). Observers at Valdez (Coulter and Migliaccio, 1965), in the Copper River Basin (Ferrians,

1966), on the Kenai Peninsula, in Prince William Sound, and at many other places also heard sounds during the quake (Chance, 1966a).

That the Alaska earthquake produced sounds audible to alert observers over a wide area seems a well established fact, though the cause of the sounds has not been determined. In all probability there were many causes, operating at different places and at slightly different times. Cracking or bending of trees, breaking of ice on water bodies or in glaciers, and ground fractures in frozen near-surface soils all probably made audible sounds. How much, if any, of the sound effects can be ascribed to deeper sources, such as breaking of rock along faults in depth or to crunching of sands and gravels as they were consolidated by vibration or as they formed slides on land or under water, is unknown. It seems possible, however, that some of the sounds, particularly those that preceded recognizable ground vibrations, were caused by processes such as these. It also seems possible that the earthquake tremors, coupled to the overlying air envelope, caused audible vibrations. This explanation would apply particularly to the fast-moving, lower amplitude P waves that can often be heard but not felt.

Although audible sound waves are not known to have been recorded, subaudible sound waves were recorded. Waves of very low, subaudible frequencies were recorded by the National Bureau of Standards at stations in Washington, D.C., Boulder, Colo., and Boston, Mass. These sound waves, generated by the earthquake itself and by seismic waves as they passed through the earth, excited the atmosphere. In addition, Rayleigh waves (surface seismic waves)

that displaced the ground created subaudible sound waves that traveled upward, with amplification, to the ionosphere. The resultant oscillation of the ionosphere was detected by means of reflected radio waves (Bolt, 1964; Davies and Baker, 1965; Leonard and Barnes, 1965; Smith, 1966; and Row, 1967).

MAGNETIC EFFECTS

A recording magnetometer in the city of Kodiak recorded several magnetic disturbances a little more than 1 hour before the earthquake struck. Moore (1964) thinks that the magnetic events so recorded may have resulted from piezo-magnetic effects of rocks undergoing a change in stress. He also suggests that magnetic monitoring may provide a means of predicting major earthquakes in time to save lives and property.

VISIBLE SURFACE WAVES

As with audible sound waves, the passage of visible waves over the surface of the ground during strong earthquakes has been reported by many observers. The Alaska earthquake of 1964 was no exception to the general rule; many observers reported seeing ground waves, but their observations were not substantiated instrumentally.

On the Kodiak island group, surface waves reportedly were seen at Ouzinkie and Afognak. These waves, perhaps propagated in ground that had become semifluid with vibration, were estimated at about 30 feet in length and about 3 feet in height (Plafker and Kachadoorian, 1966).

Many people reported seeing surface waves in various parts of the Copper River Basin. At a point 100 miles from the epicenter, the waves were said to be about 10 feet apart and 3 feet high. At

165 miles from the epicenter, they were reported as longer and lower, with lengths of 50 to 60 feet and heights of 18 to 20 inches (Ferrians, 1966).

Perhaps the most reliable observation of surface-wave amplitudes was made by an experienced geologist at Valdez. As quoted by Coulter and Migliaccio (1966), the geologist noticed a 6-foot youth standing 410 feet away from him. As crests passed the youth, he appeared in full sight, with one trough between him and the observer. Passage of troughs caused him to sink partly out of sight. The observations indicate wave heights of 3 to 4 feet and lengths of several hundred feet.

There is no question that many people saw, or thought they saw, waves on the ground surface in many places. Whether all the waves were real or imaginary, and if real, what caused them, must remain subjects for speculation.

PERMAFROST

Because it was one of the few well-studied earthquakes that has affected perenially frozen ground, the 1964 Alaska earthquake added much to our knowledge of the reaction of frozen ground to seismic shock. Permafrost, or perennially frozen ground, has long been a perplexing and exasperating engineering problem in arctic and subarctic regions. The perennially frozen unconsolidated deposits affected by the 1964 quake behaved like solid rock and were far less susceptible to seismic vibration than were similar but unfrozen deposits.

The seismic response of permafrost was studied in detail in the Copper River Basin (Ferrians, 1966). In the basin, most fine-grained sediments are perennially frozen from depths as great as 200 feet to within 1 to 5 feet of the sur-face, except beneath cleared areas where the top of the permafrost is 10 to 20 feet deep. Coarse-grained deposits along the major streams and deposits close to large deep lakes generally are free of permafrost.

There were no ground cracks and little or no vibration damage of any kind where permafrost approaches the surface. Thus ice-rich perennially frozen ground apparently behaved much like bedrock in transmitting and reacting to earthquake shocks. However, perched ground water between permafrost and the seasonally frozen layer at the surface caused some fissuring and other evidences of vibration.

CABLE BREAKS

Several underwater cables were broken by the earthquake vibrations or by subaqueous slides. The only one broken in the heavily devastated area was the Federal Aviation Agency cable under Beluga Lake at Homer (Waller, 1966a). This break was probably caused by vibration, for the lake is shallow and there is no evidence of off-shore-slides.

The Southeastern Alaska coaxial submarine cable was broken at a point 19½ miles south of Skagway, in Lynn Canal, near the mouth of the Katzehin River; a similar break occurred in this area as a result of the 1958 earthquake. The 1964 break occurred early on the morning of March 28 and was apparently caused by a submarine slide in silt that was triggered by the seismic sea wave (Lt. Col. Alexander Alvarado, USAF, written commun. to George Plafker, May 1, 1964).

Near Port Alberni, British Columbia, the Commonwealth Pacific Communication Service cable from Port Alberni to Hawaii was ruptured. This break occurred only 2 minutes after the onset of the earthquake and was evidently caused by seismic vibrations. The cables between Port Angeles, Washington, and Ketchikan and between Ketchikan and Sitka were unaffected (Comdr. H. G. Conerly, U.S. Coast and Geodetic Survey, oral commun. to George Plafker, May 1964).

TUNNELS, MINES, AND DEEP WELLS

One aspect of the earthquake's effects on manmade structures that deserves further study is the fact that no significant damage has been reported to underground openings in bedrock such as tunnels, mines, and deep wells, although some rocks and earth were shaken loose in places. The Alaska Railroad tunnel near Whittier (McCulloch and Bonilla, 1970) and the coal mines in the Matanuska Valley (Plafker and others, 1969) were undamaged. The tunnel and penstocks at the Eklutna hydroelectric project were damaged only by cobbles and boulders that were washed through the intake structures (Logan, 1967). A small longitudinal crack in the concrete floor of the Chugach Electric Association tunnel between Cooper Lake and Kenai Lake is believed to have been caused by the earthquake (Fred O. Jones, oral commun., 1967).

The collars of some drilled wells were displaced by vibration or by consolidation of adjacent soils, and a few water wells and one abandoned exploratory oil well near Yakataga were sheared off. There are, however, no reports of damage to any wells that were more than a few hundred feet deep, such as the many oil and gas wells in and along Cook Inlet. In and near the landslide areas in Anchorage, most sewers and other underground utility lines were extensively fractured or displaced (Burton, in Logan, 1967; Hansen, 1965; Eckel, 1967; McCulloch and Bonilla, 1970). Ground fissures also broke many buried pipelines in Seward (Lemke, 1967) and elsewhere. In Valdez, Coulter and Migliaccio (1966) were able to use the horizontal separation of water lines to measure the amount of lateral displacement back of the main submarine slide. Elsewhere, pipelines that traversed unfissured ground received little or no damage.

ARCHEOLOGIC REMAINS

Regional and local subsidence of Kodiak Island, as elsewhere, resulted in increased erosion of some sediments along the shore. In a few places near Ouzinkie, erosion exposed rich accumulations of stone and bone artifacts mixed with bones of sea animals. The archeologic remains occur at two horizons, separated by dark soil. Apparently they belong to the Aleut or Koniag cultures, but some may be older (Chaffin, 1966). Elsewhere in the Kodiak group of islands, many coastal archeological sites in subsided areas were made inaccessible or were subjected to accelerated erosion (Plafker and Kachadoorian, 1966).

EARTHQUAKE EFFECTS, GEOLOGY AND DAMAGE

The earthquake took 130 lives and caused more than $300 million in damage to manmade structures. Details are not recounted here, but an attempt is made to relate the loss of life and the structural damage to the earthquake and its effects, especially as these effects were modified by local geology and terrain.

Aside from a number of casualties that resulted from airplane and other accidents during the reconstruction period, all casualties to living creatures resulted either directly from the earth tremors and tectonic displacements or indirectly from water waves generated by them. Ground motion caused structural damage primarily by (1) direct shaking of some structures, (2) triggering landslides and subaqueous slides, (3) cracking underlying unconsolidated deposits, and (4) consolidating and subsiding loose sediments. The violent local waves that accompanied or followed most subaqueous slides were major indirect effects. Subaqueous slides and waves were together responsible for spreading the few major fires that had already started in petroleum storage areas. These fires, incidentally, taught another important lesson. In earthquake-prone regions, petroleum-storage tanks are especially vulnerable to earthquake vibrations; to the extent possible, they should be placed away from built-up areas and should be protected by revetments to avoid spreading of fires (Rinne, 1967).

Tectonic ground displacements, both up and down, caused long-term damage to coastal communities and shoreline facilities, either directly by changing the shore relative to sea level or indirectly by the seismic sea waves generated. In addition, widespread horizontal tectonic movements may have generated some of the destructive local waves. Local waves and seismic sea waves together took most of the human lives that were lost.

"Subaqueous slides and waves were together responsible for spreading the few major fires that had already started in petroleum storage areas."

GEOLOGIC CONTROL OF VIBRATION DAMAGE

The long-known fact that the intensity and duration of earthquake vibrations are enhanced in unconsolidated water-saturated ground was evident in the distribution of vibration damage in Alaska. The varied intensity and effect of shaking were much more closely related to the local geology than to distance from the epicenter. In general, intensity was greatest in areas underlain by thick saturated unconsolidated deposits, least on indurated bedrock, and intermediate on coarse gravel with low water table, on morainal deposits, or on moderately indurated sedimentary rocks of late Tertiary age.

Nowhere was there significant vibration damage to structures founded on indurated bedrock or on bedrock that was only thinly veneered by unconsolidated deposits. Where direct comparisons could be made, as at Whittier (Kachadoorian, 1965) and Cordova (Plafker and others, 1969), the difference in the behavior of buildings on bedrock and of those on loose material was striking.

Distance from the epicenter, too, had far less influence on the intensity of vibration damage than did the local geology. Buildings on bedrock that were only 12 to 25 miles from the instrumental epicenter were undamaged except for jostled contents (Plafker and others, 1969), and the ice on some small rock-enclosed lakes in this vicinity was not even cracked (Waller, 1966b). Buildings at Anchorage, however, more than 75 miles away from the epicenter but founded on unconsolidated materials, were demolished by earthquake vibrations (Hansen, 1965). Some structural damage resulted from shaking at even greater distances.

The lack of coincidence between structural damage and distance from the epicenter is partly explained by the fact that the generally accepted instrumental epicenter marks only one of several widely scattered points directly beneath which strong motion was centered at various moments during the history of the earthquake (Wyss and Brune, 1967). Moreover, selective damage to larger and taller buildings at Anchorage is attributed by Steinbrugge (1964) to the fact that longer period large-amplitude ground motions are dominant at some distance from earthquake epicentral regions, in contrast to the short-period motions that characterize close-in localities.

Locally, seismic vibrations caused minor structural damage to communities situated on late Tertiary sediments or on unconsolidated materials with low water table on the Kenai Peninsula, the west shore of Cook Inlet, in the Matanuska Valley, and elsewhere (Waller, 1966b; Plafker and others, 1969).

By far the most severe vibratory damage to buildings or to highway and railroad roadbeds and bridges occurred in areas of relatively thick, noncohesive unconsolidated deposits, generally where the materials were fine grained and where the water table was close to the surface. Anchorage, the Alaska transportation systems (Kachadoorian, 1968; McCulloch and Bonilla, 1970), the FAA station on the Copper River Delta, and Girdwood and Portage on Turnagain Arm (Plafker and others, 1969) are examples of sites of such vibratory damage. At most of these places, and many others, more damage resulted from foundation failure than from direct vibration of buildings. Ground cracks, differential compaction, and liquefaction of saturated materials accompanied by landspreading toward topographic depressions all were contributory factors.

"Buildings at Anchorage, however, more than 75 miles away from the epicenter but founded on unconsolidated materials, were demolished by earthquake vibrations."

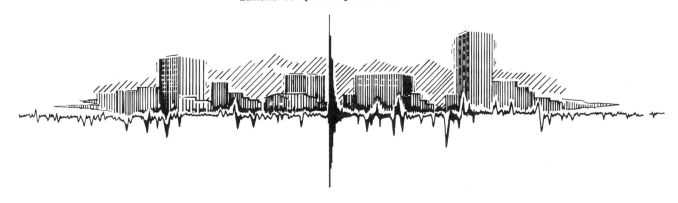

SURFACE FAULTS

From the standpoint of public safety, perhaps the most important bit of knowledge that was re-emphasized by the Alaska earthquake is that faults, with breakage and displacement of surface materials, are relatively minor causes of widespread earthquake damage. In Alaska, of course, there were no fault displacements in populated places. The only displacements on land were on uninhabited Montague Island in Prince William Sound, though there is good reason to believe that rocks on the sea floor were broken and displaced for a long distance southwestward of the island (Malloy, 1964; Plafker, 1967). Aside from the destruction and death dealt by sea waves, all of the damage was done by seismic vibration or its direct consequences.

The lesson is clear for all communities in earthquake-prone regions that the presence of an active fault, such as the San Andreas in California, constitutes only one of the dangers from future earthquakes. Delineations of such faults and predictions as to where, how, and when they may move are essential, for they may very well localize areas of great destruction when an earthquake strikes. The lesson of the Alaska earthquake, however, is that no one can take comfort simply because he, his home, or his town is some distance removed from an active fault or from the possible epicenter of a future earthquake. The foundation on which he builds is far more significant.

LANDSLIDES

Translatory slides at Anchorage (Hansen, 1966) and subaqueous slides at Whittier (Kachadoorian, 1965), Valdez (Coulter and Migliaccio, 1966), Seward (Lemke, 1967), and elsewhere were all caused indirectly by seismic vibrations, though horizontal tectonic displacement of the land may have been a factor in starting some of them. All of these slides were in soft, saturated unconsolidated materials in which the vibration caused sufficient loss of strength to make preearthquake slopes unstable. Such materials were consolidated to some extent by vibration, but it is doubtful that consolidation was sufficient to make any of the materials significantly less prone to failure in the event of future earthquakes.

Many of the violent local waves were generated by known subaqueous slides, either as backfills of the space left by the downslid material or on opposite shores where the spreading slide material pushed water ahead of it (McCulloch, 1966). Subaqueous slides that occurred as a series of small slumps apparently did not generate waves. Many of the other local waves that developed around the shores of Prince William Sound are suspected to have been caused by subaqueous slides, though some that struck the shores of fiords and semienclosed embayments must have had other causes.

VERTICAL TECTONIC DISPLACEMENTS AND SEISMIC SEA WAVES

Tectonic uplift and subsidence of the land relative to sea level wrought much long-term damage, either by inundating shore installations or by raising them above all but the highest tides. These effects were independent of local geologic conditions, except where the net amount of submergence or emergence was affected by vibration-caused surficial subsidence of unconsolidated sediments. Homer Spit (Waller, 1966a) and several communities on the Kodiak group of islands (Kachadoorian and Plafker, 1967) provided good examples of submergence resulting from both tectonic and surficial subsidence. Seldovia (Eckel, 1967), Hope, Girdwood, Portage, and several other towns (Plafker and others, 1969) all underwent tectonic subsidence; remedial raising or relocation of buildings, roadways, and wharves was necessary.

In Prince William Sound, where the land was tectonically raised, dredging of harbors and lengthening of piers were necessary to compensate for the lower

"Translatory slides at Anchorage and subaqueous slides * * * elsewhere were all caused indirectly by seismic vibrations, though horizontal tectonic displacement of the land may have been a factor in starting some."

relative water levels. Cordova, Hinchinbrook Island, and Tatitlek were the places most affected (Eckel, 1967; Plafker and others, 1969).

Of far greater importance than the tectonic uplift and subsidence, so far as damage was concerned, was an indirect effect—the generation of seismic sea waves (tsunamis) by the sudden uplift of a large expanse of the ocean floor. Besides the damage they did to Alaska, the tsunamis struck southward as far as California. They took 12 lives and wrecked the waterfront at Crescent City, Calif., and did appreciable damage to shore facilities as far away as Hawaii.

Local geologic conditions had little effect on the amount of damage caused by seismic sea waves, though local topography, both above and below water, was of great importance in guiding and refracting the waves and controlling their runups. One local geologic complication of sea-wave damage was in the Kodiak harbor; here strong currents generated by the tsunami scoured all unconsolidated material from the bedrock floor, making pile driving difficult or impossible (Kachadoorian and Plafker, 1967).

GROUND AND SURFACE WATER HYDROLOGY

Local geology helped control the earthquake's effects on water. In areas underlain by unconsolidated deposits where ground fissures occurred, there was temporary loss of water in the floors of some lakes and streams, or ground water was emitted from beneath the surface through mudspouts and waterspouts. In some places, ejected ground water flooded valley floors (McCulloch and Bonilla, 1970). Vibration caused rearrangement of particles in aquifers, with resultant surges in wells and temporary or permanent changes in water levels. Regional or local subsidence led to intrusion of sea water in some coastal aquifers.

Regional geology, too, to a large extent controlled the earthquake's effects on hydrologic systems, as shown in the conterminous United States, where McGarr and Vorhis (1968) found that seiches in wells and bodies of surface water were controlled by geologic structures of regional or continental dimensions.

BENEFICIAL EFFECTS OF THE EARTHQUAKE

SOCIOECONOMIC BENEFITS

Devastating as was the Alaska earthquake of March 27, 1964, it had many long-term beneficial effects. Most of these benefits were in the fields of socioeconomics and engineering and are only mentioned briefly here.

Economically, the Federal monies and other funds spent for reconstruction exceeded the total damage cost of the earthquake, largely because of decisions to upgrade or enlarge facilities beyond their preearthquake condition.

Many improvements resulted from the aid poured into reconstruction. One whole town, Valdez, was razed and rebuilt on a more stable site; the area of one of the most disastrous landslides in the business heart of Anchorage was permanently stabilized by a gigantic earth buttress; new and better port facilities were provided in all the affected seacoast towns; the fishing fleet acquired, under very favorable financial terms, new boats and modern floating or land-based canneries. The pattern of rail-sea transport was drastically changed, partly because of the discovery that the port of Anchorage could actually be used year-round, despite the ice in Knik Arm that had hitherto closed it in winter. (This change of pattern, of course, was hardly a benefit to Seward and Valdez.) Forced by pressures of reconstruction, builders learned that plastic tents over their buildings permitted construction work to continue during the sub-Arctic winter. These and many other direct benefits from the earthquake are summarized by George and Lyle and by Chance (in Hansen and others, 1966).

One of the more important social-political-economic developments was use by the Federal Government of a new device to channel and control reconstruction and rehabilitation aid: The Federal Reconstruction and Development Commission for Alaska represented both the legislative and the executive arms of Government and included the heads of all Federal agencies that had a part to play in the reconstruction effort. One of the Commission's offspring, the Scientific and Engineering Task Force, brought soils and structural engineers, geologists and seismologists together in an effort to apply

"Many improvements resulted from the aid poured into reconstruction. One whole town, Valdez, was razed and rebuilt on a more stable site."

their combined skills to guide decisions as to land use (Eckel and Schaem, in Hansen and others, 1966). The many opportunities that were provided by the reconstruction effort for team work and mutual understanding between engineers and earth scientists were themselves among the more valuable byproduct benefits of the earthquake. In addition, scientists learned much that helps toward a better understanding of earthquake mechanisms and effects and how to investigate them. They also learned many new basic facts about the structural and historical geology and the hydrology of a large part of south-central Alaska. Some of these scientific benefits from the earthquake and its investigation are worthy of brief mention.

DIRECT GEOLOGIC BENEFITS

Truly beneficial direct geologic effects of the earthquake were few. Navigation conditions and harbor facilities were improved in a few places by tectonic uplift or subsidence, and tidewater and beach lands were improved or extended. For example, the subsidence that led to tidal flooding of Homer Spit also exposed new deposits of material to erosion, with the result that the spit began at once to heal itself and to build new storm berms (Stanley, in Waller, 1966a; Stanley, 1968). Landslide hazards were averted, at least for some years to come, by uplift of Hinchinbrook Island; elsewhere imminent landslides and avalanches that might well have harmed people or property later were harmlessly triggered by the earthquake. Though the direct physical benefits of the earthquake were few, the earth sciences benefitted greatly from the intensive investigations of it. The knowledge thus gained added not only to the general fund of human knowledge; more importantly, it created an awareness of many potential hazards, previously unrecognized or ignored, both in Alaska and in other earthquake-prone areas, and of how to apply earth-science knowledge to reduce such hazards.

SCIENTIFIC BENEFITS

NEW AND CORROBORATIVE GEOLOGIC AND HYDROLOGIC INFORMATION

One of the richest rewards of the earthquake study lay in the additions to geological and hydrologic knowledge and in corroborations of existing theory. The myriad observations essential to understanding the effects of the Alaska earthquake threw much new light on earthquake processes and earthquake effects in general. In addition, the investigations added greatly to our scientific knowledge of a large part of Alaska. Some of the knowledge so produced might never have come to light under ordinary circumstances. Other discoveries were advanced by many years under the earthquake-generated acceleration of basic investigations.

The earthquake investigations led to better understanding of the regional tectonics of south-central Alaska. The regional gravity field was better defined than it had been before, and it was reevaluated in terms of its relation to the underlying geology and to changes caused by the earthquake. Data, hitherto unavailable, were provided on the seismicity of the region. Knowledge of the structure and age of the rocks was greatly expanded. Thanks to the need to understand the vertical tectonic displacements caused by the earthquake, new knowledge was obtained on the history of submergence and emergence throughout Holocene time. Field evidence was augmented by many new radiocarbon datings. Reconnaissance marine geological and geophysical studies were undertaken over much of the Continental Shelf, slope, and contiguous deep-sea floor. These studies have materially increased our understanding of the submarine areas.

Detailed geologic maps became available for most of the affected cities and towns. Strip geologic maps along the ramifying rail and highway net provided a skeleton control of geologic knowledge of a wide area, particularly as to the distribution and nature of the unconsolidated deposits on which man does most of his building.

Accurate and abundant geodetic control, on stable ground, is essential for evaluating tectonic movements in the mobile belts of the world; the earthquake of 1964 gave impetus to establishment of such control. For a significant part of Alaska itself, better geodetic control resulted from the earthquake-caused need for accurate triangulation and leveling and for establishment of tidal bench marks and tide gages. These data will be invaluable in any studies of future tectonic dislocations of the land surface.

Support for the hypothesis that some great landslides and avalanches travel on cushions of compressed air came from the earthquake studies. Conversely, evidence was brought to light that tends to discount a widely held theory of glacial advance as a result of earthquakes (Tarr and Martin, 1912).

One kind of landslide that has received little attention in the past from geologists and engineers—the translatory slide that was so disastrous in Anchorage—is now well understood, although extrapolation of the knowledge gained to future earthquakes will still be extremely difficult. Extensive stud-

ies led to the beginning of an explosion of new knowledge on the behavior of sensitive clays and sands under dynamic conditions. A minor byproduct of the Anchorage landslide studies was the discovery of microfossils that shed new light on the environmental conditions under which the Bootlegger Cove Clay was laid down, hitherto a puzzling point for geologists. Other byproducts of these studies were (1) production of detailed topographic maps of highly complex landslide areas and (2) development of the "graben rule" (Hansen, 1965) by which the depth to the sliding plane of a translatory slide can be easily and rather accurately estimated.

Too little study was made of the response of shore processes to sudden changes in relative sea levels, but many bits of useful information were discovered nevertheless.

The shape, character, and stability of fiord deltas built to deep water is now better known than before as a result of intensive geologic, soils, hydrographic, and hydrologic studies both on land and under water. Such studies were essential to an understanding of

"* * * the translatory slide that was so disastrous in Anchorage is now well understood, although extrapolation of the knowledge gained to future earthquakes will still be extremely difficult."

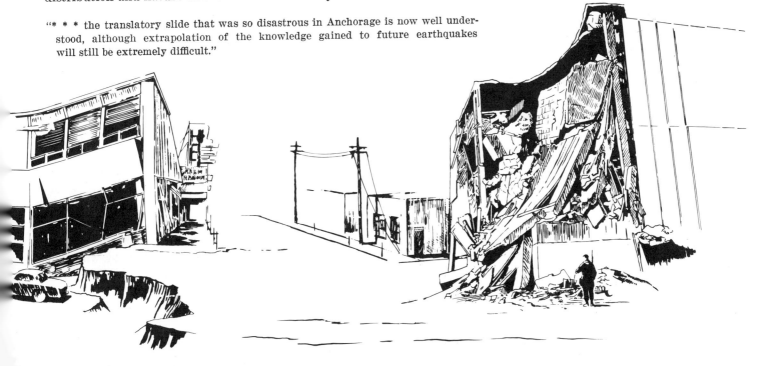

the destructive subaqueous slides that had been almost unknown as important effects of great earthquakes.

Knowledge of the water resources of south-central Alaska was increased by earthquake-prompted studies of ground and surface waters; much new information also came to light as to the relations between earthquake-caused ground fissures and local water tables. The study of hydroseisms, or seiches and surges in surface-water bodies and wells, throughout the world produced greater understanding of the relation of hydrology to seismology.

Seismic sea waves, or tsunamis, have been studied intensively for many years because of the dangers they hold for coastal communities. The Alaska earthquake of 1964, however, presented an unparalleled opportunity to relate the source, generation, and propagation of a sea-wave train to measurable tectonic dislocations of the crust.

NEW AND IMPROVED INVESTIGATIVE TECHNIQUES

Virtually all investigative techniques known to earth scientists were applied in studies of the Alaska earthquake. Some, such as scuba diving, bathymetric surveys, and use of helicopters and fixed-wing aircraft were, of course, not new, but their widespread application to specific earthquake-connected problems was either new or little-used in the past. Many unorthodox photogrammetric, engineering, biological, and geodetic techniques and data were applied in the attempts to appraise pre-earthquake conditions in areas of poor horizontal and vertical control.

Some of these techniques, discussed briefly below, were new to Alaska or to individual investiga-

tors assigned there. A secondary result of the earthquake investigations of no mean significance, therefore, was the development of a large cadre of experienced and technologically well-equipped scientists who will be available for knowledgeable investigations of future great earthquakes.

Of utmost importance for the future is the fact that the knowledge gained from the Alaskan experience can be adapted by the scientific community to underline possible hazards in other earthquake-prone areas. Thus, it should be possible to relate ground conditions to urban planning, zoning regulations, and building codes in such a manner to forestall or minimize future earthquake disasters.

USES OF RECORDING GAGES

The records from continuously recording gages served purposes not originally intended. A water-level gage at the power station on Kenai Lake, for example, enabled McCulloch (1966) to make a precise study of seiche action in a closed basin and to draw conclusions of far-reaching importance. Again, fluctuations in the recording of an automatic outside-air temperature recorder at Whittier gave a rough measure of the duration of earthquake vibrations there (Kachadoorian, 1965). Stream gages on Kodiak Island, designed to measure the levels of flowing streams, suddenly became excellent recorders of wave runup and even served as tide gages when the mouths of streams on which they were installed were brought within the reach of tides by local and regional subsidence (Plafker and Kachadoorian, 1966; Waller, 1966b). By far the most significant extension of knowledge of the usefulness of recording gages came from the study of hy-

droseisms in wells and on surface waters on continent-wide or even larger bases. Investigations showed that, among other results, a network of recording water-level gages can act as a valuable adjunct to the worldwide seismograph network. It was also shown that any earthquake near a coast that is capable of causing as great fluctuations as that recorded by the Nunn-Bush well in Wisconsin is also capable of generating a seismic sea wave (Vorhis, 1967; McGarr and Vorhis, 1968).

TELEVISION FOR UNDERGROUND OBSERVATIONS

A novel application of television to the mapping of cracks in buried utilities—and incidentally of fractures or fault displacements in the surrounding soil—is described by Burton (in Logan, 1967). To avoid costly excavation of buried utility systems, a small-diameter borehole television camera was drawn through the ducts. Cracks were clearly visible and easily measured; their location and the amount and direction of offset of the ducts added materially to the general knowledge gained from other sources as to the character of ground movements in the Anchorage landslide areas.

LAKES AS TILTMETERS

Kenai Lake was the only long lake that happened to have bench marks at both ends; hence McCulloch (1966) was able to use it as a unique giant tiltmeter. It gave a permanent record of landwarping caused by the earthquake. McCulloch's method of comparing the preearthquake height of the lake surface with preearthquake bench marks at the two ends of the lake necessarily left some ambiguity in the measurements because of difficulty in locating the preearthquake bench marks accurately, but it left no doubt whatever

"Measurement of the displacement of intertidal sessile marine organisms emerged as one of the most useful techniques for determining vertical tectonic movements along coasts."

that the Kenai Lake basin was tilted westward about 3 feet. As a direct outgrowth of the earthquake investigations, and in order to monitor future crustal changes in south-central Alaska, a network of permanent bench marks has now been established on the shores of 17 large lakes within a 500-mile radius of Anchorage. These bench marks were referenced to the water levels of the lakes so that the direction and amount of any tilting can be obtained from periodic monitoring (Hansen and Eckel, 1966). A systematic study of these lake levels was started by D. S. McCulloch and Arthur Grantz in the summer of 1966 (written commun., 1968).

MEASUREMENT OF LAND-LEVEL CHANGES

Measurement of the displacement of intertidal sessile marine organisms emerged as one of the most useful techniques for determining vertical tectonic movements along coasts. The technique had been used elsewhere, by Tarr and Martin (1912), for example, who studied the effects of the Yakutat Bay earthquake of 1899. With the aid of Dr. G Dallas Hanna, a marine biologist of the California Academy of Sciences, however, the method was greatly refined and was applied by Plafker and his associates after the Alaska earthquake of March 27, 1964, to a far larger area than ever before (Plafker, 1969).

The deeply indented rocky coast of the area affected by the 1964 earthquake was ideal for application of the method. The common acorn barnacle (*Balanus balanoides* (Linnaeus)), which is widely distributed and forms a prominent band with a sharply defined upper limit relative to tide level, was used in hundreds of "barnacle-line" measurements; in its absence the common olive-green rockweed (*Fucus distichus*) was almost equally useful. The normal preearthquake upper growth limit of barnacles and rockweed relative to mean lower low water was determined empirically for the range of tidal conditions in the area at 17 localities

where the amount of vertical displacement was known from pre- and post-earthquake tide-gage readings. Departures of the post-earthquake barnacle line from its normal altitude above mean lower low water was taken as the amount of vertical displacement at any given place along the shore. By this method, absolute land-level changes could generally be measured to an accuracy within 1 foot; even under unfavorable circumstances, the error is probably less than 2 feet.

Other methods of determining land-level changes along the coasts and elsewhere were also employed. Changes in gravity, as determined before and after the earthquake with the same instrument, were used by Barnes (1966) in computing elevation changes. In subsided areas, it was noted that wells became brackish, vegetation was killed by invasion of salt water, beach berms and stream deltas were shifted landward and built up to higher levels, and roads or other installations along the shores were inundated by the tides. In tectonically uplifted areas, indications of uplift include new reefs and islands, raised sea cliffs, and surf-cut platforms. Wherever feasible, the method used was the most accurate known—comparison of pre- and postearthquake tide-gage readings at accurately placed tidal bench marks of the U.S. Coast and Geodetic Survey. Even where gages were destroyed, some bench marks were recoverable and new series of readings could be made to determine land-level changes. Unfortunately, there were only a few permanent automatic recording gages in south-central Alaska, and also many tidal bench marks were on unconsolidated deposits where ties to bedrock were difficult or impossible to reestablish.

DISTINCTION BETWEEN LOCAL AND REGIONAL SUBSIDENCE

Clear distinctions between local subsidence caused by compaction of sediments and more widespread subsidence caused by tectonic downdrop of the region are not always easy to make. One technique used by Plafker and Kachadoorian (1966) on Kodiak and the nearby islands was to note the difference in amount of inundation of unconsolidated shoreline features as compared with nearby rock outcrops. The lowering of the rock cliffs, as measured by barnacle lines or other means, represents tectonic subsidence, whereas the lowering of beaches and delta surfaces represents a combination of tectonic subsidence and local compaction. By using a similar technique—measuring differences in the heights of piles whose tops were originally level—Plafker and Kachadoorian were able to distinguish between local compaction-subsidence of beach deposits and tectonic downdrop.

Casings of deep wells may also be helpful in distinguishing local and regional subsidence. Near the end of Homer Spit, for example, the top of a well casing that had previously been a known height above the ground stood several feet higher after the earthquake. Such protrusion could only have been caused by compaction and subsidence of the unconsolidated materials around the casing, for regional subsidence would have carried the casing down along with the land surface (Grantz and others, 1964, fig. 6).

EVIDENCE OF WAVE ACTION AND RUNUP

As part of their studies of wave-damaged shorelines, various investigators made extensive use of natural materials that indicated the relative intensity and movement direction of waves (McCulloch, 1966; Plafker and others, 1969; Plafker and Kachadoorian, 1966). Runup heights were determined from strandlines of wave-deposited debris, abraded bark or broken branches in vegetation along the shore, and water stains on snow or structures. Movement directions of the waves could be inferred from the gross distribution of damage along shores, the directions in which limbs and trunks of trees and brush were scarred, bent, and broken off, and the directions in which objects such as buoys, structures, and shoreline deposits were displaced. To aid in comparative studies of wave-damaged shorelines along the coast, Plafker and Mayo devised a scale of relative magnitude of wave damage (Plafker and others, 1969)—a scale which was also used by McCulloch and Mayo (McCulloch, 1966) in modified form for plotting wave damage along the shore of Kenai Lake. The magnitude scale evolved is summarized below in order of increasing damage.

Wave-magnitude scale

[After Plafker and others, 1969, pl. 2]

1. Brush combed and scoured in direction of wave travel. Small limbs broken and minor scarring of trees. Runup heights only a few feet above extreme high-water level. Some wooden structures floated from foundations.

2. Trees and limbs less than 2 inches in diameter broken. Small trees uprooted. Driftwood and finer beach deposits thrown up above extreme high-water level. Piling swept from beneath some structures and wooden structures

"As part of their studies of wave-damaged shorelines, * * * investigators made * * * use of * * * materials that indicated the * * * intensity and * * * direction of waves * * *"

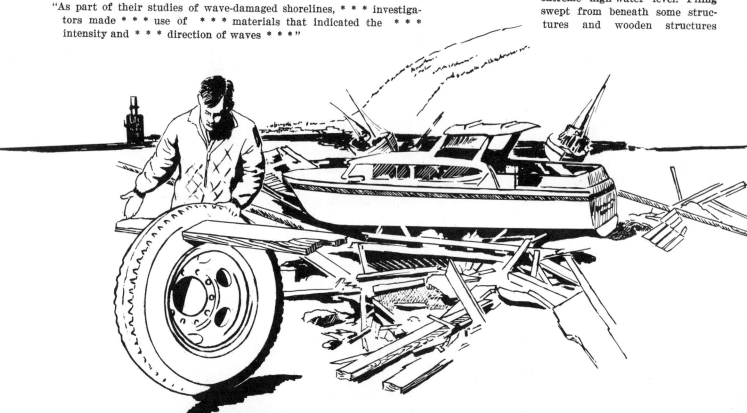

floated off their foundations. Runup reached about 25 feet on steep shores.

3. Trees and limbs as much as 8 inches in diameter broken; some large trees overturned. Rocks to cobble size eroded from intertidal zones and deposited above extreme high-water level. Soil stripped from bedrock areas. All inundated structures except those of reinforced concrete destroyed or floated away. Heavy machinery moved about. Maximum runup height 55 feet.

4. Trees larger than 8 inches in diameter broken, uprooted, and overturned. Boulders thrown above extreme high-water line. Loose rocks on cliffs moved. All struc-rocks and equipment damaged or destroyed in inundated areas. Maximum runup height 70 feet.

5. Extensive areas of total destruction of vegetation. Boulders deposited 50 feet or more above normal extreme high-water level. Maximum runup height 170 feet.

Using a wave-magnitude numbering system modified from an early version of Plafker and Mayo, to allow for the additional damage caused by ice, McCulloch (1966) mapped the distribution of intensity and maximum runup of waves on the shores of Kenai Lake. The highest runup measured there was 72 feet, where a wave struck a steep bank. By measuring the upper limit of wave damage to trees in the direction of wave travel, McCulloch also was able to show the history of the wave crests that overran several deltas.

CONCLUSIONS

SCIENTIFIC PREPARATION FOR FUTURE EARTHQUAKES

FUNDAMENTAL RESEARCH

Much more research is needed on the origins and mechanisms of earthquakes, on crustal structure and makeup, and on generation and prediction of tsunamis, local waves, and seiches. Better theoretical and experimental means of determining focal mechanisms are particularly needed, not only for scientific reasons but to aid earth scientists and structural engineers in relating focal mechanisms to ground motion and in relating the response of buildings to seismic shock. Study is needed too on all phases of rock and soil mechanics, with emphasis on the causes and nature of rock fracture in the earth's interior, on the response of different rocks to strong seismic motion, and on the behavior of soils under dynamic loading.

Well-conceived research in any of these fields is certain to show results that apply to the overall earthquake problem. Existing research projects should be supported, and new ones, designed to fill the gaps in existing knowledge, should be sought out and encouraged. In-depth studies by such groups as the Federal Council for Science and Technology (1968) have clearly defined the needs. The rate of accomplishment of research, however, is far less than it should be. It cannot be too strongly recommended that funds be provided as soon as possible to support these necessary research programs.

EARTHQUAKE FORECASTING AND EVALUATION OF EARTHQUAKE HAZARDS

An ability to predict precisely the time, place, and magnitude of future earthquakes would represent an accomplishment of the greatest importance and significance to the scientific community. Because of the sociologic, political, and economic consequences that would result from erroneous predictions, and because useful results seem to be more easily attainable, it is believed that more attention should be directed, initially, toward forecasting in terms of the probability of earthquakes of certain magnitude ranges within seismic regions, rather than as to the exact time when the next earthquake may be expected at a specific place. Every forward step will be directly applicable to the development of better and more detailed earthquake-hazard maps based on improved knowledge of regional geology, fault behavior, and earthquake mechanisms. Hopefully, each step will also lead to better guides for land-use planning, hence to closer control of new construction in areas of potential earthquake hazards.

One step toward useful forecasting of future earthquakes that should be taken at once is the preparation of earthquake-hazard maps. Such maps should be based in part on detailed knowledge of active faults and their behavior during historic and geologic times, as well as on recent instrumental observations of earthquakes and fault movements. Although an earlier version was adopted by the International Conference of Building Officials, by military construction agencies, and by some State and local governments, the official seismic risk map of the United States (U.S. Coast and Geodetic Survey, 1969) is too lacking in detail to be of value for other than very broad planning.

Preparation of useful earthquake-hazard maps, on whatever scale, will require close collaboration of earthquake engineers, seismologists, and geologists. These maps are essential to local and regional planning officials and to all others who are involved in formulation of plans for coping with earthquakes; their preparation should begin at once. They are, perhaps, especially needed by building-code officials and by designers of earthquake-resistant structures, for the response of foundation materials to seismic loads and the interactions between foundation and structure are just as important as antiseismic design of the structure. Such maps should be revised periodically as more geologic and seismic data become available.

GEOLOGIC MAPPING OF COMMUNITIES

Within the area that was tectonically elevated or depressed by the Alaska earthquake, virtually all inhabited places were damaged or devastated, though the kind, amount, and causes of damage varied widely. Unfortunately, the very features that make a site desirable for building are often the ones that make it subject to earthquake damage.

Ports, docks, and canneries obviously have to be built close to the shore. But the Alaskan experience indicates that the hazards are enormously compounded if such facilities are built on steep-faced deltas or other deposits of unconsolidated materials that are marginally stable under seismic conditions. At many places, such deposits offer the only level surfaces near tidewater for easy or economical construction. If they must be utilized, advance knowledge that they are vulnerable to future

"* * * the hazards are enormously compounded if [port, dock, and cannery] facilities are built on steep-faced deltas * * * that are marginally stable under seismic conditions. * * * If [such sites] must be utilized, knowledge that they are vulnerable to future earthquakes may stimulate planning to minimize the hazards."

earthquakes may stimulate planning to minimize the hazards.

The same reasoning applies to earthquake hazards inland. If all towns, railroads, and highways could be built on bedrock, they would be in comparatively little danger from any earthquake effects except surface faults, floods, or avalanches. There would be vibration damage, of course, but much less of it than on materials other than solid rock. Unfortunately, building sites on bedrock are scarce and tend to be economically infeasible, particularly in rugged terrain like Alaska's. Man must therefore often build on less stable terrain, including water-saturated unconsolidated sediments, on potentially unstable slopes, and on or near active faults. Even though it is necessary to build in earthquake-vulnerable areas, builders and planners should recognize the potential hazard in advance and build accordingly.

A vigorous program of geologic mapping should therefore be carried out in all inhabited earthquake-prone parts of the country.

As a direct result of the lessons learned from the earthquake of 1964, the U.S. Geological Survey began engineering-geologic studies of all of Alaska's coastal communities, whether or not they received earthquake damage. Similarly, the geology of some western cities and metropolitan complexes in the conterminous States is already known or is under study. However, many other towns and cities that may well be struck by earthquakes in the future are without adequate geologic maps. All such communities, as well as places where communities are likely to spread or develop in the future, should be geologically mapped by trained personnel as rapidly as is feasible with available funds. The need is increasing at a far faster rate than is the required geologic information.

The minimum geologic map for each community would delineate all active faults and landslides and would discriminate between areas underlain by bedrock and those underlain by unconsolidated materials. The next most needed refinement would be to distinguish areas of fine- and coarse-grained soils and to note whether the near-surface layers are normally dry or saturated. The topographic base of the geologic map would of course also show unconfined slopes bordering topographic depressions, even minor ones, where earth fissures or lateral spreading of loose materials are to be anticipated. Such maps could be prepared quickly and at relatively low cost. They would be extremely valuable in guiding authorities to wise decisions on land use, in the location of seismic instruments that would develop a maximum of useful information, and in the preparation or refinement of earthquake-hazard maps.

Much more elaborate—and more costly—geologic maps can be prepared, of course. Such maps are needed for all larger communities and for smaller ones where the geologic and soils problems are complex. Ideally, these maps should contain all the geologic, topographic, and hydrologic detail that could have any bearing on the relative reaction of parts of the community's foundations to earthquake stresses. They should depict not only the makeup of the land, but the character of contiguous water bodies and their bottom materials. Knowledge of the character, shape, and stability of off-shore deposits derived from surface observations, borings, bathymetric surveys, and bottom sampling would go far toward warning coastal residents of their danger in the event of an earthquake. Cooperative effort by soils engineers, geologists, and oceanographers is needed for this work.

Provision of good geologic maps alone is not enough, of course, to insure that the facts they show will be used effectively in reducing earthquake hazards. This lesson was forcefully taught by the Alaska experience of 1964. Modern geologic maps of Anchorage were available, and geologists had warned in print that one of the map units, the Bootlegger Cove Clay, would be unstable in the event of future earthquakes. The warnings went unheeded, however, because civic authorities, builders, and others either were unaware of the existence of the geologic information or ignored its implications.

Disastrous translatory landslides initiated by the earthquake of 1964 amply proved the correctness of the warnings.

Obviously, means must be sought to acquaint city planners, engineers, builders and the populace with the existence of useful geologic information and with its implications in terms of earthquake hazards and land use.

"Modern geologic maps were available and geologists had warned in print that * * * the Bootlegger Cove Clay would be unstable in the event of future earthquakes. * * * Disastrous translatory landslides initiated by the earthquake of 1964 amply proved the correctness of the warnings."

INSTRUMENTATION AND MEASUREMENTS

Suitable networks of recording seismographs should be installed in all areas where earthquakes are considered likely to occur. Where feasible, signals from the seismometers should be telemetered by telephone lines or by radio to a central recording and data-processing facility. The seismograph networks should be supplemented by other earthquake-sensing instruments, such as strain meters, tiltmeters, magnetometers, and gravimeters. In some areas, existing networks maintained by university and Federal agencies can be used as bases for improved modern telemetry networks. In other areas, entirely new networks must be installed.

In selecting the sites for such instruments, it is essential that the local and regional geology be known in some detail and that the instruments be placed so as to obtain the maximum amount of information on the behavior of active faults and the effects of the various kinds of rock and soils on seismic response. It is particularly important that the seismograph networks be of such geometric form that earthquakes can be located accurately and immediately by means of digital computers and related to known or suspected active faults.

In addition to the networks of standard seismographs and other earthquake-sensing instruments, the existing networks of strong-motion seismographs should be strengthened and extended to all earthquake zones. Strong-motion seismograph recordings are particularly useful in testing the interactions between buildings and different materials on which they rest when subjected to seismic shock, and it is, therefore, important that strong-motion seismographs be

sited on the basis of detailed knowledge of the local geology.

The instruments discussed above are now available and can be installed immediately. A new generation of instruments is also needed—laser strain meters, absolute-stress measuring devices, and devices for monitoring minute variations with changing stress of acoustic velocities in rock. These instruments can be developed, and should be developed without delay.

The arrays of standard and strong-motion seismographs in all earthquake-prone areas might well be supplemented by a nationwide system of test wells in confined aquifers, equipped to record long-period seismic waves and to damp out subsequent water fluctuations. Studies of well records after the Alaska earthquake demonstrated that hydroseisms can be used effectively to predict and explain certain hydrologic phenomena and can also serve as supplemental seismic recorders. In addition to a system of water-level recorders in wells, improved stream gages are needed, built to withstand earthquake shocks and to remain operational in winter. Such gages provide needed information on the reaction of streams and surface-water supplies to earthquake-induced land movements, and there is also abundant evidence that the measurements of seiches in streams and lakes can contribute greatly to the study of sites of high seismic activity.

Many more bench marks, triangulation stations, tide gages, and tidal bench marks are needed in earthquake-prone regions to permit accurate measurements of lateral or vertical crustal strains between, as well as during, major earthquakes. To the extent possible, all such stations should be established on bedrock and should

be so built as to withstand earthquake vibration, inundation by giant waves, and local land movements. Bench marks should also be established at the ends of long lakes throughout earthquake-prone regions, and their altitudes should be resurveyed periodically. With a suitable net of tidal bench marks and level lines and a suitable number of lake tiltmeters, both long-term and sudden warping of the earth's surface can be determined accurately and cheaply. Such data are required to test the hypothesis that premonitory vertical displacements sometimes precede major earthquakes; if they do, these displacements could be an important prediction tool.

More information on the normal height of barnacles and other sessile organisms relative to tide levels along all the shores of the Pacific would permit students of future earthquakes to make quick and reasonably accurate measurements of tectonic changes. Effective use of this information would also require improved tide tables based on tide-gage measurements at many localities.

Detailed geomorphic studies supplemented by many more radiocarbon dates along emergent and submergent shores are needed to clarify the Holocene history of vertical land movements. These studies would provide an understanding of the distribution and recurrence interval of earthquake-induced changes in land levels within the time range of radiocarbon-dating methods. Such studies might lead to the development of useful earthquake-forecasting techniques in some seismically active coastal regions because they can roughly define broad areas of susceptibility to future major earthquake-related tectonic displacements at specific localities.

INVESTIGATIONS OF ACTUAL EARTHQUAKES

Every large earthquake should be regarded as a full-scale laboratory experiment whose study can give scientific and engineering information unobtainable from any other source. For this reason it is essential that every earthquake strong enough to damage man-made structures or to have measurable effects on the natural environment should be studied thoroughly by scientists and engineers.

NEED FOR ADVANCE PLANNING

In total, the scientific and engineering investigations of the Alaska earthquake were remarkably successful. They resulted in accumulation and interpretation of far more knowledge, in more disciplines, than has ever been amassed before for any single earthquake. These results were obtained through the efforts of many individuals, sponsored by many governmental and private groups. There was no overall organizational plan for the investigations, and except for the work of the Committee on the Alaska Earthquake, National Academy of Sciences, and for voluntary personal interactions of individuals and groups, no determined attempt was made to coordinate and integrate all the studies. This approach, even though ultimately successful, left some gaps in the record and produced some waste and duplication of effort when time and available skills were critical. Such shortcomings in future disaster investigations could be avoided by advance planning and at least a skeletal permanent organization.

Presumably the Federal Government will be deeply involved not only in relief and reconstruction after, but also in technical investigation of, any future earthquake disaster that is at all comparable to the Alaska earthquake of 1964. For this reason, it seems imperative that the Federal Government should take the lead in contingency planning for future disastrous earthquakes. This is not to say that the Federal Government should act alone in planning for disaster or in activating the plans made. State and local governments, universities, and other groups all have major responsibilities and skills that must be brought to bear on the problems. Largely as a result of the Alaskan experience, numerous well-integrated local and State groups in several earthquake-prone regions are already (1969) active in making plans for the investigation of future earthquakes. A great earthquake, however, brings with it an immediate need for massive application of resources, both human and material, from outside the stricken locality or region. Moreover, and as the Alaskan experience made so plain, strong and immediate logistic and other support from the military is absolutely essential in dealing with a great earthquake disaster, either for technical investigations or for relief and reconstruction.

The chief objectives of a planning effort in preparation for future great earthquakes would be (1) to define the kind and scope of investigations needed for scientific purposes and for protection of life and property; (2) to provide guidelines to assume that the primary responsibilities of various organizations or individuals, governmental or private, are brought to bear on all necessary investigations; (3) to provide for coordination between investigative groups; and (4) to provide means for immediate funding and fielding of investigators when disaster strikes, including military logistic and photographic support.

It is emphasized that this proposal applies only to preplanning for disaster. Once disaster has struck, actual investigations must be left to individual groups with the requisite skills, responsibilities and funds. But the better the overall preplanning effort, the better integrated and funded will be the actual investigations and the better their chances of complete coverage.

GEOLOGIC, GEOPHYSICAL, AND HYDROLOGIC INVESTIGATIONS

Once a decision has been made to investigate a reported earthquake, a small reconnaissance party should be dispatched at once, as was done successfully by the U.S. Geological Survey for the Alaska earthquake. Preferably it should be composed of one or more mature geologists and geophysicists who have a thorough knowledge of the local and regional geology of the disaster area and who have had experience with earthquakes or other similar natural disasters. The sounder the decisions at this stage the better will be the results. The duties of the reconnaissance party would be partly to observe and record as many ephemeral features as possible but would be primarily to assess the situation and to formulate advice as to the size and character of the problem and of the task force needed to attack it. Many investigations would end with the reconnaissance phase; a few would be found worth full-scale study.

If further studies are recommended, a field team of investigators should be formed and a leader appointed. Team size and makeup depend on the character of the problem and on the skills and aptitudes required, but every effort should be made to provide coverage of all earth-science aspects of the disaster. Some team members, especially in the early phases of the investigations, should know the local and regional geology. However, both local knowledge and experience in disaster studies help in making fast, accurate observations of ephemeral geologic processes and effects.

Once the field team is formed, its members should continue to be responsible only to the team leader until all field work and reports are completed. Decisions should be made early as to the general scope and character of preliminary and final reports on the earthquake. These determinations, however, should be flexible enough as to permit pursuit of significant research problems as they unfold.

Every effort must be made to coordinate the geologists' and geophysicists' work with that of all other investigative groups in order to assure free interchange of information, to avoid confusion and duplication of effort, and to identify gaps in the investigative effort.

The work required of the field team will vary between wide limits, depending, among other things, on the size and geologic character of the affected region, on the nature and effects of the earthquake itself, and on the kind, amount, and distribution of damage done. In general, however, all work done should be aimed at two principal objectives: (1) collection of all geologic and geophysical information that has any bearing on reconstruction efforts or that can be used in preventing or alleviating the damaging effects of future earthquakes, and (2) collec-

tion of all information that can lead to better scientific understanding of earthquake processes and effects.

More specifically, the following steps should be taken in the geologic investigation, with initial emphasis on ephemeral effects that may disappear or be modified within a few hours or days:

1. Initiate immediate aerial surveys to provide complete stereo-photo coverage, at scales of 1:20,000 or larger, of all areas in which any earthquake effects are photographically recordable. The minimum coverage required might be specified by the reconnaissance party, to be expanded later as followup investigations progress. All of the studies listed below can be made or expedited with suitable airphoto coverage.

2. Study relations between the earthquake effects and the local and regional geology.

3. In cooperation with soils engineers, investigate any new faults or reactivations of preexisting faults.

4. Map ground fissures, sand spouts, and pressure ridges, especially where they affect the works of man.

5. Measure subsidence or uplift of the ground surface and distinguish between tectonic displacement and that caused by consolidation of sediments.

6. Investigate mass movements of materials, such as avalanches, landslides, and underwater slides.

7. Observe changes in stream courses and regimens.

8. Map local geology and soils, paying special attention to ground-water conditions, wherever damaging movements have occurred.

9. Ascertain the effects of tsunamis and local waves and the changes in shorelines initiated by waves or tectonic movements.

10. Study any earthquake-caused changes in volcanic activity.

11. Initiate studies, by means of portable seismographs, of aftershocks especially for the purpose of locating them and relating them to active faults.

12. Initiate geodetic and aerial surveys, both for use in studying earthquake effects and in determining

horizontal and vertical tectonic displacements.

13. In close cooperation with soils and structural engineers, examine the effects of shaking and of ground movements on structures, paying particular attention to the relationship between underlying geology and structural damage.

14. Produce good map and photographic coverage of the earthquake's effects for the permanent record.

AVAILABILITY OF MAPS AND OTHER BASIC DATA

One of the most important lessons learned from the Alaskan earthquake was the value of pre-earthquake information in studying the effects of the quake. Topographic base maps, geologic, soils, and glaciologic maps, aerial photographs, tidal and other bench marks, triangulation stations, records of building foundations—all these were invaluable to investigators.

Current base maps—topographic maps and hydrographic charts—are essential tools for scientific and engineering investigators; so are pertinent reports and maps on local geology and soils. Detailed city plans, preferably those that show utility systems as well as streets and buildings, are needed not only by technical investigators but by relief and rehabilitation workers and by the general public. All such basic materials will be needed in quantity immediately after an earthquake. The availability of such materials should, of course, be made known to city officials and other potential users.

QUESTIONNAIRES

Questionnaires, widely distributed by mail to postmasters and others or published in local newspapers, are an effective means for determining the extent, distribution, and character of an earthquake's effects, as well as for identifying alert and interested eyewitnesses who should be interviewed by investigators for more detailed facts than can be recorded on the returned questionnaire. The questionnaire method, supplemented by innumerable interviews, was widely and effectively used in studies of the Alaska earthquake by the U.S. Coast and Geodetic Survey, which routinely gathers such data on all earthquakes, by the U.S. Geological Survey, and by several other groups. The questionnaire used by the Geological Survey in Alaska is reproduced in the report by Plafker and others (1969).

SCIENTIFIC AND ENGINEERING TASK FORCE

Immediately after the Alaska earthquake, the Scientific and Engineering Task Force of the Federal Reconstruction and Development Planning Commission for Alaska (Eckel and Schaem, in Hansen and others, 1966) was set up to advise the Commission, and through it, the Federal fund-supplying agencies, as to where it was safe to permit new construction or rebuilding of earthquake-damaged structures. The Task Force's advice, based on technical studies of the earthquake's effects on geology and soils, was translated into Commission decisions as to availability of Federal funds for specific areas and purposes.

The approach of the Scientific and Engineering Task Force was highly successful during the reconstruction period after the Alaska earthquake. Its potential longer term benefits to the general public were somewhat lessened, however, because there were no provisions for continuing observance of its recommendations after the Federal Commission was dissolved and because there was no control over actions of local governments or use of non-Federal funds.

SELECTED BIBLIOGRAPHY

Barnes, D. F., 1966, Gravity changes during the Alaska earthquake: Jour. Geophys. Research, v. 71, no. 2, p. 451–456.

Bolt, B. A., 1964, Seismic air waves from the great 1964 Alaska earthquake: Nature, v. 202, no. 4937, p. 1095–1096.

Burton, L. R., 1967, Television examination of earthquake damage to underground communication and electrical systems in Anchorage, in Logan, M. H., Effect of the earthquake of March 27, 1964, on the Eklutna Hydroelectric Project, Anchorage, Alaska: U.S. Geological Survey Prof. Paper 545–A, p. A25–A30.

Case, J. E., Barnes, D. F., Plafker, George, and Robbins, S. L., 1966, Gravity survey and regional geology of the Prince William Sound epicentral region, Alaska: U.S. Geol. Survey Prof. Paper 543–C, p. C1–C12.

Chaffin, Yule, 1966, The earthquake created a hobby: Alaska Sportsman, Aug. 1966, p. 39–40.

Chance, Genie, 1966a, Chronology of physical events of the Alaskan earthquake: Prepared under a National Science Foundation Grant to the University of Alaska. Copyright by Genie Chance, 1966. 173 p.

————1966b, The year of decision and action, in Hansen, W. R., and others, The Alaska earthquake March 27, 1964—Field investigations and reconstruction effort: U.S. Geol. Survey Prof. Paper 541, p. 90–105.

Coble, R. W., 1967, Alaska earthquake effects on ground water in Iowa, in Vorhis, R. C., Hydrologic effects of the earthquake of March 27, 1964 outside Alaska: U.S. Geol. Survey Prof. Paper 544–C, p. C23–C27.

Condon, W. H., and Cass, J. T., 1958, Map of a part of the Prince William Sound area, Alaska, showing linear geologic features as shown on aerial photographs: U.S. Geol. Survey Misc. Geol. Inv. Map I–273, scale 1:125,000.

Coulter, H. W., and Migliaccio, R. R., 1966, Effects of the earthquake of March 27, 1964, at Valdez, Alaska: U.S. Geol. Survey Prof. Paper 542–C, p. C1–C36.

Crandell, D. R., and Fahnestock, R. K., 1965, Rockfalls and avalanches from Little Tahoma Peak on Mount Rainier, Washington: U.S. Geol. Survey Bull. 1221–A, p. A1–A30.

Davies, Kenneth, and Baker, D. M., 1965, Ionospheric effects observed around the time of the Alaskan earthquake of March 28, 1964: Jour. Geophys. Research, v. 70, no. 9, p. 2251–2253.

Dobrovolny, Ernest, and Schmoll, H. R., 1968, Geology as applied to urban planning—an example from the Greater Anchorage Area Borough, Alaska, in Engineering geology in country planning: Internat. Geol. Cong., 23d, Prague 1968, Proc., sec. 12, p. 39–56.

Donn, W. L., 1964, Alaskan earthquake of 27 March 1964—remote seiche stimulation: Science, v. 145, no. 3629, p. 261–262.

Donn, W. L., and Posmentier, E. S., 1964, Ground-coupled air waves from the great Alaska earthquake: Jour. Geophys. Research, v. 69, no. 24, p. 5357–5361.

Eckel, E. B., 1967, Effects of the earthquake of March 27, 1964, on air and water transport, communications, and utilities systems in south-central Alaska: U.S. Geol. Survey Prof. Paper 545–B, p. B1–B27.

Eckel, E. B., and Schaem, W. E., 1966, The work of the Scientific and Engineering Task Force—Earth science applied to policy decisions in early relief and reconstruction, in Hansen, W. R., and others, The Alaska earthquake March 27, 1964—Field investigations and reconstruction effort: U.S. Geol. Survey Prof. Paper 541, p. 46–69.

Engineering Geology Evaluation Group, 1964, Geologic report—27 March 1964 earthquake in Greater Anchorage area: Prepared for Alaska Housing Authority and the City of Anchorage; Anchorage, Alaska, 34 p.

Federal Council for Science and Technology, 1968, Proposal for a ten-year national earthquake hazards program: Ad hoc Interagency Working Group for Earthquake Research, prepared for the Office of Science and Technology and the Federal Council for Science and Technology, Washington, D.C., 81 p.

Federal Reconstruction and Development Planning Commission for Alaska, 1964, Response to disaster, Alaskan earthquake, March 27, 1964: Washington, U.S. Govt. Printing Office, 84 p.

Ferrians, O. J., Jr., 1966, Effects of the earthquake of March 27, 1964, in the Copper River Basin area, Alaska: U.S. Geol. Survey Prof. Paper 543–E, p. E1–E28.

Foster H. L., and Karlstrom, T. N. V., 1967, Ground breakage and associated effects in the Cook Inlet area, Alaska, resulting from the March 27, 1964, earthquake: U.S. Geol. Survey Prof. Paper 543–F, p. F1–F28.

George, Warren, and Lyle, R. E., 1966, Reconstruction by the Corps of Engineers—methods and accomplishments, in Hansen, W. R., and others, The Alaska earthquake March 27, 1964—Field investigations and reconstruction effort: U.S. Geol. Survey Prof. Paper 541, p. 81–89.

Grantz, Arthur, Plafker, George, and Kachadoorian, Reuben, 1964, Alaska's Good Friday earthquake, March 27, 1964—a preliminary geologic evaluation: U.S. Geol. Survey Circ. 491, 35 p.

Gronewald, G. J., and Duncan, W. W., 1966, Study of erosion along Homer Spit and vicinity, Kachemak Bay, Alaska, in Coastal engineering; Santa Barbara Specialty Conference, 1965: New York, Am. Soc. Civil Engineers, p. 673–682.

Hackman, R. J., 1965, Photointerpretation of post-earthquake photography, Alaska: Photogrammetric Eng., v. 31, no. 4, p. 604–610.

Hansen, W. R., 1965, Effects of the earthquake of March 27, 1964, at Anchorage, Alaska: U.S. Geol. Survey Prof. Paper 542–A, p. A1–A68.
————1966, Investigations by the Geological Survey, in Hansen, W. R, and others, The Alaska earthquake March 27, 1964—Field investigations and reconstruction effort: U.S. Geol. Survey Prof. Paper 541, p. 38–45.

Hansen, W. R., and Eckel, E. B., 1966, A summary description of the Alaska earthquake—its setting and effects, in Hansen, W. R., and others, The Alaska earthquake March 27, 1964—Field investigations and reconstruction effort: U.S. Geol. Survey Prof. Paper 541, p. 1–37.

Hansen, W. R., and others, 1966, The Alaska earthquake March 27, 1964—Field investigations and reconstruction effort: U.S. Geol. Survey Prof. Paper 541, 111 p.

Harding, S. T., and Algermissen, S. T., 1969, The focal mechanism of the Prince William Sound earthquake of March 28, 1964, and related earthquakes, in Leipold, 1969a, p. 185–221.

International Conference of Building Officials, 1964, Uniform building code: Los Angeles, Calif., 1964 ed., v. 1, 503 p.

Kachadoorian, Reuben, 1965, Effects of the earthquake of March 27, 1964, at Whittier, Alaska: U.S. Geol. Survey Prof. Paper 542–B, p. B1–B21.
————1968, Effects of the earthquake of March 27, 1964 on the Alaska highway system: U.S. Geol. Survey Prof. Paper 545–C, p. C1–C66.

Kachadoorian, Reuben, and Plafker, George, 1967, Effects of the earthquake of March 27, 1964, on the communities of Kodiak and nearby islands: U.S. Geol. Survey Prof. Paper 542–F, p. F1–F41.

Kirkby, M. J., and Kirkby, A. V., 1969, Erosion and deposition on a beach raised by the 1964 earthquake, Montague Island, Alaska: U.S. Geol. Survey Prof. Paper 543–H, p. H1–H41.

Lemke, R. W., 1967, Effects of the earthquake of March 27, 1964, at Seward, Alaska: U.S. Geol. Survey Prof. Paper 542–E, p. E1–E43.

Leonard, R. S. and Barnes, R. A., Jr., 1965, Observation of ionospheric disturbances following the Alaska earthquake: Jour. Geophys. Research, v. 70, no. 5, p. 1250–1253.

Logan, M. H., 1967, Effect of the earthquake of March 27, 1964, on the Eklutna Hydrolelectric Project, Anchorage, Alaska, with a section on Television examination of earthquake damage to underground communication and electrical systems in Anchorage, by Lynn R. Burton: U.S. Geol. Survey Prof. Paper 545–A, p. A1–A30.

Long, Erwin, and George, Warren, 1967a, Buttress design earthquake-induced slides: Am. Soc. Civil Engineers Proc., v. 93, paper 5332, Jour. Soil Mechanics and Found. Div., no. SM4, p. 595–609.

Lyle, R. E., and George, Warren, 1966, Activities of the Corps of Engineers—cleanup and early reconstruction, in Hansen, W. R., and others, The Alaska earthquake March 27, 1964—Field investigations and reconstruction effort: U.S. Geol. Survey Prof. Paper 541, p. 70–80.

McCulloch, D. S., 1966, Slide-induced waves, seiching, and ground fracturing caused by the earthquake of March 27, 1964, at Kenai Lake Alaska: U.S. Geol. Survey Prof. Paper 543–A, p. A1–A41.

McCulloch, D. S., and Bonilla, M. G., 1970, Effects of the Alaska earthquake, March 27, 1964, on The Alaska Railroad. U.S. Geol. Survey Prof. Paper 545–D.

McGarr, Arthur, and Vorhis, R. C., 1968, Seismic seiches from the March 1964 Alaska earthquake: U.S. Geol. Survey Prof. Paper 544–E, p. E1–E43.

Malloy, R. J. 1964, Crustal uplift southwest of Montague Island, Alaska: Science, v. 146, no. 3647, p. 1048–1049.
————1965, Gulf of Alaska—seafloor upheaval: Geo-Marine Technology, v. 1, no. 5, p. 22–26.

Miller, D. J., 1960, Giant waves in Lituya Bay, Alaska: U.S. Geol. Survey Prof. Paper 345–C, p. 51–86.

Miller, R. D., and Dobrovolny, Ernest, 1959, Surficial geology of Anchorage and vicinity, Alaska: U.S. Geol. Survey Bull. 1093, 128 p.

Moore, G. W., 1964, Magnetic disturbances preceding the Alaska 1964 earthquake: Nature, v. 203, no. 4944, p. 508–509.

Pararas-Carayannis, George, 1967, A study of the source mechanism of the Alaska earthquake and tsunami of March 27, 1964—pt. 1, Water waves: Pacific Sci., v. 21, no. 3, p. 301–310.

Parkin, E. J., 1966, Horizontal displacements, pt. 2 of Alaskan surveys to determine crustal movement: Am. Congress Surveying and Mapping Proc., v. 27, no. 3, p. 423–430; also U.S. Coast and Geod. Survey, 11 p.

————1969, Horizontal crustal movements determined from surveys after the Alaskan earthquake of 1964, in Leipold, 1969b, p. 35–98.

Plafker, George, 1965, Tectonic deformation associated with the 1964 Alaska earthquake: Science, v. 148, no. 3678, p. 1675–1687.

————1967, Surface faults on Montague Island associated with the 1964 Alaska earthquake: U.S. Geol. Survey Prof. Paper 543–G, p. G1–G42.

————1968, Source areas of the Shattered Peak and Pyramid Peak landslides at Sherman Glacier: in The Great Alaska Earthquake of 1964, Hydrology: Natl. Acad. Sci. Pub. 1603, p. 374–382.

————1969, Tectonics of the March 27, 1964, Alaska earthquake U.S. Geol. Survey, Prof. Paper 543–I, p. I1–I74.

Plafker, George, and Kachadoorian, Reuben, 1966, Geologic effects of the March 1964 earthquake and associated seismic sea waves on Kodiak and nearby islands, Alaska: U.S. Geol. Survey Prof Paper 543–D, p. D1–D46.

Plafker, George, Kachadoorian, Reuben, Eckel, E. B., and Mayo, L. P., 1969, Effects of the earthquake of March 27, 1964, at various communities: U.S. Geol. Survey, Prof. Paper 542–G, p. G1–G50.

Plafker, George, and Mayo, L. R., 1965, Tectonic deformation, subaqueous slides, and destructive waves associated with the Alaskan March 27, 1964 earthquake—an interim geologic evaluation: U.S. Geol. Survey open-file report, 21 p.

———— 1967, Effects of the March 1964 Alaska earthquake on glaciers: U.S. Geol. Survey Prof. Paper 544–D, p. D1–D42.

Press, Frank, and Jackson, David, 1965, Alaskan earthquake, 27 March 1964—Vertical extent of faulting and elastic strain energy release: Science, v. 147, no. 3660, p. 867–868.

Reimnitz, Erk, and Marshall, N. F.,

1965, Effects of the Alaska earthquake and tsunami on recent deltaic sediments: Jour. Geophys. Research, v. 70, no. 10, p. 2363–2376.

Rinne, J. E., 1967, Oil storage tanks, in Wood, F. J., ed.-in-chief, Research studies: seismology and marine geology, pt. A, Engineering seismology, v. 2 of The Prince William Sound, Alaska, earthquake of 1964 and aftershocks: U.S. Coast and Geod. Survey Pub. 10–3, p. 245–252.

Row, R. V., 1967, Acoustic-gravity waves in the upper atmosphere due to a nuclear detonation and an earthquake: Jour. Geophys. Research, v. 72, no. 5, p. 1599–1610.

Savage, J. C., and Hastie, L. M., 1966, Surface deformation associated with dip slip faulting: Jour. Geophys. Research, v. 71, no. 20, p. 4897–4904.

Seed, H. B., and Wilson, S. D., 1967, The Turnagain Heights landslide, Anchorage, Alaska: Am. Soc. Civil Engineers Proc. v. 93, paper 5320, Jour. Soil Mechanics and Foundation Div., no. SM4, p. 325–353.

Shannon and Wilson, Inc., 1964, Report on Anchorage area soil studies, Alaska, to U.S. Army Engineer District, Anchorage, Alaska: Seattle, Wash., 109 p., app. A–K.

Shreve, R. L., 1959, Geology and mechanics of the Blackhawk landslide, Lucerne Valley, California: California Inst. Technology, Pasadena, Ph. D. thesis, 79 p.

*———— 1966a, Air-layer lubrication of large avalanches [abs.]: Geol. Soc. America Spec. Paper 87, p. 154.

———— 1966b, Sherman landslide, Alaska: Science, v. 154, no. 3757, p. 1639–1643.

*———— 1968, The Blackhawk landslide: Geol. Soc. Am. Spec. Paper 108, 47 p.

Small, J. B., and Parkin, E. J., 1967, Alaskan surveys to determine crustal movement—pt. 1, Vertical bench mark displacement: Surveying and Mapping, v. 27, no. 3, p. 413–422.

Small, J. B., and Wharton, L. C., 1969, vertical displacements determined by surveys after the Alaskan earthquake of March 1964, in Leipold, 1969b, p. 21–33.

Smith, S. W., 1966, Free oscillations excited by the Alaskan earthquake: Jour. Geophys. Research, v. 71, no. 4, p. 1183–1193.

Spaeth, M. G., and Berkman, S. C., 1965, The tsunami of March 28, 1964, as recorded at tide stations: U.S. Coast and Geod. Survey, 59 p.

Stanley, K. W., 1966, Beach changes on Homer Spit, Alaska, in Waller, R. M., 1966, Effects of the earthquake of March 27, 1964, in the Homer area, Alaska: U.S. Geol. Survey Prof. Paper 542–D, p. D20–D27.

———— 1968, Effects of the Alaska earthquake of March 27, 1964 on shore processes and beach morphology: U.S. Geol. Survey Prof. Paper 543–J, p. J1–J21.

Stauder, William, and Bollinger, G. A., 1966, The focal mechanism of the Alaskan earthquake of March 28, 1964, and its aftershock sequence: Jour. Geophys. Research, v. 71, no. 22, p. 5283–5296.

Steinbrugge, K. V., 1964, Engineering seismology aspects, in Prince William Sound, Alaskan earthquakes, March–April 1964: U.S. Coast and Geod. Survey Seismology Div., prelim. rept., p. 58–72.

Tarr, R. S., and Martin, Lawrence, 1912, The earthquakes at Yakutat Bay, Alaska, in September, 1899: U.S. Geol. Survey Prof. Paper 69, 135 p.

Tuthill, S. J., and Laird, W. M., 1966, Geomorphic effects of the earthquake of March 27, 1964, in the Martin-Bering Rivers area, Alaska: U.S. Geol. Survey Prof. Paper 543–B, p. B1–B29.

U.S. Coast and Geodetic Survey, 1969, Seismic risk map of the United States: U.S. Coast and Geod. Survey, Environmental Sci. Services Adm., Washington, D.C.

Van Dorn, W. G., 1959, Local effects of impulsively generated waves: Scripps Inst. Oceanography Rept. II, 80 p., Univ. Calif., La Jolla, Calif.

Van Dorn, W. G., 1964, Source mechanism of the tsunami of March 28, 1964, in Alaska: Coastal Eng. Conf., 9th, Lisbon, 1964, Proc., p. 166–190.

Varnes, D. J., 1958, Landslide types and processes, in Eckel, E. B., ed., Landslides and engineering practice: Natl. Research Council, Highway Research Board Spec. Rept. 29 (NAS–NRC Pub. 544), p. 20–47.

Vorhis, R. C., 1967, Hydrologic effects of the earthquake of March 27, 1964, outside Alaska, with sections on Hydroseismograms from the

Nunn-Bush Shoe Co. well, Wisconsin, by E. E. Rexin and R. C. Vorhis, *and* Alaska earthquake effects on ground water in Iowa, by R. W. Coble: U.S. Geol. Survey Prof. Paper 544–C, p. C1–C54.

Waller, R. M., 1966a, Effects of the earthquake of March 27, 1964, in the Homer area, Alaska *with a section on* Beach changes on Homer Spit, by K. W. Stanley: U.S. Geol. Survey Prof. Paper 542–D, p. D1–D28.

—— 1966b, Effects of the earthquake of March 27, 1964, on the hydrology of south-central Alaska: U.S. Geol. Survey Prof. Paper 544–A, p. A1–A28.

—— 1966c, Effects of the earthquake of March 27, 1964, on the hydrology of the Anchorage area, Alaska: U.S. Geol. Survey Prof. Paper 544–B, p. B1–B18.

Wilson, B. W., and Tørum, Alf, 1968, The Tsunami of the Alaskan earthquake, 1964—engineering evaluation: US. Army Corps of Engineers, Coastal Eng. Research Center, Tech. Mem. 25, 448 p., 232 ills., 5 appen.

Wyss, Max, and Brune, J. N., 1967, The Alaska earthquake of 28 March 1964: A complex multiple rupture: Seismol. Soc. America, Bull. v. 57, no. 5, p. 1017–1023.

CLARIFICATION

Geology Vol. Page	USGS Page	Column	Line	Remarks
774	28	1	14	Also reported as 131: 115 in Alaska, 12 in California (including 11 in the Crescent City area and 1 at Bolinas Bay), and 4 in Oregon (Weller, in press, in Oceanography and Coastal Engineering volume)

Appendixes

ENGLISH–METRIC CONVERSION TABLE

LENGTH

1 inch (in.)	=	2.54	centimeters (cm)
1 foot (ft) [12 in.]	=	30.48	cm
1 yard (yd) [3 ft]	=	91.44	cm
	=	0.914	meter (m)
1 mile (mi) [5280 ft]	=	1.610	kilometer (km)

AREA

1 square inch (in.²)	=	6.45	square centimeters (cm²)
1 square foot (ft²)	=	929.0	. cm²
	=	0.0929	square meter (m²)
1 square yard (yd²)	=	0.836	m²
1 acre (a) [43560 ft²]	=	0.4047	hectare (ha)
1 square mile (mi²)	=	2.59	square kilometers (km²)

VOLUME

1 cubic inch (in.³)	=	16.4	cubic centimeters (cm³)
1 cubic foot (ft³)	=	28.3	× 10³ cm³
	=	0.0283	m³
1 cubic yard (yd³)	=	0.7646	cubic meter (m³)
1 cubic mile (mi³)	=	4.17	cubic kilometers (km³)
1 quart (qt) [0.25 U.S. gallon (gal)]	=	0.95	liter (1)
1 gal [4 qt]	=	3.79	liter
1 bushel (bu) [U.S. dry]	=	35.24	liter

MASS

1 pound (lb) [16 ounces (oz)]	=	453.6	grams (g)
	=	0.4536	kilogram (kg)
1 U.S. ton (tn) [2000 lb]	=	907.2	kg
	=	0.9072	metric ton (MT)
1 long ton (LT) [2240 lb]	=	1.016	MT

PRESSURE

1 pound per square inch (lb/in.² or psi)	=	0.0704	kilogram per square centimeter (kg/cm²)
1 pound per square foot (lb/ft²)	=	4.8824	kilograms per square meter (kg/m²)
1 bar [1000 millibars (mb)]	=	1.020	kg/cm²

VELOCITY

1 foot per second (ft/s)	=	0.3048	meter per second (m/s)
	=	1.097	kilometer per hour (km/h)
	=	0.5925	international knot (kn)
1 mile per hour (mi/h)	=	1.609	km/h
	=	0.869	kn

METRIC-ENGLISH CONVERSION TABLE

LENGTH

1 millimeter (mm) [0.1 centimeter (cm)]	=	0.0394 inch (in.)
1 cm [10 mm]	=	0.3937 in.
1 meter (m) [100 cm]	=	39.37 in.
	=	3.28 feet (ft)
1 kilometer (km) [1000 m]	=	0.621 mile (mi)
1 international nautical mile [1852 m]	=	6076.1 ft

AREA

1 square centimeter (cm²)	=	0.155 square inch (in.²)
1 square meter (m²)	=	10.76 square feet (ft²)
	=	1.196 square yards (yd²)
1 hectare (ha)	=	2.4710 acres (a)
1 square kilometer (km²)	=	0.386 square mile (mi²)

VOLUME

1 cubic centimeter (cm³)	=	0.0610 cubic inch (in.³)
1 cubic meter (m³)	=	35.314 cubic feet (ft³)
	=	1.31 cubic yards (yd³)
1 cubic kilometer (km³)	=	0.240 cubic mile (mi³)
1 liter	=	1.06 quarts (qt)
	=	0.264 gallon (gal)

MASS

1 kilogram (kg) [1000 grams (g)]	=	2.20 pounds (lb)
	=	0.0011 ton
1 metric ton (MT) [1000 kg]	=	1.10 ton
	=	0.9842 long ton (LT)

PRESSURE

1 kilogram per square centimeter (kg/cm²)	=	14.20 pounds per square inch (lb/in.²)
	=	2,048 pounds per square foot (lb/ft²)

VELOCITY

1 meter per second (m/s)	=	3.281 feet per second (ft/s)
1 kilometer per hour (km/h)	=	0.9113 ft/s
	=	0.621 mile per hour (mi/h)
1 knot (kn) [1852 m/h]	=	1.6878 ft/s
	=	1.151 mi/h

Annotated Bibliography

Aki, Keiiti, Minoru Hori, and Hideteru Matumoto. Microaftershocks observed at a temporary array station on the Kenai Peninsula from May 19 to June 7, 1964 *in* Volume II-B,C: The Prince William Sound, Alaska, earthquake of 1964 and aftershocks. Environmental Science Services Administration, U.S. Coast and Geodetic Survey. Washington: Government Printing Office, 1969. p. 131–156. Also *in* The Great Alaska Earthquake of 1964: Seismology and Geodesy. NAS Pub. 1602. Washington: National Academy of Sciences, in press.
Concludes that about one tenth of the aftershocks (as studied at a temporary-array station on the Kenai Peninsula) originate in the upper mantle to a depth of about 200 km.

Alaska Department of Health and Welfare. Preliminary report of earthquake damage to environmental health facilities and services in Alaska. Mimeographed report of the Division of Public Health. Juneau: Branch of Environmental Health, 1964. 47 p.
Surveys landslide and crevasse effects on waterworks, sewerage, and food and drug supplies.

Alaska Division of Mines and Minerals. The great Alaska earthquake, March 27, 1964. Miscellaneous Paper No. 1. Juneau: Alaska Division of Mines and Minerals, 1964. 4 p.
Stresses the fact that earthquake phenomena are the consequence of natural geologic processes, with rocks in zones of active mountain building being suddenly broken along a fault surface and generating an earthquake; points out that the surface trace of the fault in the 1964 Alaska earthquake was under the waters of Prince William Sound.

Alaskan Construction Consultant Committee. Reconstruction and development survey of earthquake damages in Alaska. Committee Report. Washington: Federal Reconstruction and Development Planning Commission for Alaska [1964]. 98 p.
Recommends completion of an overall geological survey of the Alaska area before replacement or repair of utilities and suggests special studies of the subsidence on the Homer Spit and Seldovia areas.

Alaskan Publishing Company. Great Alaska earthquake: A pictorial review [revised edition]. Anchorage: Alaskan Publishing Company, 1964. 48 p.
Presents a photographic record of building damage and ground breakage in Anchorage as a result of the earthquake.

Algermissen, S. T. Introduction: Foreshocks and aftershocks *in* The Great Alaska Earthquake of 1964: Seismology and Geodesy. NAS Pub. 1602. Washington: National Academy of Sciences, in press.
Points out need for studies of seismicity and mentions that most of the aftershocks occurred at shallow depths.

Algermissen, S. T. Seismic hazards reduction in Alaska *in* The Great Alaska Earthquake of 1964: Seismology and Geodesy. NAS Pub. 1602. Washington: National Academy of Sciences, in press.
Describes the efforts made during reconstruction after the 1964 Alaska earthquake, to reduce the earthquake-associated hazards by engineering and geological work.

Algermissen, S. T. Seismological investigation of the Prince William Sound, Alaska, earthquake and aftershocks (Abstract). *Transactions, American Geophysical Union,* 45 (December 1964), 633.
Presents fault plane solutions for the main shocks and several of the larger aftershocks and discusses the energy released by the aftershocks.

Algermissen, S. T., W. A. Rinehart, R. W. Sherburne, and W. H. Dillinger, Jr. Preshocks and aftershocks of the Prince William Sound earthquake of March 28, 1964 *in* Volume II-B, C: The Prince William Sound, Alaska, earthquake of 1964 and aftershocks. Environmental Science Services Administration, U.S. Coast and Geodetic Survey. Washington: Government Printing Office, 1969. p. 79–130. Also *in* The Great Alaska Earthquake of 1964: Seismology and Geodesy. NAS Pub. 1602. Washington: National Academy of Sciences, in press.
Gives data on 2,210 aftershocks and preshocks, showing that 79 percent of those aftershocks with depths computed had hypocenters less than 40 km deep and that the energy released in the aftershock sequence during the first 1,000 days totaled about one tenth of that released in the main shock.

Aune, Quintin A. Geologic hazards: Quick clays and California's clays: No quick solutions. *Mineral Information Service,* 19 (August 1966), 119–123.
Examines landslides at Anchorage in 1964 due to local failure of the Bootlegger Cove Clay (some of it quick clay) and contrasts it with the geological environment in California.

Barnes, David F. Gravity changes during the Alaska earthquake. *Journal of Geophysical Research,* 71 (January 15, 1966), 451–456. Also *in* The Great Alaska Earthquake of 1964: Seismology

and Geodesy. NAS Pub. 1602. Washington: National Academy of Sciences, in press.
Finds the maximum change of elevation produced by the 1964 earthquake along the Richardson Highway was only about 0.6 m, and that elevation changes were accompanied by a net change of the total mass affecting the gravity readings.

Barrett, Peter J. Effects of the 1964 Alaskan earthquake on some shallow-water sediments in Prince William Sound, southeast Alaska. *Journal of Sedimentary Petrology,* 36 (December 1966), 992–1006. Also in The Great Alaska Earthquake of 1964: Geology. NAS Pub. 1601. Washington: National Academy of Sciences, 1971.
Records the effects of the great Alaska earthquake on four shallow subtidal and intertidal areas in Prince William Sound (Rude River Delta, Cordova, MacLeod Harbor, and Hanning Bay) with mass movement of preearthquake sediment and changes in grain-size distribution of postearthquake sediment.

Berg, Eduard. Crustal structure in Alaska in The Great Alaska Earthquake of 1964: Seismology and Geodesy. NAS Pub. 1602. Washington: National Academy of Sciences, in press.
Summarizes recent investigations of crustal structure by seismic, gravity, or magnetic methods.

Berg, Eduard. Triggering of the Alaskan earthquake of March 28, 1964, and major aftershocks by low ocean tide loads. *Nature,* 210 (May 28, 1966), 893–896. Also in The Great Alaska Earthquake of 1964: Seismology and Geodesy. NAS Pub. 1602. Washington: National Academy of Sciences, in press.
Indicates that the March 1964 earthquake and aftershocks were possibly triggered by low-ocean-tide loads.

Berg, Glen V., and James L. Stratta. Anchorage and the Alaska earthquake of March 27, 1964. New York: American Iron and Steel Institute, 1964. 63 p.
Reports on structural damage in the Anchorage area caused by ground displacement and vibration.

Blum, P. A., R. Gaulow, Georges Jobert, and Nelly Jobert. On ultra-long period seismometers operating under vacuum. Royal Society of London Proceedings, Series A, 290 (No. 1422, 1966), 318–322.
Gives results of the study of free oscillations from the 1964 Alaska earthquake; describes use of ultralong-period seismometer, operating in a vacuum.

Blume, John A. A structural-dynamic analysis of an earthquake damaged 14-story building in Volume II-A: The Prince William Sound, Alaska, earthquake of 1964 and aftershocks. Environmental Science Services Administration, U.S. Coast and Geodetic Survey. Washington: Government Printing Office, 1967. p. 357–382.
Analyzes data on a 14-story building at Anchorage, in light of forced-vibration tests after damage by the 1964 earthquake; also studies the building's calculated preearthquake dynamic properties.

Blume, John A., and Associates Research Division. Report on structural damage in Anchorage, Alaska, caused by the earthquake of March 27, 1964. Report prepared for Structural Response Program, Operational Safety Division, Nevada Operations Office, U.S. Atomic Energy Commission. San Francisco: John A. Blume and Associates Research Division, 1966. 91 p.
Observes and evaluates the response of typical structures to ground

motion caused by the Alaska earthquake; points out that the presence of a thick layer of sediment underlying Anchorage increased damage by amplifying ground motion and by causing landslides.

Bolt, Bruce A. Seismic air waves from the great 1964 Alaskan earthquake. *Nature,* 202 (June 13, 1964), 1095–1096.
Describes exceptional atmospheric waves, resembling those from large nuclear explosions, recorded at Berkeley after the great Alaska earthquake, and suggests the use of such detection as an additional method of tsunami prediction.

Bredehoeft, John D., Hilton H. Cooper, Jr., Istavros S. Papadopulos, and Robert R. Bennett. Seismic fluctuations in an open artesian water well in Geological Survey Research 1965: Chapter C. U.S. Geological Survey Professional Paper 525-C. Washington: Government Printing Office, 1965. p. 51–57.
Illustrates the theory of seismically induced water-level fluctuations by an analysis of the fluctuations in a northern Florida well in response to the 1964 Alaska earthquake.

Bull, Colin. The 1978–1980 surge of the Sherman Glacier, south-central Alaska. *Canadian Journal of Earth Sciences,* 6 (No. 4, 1969), 841–843.
Predicts surge-type advance in the Sherman Glacier in the near future because of the observed changes in the mass balance and movement regime of the glacier after the 1964 Alaska earthquake.

Bull, Colin, and Cedomir Marangunic. Glaciological effects of debris slide on Sherman Glacier in The Great Alaska Earthquake of 1964: Hydrology. NAS Pub. 1603. Washington: National Academy of Sciences, 1968. p. 309–317.
Notes changes in Sherman Glacier observed in 1965 and 1966, including measurements of ablation ice-surface velocities, strain nets, and the behavior of the terminus; concludes that the regimen has become strongly positive as a result of the insulating effect of the slides.

Bull, Colin, and Cedomir Marangunic. The earthquake-induced slide on the Sherman Glacier, south-central Alaska, and its glaciological effects in Physics of snow and ice. Proceedings of the International Conference on Low Temperature Science, Sapporo, Japan, 1966, Vol. 1, Part 1. Sapporo: Institute of Low Temperature Science, 1967. p. 395–408.
States that the 1964 earthquake dislodged 10^7 m^3 of rock onto a tributary of Sherman Glacier and that the debris covered about 8 km^2 of the ablation zones of the two glaciers with a layer 1–3 m thick.

Burton, Lynn R. Television examination of earthquake damage to underground communication and electrical systems in Anchorage in Effect of the earthquake of March 27, 1964, on the Eklutna Hydroelectric Project, Anchorage, Alaska. U.S. Geological Survey Professional Paper 545-A. Washington: Government Printing Office, 1967. p. 25–30.
Details the use of a small-diameter closed-circuit television camera, normally used to obtain geologic data, to locate fractures in underground communication and electrical systems after the great Alaska earthquake.

California Division of Mines and Geology. Geological hazards: Land level changes in Alaskan earthquake. *Mineral Information Service,* 18 (October 1965), 184.
Reports that the 1964 Alaska earthquake brought about the largest known surface movement of land from a single earthquake in re-

corded history and that land level was altered in a 65,000- to 77,000-mi^2 area.

California Division of Mines and Geology. Spectacular surges of glaciers reported. *Mineral Information Service,* 20 (May 1967), 51–53.
Indicates that renewed activity of Bering Glacier is probably not related to the 1964 earthquake but that surges (or sudden movements of the glaciers at speeds of 10 or 100 times faster than normal glacier flow) appear to be related to some occurrence within the glacier.

Campbell, Ian. Preparedness for disaster—The geologist's role. *Mineral Information Service,* 18 (March 1965), 51–53.
Points out that the geologic information on hand prior to the great Alaska earthquake, if it had been used, could have lessened the amount of damage. The U.S. Geological Survey had already completed and published an excellent geologic map of the area and Bulletin 1093 (Surficial Geology of the Anchorage Area, by Miller and Dobrovolny, 1959) that called attention to the seismic hazard of the Bootlegger Cove Clay.

Case, J. E., D. F. Barnes, George Plafker, and S. L. Robbins. Gravity survey and regional geology of the Prince William Sound epicentral region, Alaska. U.S. Geological Survey Professional Paper 543-C. Washington: Goverment Printing Office, 1966. 12 p. Also *in* The Great Alaska Earthquake of 1964: Geology. NAS Pub. 1601. Washington: National Academy of Sciences, 1971.
Mentions that about 500 gravity stations were established in the Prince William Sound region in conjunction with postearthquake geologic investigations, which included stratigraphy of the Valdez and Orca Groups.

Chaffin, Yule. The earthquake created a hobby. *Alaska Sportsman,* 32 (August 1966), 39–40.
Describes the finding of artifacts and ancient village sites along the beaches near Kodiak after erosion caused by the 1964 Alaska earthquake.

Chance, Genie. Chronology of physical events of the Alaskan earthquake (unpublished report). Anchorage: University of Alaska, 1966. 176 p. (Copy on file, Library, National Academy of Sciences–National Academy of Engineering, Washington, D.C.) Condensed version *in* The Great Alaska Earthquake of 1964: Summary and Recommendations. NAS Pub. 1608. Washington: National Academy of Sciences, in press.
Includes eyewitness accounts of earthquake aspects by laymen and scientists, such as Ralph Migliaccio, District Geologist, Alaska State Highway Department.

Chance, Genie. The year of decision and action *in* The Alaska earthquake, March 27, 1964: Field investigations and reconstruction effort. U.S. Geological Survey Professional Paper 541. Washington: Government Printing Office, 1966. p. 90–105.
Reports on responses of Seward, Homer, Kodiak, Cordova, Valdez, Whittier, Girdwood, Anchorage, and the native communities; describes decisions made with respect to reconstruction aided by the federal government.

Chapman, Robert M. A reconnaissance geological examination of the earthquake features in the Valdez area and along the Richardson Highway (unpublished manuscript). [Fairbanks: U.S. Geological Survey, 1964.] 9 p. (Copy on file, Library, National

Academy of Sciences–National Academy of Engineering, Washington, D.C.)
Ascribes damage in Valdez to tremors, cracking and differential rise or fall in the gravel–sand–silt alluvium and glacial outwash, the force of two waves, the soaking by salt water, and the mud and debris washed in.

Chouhan, R. K. S. Aftershock sequence of Alaskan earthquake of 28th March 1964. *Pure and Applied Geophysics,* 64 (No. II, 1966), 43–48.
Studies the aftershock sequence, using Benioff's creep theory of aftershocks, and finds that the major portion of seismic-wave energy is due to shear type of recovery.

Christensen, Mark N., and Bruce A. Bolt. Earth movements: Alaskan earthquake, 1964. *Science,* 145 (September 11, 1964), 1207–1216.
Reports that the earthquake caused numerous snow avalanches in the mountains and that these avalanches are inadequate to trigger glacier advances.

Cloud, William K., and Nina H. Scott. Distribution of intensity, Prince William Sound earthquake of 1964 *in* Volume II-B, C: The Prince William Sound, Alaska, earthquake of 1964 and aftershocks. Environmental Science Services Administration, U.S. Coast and Geodetic Survey. Washington: Government Printing Office, 1969. p. 5–48. Also *in* The Great Alaska Earthquake of 1964: Seismology and Geodesy. NAS Pub. 1602. Washington: National Academy of Sciences, in press.
Summarizes effects of the 1964 earthquake (from eyewitness accounts) on a map indicating distribution of intensity; estimates the felt area of the earthquake at approximately 700,000 mi^2, and the damage area at about 80,000 mi^2.

Committee on Earthquake Engineering Research. Earthquake engineering research. A report to the National Science Foundation prepared by the National Academy of Engineering, Division of Engineering–National Research Council. Springfield [Virginia]: Federal Clearinghouse for Scientific and Technical Information, 1969, 313 p.
Discusses problems of strong-motion seismology; soils, foundations, and earth structures; structural dynamic analysis; and postearthquake study of behavior of structures, to provide evaluation of earthquake engineering effectiveness.

Committee on the Alaska Earthquake. Toward reduction of losses from earthquakes: Conclusions from the Great Alaska Earthquake of 1964. Washington: National Academy of Sciences, 1969. 34 p.
Makes 12 recommendations on measures that can be taken to minimize loss of life and property in future earthquakes, basing the recommendations on experience from the March 27, 1964, Alaska earthquake.

Cooper, Hilton H., Jr., John D. Bredehoeft, Istavros S. Papadopulos, and Robert R. Bennett. The response of well-aquifer systems to seismic waves. *Journal of Geophysical Research,* 70 (August 15, 1965), 3915–3926. Also *in* The Great Alaska Earthquake of 1964: Hydrology. NAS Pub. 1603. Washington: National Academy of Sciences, 1968. p. 122–132.
Discusses parameters of seismic water-level fluctuations in wells and applies theory to a hydroseism of the Alaska earthquake as recorded in a Florida well.

Coulter, Henry W., and Ralph R. Migliaccio. Effects of the earthquake of March 27, 1964, at Valdez, Alaska. U.S. Geological Survey Professional Paper 542-C. Washington: Government Printing Office, 1966. 36 p. Also in The Great Alaska Earthquake of 1964: Geology. NAS Pub. 1601. Washington: National Academy of Sciences, 1971.
Discusses massive submarine landslide off the face of delta, strong waves generated by the slide, extensive fissures in the delta, and resulting damage; contrasts seismically hazardous characteristics of Valdez site to nearby Mineral Creek townsite.

Cravat, H. R., and Capt. V. Ralph Sobieralski. 1965 and 1966 photogrammetric operations in Volume III: The Prince William Sound, Alaska, earthquake of 1964 and aftershocks. Environmental Science Services Administration, U.S. Coast and Geodetic Survey. Washington: Government Printing Office, 1969. p. 121–155. Anchorage portion in The Great Alaska Earthquake of 1964: Seismology and Geodesy. NAS Pub. 1602. Washington: National Academy of Sciences, in press.
Presents aerial photogrammetric study of crustal movement in the Bootlegger Cove area of Anchorage, as well as aerial photographs of Cordova, Valdez, and Seward.

Davies, Kenneth, and Donald M. Baker. Ionospheric effects observed around the time of the Alaskan earthquake of March 28, 1964. Journal of Geophysical Research, 70 (May 1, 1965), 2251–2253.
Draws attention to ionospheric disturbances observed near Boulder, Colorado, about the time of the 1964 Alaska earthquake, and finds that they may have been caused by pressure waves generated by the movement of the earth.

Dobrovolny, Ernest. Landslide susceptibility in and near Anchorage, as interpreted from topographic and geologic maps in The Great Alaska Earthquake of 1964: Geology. NAS Pub. 1601. Washington: National Academy of Sciences, 1971.
Contains landslide-susceptibility map based in part on observations made after the great Alaska earthquake; shows how topographic and geologic maps may be used to determine possible landslide areas in the event of a strong earthquake.

Dobrovolny, Ernest, and Henry R. Schmoll. Geology as applied to urban planning—An example from the Greater Anchorage Area Borough, Alaska in Engineering geology in country planning. Proceedings of the 23rd International Geological Congress, Prague, 1968. p. 39–56.
States (1) that a 1959 geologic report, containing Anchorage lowland information useful in development planning and identifying the Bootlegger Cove Clay, reached few local planners; and (2) that special-purpose interpretive maps are being made to provide planners with necessary geologic data for future land development for human needs in Alaska.

Donn, William L. Alaskan earthquake of 27 March 1964: Remote seiche stimulation. Science, 145 (July 17, 1964), 261–262.
Discusses water waves (up to 6 ft in height) occurring along the Louisiana and Texas coasts at the time of the Alaska earthquake and finds that they were generated by and in resonance with the seismic waves.

Donn, William L., and Eric S. Posmentier. Ground-coupled air waves from the great Alaskan earthquake. Journal of Geophysical Research, 69 (December 15, 1964), 5357–5361.
Concludes that microbarographic oscillations at Palisades (New York), Berkeley (California), and Honolulu (Hawaii) at the time of arrival of seismic surface waves are real pressure variations and that they are air waves coupled to the local Rayleigh waves traveling from the epicenter.

Eckel, Edwin B. Effects of the earthquake of March 27, 1964, on air and water transport, communications, and utilities systems in south-central Alaska. U.S. Geological Survey Professional Paper 545-B. Washington: Government Printing Office, 1967. 27 p. Also in The Great Alaska Earthquake of 1964: Geology. NAS Pub. 1601. Washington: National Academy of Sciences, 1971.
Notes that utilities, communications, and all forms of transportation were wrecked or hampered by the 1964 earthquake; several, such as air facilities, were at least partly operational within hours after the earthquake.

Eckel, Edwin B. The Alaska earthquake, March 27, 1964: Lessons and conclusions. U.S. Geological Survey Professional Paper 546. Washington: Government Printing Office, 1970. 47 p. Also in The Great Alaska Earthquake of 1964: Geology. NAS Pub. 1601. Washington: National Academy of Sciences, 1971.
Summarizes geologic and hydrologic findings of the U.S. Geological Survey and includes sections on tectonics, vibration and deformation of the land surface, downslope mass movements, ground cracks, and geologic control of vibration damage.

Eckel, Edwin B., and William E. Schaem. The work of the scientific and engineering task force—Earth science applied to policy decisions in early relief and reconstruction in The Alaska earthquake, March 27, 1964: Field investigations and reconstruction effort. U.S. Geological Survey Professional Paper 541. Washington: Government Printing Office, 1966. p. 46–69. Revised in The Great Alaska Earthquake of 1964: Human Ecology. NAS Pub. 1607. Washington: National Academy of Sciences, 1970. p. 168–182.
Describes immediate response of the federal government and the work accomplished by the Federal Reconstruction and Development Planning Commission and by the Scientific and Engineering Task Force; gives objectives, accomplishments, and recommendations of the Task Force, which gathered information on parts of earthquake-damaged cities where reconstruction was inadvisable because of land-stability problems.

Engineering Geology Evaluation Group [Anchorage]. Geologic report: 27 March 1964 earthquake in Greater Anchorage area. Alaska State Housing Authority and City of Anchorage Report (unpublished). Anchorage: Alaska State Housing Authority and City of Anchorage, 1964. 47 p. plus maps and charts. (Copy on file, Library, National Academy of Sciences–National Academy of Engineering, Washington, D.C.)
Provides a very early assessment of the geological changes, with emphasis on the engineering geology of landslides in the Anchorage area, Bootlegger Cove Clay, and the monitoring of possible ground movements.

Environmental Science Services Administration. Earthquakes. Washington: Government Printing Office, 1969. 16 p.
Discusses release of strain or physical deformation of the rock structure, the four basic seismic waves (P, S, Love, and Rayleigh), earthquake magnitude, and epicenter location.

Environmental Science Services Administration. ESSA Symposium

on Earthquake Prediction, Rockville, Maryland, February 7, 8, 9, 1966. Washington: Goverment Printing Office, 1966. 167 p.
Summarizes work on the physical basis of earthquakes, instrumentation in earthquake fault zones, strong-motion seismology and soil mechanics, and geological studies of fault zones, including studies of focal mechanism and seismicity in Alaska after the 1964 earthquake.

Federal Reconstruction and Development Planning Commission for Alaska. Response to disaster: Alaskan earthquake–March 27, 1964. Washington: Goverment Printing Office, 1964. 84 p.
Describes need for accurate knowledge of the geology and soil conditions of the earthquake area, as well as judgment as to future slides and subsidence and as to precautions to minimize their occurrence.

Federal Reconstruction and Development Planning Commission for Alaska. "Thirty-day" report. Report of the Task Force on Natural Resources Development. Washington: Federal Reconstruction and Development Planning Commission for Alaska, 1964. 39 p.
Assesses the impact of the great Alaska earthquake on such natural resources of Alaska as agriculture, forests, fisheries, facilities for outdoor recreation, electric-power supply, and minerals (oil, gas, and coal).

Ferrians, Oscar J., Jr. Effects of the earthquake of March 27, 1964, in the Copper River Basin area, Alaska. U.S. Geological Survey Professional Paper 543-E. Washington: Government Printing Office, 1966. 28 p. Abstract in The Great Alaska Earthquake of 1964: Geology. NAS Pub. 1601. Washington: National Academy of Sciences, 1971.
Describes effects in water wells, sublacustrine slides off fronts of deltas, cracking of ice on lakes, ground cracks in relation to different geologic materials, snowslides, and avalanches.

Field, William O. Avalanches caused by the Alaska earthquake of March 1964 in International Symposium on Scientific Aspects of Snow and Ice Avalanches. International Association of Scientific Hydrology Publication 69. Gentbrugge [Belgium]: International Association of Scientific Hydrology, 1966. p. 326–331.
Discusses the effect of the 1964 earthquake-induced avalanches on glaciers, especially the massive rockslides that are expected to affect glacier regimen; includes details of observations during the first season of the slide on Sherman Glacier.

Field, William O. Introduction: Effects on glaciers in The Great Alaska Earthquake of 1964: Hydrology. NAS Pub. 1603. Washington: National Academy of Sciences, 1968. p. 249–251.
Gives brief review of earthquake effects on glaciers, with historical perspective and outline of the observations made after the 1964 earthquake.

Field, William O. The effect of previous earthquakes on glaciers in The Great Alaska Earthquake of 1964: Hydrology. NAS Pub. 1603. Washington: National Academy of Sciences, 1968. p. 252–265.
Reviews literature, including the Tarr-Martin theory, on observed and conjectured effects of previous earthquakes on glaciers; finds role of earthquakes in influencing glacier variations to be less than previously believed.

Field, William O., John E. Sater, and Richard H. Ragle. Effects on

glaciers of the Alaskan earthquake of March 1964: Report of an aerial reconnaissance, 14 to 19 April 1964. Arctic Institute of North America Research Paper 28 (unpublished manuscript). Washington: Arctic Institute of North America, 1964. 26 p. (Copy on file, Library, National Academy of Sciences–National Academy of Engineering, Washington, D.C.)
Summarizes the effects of the 1964 earthquake on glaciers as observed in photographic flights.

Fisher, Walter E., and Douglas H. Merkle. The great Alaska earthquake (2 vols.). Air Force Weapons Laboratory Technical Report AFWL-TR-65-92. Kirtland Air Force Base [New Mexico]: Air Force Systems Command, Research and Technology Division, 1965. 100 p. (vol. I); 312 p. (vol. II).
Summarizes crevasses, pressure ridges, and landslides produced by the Alaska earthquake; also evaluates engineering structures damaged by the shocks.

Foley, Robert E. Crescent City: Tidal waves. Shore and Beach, 32 (April 1964), 28.
Describes Crescent City damage caused by tidal lifting of some structures, with washout underneath, and by deposited sand washed away from the shore.

Foster, Helen L., and Thor N. V. Karlstrom. Ground breakage and associated effects in the Cook Inlet area, Alaska, resulting from the March 27, 1964, earthquake. U.S. Geological Survey Professional Paper 543-F. Washington: Government Printing Office, 1967. 28 p. Abstract in The Great Alaska Earthquake of 1964: Geology. NAS Pub. 1601. Washington: National Academy of Sciences, 1971.
Describes ground cracks and deposits from groundwater eruptions (extrusions) throughout Kenai Lowland; discusses origin by faulting, settling, and sliding.

Furumoto, Augustine S. A study of the source mechanism of the Alaska earthquake and tsunami of March 27, 1964: Part II, Analysis of Rayleigh wave. Pacific Science, 21 (July 1967), 311–316. Also in The Great Alaska Earthquake of 1964: Seismology and Geodesy. NAS Pub. 1602. Washington: National Academy of Sciences, in press. See also Report HIG-65-17. Honolulu: University of Hawaii, Institute of Geophysics, 1965. p. 31–42.
Investigates the source mechanism of the 1964 earthquake by analyzing the Rayleigh wave recorded on the strain seismograph at Kipapa Station, Hawaii; finds that results compare favorably with field data on the earthquake.

Gabert, G. M. Groundwater-level fluctuations in Alberta, Canada, caused by the Prince William Sound, Alaska, earthquake of March, 1964. Canadian Journal of Earth Sciences, 2 (April 1965), 131–139. Also in The Great Alaska Earthquake of 1964: Hydrology. NAS Pub. 1603. Washington: National Academy of Sciences, 1968. p. 190–195.
Finds that groundwater-level fluctuations caused by the 1964 earthquake had amplitudes ranging from less than 0.01 ft to greater than 5 ft in 24 wells in Alberta, the largest being recorded in a well completed in a thick, permeable, confined aquifer.

Galliett, Harold H., George C. Silides, and Michael Baker, Jr. The Alaska Railroad, U.S. Department of the Interior: Proposal for investigation, report, and design of relocations and grade changes, Anchorage to Portage–A joint venture. Washington: U.S. Department of the Interior [1964]. 43 p.

Proposes securing available information on the geology, soils, and hydrology of the area from Anchorage to Portage; preparing a soils map; and submitting recommendations for work needed.

George, Warren, and Robert E. Lyle. Reconstruction by the Corps of Engineers—Methods and accomplishments *in* The Alaska earthquake, March 27, 1964: Field investigations and reconstruction effort. U.S. Geological Survey Professional Paper 541. Washington: Government Printing Office, 1966. p. 81–89.
Details the need for geologic and soils studies, which, when completed, gave conclusions regarding the ground-motion waves, soil failure, and future movements of slide areas.

Goldthwait, Richard P. General introduction: The effects of the Alaska earthquake on the hydrologic regimen *in* The Great Alaska Earthquake of 1964: Hydrology. NAS Pub. 1603. Washington: National Academy of Sciences, 1968. p. 1–4.
Introduces the Hydrology volume and notes such hydrologic effects of the 1964 earthquake as lasting water-level changes, earthquake magnitudes from well-water reactions, avalanche cushioning, and the lack of glacier-surge reaction.

Goldthwait, Richard P. Hydrologic hazards from earthquakes *in* The Great Alaska Earthquake of 1964: Hydrology. NAS Pub. 1603. Washington: National Academy of Sciences, 1968. p. 405–414.
Evaluates hazards to life and property from snowslides, far-traveling debris avalanches, floods, seiches, and groundwater spouts; suggests 11 steps to prevent or reduce losses.

Goodman, Richard E., and H. Bolton Seed. Earthquake-induced displacements in sand embankments. *Journal of the Soil Mechanics and Foundations Division*, 92 (March 1966), 125–146.
States that if an embankment of dense granular material is accelerated so that all points of the slope experience approximately the same acceleration at the same time, the result of overstressing is a surface slide involving a thin layer of soil.

Grantz, Arthur, George Plafker, and Reuben Kachadoorian. Alaska's Good Friday earthquake, March 27, 1964: A preliminary geologic evaluation. U.S. Geological Survey Circular 491. Washington: U.S. Geological Survey, 1964. 35 p.
Describes areas of tectonic uplift and subsidence; effects on land, on coasts; hydrologic effects; and damage to communities, transportation routes, and industries.

Gronewald, Gail J., and Walter W. Duncan. Study of erosion along Homer Spit and vicinity, Kachemak Bay, Alaska. Proceedings of the Specialty Conference (1965) on Coastal Engineering, Santa Barbara (Chapter 27). New York: American Society of Civil Engineers, 1966. p. 673–682.
Presents information on the rapid acceleration of the erosion processes due to the subsidence of Homer Spit during the 1964 earthquake.

Gryc, George. Earthquake questionnaire results. Memorandum from Chief, Alaskan Geology Branch, to USGS Geologists in Alaska. Menlo Park, California: U.S. Geological Survey, 1964. 8 p. (Copy on file, Library, National Academy of Sciences–National Academy of Engineering, Washington, D.C.)
Gives first-hand information on pressure ridges, landslides, subsidences, water spouts, trees broken during the earthquake, and other features of interest to geologists.

Hackman, Robert J. Interpretation of Alaskan post-earthquake photographs. *Photogrammetric Engineering*, 31 (July 1965), 604–610. Also *in* The Great Alaska Earthquake of 1964: Hydrology. NAS Pub. 1603. Washington: National Academy of Sciences, 1968. p. 40–46.
Reports on stereoscopic examination of 2,000 aerial photographs taken after the March 1964 earthquake that show uplifted shorelines where landslides overlapped the former beach lines.

Hanna, G Dallas. Biological effects of an earthquake. *Pacific Discovery,* 17 (November–December 1964), 24–26. Also *in* The Great Alaska Earthquake of 1964: Biology. NAS Pub. 1604. Washington: National Academy of Sciences, 1971.
Reports use of the upper limit of recently killed barnacles as a datum plane from which to measure uplift. The algae above the line of demarcation, at first thought to be *Ralfsia,* has since been identified as *Verrucaria.*

Hanna, G Dallas. Introduction: Biological effects of the earthquake as observed in 1965 *in* The Great Alaska Earthquake of 1964: Biology. NAS Pub. 1604. Washington: National Academy of Sciences, 1971.
Introduces three other biological papers and describes the 33 stations and transects in Prince William Sound made by the biologists and geologists on the special 1965 survey of earthquake effects conducted by the California Academy of Sciences from M.V. *Harmony*.

Hanna, G Dallas. The great Alaska earthquake of 1964. *Pacific Discovery,* 20 (May–June 1967), 25–30.
Evaluates effect of the 1964 earthquake on the animal and plant populations of the Prince William Sound area; mentions loss of animal and plant life due to their exposure to air when the tide failed to return as a result of the uplift.

Hansen, Wallace R. Effects of the earthquake of March 27, 1964, at Anchorage, Alaska. U.S. Geological Survey Professional Paper 542-A. Washington: Government Printing Office, 1965. 68 p. Also *in* The Great Alaska Earthquake of 1964: Geology. NAS Pub. 1601. Washington: National Academy of Sciences, 1971.
Describes and analyzes the most damaging ground response, the translatory slides; describes characteristics of Bootlegger Cove Clay in relation to slides; and summarizes vibratory damaging effects.

Hansen, Wallace R. Investigations by the Geological Survey *in* The Alaska earthquake, March 27, 1964: Field investigations and reconstruction effort. U.S. Geological Survey Professional Paper 541. Washington: Government Printing Office, 1966. p. 38–45.
Reviews the contributions of many geologists to solving geologic problems relating to pattern of sea-level changes, outlook for fisheries, effects on water supply and soil environments.

Hansen, Wallace R. The Alaska earthquake of 1964. *Nature,* 215 (July 22, 1967), 348–351.
Discusses magnitude of the main shock and aftershocks, intensity deformation, effect on flora and fauna, and effects on the fishing industry.

Hansen, Wallace R., and Edwin B. Eckel. A summary description of the Alaska earthquake—Its setting and effects *in* The Alaska earthquake, March 27, 1964: Field investigations and reconstruction effort. U.S. Geological Survey Professional Paper 541. Washington: Government Printing Office, 1966. p. 1–37. Also

in The Great Alaska Earthquake of 1964: Geology. NAS Pub. 1601. Washington: National Academy of Sciences, 1971.
Summarizes the physiographic and geologic setting of the great Alaska earthquake tectonic effects, damage to transportation, and atmospheric and possible magnetic effects.

Hansen, Wallace R., Edwin B. Eckel, William E. Schaem, Robert E. Lyle, Warren George, and Genie Chance. The Alaska earthquake, March 27, 1964: Field investigations and reconstruction effort. U.S. Geological Survey Professional Paper 541. Washington: Government Printing Office, 1966. 111 p.
Deals with the geologic setting and effects, the field investigations, and the public and private reconstruction efforts after the 1964 earthquake.

Harding, Samuel T., and S. T. Algermissen. The focal mechanism of the Prince William Sound earthquake of March 28, 1964, and related earthquakes *in* Volume II-B,C: The Prince William Sound, Alaska, earthquake of 1964 and aftershocks. Environmental Science Services Administration, U.S. Coast and Geodetic Survey. Washington: Government Printing Office, 1969. p. 185–221. Also *in* The Great Alaska Earthquake of 1964: Seismology and Geodesy. NAS Pub. 1602. Washington: National Academy of Sciences, in press.
Presents focal mechanism solutions for the main shock, two pre-shocks, and six aftershocks of the 1964 earthquake, as well as composite focal mechanisms.

Hirshberg, Joan, Robert G. Currie, and Sheldon Breiner. Long period geomagnetic fluctuations after the 1964 Alaskan earthquake. *Earth and Planetary Science Letters* (Amsterdam), 3 (February 1968), 426–428. Also *in* The Great Alaska Earthquake of 1964: Seismology and Geodesy. NAS Pub. 1602. Washington: National Academy of Sciences, in press.
Contains power spectra of the geomagnetic field (after the 1964 earthquake) that show lines with frequencies of several of the greatest torsional eigenmodes of the earth.

Hoyer, Marcus C. Puget Peak avalanche, Alaska. *Geological Society of America Bulletin*, 82 (May 1971), 1267–1284. Abstract *in* The Great Alaska Earthquake of 1964: Geology. NAS Pub. 1601. Washington: National Academy of Sciences, 1971.
Describes large rockfall avalanche from Puget Peak (1,198 m) 32 mi ESE of Seward, with large amounts of snow and soil incorporated into the debris as it moved and evidence that snow acted as the slide plane.

Johnson, Noye M., and Richard H. Ragle. Analysis of flow characteristics of Allen II slide from aerial photographs *in* The Great Alaska Earthquake of 1964: Hydrology. NAS Pub. 1603. Washington: National Academy of Sciences, 1968. p. 369–373.
Observes that the form of some slides suggests complete turbulence during flow and that others give evidence for controlled shearing; states that many of the features observed in the slides can be explained by a steady-state flow model and the effects of vertical shear.

Kachadoorian, Reuben. Effects of the earthquake of March 27, 1964 at Whittier, Alaska. U.S. Geological Survey Professional Paper 542-B. Washington: Government Printing Office, 1965. 21 p. Also *in* The Great Alaska Earthquake of 1964: Geology. NAS Pub. 1601. Washington: National Academy of Sciences, 1971.
Ascribes earthquake damage at Whittier to a 5.3-ft subsidence of the landmass, seismic shock, fracturing of fill, compaction of fill, submarine landslides, two or three waves generated by landslides, and fire.

Kachadoorian, Reuben. Effects of the earthquake of March 27, 1964, on the Alaska highway system. U.S. Geological Survey Professional Paper 545-C. Washington: Government Printing Office, 1968. 66 p. Also *in* The Great Alaska Earthquake of 1964: Geology. NAS Pub. 1601. Washington: National Academy of Sciences, 1971.
Concludes that the intensity of earthquake damage to the Alaska highway system was controlled primarily by the geologic environment (including the depth of the water table) upon which the highway structures rested, and secondarily by the engineering characteristics of the structures.

Kachadoorian, Reuben, and George Plafker. Effects of the earthquake of March 27, 1964, on the communities of Kodiak and nearby islands. U.S. Geological Survey Professional Paper 542-F. Washington: Government Printing Office, 1967. 41 p. Abstract *in* The Great Alaska Earthquake of 1964: Geology. NAS Pub. 1601. Washington: National Academy of Sciences, 1971.
Reports that damage to Kodiak was caused chiefly by 5.6 ft of tectonic subsidence and 10 tsunamis.

Kanamori, Hiroo. The Alaska earthquake of 1964: Radiation of long-period surface waves and source mechanism. *Journal of Geophysical Research*, 75 (September 10, 1970), 5029–5040. Also *in* The Great Alaska Earthquake of 1964: Seismology and Geodesy. NAS Pub. 1602. Washington: National Academy of Sciences, in press.
Compares the seismograms recorded by the World-Wide Network of Standard Seismographs (WWNSS stations) with synthetic seismograms for radiation pattern and amplitude to estimate source parameters; finds that the moment and width of the fault plane of the Alaska earthquake are much larger than those of any other earthquake reported.

Kawasumi, Hirosi, and Etsuzo Shima. Spectra of microtremors observed in the city of Anchorage and their relation to soils *in* Volume II-A: The Prince William Sound, Alaska, earthquake of 1964 and aftershocks. Environmental Science Services Administration, U.S. Coast and Geodetic Survey. Washington: Government Printing Office, 1967. p. 299–331.
Studies the frequency characteristics of the ground surface and their relationships to subsoil structures in Anchorage and finds that the subsoil layers at the shoreline are thicker than inland.

Kerr, Paul F., and Isabella M. Drew. Quick clay movements, Anchorage, Alaska: A preliminary report. Air Force Cambridge Research Laboratories Scientific Report 5 (AFCRL-66-78). Bedford, Massachusetts: U.S. Air Force, Office of Aerospace Research, 1965. 133 p.
Notes that during the 1964 earthquake, quick clay movement at Anchorage initiated slide action with deformation in overlying silts and gravel; also, that old slide areas along the bluffs contains heterogeneous materials that appear to form a mass resistant to quick clay flowage.

Kirkby, M. J., and Anne V. Kirkby. Erosion and deposition on a beach raised by the 1964 earthquake, Montague Island, Alaska. U.S. Geological Survey Professional Paper 543-H. Washington: Government Printing Office, 1969. 41 p. Abstract *in* The Great Alaska Earthquake of 1964: Geology. NAS Pub. 1601. Washington: National Academy of Sciences, 1971.
Finds no appreciable erosion of bedrock on the raised beach 15 months after the earthquake; uses the 1964 raised beach to test accuracy of identification of former sea-level elevations from raised beach features.

LaChapelle, Edward R. The character of snow avalanching induced by the Alaska earthquake *in* The Great Alaska Earthquake of 1964: Hydrology. NAS Pub. 1603. Washington: National Academy of Sciences, 1968. p. 355–361.
Finds a clear pattern of two separate avalanche cycles generated by the 1964 earthquake, with the first shock triggering the displacement of already unstable surface layers of large cornices and with the fracturing of deep drifts causing the second series of avalanches.

Lantz, Bill, and Mildred Kirkpatrick. Seward quake: Good Friday 1964. Seward: Kirkpatrick Printing Co., 1964. 56 p.
Recounts destruction in Seward and graphically illustrates geologic conditions; includes Seward map of high-risk areas of unstable land and of nominal-risk areas.

Lemke, Richard W. Effects of the earthquake of March 27, 1964, at Seward, Alaska. U.S. Geological Survey Professional Paper 542-E. Washington: Government Printing Office, 1967. 43 p. Also *in* The Great Alaska Earthquake of 1964: Geology. NAS Pub. 1601. Washington: National Academy of Sciences, 1971.
Describes and analyzes submarine landslide off face of delta, the geologic setting (bedrock and kinds of surficial deposits), responses of various geologic materials, and relation to damage.

Leonard, Robert S., and R. A. Barnes, Jr. Observation of ionospheric disturbances following the Alaska earthquake. *Journal of Geophysical Research,* 70 (March 1, 1965), 1250–1253.
Analyzes ionospheric disturbances recorded by ionosondes at College and Adak (Alaska), Palo Alto (California), and Maui (Hawaii) after the great Alaska earthquake; also observes pressure disturbances at ground level.

Logan, Malcolm H. Effect of the earthquake of March 27, 1964, on the Eklutna Hydroelectric Project, Anchorage, Alaska (*with a section on* Television examination of earthquake damage to underground communication and electrical systems in Anchorage, by Lynn R. Burton). U.S. Geological Survey Professional Paper 545-A. Washington: Government Printing Office, 1967. 30 p. Abstract *in* The Great Alaska Earthquake of 1964: Geology. NAS Pub. 1601. Washington: National Academy of Sciences, 1971.
Indicates that the intake structure in Eklutna Lake was damaged by densification of unconsolidated sediments and overburden.

Long, Erwin, and Warren George. Buttress design earthquake-induced slides. *Journal of the Soil Mechanics and Foundations Division,* 93 (July 1967), 595–609.
Explains that stabilization of the Fourth Avenue slide in Anchorage was accomplished by construction of a gravel buttress designed to resist forces caused by sand or clay liquefaction, horizontal or circular sliding, or slumping.

Long, Erwin, and Warren George. Turnagain slide stabilization, Anchorage, Alaska. *Journal of the Soil Mechanics and Foundations Division*, 93 (July 1967), 611–627.
Mentions tests conducted in early 1966 that show that soil strength under the seaward toe of the Turnagain slide would not fail in an equivalent future earthquake.

Lyle, Robert E., and Warren George. Activities of the Corps of Engineers—Cleanup and early reconstruction *in* The Alaska earthquake, March 27, 1964: Field investigations and reconstruction effort. U.S. Geological Survey Professional Paper 541. Washington: Government Printing Office, 1966. p. 70–80.
Deals with the damage surveys and restoration work done in An-

chorage, Seward, Cordova, Homer, Seldovia, Whittier, and other communities.

McCulloch, David S. Slide-induced waves, seiching, and ground fracturing caused by the earthquake of March 27, 1964, at Kenai Lake, Alaska. U.S. Geological Survey Professional Paper 543-A. Washington: Government Printing Office, 1966. 41 p. Also *in* The Great Alaska Earthquake of 1964: Hydrology. NAS Pub. 1603. Washington: National Academy of Sciences, 1968. p. 47–81. Abstract *in* The Great Alaska Earthquake of 1964: Geology. NAS Pub. 1601. Washington: National Academy of Sciences, 1971.
Describes ground fractures produced by the earthquake on Lakeview and Rocky Creek deltas in Kenai Lake.

McCulloch, David S., and Manuel G. Bonilla. Effects of the earthquake of March 27, 1964, on The Alaska Railroad. U.S. Geological Survey Professional Paper 545-D. Washington: Government Printing Office, 1970. 161 p. Condensed *in* The Great Alaska Earthquake of 1964: Geology. NAS Pub. 1601. Washington: National Academy of Sciences, 1971.
Stresses that damage to The Alaska Railroad from the earthquake was caused by landslides, regional tectonic subsidence, and land-spreading (lateral displacement and distension of mobilized sediments).

McGarr, Arthur. Excitation of seiches in channels by seismic waves. *Journal of Geophysical Research*, 70 (February 15, 1965), 847–854. Also *in* The Great Alaska Earthquake of 1964: Hydrology. NAS Pub. 1603. Washington: National Academy of Sciences, 1968. p. 133–139.
Discusses seiche of Alaska earthquake recorded at Freeport, Texas, and develops theory to explain the generation, distribution, and damping of seiches.

McGarr, Arthur, and Robert C. Vorhis. Seismic seiches from the March 1964 Alaska earthquake. U.S. Geological Survey Professional Paper 544-E. Washington: Government Printing Office, 1968. 43 p. Also *in* The Great Alaska Earthquake of 1964: Hydrology. NAS Pub. 1603. Washington: National Academy of Sciences, 1968. p. 196–236.
Relates occurrence of seismic seiches throughout North America to seismic and geologic parameters.

McKenzie, D. P., and R. L. Parker. The North Pacific: An example of tectonics on a sphere. *Nature*, 216 (December 30, 1967), 1276–1280.
Indicates that individual aseismic areas move as rigid plates on the surface of a sphere and that the paving-stone theory of world tectonics is correct and applies to about a quarter of the earth's surface. Refers to 1964 Alaska earthquake work of Stauder and Bollinger (1966).

Malloy, Richard J. Crustal uplift southwest of Montague Island, Alaska. *Science*, 146 (November 20, 1964), 1048–1049.
Compares submarine crustal uplift studied by the U.S. Coast and Geodetic Survey ship *Surveyor* in June and July 1964 with a hydrographic survey made in 1927; finds maximum submarine uplift just north of the fault southwest of Montague Island.

Malloy, Richard J. Gulf of Alaska: Seafloor upheaval. *Geo-Marine Technology*, 1 (May–June 1965), 22–26.
Finds that maximum uplift on land was 33 ft on Montague Island's southwest end; investigates the earthquake's effect on the sea floor in the area of suspected maximum uplift.

[803]

Malloy, Richard J. Marine geological reconnaissance of epicentral and aftershock regions 1964 Alaska earthquake (unpublished manuscript). Rockville, Maryland: Environmental Science Services Administration, Institute for Oceanography, 1967. 45 p. (Copy on file, Library, National Academy of Sciences–National Academy of Engineering, Washington, D.C.)
Determines that only a portion of the sea floor in the regions of the 1964 earthquake exhibited measurable open-water submarine tectonic deformation; states that the Aleutian Trench appears to be in a period of active submergence.

Malloy, Richard J., and George F. Merrill. Vertical crustal movement of the sea floor associated with the Prince William Sound, Alaska, earthquake in Volume II-B,C: The Prince William Sound, Alaska, earthquake of 1964 and aftershocks. Environmental Science Services Administration, U.S. Coast and Geodetic Survey. Washington: Government Printing Office, 1969. p. 327–338. Also in The Great Alaska Earthquake of 1964: Oceanography and Coastal Engineering. NAS Pub. 1605. Washington: National Academy of Sciences, in press.
Reveals a sea-floor uplift of more than 15 m in areas southwest of Montague Island, with fresh fault scarps traced seaward a distance of 19 km.

Mansinha, L., and D. E. Smylie. Effect of earthquakes on the Chandler wobble and the secular polar shift. Journal of Geophysical Research, 72 (September 15, 1967), 4731–4743. See revised version by Smylie and Mansinha in The Great Alaska Earthquake of 1964: Seismology and Geodesy. NAS Pub. 1602. Washington: National Academy of Sciences, in press.
Concludes that both the Chandler-wobble excitation and the secular polar shift could be caused by earthquakes; finds the far-field displacements to be remarkably extensive according to the elasticity theory of dislocation.

Marangunic, Cedomir, and Colin Bull. The landslide on the Sherman Glacier in The Great Alaska Earthquake of 1964: Hydrology. NA NAS Pub. 1603. Washington: National Academy of Sciences, 1968. p. 383–394..
States that the slide dislodged about 1.1×10^7 m³ of rock from the east wall of a tributary glacier; that the debris sheet, supported on an air cushion, moved to cover about 8.5 km² of the glacier's ablation zone with a layer 1.3 m thick; and that the slide scar is about 700 m wide and more than 1,000 m long in the direction of the slip.

Marcus, Melvin G. Effects on glacier-dammed lakes in the Chugach and Kenai mountains in The Great Alaska Earthquake of 1964: Hydrology. NAS Pub. 1603. Washington: National Academy of Sciences, 1968. p. 329–347.
Considers ice-dammed lakes in which minor disturbances attributed to the earthquake were observed but no major changes were identified.

Matthews, D. H. Earthquake in Alaska 28 March 1964. Polar Record, 12 (September 1964), 309–311.
Relates the earthquake to the geological age and origin of prominently affected areas and to earthquake zones in the region. The rocks range in age from the Mesozoic sediments of the Chugach geosyncline to the unconsolidated fluvioglacial deposits of the Quaternary at Anchorage.

Matumoto, Tosimatu, and Robert A. Page, Jr. Microaftershocks following the Alaska earthquake of March 28, 1964: Determination of hypocenters and crustal velocities in the Kenai Peninsula–Prince William Sound area in Volume II-B,C: The Prince William Sound, Alaska, earthquake of 1964 and aftershocks. Environmental Science Services Administration, U.S. Coast and Geodetic Survey. Washington: Goverment Printing Office, 1969. p. 157–173. Also in The Great Alaska Earthquake of 1964: Seismology and Geodesy. NAS Pub. 1602. Washington: National Academy of Sciences, in press.
Describes program at Lamont Geological Observatory to record microaftershocks, most of which occurred in the uplifted tectonic block.

Meade, Buford K. Precise surveys of the Anchorage monitoring system in Volume III: The Prince William Sound, Alaska, earthquake of 1964 and aftershocks. Environmental Science Services Administration, U.S. Coast and Geodetic Survey. Washington: Government Printing Office, 1969. p. 113–118. Also in The Great Alaska Earthquake of 1964: Seismology and Geodesy. NAS Pub. 1602. Washington: National Academy of Sciences, in press.
Gives the observations, adjustments, and results of the program for re-observing the primary triangulation networks in the Anchorage–Prince William Sound area.

Meehan, John F. The response of several public school buildings in Anchorage, Alaska, to the March 27, 1964, earthquake in Volume II-A: The Prince William Sound, Alaska, earthquake of 1964 and aftershocks. Environmental Science Services Administration, U.S. Coast and Geodetic Survey. Washington: Government Printing Office, 1967. p. 219–243.
Recommends that a definite, adequate, and logical path of lateral load resistance must be provided in structures located in earthquake areas; suggests consideration of geologic conditions of the geographical area.

Migliaccio, Ralph R. Earthquake damage to highways in the Valdez district, Alaska in Highway Research Record Number 91: Road Crown, Testing, Compaction, Soil Bitumen; The Alaska Earthquake, 7 Reports. Highway Research Board of the National Academy of Sciences–National Research Council. NAS Pub. 1307. Washington: National Academy of Sciences. 1965. p. 64–72.
Points out that the degree of earthquake damage to the highways around Valdez is a direct reflection of the geologic environment of the structure or highway.

Migliaccio, Ralph R. Earthquake of March 27, 1964. Report of District Geologist, Valdez, to Chief Geologist, College. Valdez: Office of the District Geologist, 1964. 6 p. (Copy on file, Library, National Academy of Sciences–National Academy of Engineering, Washington, D.C.)
Describes the sequence of events in Valdez at the time of the earthquake and gives the opinion of a geologist on the causes.

Mikumo, Takeshi. Atmospheric pressure waves and tectonic deformation associated with the Alaskan earthquake of March 28, 1964. Journal of Geophysical Research, 73 (March 15, 1968), 2009–2025.
Concludes that large-scale ground deformations such as those accompanying the Alaska earthquake could generate atmospheric pressure waves observable at long distances.

Moore, George W. Magnetic disturbances preceding the 1964 Alaska earthquake. Nature, 203 (August 1, 1964), 508–509. Also in The Great Alaska Earthquake of 1964: Seismology and Geodesy. NAS Pub. 1602. Washington: National Academy of Sciences, in press.
Suggests that large positive magnetic disturbances recorded before

the earthquake indicate magnetic monitoring as a means of predicting a major earthquake.

National Board of Fire Underwriters and Pacific Fire Rating Bureau. The Alaska earthquake, March 27, 1964. San Francisco: The National Board of Fire Underwriters, 1964. 35 p.
Emphasizes the elevation change of large land masses, earthslides, and ground settlements as requiring provisions for earthquake-resistive design and consideration of soil conditions at building sites.

Nickerson, Richard B. Fish and the big shake. *Alaska Sportsman,* 35 (March 1969), 6–9, 51–52.
Reports on the fisheries rehabilitation made necessary by the uplift and subsidence resulting from the 1964 earthquake on Prince William Sound; describes a large-scale program encompassing a heavy outlay of engineering equipment operated under sound biological concepts.

Nielsen, Lawrence E. Earthquake-induced changes in Alaskan glaciers. *Journal of Glaciology,* 5 (October 1965), 865–867.
States that the 1964 earthquake created many rock avalanches that discharged onto the glaciers from the surrounding mountains, with more open crevasses than before the earthquake.

Northrop, John. *T* phases from 80 Alaskan earthquakes, March 28–31, 1964. *Bulletin of the Seismological Society of America,* 55 (February 1965), 59–63.
Points out that a large *T*-phase signal was received at Pt. Sur, California, from the 1964 earthquake and that additional *T* phases were received from 90 percent of the 80 aftershocks in the Kodiak Island area, with the largest ones being received from hypocenters beneath the upper portion of the Continental Shelf.

Nowroozi, Ali A. Eigenvibrations of the earth after the Alaskan earthquake. *Journal of Geophysical Research,* 70 (October 15, 1965), 5145–5156. Also *in* The Great Alaska Earthquake of 1964: Seismology and Geodesy. NAS Pub. 1602. Washington: National Academy of Sciences, in press.
Discusses measurements of the free oscillations of the earth after the earthquake and mentions the determination of an azimuthal order number *m* and the amplitude variations of the spectrums in terms of the pattern of nodal lines.

Nowroozi, Ali A. Measurement of *Q* values from the free oscillations of the earth. *Journal of Geophysical Research,* 73 (February 15, 1968), 1407–1415.
Estimates the *Q* values for spheroidal and torsional oscillations of the earth from time decay of spectral amplitudes for each mode, by using data from the 1964 Alaska earthquake and the 1965 Aleutian earthquake.

Office of Science and Technology. Earthquake prediction: A proposal for a ten year program of research. A report prepared by the Ad Hoc Panel on Earthquake Prediction. Washington: Office of Science and Technology, 1965. 136 p.
Recommends programs for a 10-year research effort to accomplish earthquake prediction; suggests geophysical and geological surveys of earthquake fault zones, as well as research on the physical basis of earthquakes and on earthquake engineering.

Office of Science and Technology. Proposal for a ten-year national earthquake hazards program: A partnership of science and the community. Prepared by the Ad Hoc Interagency Working Group

for Earthquake Research of the Federal Council for Science and Technology. Washington: Office of Science and Technology, December 1968. 81 p.
Proposes a program to study guidelines for safe development of U.S. urban areas vulnerable to earthquake hazards, based on evaluation of such hazards in previous earthquakes such as that in Alaska in 1964.

Oliver, Jack. Earthquake prediction. *Science,* 153 (August 26, 1966), 1024–1026.
Comments on the increasing interest in earthquake mechanisms and prediction as shown at the Conference on Research Related to Earthquake Prediction, where George Plafker described the geological setting of the Alaska earthquake.

Orlin, Hyman. Gravity surveys *in* ESSA Symposium on Earthquake Prediction. Washington: Government Printing Office, 1966. p. 128–130.
Stresses the need for geophysical surveys, with the Alaska earthquake providing an ideal opportunity to determine gravity variations over a short time period.

Page, Robert. Aftershocks and microaftershocks of the great Alaska earthquake of 1964. *Bulletin of the Seismological Society of America,* 58 (June 1968), 1131–1168.
Gives results of a field program to record microaftershocks of the Alaska earthquake for the purpose of furnishing new information on the aftershock process.

Paige, Russell A. Advance of Walsh Glacier. *Journal of Glaciology,* 5 (October 1965), 876–878.
Suggests that the spectacular advance of Walsh Glacier (in the St. Elias Range, Yukon Territory, near the Alaska border) is related to the 1964 Alaska earthquake.

Pakiser, L. C., J. P. Eaton, J. H. Healy, and C. B. Raleigh. Earthquake prediction and control. *Science,* 166 (December 19, 1969), 1467–1474.
Looks beyond earthquake prediction to controlled release of stored strain energy in active fault zones.

Pararas-Carayannis, George. Water waves, Part I *in* Source mechanism study of the Alaska earthquake and tsunami of 27 March 1964. Report HIG-65-17. Honolulu: University of Hawaii, Institute of Geophysics, 1965. p. 1–30. Also *in* The Great Alaska Earthquake of 1964: Seismology and Geodesy. NAS Pub. 1602. Washington: National Academy of Sciences, in press. See also *Pacific Science,* 21 (July 1967), 301–310.
Determines the tsunami-generating area and discusses the extent of crustal displacement and the limits of the areas of subsidence and uplift revealed by geologic evidence.

Pararas-Carayannis, George, and Augustine S. Furumoto. Source mechanism study of the Alaska earthquake and tsunami of 27 March 1964. Report HIG-65-17. Honolulu: University of Hawaii, Institute of Geophysics, 1965. 42 p.
Determines the dimensions of the tsunami-generating area, its volume of crustal displacement, and the energy associated with the tsunami; investigates the source mechanism by analyzing the Rayleigh wave recorded at Kipapa Station, Hawaii.

Parkin, Ernest J. Alaskan surveys to determine crustal movement. Part II: Horizontal displacement. Paper presented at Annual Meeting of American Congress on Surveying and Mapping,

Washington, D.C., March 10, 1966. Rockville, Maryland: U.S. Coast and Geodetic Survey, 1966. 15 p. See also *Surveying and Mapping*, 27 (1967), 423–430.
Discusses the horizontal displacement of the earth's crust, as shown by a comparison of the results of triangulation and traverse surveys made before and after the earthquake.

Parkin, Ernest J. Horizontal crustal movements determined from surveys after the Alaskan earthquake of 1964 *in* Volume III: The Prince William Sound, Alaska, earthquake of 1964 and aftershocks. Environmental Science Services Administration, U.S. Coast and Geodetic Survey. Washington: Goverment Printing Office, 1969. p. 35–98. Also *in* The Great Alaska Earthquake of 1964: Seismology and Geodesy. NAS Pub. 1602. Washington: National Academy of Sciences, in press.
Finds that a comparison of pre- and postearthquake geographic positions indicates horizontal displacements of 50 ft or more.

Péwé, Troy L. Introduction: Avalanches on glaciers and the effects of snowslides *in* The Great Alaska Earthquake of 1964: Hydrology. NAS Pub. 1603. Washington: National Academy of Sciences, 1968. p. 351–354.
States that the amount of snow that cascaded from the peaks was small compared with the size of the included area, that the majority of the debris slides were small, and that many avalanches with snow were deposited on glaciers.

Péwé, Troy L. Preliminary geologic observations of March 27 earthquake in Alaska. *Fairbanks Daily News-Miner* ["Earthquake Disaster Edition"], 42 (Good Friday, March 27, 1964), 21, col. 1–9.
Represents the first geologic report on the earthquake to appear in print; mentions that lake and river ice in the Kenai Peninsula area was cracked and that snowslides were observed in the Kenai Mountains.

Plafker, George. Source areas of the Shattered Peak and Pyramid Peak landslides at Sherman Glacier *in* The Great Alaska Earthquake of 1964: Hydrology. NAS Pub. 1603. Washington: National Academy of Sciences, 1968. p. 374–382.
Calculates the volumes of debris from the two landslides (33.7 and 6.4 million yd^3, respectively) by comparing pre- and postearthquake topographic maps of the peak area; states that the slide failures were due to steep unstable slopes and to fractures and steeply dipping bedding planes.

Plafker, George. Surface faults on Montague Island associated with the 1964 Alaska earthquake. U.S. Geological Survey Professional Paper 543-G. Washington: Government Printing Office, 1967. 42 p. Also *in* The Great Alaska Earthquake of 1964: Geology. NAS Pub. 1601. Washington: National Academy of Sciences, 1971.
Contains description and tectonic analysis of ground breakage and surface warping along two reverse faults reactivated during the Alaska earthquake–the Patton Bay and Hanning Bay faults.

Plafker, George. Tectonic deformation associated with the 1964 Alaska earthquake. *Science*, 148 (June 25, 1965), 1675–1687.
Points out that the Alaska earthquake was accompanied by vertical tectonic deformation over an area of 170,000 to 200,000 km^2; postulates that the earthquake is genetically related to the Aleutian Arc.

Plafker, George. Tectonics of the March 27, 1964, Alaska earth-

quake. U.S. Geological Survey Professional Paper 543-I. Washington: Goverment Printing Office, 1969. 74 p. Also *in* The Great Alaska Earthquake of 1964: Geology. NAS Pub. 1601. Washington: National Academy of Sciences, 1971.
Presents and summarizes available data on the distribution and nature of displacements and effects of tectonic movements that accompanied the Alaska earthquake; suggests that the primary fault motion was along a complex, gently dipping thrust fault beneath the continental margin near the Aleutian Trench.

Plafker, George, and Reuben Kachadoorian. Geologic effects of the March 1964 earthquake and associated seismic sea waves on Kodiak and nearby islands, Alaska. U.S. Geological Survey Professional Paper 543-D. Washington: Goverment Printing Office, 1966. 46 p. Also *in* The Great Alaska Earthquake of 1964: Geology. NAS Pub. 1601. Washington: National Academy of Sciences, 1971.
Describes tectonic vertical displacements, subsidence due to failure of noncohesive granular materials, landslides, effects on hydrologic regimen, and tsunamis.

Plafker, George, Reuben Kachadoorian, Edwin B. Eckel, and Lawrence R. Mayo. Effects of the earthquake of March 27, 1964, on various communities. U.S. Geological Survey Professional Paper 542-G. Washington: Government Printing Office, 1969. 50 p. Also *in* The Great Alaska Earthquake of 1964: Geology. NAS Pub. 1601. Washington: National Academy of Sciences, 1971.
Discusses vertical tectonic displacements over an area in excess of 50,000 m^2, local surface faulting, uplift of Continental Shelf and resultant tsunamis, widespread subaqueous sliding and sedimentation, and local violent surges of water.

Plafker, George, and L. R. Mayo. Tectonic deformation, subaqueous slides and destructive waves associated with the Alaskan March 27, 1964 earthquake: An interim geologic evaluation. U.S. Geological Survey Open-File Report. Menlo Park, California: U.S. Geological Survey, 1965. 34 p.
Includes statement on sublacustrine slides at Kenai Lake, the slides being indicated by missing segments of shoreline and by onshore damage from waves and ice floes.

Plafker, George, and Meyer Rubin. Vertical tectonic displacements in south-central Alaska during and prior to the great 1964 earthquake. *Journal of Geoscience*, 10 (March 1967), 53–66.
Examines vertical tectonic deformation in relation to the geologic record of Holocene (Recent) movement along coasts of south central Alaska; finds that recent submergence may be related to preearthquake strain buildup.

Pope, Allen J. Strain analysis of horizontal crustal movements in Alaska based on triangulation surveys before and after the Prince William Sound earthquake of March 27, 1964 *in* Volume III: The Prince William Sound, Alaska, earthquake of 1964 and aftershocks. Environmental Science Services Administration, U.S. Coast and Geodetic Survey. Washington: Government Printing Office, 1969. p. 99–111. Also *in* The Great Alaska Earthquake of 1964: Seismology and Geodesy. NAS Pub. 1602. Washington: National Academy of Sciences, in press.
Discusses method of computation of strain components, summarizes factors limiting or increasing usefulness of these components in interpreting crustal movements, and presents the components in tabular and graphic form.

Post, Austin S. Alaskan glaciers: Recent observations in respect to the earthquake-advance theory. *Science*, 148 (April 16, 1965), 366–368.
Indicates that aerial photographic studies show that the Alaska earthquake had little visible immediate effect on the glaciers, except for some localized rockfalls, produced no significant snow and ice avalanches, and failed to support the earthquake-advance theory of Tarr and Martin.

Post, Austin. Effects of the March 1964 Alaska earthquake on glaciers. U.S. Geological Survey Professional Paper 544-D. Washington: Government Printing Office, 1967. 42 p. Also *in* The Great Alaska Earthquake of 1964: Hydrology. NAS Pub. 1603. Washington: National Academy of Sciences, 1968. p. 266–308.
Analyzes 1964 earthquake effects, including rock avalanches, changes in ice-dammed lakes, river drainage, and the termini of tidewater glaciers; reviews the Tarr-Martin theory and the problem of surges.

Press, Frank. Displacements, strains, and tilts at teleseismic distances. *Journal of Geophysical Research,* 70 (May 15, 1965), 2395–2412. Also *in* The Great Alaska Earthquake of 1964: Seismology and Geodesy. NAS Pub. 1602. Washington: National Academy of Sciences, in press.
Reports that the vertical displacement field from the Alaska earthquake indicates that the primary fault extended to a depth of 150-200 km and that it probably came to within 15 km of the surface; examines observations of residual strains and tilts.

Press, Frank, and W. F. Brace. Earthquake prediction: Recent developments reopen the question of the predictability of earthquakes. *Science,* 152 (June 17, 1966), 1575–1584.
Points out that forewarning of a large earthquake might come from tilts and strains in the epicentral region, general increase in the number of small seismic events, and changes in physical properties of rocks near the fault as they are strained; also gives vertical extent of faulting in the Alaska earthquake.

Press, Frank, and David Jackson. Alaskan earthquake, 27 March 1964: Vertical extent of faulting and elastic strain energy release. *Science,* 147 (February 19, 1965), 867–868. Also *in* The Great Alaska Earthquake of 1964: Seismology and Geodesy. NAS Pub. 1602. Washington: National Academy of Sciences, in press.
Announces that the vertical extent of the Alaska earthquake is an order of magnitude greater than that reported for all other earthquakes, that elastic strain energy of 10^{25} ergs was released, and that about 12,000 aftershocks probably occurred in a 69-day period.

Ragle, Richard. Letter to Dr. Troy Péwé, Department of Geology, University of Alaska, 17 April 1964, Relating Personal Observations of Wavelength, Amplitude, Velocity of the Earthquake in Anchorage. 2 p. (Copy on file, Library, National Academy of Sciences–National Academy of Engineering, Washington, D.C.)
Provides data from observation of two cars parked at Elmendorf Air Force Base during Alaska earthquake, with slow and massive waves observed, frequency of 70 pulses per minute, and velocity of more than 5 fps.

Ragle, Richard H., John E. Sater, and William O. Field. Effects of the 1964 Alaskan earthquake on glaciers and related features. Arctic Institute of North America Research Paper 32. Washington: Arctic Institute of North America, 1965. 44 p.
Finds that landslide materials on the glaciers constitute one of the most conspicuous and impressive effects of the 1964 earthquake and that apparently there was more activity of glacier fronts terminating in lakes than those terminating in tidewater.

Reimnitz, Erk. Effects in the Copper River Delta *in* The Great Alaska Earthquake of 1964: Oceanography and Coastal Engineering. NAS Pub. 1605. Washington: National Academy of Sciences, in press.
Reports on sedimentary structures including sand dikes, sand pipes, faults, joints, slumps, and distorted bedding; anticipates a seaward shift of broad lithofacies and plant zones by as much as 10 km.

Reimnitz, Erk, and Neil F. Marshall. Effects of the Alaska earthquake and tsunami on recent deltaic sediments. *Journal of Geophysical Research,* 70 (May 15, 1965), 2363–2376. Also *in* The Great Alaska Earthquake of 1964: Geology. NAS Pub. 1601. Washington: National Academy of Sciences, 1971.
Discusses ground fractures, lake ice fractures, earthquake fountain craters and related phenomena, avalanches, and regional uplift.

Rice, Donald A. Gravity observations in Alaska, 1964–1965, including some repeat observations *in* Volume III: The Prince William Sound, Alaska, earthquake of 1964 and aftershocks. Environmental Science Services Administration, U.S. Coast and Geodetic Survey. Washington: Government Printing Office, 1969. p. 5–20. Also *in* The Great Alaska Earthquake of 1964: Seismology and Geodesy. NAS Pub. 1602. Washington: National Academy of Sciences, in press.
Finds that the 1964–1965 gravity observations made by USC&GS provide a sound basis for future study of tectonic changes in the Prince William Sound area; suggests that future repeat gravity observations will be most useful if made concurrently with releveling in an earthquake region.

Rinne, John E. Oil storage tanks *in* Volume II-A: The Prince William Sound, Alaska, earthquake of 1964 and aftershocks. Environmental Science Services Administration, U.S. Coast and Geodetic Survey. Washington: Government Printing Office, 1967. p. 245–252.
Analyzes damage to steel tanks for oil storage caused by the ground motion directly associated with the Alaska earthquake or by earthquake-triggered subsidence or landslides.

Ross, Grant A., H. Bolton Seed, and Ralph R. Migliaccio. Performance of highway bridge foundations during the Alaska earthquake *in* The Great Alaska Earthquake of 1964: Engineering. NAS Pub. 1606. Washington: National Academy of Sciences, in press.
Reports on the foundation conditions, bridge and channel configurations, and foundation displacements; assesses the effects of foundation support conditions on bridge performance during the earthquake.

Row, Ronald V. Acoustic-gravity waves in the upper atmosphere due to a nuclear detonation and an earthquake. *Journal of Geophysical Research,* 72 (March 1, 1967), 1599–1610.
Develops theory for pulse propagation in a neutral atmosphere and compares ionospheric disturbances due to Novaya Zemlya nuclear detonation (1961) and the great Alaska earthquake (1964).

Savage, J. C., and L. M. Hastie. Surface deformation associated with dip-slip faulting. *Journal of Geophysical Research,* 71 (October 15, 1966), 4897–4904. Also *in* The Great Alaska Earthquake of 1964: Seismology and Geodesy. NAS Pub. 1602. Washington: National Academy of Sciences, in press.
Deals with fault surfaces with reasonable values of dip and gives the preferred fault models for the 1964 Alaska earthquake.

Savarenskiy, Ye. F., O. E. Starovoyt, and S. A. Fedorov. Long-period

Rayleigh waves of the Alaskan earthquake on March 28, 1964. *Akademiya Nauk SSSR Izvestiya, Seriya Geofizicheskaya* [Academy of Sciences of the USSR Bulletin, Geophysics Series], (No. 12, December 1964), 1103–1106.
Analyzes the dispersion of group and phase velocities of the Rayleigh waves registered in the central seismic station in Moscow.

Schmidt, Ruth A. M. Alaskan earthquake: geology color slides. Anchorage: Consulting Geologist [1966]. (Copy of one-page description on file, Library, National Academy of Sciences–National Academy of Engineering, Washington, D.C.)
Consists of thirty 35-mm Kodachrome slides (with a 5-page descriptive text), providing a technical account of landslides, structural damage, ground crack, changes in land level, and other geologic effects.

Schmidt, R[uth] A. M., B. Bedford, K. W. Calderwood, G. Ganopole, J. A. Hamilton, D. N. Helmuth, N. J. Moening, and D. H. Richter. Earthquake-triggered landslides in the Anchorage area March 27, 1964, *in* Science in Alaska, 1964: Proceedings Fifteenth Alaskan Science Conference, College, Alaska, August 31 to September 4, 1964. George Dahlgren, editor. College: Alaska Division American Association for the Advancement of Science, March 15, 1965. p. 239–252.
Describes detailed field mapping of the Anchorage area from air photos; drill sampling program; landslide areas; and weak zones in bluff areas.

Scientific and Engineering Task Force (Task Force No. 9). 30 Day Report of the Scientific and Engineering Task Force. Washington: Federal Reconstruction and Development Planning Commission for Alaska, 1964. 52 p.
Evaluates disaster effects, reports interim status of field investigations and actions, and gives guidelines for reconstruction.

Scott, Ronald F. Soil mechanics and foundation engineering aspects of the Alaskan earthquake of March 27, 1964. Proceedings 3d World Conference on Earthquake Engineering, New Zealand, 1965, Vol. I. Wellington: New Zealand Institute of Engineers, 1966. p. 157–172.
Summarizes the geology and soil profiles of the Anchorage area, describes earthquake effects with respect to soil engineering, and discusses stability of slopes in the region.

Seaborg, Harold J. Alaska earthquake damage report–Ship *Pathfinder*, April 10–June 5, 1964 (unpublished report by the Captain commanding the U.S. Coast and Geodetic Survey Ship *Pathfinder*). (Copy on file, Library, National Academy of Sciences–National Academy of Engineering, Washington, D.C.)
Reports on reconnaissance hydrography in Resurrection Bay and Cook Inlet between April 10 and June 5, 1964; notes that great changes along the waterfront at Seward were caused by sliding of the unstable ground mass, which, in turn, caused a mound effect in the center of the upper portion of the bay.

Seed, H. Bolton. Soil stability problems caused by earthquakes. Soil Mechanics and Bituminous Materials Research Laboratory Report. Berkeley: University of California, Department of Civil Engineering, January 1967. 57 p.
Classifies types of soil-instability problems, including settlement of cohesionless soils, liquefaction of saturated sands, and failures of fills on weak foundations.

Seed, H. Bolton, and Clarence K. Chan. Clay strength under earthquake loading conditions. *Journal of the Soil Mechanics and Foundations Division,* 92 (March 1966), 53–78.
Presents procedure for determining the combinations of sustained stress and pulsating stress that will cause failure of a given soil.

Seed, H. Bolton, and Stanley D. Wilson. The Turnagain Heights landslide in Anchorage, Alaska. Soil Mechanics and Bituminous Materials Research Laboratory Report. Berkeley: University of California, Department of Civil Engineering [1966]. 55 p. See also *Journal of the Soil Mechanics and Foundations Division,* 93 (July 1967), 325–353. Also *in* The Great Alaska Earthquake of 1964: Engineering. NAS Pub. 1606. Washington: National Academy of Sciences, in press.
Analyzes soil conditions in the Turnagain Heights slide area and concludes that the slide developed as a result of a loss in strength of the soils underlying the area.

Shannon & Wilson, Inc. Electro-osmosis field test section. Preliminary stabilization studies for the Turnagain buttress for U.S. Army Corps of Engineers. Seattle: Shannon & Wilson, Inc., 1966. 153 p.
Concludes that stabilization of the Turnagain area cannot be accomplished by electroosmosis.

Shannon & Wilson, Inc. Preliminary report to U.S. Army Corps of Engineers on 4th Avenue slide, Anchorage, Alaska. Seattle: Shannon & Wilson, Inc., 1964. 10 p.
Summarizes surface observations in area of 4th Avenue slide, outlines subsurface explorations, describes laboratory testing program, summarizes interpretations of soil formations, discusses possible landslide mechanisms, and gives conclusions on the stability of this area, along with forthcoming remedial measures.

Shannon & Wilson, Inc. Preliminary report to U.S. Army Corps of Engineers on Turnagain slide, Anchorage, Alaska. Seattle: Shannon & Wilson, Inc., 1964. 10 p.
Presents a summary of findings from subsurface exploration description of soil conditions around the Turnagain slide area and an analysis of the mechanism of failure.

Shannon & Wilson, Inc. Remolding of Bootlegger Cove Clay with explosives. Preliminary stabilization studies for the Turnagain buttress for U.S. Army Corps of Engineers. Seattle: Shannon & Wilson, Inc., 1965. 180 p.
Describes field tests with a series of alternating explosive shots of small magnitude, fired with a time delay of more than 0.5 second between shots, is more effective in creating a disturbance to the clay structure and is less likely to cause critical vibrations in the Turnagain residential area.

Shannon & Wilson, Inc. Report on Anchorage area soil studies, Alaska, to U.S. Army Engineer District, Anchorage, Alaska. Seattle: Shannon & Wilson, Inc., 1964. 300 p.
Analyzes earthquake-triggered landslides at Anchorage and concludes that all slide areas are stable under present static conditions but may experience additional movements in another great earthquake; recommends stabilization of area and a program of future observations.

Shannon & Wilson, Inc. Report on subsurface investigation for city of Seward, Alaska, and vicinity, to U.S. Army Engineer District, Anchorage, Alaska. Seattle: Shannon & Wilson, Inc., 1964. 77 p.
Reports on probable factors responsible for the submarine landslide that destroyed most of Seward's waterfront; presents an evaluation of the area's stability under both static and earthquake conditions.

Shannon & Wilson, Inc. Report on subsurface investigation for Mineral Creek townsite, city of Valdez, Alaska, to U.S. Army Engineer District, Anchorage, Alaska. Seattle: Shannon & Wilson, Inc., 1964. 34 p.
Explores the subsurface conditions of the Mineral Creek townsite and determines the suitability of the area for the reconstruction of Valdez.

Sherburne, R. W., S. T. Algermissen, and Samuel T. Harding. The hypocenter, origin time, and magnitude of the Prince William Sound earthquake of March 28, 1964 in Volume II-B,C: The Prince William Sound, Alaska, earthquake of 1964 and aftershocks. Environmental Science Services Administration, U.S. Coast and Geodetic Survey. Washington: Government Printing Office, 1969. p. 49–69. Also in The Great Alaska Earthquake of 1964: Seismology and Geodesy. NAS Pub. 1602. Washington: National Academy of Sciences, in press.
Calculates the earthquake epicenter in 10 separate computations; finds preferred epicenter to be latitude 61.04°N and longitude 147.73°W, origin time 03:36:14.0, and surface-wave magnitude 8.3 ± 0.33 magnitude unit.

Shreve, Ronald L. Sherman landslide, Alaska. Science, 154 (December 30, 1966), 1639–1643. Also in The Great Alaska Earthquake of 1964: Hydrology. NAS Pub. 1603. Washington: National Academy of Sciences, 1968. p. 395–401.
Develops the hypothesis that the Sherman Glacier landslide moved on an air cushion.

Slichter, Louis B. Spherical oscillations of the earth in International Upper Mantle Committee Symposium on non-elastic processes in the mantle. Proceedings of the Royal Astronomical Society, 1966, Newcastle-upon-Tyne. Geophysical Journal, 14 (Nos. 1–4, 1967), 171–177.
Estimates that, for the lower-degree modes in the spheroidal free oscillations observed at Los Angeles as a result of the Alaska earthquake, the values are generally an order of magnitude more precise than those customarily reported.

Small, James B., and Ernest J. Parkin. Alaskan surveys to determine crustal movement: Part I, Vertical bench mark displacement. Surveying and Mapping, 27 (No. 3, 1967), 413–422.
Gives subsidence of bench marks, along with evidence of upheaval observed by the USC&GS in 1964 and 1965 during its program of 1,579 mi of first-order leveling.

Small, James B., and Lawrence C. Wharton. Vertical displacements determined by surveys after the Alaskan earthquake of March 1964 in Volume III: The Prince William Sound, Alaska, earthquake of 1964 and aftershocks. Environmental Science Services Administration, U.S. Coast and Geodetic Survey. Washington: Government Printing Office, 1969. p. 21–33. Also in The Great Alaska Earthquake of 1964: Seismology and Geodesy. NAS Pub. 1602. Washington: National Academy of Sciences, in press.
Describes vertical control surveys after the earthquake when 1,191 mi of first-order lines were releveled for engineering and mapping purposes.

Smith, Charles P. Highway destruction in Alaska: Part I, Alaska bridges experience an earthquake. American Highway, 43 (January 1965), 23–27.
Examines damage to bridges in the area affected by the 1964 earthquake and finds that these bridges suffered substructure failures due to massive inertial movements of the superstructures and gross displacement of the substructures.

Smith, Stewart W. Free oscillations excited by the Alaskan earthquake. Journal of Geophysical Research, 71 (February 15, 1966), 1183–1193. Also in The Great Alaska Earthquake of 1964: Seismology and Geodesy. NAS Pub. 1602. Washington: National Academy of Sciences, in press.
Determines periods of spheroidal and toroidal modes for the Alaska earthquake and generally confirms measurements made after the Chilean earthquake.

Smith, Stewart W. Introduction: Related geophysical effects in The Great Alaska Earthquake of 1964: Seismology and Geodesy. NAS Pub. 1602. Washington: National Academy of Sciences, in press.
Notes the importance of thoroughly documenting geophysical phenomena related to the 1964 earthquake, so that data will be available later for checking new hypotheses.

Smylie, D. E., and L. Mansinha. Chandler wobble and secular motion of the pole in The Great Alaska Earthquake of 1964: Seismology and Geodesy. NAS Pub. 1602. Washington: National Academy of Sciences, in press. (Revised and updated version of Mansinha and Smylie paper.)
Concludes that earthquakes must be considered as possible causes in attempts to explain the Chandler-wobble excitation and the secular polar shift.

Spaeth, M. G., and S. C. Berkman. The tsunami of March 28, 1964, as recorded at tide stations. U.S. Coast and Geodetic Survey Publication. Rockville, Maryland: U.S. Coast and Geodetic Survey, 1965. 59 p.
Mentions the vertical tectonic displacements that occurred over a large area of ocean bottom and the uplift of the seaward edge of the tectonic hinge zone.

Spaeth, Mark G., and Saul C. Berkman. The tsunami of March 28, 1964, as recorded at tide stations. ESSA [Environmental Science Services Administration] Technical Report C&GS 33. Washington: Government Printing Office, 1967. 86 p. Also in The Great Alaska Earthquake of 1964: Oceanography and Coastal Engineering. NAS Pub. 1605. Washington: National Academy of Sciences, in press.
Refers to oscillations induced by the long-period seismic waves and to the broad crustal warping along a northeast–southwest hinge line.

Stacey, F. D., and P. Westcott. The record of a vector proton magnetometer after the March 1964 Alaskan earthquake. Journal of Geophysical Research, 70 (July 15, 1965), 3321–3323. Also in The Great Alaska Earthquake of 1964: Seismology and Geodesy. NAS Pub. 1602. Washington: National Academy of Sciences, in press.
Finds (in power spectra of data from a digitally recording, vector proton-precession magnetometer operating during the Alaska earthquake) no evidence of magnetic fluctuations with frequencies of torsional modes in the earth's free-oscillation spectrum.

Stanley, Albert A. Crescent City: Sea wave. Shore and Beach, 32 (April 1964), 29.
Describes the disastrous fourth tsunami on March 28, 1964, at Crescent City, California, and explains tsunami propagation.

Stanley, Kirk W. Alaska earthquake. Shore and Beach, 32 (April 1964), 25–27.
Presents early report of damage from the tsunamis after the great Alaska earthquake and of the subsequent widespread changes in sea level.

Stanley, Kirk W. Beach changes on Homer Spit *in* Effects of the earthquake of March 27, 1964, in the Homer area, Alaska. U.S. Geological Survey Professional Paper 542-D. Washington: Government Printing Office, 1966. p. 20–28. Also *in* The Great Alaska Earthquake of 1964: Geology. NAS Pub. 1601. Washington: National Academy of Sciences, 1971.
Indicates that the increased supply of material to Homer Spit (as a result of accelerated erosion in the spit's source area after the 1964 earthquake) will provide further deposition on the Cook Inlet side of the beach.

Stanley, Kirk W. Effects of the Alaska earthquake of March 27, 1964, on shore processes and beach morphology. U.S. Geological Survey Professional Paper 543-J. Washington: Government Printing Office, 1968. 21 p. Also *in* The Great Alaska Earthquake of 1964: Geology. NAS Pub. 1601. Washington: National Academy of Sciences, 1971.
Reports that about 10,000 mi of shoreline in southeastern Alaska were affected by subsidence or uplift associated with the great Alaska earthquake; tells of effects on frontal beach ridges and stream mouths.

Stauder, William. Introduction: Parameters *in* The Great Alaska Earthquake of 1964: Seismology and Geodesy. NAS Pub. 1602. Washington: National Academy of Sciences, in press.
Describes the efforts to determine the different parameters of an earthquake, the collection of information on the source, and the evidence afforded by the data that have been collected.

Stauder, William. Tensional character of earthquake foci beneath the Aleutian Trench with relation to sea-floor spreading. *Journal of Geophysical Research*, 73 (December 15, 1968), 7693-7701.
Claims that study of the tensional character of foci under the Aleutian Trench supports the hypothesis of sea-floor spreading and underthrusting of the island area.

Stauder, William, and G. A. Bollinger. The focal mechanism of the Alaska earthquake of March 28, 1964, and of its aftershock sequence. *Journal of Geophysical Research*, 71 (November 15, 1966), 5283-5296. Also *in* The Great Alaska Earthquake of 1964: Seismology and Geodesy. NAS Pub. 1602. Washington: National Academy of Sciences, in press.
Illustrates uniformity of motion in the entire Alaska earthquake sequence by considering one preshock, the main shock, and more than 25 aftershocks; shows that criteria favor the hypothesis of thrust faulting.

Steinbrugge, Karl V. Earthquake hazard in the San Francisco Bay area: A continuing problem in public policy. Berkeley: University of California, Institute of Governmental Studies, 1968. 80 p.
Mentions soil liquefaction as a cause of the spectacular land movements in Anchorage during the Alaska earthquake; directs attention to seismic risk from vibrational forces in buildings.

Steinbrugge, Karl V. Introduction to the earthquake engineering of the 1964 Prince William Sound, Alaska, earthquake *in* Volume II-A: The Prince William Sound, Alaska, earthquake of 1964 and aftershocks. Environmental Science Services Administration, U.S. Coast and Geodetic Survey. Washington: Government Printing Office, 1967. p. 1–6.
Introduces papers on performance of structures and soils in Anchorage and vicinity and reviews briefly some of the seismological data previously developed.

Steinbrugge, Karl V., and Vincent R. Bush. Review of earthquake

damage in the western United States, 1933–1964 *in* Earthquake investigations in the western United States, 1931–1964. U.S. Coast and Geodetic Survey Pub. 41-2. Washington: Government Printing Office, 1965. p. 223–256.
Stresses proper earthquake-resistant design of foundations and superstructure of buildings; finds that long-period ground motion has been particularly destructive to multistory structures.

Steinbrugge, Karl V., John H. Manning, and Henry J. Degenkolb. Building damage in Anchorage *in* Volume II-A: The Prince William Sound, Alaska, earthquake of 1964 and aftershocks. Environmental Science Services Administration, U.S. Coast and Geodetic Survey. Washington: Government Printing Office, 1967. p. 7–217.
Studies vibrational damage and related effects to buildings in Anchorage and vicinity as well as the 14-story Hodge Building at Whittier; discusses predominant periods of ground motion.

Stephenson, J. M. Earthquake damage to Anchorage area utilities—March 1964. U.S. Naval Civil Engineering Laboratory Technical Note N-607. Port Hueneme, California: U.S. Naval Civil Engineering Laboratory, 1964. 47 p.
Relates the damage suffered by the utilities at Anchorage to shock waves traveling through the soil and to the nature of the Bootlegger Cove Clay, which was responsible for large landslides.

Tobin, Don G., and Lynn R. Sykes. Relationship of hypocenters of earthquakes to the geology of Alaska. *Journal of Geophysical Research*, 71 (March 15, 1966), 1659-1667.
Reports renewed interest in seismicity of Alaska since 1964 earthquake and contains results of 10-year study (before 1965) of the relation of epicenters to geologic and tectonic features such as island arcs, deep-sea trenches, and faults.

Tocher, Don. General introduction: Tectonics and seismic effects of the Alaska earthquake and the seismicity of Alaska *in* The Great Alaska Earthquake of 1964: Seismology and Geodesy. NAS Pub. 1602. Washington: National Academy of Sciences, in press.
Discusses tectonics and the manner of assessing seismic effects of the Alaska earthquake; concludes that 17 percent of worldwide seismic energy release between 1953 and 1965 took place in the Aleutian–Alaska arc and in the interior of Alaska.

Tocher, Don. Seismologic conclusions *in* The Great Alaska Earthquake of 1964: Seismology and Geodesy. NAS Pub. 1602. Washington: National Academy of Sciences, in press.
Summarizes the seismologic lessons learned and presents the Panel's conclusions.

Trainer, Frank W., and Roger M. Waller. Subsurface stratigraphy of glacial drift at Anchorage, Alaska *in* Geological Survey Research 1965: Short Papers in the Geological Sciences. U.S. Geological Survey Professional Paper 525-D. Washington: Government Printing Office, 1965. p. 167–174.
Indicates that glacial drift at Anchorage reaches a thickness greater than 500 ft and concludes that disastrous slides during the earthquake were caused by failure of a thick clay unit exposed in the Anchorage bluffs.

Tuthill, Samuel J. Earthquake origin of superglacial drift on the glaciers of the Martin River area, south-central Alaska. *Journal of Glaciology*, 6 (February 1966), 83-88. Also, revised *in* The Great Alaska Earthquake of 1964: Hydrology. NAS Pub. 1603. Washington: National Academy of Sciences, 1968. p. 362–368.
Suggests that earthquake-triggered avalanching is a major source of

superglacial debris on the terminal areas of the Martin River and Slide (formerly Sioux) glaciers; also suggests that some glaciers in south central Alaska may have stagnated due to rock debris that resulted from prehistoric earthquakes.

Tuthill, Samuel J., William O. Field, and Lee Clayton. Postearthquake studies at Sherman and Sheridan glaciers *in* The Great Alaska Earthquake of 1964: Hydrology. NAS Pub. 1603. Washington: National Academy of Sciences, 1968. p. 318–328.
Uses observations of Sherman and Sheridan glaciers to establish a basis for determining the future effect of the earthquake-induced debris avalanche on the Sherman terminus.

Tuthill, Samuel J., and Wilson M. Laird. Geomorphic effects of the earthquake of March 27, 1964, in the Martin-Bering rivers area, Alaska. U.S. Geological Survey Professional Paper 543-B. Washington: Government Printing Office, 1966. 29 p. Abstract *in* The Great Alaska Earthquake of 1964: Geology. NAS Pub. 1601. Washington: National Academy of Sciences, 1971.
Discusses snow and rock avalanches and deposits of dust on the glaciers and describes effect of earthquake on lakes along ice margins of Martin River Glacier and water-borne mudvent deposits, mud cones, and snow avalanches.

Undersea Technology. Montague Island raised 30 feet by quake. *Undersea Technology*, 5 (November 1964), 7.
Draws attention to Ocean Survey Ship (OSS) *Surveyor* investigations, showing extensive fractures for 30 mi in the ocean floor, with some marked by 50-ft vertical escarpments.

U.S. Army Engineering Division. Report on analysis of earthquake damage to military construction in Alaska, 27 March 1964. Washington: U.S. Army, Office, Chief of Engineers, Directorate of Military Construction, 1964. 113 p.
Discusses the geology of the Alaska earthquake area (in Appendix I) and reports on the soil mechanics and foundation-engineering aspects (in Appendix II).

U.S. Coast and Geodetic Survey. Assistance and recovery, Alaska/ 1964: A report covering the activities of the U.S. Coast and Geodetic Survey in conjunction with the Prince William Sound, Alaska, earthquake of 1964 for the period March 27–December 31, 1964. Washington: U.S. Department of Commerce, 1965. 45 p.
Outlines progress made by the USC&GS in restoring the technical foundation for the reconstruction of Alaska during the 9 months after the 1964 earthquake; details the horizontal and vertical control surveys; and gives the results of geodetic, gravity, and field surveys.

U.S. Coast and Geodetic Survey. Preliminary report—Prince William Sound, Alaskan earthquakes March–April 1964 (second printing). Seismology Division Report. Washington: U.S. Coast and Geodetic Survey, 1964. 101 p.
Provides information on the geological setting of the epicentral area and attempts to correlate local damage to specific geological or lithological conditions.

U.S. Coast and Geodetic Survey. The Prince William Sound, Alaska, earthquake of 1964 and aftershocks. Fergus J. Wood, editor. Volume I: Operational phases of the Coast and Geodetic Survey program in Alaska for the period March 27 to December 31, 1964. Washington: Government Printing Office, 1966. 263 p.
Summarizes USC&GS operations in Alaska between March 27 and December 31, 1964; contains an account of the seismic history and setting of the area.

U.S. Coast and Geodetic Survey. The Prince William Sound, Alaska, earthquake of 1964 and aftershocks. Fergus J. Wood, editor. Volume II-A: Research studies–Engineering seismology. Washington: Government Printing Office, 1967. 392 p.
Combines nine engineering seismology papers, within a single binding, as a study of vibrational effects on various types of building construction, mainly in the Anchorage area.

U.S. Coast and Geodetic Survey. The Prince William Sound, Alaska, earthquake of 1964 and aftershocks. Louis E. Leipold, editor. Volume II-B, C: Research studies–Seismology and marine geology. Washington: Government Printing Office, 1969. 350 p.
Gathers 11 seismology papers in Part B and 1 marine geology paper in Part C into a single binding; includes articles on seismological aspects of the Alaska earthquake, the mapping of crustal deformation in the Gulf of Alaska, and focal mechanism studies.

U.S. Coast and Geodetic Survey. The Prince William Sound, Alaska, earthquake of 1964 and aftershocks. Louis E. Leipold, editor. Volume III: Research studies and interpretive results–Geodesy and photogrammetry. Washington: Government Printing Office, 1969. 161 p.
Presents seven geodesy and photogrammetry papers in a single volume that also contains papers on gravity observations, vertical displacements, horizontal crustal movements, and strain analyses.

U.S. Geological Survey. Color slides showing geologic effects and damage to the works of man caused by the great Alaska earthquake of March 27, 1964. Arthur Grantz, compiler and annotator. U.S. Geological Survey Photographic Library [Federal Center, Denver, Colorado]. Annotated List of Slides. Washington: U.S. Geological Survey, 1965. 12 p. (Copy on file, Library, National Academy of Sciences–National Academy of Engineering, Washington, D.C.)
Offers 75 color and black-and-white 35-mm slides documenting evidence of several dynamic geologic processes.

U.S. Geological Survey. The Alaskan earthquake, 1964. 20-minute, 16-mm color documentary film. Washington: U.S. Geological Survey [1966]. (Copy of one-page film description on file, Library, National Academy of Sciences–National Academy of Engineering, Washington, D.C.)
Incorporates on-the-scene film to illustrate the geologic conditions that produced seismic vibrations, landslides, and tsunamis.

Universities Council for Earthquake Engineering Research. UCEER Information report. A Report Prepared with the Cooperation of the Engineering Division of the National Science Foundation. Pasadena, California: Universities Council for Earthquake Engineering Research, 1966. 153 p.
Announces the formation of the Universities Council for Earthquake Engineering Research; reprints the engineering sections of the Office of Science and Technology report on earthquake predictions and also several reports on the UNESCO program in earthquake engineering; and uses aspects of the 1964 Alaska earthquake as examples to illustrate particular points.

Van Dorn, William G. Source mechanism of the tsunami of March 28, 1964 in Alaska. Proceedings of the Ninth Conference (1964) on Coastal Engineering (Chapter 10). New York: American So-

ciety of Civil Engineers, 1965. p. 166–190. Also *in* The Great Alaska Earthquake of 1964: Oceanography and Coastal Engineering. NAS Pub. 1605. Washington: National Academy of Sciences, in press.
Concludes that the tsunami from the Alaska earthquake was produced by a dipolar movement of the earth's crust and that the initial positive phase contained about 2.3×10^{21} ergs of energy.

von Huene, Roland. Geologic structure of the continental margin in the area of the Alaska earthquake *in* The Great Alaska Earthquake of 1964: Seismology and Geodesy. NAS Pub. 1602. Washington: National Academy of Sciences, in press.
Suggests that the earthquake may have occurred along the fault off Montague and Kodiak islands and that the absence of a large active thrust fault in the Aleutian Trench points to slippage of a near-vertical fault.

von Huene, Roland. Introduction: Marine and shoreline geological effects *in* The Great Alaska Earthquake of 1964: Oceanography and Coastal Engineering. NAS Pub. 1605. Washington: National Academy of Sciences, in press.
Introduces papers presenting data on sea-floor deformation and geologic structures, to provide a better understanding of major earthquakes.

von Huene, Roland. [Untitled notes of consulting geologist to U.S. Coast Guard regarding his reconnaissance of Cape Hinchinbrook Light after the Alaska earthquake. China Lake, California: U.S. Naval Ordnance Test Station, 1966.] 14 p. (Copy on file, Library, National Academy of Sciences–National Academy of Engineering, Washington, D.C.)
Describes strong earthquake effects on the morale of the men at a remote lighthouse and reveals that they had used binoculars for their observations rather than leave the lighthouse area to make inspections; concludes that the slides or fault slippage would not immediately endanger the station and personnel.

von Huene, Roland, Richard J. Malloy, George G. Shor, Jr., and Pierre St.-Amand. Geologic structures in the aftershock region of the 1964 Alaskan earthquake. *Journal of Geophysical Research*, 72 (July 15, 1967), 3649-3660.
Indicates a preexisting zone of discontinuous faults in the area of maximum aftershock strain release; states that an anticline at the continental margin with local large structural relief was also uplifted during the earthquake.

von Huene, Roland, George G. Shor, Jr., and Richard J. Malloy. Offshore tectonic features in the affected region *in* The Great Alaska Earthquake of 1964: Oceanography and Coastal Engineering. NAS Pub. 1605. Washington: National Academy of Sciences, in press.
Discusses the tectonism along the Alaska and Aleutian trends, deformation on the Continental Shelf, and the thrust-fault and steep-fault models.

von Huene, Roland, George G. Shor, Jr., and Erk Reimnitz. Geological interpretation of seismic profiles in Prince William Sound, Alaska. *Geological Society of America Bulletin*, 78 (February 1967), 259-268.
Finds in the seismic reflection profiles (Alaska 1964) an ice-sculptured metamorphic basement, overlain by probable glacial drift, and Holocene marine sediments.

Vorhis, Robert C. Calculation and use of hydroseismic magnitudes *in* The Great Alaska Earthquake of 1964: Hydrology. NAS Pub. 1603. Washington: National Academy of Sciences, 1968. p. 237–245.
Compares magnitudes of the Alaska earthquake and others with hydroseismic magnitude as determined for a well in Georgia.

Vorhis, Robert C. Ground-water data from the Prince William Sound earthquake. *Georgia Mineral Newsletter*, 17 (1964–1965), 46.
Shows, by state, the largest hydroseisms of the earthquake and the number of wells in which hydroseisms were recorded.

Vorhis, Robert C. Hydrologic effects of the earthquake of March 27, 1964, outside Alaska (*with sections on* Hydroseismograms from the Nunn-Bush Shoe Co. well, Wisconsin, by Elmer E. Rexin and Robert C. Vorhis *and* Alaska earthquake effects on ground water in Iowa, by R. W. Coble). U.S. Geological Survey Professional Paper 544-C. Washington: Government Printing Office, 1967. 54 p. Also *in* The Great Alaska Earthquake of 1964: Hydrology. NAS Pub. 1603. Washington: National Academy of Sciences, 1968. p. 140–189.
Assembles data on hydrologic effects as recorded at water wells in 47 of the states and also in Canada, Europe, Africa, Asia, and Australia and surface-water gages in 38 states and in Canada and Australia.

Vorhis, Robert C. Introduction: Groundwater and surface water: Effects outside Alaska *in* The Great Alaska Earthquake of 1964: Hydrology. NAS Pub. 1603. Washington: National Academy of Sciences, 1968. p. 119–121.
Summarizes the hydroseismic effects of the Alaska earthquake that were recorded on every continent except South America.

Waller, Roger M. Effects of the earthquake of March 27, 1964, in the Homer area, Alaska (*with a section on* Beach changes on Homer Spit, by Kirk W. Stanley). U.S. Geological Survey Professional Paper 542-D. Washington: Government Printing Office, 1966. 28 p. Also *in* The Great Alaska Earthquake of 1964: Geology. NAS Pub. 1601. Washington: National Academy of Sciences, 1971.
Describes geologic and hydrologic effects and relation to damage: tectonic subsidence, subsidence from compaction, submarine slides, postearthquake beach modifications.

Waller, Roger M. Effects of the March 1964 Alaska earthquake on the hydrology of the Anchorage area. U.S. Geological Survey Professional Paper 544-B. Washington: Government Printing Office, 1966. 18 p. Also *in* The Great Alaska Earthquake of 1964: Hydrology. NAS Pub. 1603. Washington: National Academy of Sciences, 1968. p. 82–96.
Describes immediate effects of stream-flow changes and ground-water fluctuations; explains lowered water levels and increased pore pressure.

Waller, Roger M. Effects of the March 1964 Alaska earthquake on the hydrology of south-central Alaska. U.S. Geological Survey Professional Paper 544-A. Washington: Government Printing Office, 1966. 28 p. Also *in* The Great Alaska Earthquake of 1964: Hydrology. NAS Pub. 1603. Washington: National Academy of Sciences, 1968. p. 12–39.
Contains descriptions of water-level fluctuations, ejection of sediment-laden water, seiching of ice-covered lakes and streams, and changes in stream regimen.

Waller, Roger M. Introduction: Groundwater and surface water:

Effects in Alaska *in* The Great Alaska Earthquake of 1964: Hydrology. NAS Pub. 1603. Washington: National Academy of Sciences, 1968. p. 7-11.
Introduces section on hydrologic effects in Alaska, describing significant events and furthering concepts of aquifer changes created by the earthquake.

Waller, Roger M. Water-sediment ejections *in* The Great Alaska Earthquake of 1964: Hydrology. NAS Pub. 1603. Washington: National Academy of Sciences, 1968. p. 97-116.
Summarizes and analyzes the sites and features of the ejections.

Waller, Roger M., Harold E. Thomas, and Robert C. Vorhis. Effects of the Good Friday earthquake on water supplies. *Journal American Water Works Association*, 57 (February 1965), 123-131.
Lists various water-related effects of the earthquake, such as tsunamis, sandspouts, rearrangement of solid material in the aquifer system, damage to water installations, and water fluctuations.

White, W. R. H. The Alaska earthquake—Its effect in Canada. *Canadian Geographical Journal*, 72 (June 1966), 210-219.
Tells of movement of ice 2 ft higher along the shore of Lakelse Lake and of the fracturing of ice on Francois Lake.

Whitten, Charles A. An evaluation of the geodetic and photogrammetric surveys *in* Volume III: The Prince William Sound, Alaska, earthquake of 1964 and aftershocks. Environmental Science Services Administration, U.S. Coast and Geodetic Survey. Washington: Government Printing Office, 1969. p. 1-4. Also *in* The Great Alaska Earthquake of 1964: Seismology and Geodesy. NAS Pub. 1602. Washington: National Academy of Sciences, in press.
Evaluates geodetic surveys made after the Alaska earthquake and concludes that some postearthquake monitoring is essential for the future economic development of Anchorage.

Whitten, Charles A. Earthquake damage, Montague Island, Alaska *in* Manual of color aerial photography. Falls Church, Virginia: American Society of Photogrammetry, 1968. p. 390-391.
Shows (in a color photograph of the Hanning Bay fault scarp, taken 4 months after the 1964 earthquake) the differential uplift in the area, the greater seaward displacement of 15 ft along this section of the fault, and the newly formed beach.

Wilson, Basil W., and Alf Tørum. The tsunami of the Alaskan earthquake, 1964: Engineering evaluation. Coastal Engineering Research Center Technical Memorandum No. 25. Washington: U.S. Army Corps of Engineers, May 1968. 444 p.
Describes the nature of the earth dislocation in the Alaska earthquake and relates it to generation of the main tsunami waves; presents an engineering evaluation for severely damaged areas.

Wilson, Stanley D. Landslides in the city of Anchorage *in* Volume II-A: The Prince William Sound, Alaska, earthquake of 1964 and aftershocks. Environmental Science Services Administration, U.S. Coast and Geodetic Survey. Washington: Government Printing Office, 1967. p. 253-297.
Gives a digest of the Shannon & Wilson, Inc. (1964) report on Anchorage-area soil studies.

Wyss, Max, and James N. Brune. The Alaska earthquake of 28 March 1964: A complex multiple rupture. *Bulletin of the Seismological Society of America*, 57 (October 1967), 1017-1023. Also *in* The Great Alaska Earthquake of 1964: Seismology and Geodesy. NAS Pub. 1602. Washington: National Academy of Sciences, in press.
Notes that the multiple *P*-phases on seismograms of the Alaska earthquake suggest a multiple-event source mechanism where the propagating rupture triggers larger distinct events; the average rupture velocity is 3.5 km/sec.

Contributors to This Volume

DAVID F. BARNES, U.S. Geological Survey, 345 Middlefield Road, Menlo Park, California 94025

PETER J. BARRETT, Geology Department, Victoria University of Wellington, Wellington, New Zealand

MANUEL G. BONILLA, U.S. Geological Survey, 345 Middlefield Road, Menlo Park, California 94025

JAMES E. CASE, Department of Geology, University of Missouri, Columbia, Missouri 65201

HENRY W. COULTER, U.S. Geological Survey, GSA Building, Washington, D.C. 20242

ERNEST DOBROVOLNY, U.S. Geological Survey, Federal Center, Denver, Colorado 80225

EDWIN B. ECKEL, The Geological Society of America, P. O. Box 1719, Boulder, Colorado 80302

OSCAR J. FERRIANS, JR., U.S. Geological Survey, 345 Middlefield Road, Menlo Park, California 94025

HELEN L. FOSTER, U.S. Geological Survey, 345 Middlefield Road, Menlo Park, California 94025

WALLACE R. HANSEN, U.S. Geological Survey, Federal Center, Denver, Colorado 80225

MARCUS C. HOYER, Department of Geology, The Ohio State University, Columbus, Ohio 43210

REUBEN KACHADOORIAN, U.S. Geological Survey, 345 Middlefield Road, Menlo Park, California 94025

THOR N. V. KARLSTROM, U.S. Geological Survey, 601 E. Cedar Avenue, Flagstaff, Arizona 86001

ANNE V. KIRKBY, Department of Geography, University of Bristol, Bristol, England

M. J. KIRKBY, Department of Geography, University of Bristol, Bristol, England

WILSON M. LAIRD, American Petroleum Institute, 1801 K St., N.W., Washington, D.C. 20006

RICHARD W. LEMKE, U.S. Geological Survey, Federal Center, Denver, Colorado 80225

MALCOLM H. LOGAN, U.S. Bureau of Reclamation, Federal Center, Denver, Colorado 80225

DAVID S. McCULLOCH, U.S. Geological Survey, 345 Middlefield Road, Menlo Park, California 94025

NEIL F. MARSHALL, Scripps Institution of Oceanography, La Jolla, California 92037

LAWRENCE R. MAYO, U.S. Geological Survey, 310 First Avenue, Fairbanks, Alaska 99701

RALPH R. MIGLIACCIO, R&M Engineering and Geological Consultants, Fairbanks, Alaska 99701

GEORGE PLAFKER, U.S. Geological Survey, 345 Middlefield Road, Menlo Park, California 94025

ERK REIMNITZ, U.S. Geological Survey, 345 Middlefield Road, Menlo Park, California 94025

STEPHEN L. ROBBINS, U.S. Geological Survey, 345 Middlefield Road, Menlo Park, California 94025

KIRK W. STANLEY, P. O. Box 3-3956, Anchorage, Alaska 99501

SAMUEL J. TUTHILL, Iowa Geological Survey, 16 W. Jefferson Street, Iowa City, Iowa 52240

ROGER M. WALLER, U.S. Geological Survey, 1815 University Avenue, Madison, Wisconsin 53706

Index

Figures in italic indicate major discussion of topic.

Abercrombie, W. R., 364
advance planning, need, 787
Advanced Research Projects Agency, *xv*
Afognak, damage, 539
  ground undulations, 190
  muddied wells, 201
  subsidence, 539
Afognak airstrip, subsidence, 710
Afognak Island, Malina Bay, barnacle line, (photo), 63
  seismic sea wave damage (photo), 216
  subsidence, 203
  undermined trees (photo), 208
aftershock belt, 51
aftershocks, Alaska earthquake, *51*
  depth distribution, 51; (map), 52
  Kodiak Island area, *190*
  Valdez, 378
air transport system, Anchorage, damage, 707
  effects of earthquake, *706*
airports, tectonic effects, *33*
Alaska, Cretaceous deformation, *100*, 101
  damaged communities (table), 490, 491
  earthquake epicenters (map), 96
  Eocene deformation, *99*
  ground deformation (map), part B, Plate A
  highway damage, estimated repairs (table), 644
  highway system (map), 643
  Jurassic deformation, 101
  major surface faults, *101*
  mean tide variations (map), 61
  Oligocene deformation, *99*
  post-Miocene deformation, *98*
  power transmission lines (map), 705
  rail and highway net (map), 29
  seismicity, *50*
  shorelines affected by earthquake (map), 228
  south-central, physiography (map), 180
  tectonic change (map), 756
  tectonic history, summary, *98*
  tectonic uplift and subsidence (map), 55

Tertiary deformation *100*
  tidal parameters (figure), 62
  vibration-induced damage (map), Part B, Plate P
Alaska Aggregate Company tanks, vibration damage, 315
Alaska and adjacent areas, 1964 earthquake (map), 49
Alaska communications facilities, damage, 722
Alaska Department of Highways, Mineral Creek fan investigation, 364
  Valdez drilling, 373
Alaska Division of Lands, 245
Alaska earthquake, aftershocks, 9, 51, 183
  astronomic origin, 755
  atmospheric effects, 37
  biologic effects, *38*
  damage estimates (figure), 22
  damage outside Alaska, *40*
  damage to communities (table), 23
  damage to highway bridges and approaches, *669*
  damage to transportation facilities, *29*
  deformation, *54*
  deformation and vibration, *755*
  duration and extent, 7
  effects on air transport system, 706; communications facilities, 722; economic patterns, 711; highways, 641; (table), 644; navigation aids, 711; property values and manmade structures, *247*; shipping, 710; shorelines, *229*; utilities, 722
  epicenter, *5*; (map), 549
  focal mechanism studies, *53*
  geologic setting, *10*
  geology, conclusions, *783*
  ground motion, *183*
  horizontal displacement (map), 550
  importance, 1
  lessons learned, *747*
  magnitude, 5
  main shock, *50*

mechanism, *111*
  physiographic setting, *10*; (illus.), 6
  possible magnetic effects, *37*
  regional tectonics, summary and conclusions, *118*
  regional vertical displacements, *54*
  relation to Holocene movement, 110
  reports by the U.S. Geological Survey, *749*
  seismic vibrations (map), 750
  setting and effects, *5*
  summary of events at Valdez, *367*
  tectonic effects, *18*; (map), 19
  communities, *20*
  tectonic setting, *92*
  tectonics, comparison with other earthquakes, *90*
  time, 5
Alaska earthquake (1908), effects at Valdez, 365
Alaska earthquake (1911), effects at Valdez, 366
Alaska earthquake (1912), effects at Valdez, 367
Alaska earthquake (1925), effects at Valdez, 367
Alaska earthquakes, 1898–1961, epicenters (map), 11
Alaska earthquakes, previous, *10*
Alaska eruption (1883), effects at Homer, 478
Alaska Methodist University, vibration damage, 311
Alaska Pipeline Company, 725
Alaska placenames, principles, *xvi*
Alaska Psychiatric Institute, vibration damage, 311
Alaska Railroad (map), 547
  bench-mark lowering (map), 623
  bridge 3.0, damage, (illus.), 581
  bridge 3.2, damage (photo), 583
  bridge 3.3, damage (illus.), 585
  bridge 14.5, damage (photo), 587
  bridge 34.5, damage (illus.), 594
  bridge 61.9, damage (photo), 596

bridge approaches, typical fractures (illus.),
  609
bridge construction (illus.), 552
bridge damage (table), 558; (photo),
  565, 567, 584
bridge damage, fractures (photo), 570
bridge damage by foundation movement,
  551
bulkhead filler, failure, 602
construction in potential landspreading
  area, *636*
cost distribution of damage, *627*
damage, 29; (table), *627*
  cost distribution, *627*
  geographic distribution of cost (table),
    630
  summary, *630*
effects of earthquake, *543, 551*
embankment damage, *601*
  wave erosion (photo), 626
ground cracking, *595*
Hunter Flats bridge, damage, 593
Knik River bridge, damage, 591
landslide damage, 319, *614*
  mile 138.4, 622; (photo), 622
Nash Road deformation (photo), 608
physiographic setting, 546
Portage, flooding, 622
postearthquake elevations (table), 654
Potter Hill landslides, *614*; (photo),
  30, 615
  reconstruction sliding, 617
restoration activity, 545
Rocky Creek delta, landslides, *618*
Seward, damage (photo), 406
Ship Creek Bridge, damage, 587; (illus.),
  590
Snow River bridge, damage, 586; (photo),
  586
Sutton Branch landslide, *621*; (photo),
  621
subsidence damage, *622*
top-of-rail profile, pre- and postearthquake
  (illus.), 625
track bending (photo), 566
track damage, *601*
  lateral offsetting (photo), 609
Turnagain Arm bridge, damage (photo), 30
Twentymile River bridge, damage, 587;
  (photo), 590
Whittier, flooding, 622
Alaska Railroad dock, Seward, damage, 407
Alaska Range, physiography, 12
  slight uplift, 71
Alaska Standard (vessel), 530
Alaska State Housing Authority, Mineral
  Creek fan investigation, 364
  Seward, 419
Alaska Steamship Line, use of Anchorage,
  711
Aleutian Arc, Cenozoic deformation, 99
  hypocenters, 93
  inferred regional stress patterns, *97*
  seismicity, *93*

tectonic setting, *92*
  volcanoes, 93
Aleutian Islands, geology, 93
Aleutian Range, geology, 93
  landslides, 12
  physiography, 12
Aleutian Ridge, volcanic chain, 92
Aleutian trench, aftershocks, 51
  stress patterns, 97
  tectonics, 93
Algermissen, S. T., 48, 111, 161, 183
Allen, Clarence, 1
Allen River, road fractures (photo), 659
alluvial fan, Jap Creek, 414
  Seward area, 412
alluvial fan-deltas, Fourth of July Creek, 415
  Lowell Point, 415
alluvium, Seward area, *415*
alluvium subsidence, Buskin Lake, 193
  Lake Rose Tead, 193
  Saltery Lake, 193
Alnus sp., post-Mesozoic, 126
Alvarado, Alexander, 773
amateur radio network, value in restoration,
  722
American Geophysical Union, *xv*
American Legion, aid to Seward, 420
American Red Cross, aid to English Bay, 524
  aid to Seward, 420
Anchorage, air transport system, damage,
  707
  Alaska Fish and Farm Products, ground
    cracks, 317
  Alaska Railroad yards, vibration damage,
    311; (photo), 298
  Alaska Sales and Service Building, vibra-
    tion damage, 311; (photo), 27
  Bootlegger Cove Clay (map), 740
  City Dock, mud extrusion, 317
  Cordova Building, vibration damage, 312
  damage estimates, 292
  direct seismic effects, *309*
  earthquake effects, *290, 309*
  Fifth Avenue Chrysler Center, vibration
    damage, 312
  First Avenue landslide, 337
  First Federal Savings and Loan Association
    Building, vibration damage, 312
  Four Seasons Apartment Building, vibra-
    tion damage, 312; (photo), 313
  Fourth Avenue landslide, *329*; (map), 330;
    (photo), 296
    graben (photo), 24
  furniture movement, 292
  gas main rupture (photo), 726
  geologic setting, *299*
  Government Hill, pre-1964 landslide, 354
  Government Hill landslide, *341*; (map),
    345; (photo), 342
    geologic section (illus.), 344
  Government Hill school, damage (photo),
    294, 343
  gravity base station, 128
  ground cracks, 315

ground displacements, *315*
  Hill Building, vibration damage, 313
  Hillside Apartments, vibration damage,
    313
  immediate aftermath, *290*
  increased port usage, 711
  J. C. Penney Department Store Building,
    vibration damage, 314; (photo), 297
  Knik Arm Apartment Building, vibration
    damage, 314
  L Street landslide, *331*; (map), 333; (illus.),
    336; (photo), 28
    fractures (photo), 334
  landslide pressure ridge (photo), 332
  landslide susceptibility, *735*
  landslides, 297
    Alaska Railroad, *618*
  landslides (1954), 354
  motion directions, 292
  Mount McKinley Building, vibration
    damage, 314
  Native Hospital landslide, *337*; (map), 338;
    (photo), 339
    geologic sections (illus.), 340
    pressure ridge (photo), 341
  natural gas distribution damage, 725
  Pleistocene deposits, 300
  Port of Anchorage, damage, 36, 297
    ground cracks (map), 316
  Port of Anchorage area, vibration damage,
    315
  Potter Hill landslides, *319*
  power systems, damage, *723*
  pre-1964 landslides, *354*
  pressure ridges (photo), 335
  sand boils and mud fountains, *317*
  sewage system, damage, 727
  Ship Creek area, landslides (map), 620
  slope map, 736
  tectonic effects, 21, 22
  telephone system, damage, 727
  translatory slides, *326*, 763
  Turnagain Heights landslide, *347*; (map),
    part B, Plate E, F; (photo), 28
    clay ridge (photo), 349
    cross section (illus.), 353
    damage (photo), 346
    eyewitness account, 352
    furrowed ridge (photo), 348
    shattered trees (photo), 347
    slip surface (photo), 351
  1200 L Street Building, vibration damage,
    314; (photo), 26
  utilities damage, 727
  vibration damage (photo), 27
  water system, damage, 727
  West Anchorage High School, vibration
    damage, 315
Anchorage area, Bluff Road, rotational
  slides, *324*; (illus.), 325
    pressure ridge (photo), 324
  dominant slope (map), 738
  earthquake effects (map), 291
  geology, 736, 741; (map), 739

lake-ice cracks, 318
landslide-susceptibility (map), 742
landslides, *318*; (map), 619
landslides and cracks (map), 744
Potter Hill landslides (map), 320
topography (map), 737
Anchorage harbor, effects of earthquake, 712
Anchorage International Airport, control
    tower damage (photo), 299, 706
control tower restoration (photo), 707
damage, 708
vibration damage, 296, 311
Anchorage municipal gas-turbine power
    plant, damage, 724
Anchorage municipal wharf, postearthquake
    (photo), 713
Anchorage Natural Gas Corp., 725
Anchorage Westward Hotel, vibration
    damage, 311
Anderson Bay, damage, 501
Andreanof-Fox Island earthquake (1957),
    faulting, 97
anomaly interpretation, Knight Island (illus.),
    132
Anten, Ivan D., 518
Aranson, Carl, 518
archeologic effects, summary, 774
[U.S.] Army dock, Seward, disappearance,
    407
[U.S.] Army Research Office, *xv*
artesian well records (illus), 89
artesian wells, changes in levels, *88*
atmospheric effects, *87*
[U.S.] Atomic Energy Commission, *xv*, 264
Atterberg limits, Bootlegger Cove Clay, *303*
Aucella sp., Jurassic-Cretaceous, 126
Augustine Island volcano, ground breakage,
    12
avalanche, Puget Peak, 285
avalanches, extent, 495
highway damage, *667*
avulsion, legal problems, 248

Baier, Karl, 463
Balanus balanoides, 58, 781
Balanus glandula, 58
Barbee, W. D., 48, 179
barnacle line, 58, 62, 781
    Kizhuyak Bay, Kodiak Island, (photo), 66
    Port Bainbridge (photo), 59
    S. S. Coldbrook (vessel) (photo), 60
    Whale Bay (photo), 60
barnacles, height of upper growth limit
    (table), 65
mixed with terrestrial plants, Middleton
    Island (photo), 67
postearthquake yearling (photo), 63
Barnes, D. F., 50, 90
Barnett, Bob, 48
Barney, Lt. C. R., 80
barrier beach, Breving Lagoon, alteration,
    236
Bastian, William H., 48, 128
Baxter, Rae, 276

Beach, Rex, 676
beach changes, Homer Spit, 480, *487*
beach deposits, Kodiak Island, surficial
    subsidence, *191*
beach erosion, Montague Island, 281
beach-face recession, Homer Spit (illus.), 482
beach features (illus.), 231
beach material and transport, Homer Spit,
    484
beach ridges, alteration by earthquake, 235
ancient, earthquake evidence, *237*
migration, 236
beaches, changes in profile and gradient, 231
effects of earthquakes, *231*
response to uplift and submergence, *235*
ridge and runnel changes, *234*
Beaty, Joe, 193, 203, 210
Beaty ranch, inundation (photo), 224
beavers crushed by ice, Tuxedni Bay, 532
Beluga Lake, seiche, 475
Beluga Lake outlet, slumping, 280
benefits of earthquake, *777*
geologic, 778
scientific, 778
socioeconomic, 777
Benson, Carl S., *xv*
Bering Glacier, fissured deposits (photo), 520
Bering Lake, emergence effects, 82
berm development, Homer Spit, 483
Bernice Lake power plant, circuit overloads,
    51
damage, 724
bibliography, annotated, 796–813
Bilderback, Charles, 522
Billings, Al, 461
Binkley, William G., 314
biologic changes, *84*
Bishop, Elna, 754
Blake, Charles H., 361, 377
Blindheim, Carl, 518
Bohannan, William, 594
Bonilla, Manuel G., 48, 136, 169, 290, 319,
    320, 564, 603, 642, 686, 704
Bootlegger Cove Clay, Pleistocene,
    Anchorage area, *300*
Atterberg limits, *303*
depositional environment, *308*
failure, 301
Foraminifera, 308; (table), 309
liquid-limit sensitivity curves, 305
mineralogy, *307*
particle size distribution (table), 308
physical properties, *301*
physicochemical tests, *307*
plasticity charts (illus.), 303
Potter Hill landslides, 614
pulsating-load tests, *305*
sensitivity, *302*
shear strength, *301*
specific gravity, *306*
statistical liquid-limit distribution curves,
    304
torsional-vane-shear strengths (illus.), 302
vibration tests, *305*

water–plasticity ratio (illus.), 306
Borcherdt, R., 570
bore-hole data, Potter Hill slide (illus.), Part
    B, Plate U
bore-hole logs, Valdez area (illus.), Part B,
    Plate I
bore holes, Anchorage–Seward Highway, 652
Copper River Highway, 653
Richardson Highway, 654
borings, penetrometer values, Knik–
    Matanuska River floodplain (chart), 613
Portage River, penetrometer values (chart),
    612
Boulder Creek, *see* Rocky Creek
Brabb, Earl, 491
Bradley Lake delta, slumping, 280
Branson, Guy, 79, 530
Brevdy, June, 179
Breving Lagoon, barrier beach (photo), 237
alteration, 236
bridge, Resurrection River, pier damage
    (photo), 554
Twentymile River, collapse (photo), 676
bridge-approach damage (photo), 674
Chickaloon River, 674
Copper River Highway, 674; (table),
    696–699
Glenn Highway, 701
Little Nelchina River, 674
Puritan Creek, 674
Richardson Highway (table), 702
Seward-Anchorage Highway (table),
    699–701
Sterling Highway (table), 703
bridge-approach embankments, damage, 605
bridge-approach subsidence (photo), 673
geologic factors, 672
bridge construction, Alaska Railroad (illus.),
    552
influence on damage, 688
Knik–Matanuska River floodplain, damage,
    611
bridge damage (table), 695
Alaska Railroad (illus.), 594; (photo),
    565, 567, 580, 596; (table), 558
Twentymile River, 587; (illus.), 589;
    (photo), 588, 590
foundation movement, 551
fractures, (photo), 570
California earthquake (1906), 554
Clear Creek (photo), 682
compressive forces on stringers (graph),
    595
Copper River Highway (photo), 680, 679,
    688; (table), 696–699
drift-pin pounding (photo), 593
foundation failure, *565*
Glenn Highway (table), 701
grain size of foundation, influence, 608
horizontal movement, 551
horizontal pounding (photo), 592
horizontal skewed (illus.), 606, 607
Hunter Flats, 593
influence of construction, 688

Knik River, 591; (illus.), 591
landspreading (illus.), 604
Million Dollar Bridge, (photo), 677
Mineral Creek, 577, 582
Niigata earthquake (1964), 613
pile penetration influence (illus.), 555, 556
primary and secondary roads (table), 695
Quartz Creek, 681
relation of horizontal displacement to
  bridge length (illus.), 557
relation of pile spacing to bridge length,
  554
relation to foundation density (chart),
  614; foundation material, 608; foundation properties, 614; grain size, 610;
  pile-embedding material (chart), 610;
  sediment grain size (chart), 612; sediment thickness, 610, 681; (chart), 611
Resurrection Creek, 577
Resurrection River (photo), 582
Richardson Highway (table), 702
seismic shaking, 672
Seward–Anchorage Highway (table),
  699–701
Ship Creek, damage, 587, 590
Snow River, 586; (photo), 676
Sterling Highway (table), 703
summary, 591
(highway), summary, 689
transient horizontal displacement, 592
type (chart), 687
bridge failure, factors, 674
bridge piles, typical displacement (illus.), 553
bridge settling, sand ejects (photo), 569
compression compared to length (graph),
  564
deck arching compared with pile penetration (illus.), 568
embankment failures (illus.), 596
foundation displacement, 577
pile settling, 675
pile shattering, 679
subsidence effects, 683
vertical movement, 553
bridges and approaches, highways, damage,
  669
Bristol Bay, 532
British Columbia, Hot Springs Cove, damage,
  41
  Port Alberni, cable breakage, 773
  damage, 41
Brooks, A. H., 366
Brooks, J. W., 40
Bruce, Dick, 545
Brunton, Gordon, 361
Bryant, F. J., 361
Burford, R. O., 50, 115
Burk, Creighton A., xv
Burma earthquake (1762), deformation, 91
Burnside (vessel), 365
Burr, A. J., 367
Bush, E. R., 352
Buskie, Frank, 546
Buskin Lake, alluvial subsidence, 193

cable breaks, summary, 773
California, Berkeley, atmospheric pressure
  wave, 37, 87, 218
  coastline damage, 41
  Crescent City, damage, 41
  Kern County earthquake (1952), faulting,
    136
  La Jolla, atmospheric pressure wave, 87,
    218
  San Francisco Bay, damage, 41
  San Francisco earthquake (1906), bridge
    damage, 554
    deformation, 92
    railroad embankment failure, 604
    raised marshlands, 565
  Santa Cruz, damage, 41
  Scripps Institute, atmospheric pressure
    wave, 37, 87, 218
California Academy of Sciences, biology
  program, 264
California Institute of Technology, xv
Campbell, Bruce A., 546, 642
Campbell, Catherine, 754
Canada goose, loss of feed grass, 246
cannery destruction, Kodiak Island area,
  223
Cannon, Bruce E., 440, 545, 546
Cape Chiniak station, U. S. Coast Guard,
  tsunami, 210
Cape Hinchinbrook Light Station, effects
  of earthquake, 711
Cape Hinchinbrook Light Station area (map),
  510
Cape Saint Elias, damage, 521
  Pinnacle Rock, rockfall (photo), 521
  waves, 521
Cape St. Elias lighthouse, damage, 36
Cape Suckling, uplift (photo), 67
Carey, Dawn, 278
Case, J. E., 48, 123, 136
Cason, Velton, 464
casualties, Kodiak Island area, 225
cattle ranches, Kodiak Island, effects of
  earthquake, 224
Cenozoic deformation, Aleutian Arc, 99
  Cook Inlet–Susitna Lowland, 99
  Copper River lowland, 99
Cenozoic rocks, Kodiak Island, 99
Cenozoic tectonism, Alaska, 98
Chapman, R. M., 361
chartlets, new water maps, 712
Chena (vessel), 368, 372
Chenega (photo), 503
  earthquake damage, 503, 715; (photo),
    504
  local-origin waves, 504
  remains (photo), 24
  tectonic effects, 21
  water displacement, 88
  wave damage (map), 505
Chile earthquake (1822), deformation, 91
Chile earthquake (1960), compared to
  Alaskan (1964), 90
  landslides, 326

Chirikof Island earthquake (1880), faulting,
  101
Chirikof Islands, Oligocene rocks, 99
  undeformed Tertiary rocks, 99
Chisik Island cannery, damage, 533
Chitina airstrip, damage, 710
Chugach Electric Association, 193, 418
Chugach Electric Association, system
  damage, 724
Chugach Mountains, snowslides, 282
Chugach–Saint Elias mountains, Cenozoic
  gravity sliding, 99
Church, Jack, 545, 546
cirque floors, elevation differences, relation
  to submergence, 106
City Planning Associates, Inc., 419
Clair A. Hill and Associates, Inc., 546, 616,
  617
clam bed uplifted, Rude River Delta (photo),
  253
clamming, improvement, Kodiak Island area,
  224
clams, effects of uplift, 246
  Copper River delta (photo), 275
  Cordova (photo), 255
Clark, Charles H., 361, 367
Clark, Joe, 496, 535
Clark University, xv
clastic dikes, Snow River Delta (photo), 15
Clear Creek bridge, damage (photo), 682
Cliff Mine, damage, 501
Clinocardium nuttalli, 276
Clock, Mr. and Mrs. Jerry, 535
Cluff, L. C., 136, 158
coastal erosion, 240
coastal facilities, influence of changes of
  level, 89
coastal features, earthquake effects, 231
Coats, R. R., 50
S. S. Coldbrook (vessel) (photo), 60
Colinvaux, Paul, 250
collapse pit, Valdez Glacier stream flood-
  plain (photo), 386, 387
Colner, Alec, 509
Colorado, ionospheric effects, 87
  sound waves, 37
communications facilities, damage, 722
compressive force on bridge stringers (chart),
  595
Comstock, "Chick," 511
Comstock, "Red," 511
Condon, W. H., 179
Conerly, H. G., 773
Conger, Dan K., 546, 617
consolidation subsidence, summary, 767
continental shelf, aftershocks, 51
  gravity anomaly trends, 130
  tectonic uplift, 69
Controller Bay area, fissures (photo), 520
  structural trends, 98
  submergence, 108
Cook, Irvin P., 440, 545, 546
Cook Inlet, beach changes, 231
  ridge and runnel features, 234

slight uplift, 71
submergence of beaches (photo), 237
subsidence and erosion (photo), 241
wave erosion of landslides, 243
west coast, earthquake effects, 532
Cook Inlet area, ground breakage, 280
submergence, 108
Cook Inlet Tug and Barge Lease, ground
cracks, 317
Cook Inlet–Susitna Lowland, Cenozoic
deformation, 99
physiography, 13
Cooper Landing, damage, 524
Copeland, Top, 533
Copper River, drainage change, 83
Copper-River-2 Bridge, damage (photo), 680
Copper-River-5 Bridge, collapsed, bent
(photo), 679
collapsed deck (photo), 680
Copper-River-9 bridge, damage (photo), 688
Copper River Basin area, cracked lake ice,
282
earthquake effects, 282
Copper River Delta, beach changes, 233
cracks (photo), 270
cracks and faults, 269
depth of influence of seiches and tsunamis,
277
effects of seiches, 276; tsunamis, 276;
uplift, 273
fissured sand dune (photo), 519
marsh-bank upheaval (photo), 274
new drainage, 274
non-desiccation cracks, 274
rapid gullying (photo), 240
ridge and runnels, 234
sand dike (photo), 273
sandspouts, 267
sediment ridges (photo), 272
sediments, shock effects, 267
slough-bank upheaval, 271
slough-slumping (photo), 272
slump cracks (photo), 271
tidal flat erosion, 277
tidal marshes, changes, 276
uplift, dead clams (photo), 275
effect on streams, 239
new land (photo), 239
Copper River Delta area (map), 266
Copper River Highway, bore holes (illus.),
653
bridge-approach damage (table), 696–699
bridge-approach subsidence, 674
bridge damage (table), 696–699
damage (map), 649
fractures (photo), 657, 658
pre- and postearthquake profiles (illus.),
661
sediment analysis (table), 693
Copper River Lowland, Cenozoic deformation, 99
physiography, 14
Copper River region, submergence, 108
Cordova, Copper River bridges, damage, 506

core-logs (illus.), 254
damage and repair (photo), 507
effects of emergence, 247
fissures (photo), 508
geological control, 708
port and harbor damage, 35
sewage system, damage, 728
shallow-water sample sites (map), 254
shallow-water sediments, 253; analyses,
261
tectonic effects, 21
uplift, 509
effect on clams (photo), 255
utilities damage, 728
water system, damage, 728
wave damage, 506; (photo), 508
Cordova Airfield, damage, 708; (photo), 33
Cordova area, damage, 506
shock effects, 267
Cordova harbor, damage, 714
postearthquake (photo), 714
Cordova post office, gravity base station,
128
core-logs, Cordova area (illus.), 254
Hanning Bay, 258
MacLeod Harbor (illus.), 255
Rude River Delta (illus.), 252
Coulomb failure, bridge embankments
(illus.), 596
Coulter, H. W., 40
Cowles, Ralph, 463
cracked ice, extent, 495
cracks, Copper River Delta, 269; (photo),
270
non-desiccation, Copper River Delta, 274
summary, 765
crater, Copper River Delta (photo), 269
Cratty, Al, 48, 179
Cravat, H. R., 48
Cretaceous rocks, Seward, 410
Valdez Group, Valdez area, 361
Whittier, 441
Cretaceous deformation, south-central
Alaska, 100, 101
Crystal Falls cannery, abandonment, 509
loss by uplift, 712
Curray, J. R., 278

damage, Alaska Railroad (table), 627;
geographic distribution of cost (table),
630; summary, 630
geologic controls, 534
Prince William Sound, extent, 499
summary, 774
Dayville cannery, damage, 501
debris avalanche, Kodiak Island (photo), 188
debris flow, Upper Miles Glacier (photo), 14
debris slide, Kodiak Island area, 198
deformation, Alaska and other earthquakes
(table), 91
Alaska earthquake, 54
earthquake-related movements, 79
eyewitness accounts, 79
geometry, 72

time and rate, 79
Valdez–Orca Groups, Prince William Sound
area, 127
delta-fans, future stability, Seward, 425
delta fronts, future danger, 763
delta sediments, effects of tsunamis, 265
Denali fault system, 102
densities of rocks, Prince William Sound
area, 127
[U.S.] Department of Defense, xv
[U.S.] Department of Housing and Urban
Development, xv
[U.S.] Department of the Interior, xv
Detterman, R. L., 48, 71
Dick, Sam, 523
Dickinson, M., 434
Dickinson Oswald and Associates, Inc., 348
Dieringer, James, 375
Dixon, M. J., 444
Dobrovolny, Ernest, 1, 290
Dodd, A. B., 290
Dodson, A. L., 179
Don J. Miller (vessel), 48, 423, 424
drainage, Valdez area, 364
drainage changes, Copper River Delta, 274
Drier, Calvin, 524
drill holes, Whittier (illus.), 443
drowned brush, Harriman fiord, Prince
William Sound (photo), 66

Eagle River floodplain, fractures, 280
Earl and Wright, civil engineers, 546
earthflow, Homer, 467
Kodiak Island area, 199
Sitkinak Island (photo), 199
earthquake damage, Anchorage International
Airport, 708
categories, 493
Cordova Airport, 708
Kenai Peninsula airstrips, 709
Kodiak Naval Station airfield, 708
earthquake effects, Anchorage, 290, 309
Homer, 461
Seward, 395
Valdez, 359
Whittier, 447
earthquake belts of the world (map), 10
earthquake benefits, 777
earthquake forecasting, 783
future, geologic, 787
geophysical activity, 787
hydrologic investigations, 787
recommendations, 787, 788
earthquake mechanism, interpretations
(illus.), 111
major unresolved problems, 115
steep-fault model, 116
dislocation theory, 117
summary, 759
thrust-fault model, 112
dislocation theory, 115
earthquake questionnaire, 491
earthquake sounds, Kodiak Island area, 191
summary, 772

earthquakes, severe, 856 A.D.–1964 (table), 8
Eberlein, G. D., 50
Eckel, Edwin B., 1, 3, 50, 290
economic pattern, effect of earthquake, *711*
Edgerton Highway, damage (map), 648
Egan, William A., 367
ejecta from fissures, Valdez, 381
 (photo), 382
Eklutna hydroelectric power system, earthquake effects, *732*
Eklutna Lake Delta, slumping, 280
Eklutna powerplant, damage, 732
electric service, Seward, damage, 729
Eleshansky, Mike, 503
Ellamar cannery, damage, 715
Ellamar Peninsula, greenstone outcrops, 133
Elmendorf Air Force Base, damage, 312, 708
Elmendorf Air Base powerplant, damage, 724
Elrington Island, greenstone outcrops, 133
emerged shoreline, plant invasion, 85
emergence, effects on manmade structures, *247*
 legal problems, *247*
Emory University, *xv*
engineering factors in highway damage, *687*
engineering geology, Seward, 418
Engineering Geology Evaluation Group, 290, 313
 Fourth Avenue Slide, Anchorage, 331
 L Street Slide, 336
 role in Anchorage, 298
 Turnagain Heights Slide, 350
English Bay, damage, 524
[U.S.] Environmental Science Services Administration, *xv*
Eocene deformation, south-central Alaska, *99*
epicenter, Alaska earthquake (map), 549
Erickson, George S., 432
erosion, coastal, *240*
 Copper River Delta, tidal flats, 277
 Homer Spit groins (photo), 484
 Montague Island, southern, 281
 Munson Point, Homer, postearthquake (photo), 466
Estes, Don, 686
Estes, Ed, 686
Evans Island, Sawmill Bay, tectonic effects, 21
 uplift, 58
Evitt, W. R., 126
exposed stumps, emergence (photo), 109
eyewitness accounts, Homer, 463

Fairbanks, earthquake effects, 533
 Alaska Motel, damage, 533
Fairbanks Committee for Alaska Earthquake Recovery, 361
Fairweather Fault, 102
 1958 movement, 101
Fairweather Range, physiography, 18
Fallwell, Col. M. L., 48, 440
fan-delta deposits, Seward, 412
Farnsworth, Jack, 440

fathometer profiles, Homer Spit, 472
Faulkner, Glen L., 312
faults, *73*
 Copper River Delta, *269*
 Montague Island, *140*
 post-Miocene movement, 101
 relation to vertical displacement, *78*
 south-central Alaska, *101*
 subsurface, 758
 surface, summary, *758*
Fault Cove, Hanning Bay Fault, extension crack (photo), 169
 Hanning Bay fault scarp (photo), 166, 167
 Montague Island, 163
 pre- and postearthquake tides (photos), 164
fault scarp, Hanning Bay (photo), 17
Federal Reconstruction and Development Planning Commission, damage estimates, 22
Felland, Robert, 361
Ferrians, Oscar, 596
Ferrier, Delbert, 502
Ferrier, Red, 372, 502
fill failure, railroad embankments, 602
fiord deltas, increased knowledge, 779
fire damage, Whittier, 458
fish, dead, Knight Island Passage, 504
 Valdez Narrows, 503
 Whittier, 446
fishing industry damage, Kodiak Island, *222*
fissure, Valdez (photo), 381
fissured ground, definition, 494
fissures, Bering Glacier deposits (photo), 520
 Controller Bay (photo), 520
 Cordova (photo), 508
 Homer, 467
 Kodiak Island, *191*
 Portage, 528
 summary, 765
 Valdez, *379*, 383
 Valdez Glacier stream floodplain (photo), 380, 384, 386
 Whidbey Bay, 532
 Yakataga (photo), 522
Fitzgerald, Mrs., 464
Fleet Weather Central, Kodiak Island, 179
 preearthquake movement, 80
 tide records, *213*
Flemming, George, 513
floodplain, Resurrection River, 415
 Salmon Creek, 416
focal mechanism studies, Alaska earthquake, *53*
Foraminifera, Bootlegger Cove Clay, 309
Fort Richardson powerplant, damage, 724
Fort Wainwright, damage, 533
Fortress (vessel), 210
fossil trees, Jap Creek Fan, 414
Foster, Helen, 642
foundation, Seward–Anchorage Highway, correlation with fractures (table), 694
foundation density, relation to bridge damage (chart), 614
foundation displacements, ground cracks, 596

foundation failure, bridge damage, *565*
 model studies, *570*
foundation material, Glenn Highway, earthquake effects (table), 691
 Richardson Highway, earthquake effects, 691
 Seward–Anchorage Highway, effects of earthquake (table), 690
 Sterling Highway, earthquake effects (table), 690
foundation properties, relation to bridge damage, 614
Fourth of July Creek fan-delta, 415
Fox River floodplain, fractures, 280
fracture, Forest Acres, Seward (photo), 431
fractured ground, Seward, *427*, 434
fractures, Alaska Railroad, bridge approaches, typical (illus.), 609
 Allen River Road (photo), 659
 Copper River Highway (photo), 657, 658
 Eagle River floodplain, 280
 Forest Acres, Seward, 428
 Fox River floodplain, 280
 highway, *651*
 normal to roadway, *654*
 oblique, 658
 origin, 658; (illus.), 655
 highway centerline, *657*
 highway edges, 657
 Seward, coordinate causes, *432*
 Seward–Anchorage Highway (photo), 656, 666
 correlation with foundation (table), 694
 Seward waterfront, 427
 Skilak River floodplain, 280
 summary, 765
 Whittier, 453
Fribrock, Joe, 533
Fucus, 61, 62
 barnacle line, Glacier Island (photo), 64
 land-level variations, 65
Fucus distichus, 58, 781
Fugelstad, T. Clifford, 440, 545, 546, 601, 617
furniture movement trace, Anchorage (illus.), 293
future earthquakes, scientific preparation, *783*

Gardiner, Paul, 463
Gates, George, 2
geographic setting, Kodiak Island, *179*
geologic effects, summary, *760*
geologic influence, summary and conclusions, 534
geologic mapping of communities, 784
geologic maps, landslide susceptibility, *735*
 purpose, 736
 use in hazard prediction, *784*
Geological Society of America, *xv*
geology, Anchorage area, *299*, 736, 741
 highway system, 642
 Homer Spit, 480
 influence on damage, *534*; damage intensity, *683*; vibration damage, *775*

Kodiak Island, *182*
Mineral Creek alluvial fan, 364
Seward, *410*
summary, *774*
translatory landslides, Anchorage, 326
Valdez area, 359, *361*
Whittier, *441*
geometry, major zone of uplift, *72*
probable zone of slight uplift, 72
zone of subsidence, *72*
Geo-Recon, Inc., 421
George, Warren, 427
Gervais, Arthur, 290
Gillette, Edward, 364
Gilluly, James, 1
Girdwood, damage, 524
marine inundation, 38
submergence, radiocarbon dates, 107
Girdwood airstrip, subsidence damage, 710
glacial deposits, Seward, 412
Glacier Island, greenstone outcrops, 133
glaciers, summary, *767*
Glenn Highway, bridge-approach damage
(table), 701
bridge damage (table), 701
damage (map), 647
foundation material, earthquake effects
(table), 691
Goldthwait, Richard P., 264
Golub, Harry, 677
Gorman, A. T., 523
graben formation, translatory landslides, 328
graben rule, *329*, 779
grabens, Passage Canal, 758
Resurrection Bay, 758
grain-size analysis, Valdez delta (table), 363
granitic rocks, Prince William Sound area,
126
Grant, U.S., 366
Grantz, Arthur, 781
gravity, Prince William Sound area, *128*
gravity change, Middleton Island, 80
vertical displacements, *90*
gravity gradient, regional, Prince William
Sound, 131
gravity high, Prince William Sound, *132*
gravity low, Port Gravina, *131*
gravity map, Prince William Sound area,
general features, *130*
gravity profile, Prince William Sound (illus.),
130
gravity sliding, Cenozoic, Chugach–Saint
Elias mountains, 99
graywacke, engineering properties (table),
411
Green, A. G., 464
Greer, Mr. and Mrs. Albert, 463
Griffith, Charles L., 440, 545, 546, 602
groins, Homer Spit, updrift and downdrift
fill (illus.), 244
ground breakage, Cook Inlet area, 280
Kenai Lowland, 280
other earthquakes, documented 378
Valdez, 378

ground cracks, Alaska Fish and Farm
Products lease, Anchorage, 317
Anchorage area, 315
building corners on floodplains (illus.),
599
controls, 282
Cook Inlet Tug and Barge lease, Anchorage,
317
effects on Alaska Railroad, *595*
foundation displacements, 596
India earthquake (1897), 600
Knik–Matanuska River floodplain (photo),
Part B, Plate R
landsliding and lurching, 598
lateral displacement, 597
mechanisms, 282
origin by spreading (illus.), 597
Port of Anchorage area (map), 316
Portage, related to embankment (photo),
600
Portage area (photo), part B, Plate T
Portage Creek, Forest Service house
(photo), 598
produced by embankments, 599
Union Oil Company of California tank
farm, Anchorage, 317
ground displacement, Anchorage, *315*
Valdez, *376*
ground fissures, summary, 765
ground fractures, Kenai Lake, 279
ground water, Homer, 475, 476
Kodiak Island area, effects of earthquake,
201
Seward, 421
summary, *768*
ground water hydrology, summary, *777*
Gulf of Alaska, greenstone belt, 133
Gulf of Alaska coastal section, physiography,
18
Gulf of Mexico, seiches, 41
Gulkana Upland, 14

Haas, J. E., 728
Haltness, Edward A., Sr., 278
Hanna, G Dallas, 39, 48, 58, 84, 85, 235,
255, 264, 781
Hanning Bay, core logs (illus.), 258
pre- and postearthquake sediments (photo),
259
shallow-water sediments, *257, 262*
Hanning Bay Fault, 73, *161*; (photo), 172
extension cracks (photo), 168
Fault Cove (photo), 165, 171
extension cracks, 168
fault trace (photo), 170
fault scarp (photo), 17, 161, 162, 173
vertical displacement, 92
Hansen, Wallace R., 754
Harmony (vessel), 264
Harned, C. H., 546
Harrison, James W., 397, 407, 418
Harry, G. Y., Jr., 245
Hart, Keith, 16
Hartney Bay, bridge damage, 509
Hatfield, Sam, 529

Hayden, H. H., 564
Hayes, Webb, 546
Haven, Stoner B., 246
Hawaii, Kipapa, strain seismometer, 51
Helm, J. R., 290
Henderson, Harry, 501
Hesness, Arnie, 546
Hess, Harley D., 464, 530
highways, effects of earthquake, *641*;
(table), 644
effects of tectonic subsidence, *659, 669*
lateral displacement, *666*
sand ejecta blankets, 667
Snow River Crossing, bore holes (illus.),
651
highway bridge damage, relation to epicenter,
669
highway bridge segments (illus.), 672
highway bridges, effects of seismic sea
waves, 682
highways damage, 31, *644*
avalanches, *667*
Copper River Highway, 651; (map), 649
Edgerton Highway (map), 648
engineering factors, *687*
estimated repairs (table), 644
fracture, *651*
geological conditions, 651
Glenn Highway (map), 647
Hope Road (map), 646
influence of lateral displacement, 686;
sediment thickness, 684; water-table
depth, 684
intensity, influence of geology, *683*
Kodiak Island, *219*; (map), 650; (photo),
222
landslides, *666*
Point Whitshed Road (map), 649
Portage Glacier Road (map), 646
Richardson Highway, 651; (map), 648
relation of sediment compaction, 684
sediment liquefaction, 685
Seward–Anchorage (map), 645, 646
Snow River Crossing, 651
Sterling Highway (map), 645
summary, 642, *689*
highway fractures, centerline, *657*
edges, 657
normal to highway, *654*
oblique, 658
origin, 658; (illus.), 655
patterns, 651
highway system, geology, 642
Hill, C. A., 546
Hinchinbrook Island, Orca Group, Tertiary,
126
Hinchinbrook Light Station, damage, *509*
dock, uplift (photo), 24
Hoisington, Neal, 69
Holocene sea-level changes, 103
Holocene vertical movements, *103*
long-term, *103*
tectonic implications, *110*
Homer, 716
earthflow, 467

effects of 1883 eruption, 478
effects of historic earthquakes, *461,* 466, 479
eyewitness accounts, *463*
fissures, 467; (map), 466
ground water, 475, *476*
hydrographs of water wells, 476
Inlet Inn Hotel, damage (photo), 465
landslide, 466
local waves, 88
Munon Point, postearthquake erosion (photo), 466
port facilities damage, 36
seismic history, *478*
shoreline, source of Homer Spit (photo), 481
subsidence and erosion, 241
tectonic effects, 22
tsunamis, 464
waves, 465
well failure, 475
Homer area (map), 460, 462
muddied well-water, 475
Homer Spit (map), 480
bar building (photo), 486
beach alteration (photo), 236
beach changes, 233, *480;* (illus.), 233
summary, *487*
beach-face recession diagram, 482
beach material and transport, 484
bench-mark altitudes, (table), 473
berm development, 483
berm-face-recession relationships, 483
bottom slopes (illus.), 472
damage, 36
earthquake effects, *467*
erosion at groins (photo), 484
erosion prevention measures (photo), 485
fathometer profiles, 472
fissure patterns (map), Part B, Plate O
geology, 480
groin alteration (photo), 484
groin fill, updrift and downdrift (illus.), 244
hydrologic effects, 474
Land's End Hotel (photo), 469
minor beach changes, 231
offshore bathymetry (map), Part B, Plate O
offshore profiles (illus.), 471
pre- and postearthquake road profiles (illus.), 473
pre- and postearthquake tidelines (illus.), 481
preearthquake photo, 468
postearthquake changes, *482*
postearthquake high tide (photo), 468
postearthquake seawall (photo), 242
sea-bottom changes, 235
shore protection works, *485*
small-boat harbor, restoration (photo), 716
storm berm (photo), 482
submarine landslide, 470
submergence (photos), 470

subsidence, 467, 473
effect on beaches, 235
tidal inlets, 487
tide-gage readings, 57
topography (map), Part B, Plate O
well log (table), 474
Hope, damage, 524
Hope airstrip, damage, 709
Hope Road, damage (map), 646
horizontal deformation, *757*
horizontal displacements, *74;* (map), *75*
amount and distribution, *77*
methods of measurement, *74*
Montague Island faults, *174*
transient, bridge damage, *592*
water disturbances, *87*
horizontal movement, bridge damage, 551
Valdez, 377
Hose, R. K., 112
Hudson, Oren, 48
Hunter Flats, avalanches (map), Part B, Plate S
flooding (map), Part B, Plate S
ground cracks (map), Part B, Plate S
Hurst, Paul, 365
Hurst, Ron, 193
hydrographs, Homer, 476
hydroseisms, 769

Ibex Mining Company, 366
ice breakage, summary, *768*
ice cracks, Anchorage area, 318
Kodiak Island area, 201
India earthquake (1762), deformation, 91
India earthquake (1874), deformation, 91
India earthquake (1897), ground cracks, 600
vertical fault-movement, 92
Ingraham, John, 551
Inoceramus sp., Jurassic, 126
instrumental records, Whittier, 50
instruments and measurements, conclusions, *786*
International Conference of Building Officials, 783
intertidal organisms, sessile, extremes, 65
zonation, (photo), 63
inundation, effects, 82, 84
Ireton, J. C., 414, 423

Jack Bay, wave damage, 497
Jap Creek Fan, 414
fossil trees, 414
Japan, Kwanto earthquake (1923), deformation, 91, 92
Mikawa earthquake (1945), faulting, 136
Nankaido earthquake (1946), deformation, 91
Niigata earthquake (1964), bridge damage, 613
deformation, 91
Tokachioki earthquake (1968), embankment failures, 603
Johnson, Arvid M., 546, 593
Jones, D. L., 126
Jones, Fred O., 179, 193, 773

Jurassic deformation, south-central Alaska, *101*
Jurassic rocks, Seward, 410

Kachadoorian, Reuben, 16, 48, 179, 290, 461, 464, 603, 704, 712
Kachemak Bay, seiche, 475
slope-break on beach (photo), 231
submergence, 108
Kadiak Fisheries, damage (photo), 189
Kadiak Fisheries cannery, beach compaction, 191
pile foundation (photo), 191
sand liquefaction, 196
vibration damage, 189
Kaguyak, seismic sea waves, 540
Kalea, Albert S., Jr., 533
Karlstrom, Thor N. V., 48, 642
Kasilov River, basin tilting, 83
Katalia, emerged beach ridges (photo), 107
emergence, radiocarbon dates, 107
Kaye, C. A., 290
Keating, Mrs. D., 443
Kehdon, John, 551
Kenai, subsidence and erosion (photo), 241
Kenai airstrip, damage, 709
Kenai area, damage, 525
Kenai–Chugach mountains, physiography, 16
Kenai Lake, ground fracturing, 279
slide-induced seiching, 279
slide-induced waves, 279
tilting, 82
water displacement, 87
Kenai lineament, 74, 101
Kenai Lowland, ground breakage, 280
Kenai Peninsula, airstrip damage, 709
Mesozoic rocks, structure (illus.), 101
Port Bainbridge, barnacle line (photo), 59
power systems, damage, 723
submerged coast (photo), 106
Kenai River, flow reversal, 83
Kenai River bridge, collapse (photo), 683
Kenai River bridge-approach, subsidence, 674
Kennedy, Arthur, 546, 588, 597
Khantaak Island, earthquake noises, 523
King, Philip Burke, 95
King Salmon, damage, 532
King Salmon Air Force Base, damage, 532
King's Bay, shoreline damage (photo), 514
Kjelsted, Nels, 361
Klutina Lake, ice breakage, submarine slides, 282
Knight Island, gravity anomaly, 131
interpretation (illus.), 132
greenstone outcrops, 133
shear zones, 128
Thumb Cove, local waves, 516
Knight Island Passage, overthrust, 128
Knik Arm, Cairn Point, landslides, 321
Point Woronzof, landslides, 321
Sleeper landing strip, compound slump (illus.), 323; (photo), 322
west side, landslides, 322
Knik Arm powerplant, damage, 724

Knik–Matanuska River floodplain, borings, penetrometer values (chart), 613
ground cracks (map), Part B, Plate R; (photo), Plate R
Kodiak, damage, 718
earthquake effects, *539*
magnetic field changes, 37
sea-bottom scour, 217, 539
sea-level rise, pre-tsunami, 210
seismic sea waves, 539
seismic sea wave damage, 719; (photo), 223
sewage system, damage, 728
subsidence, 539
tectonic effects, 35
telephone service damage, 728
tidal mud removal, 217
utilities, damage, *728*
water system damage, 728
Kodiak area, earthquake effects, *539*
Kodiak Electric Association powerplant, circuit response, 728
damage, 728
low-water withdrawal, 212
Kodiak Island, ash from Katmai eruption, 183
Cenozoic rocks, 99
earthflows, 199
effects on cattle ranches, *224*
emptied lakes, 202
fishing industry damage, *222*
fissures, *191*
geographic setting, *179*
geology, *182*
Gibson Cove, small-boat basin, 719
highway damage, *219*; (map), 220, 650; (photo), 222
seismic sea waves, *667*
Kiliuda Bay, submergence and emergence (photo), 64
Kizhuyak Bay, barnacle line (photo), 66
Larsen Bay, seawall, postearthquake (photo), 243
Middle Bay, subsidence (photo), 207
Narrow Cape, landslide, 199
muddied wells, 201
uplift, 205
physiography (map), 181
population 1960, 183
pre- and postearthquake shorelines (map), 668
inundations (map), 668
property losses, estimate (table), 179
Quaternary deposits, severe shaking, 189
rockfalls, 198
seismic sea waves, heights and times (table), 214
highway destruction, *222*
submergence, 108
effect on salmon, 246
subsidence, beach deposits, *191*
surficial subsidence, *191*
alluvial and lacustrine deposits, *193*
artificial fills and embankments, *193*
stream-mouth changes, 237
Terror Bay, seiching, 215

tidal constants (table), 182
Ugak Bay, drowned estuary (photo), 187
landslide (photo), 198
Ugak–Kiliuda Bays, debris avalanche (photo), 188
uplift, 203
Womens Bay, seaplane ramps, submergence, 708
seismic sea wave damage to bridge (photo), 221
tide-gage readings, 57
submerged road (photo), 90
Kodiak Island area, aftershocks, *190*; (map), 185
cannery destruction, 223
casualties, *225*
changes, regional setting, *206*
clam industry, improvement, 224
deformation (map), 204
damage and casualties, *219*
debris slides, 198
earthquake sounds, *191*
effects on groundwater, 201; logging industry, *224*; shorelines, *205*; surface water, 201
geology (map), 184
ground motions (map), 186
lake ice cracked, 201
landslides, *196*; (map), 197
causes, *200*
related to Tertiary rocks, 200
effects on logging industry, *224*; shorelines, *205*
rotational slump, 198
seismic sea waves, *210*
chronology, *210*
crest heights, *213*
damage (map), 211
effects on shorelines and sea bottoms, *217*
origin, *217*
periods, *215*
stream flow variation, 202
surface waves, *190*
tidal inundation (table), 205
vertical displacement (map), 209
vertical tectonic deformation, *203*
vessels lost, 223
Kodiak Mountains, physiography, 16
Kodiak Naval Station, airfield damage, 708
damage, 539, 718
high-water mark (photo), 212
radioactive contamination, 539
seismic sea waves, 539
Koelbl, H. T., 113
Kola, Oliver V., 293
Kolb, Farrian, 444, 455
Kolb, Mrs. Farrian, 444
Komkoff, Joe, 504
Kompkoff, Karol, 518
Kukak Bay, stable, radiocarbon dates, 107

LaCoste and Romberg portable geodetic meter, 128
lake basins, tilting, *82*

Lake George, slumping, 280
Lake Hood seaplane facility, use in restoration, 708
lake levels, changes, 89
Lake Louise Plateau, 14
Lake Rose Tead, alluvium subsidence, 193
submergence (photo), 192
lakes, change in biota, 86
marine inundation, 38
lakes as tiltmeters, 780
Lall, Dexter, 179, 202
land-level changes, distribution, *68*
estimates by residents, 67
major zone of uplift, *69*
pre- and postearthquake depth soundings, 68
pre- and postearthquake levelings, 68
tidal bench marks, 67
tide-gage readings (table), 56
Whittier, 447
zone of slight uplift, *71*
zone of subsidence, *68*
land-level measurements, new methods, *781*
land-level variations, storm-beach heights, 65
terrestrial vegetation, 65
landslide causes, Kodiak Island area, *200*
landslide damage, Alaska Railroad, *614*
landslide graben, L Street slide, Anchorage (photo), 334
landslide potential, Seward area, 427
landslide susceptibility, Anchorage, *735*
geologic maps, *735*
landslide waves, Seward, 435
Whittier, 454
landslides, Alaska Railroad, 319
Anchorage, *618*
mile 138.4, 622
Sutton Branch (photo), 621
Anchorage, 297
(1954), 354
Anchorage area, *318*
Cairn Point, Knik Arm, 321
Chile earthquake (1960), 326
extent, 495
Fourth Avenue slide, Anchorage, *329*
Government Hill, Anchorage, *341*; (photo), 342
geologic section (illus.), 344
pre-1964, 354
highway damage, *666*
Homer, 466
Knik Arm, west side, 322
Kodiak Island area, *196*
relation to Tertiary rocks, 200
L Street slide, Anchorage, *331*
lessons learned, *776*
Narrow Cape, Kodiak Island (photo), 199
Native Hospital, Anchorage, *337*; (photo), 334
geologic section (illus.), 340
pressure ridge (photo), 341
New Madrid earthquake (1811), 326
Resurrection Bay, 422
Rocky Creek delta, Alaska Railroad, *618*
Point Woronzof, Knik Arm, 321

Potter Hill, Anchorage, *319*
   railroad damage, *614*
pre-1964, Anchorage, *354*
Puget Bay, 529
Seward, *408*, 416, *422*
Seward–Anchorage Highway (photo), 667
Seward waterfront, 422, 423
Sitkalidak Island, 200
Sitkinak Island (photo), 198
Sutton Branch, Alaska Railroad, *621*
Turnagain Arm, 318
Turnagain Heights, Anchorage *347*; (map),
   Part B, Plate F
   clay ridges (photo), 349
   cross section (illus.), 353
   damage (photo), 346
   eyewitness accounts, 352
   furrowed ridges (photo), 348
   shattered trees (photo), 347
   slip surface (photo), 351
   Ugak Bay, Kodiak Island (photo), 198
   wave erosion, Cook Inlet, 243
   Whittier, 453
landspreading, *599, 762*
landspreading areas, construction, *636*
Laneville, David, 369
LaPointe, L. J., 128
Larsen, Neal L., 372
Larsen Bay, subsidence, 540
Larson, George, 528
LaRue, W. P., 443
lateral displacement, highways, *666*
   influence on highway damage, 686
Latouche area, damage, *510*
   wave damage (map), 511
Latouche Island, exposed stumps from
   emergence, (photo), 109
   greenstone outcrops, 133
   tectonically elevated shoreline (photo),
   39
Latouche waterfront, damage (photo), 512
LaZelle, Harriet, 546
Lee, K. L., 305
legal problems, uplift and subsidence, *247*
Lemke, Richard W., 22, 642
Leonard, Bob, 48, 179
life loss, Seward, *407*
liquid-limit distribution curves, Bootlegger
   Cove Clay, 304
liquid-limit sensitivity curves, Bootlegger
   Cove Clay, 305
liquefaction, highway damage, 685
   railroad embankments (illus.), 604
Lisiansky, Capt., 210
Little Nelchina River bridge approach,
   subsidence, 674
littoral deposits, Seward, 416
Littorina sp., 84
Lloyd, C. R., 50
logging industry, Kodiak Island area, effects
   of earthquake, *224*
longshore material movement, *243*
Lorensen, Rudy, 189, 201, 202
Lowcock, Mr. and Mrs. D. P., 463, 464
Lowell Creek Fan, Seward, 411

Lowell Point Fan-delta, 415
low-water features, *234*

McClure, Frank, 546
McClure and Messinger, structural engineers,
   546
McCulloch, David S., 74, 290, 319, 320,
   439, 666, 704, 754, 781
McDonough, L., 444, 455
McMahon, Gordon. 79
magnetic effects, summary, 772
Malloy, R. J., 48, 132, 138
Manley, John E., 545, 546
maps, aftershock depth distribution, 52
   Alaska, earthquake-affected shorelines, 228
      earthquake epicenters, 96
      ground deformation, Part B, Plate A
      highways, 643
      major aftershocks, 19
      mean tide variations, 61
      physiographic, south-central, 180
      physiographic divisions of Alaska, 11
      physiographic setting, 6
      power transmission lines, 705
      rail and highway net, 29
      seismic vibrations, 750
      tectonic, southern 95
      tectonic change, 756
      tectonic land-level changes, 19
      tectonic uplift and subsidence, 55
      vertical displacements, 104
      vibration-induced damage, Part B,
      Plate P
   Alaska and vicinity, area affected, 49
   Alaska earthquakes, 1898-1961, 11
   Alaska Railroad, 547
      bench-mark lowering, 623
   Anchorage, Fourth Avenue landslide, 330
      Government Hill landslide, 345
      L Street landslide, 333
      Native Hospital landslide, 338
      Port of Anchorage area, ground cracks,
      316
      Potter Hill, landslide area, 320
      Ship Creek, landslides, 620
      Turnagain Heights landslide, Part B,
      Plate F
      Turnagain Heights landslide area, Part B,
      Plate E
   Anchorage and vicinity, earthquake effects,
      291
   Anchorage area, Bootlegger Cove Clay, 740
      dominant slope, 738
      ground cracks, 744
      landslide-susceptibility (map), 742
      landslides, 619, 744
      surface geology, 739
      topography, 737
   Chenega, wave damage, 505
   Copper River Delta area, 266
   Copper River Highway, damage, 649
   Cordova, shallow-water sample sites, 254
   earthquake belts of the world, 10
   Edgerton Highway, damage, 648
   epicenter, 19, 549

   geologic, purpose, 736
   Glenn Highway, damage, 647
   Hanning Bay Fault, Part B, Plate D
   Hinchinbrook Light Station area, 510
   Homer, U.S. Bur. Land Management
      station, fissures, 466
   Homer area, 462
   Homer Spit, 480
      fissure patterns, Part B, Plate O
      offshore bathymetry, Part B, Plate O
      topography, Part B, Plate O
   Hope Road, damage, 646
   horizontal displacement, 75, 550
   Hunter Flats, avalanche, Part B, Plate S
      flooding, Part B, Plate S
      ground cracks, Part B, Plate S
   Knik-Matanuska River floodplain, ground
      cracks, Part B, Plate R
   Kodiak Island, highway damage, 220, 650
      physiographic, 181
      seismic sea wave inundations, 668
   Kodiak Island area, aftershocks, 185
      deformation, 204
      geology, 184
      ground motions, 186
      landslides, 197
      seismic-sea-wave damage, 211
      vertical displacement, 209
   Latouche area, wave damage, 511
   Mineral Creek bridge, ground cracks, 578
   Montague Island, faults, 139
      Hanning Bay, 257
      Jeanie Point, Patton fault, 144
      MacLeod Harbor, shallow-water sediment
      sites, 255
      Patton Bay Fault, Part B, Plate C
      regional tectonic setting, 137
   Orca Inlet, postearthquake deposition, 276
      postearthquake sounding, 276
   Point Whitshed Road, damage, 649
   Point Woronzof, landslides, 321
   Port Oceanic area, wave damage, 515
   Port Valdez area, 500
   Portage area, fissures, 528
      ground cracks, Part B, Plate T
      pre- and postearthquake tides, 624
   Portage Creek, ground cracks, 571
   Portage Glacier Road, damage, 646
   Potter Hill slide, Part B, Plate U
   Prince William Sound, 251
      Bouguer gravity, 129
      ground deformation, Part B, Plate B
      subaqueous slides, Part B, Plate Q
      submarine extension of uplift, 70
      wave distribution, Part B, Plate Q
   Prince William Sound area, geologic, 124
   Resurrection River bridge, ground cracks,
      578
   Richardson Highway, damage, 648
   Rude River Delta, 252
   Sawmill Bay, wave damage, 517
   Seward, damage area, 404
      Forest Acres, fractures, 430
      Forest Acres and Clearview, fractured
      ground, 429

Seward and vicinity, 397
Seward-Anchorage highway, 646
  damage, 645
Seward area, geology, Part B, Plate J
Sterling Highway damage, 645
Turnagain Arm, preearthquake shoreline
  and inundation, 671
Valdez, ground conditions, 362
Valdez area, 360
  earthquake effects, Part B, Plate G
Valdez Glacier stream floodplain, fissures,
  385
Valdez Glacier termini, 365
Valdez harbor, submarine contours, Part
  B, Plate H
value, *788*
Whittier, Buckner Building, core drilling,
  452
  Hodge Building, drill holes, 442
  submarine topography, Part B, Plate M
  preearthquake topography, Part B,
    Plate N
  wave damage, Part B, Plate N
Whittier area, 438
  earthquake effects, Part B, Plate L
  geology, Part B, Plate L
Marmot Island, subsidence, 203
marsh-bank upheaval, Copper River delta
  (photo), 274
Marston, Brooke, 352
Martin, Ed, 361
Martin-Bering Rivers area, geomorphic
  effects, 284
mass movements, summary, 760
Massachusetts, sound waves, 37
Matanuska Valley, earthquake effects, 533
  power systems, damage, *723*
Mathes, John, 268
Maxwell, John C., *xv*
Mayo, L. R., 48, 123, 128, 136, 439, 506,
  513
mechanism of the earthquake, *111*
Meeks, Dwight, 522
Meleau, Wilkie, 532
Merrill Field, damage, 707
Mesozoic, Valdez Group, Prince William
  Sound area, *126*
Mesozoic structures, Kenai Peninsula (illus.),
  101
Mesozoic tectonism, Alaska, 98
Middleton Island, barnacle line, S. S.
  Coldbrook (photo), 60
  damage, 522
  emergence, radiocarbon dates, 107,108
  flowers and barnacles mixed (photo), 67
  gravity change, 80
  muskeg-covered preearthquake emerged
    terrace (photo), 107
  seismic sea wave, 522
  tilted Pleistocene rocks, 99
Migliaccio, Ralph, 642
Miller, Don J., 99
Miller, Robert D., 16, 290, 317, 397, 431
Million Dollar Bridge, damage, *676*
  (photo), 32, 677, 678

Mineral Creek alluvial fan, geology, 364
  Pleistocene, Valdez, 361
  townsite, advantage, 392
Mineral Creek bridge, damage, 577, 582;
  (photo), 579
  ground cracks (map), 578
Mineral Creek fan area (photo), 392
  new Valdez townsite (photo), 392
mineralogy, Bootlegger Cove Clay, *307*
mines, earthquake effects, *773*
Minta, J. T., 50
Mirsky, Arthur, 264
Mission Lake, high-tide flooding, 539
Missouri, New Madrid earthquake (1811),
  landslides, 326
Mitchell, J. K., 307
Mongolia, Gobi-Altai, earthquake (1957),
  faulting, 136
Montague Island, Braided Creek, Patton Bay
  fault trace, 155
  Cape Cleare, exposed surf-cut platform
    (photo), 83
    surf-cut surface (photo), 85
    uplifted kelp (photo), 38
    uplifted sea floor (photo), 21
  faults, *73*, 140; (map), 139
    horizontal displacement, *174*
  geographic setting, *138*
  geologic setting, *138*
  Hanning Bay (map), 257
  Hanning Bay Fault (map), Part B, Plate D
  Jeanie Creek area, Patton Bay fault
    (photo), 151
  Jeanie Point, Patton Bay fault (map), 144;
    (photo), 142
  MacLeod Harbor, core logs, (illus.), 255
    preearthquake beach sands (illus.), 256
    preearthquake cut and fill (photo), 256
    preearthquake subtidal channel (photo),
      256
    raised bay-head deposits (photo), 83
    shallow-water sediment sites (map), 255
    shallow-water sediments, 256, *261*, 262
    Tertiary Orca Group (illus.), 100
    uplifted preearthquake and postearth-
      quake material (photo), 256
  Neck Point, Patton Bay fault, *141*
  Nellie Martin River, postearthquake in-
    cisement, 154
  Patton Bay Fault (map), Part B, Plate C;
    (photo), 143
    deformed muskeg (photo), 148
  Purple Bluff, lineaments (photo), 159
  regional tectonic setting, *136*; (map), 137
  southern, erosion, 281
  storm-beach variations, 65
  Tortuous Creek, fissures (photo), 149
  uplift, effect on streams, 240
Montague Strait, gravity low, 131
Montana, Fallon-Stillwater earthquake
  (1954), fissures, 565
Moonan, Mickey, 525
Moore, Fran, 546
Moore, George W., 48, 101, 179, 184, 199
Moran, Robert H., 421

Moriarity, James, 278
Morrison, James A., 440, 546, 616, 618
Moss, J. M., 464
motion directions, Anchorage, 292
movements, preearthquake, 80
  postearthquake, 80
mud extrusion, City Dock, Anchorage, 317
mud fountains, Anchorage area, *317*
mudspout crater, Orca Inlet, mud flats
  (photo), 268
Munger, Mr. and Mrs. George, 533
Muttart, John, 48
Mya sp., 253
Myers, "Stinky," 48

Naked Island, local waves, 88
National Academy of Sciences, Committee
  on the Alaska Earthquake, 767, 787
National Oceanic and Atmospheric Administration, *xv*
National Science Foundation, *xv*, 264
native villages, tectonic effects, 23
natural disasters, 1357 A.D.–1964 (table), 9
natural gas distribution, Anchorage, damage,
  725
natural gas facilities, damage, *725*
natural gas pipeline, damage, 725
  rupture (photo), 726
  stress-relief by geologic maps, 726
navigation aids, effects of earthquake, 711
Nelson, Carl, 546
Nelson, Hal, 69, 205
Nelson, Mr. and Mrs. Vic, 463
Neva (vessel), 210
new techniques, *780*
New Zealand, Hawke Bay, earthquake
  (1931), faulting, 136
New Zealand earthquakes, deformation, 91
Ninilchik airstrip, damage, 709
Nikishka refinery, damage, 725
Nikiski refinery, damage (photo), 527
Nikiski tank farm, damage, 525
Nolde, H. E., 440
Northwestern (vessel), 366
Norton, F. R. B., 728
Norway, Bekkelaget slide, 326
Nuka Passage, inundated trees (photo), 84

oceanographic effects, *769*
[U.S.] Office of Emergency Preparedness,
  xv
  Anchorage damage estimates, 292
[U.S.] Office of Naval Research, *xv*, 278
offshore borings, Seward (illus.), 422
Ohio State University, *xv*
  Institute of Polar Studies, 264
Old Harbor, beach subsidence, 193
  damage, 540
  salty wells, 201
  seismic sea waves, 540
  subsidence, 540
Old Harbor airstrip, submergence, 710
Olds River, stream gravel displacement, 217
Olds River estuary, subsidence, 205

Oligocene deformation, south-central Alaska, *99*
Oligocene plutons, Prince William Sound region, 99
Oligocene rocks, Chirikof Island, 99
O'Neal, William B., 521
Orca Group, Tertiary, deformation, 127
    Prince William Sound area, *126*
Orca Inlet, dredging, U.S. Army Corps of Engineers, 509
    effects of seiches, 276
    emergence (photo), 90
    mud flats, mudspout crater (photo), 268
    postearthquake areas of deposition (map), 276
    postearthquake soundings (map), 276
    shoaling, 36
    sounding profiles (illus.), 277
    water oscillation, 267
Oregon, Cannon Beach, damage, 41
    Coos Bay, seismic sea wave, 41
    DePoe Bay, drownings, 41
    Gold Coast, damage, 41
    Portland, aid to Seward, 420
    Seaside, damage, 41
organisms, sessile, upper growth limits, 58
Osborne, Jim, 48, 79
Ouzinkie (also *as* Uzinki), damage, 540
    undulations, 190
    seismic sea waves, 540
    subsidence, 540
Ouzinkie airstrip, submergence, 710

Page, R. A., Jr., 48
Palmer, earthquake effects, 533
Palmer airstrip, damage, 710
Panel on Geology, role, 1
Parkin, E. J., 48
particle size distribution, Bootlegger Cove Clay (table), 308
Passage Canal, grabens, 758
Pathfinder (vessel), 419
Patton Bay Fault, 73, *141*
    deformed muskeg (photo), 149
    fissures (photo), 147, 158
    landslide scars (photo), 152
    Patton River area, fissures (photo), 157
        tilted trees (photo), 156
    sheared boudins (photo), 153
    submarine extension, *160*
    surface cracks, 141; (photo), 145, 146
    vertical displacement, 92
pebble dents, estimation of bridge damage energy, 593
Pennsylvania, Allentown, aid to Seward, 420
Perl Island, inundation, 530
permafrost, earthquake effects, *773*
Permanente Cement Company tanks, vibration damage, 315
Perry Island, damage, *511*
    water displacement, 88
Pestrikoff, Edward, 193
Pestrikoff, Sergei, 189
Petrie, W. L., 84
petroleum pipe-lines, damage, *725*

petroleum storage tanks, development of leaks, 725
Péwé, Troy L., 391
physical environment, effects, summary, *760*
physicochemical tests, Bootlegger Cove Clay, *307*
physiographic changes, *82*
physiographic divisions of Alaska (map), 11
physiography, Alaska-Aleutian province, 12
    Alaska Railroad area, 546
    Coastal Trough province, *13*
    Pacific Border ranges, *16*
    Prince William Sound, 496
pile-embedding material, relation to bridge damage (chart), 610
pile penetration, influence on bridge damage (illus.), 555, 556
place names, Alaska, terminology, *xvi*
Plafker, George, 16, 18, 39, 123, 169, 179, 435, 436, 439, 461, 642, 704, 712, 754
plasticity charts, Bootlegger Cove Clay (illus.), 303
Pleistocene, Anchorage area, 300
    Bootlegger Cove Clay, *300*
    Mineral Creek alluvial fan, Valdez, 361
    outwash complex, Valdez, 361
Point Nowell, damage, 512
Point Whitshed, damage, 509
Point Whitshed Road, damage (map), 649
    damage by seismic sea waves (photo), 670
Point Woronzof, landslide area (map), 321
ponds, Hanning Bay fault scarp (photo), 172
Port Ashton, damage, 518
    water displacement, 88
Port Bailey cannery, dry wells, 201
Port Crawford, sawmill damage, 510
Port Graham, damage, 525
    waves, 525
Port Gravina, gravity low, *131*
    subsidence, 81
Port Nellie Juan, boat damage (photo), 514
    damage, 512, 715; (photo), 513
    water displacement, 88
Port Nowell, water displacement, 88
Port Oceanic, damage, *513*, 715; (photo), 516
    water displacement, 88
Port Oceanic area, wave damage (map), 515
Port San Juan, water displacement, 88
Port Valdez, Shoup Bay, slump (photo), 501
Port Valdez area (map), 500
Port Wells, local waves, 88
Portage, damage, 528
    fissures, 528
    ground cracks at embankments (photo), 600
    marine inundation, 38; (photo), 529
    postearthquake high tide (photo), 625
    submerged roadway (photo), 670
Portage airstrip, damage, 710
Portage area, fissures (map), 528
    ground cracks (map), Part B, Plate T; (photo), Part B, Plate T

pre- and postearthquake high tides (map), 624
Portage Creek, Forest Service house, ground cracks (photo), 598
    ground cracks (map), 571
Portage Creek bridges, damage (photo), 675
Portage Glacier road, bridge damage, 682
    damage (map), 646
Portage River, borings, penetrometer values (chart), 612
Ports and harbors, damage losses (table), 35
    tectonic effects, 34
postearthquake movement, 80
post-Miocene deformation, Alaska, *98*
Potato-patch Lake, high-tide flooding, 539
Potter Hill Landslide (illus.), Part B, Plate U; (map), Part B, Plate U; (photo), 615
    bore-hole data (illus.), Part B, Plate U
    borings, 616
    preearthquake landslide history, 618
    pressure ridges, 616; (photo), 616
    railroad reconstruction, continued failure (illus.), 617
powerline loss, Cordova, 728
powerplant, Eklutna, damage, 732
    Kodiak, damage, 728
power systems, Anchorage, damage, *723*
    Kenai Peninsula, damage, 723
    Matanuska Valley, damage, 723
power-transmission lines, Turnagain Arm, damage, 725
power-transmission poles, Turnagain Arm, tilting (photo), 723
preearthquake movements, *80*
pressure ridge, Anchorage (photo), 332, 335
    Bluff Road, (photo), 324
    origin, 335
    Potter Hill landslides, 616; (photo), 616
Prince William Sound (map), 251
    crustal thickness, 131
    damage to communities, *499*
    Glacier Island, *Fucus* spp., barnacle line (photo), 64
    gravity high, 130, *132*
    gravity profile (illus.), 130
    gravity stations, 129
    ground deformation (map), Part B, Plate B
    Harriman fiord, drowned brush (photo), 66
    regional gravity gradient, *131*
    shallow-water sediments, *250, 259, 261*
    sparker survey, 132
    stratigraphy, *123*
    subaqueous slides (map), Part B, Plate Q
    submergence, 108
    wave distribution (map), Part B, Plate Q
    Whale Bay, barnacle line (photo), 60
Prince William Sound area, Bouguer gravity map, 129
    geologic map, 124
    granitic rocks, *126*
    gravity, *128*
    physiography, 496
    Quaternary unconsolidated deposits, *127*
    rock densities, *127*

structural geology, *127*
property values, effects of earthquake, *247*
Providence Hospital, vibration damage, 311
Puget Bay, damage, 529
  landslides, 529
  waves, 529
Puget Peak avalanche, 285
pulsating load tests, Bootlegger Cove Clay, *305*
Puritan Creek bridge-approach, subsidence, 674

Quartz Creek Bridge, damage, 681
Quaternary, Seward fan-delta, 412
  Seward, surficial deposits, *412*
Quaternary deposits, Homer Spit, well log, 474
  Prince William Sound area, *127*
  Whittier, 441
questionnaire, earthquake damage, 491
  value. *788*

radio service, damage, *722*
radioactive contamination, Kodiak Naval Station, 539
radiocarbon-dated samples, pre-1964 positions (illus.), 105
radiocarbon dates, drowned trees, 110
  Middleton Island emergence, 108
  shoreline features (table), 102
Ragged Mountain Fault, 101
railroad embankments, active failures, 602
  failure on deltas and fans, 608
  fill failure, 602
  floodplain failures, 605
  liquefaction (illus.), 604
  passive failures, 604
  restoration, 627
  settlement cross sections (illus.), 603
  submergence, effect of tides, 625
  typical cross section (illus.), 602
railroad embankment damage, Alaska Railroad, *601*
  inertial forces (graph), 601
  Resurrection River fill, 608
railroad embankment failure, stream crossings, 604
railroad fill, failure, Alaska Railroad (photo), 608
railroad track damage, Alaska Railroad, *601*
  floodplain bridges, 605
Raleigh, C. B., 50
Rat Island, earthquake (1964), transverse faults, 97
Rautio, Dorothy, 278
Rautio, Emil, 267, 278
Reardon, James D., 83, 464
reconstruction effort, Seward, *418*
recording gages, use in earthquake study, 780
Reed, B. L., 48
Reilly, Robert A., 754
Resurrection Bay, drowned trees (photo), 20
  grabens, 758

seiching, 436
  submerged trees (photo), 82
Resurrection Creek bridges, damage, 577
Resurrection River, floodplain deposits, 415
  railroad embankment damage, 608
Resurrection River bridge, damage (photo), 579, 582
  ground cracks (map), 578
  pier damage (photo), 554
Rhodes, Mrs. Leo, 463
Richards, E. W., 48, 265
Richardson Highway, bore holes (illus.), 654
  bridge-approach damage (table), 702
  bridge damage (table), 702
  damage (map), 648; (photo), 31
  foundation material, earthquake effects (table), 691
  pre- and postearthquake profiles (illus.), 660
  sediment-analysis (table), 693
Rimling, Mrs. Vern, 525
river drainage, tilting, *83*
roadway damage, Alaska, *644*
Roald (vessel), 496
Robbins, S. L., 48
Roberts, Mrs. Hadley, 686
rock avalanche, Surprise Glacier (photo), 13
rockfalls, Kodiak Island, 198
rockslide avalanches, summary, 761
Rocky Bay, damage, 530
  seismic sea waves, 530
  subsidence, 530
Roddy, K. A., 466
Rose Tead Lake, submergence (photo), 192
rotational slides, Bluff Road, Anchorage area, *324, 325*
Rouse, John T., *xv*
Rude River Delta (map), 252
  clam bed uplifted (photo), 253
  core logs (illus.), 252
  effects on preearthquake sediments, 263
  grain-size analyses (illus.), 260
  post-, preearthquake sediments compared, 253
  pre- and postearthquake sediments (photo), 253
  preearthquake mudcracks and postearthquake mud (photo), 253
  sediment analyses, *259*
  shallow-water sediments, *251*
Rusnak, G. A., 423, 424, 758

salmon, damage to environment, 245
  effects of seismic sea waves, 246
  effects of submergence, 246
Salmon Creek, floodplain, 416
salmon spawning, effects, 85
Saltery Lake, alluvium subsidence, 193
Salvation Army, aid to Seward, 420
San Juan dock, Seward, disappearance, 407
sand bars, submarine, *234*
  Turnagain Heights slide area (photo), 317
sand boils, Anchorage area, *317*

Seward, 431
  analysis (illus.), 432
sand dike, Copper River Delta (photo), 273
sand ejecta blankets, highways, *667*
sandbox, soil compaction models (illus.), 573
sandbox experiments, four-layer model (photo), 575; (illus.), 576
  grain size analysis (illus.), 573
  soil movement (illus.), 574
Sawmill Bay, damage, *516*, 715
  local waves, 518
Sawmill Bay area, wave damage (map), 517
Schizothaerus sp., 255
Schizothaerus capax, 276
Scientific and Engineering Task Force, 426, 777
  Homer Spit, 471
  Seward, 420
  value *785, 789*
Scott-Glacier-5 Bridge, damage (photo), 681
Scott-Glacier-6 Bridge, broken piles (photo), 679
Scripps Institution of Oceanography, 93
Seabastolobus sp. (or *Sebastolobus*), 446
Sebastodes sp. (now *Sebastes*), 446
Sedge (vessel), 267
sediment-analysis, Copper River Highway (table), 693
  Richardson Highway, 693
  Seward–Anchorage Highway (table), 692
  Snow River Crossing (table), 692
sediment compaction, relation to highway damage, 684
  sandbox experiments, 570
  Whittier, 453
sediment grain-size, influence on highway damage, 683
  relation to bridge damage, 611; (illus.), 612
sediment liquefaction, 566
sediment movement, bends in railroad bridge piles (illus.), 572
sediment ridges, Copper River Delta (photo), 272
sediment thickness, influence on highway damage, 684
  relation to bridge damage, 610, 681; (chart) 611
sediments, post- and preearthquake compared, Rude River Delta, 253
Seed, H. B., 2, 305
seiche, Beluga Lake, 475
  Copper River Delta, 276
  Kachemak Bay, 474
  Orca Inlet, 275
  seismic, 769
  Terror Bay, Kodiak Island, 215
  Valdez Bay, 372
seiching, Passage Canal, Whittier, 456
  Resurrection Bay, 436
  slide-induced, Kenai Lake, 279
seismic activity, tectonic displacement (illus.), 113

seismic air waves, Berkeley, California, 218
La Jolla, 218
seismic damage, Whittier, *448*
seismic history, Homer, 478
Valdez, *365*
seismic profiles, Seward area (illus.), Part B,
Plate K
seismic sea waves, *see also* tsunamis
California, Crescent City, 41
Cordova, damage (photo), 508
destruction of submarine sand bars, 235
effects on highway bridges, 682; highways, 667; salmon, 246
extent, *498*
Kaguyak, 540
Kodiak, 539
Kodiak Island, heights and times (table),
214
highway damage, 219, 222
Kodiak Island area, *210*
crest heights, *213*
effects on shorelines and sea bottoms,
217
origin, *217*
periods, *215*
runup heights, *214*
Kodiak Naval Station, 539
lessons learned, 771
Middleton Island, 522
Old Harbor, 540
Oregon, Coos Bay, 41
Ouzinkie, 540
relation to vertical tectonic displacement,
776
Rocky Bay, 530
Seldovia, 464, 530
Seward, 399, 435
source determinations, 69
tectonic generation, *86*
travel times (table), 71
Whidbey Bay, 532
Yakataga, 522
seismic sea wave damage, Afognak Island
(photo), 216
Kodiak (photo), 223
Kodiak Island, Womens Bay (photo), 221
Seismic Sea Wave Warning System, *225*
seismic seiches, 769
seismic shaking, highway bridge damage, *672*
seismic studies, Seward, 421
Seward alluvial fan, 414
seismic vibration damage, definition, 493
seismicity, Alaska, *50*
Aleutian Arc, *93*
seismograph network, need, 786
Seldovia, airstrip submergence (photo), 709
damage, 530, 717
port facilities, damage, 36
restored view (photo), 531
seismic sea waves, 464, 530
subsidence, 530
Seldovia waterfront, postearthquake (photo),
718
Selkregg, Lidia, 298
sensitivity, Bootlegger Cove Clay, *302*

sessile organisms, tectonically disturbed, 39
sewage system, Anchorage, damage, 727
Cordova, damage, 728
Kodiak, damage, 728
Seward, damage, 729
Valdez, damage, 729
Whittier, damage, 730
Seward, A Street fractures (photo), 428
aid from Allentown, Pa., 420; American
Legion, 420; American Red Cross, 420;
Portland, Oregon, 420; Salvation Army,
420
Alaska State Housing Authority, 419
Alaska Railroad, cranes, damage, 398;
(photo), 406
dock, damage, 407
All-America City, 1963, 418
Army dock disappearance, 407
artificial fill, 417
bedrock, *411*
Clearview area, fractured ground (map),
429
Cretaceous rocks, 410
damage, 716; (photo), 24, 409
damage area (map), 404
earthquake effects, *395*
electric service, damage, 729
engineering geology, *418*
Forest Acres, fractures (map), 430
(photo), 431
Forest Acres fractured ground (map), 429
Forest Acres area, fractures, 428
fractured ground, *427*
stability, 434
fracturing, coordinate causes, *432*
geological studies, 420
geology, *410*
glacial deposits, 412
ground water, 421
incipient landsliding (photo), 423
intertidal deposits, 416
Jurassic rocks, 410
landslide deposits, 416
landslide mechanics, 423
landslide waves, 435
landslides, *408, 422*
loss of life, *407*
Lowell Creek fan, 411
offshore borings (illus.), 422
port damage (photo), 35
port facilities damage (photo), 35
postearthquake photo, 400, 401
potential future damage, 436
preearthquake photo, 400, 401
railroad yard, damage (photo), 30, 408
reconstruction effort, *418*
Resurrection Bay landslide, 422
San Juan dock, disappearance, 407
sand boils, 431
sedimentary analysis (illus.), 432
Scientific and Engineering Task Force,
420
seismic sea waves, 399, 435
seismic studies, 421
sewage system, damage, 729

Small Business Administration, 420
Standard Oil dock, disappearance, 407
standby power generators (photo), 729
surficial deposits, *412*
tectonic effects, 21, 22, 35
tectonic land changes, *410*
telephone system, damage, 729
tide-gage readings, 57
U.S. Army Corps of Engineers, 420
U.S. Geological Survey, 420
U.S. Urban Renewal Administration, 419
utilities damage, *729*
water system, damage, 729
water wells, 410
waterfront damage (photo), 402, 403,
405, 407, 419
waterfront landslide, 422
Seward Airport, damage, 710
Seward and vicinity (map), 397
Seward–Anchorage Highway, bore holes
(illus.), 652
bridge damage (table), 699–701
damage (map), 646
foundation–fracture correlation (table),
694
foundation material and earthquake
effects (table), 690
fractures (photo), 656, 666
landslide (photo), 667
pre- and postearthquake profiles (illus.),
662, 663
sediment-analysis (table), 692
Seward area, geology (map), Part B, Plate J
landslide potential, 427
seismic profiles (illus.), Part B, Plate K
snowslides, 408
valley alluvium, *415*
water waves, *435*
Seward alluvial fans, 412; (photo), 413
seismic studies, 414
Seward fan-delta deposits, 412
Seward harbor, restoration (photo), 717
Seward Highway, fissure (photo), 31
Sewell, Glen, 463, 464
shallow-water sediments, Hanning Bay, *257*
Prince William Sound, *250*
sampling techniques, *250*
shallow wells, changes, 89
Shannon & Wilson, Inc., 299, 397, 364,
420, 421
Sharp, Tex, 463
shear strength, Bootlegger Cove Clay, *301*
Shearwater Bay, cannery damage, 36
Shelikof Strait, water fluctuations, 213
Shelikof Strait–Cook Inlet area, aftershocks,
51
shellfish, effects of earthquake, *246*
Shepard, F. P., 278
Shepherd, Peter E. K., 246, 276
Sheridan, W. L., 246
Shevlin, T. S., 307
shipping industry, earthquake damage, *710*
shore processes, summary, *767*
shore protection measures, *241*
shore protection works, Homer Spit, *485*

shoreline changes, biologic effects, *245*
   tectonic influence, 110
shoreline damage (photo), 217
shoreline erosion, Kodiak Island area, 217
shoreline features, radiocarbon dates,
   (table), 102
shorelines *230*
   Alaska, effects of earthquake, *229*
   Kodiak Island area, *205*
   upslope material movement, *245*
Shoup Bay, boulder movement (photo), 502
   wave-damaged trees (photo), 502
Shoup Glacier, moraine, submarine slides,
   501
Shuyak Island, emptied lakes, 202
   subsidence, 203
Silver Lake, gravity anomaly, 133
Sitka, earthquake damage, 711
Sitkalidak Island, landslides, 200
   McCord ranch, subsidence, 193
   uplift, 203
Sitkinak Island, earthflow (photo), 199
   landslide (photo), 198
Skilak Lake, tilting, 280
Skilak Lake Delta, slumping, 280
Skilak River floodplain, fractures, 280
slope map, Anchorage, 736
slope stability chart, 327
slough banks, upheaval, Copper River Delta,
   271
slough-slumping, Copper River Delta
   (photo), 272
slumping, Beluga Lake outlet, 280
   Bradley Lake Delta, 280
   Eklutna Lake Delta, 280
   Kodiak Island area, 198
   Lake George Delta, 280
   Skilak Lake Delta, 280
   Sleeper landing strip, Knik Arm (illus.),
   323
   Susitna River Delta, 280
   Tustumena Lake Delta, 280
slump cracks, Copper River Delta (photo),
   271
Small, J. B., 48
[U.S.] Small Business Administration,
   Seward, 420
Smas, Steve, 522
Smith, Patsy J., 307, 308
Snow River Bridge, pre- and postearthquake
   penetrometer tests (illus.), 685; (photo)
   676
Snow River Crossing, arched bridge (photo),
   665
   bridge pier displacement (photo), 664
   pre- and postearthquake bridge pier elevations (illus.), 664
   sediment-analysis (table), 692
   clastic dikes (photo), 15
snowslides, Seward area, 408
Society of Economic Paleontologists and
   Mineralogists, *xv*
soil, mobilized, horizontal movement,
   summary, 762
Soldatna airstrip, damage, 709

sound waves, Boston, Massachusetts, 772
   Boulder, Colorado, 772
   Washington, D. C., 772
sounding profiles, post- and preearthquake,
   Copper River Delta (illus.), 277
South American earthquakes, deformation,
   compared with Alaska (1964), 91
South Campbell airstrip, damage, 710
South Naknek, damage, 532
Sozen, M. A., 293
Spaeth, M. G., 69
Spangler, John A., 397
sparker survey, Prince William Sound, 132
specific gravity, Bootlegger Cove Clay, *306*
Stacey, Capt. John, 48
St. Amand, Pierre, 179, 199
Standerwick, J., 176
Standard Oil dock, Seward, disappearance,
   407
Stanford University, *xv*
Starbuck, S. I., 506
starfish, stranded and dead (photo), 85
Stauder, William 50
St. Elias Mountains, physiography, 18
Sterling Highway, bridge damage (table),
   703
   bridge-approach damage (table), 703
   damage (map), 645
   foundation material, earthquake effects
   (table), 690
Stewart, M. D., 368
Stockton, Perry, 397, 418
storm-beach variations, Montague Island, 65
storm berm, Homer Spit (photo), 482
stratigraphy, Prince William Sound area, *123*
stream flow, changes, 89
   Kodiak Island area, 202
stream-mouth changes, *237*
stress-reversing test, 305
structural damage, Valdez, *388*
structural geology, Prince William Sound
   area, *127*
Stump, W. J., *726*
subaqueous slides, summary, *762*
subaqueous slides and related waves, *496*
submarine sand bars, *234*
   destruction by seismic sea waves, 235
submarine slides, ice breakage, 282
submarine landslide, Homer Spit, 470
   Valdez, *372*; (illus.), 369
   Valdez, damage, 388
   Valdez, effects, 368
   Valdez, mechanics, *373*
   Valdez, pre-1964, 374
   Whittier (photo), 454
   Whittier, mechanism for waves (illus.), 455
   Whittier, slopes (table), 454
submerged coast, Kenai Peninsula (photo),
   106
submerged shorelines, 103
submerged trees, Resurrection Bay (photo),
   82
submergence, effect on coastal erosion, 240;
   intertidal organisms, 84; manmade
   structures, *247*; stream mouths, 237

Homer Spit (photos), 470
   response by beaches, *235*
   short-term, *108*
   Womens Bay seaplane ramps, 708
subsidence, Afognak, 539
   Afognak Island, 203
   Alaska highways, damage, *659*
   Alaska Railroad, damage, *622*
   artificial fills and embankments, *193*
   effects on highway bridges, 683
   extent, 495
   Homer Spit, 467, 473
     effect on beaches, 235
   Kodiak, 539
   Kodiak Island, 203
   Kodiak Island area, *203*
     effects on salmon spawning grounds,
     224
   Larsen Bay, 540
   legal problems, *247*
   local and regional, *782*
subsidence, Marmot Island, 203
   Old Harbor, 540
   Ouzinkie (Uzinki), 540
   Rocky Bay, 530
   Seldovia, 530
   Shuyak Island, 203
   Whittier, 447
subsidence by consolidation, summary, *767*
surface faults, geology, 776
   lessons learned, 776
   summary, *758*
surface water, Kodiak Island, effects of
   earthquake, *201*
   summary, *769*
surface water hydrology, summary, *777*
surface displacement profiles, thrust fault,
   observed and inferred (illus.), 117
   steep-fault, observed and inferred (illus.),
   116
surface waves, Kodiak Island area *190*
surficial deposits, Seward, *412*
surficial subsidence, causes, *193*
   Kodiak Island, *191*
surges, glacial, relation to earthquakes, 768
Surprise Glacier, rock avalanche (photo), 13
Surveyor (vessel), 128, 131, 132
Susitna River Delta, slumping, 280
Sutton, earthquake effects, 534
Swanson River oil field, no tectonic change,
   88
Sweden, Skottorp slide, 326
Sweeney, Bill, 530, 532

Talkeetna Mountains, physiography, 14
Tarbelt, Clarence, 522
Tatitlek, damage, 715
   local waves, 88
   tectonic effects, 21
Tatitlek area, damage, 518
Taylor, Ralph, 361
Tazlina Lake, ice breakage, submarine slides,
   282
tectonic displacements, effects, *81*
   measured and inferred (illus.), 78

tectonic effects, Alaska earthquake, *18*
tectonic land changes, Seward, *410*
tectonic setting, Alaska earthquake, *92*
tectonic map, southern Alaska, 95
tectonic submergence, short-term, *108*
tectonic subsidence, effects on highways, 669
tectonics, lessons learned, *754*
telephone poles, Turnagain Arm, tilting (photo), 723
telephone service, Kodiak, damage, 728
telephone system, damage, *722*
   Anchorage, 727
   Seward, 729
television, loss of power, *722*
   use in underground observations, 780
terrestrial vegetation, killed by inundation, 84
Terror Lake, delta subsidence (photo), 194
   ejected sand (photo), 195
Terror Lake Delta, subsidence, 193
Tertiary, Orca Group, MacLeod Harbor (illus.), 100
   Prince William Sound area, *126*
Tertiary deformation, south-central Alaska, *100*
Tertiary rocks, Chirikof Island, 99
   Trinity Islands, 99
Texas A & M University, *xv*
Thomas, H. E., 202
Thompson, H. S., 464
Thompson Pass airstrip, damage, 710
Thorn, A. H., 476
Thornton, Jerry, 274
tidal constants, Kodiak Island (table), 182
tidal inlets, Homer spit, 487
tidal inundation, Kodiak Island area (table), 205
tidal marshes, Copper River Delta, changes, 276
tide-gage readings, pre- and postearthquake, 56
tides, Portage area, effects on railroad embankments, 625
Tilley, Jerry, 210, 217
tilting, Skilak Lake, 280
   Tustumena Lake, 280
tilting of lake basins, *82*
tilting of river drainages, *83*
tiltmeters, use of lakes, 780
time-sequential cross sections (illus.), 114
Tonsina Lake, ice breakage, submarine slides, 282
torsional vane-shear strength, Bootlegger Cove Clay (illus.), 302
track damage, Alaska Railroad (photo), 566
translatory slides, Anchorage, *326*
   geology, 326
   summary, 763
  block diagram (illus.), 328
  geometry and mode of failure, 328
  graben formation, 328
trestle, open wood (illus.), 569
triangulation adjustment, schematic illustration, 77

triangulation coordinates, pre- and post-earthquake (table), 76
Trinity Islands, Tertiary rocks, 99
tsunamis, *see also* seismic sea waves, Copper River Delta, *276*
   effects on delta sediments, *265*
   Homer, 464
tunnels, earthquake effects, *773*
Turnagain Arm, landslides, *318*
   Point Campbell, bluff failure (illus.), 318
   pre-earthquake shoreline and inundation (map), 671
   stream-mouth changes, 239
   telephone poles, tilting (photo), 723
Tustumena Lake, tilting, 83, 280
Tustumena Lake Delta, slumping, 280
Tuxedni Bay, submarine slump, 532
Twentymile River Bridge, collapse (photo), 676
Twentymile River Bridge, damage (illus.), 589; (photo), 32, 588
Two Brothers Lumber Company, 447
Tyonek, earthquake effects, 532

Unakwik Inlet, local waves, 88
undulations, Afognak, 190
   Ouzinkie (Uzinki), 190
Unga (vessel), 398
Union Oil Company of California, tank farm, ground cracks, 317
United States, ground-water regimen, 41
U.S. Air Force, *xv*
U.S. Army, *xv*
   assistance in highway surveys, 642
U.S. Army–Alaska, 440
U.S. Army Corps of Engineers, 290, 418
   Cordova, harbor dredging, 714
   Homer Spit, bathymetry survey, 471
   Fourth Avenue slide, 331
   L Street landslide, 336
   Mineral Creek fan investigation, 364
   Orca Inlet dredging, 509
   Seldovia restoration, 718
   Seward, 397, 420, 421
   Tatitlek, harbor dredging, 518
   Turnagain Heights landslide, 349, 350
   Valdez, docks, 719
U.S. Army District Engineer, role in Anchorage, 299
U.S. Bureau of Commercial Fisheries, *xv*
U.S. Bureau of Land Management, 466
U.S. Coast Guard, Cape Chiniak station, tsunami, 210
U.S. Coast Guard, Loran facility, damage, 193
U.S. Coast and Geodetic Survey, *xv*, 93, 789
   hydrographic surveys, 160
   recharting new waters, 712
   resurvey, 74
   re-triangulation, Montague Island, 174
   role in data accumulation, 48
   Seismic Sea Wave Warning System, 225
   Seward Harbor resurvey, 419
U.S. Geological Survey, *xv*
   Alaska mapping, 784

fault-finding mission, 135
landslide-susceptibility mapping, 734
Mineral Creek fan investigation, 364
mobile seismic arrays, San Francisco Bay, 570
relation to Panel on Geology, 2
reports on the Alaska earthquake (1964), *749*
Seward, 420
U.S. Navy, aid to Kodiak fishing fleet, 719
   assistance in highway surveys, 642
U.S. Navy seaplane tender, power for naval station, 719
U.S. Steel Foundation, 278
University of California at Berkeley, *xv*
University of Colorado, *xv*
University of Hawaii, *xv*
University of Idaho, *xv*
University of Southern California, *xv*
upland owner, 247
uplift, Cape Suckling (photo), 67
   Cordova, 509
   effect on clams, 246; coastal erosion, 240; Copper River Delta, *273*; littoral biota, 84; stream mouths, *239*
   Kodiak Island area, 203
   response by beaches, *235*
   Sitkalidak Island, 203
   submarine extension (map), 70
uplifted areas, marine mortality, 85
Upper Miles Glacier, debris flow (photo), 14
[U.S.] Urban Renewal Administration, Seward, 419
Utermole, George E., Jr., 685
utilities, damage, *722*
   Cordova, *728*
   Kodiak, *728*
   Seward, *729*
   Valdez, *729*
   Whittier, *730*
Uzinki, *see* Ouzinkie

Valdez, aftershocks, 378
   Alaska Communications System tower, damage, 392
   Alaska Hotel, damage (photo), 390
   conclusions, *393*
   damage, 719
   damage to structures, *388*
   dock failure 1920 (photo), 375
   earthquake effects, *359*
   earthquake, (1908), 365
   earthquake, (1911), 366
   earthquake, (1912), 367
   earthquake, (1925), 367
   Yakutat earthquake (1899), 365
   eyewitness account, 367
   fissures, *379*; (photo), 22
   origin, 383
   geology, 359, *361*
   ground breakage, *378*
   ground conditions (map), 362
   ground displacement, *376*
   high-water mark (photo), 389
   horizontal movement, 377

large fissure (photo), 381
new townsite (photo), 720, 721
old townsite, postearthquake (photo), 720
Pleistocene outwash complex, 361
postearthquake photo, 371
preearthquake photo, 370
preearthquake submarine slides, 374
seismic history, *365*
sewer system, damage, 729
submarine landslide, *372*; (illus.), 369
   damage, 388
   effects, 368
   mechanics, *373*
subsurface conditions, *372*
summary of events, *367*
tectonic effects, 21, 22, 35
Union Oil Company tank farm, damage, 391
utilities damage, *729*
Valdez Group, Cretaceous, 361
vertical movement, 376
water-line separations (table), 377
water system, damage, 729
wave and water damage, 388
Valdez airstrip, damage, 710
Valdez area (map), 360; (photo), 358
   bore-hole logs (illus.), Part B, Plate I
   drainage, *364*
   earthquake effects (map), Part B, Plate G
   gravity values, 133
Valdez Arm area, recent faulting, 128
Valdez Bay, dead fish from water concussion, 367
   seiching, 372
Valdez Delta, grain-size analysis (table), 363
Valdez Glacier, stream floodplain, collapse
   pits (photo), 386, 387
   fissure ejecta (photo), 382
   fissures (map), 385; (photos), 380, 384, 386
   termini (map), 365
Valdez Group, Mesozoic, *126*
   deformation, 127
Valdez harbor, submarine contours (map), part B, Plate H
Valdez High School, fissure in floor (photo), 391
Valdez Narrows navigation light, loss, 501
Valdez waterfront, postearthquake stability, *374*
Vancouver, George, 108
Verrucaria spp., 58
vertical deformation, Kodiak Island area, *203*
   summary, *757*
vertical displacement (map), 104
   bridges, 553
   extent, *495*
   measurement methods, 54
   regional, *54*
   relation to faults, *78*
   relation to seismic sea waves, *776*
   Valdez, 376
vertical shoreline movements, preearthquake, *103*

vessels lost, Kodiak Island area, 223
vibration damage, Alaska Railroad marshaling yards, 311
   Anchorage, Alaska Methodist University, 311
   Alaska Psychiatric Institute, 311
   Alaska Sales and Service Building, 311
   Anchorage Westward Hotel, 311
   Cordova Building, 312
   Fifth Avenue Chrysler Center, 312
   First Federal Savings and Loan Building, 312
   Four Seasons Apartment Building, 312
   Hill Building, 313
   Hillside Apartments, 313
   Knik Arm Apartment Building, 314
   Mount McKinley Building, 314
   Penney's Department Store Building, 314
   Providence Hospital, 311
   1200 L Street Building, 314
   West Anchorage High School, 315
   Anchorage International Airport, 311
   Elmendorf Air Force Base, 312
   extent, 494
   geologic control, *775*
   Port of Anchorage 315
      Alaska Aggregate Company tanks, 315
      Permanente Cement Company tanks, 315
vibration tests, Bootlegger Cove Clay, 305
von Huene, Roland, 50, 271
Vorhis, Robert C., 41

Wakefield cannery, relocation, 247
Waller, Roger M., 12, 202, 290, 312, 315, 354, 619, 642
Waltz, Fred, 397
Washington, D. C., sound waves, 37
Washington, Grays Harbor County, damage, 41
water damage, distribution, 497
water fluctuations, Kodiak Island area, causes, *202*
water-line separations, Valdez (table), 377
water movement, enclosed basin, horizontal displacement (illus.), 87
water-plasticity ratio, Bootlegger Cove Clay (illus.), 306
water system, Anchorage, damage, 727
   Cordova, damage, 728
   Kodiak, damage, 728
   Seward, damage, 729
   Valdez, damage, 729
   Whittier, damage, 730
water-table depth, influence on highway damage, 684
water wells, earthquake effects, 773
   failure, Homer, 475
   Seward, 410
Watts, Paul, 545
wave damage, Jack Bay, 497
   Valdez, 388
wave-magnitude scale, 782
wave runup, new techniques, *782*

waves, Homer, 465
   local origin, *770*
   Port Graham, 525
   Puget Bay, 529
   Sawmill Bay, local, *518*
   Seward area, *435*
   slide-induced, Kenai Lake, 279
   surface, visible, summary, *772*
   time and sequence, 497
   Whittier, landslide-generated, 454
   Yakutat, 523
waves from horizontal displacement, 88
waves related to subaqueous slides, extent, 496
Webb, William, 564
Weber, Mrs. Gus, 463
Weeks, Francis, 546
Weiss, Malcolm P., 264
Wennerstrom, Bert, 319, 618
Wheeler, Glenn, 48
Whidbey Bay, damage, 530
   fissures, 532
   seismic sea waves, 532
Whitnal, William, 361
Whitten, Charles A., 2, 48, 77
Whittier, air-temperature chart, 444
   Alaska Railroad station, damage (photo), 456
   bedrock, Cretaceous(?), 441
   Buckner Building (photo), 451
      core drilling (map) 452
      damage, 451
   climate, 440
   climatological data (table), 440
   Columbia Lumber Company, damage (photo), 446
   conclusions, *458*
   core logs (illus.), 453
   damage (photo), 450
      relation to geology, 458
   dead fish, 446
   drill holes (illus.), *443*
   earthquake effects, *447*
   eyewitness accounts, *443*
   fire damage, 458
   fracturing, 453
   geographic setting, 440
   geology, *441*
   Hodge Building, damage, 451
      drill holes (map), 442
   instrumental records, 50
   land-level changes, 447
   landslide damage (photo), 454
   landslide-generated waves, 454
   landslide slopes (table), 454
   landslides, 453
   Passage Canal, seiching, 456
   Passage Canal Delta (photo), 448
      pre- and postearthquake photos, 448
   plank driven through tire (photo), 457
   port facilities, damage (photo), 448
   postearthquake (photo), 447
   postearthquake submarine topography (map), Part B, Plate N
   preearthquake (photo), 445, 477

preearthquake submarine topography (map), Part B, Plate M
Quaternary deposits, *441*
sediment compaction, 453
seismic damage, *448*
sewer system, damage, 730
subsidence, 447
surge-wave violence (photo), 33
tectonic effects, 21, 22, 35
utilities damage, *730*
water system, damage, 730
waterfront damage (photo), 34, 445
wave damage (map), Part B, Plate N
Whittier airfield, damage, 710
Whittier area (map), 438
earthquake effects (map), Part B, Plate L
geology (map), Part B, Plate L
Whittier harbor, damage, 715

wildfowl, effects of earthquake, *246*
Wildwood Station, damage, 525; (photo), 527
Wilimovsky, N. J., 446
Williams, Jack, 523
Wilson, M. L., 377
Winterer, E., 278
Woodford, Bruce, 360
Woodward-Clyde-Sherard and Associates, 136, 158
Woody Island FAA facility, damage, 36, 710
World-Wide geodetic meter, 128
Wrangell Mountains, physiography, 15
volcanoes, relation to Aleutian Arc, 93

Yakataga, damage, 522
fissured road (photo), 522

seismic sea waves, 522
Yakataga airstrip, damage, 710
Yakutat, damage, 523
waves, 523
Yakutat Airport, damage, 710
Yakutat Bay earthquake (1899), deformation, 91
effects at Valdez, 365
faulting, 101
landslide trigger, 354
tectonic effects, 81
Yukon Island, submergence, radiocarbon dates, 107

Zentmeyer, Delmar, 418
zoned intertidal marine organisms (photo), 59